Steve Williams

AAPG Treatise of Petroleum Geology

The American Association of Petroleum Geologists
gratefully acknowledges and appreciates
the leadership and support of the
AAPG Foundation in the development of the
Treatise of Petroleum Geology

STEVE WILLIAMS
UNIVERSITY OF HOUSTON
ENGINEERING DEPT.

DIAMOND JUBILEE
AAPG
1917-1991

AAPG's
Distinguished Publication of the Millennium

EXPLORING FOR OIL AND GAS TRAPS

EDWARD A. BEAUMONT
NORMAN H. FOSTER
Editors

TREATISE OF PETROLEUM GEOLOGY
HANDBOOK OF PETROLEUM GEOLOGY

TREATISE EDITORS:
NORMAN H. FOSTER
AND
EDWARD A. BEAUMONT

DIAMOND JUBILEE
AAPG
1917-1991

Published by
The American Association of Petroleum Geologists
Tulsa, Oklahoma, U.S.A. 74101

ISBN: 0-89181-602-X

Association Editor: Neil F. Hurley
Science Director: Jack Gallagher
Publications Manager: Kenneth M. Wolgemuth
Managing Editor, Publications: Anne H. Thomas
Project Editors: Kathryne E. Pile, Michael Blechner
Production: Patsy Ann Dock, Rusty Johnson, Janet Brister

This and other AAPG publications are available from:

The AAPG Bookstore
P.O. Box 979
Tulsa, OK 74101-0979
Telephone: 1-918- 584-2555 or 1-800-364-AAPG (USA)
Fax: 1-918-560-2652 or 1-800- 898-2274 (USA)
www.aapg.org

Geological Society Publishing House
Unit 7, Brassmill Enterprise Centre
Brassmill Lane, Bath, U.K.
BA1 3JN
Tel +44-1225-445046
Fax +44-1225-442836
www.geolsoc.org.uk

Australian Mineral Foundation
AMF Bookshop
63 Conyngham Street
Glenside, South Australia 5065
Australia
Tel. +61-8-8379-0444
Fax +61-8-8379-4634
www.amf.com.au/amf

Affiliated East-West Press Private Ltd.
G-1/16 Ansari Road Darya Ganj
New Delhi 110 002
India
Tel +91 11 3279113
Fax +91 11 3260538
e-mail: affiliat@vsnl.com

Table of Contents

Table of Contents, continued

Part II
(continued)

Part III Critical Elements of the Trap

Table of Contents, continued

Part III
(continued)

Part IV

Predicting the Occurrence of Oil and Gas Traps

Table of Contents, continued

Part IV
(continued)

Treatise of Petroleum Geology Advisory Board

Norman S. Neidell
Ronald A. Nelson
Charles R. Noll
Clifton J. Nolte
David W. Organ
John C. Osmond
Philip Oxley*
Susan E. Palmer
Arthur J. Pansze
John M. Parker
Stephen J. Patmore
Dallas L. Peck
William H. Pelton
Alain Perrodon
James A. Peterson
R. Michael Peterson
Edward B. Picou, Jr.
Max Grow Pitcher
David E. Powley
William F. Precht
A. Pulunggono
Bailey Rascoe, Jr.
R. Randy Ray
Dudley D. Rice
Edward P. Riker
Edward C. Roy, Jr.
Eric A. Rudd
Floyd F. Sabins, Jr.
Nahum Schneidermann
Peter A. Scholle
George L. Scott, Jr.
Robert T. Sellars, Jr.
Faroog A. Sharief
John W. Shelton
Phillip W. Shoemaker
Synthia E. Smith
Robert M. Sneider
Frank P. Sonnenberg
Stephen A. Sonnenberg
William E. Speer
Ernest J. Spradlin
Bill St. John
Philip H. Stark
Richard Steinmetz
Per R. Stokke
Denise M. Stone
Donald S. Stone
Douglas K. Strickland
James V. Taranik
Harry Ter Best, Jr.
Bruce K. Thatcher, Jr.
M. Ray Thomasson
Jack C. Threet
Bernard Tissot
Don F. Tobin
Don G. Tobin
Donald F. Todd
Harrison L. Townes
M. O. Turner
Peter R. Vail
B. van Hoorn
Arthur M. Van Tyne
Kent Lee Van Zant
Ian R. Vann
Harry K. Veal*
Steven L. Veal
Richard R. Vincelette
Fred J. Wagner, Jr.
William A. Walker, Jr.
Carol A. Walsh
Anthony Walton
Douglas W. Waples
Harry W. Wassall, III
W. Lynn Watney
N. L. Watts
Koenradd J. Weber
Robert J. Weimer
Dietrich H. Welte
Alun H. Whittaker
James E. Wilson, Jr.
Thomas Wilson
John R. Wingert
Martha O. Withjack
P. W. J. Wood
Homer O. Woodbury
Walter W. Wornardt
Marcelo R. Yrigoyen
Mehmet A. Yukler
Zhai Guangming
Robert Zinke

*Deceased

AMERICAN ASSOCIATION OF PETROLEUM GEOLOGISTS FOUNDATION
TREATISE OF PETROLEUM GEOLOGY FUND*

Major Corporate Contributors
($25,000 or more)

Amoco Production Company
BP Exploration Company Limited
Chevron Corporation
Exxon Company, U.S.A.
Mobil Oil Corporation
Oryx Energy Company
Pennzoil Exploration and Production Company
Shell Oil Company
Texaco Foundation
Union Pacific Foundation
Unocal Corporation

Other Corporate Contributors
($5,000 to $25,000)

ARCO Oil & Gas Company
Ashland Oil, Inc.
Cabot Oil & Gas Coporation
Canadian Hunter Exploration Ltd.
Conoco Inc.
Marathon Oil Company
The McGee Foundation, Inc.
Phillips Petroleum Company
Transco Energy Company
Union Texas Petroleum Corporation

Major Individual Contributors
($1,000 or more)

John J. Amoruso
Thornton E. Anderson
C. Hayden Atchison
Richard A. Baile
Richard R. Bloomer
A. S. Bonner, Jr.
David G. Campbell
Herbert G. Davis
George A. Donnelly, Jr.
Paul H. Dudley, Jr.
Lewis G. Fearing
Lawrence W. Funkhouser
James A. Gibbs
George R. Gibson
William E. Gipson
Mrs. Vito A. (Mary Jane) Gotautas
Robert D. Gunn
Merrill W. Haas
Cecil V. Hagen
Frank W. Harrison
William A. Heck
Roy M. Huffington
J. R. Jackson, Jr.
Harrison C. Jamison
Thomas N. Jordan, Jr.
Hugh M. Looney
Jack P. Martin
John W. Mason
George B. McBride
Dean A. McGee
John R. McMillan
Lee Wayne Moore
Grover E. Murray
Rudolf B. Siegert
Robert M. Sneider
Estate of Mrs. John (Elizabeth) Teagle
Jack C. Threet
Charles Weiner
Harry Westmoreland
James E. Wilson, Jr.
P. W. J. Wood

The Foundation also gratefully acknowledges the many who have supported this endeavor with additional contributions.

*Based on contributions received as of June 30, 1992.

PREFACE TO THE *HANDBOOK OF PETROLEUM GEOLOGY*

Exploring for Oil and Gas Traps is one of four books of the *Handbook of Petroleum Geology*, which is part of the *Treatise of Petroleum Geology.* The Treatise comprises three different publication sets: the *Reprint Series*, the *Atlas of Oil and Gas Fields*, and the *Handbook of Petroleum Geology*. The Treatise is AAPG's Diamond Jubilee project, commemorating AAPG's 75th Anniversary in 1991.

With input from an advisory board of more than 250 geologists and geophysicists from around the world, we designed this entire effort so that the set of publications will represent the cutting edge in petroleum exploration knowledge and application. The Reprint Series provides useful literature from various geological, geophysical, and engineering publications. In some cases, reprinted articles are from obscure sources. The Atlas is a collection of detailed field studies that illustrate the myriad ways oil and gas are trapped. It is also a guide to the petroleum geology of the basins where these fields are found. Field studies like those published in the Atlas are the documentation of petroleum geology. They form the basis for all of our assumptions regarding petroleum geology. From the standpoint of the explorationist who is building and selling prospects, details from field studies can be stored as memories and used to build stronger prospects and convince doubters of the validity of any unique features of a prospect—nothing is more convincing than a close analogy. The third part of the Treatise, the *Handbook of Petroleum Geology*, is a professional explorationist's guide to the methodology and technology used to find fields similar to those described in the Atlas.

The Handbook set is divided into four volumes, each of which addresses one of the four steps of oil and gas prospecting—evaluation of source rocks and migration, evaluation of reservoir quality and properties, evaluation of trapping conditions, and evaluation of economic opportunity. Accordingly, the four volumes of the Handbook are *Source and Migration Processes and Evaluation Techniques*; *Reservoirs*; *Exploring for Oil and Gas Traps;* and *The Business of Petroleum Exploration*. These publications should be kept close at hand so that when a question arises, an answer can be found quickly and easily.

Edward A. Beaumont and Norman H. Foster
Editors of the *Treatise of Petroleum Geology*

Preface

Purpose of the book

This book presents, in succinct form, basic concepts of petroleum geology and proven petroleum exploration techniques for locating oil and gas accumulations.

Book theme

This volume is a handbook about prospecting for oil and gas traps. It is a how-to discussion of techniques used to evaluate the critical elements necessary for discovering oil and gas accumulations. For the most part, the chapters focus on procedures first and then discuss concepts that one must understand to apply the procedures effectively.

Book format

The book format is a structured technical writing style known as information mapping. Information mapping makes information more accessible, easier to understand, and easier to remember. It is especially well suited for procedure-based books such as this one.

Intended audience

This volume is directed at professionals with two or more years' experience. It assumes a basic knowledge of most aspects of petroleum geology and petroleum exploration methods. Basic well log analysis, seismic theory, structural geology, stratigraphy, or sedimentology are not detailed. Instead it concentrates on elements of petroleum geology and petroleum exploration methods that are critical for generating viable prospects.

Contents

The book consists of twenty-one chapters subdivided into four parts. The first chapter serves as a jump-off point for the book's vision. It contains five sections that discuss various aspects of developing an exploration philosophy. Exploration begins in the mind. How one approaches exploration for oil and gas traps is a result of a philosophy developed through experience, interaction with others such as a mentor, and reading.

Part I contains chapters that deal with the concept of a trap and the geological context of a trap in a petroleum system.

Part II contains chapters discussing sedimentary basin analysis and the behavior of fluids within the basin. These chapters show methods of understanding the development and current condition of a basin and its plumbing system.

Part III narrows the focus to specific critical elements of the trap. It contains chapters that discuss tried-and-true methods for predicting the critical elements of a trap, including reservoir performance, seal existence and quality, and preservation of traps.

Part IV contains chapters that discuss various exploration methods and methods for predicting the location of structural and stratigraphic traps.

Acknowledgments

Our thanks to the authors of this book for their contributions and their patience with us during the editing process. We thank companies and individuals who supported the *Treatise* project through financial contributions and the committee that asked companies for financial support: P.W.J. Wood, James E. Gibbs, David S. Holland, and Jack C. Threet. Special thanks go to the AAPG Foundation and its trustees: Larry Funkhouser, John Amoruso, Jack Threet, Lewis "Bud" Fearing, and Paul Dudley. We especially appreciate the support of Executive Director Fred Dix. Finally, we gratefully acknowledge the persistence, patience, and professionalism of the book's Project and Content Editor, Kathryne E. Pile. Its quality is the result of her skill and diligence.

Dedication

Norman H. Foster was an oil and gas finder. During his lifetime, he found lots of it. He found it in basins where others had found it and he found it in basins where others said it couldn't be found. What made Norm Foster so good at finding oil and gas?

Finding oil and gas results from the skillful application of geologic concepts; it is not merely a matter of being lucky. The successful application of the science of petroleum geology is an art that requires the creative flair. That was Norm Foster's philosophy. That is the philosophy of this book. Using an analogy from golf, he used to say, "You have to get the ball close to the hole in order to have a chance for luck." He hoped that this book will help get you close.

Norman Foster was a geologist's geologist. He was the model of what all professionals should strive to be. At the local level (as a member of the Rocky Mountain Association of Geologists, in Denver, Colorado) he published, led field trips, worked on committees, and served in various offices including president. At the national level (AAPG) he published, taught continuing education courses, served on committees, and was Treasurer and President. AAPG and RMAG recognized Norm for his involvement and contributions. The RMAG made him a honorary member and presented him with its most prestigious award, Explorer of the Year. The AAPG made him an honorary member and presented him with its most prestigious award, The Sidney Powers Medal.

This book is about finding oil and gas. People working together to find oil and gas. People who are good at finding oil and gas are optimistic, creative, persistent, resourseful, and enthusiastic. Norman Foster was all of those things and more. He wanted to help others become oil and gas finders, and that is why he served as co-editor of this book. We dedicate this book to Norman H. Foster—to his spirit, to his professionalism, and to his generosity.

Chapter 1

Developing a Philosophy of Exploration

by

Edward A. Beaumont,

Norman H. Foster,

Richard R. Vincelette,

Marlan W. Downey,

and

James D. Robertson

Norman H. Foster

Norman H. Foster received a bachelor's degree (1957) and a master's degree (1960) in geology at the University of Iowa. In 1963 he completed his Ph.D. in geology at the University of Kansas. His geological career began in 1962, with Sinclair Oil in Casper, Wyoming. When Sinclair merged with Arco in 1969, Foster was offered expanding opportunities to participate in a number of important discoveries, including the giant Irian Jaya field in Indonesia. In 1979, he became an independent geologist and continued to prospect both in the United States and abroad. In addition to winning AAPG's Sidney Powers Memorial Medal for 1999, the former AAPG president received the Levorsen Award (1980), two Certificate of Merit awards (1987 and 1992), and the Distinguished Service Award (1985). He was a member of the AAPG Foundation and an AAPG Trustee Associate since 1979. His professional activities included GSA, SEG, SPE, SIPES, SEPM, and the National Academy of Sciences.

Edward A. Beaumont

Edward A. (Ted) Beaumont is an independent petroleum geologist from Tulsa, Oklahoma. He holds a BS in geology from the University of New Mexico and an MS in geology from the University of Kansas. Currently, he is generating drilling prospects in Texas, Oklahoma, and the Rocky Mountains. His previous professional experience was as a sedimentologist in basin analysis with Cities Service Oil Company and as Science Director for AAPG. Ted is coeditor of the Treatise of Petroleum Geology. He has lectured on creative exploration techniques in the U.S., China, and Australia and has received the Distinguished Service Award and Award of Special Recognition from AAPG.

Richard R. Vincelette

Richard Vincelette graduated with a B.S. degree in geological engineering from Montana Tech. in 1960 and received a Ph.D. in geology from Stanford in 1964. He has spent the last 35 years searching for, and occasionally finding, the elusive hydrocarbon trap. At present he is a geologist and chief curmudgeon with JOG Corporation in Healdsburg, California.

Marlan W. Downey

Marlan W. Downey is the J. Denny Bartell Professor and chief scientist of the Sarkeys Energy Center at the University of Oklahoma. He holds a B.A. degree in chemistry from Peru State College and both B.S. and M.S. degrees in geology from the University of Nebraska. Mr. Downey joined Shell Oil Company in 1957 and became its youngest chief geologist and the first Alaska Division exploration manager. In 1977 he became vice president of Shell's International Exploration and Production Division and later president of subsidiary Pecten International. Downey retired from Shell in 1987 but subsequently joined ARCO International in 1990 as senior vice president of exploration, then president. He retired from ARCO in 1996. He has been recognized as a Distinguished Alumni by both Peru State College and the University of Nebraska, knighted by President Biya of Cameroon for his service to that country, elected a Fellow of the American Association for the Advancement of Science, served as an AAPG Distinguished Lecturer (1986 and 1987), and named the AAPG Huffington Lecturer for the Far East (1996).

James D. Robertson

James D. Robertson, Vice President of Exploration for ARCO International Oil and Gas Company, received a B.S.E. degree in civil and geological engineering from Princeton University in 1970 and a Ph.D. degree in geophysics from the University of Wisconsin in 1975. He joined ARCO in 1975 and has held various technical and management positions, including director of geophysical research, geophysical manager of the offshore Gulf of Mexico exploration group, vice president of geoscience operations, and chief geophysicist of ARCO's international exploration and production division. Robertson has been active in the professional activities of various geological and geophysical societies and was the 1994–95 president of the Society of Exploration Geophysicists. He is a past president and honorary member of the Dallas Geophysical Society and serves on the advisory boards of the geology and geophysics departments of Princeton University, the University of Wisconsin, and the Colorado School of Mines.

Overview

Introduction

Developing a philosophy of exploration is an important step toward becoming a more effective explorationist, both individually and on a team. This chapter discusses various aspects of exploration philosophy with the intent of helping individuals develop their own philosophies.

In this chapter

This chapter contains the following sections.

Section A

The Art and Science of Exploring for Oil and Gas

by
Norman H. Foster and Edward A. Beaumont

Introduction

Great oil, gas, and mineral finders have common characteristics that allow them to succeed. By surveying a select group of successful explorationists, we discovered they love the thrill of discovery and the deep satisfaction of being able to use science and art to find a valuable resource for the benefit of all mankind. Specifically, we identified the following common characteristics:

1. Think positively (negative-thinking people do not find oil and gas)
2. Are self-motivated and self-starting
3. Are persistent
4. Have vivid imaginations controlled by facts
5. Develop creativity through visual thinking

In this chapter we concentrate on the role of creativity in petroleum exploration and how that creativity can be enhanced.

In this section

This section contains the following topics.

Who Finds Oil?

Introduction

Only a small percentage of people exploring for oil, gas, and other natural resources actually find those resources in commercial quantities. We fervently believe, however, that one learns to be an oil and gas finder. Two of the best ways to learn to become oil finders are (1) to familiarize ourselves with the successful approaches and techniques of other oil and gas finders and (2) to develop our visual thinking skills.

Academic training

Theoretically, every geologist with a master's degree or higher from an accredited institution has the necessary scientific background to be a successful explorationist. Thorough training in structural geology, stratigraphy, sedimentology, geomorphology, paleontology, remote sensing, mineralogy, petrology, volcanism, economic geology, geophysics, and geochemistry are fundamental. A course in petroleum engineering is very helpful. Also, a rigorous field geology course is absolutely essential because one must learn to observe and record information accurately in the field, thinking in the third and fourth dimensions and developing a sense of the size of geological features.

Impact of technology

A few years of experience in the industry should prepare an individual to use the latest technology. Computers process data rapidly, which was impossible just a short time ago. This has allowed us, for example, to develop 3-D and 4-D seismic data gathering and processing. In addition, computers allow us to compare thousands of data sets rapidly, as in surface geochemical ratios. But even with all the new technology, thorough scientific training, and new scientific and engineering understanding, only a small percentage of people searching for oil, gas, and minerals ever find them in commercial quantities.

Teams

To overcome the huge amount of technological know-how needed for successful exploration, most companies form multidisciplinary teams. The synergies achieved by several individuals with different specialized skills working to solve a problem can be a successful approach. However, the creative spark of one or more members of the team to correctly interpret the geology (with the aid of scientific understanding and technology) is the essential element for success.

Creativity

Given that most geologists and geophysicists are scientifically and technically competent, what is it that separates the oil and gas finders from the crowd? Creativity is the most important ingredient in exploration, and creativity is enhanced through visual thinking. We define creativity as the ability to look at the same data that everyone else has but to see something different. It involves looking at data from many different perspectives—thinking outside "the box," yet always honoring known facts to make an interpretation that varies from the beaten path. One must constantly attempt to see what might be there, instead of discounting what may not be known to us.

Visual training

Geology is a visual science. To make insightful observations and dream more imaginative concepts, the visual skills of the geologist must be developed fully.

In the past, some geology or earth science departments required a basic course in drawing for a baccalaureate degree. The ability to draw freehand and illustrate various geological phenomena was deemed indispensable. Many geologists became quite proficient in sketching thin sections, fossils, outcrops, and other geological features. But beginning in the 1930s, the drawing requirement was dropped. With the development of the camera and the ease and economy of its use came the belief that drawing proficiency was no longer necessary. All one needed was to snap the camera with the proper exposure and focus, and an even more accurate record (more accurate than drawing the feature oneself) could be obtained.

Today, of course, there is the choice of black-and-white or living color. Earth scientists have retained some of the knowledge of how to diagram and draw by making maps, cross sections, and block diagrams. Unfortunately, by not learning to draw at an adult level, we have largely given up one of our most powerful tools of learning: to think visually and to observe critically. These are the keys to creative thinking, problem-solving, and developing new concepts.

The Thinking Process

Introduction

In the 1960s, Roger Sperry published his Nobel prize-winning brain hemisphere research based on split-brain studies. He and his students found that the two lobes of the cerebrum think in fundamentally different modes.

Thinking styles

The two lobes of the cerebrum are referred to as the left and right hemispheres. Betty Edwards, in *Drawing on the Artist Within,* refers to the thinking style as L-mode and R-mode.

The table below summarizes the styles.

L-Mode Thinking	R-Mode Thinking
Linear	Lateral
Conscious	Subconscious
Logical	Spatial/Visual

In addition to identifying thinking styles, Sperry's research showed that the left and right hemispheres have different functions. L-mode thinking functions include language, mathematics, logic, and sense of time. R-mode thinking functions include intuition, emotion, visualization, spatial movement, and interpretation of the whole from fragments of data. Some endeavors tend to be dominated by left-brain thinking and others by right-brain thinking. Earth scientists should attempt to achieve a balance between L- and R-mode thinking, which is called whole-brain thinking.

Thinking Creatively

Introduction

The creative thinking process consists of six stages and involves switching back and forth between L- and R-mode thinking. The table below shows the six stages. The first five stages are well established in the literature, and we have added a sixth stage—application. Unless we *do* something about our creative idea, no progress will be made.

Stage	Thinking Mode	Description
First Insight	R-mode	Noticing something seems wrong or is missing
Saturation	L-mode	Saturating the brain with information
Incubation	R-mode	Putting a problem away for awhile
Illumination	L-mode	Becoming aware of a solution to a problem
Verification	L-mode	Testing the solution
Application	L-mode	Applying the solution

First insight

In petroleum exploration, with first insight (primarily a right-brain activity) one might become aware of an area's potential because of good hydrocarbon shows and reservoirs, or because of the presence of an accumulation that may have analogs nearby, or because a new technique might change the economics of a play.

Saturation

Saturation follows first insight and involves the complete study of all available information pertaining to the problem. This is mainly a left-brain activity. When the mind becomes fully saturated with all the available data, such as well control, surface geology, and seismic data, then it is time to incubate, which involves switching back to the subconscious right side and analyzing the data.

Incubation

One of the main blocks to creativity comes at the end of the saturation stage. Our educational system trains mainly the left side with subjects such as reading, writing, and arithmetic. We become conditioned to believe that once the data have been gathered and studied, we should be able to plug these into a formula and come up with a quick answer. That is not the way creative thought occurs. The information must be processed on the right side to find patterns and solutions to the problem. After saturation, it is best to relax and allow the subconscious mind to work on an answer. We need to let the problem "simmer." This is known as the incubation stage.

Illumination

Usually at a quiet moment in the middle of the night or on a walk or when you have your feet on the desk and are gazing out the window, the answer will come as a flash of insight. Suddenly, the left side becomes aware of the solution to the problem that the right side developed. This relatively short period is the illumination stage. The answer usually is in almost complete form.

Verification

The new insight to the problem may or may not be correct. Therefore, one must switch back to the left side and rigorously test the idea against the data. In petroleum exploration this includes all well and surface control. If, after thorough verification, it is still possible that the idea is correct (and it may not be), then we move to the final stage—application.

Application

The application stage is another major block to creativity in exploration because so many outstanding prospects go untested. If an idea can be right, then we must find a way to drill a well or, at an earlier stage, to conduct field work or perhaps shoot seismic data. Managers and individuals must find the funds to get the good ideas drilled because, of course, no petroleum will be found without drilling the creative plays. The newly created idea must be applied to have value.

Enhancing the Creative Thinking Process

Introduction

Three conditions promote creative thinking: motivation, information, and flexibility (McKim, 1980). We must be motivated because creative thinking is hard work. We must have the right information; valid new exploration concepts are created from information that is correct and readily available. Finally, we must be flexible. When our concepts are wrong, we must be flexible enough to change them. Once we have met these three conditions, what else can we do to enhance our creativity? There are many methods for enhancing creativity in petroleum exploration, such as building a knowledge of oil and gas field case histories or overcoming mental blocks. However, one of the most important methods for enhancing creativity in petroleum exploration is improving our ability to visualize.

Visualization

Both Betty Edwards and Robert H. McKim, in his book *Experiences in Visual Thinking,* stress the importance of learning to draw and diagram to aid visual-perceptual thinking. Through drawing and other visual exercises, one can learn to bring the right side to a conscious level and thus greatly improve our creative abilities.

Visualization & petroleum exploration

The great oil finders have long stressed developing creativity through visualization. Wallace Pratt said, "Where no one any longer believes that more oil is left to be found, no more oil fields will be discovered, but so long as a single oilfinder remains with a mental vision of a new oil field to cherish, along with freedom and incentive to explore, just so long new oil fields may continue to be discovered." In the same paper, Pratt said, "One indispensable attribute of the oilfinder is vision. If it is in the mind of the geologist or oilfinder that new fields first take form, then discovery must wait on our mental visualization—our imagination."

Drawing

Learning to sketch and draw is perhaps the best way to enhance creative visual thought. As Betty Edwards discovered, turning the object upside down turns off the dominant logical L-mode of thought because it does not like to deal with upside down. This allows the subdominant R-mode to take over. We see an object's shape, shading, highlights, negative space, and other visual features, and we can draw the object much more easily. For an observationally based science such as geology, a person who knows how to draw will be much more observant and imaginative than someone who does not know how to draw. Drawing forces one to abstract only the important elements of a subject. For numerous techniques and exercises to enhance visual thinking, refer to McKim and Edwards.

Geologists who draw

Many great earth scientists have or have had an artistic flair. The outcrop sketches and abstractions of geology from the drawings of people such as William Henry Holmes and P.B. King are legendary, as were the drawings and paintings of many early geologists. Shown below is a P.B. King outcrop field sketch (A) and extrapolated cross section (B) of the Victorian flexure from the Permian basin in the United States. By drawing the outcrop and abstracting stratigraphic relationships, King was able to understand and demonstrate the progradational nature of the carbonate platform.

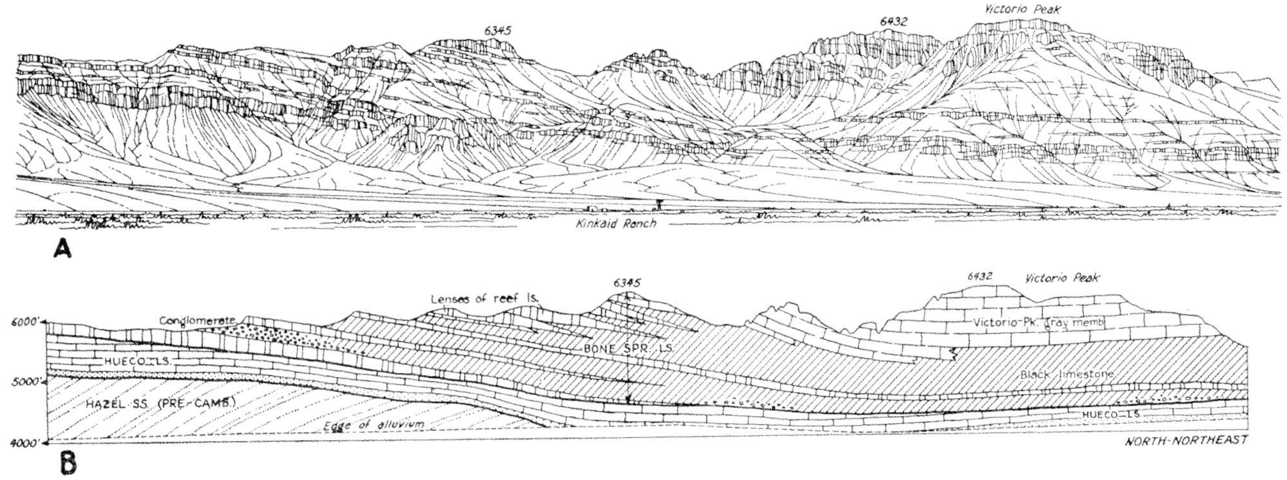

Figure 1–1. From King (1942); courtesy AAPG.

Section B

Characteristics of Oil Finders

by

Edward A. Beaumont, Norman H. Foster, and Richard R. Vincelette

Introduction

What is an oil finder? Oil finders are people who have not only found oil or gas but who seem to have a nose for it. This section presents the results of a survey of oil finders that gives insight into the personality characteristics of oil finders and their philosophic approach to exploration.

In this section

This section contains the following topics.

Characteristics of Oil Finders

Introduction

What are the characteristics of people who are effective at finding oil and gas? What do they do when exploring for oil or gas that sets them apart? What are their hobbies? How do they approach exploration? How do they overcome creative blocks? To gain insight into the traits and work habits of oil finders, we surveyed a select group of 44 explorationists who had found oil or gas to see if similarities emerged. Respondents answered the questions enthusiastically. Their answers are fascinating and fun to read. We can all learn from their philosophies and approaches to exploration.

Survey respondents

The survey was sent to a wide variety of explorationists: women and men, major company employees and consultants, old and young, domestic and international. Although broadly different in background, this select group of explorationists had one thing in common: not only have they found oil or gas, but they have found it often enough that one would have to conclude they are not just lucky. They all fit the definition of oil finder.

Survey Responses

Survey questions

The survey questions were grouped into eight categories:

- General
- Personal attributes
- Education/training
- Visual skills
- Methodology
- Business and personal contacts
- Blocks to creativity
- Working environment

Responses to the survey showed the individualism and diversity of participants. Answers to questions were varied. The differences and similarities were significant and informative. Typical responses to a few of the questions are noted below. Anyone wishing to become an oil finder should find them fascinating and useful.

Advice for aspiring oil finders

Question: What advice would you give to someone who wishes to become an oil finder?

Summary: Get a good education, work with an oil finder mentor, study oil and gas field case histories, and use every scrap of information.

Typical responses:

"1. Love the excitement of the oil industry. 2. Love the smell of sulfur and crude oil. 3. Study what oil finders have written. 4. Know that finding oil requires endless effort. 5. Associate with an oil-finder, if possible. 6. Pay very close attention to oil tracks—shows." (Gerald Loucks)

"Find space to dream. Believe in yourself and your capabilities, and believe that if you keep trying, tomorrow you'll win. Keep an open mind and be willing to change it. Learn to be a realistic business person. Maintain a good sense of humor. Marry someone who also believes in you." (Donald Todd)

"1. Educate yourself widely in geology, geophysics, and engineering. 2. Work in several different basins of varied stratigraphy, structure, etc. 3. Learn the petroleum history of your area. Know what people were thinking when wells were drilled in the '40s, '50s, '70s, etc. 4. Input every scrap of information you can find, continually." (John Masters)

Learning to find oil

Question: Can explorationists be taught to find oil?

Summary: Most said "yes." Many said desire is critical.

Typical responses:

"Yes, it is much more a learned skill than a natural talent. However, a good oil finder must be an optimist. He has to believe that he can find prospects that others overlook in order to be effective." (Jack Elam)

"Yes, but only if that's what they want to do. Most do not want to be oil finders, or at most it is a secondary objective. Also, most explorationists think they already know how to do it—they don't!" (James Lantz)

"1. Yes, to a point! 2. The exceptional hydrocarbon finders, I believe, have 'powers' (understanding and visualization) that may be intuitive." (Robert Sneider)

Skill versus luck

Question: Which is more important, skill or luck?

Summary: Skill. Many said luck plays a role, but skill makes the difference over the long term.

Typical responses:

"A skilled practitioner employs controlled, creative imagination. The control consists of utilizing all geological and geophysical data available. Creative imagination involves the application of a broad academic and experience background. I will be grateful for luck but to depend on it is no better than your chances of hitting a moving target with a dart in a high wind." (Dan Busch)

"Although many discoveries are attributed to luck, if investigated, it would be found that many hours of consideration, thinking, construction, and data presentation were involved in creating the 'luck.' I think circumstances that involve good or bad results because of a myriad of reasons have been the basis for many a philosophical discussion through the history. 'Lucky' is in my vocabulary, but whether it be true or not, I do not know, and I don't think I want to know." (Graham Curtis)

"As important as the basic skills are in becoming an oil finder, these aren't of much consequence without a bit of luck. Luck doesn't happen if you don't expose yourself and take changes. For those you have included in your survey, many times more were equally capable and took big risks but luck was not with them." (Donald Todd)

"Skill! Luck is what others call an oil finder's skill. I have some regrets of permitting salesmen of 'luck' to persuade me to forego good judgment and take a chance on 'luck.'" (Gerald Loucks)

Survey Responses, continued

Productive age

Question: What was the most productive period in your life?

Summary: Most respondents said they were not successful until they had five or more years' experience. Many said they are most productive now, indicating they feel experience is critical.

Typical Responses:

"From 1948 to 1975, which is when I was between 30 and 58 years of age. I was involved in 15 discoveries between 1948 and 1965." (Ted Bear)

"Different tasks are more easily accomplished at different ages. I fortunately feel I have been very productive at all mature stages of my life. When I lose that a feeling, I will retire." (Roy Huffington)

"Ages 18 through 50, when I was actually allowed to explore. I directly found 7 large fields and participated in about 20 other discoveries (2 giants). I also found one hard rock ore body which became a commercial mine." (David Powley:)

"Between 40 and 70 years of age." (Dan Busch)

"I am still productive at 89 years of age. I have been productive in every decade of my professional life, which spans 70 years, indicating that I have not slackened my pace." (Michel Halbouty)

Motivation

Question: We all recognize that successful exploration is related to a number of important factors: motivation, opportunity, and environment. What has motivated you in your career, and what do you think are the most important motivating factors in general?

Summary: The excitement of the hunt; money is nice, but it isn't the real motivator.

Typical responses:

"I think that motivation changes throughout one's life. The early years of survival and family maintenance require more of a technical adherence. Eventually there is the emergence of that inner challenge of you vs. Mother Nature and the need for the thrill and satisfaction of discovery—and then just one more! I believe motivation and the best scientific oil finders come from a basic love, understanding, and appreciation of their science, as well as the exploration business, i.e., playing the game for the game's sake!" (Graham Curtis)

"First was appreciation by my superiors for a job well done. Then it was acceptance of my ideas by my peers. Then it was financial success. But overall it was the fun and challenge of the 'race' and the pride of accomplishment." (Donald Stone)

"My greatest motivation has always been the thrill of the hunt, of looking for the pot of gold at the end of the rainbow. I just happen to really enjoy using my skills and talents in exploring for oil and gas. And once you have had success and felt the thrill of victory, it motivates you even more." (Richard Vincelette)

Survey Responses, continued

Training

Question: How did you learn to find oil? Did someone teach you, or were you largely self-taught?

Summary: Although earlier the respondents said mentors were very important, most said they were self-taught.

Visual thinking

Question: Do you consider yourself to be a visual thinker?

Summary: Yes.

Sketching

Question: Do you like to draw or sketch?

Summary: Yes (86%).

Typical responses:

"Yes, I draw and sketch landscapes, seascapes, people, things—outcrops in the field. It helps me to visualize, to see things I otherwise would never notice. I keep sketch (visual) notebooks. Drawing and sketching are the most important ways to learn to think visually." (Norman Foster)

"Yes. Even though I am very adept at 3-D visualization, I still have to put it down on paper to get it properly in mind. I continually redraw cross and seismic sections in 3-D, taking the earth's curvature into consideration." (Jack Elam)

"Absolutely. I believe I understand concepts, etc., only after I can draw it for myself and explain it to others." (Robert Sneider)

"Yes, all the time—have even tried etching and monoprints. Took up watercolor as a well-site geologist. Used blank DST charts to scratch pictures on. I have done some carving. Mostly I paint in oils and acrylics." (Donald Todd)

"My imagination and the pages of my books are my best, most used visual aids. From these I sketch, I interpret, I classify, I discard, and I refine each concept based on the information available. When everything meshes and I feel good and secure, I become fairly sure I have found oil or gas—reached my goal." (Gerald Loucks)

Idea development

Question: Where do you get your best ideas for new plays?

Summary: Developing and applying analogs from a strong knowledge of case histories is valuable.

Typical responses:

"From surface geology, either directly from the field or from aerial photos compared to surface expression of analogs. From the patterns of productive trends in similar basin settings. From studying nearby analogs and looking for similar anomalies. From analogs in faraway basins and applying them to the prospect area." (Norman Foster)

"Most of the best ideas I have had were based on plays that developed in other parts of the U.S. that were look-alikes to things that I was already doing." (A.V. Jones)

"Sometimes while driving, sometimes while sleeping, sometimes in church, sometimes through field studies, once by looking at a map of the northern polar region of Mars." (Douglas Strickland)

"Reading and hearing professional talks are first. Sometimes in teaching or preparing to teach. Also on airplanes when listening to music." (Robert Sneider)

"In the shower. While doing rig operations, short-term input for drilling wells. While messing around in my databases, doing things that 'I ought to let someone else do.'" (James Lantz)

Frontier vs. mature basins

Question: Do you prefer frontier or mature basins?

Summary: Frontier, 60%; mature, 20%; both, 20%.

Peers

Question: Discuss other oil finders you know or have known. What characteristics made them oil finders?

Typical responses:

"The scientific oil finders' characteristics, I believe, are as follows: observant, curious, logical, intelligent, creative, dedicated, outdoorsy, risk oriented, independent, derives pleasure when making order out of chaos. I hope the above does not sound too much like a horoscope reading, but all or parts of each are needed." (Graham Curtis)

"They are optimistic, positive thinkers (negative-thinking people do not find oil). They develop creativity through visual thinking, they have vivid imaginations controlled by facts, they are also very curious, they have a great desire to find oil, they are self-motivating and self-starting, they are persistent, and they love the trill of discovery and the deep satisfaction of finding something of value for the betterment of mankind." (Norman Foster)

"They were there first. Even before geophysicists, there was no substitute for being there first. As for characteristics, 1. Persistence is #1. 2. Enthusiasm for oil exploration. 3. Self-confidence. 4. Risk-takers. 5. Intuitive sense of where exploration opportunities exist. 6. Ability to diagnose critical elements of a play." (David Powley)

Blocks to creativity

Question: What do you think are the biggest blocks to creativity in petroleum exploration?

Summary: Management that doesn't understand oil and gas exploration or the creative process. On the other hand, a boost to creativity was working in a place that has the resources to test ideas.

Typical responses:

"Most explorationists are under too much pressure to produce. Exploration is an art form, and you don't stand over an artist and criticize his work. Large companies have to show a profit every year. Even if they are doing their jobs, they are going to have a bad year. Bosses and stockholders should look at the longer term and overall results." (A.V. Jones)

"Extraneous activities which constantly interrupt the concentration of the explorationist." (Frank Harrison)

"The single, most destructive block is the desire to quantify results and relate those to economic rates of return. Usually this takes the form of a single answer which is subjective and doomed to be wrong! Another block is attitudinal—it is always easier to destroy a hypothesis than it is to nurture one. Nurturing ideas is hard work!" (Harry Jamison)

"A management lacking geologic knowledge and exploration know-how. In the case of an independent, lack of sufficient resources to acquire necessary geologic data, well data, maps, and pertinent information." (Howard Lester)

Overcoming prospector's block

Question: How do you overcome prospector's block?

Summary: Typically, respondents said they put the problem away for awhile—they let it incubate.

Typical responses:

"I usually work on two or three projects during the same time period. When I get bogged down on one, I go concentrate on one or two of the others. This usually works for me every time." (Robert Sneider)

"If I understand what you mean, I clean up the office, put things away, and start by studying regional maps and doing some general reading. Or perhaps going through old files for leads never followed up." (Donald Stone)

"Yes. I go for drives in the country, go camping, go fossil collecting, etc." (Douglas Strickland)

"Cleaning my desk and my office helps clear my mind. (Sometimes this takes a few days.) Quit your job. Twice in my career I quit good jobs because I was left no room to dream." (Donald Todd)

Survey Responses, continued

Working environment

Question: Describe what you consider to be the best working environment.

Summary: Most individuals described a comfortable environment where other optimistic colleagues worked and with whom they could interact.

Typical responses:

"In an office with all the data, around a number of optimistic geologists, and with a supervisor tht doesn't have preconceived ideas, does have an open mind, and is a smart geologist." (Ted Bear)

"Large room; lots of (magnetic) wall space; long layout table; easy access to database and exploration files and well-stocked library. Experienced, enthusiastic teammates. Ample freedom within framework of time and company's strategic targets." (H.M. Helmig)

"Comfortable, well-lighted working areas with access to all the better exploration aids and no worry about financing your projects. Optimistic exploration friends are also quite valuable in helping to overcome some occasional exploration slumps." (Roy Huffington)

Working alone versus working on a team

Question: Do you function best alone or on a team?

Summary: They like an office where they can be alone but, when they need to test an idea, have someone there to help.

Typical response:

"Alone, I think pure individualism is essential because, in my case, committee efforts tend to defuse my aim. With total concentration, I am able to massage my data and imaginatively draw or conceptualize my targets without diversion. After my study is complete, I consider it important to subject it to constructive expert review (provided they agree with me)." (Robert Gunn)

"Initially, I function best alone; but as an exploration idea develops, more and more teamwork is required in order to bring to bear all of the talents and disciplines of the team. This is particularly true now and in the future as geology becomes more and more a multi-disciplined science." (Howard Lester)

"I like to work alone, essentially, but with access to a team of specialists because I am not very strong technically." (John Masters)

"Creatively I have always functioned best alone. After the conceptional stage, however, team effort is most necessary. Rarely does a creative oil finder fit into a bureaucratic corporate mold for very long. I function best out of my hip pocket." (Donald Todd)

"I have had my greatest success in a team environment, but where independent thought and action are also encouraged. Most creative ideas are probably developed by the individual pondering alone on a problem or goal. But those ideas are immeasurably enhanced through brainstorming and interaction with others concerned with the same problem or goal." (Richard Vincelette)

Section C

Leading and Managing Explorationists

by
Norman H. Foster

Introduction

People who understand the creative process and how it applies to petroleum exploration are best qualified to lead and manage explorationists in an exploration program. Explorationists are more creative when their ideas are nurtured and they are surrounded by a supportive team.

In this section

This section contains the following topics.

Developing and Leading Multidisciplinary Teams

An analogy

Metaphors help develop an understanding of any subject. To help understand the highly effective dynamics of teams, let's consider the four-person scramble in golf. Many professional golf tournaments are usually straight medal play for the championship, where the person with the best score wins. In these tournaments, scores are determined by individual handicaps so anyone has a chance to win.

In a scramble, teams are assembled. Everyone on a team tees off and plays every shot. After a shot, members of a team decide where the best ball is located. Each team member participates in the next shot, and so on. Compared with medal play, the transformation in attitude and teamwork is amazing. Each team member wants his teammates to succeed. The members are no longer competing against each other but are working toward a common goal. The enthusiasm feeds on itself, resulting in a greater enjoyment of the game. The team shoots a much better score than any one individual could post, and team members share equally in any prizes that may be won.

Past and present

Multidisciplinary teams of geologists, geophysicists, engineers, geochemists, petrophysicists, landmen, and businessmen are far superior to any one individual working under the old district concept if arranged in the proper scramble format. The district concept of petroleum exploration used by the industry tended to pit fellow workers against each other, as well as groups of specialists such as geologists and engineers. Fiefdoms tended to form to protect turf.

Maximum brain power

Early in my career at Sinclair Oil Corp., I was inspired by Michel Halbouty's paper entitled "Maximum Brain Power." Halbouty advocated the formation of multidisciplinary teams to maximize the exploration effectiveness of an organization. I proposed this type of organization to Sinclair's exploration manager, S. K. Van Steenburg, and he formed the Williston Basin Exploration Team.

The original group consisted of geologists (a carbonate stratigrapher, a structural geologist, and a photogeologist), a petrophysicist, a geophysicist, and a landman. The team was so highly effective that within six months the entire Western Region was reorganized into exploration teams. The Williston basin team developed more prospects in about a year than the entire corporation did worldwide. It leased acreage quickly after generating the prospects, and its work led to several important discoveries, including the Weldon oil field in Montana (the best field on a per-well basis in Montana).

Take dead aim

Just as in golf, if you take dead aim, you will be more effective. What are you trying to do? Make a profit for the company. How do you do this? Find and produce commercial accumulations of hydrocarbons. When you focus on the goal—to find and produce commercial accumulations of hydrocarbons—all sorts of things start to fall into place, especially when individuals are organized into teams.

Unfortunately, we frequently tend to get sidetracked into many extraneous areas that have little or no bearing on where commercial hydrocarbons are located. When this happens, we need to focus again on the goal, asking the same fundamental questions for every prospect:

1. Are mature source rocks present?
2. Have the source rocks generated and expelled enough oil to provide commercial accumulations?
3. What are the migration pathways?
4. Are sufficient reservoirs present?
5. What types of traps are probable, and where are the traps located in which the hydrocarbons may have accumulated?

Leadership

Leaders and managers have a unique opportunity to help the effectiveness of exploration teams. Their experience in widely diverse areas and traps enables them to provide many helpful and sometimes critical ideas for generating and evaluating prospects. Their experience of evaluating many widely different types of plays can be applied in innumerable ways to help a team take dead aim. Leaders and managers should always put people first. Stephen Covey, author of *The 7 Habits of Highly Effective People,* says, "The first imperative for today's leaders is the top line, not the bottom line." By this, he means that if we concentrate on people (the top line), the bottom line will take care of itself. Try to provide an environment that nurtures creative thinking—one that encourages taking a different path.

Test ideas

If a creative idea has held up under the closest scrutiny, then the idea is ready for the drill and it is the duty of the manager to do everything possible to get the idea evaluated. Find the money to drill inside the company or, if not available internally, farm out the prospect. One of the great killers of creativity is that new ideas frequently are not evaluated.

Getting ideas

Managers must make sure they and their employees keep abreast of developments in their field. Managers should encourage explorationists to attend conventions, present talks for professional societies, publish papers, take/lead seminars, enroll in continuing education courses, participate in study groups, serve on committees and as officers of professional societies, and read the published literature. One of the lamest excuses is "My company won't let me publish." Companies will succeed if their people are able to reach their maximum potential by interacting with professionals outside their companies.

Developing and Leading Multidisciplinary Teams, continued

Team life cycles

Effective exploration teams are extremely flexible and are formed for a specific purpose and goal. When those goals are achieved, the team should be disbanded.

Recognizing oil finders

How do managers and leaders recognize oil and gas finders? Finders are positive thinkers (negative-thinking people do not find oil), they develop creativity through visual thinking, they have vivid imaginations controlled by facts, they have a great desire to find hydrocarbons, they are self-motivating and self-starting, they are optimistic, they are persistent, and above all they love the thrill of discovery and the deep satisfaction of being able to use science and art to find a valuable deposit for the benefit of all mankind.

Establishing a Creative Environment

Idea killers

The great enemy of ideas and a creative environment is the killer phrase. New ideas are very fragile and must be nurtured until they can be tested. Most new ideas fail because they are not correct; however, a small percentage of new ideas will prove to be right. If an organization is to survive and prosper, an environment must be established where new ideas are allowed to come forward, be tested, and, if workable, be integrated into the business.

What is a killer phrase?

A killer phrase is a negative word or statement that is inevitably hurled at any new idea. Frequently the result is to shoot down the idea without a fair evaluation. Examples of killer phrases are . . .

- "We tried that before."
- "That's irrelevant."
- "Don't waste time thinking."
- "It's not in the budget."
- "Your ideas only have limited use in their present format."
- "It will be more trouble than it's worth."
- "We've done all right so far."
- "No."
- silence

Killer phrase generators

Everyone issues killer phrases: you, me, our spouses, our bosses—everyone. It's part of human nature, our culture, and our upbringing. One study showed that negative no-can-do statements outweigh positive can-do statements by big margins. At home, parents say, on the average, 18 negative statements for every one positive statement they utter. We even issue killer phrases to ourselves by creating self-doubt: "I'll look stupid" or "Somebody has already done it" or "I don't have time." How often have you had a great idea but failed to follow through? Idea generators must be aware of killer phrases, know how to recognize them (no matter how subtle), and be prepared to defuse them.

Defusing killer phrases

Killer phrases become institutionalized. Every organization has its own favorite negative statements. To defuse the inevitable killer phrases that appear at any stage of a new idea, be prepared. Anticipate them, and have a response ready such as the following:

Killer phrase—"We did that 10 years ago."

Possible response—"Lots of improvements and new understanding have occurred since then. Let me gather the details for you so we can review them at our next meeting and avoid previous mistakes."

Institutionalize the term "killer phrase" so everyone learns to recognize one. This will greatly reduce their use. Point out old ways of thinking in a fun way, such as by throwing paper wads at each other whenever a killer phrase is hurled at a new idea. Before long, you won't let the "It hasn't worked in the past" way of thinking affect the way you operate today.

Section D

Applying the Scientific Method to Petroleum Exploration

by
Marlan W. Downey and James D. Robertson

Introduction

Successful exploration results when we apply technology and intelligence to the task of finding oil cheaply. We must know whether intelligence and technology are being properly harnessed to deliver exploration success. If technology is being properly utilized, it should lead to predictable outcomes and improvement in performance measures such as exploration costs. On the other hand, if the application lacks focus or direction, technology will have no benefit, even though it may be intellectually interesting. Proper application of technology in petroleum exploration is geologically directed and follows the scientific method. It is important for all explorationists to realize that scientifically directed petroleum exploration reduces risk and therefore impacts the economic success of any petroleum exploration program.

This chapter reviews the scientific method and discusses its application to exploration. Also discussed are ways to measure and evaluate the confidence level of a scientific interpretation.

In this section

This section covers the following topics.

What is the Scientific Method?

Introduction

In looking at past actions and past outcomes, it is easy to analyze whether exploration predictions were correct. If they were correct, the technology used for the predictions was probably proper and correct.

In real-time monitoring of whether technology is used properly, managers must rely on subjective measures. One helpful approach is to assess whether a company's technical efforts are truly part of a scientific approach to exploration. A scientific approach requires that technology be used in a logic sequence to solve problems, i.e., be deployed not for its own sake but as part of a scientific methodology.

The scientific method

The logic sequence, or *scientific method,* has been the basis of scientific work since the time of Copernicus and takes the form shown in the following table.

Step	Action
1	State a problem.
2	Collect observations relevant to the problem.
3	Formulate a hypothetical solution (interpretation) of the problem, consistent with the observations.
4	Predict other observable phenomena from the hypothesis.
5	Test predictions by observing occurrences or nonoccurrences of the predicted phenomena.
6	Accept, modify, or reject the hypothesis (interpretation) in accordance with the degree of fulfillment of the predictions.

Measuring the merit of predictions

Technical work in exploration is most valuable when it both conforms to and lasts through the entire logic sequence. We can appreciate a solid technical effort that produces a good initial interpretation. However, the true measure of merit is the accuracy of the predictions inherent in this first hypothesis and the robustness of the interpretation when these predictions are tested by new data.

Applying the Scientific Method to Exploration

Introduction

Technical effort in petroleum exploration that follows the six steps of the scientific method is the only effort that can consistently progress toward an acceptable solution. The table below shows how to apply the scientific method to petroleum exploration.

Examples

Step	Action	Example(s)
1	State the problem	Asking "Where are the economical hydrocarbon accumulations?"
2	Collect observations	Collecting outcrop, seismic, and well log data
3	Formulate hypothesis	Correlating seismic records with well logs Contouring structural and thickness data
4	Make predictions	Recommending lease purchases Recommending drilling a test well on the basis of map interpretation
5	Test predictions by observing phenomena	Seismically detailing a structural prospect Drilling a wildcat well
6	Accept, modify, or reject the hypothesis	Drilling another wildcat well Promoting a well to test a modified hypothesis Dropping acreage

Step 1: State objectives

In exploration, the general problem is locating substantial quantities of hydrocarbons that are economical to produce. A host of specific problems arise in given instances, but we should recognize that the major problem (objective) of an exploration effort is to find large amounts of oil or gas cheaply.

Step 2: Collect observations

Much of the technical work done in exploration can be categorized as collecting observations (data). Under this heading comes work such as logging samples, recording shows, compiling sediment interval thicknesses, acquiring field seismic data, and identifying paleontologic data.

Step 3: Formulate a hypothesis

In step 3, explorationists formulate hypothetical solutions (interpretations) to the problem stated in step 1 (Where are the hydrocarbons?) that are consistent with the observations of step 2. When explorationists interpret data, they formulate hypothetical solutions to the problem of finding commercial accumulations of hydrocarbons.

Unfortunately, exploration technical work often bogs down at step 3. Many people believe a modern interpretation derived from recently collected and carefully measured data is a high-level scientific piece of work that deserves a high level of confidence. In the rigorous context that we are attempting to describe, such an interpretation is only an untested hypothesis (step 3).

Applying the Scientific Method to Exploration, continued

Step 3: Formulate a hypothesis (continued)

We should continuously evaluate whether the products of an exploration effort have passed step 3. For example, compare these two pieces of stratigraphic work:

- A simple gross sand isopach map that is essentially unaltered by results of considerable additional drilling. Such correct predictions represent work that has earned a high scientific confidence level and therefore is well past step 3.
- A newly prepared environmental, lithofacies, and seismic–stratigraphic interpretation of a similar sand unit. Although prepared with an impressive degree of advanced technical competence, this is only an untested hypothesis and therefore has only reached step 3.

The scientific method recognizes the degree of proof of the hypothesis, not the sophistication of the data used to prepare it.

Step 4: Predict results

Step 4 in the scientific method sequence is predicting that hydrocarbons can be found and economically produced at a specific location, using the maps, cross sections, etc., made in step 3. Predictions are of most value when their specific components are properly recorded in advance of verification along with some estimate of the degree of confidence in the components.

Step 5: Test predictions

Next, we must check or observe the predictions of step 4 against the outcome of some test, such as drilling a well or seismically detailing (reshooting) a prospect.

Step 6: Accept, modify, or reject the hypothesis

Drilling a wildcat well on a prospect rarely completely proves or disproves the original interpretation. Generally the test performed at step 5 modifies the interpretation to a greater or lesser extent and always alters the confidence level attributable to the interpretation. Depending on the confidence retained in the interpretation, we may drill another wildcat well, promote a test, or drop the acreage, in descending orders of confidence. Step 6 of the scientific method as applied to petroleum exploration is accepting, modifying, or rejecting the hypotheses or interpretation developed at step 4.

Measuring and Evaluating Scientific Predictions

Introduction

There is a common tendency to regard a single well on a prospect as conclusive proof or disproof of an interpretation. However, we need to analyze the wildcat well far more intensively than "Is it a dry hole or not?" We need to provide a series of specific predictions about what the well will find to compare with what the well did find.

Evaluating predrilling hypothesis

How do we know when a predrilling hypothesis is correct? If drilling proves we were correct on most or all of our predictions, then we can be confident in our interpretation. If the well comes in low with very thin, tight reservoirs and no oil shows, then we need to give our interpretation and ourselves a failing grade.

Measuring confidence level

Is it possible to measure the confidence level (degree of scientific proof) of a mapping interpretation without drilling numerous additional wildcats or shooting more seismic? Certainly! Where possible, maps should be constructed in two stages:

Stage 1. A preliminary interpretation that deliberately excludes a random portion of the available information.

Stage 2. A revised map incorporating all the information to compare and test the interpretation.

Such a two-stage mapping procedure lets us test our interpretation with available data rather than drilling expensive new wildcats and shooting seismic surveys.

Follow these steps to measure the confidence level of a mapping interpretation before drilling.

Step	Action
1	Construct a first-stage map, leaving out a random and significant portion of the available data.
2	Insert all withheld well data into a second-stage map and compare predicted vs. actual.
3	If predicted vs. actual does not match, review the original contouring hypothesis and adjust it to fit the data.

Example

The following is a hypothetical example of a two-stage mapping to measure confidence before drilling:

Assumption: Commercial oil production in the zone of interest in the map area shown below requires more than 15 m of sand.

Example (continued)

Task: Map sand thickness in available wells and select the area most favorable for leasing and drilling.

Procedure: Follow the procedure detailed on the preceding page.

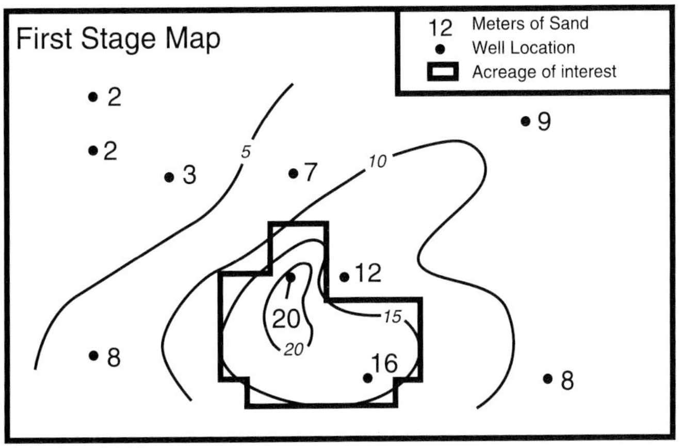

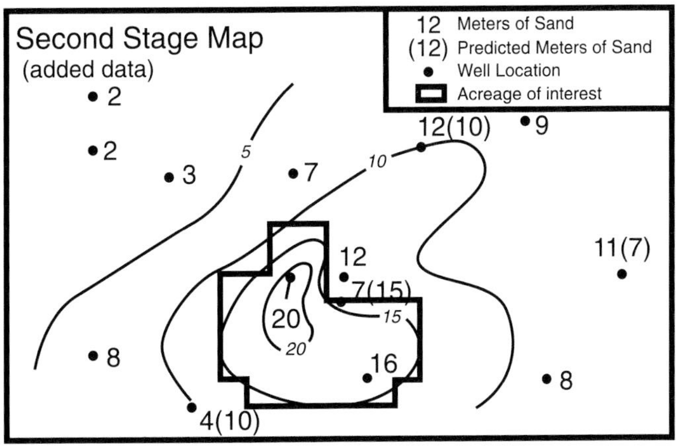

Conclusion: Four wells were left out of the first map. The second map shows that the two wells closest to the prospect outline had thinner sand than predicted. The two wells away from the outline had thicker sand. The interpretation should be adjusted by recontouring the data.

Judging confidence level

The most difficult single decision in exploration is judging the level of confidence to place on an interpretation. If we want exploration technical work to be scientific work, we must learn to recognize the real usefulness of our technical work: What step in the scientific method are we actually attaining? Our technical work needs to provide internal measures of its uncertainty.

A common approach of developing confidence in an interpretation might be to drench the area in data—drilling wells and acquiring 3-D seismic data. A more thoughtful and economic approach would be to test the robustness of the original interpretation. If we conduct our exploration technical studies with scientific logic, we will be more successful in our exploration business ventures.

Section E
Analog Exploration

by
Norman H. Foster

Introduction

Each trap is unique because of the complex combination of all the geologic variables that define it. Some argue that this fact makes the analog approach weak. But the analog approach does not assume there is an exact look-alike. Instead, the analog approach draws look-alike features that are critical elements of the play from appropriate fields both within and outside the basin of interest. This section discusses how to apply analogs to petroleum exploration.

In this section

This section contains the following topics.

Using Analogs to Identify Critical Elements

Introduction

Many people looking for oil and gas do not have a mental image of what they are searching for. How can one recognize something if they do not know what it looks like? A hunter would not have much luck finding rabbits if he had very little idea of the appearance of a rabbit. He also would not have much luck finding rabbits if he did not understand their habits—where they live or what and when they eat. In the same way, we learn about oil and gas fields by studying their habitat.

Visualizing the trap

Visualizing an accumulation is the key to exploring for any type of trap. The explorer must have a mental image constantly before him to maximize his chances of success. Keeping visually focused on what you are looking for (the critical elements derived from analogs) helps define exploration methods, wellbore location, and penetration direction. This is known as the analog method of exploration.

The analog method is the most effective method, in the author's opinion. It closely follows the scientific method: establishing the critical factors of the known and then looking for the same critical factor in an unknown area. In essence, if you can visualize it, you can find it.

Finding analogs

Oil and gas accumulations fall into broad categories, i.e., structural and stratigraphic traps, but there are hundreds of variations of these trap types. The explorer must carefully study the many ways in which oil and gas accumulate. Many local and international geological societies publish field studies that can serve as analogs. AAPG's 11-volume *Treatise of Petroleum Geology, Atlas of Oil and Gas Fields* is an excellent example of where to find analogs.

Critical elements

These excellent descriptions and analyses provide the explorer with mental images of various trap types, which are essential in recognizing certain critical elements of traps. Usually, at least three to five critical factors must be present for a particular type of trap to work. When we study local analog fields within a region or basin, or perhaps in a similar productive setting in another part of the world, we can develop the critical elements of a specific play, which in turn lead to discovery.

An Example of Applying Critical Elements

Critical elements of the Niobrara play

In the fractured Upper Cretaceous Niobrara play of the central Rocky Mountain region, specific critical elements must be present for a prospect to be successful. Since the Niobrara Formation is its own oil source rock, there is no bottom water; gas expansion along with gravity drainage provide the main reservoir energy, so the structural position of a well is not a critical factor. Synclines, anticlines, and any structural location in between will work. The main critical element is to find a sufficiently fractured sweet spot in which the fractures remain open during production. Careful study of numerous excellent Niobrara producing fields shows that the following critical elements must be present to achieve commercial success.

- Maximum bed curvature
- Normal fault cutting through area of maximum bed curvature
- Presence of a cross-lineation
- Open calcite crystals lining the fractures
- Well must penetrate above critical elements in a more fracturable (more calcareous) bench within the Niobrara
- Completion must be open hole (hang a slotted liner) with cement-block fractures
- Drilling must be conducted with underbalanced mud or air to prevent fracture damage. The Niobrara is an underpressured reservoir with petrostatic (0.33 lb/ft gradient) rather than hydrostatic (0.43 lb/ft gradient) pressure.

Applying the critical factors

Once the critical factors from the analog field(s) are fully understood, we can devise the best exploration methods to delineate the critical factors.

An Example of Applying Critical Elements, continued

Niobrara structure

In the Niobrara play, a subsurface structure map on top of the Niobrara formation is a first step to locate areas of maximum bed curvature. Normal faults should then be mapped from subsurface well control, photogeology, and good old-fashioned field work. Cross-linears may be mapped from photogeology and satellite imagery. Below is an example Niobrara structure map.

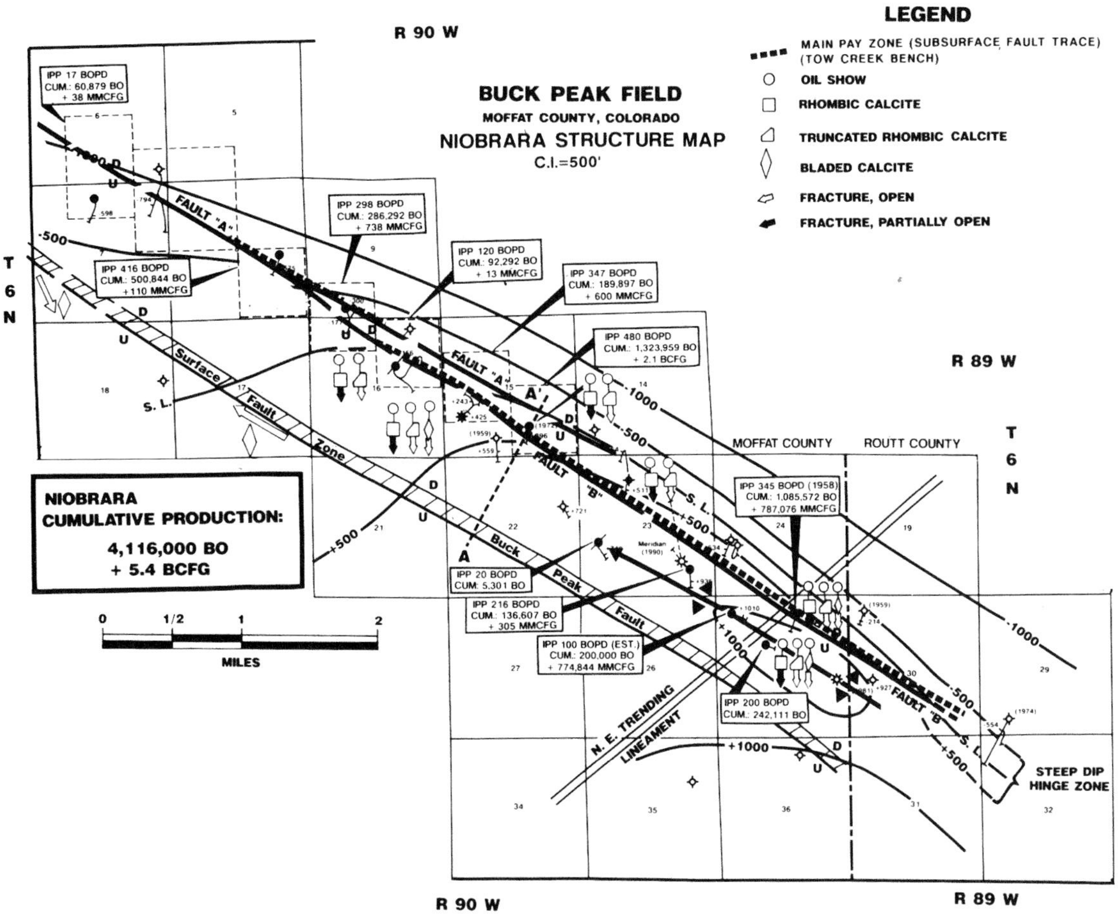

Figure 1–2.

Niobrara maximum bed curvature

Higher resistivity on electrical logs shows the brittle, more fracturable benches within the Niobrara. Constructing a detailed cross section, showing fracturable benches, maximum bed curvature, and any surface and subsurface normal faulting, allows the explorer to visualize and accurately plot the angle at which the well bore must be drilled to penetrate the critical elements.

Seismic surveys are not particularly helpful in mapping normal faults because they are listric with about 100–300 ft of throw at the surface and about 30–80 ft of throw in the Niobrara. The faults are usually not present below the Niobrara. Therefore, although the Mesa Verde provides good seismic marker beds, the underlying Mancos and Niobrara

An Example of Applying Critical Elements, continued

Niobrara maximum bed curvature (continued)

Formations usually do not have them. Occasionally, upward-lying normal faults will produce. Seismic data are useful in delineating these faults because good marker beds are usually present below the Niobrara. The fault can then be projected upward and is sometimes associated with a dim spot due to attenuation of seismic data in fracture zones.

Below is a Niobrara structure cross section.

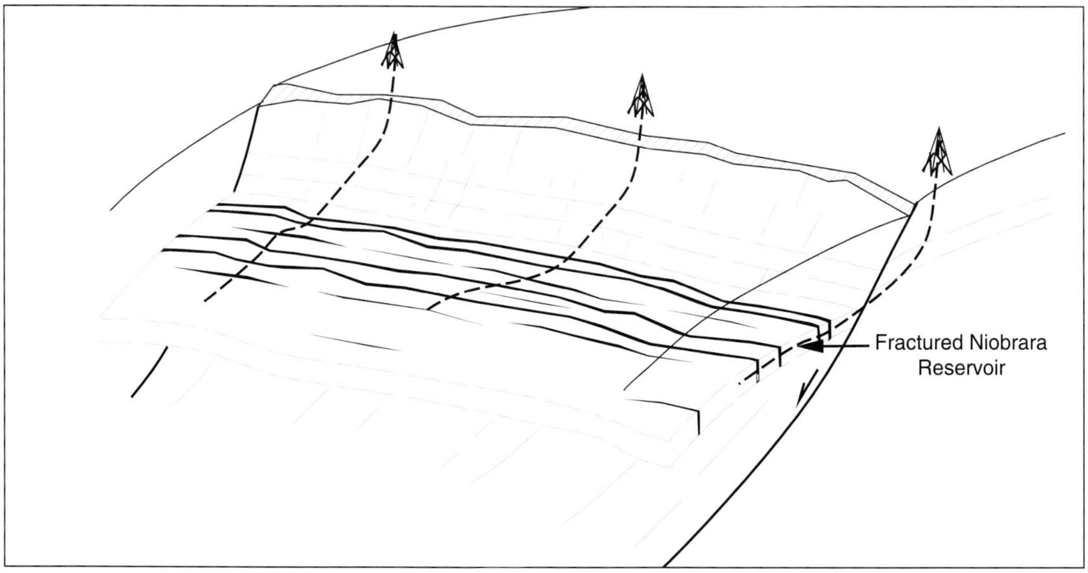

Figure 1–3.

Niobrara open fractures

Running samples on Niobrara wells will reveal whether open calcite crystals are present in the fractures. In addition, field work has shown that the same kind of calcite present in subsurface fractures within the Niobrara also occurs in fractures associated with brittle beds at the surface, such as the Mesa Verde group.

Surface geochemistry applied to Niobrara play

Surface geochemical methods—specifically, soil gas surveys—have proven useful in exploring for these types of traps. The computer compares hundreds of soil–gas ratios very quickly. Also, very sensitive chromatographs have improved the detection of vertical microseepages of hydrocarbons above these fractured reservoirs. The main method of exploration with this technique is to conduct surveys over a number of known commercial accumulations to establish productive signatures. Then a survey over the prospect may provide useful information that can be integrated with the other exploration techniques to help locate a drillsite.

Conclusion

Critical elements of the Niobrara play were identified by studying known accumulations. Knowing what elements were critical allowed a focused effort that saved time and improved effectiveness. Study known examples of trap types of interest to discover critical elements, and the result will be a more effective program.

Section F
References

Covey, Stephen R., 1989, The 7 Habits of Highly Effective People: New York, Simon and Schuster, 358 p.

Edwards, Betty, 1987, Drawing on the Artist Within: New York, Simon and Schuster.

Foster, Norman H., and Edward A. Beaumont, Eds., 1992, Oil is First Found in the Mind: The Philosophy of Exploration: AAPG Treatise of Petroleum Geology, Reprint Series No. 20, Tulsa, AAPG.

Halbouty, Michel T., 1966, Maximum brain power: AAPG Bulletin, vol. 49, no. 10, p. 1597–1600.

King, P.B., 1942, Permian of West Texas and New Mexico: AAPG Bulletin, vol. 26, no. 4, p. 535–763.

McKim, Robert H., 1980, Experiences in Visual Thinking: Boston, PWS Publishing, 183 p.

Pratt, Wallace, 1952, Toward a philosophy of oil-finding: AAPG Bulletin, vol. 36, p. 2231–2236.

Part I

Traps, Trap Types, and the Petroleum System

Introduction

Each trap is unique. Enough similarities exist, however, for traps to be classified. Different classifications serve different purposes. The purpose of the classification presented in Part I is to aid in conceptualizing traps and knowing how to explore for them. The classification of each trap says something about the manner in which one would explore for it. A trap exists in a context of geologic elements and processes that constitute a petroleum system. The probability that a trap will be filled depends on the right combination of source, maturation, migration, trap location, and timing. Studying the petroleum systems within a basin can lead to the creation of new plays and prospects.

In this part

The two chapters of Part I discuss the concept of a trap, how traps are classified, and the context that a trap has within a petroleum system.

Chapter 2

Classification of Exploration Traps

by

Richard R. Vincelette,

Edward A. Beaumont,

and

Norman H. Foster

Richard R. Vincelette

Richard Vincelette graduated with a B.S. degree in geological engineering from Montana Tech. in 1960 and received a Ph.D. in geology from Stanford in 1964. He has spent the last 35 years searching for, and occasionally finding, the elusive hydrocarbon trap. At present he is a geologist and chief curmudgeon with JOG Corporation in Healdsburg, California.

Edward A. Beaumont

Edward A. (Ted) Beaumont is an independent petroleum geologist from Tulsa, Oklahoma. He holds a BS in geology from the University of New Mexico and an MS in geology from the University of Kansas. Currently, he is generating drilling prospects in Texas, Oklahoma, and the Rocky Mountains. His previous professional experience was as a sedimentologist in basin analysis with Cities Service Oil Company and as Science Director for AAPG. Ted is coeditor of the Treatise of Petroleum Geology. He has lectured on creative exploration techniques in the U.S., China, and Australia and has received the Distinguished Service Award and Award of Special Recognition from AAPG.

Norman H. Foster

Norman H. Foster received a bachelor's degree (1957) and a master's degree (1960) in geology at the University of Iowa. In 1963 he completed his Ph.D. in geology at the University of Kansas. His geological career began in 1962, with Sinclair Oil in Casper, Wyoming. When Sinclair merged with Arco in 1969, Foster was offered expanding opportunities to participate in a number of important discoveries, including the giant Irian Jaya field in Indonesia. In 1979, he became an independent geologist and continued to prospect both in the United States and abroad. In addition to winning AAPG's Sidney Powers Memorial Medal for 1999, the former AAPG president received the Levorsen Award (1980), two Certificate of Merit awards (1987 and 1992), and the Distinguished Service Award (1985). He was a member of the AAPG Foundation and an AAPG Trustee Associate since 1979. His professional activities included GSA, SEG, SPE, SIPES, SEPM, and the National Academy of Sciences.

Overview

Introduction

Traps are the product of the interaction of many geologic elements and processes. The outcome of all the possible combinations of geologic elements makes each trap unique. Yet each trap generally shares enough similarities with other traps in the same basin or in other basins that traps may be classified. The classification chosen depends on one's purpose. The ultimate purpose of the trap classification presented in this chapter is to facilitate the discovery of oil and gas accumulations. This chapter discusses the philosophy of classification, shows how to classify traps in a scientifically rigorous and systematic way, and presents a classification scheme for traps found to date. The classification scheme is designed to be flexible and therefore will evolve as new trap types are found and trapping concepts change.

In this chapter

This chapter contains four sections.

Section A
Classification Philosophy

Introduction

Most petroleum geologists classify traps according to the scheme proposed by Levorsen (1954). Levorsen's scheme breaks traps into three basic types: structural, stratigraphic, and combination. The trap classification scheme proposed here uses Levorsen's scheme as a foundation and adds new trap types discovered since 1954. The proposed scheme attempts to formalize the schemes of Levorsen and others (Rittenhouse, 1972; North, 1985; Melton and Bertram, 1992; and Biddle and Weilchowsky, 1994) by developing a more systematic and rigorous approach. It uses elements critical to petroleum exploration to group traps into levels. The method is similar to the one used by biologists to classify plants and animals.

In this section

This section discusses the following topics

What is a Trap?

Early concepts of traps

The earliest concept of a trap was made by William Logan in 1844 when he noted the occurrence of oil on anticlines. I.C. White took Logan's anticlinal trap concept and applied it to search for oil and gas in 1855. Since then, models and applications of trap concepts have evolved as new trap types have been discovered.

Trap definition

A trap consists of a geometric arrangement of permeable (reservoir) and less-permeable (seal) rocks which, when combined with the physical and chemical properties of subsurface fluids, can allow hydrocarbons to accumulate.

Trapping elements

Three main trapping elements comprise every subsurface hydrocarbon accumulation:

1. **Trap reservoir**—storage for accumulating hydrocarbons and can transmit hydrocarbons.
2. **Trap seal**—an impediment or barrier that interferes with hydrocarbon migration from the reservoir.
3. **Trap fluid**s—physical and chemical contrasts—especially differences in miscibility, solubility, and density—between the common reservoir fluids (primarily water, gas, and oil) that allow hydrocarbons to migrate, segregate, and concentrate in the sealed reservoir.

Trap boundaries

Trap boundaries define the limits of the trap and usually consist of (1) boundaries between solids, such as the contact between reservoir and seal, or (2) boundaries between fluids, such as oil–water or gas–water contacts. Temperature can also control a trap boundary as displayed by gas hydrate traps.

Traps vs. accumulations

A trap may or may not contain oil or gas. Accumulations, or pools, are traps that contain oil or gas.

Trapping conditions

Subsurface conditions that impede oil or gas migration include the following:

- Capillary contrasts in pore throats in the seal vs. the reservoir
- Contrasts in physical/chemical properties of subsurface fluids (primarily oil, gas, and water)
- Rock/fluid chemical and physical interactions

Capillary contrasts

Capillary contrasts are differences in the capillary properties of the pore-throat apertures of seal and reservoir rocks, generally caused by a difference in pore-throat aperture sizes. These capillarity contrasts commonly create the trap boundaries between reservoir and seal.

What is a Trap? continued

Trap closure

Trap closure is a measure of the potential storage capacity or size of the trap defined by the trap boundaries. Vertical closure is a measure of the maximum potential hydrocarbon column of the trap. Areal closure is a measure of the maximum area of the potential hydrocarbon accumulation within the trap boundaries. Volumetric closure integrates vertical and areal closure with pay thickness, porosity, and hydrocarbon saturation to provide the volume of the potential hydrocarbon accumulation within the trap boundaries.

Trap classification

A meaningful trap classification scheme must consider reservoir, seal, and fluid properties and how these properties relate to one another to form closure. Since closure is defined by trap boundaries, the proposed classification scheme is based on the geometry, composition, and genesis of trap boundaries.

Classification Basis

Introduction

All classification schemes have a basis from which they are organized. Some are more organized and systematic than others. The basis used for classification depends on the purpose of the classification. The bases for this scheme are the geologic elements critical to finding similar traps.

Purpose

The main purpose of the proposed scheme is to help explorationists find more oil or gas traps. A well-constructed classification scheme for traps can serve other useful purposes:

- It provides a means whereby traps can be organized and cataloged in an orderly manner. Once properly organized, the various trap types can be analyzed and compared to one another to provide valuable information for the exploration and development of similar features.
- A good classification scheme provides standardized terminology that can be used in communicating information to others about oil and gas accumulations.

Considering other schemes

Several classification schemes were analyzed and, where appropriate, were used as a basis for setting up the proposed trap classification scheme. Of particular interest was the biological classification scheme used to catalog and describe plants and animals. First proposed by Aristotle and then expanded and improved by Linnaeus, this system has stood the test of time. Although competing schemes have been proposed and modifications to the scheme are the basis of ongoing debate, the scheme has provided a valuable method of organizing and studying organisms.

Basis for biological classification

The basis for the biological classification scheme is similarity of morphology (shape) and phylogeny (evolutionary history) (Curtis, 1983). In addition, the processes that led to these similarities are also used in biological classification. For example, one of the major differences between plants and animals is that animals are mobile and can search for food, whereas plants are fixed or rooted and rely on food to be brought to them (Curtis, 1983).

Classification Basis, continued

Ranking classes of organisms

The biological classification scheme places organisms in seven ranked levels, going from general to specific:

1. Kingdom
2. Phylum
3. Class
4. Order
5. Family
6. Genus
7. Species

The species represents one certain type of organism, which, by definition, cannot interbreed with an organism of a different species. The largest or most general grouping is at the kingdom level, which Aristotle originally used to separate plants (plant kingdom) and animals (animal kingdom). Interestingly, Aristotle also identified a third kingdom—the mineral kingdom—in which hydrocarbon traps presumably belong.

Similarities of classifying traps and organisms

The use of shape and evolutionary history in the biological classification scheme provides a basis for the use of similar attributes in a trap classification scheme. We propose to utilize similarities in geometry, composition, and genesis as the basis for classifying traps. These similarities are really critical geological elements that can guide exploration. Unfortunately, using a scheme identical to that used in biology has limitations in trap classification, primarily because our trap "species" are prolific interbreeders. Trying to classify most traps would be like trying to classify an organism that is a cross between an elephant and a bee with an apple tree growing out of its head. The "treephantbee" might be difficult to classify in the standard biological classification. However, if a proper classification would enable us to locate a herd of treephantbees, and if honey were oil, we might become rich indeed!

Classifying Traps

Classification flexibility

The common occurrence of combination traps, which involve many different types and varieties of trapping elements, requires a scheme that allows for such variations. Consequently, a classification scheme such as that used to organize a stamp or coin collection might be more useful, especially one in which a variety of flexible methods of organization can be used.

For example, stamps can be organized or classified in many different ways: stamps from one country, stamps from all countries for a certain period, stamps from different countries with similar themes or colors, etc. Depending upon the needs of the stamp collector, the ability to search through a stamp classification scheme and pick out whatever combination of stamps is desirable would be a powerful research tool. In a similar manner, a flexible trap classification scheme should allow for different methods of classifying and cataloging hydrocarbon traps, depending upon the needs of the investigator. The intent is that the proposed classification scheme allows for such flexibility.

Classification levels

The proposed classification scheme places traps into four ranked levels, from general to specific:

1. System
    2. Regime
        3. Class (Superclass if necessary)
            a. Subclass
            b. Style (if necessary)
                4. Family (Superfamily if necessary)
                    a. Subfamily
                    b. Variety (if necessary)

Basis for each level

Most of the levels and sublevels (outlined above) are necessary to adequately describe, in the classification scheme, all of the different elements that characterize a trap. Each level has its own unique basis for classification. Trap systems are based on the controlling geologic elements that created the traps, trap regimes are based on the geologic processes that caused the traps in each system, traps classes are based on the geometry and composition of the traps within the trap regimes, and trap families are based on the genesis or origin of the traps within the trap classes.

Trap Systems: Structural, Stratigraphic, and Fluidic

Introduction

The proposed classification scheme divides traps into three main groups or systems, based on the controlling geologic element that created the trap:

1. Structural
2. Stratigraphic
3. Fluidic

System definition

Following are definitions for the three systems.

Trap Type	Trapping element is ...
Structural	Post- or syndepositional deformation or displacement of reservoir and/or sealing units
Stratigraphic	Depositional, erosional, or diagenetic configuration of reservoir and/or sealing units
Fluidic	Physical and/or chemical property or condition of reservoir fluids

Discussion

Structural and stratigraphic traps are well established in geological literature. The fluidic system is new; often, traps of this nature are referred to as "miscellaneous" or "other" or "unconventional" but seem to fit nicely into a distinct system of their own.

Classifying combinations

One of the more difficult tasks in categorizing an oil or gas accumulation into a specific trap type is determining the dominant element that creates the trap boundaries since often more than one element is involved, giving rise to the *combination trap.* We recognize this problem but hope that, by determining the primary, secondary, and, in some cases, tertiary trapping elements, explorationists can give combination traps useful labels. The label would combine classification labels such as structural/fluidic trap, stratigraphic/structural trap, anticline/fault trap, and tilted fault-block/unconformity truncation trap, with the primary element listed first.

Trap Classification Levels

Basis for each level

A fairly flexible classification scheme has been devised in which each of the three trap systems is divided into three trap regimes, based primarily on the processes that control trap formation in the systems. The trap regimes can be divided into geometric classes and the classes into genetic families. Classifying traps using levels and the same basis at each level brings more consistency and value to classification. The table below shows the basis for each classification level and its definition.

Classification Level	Basis	Function/Definition
System	Controlling geologic element	Dominant control of the trap—structural, stratigraphic, or fluidic.
Regime	Process	The dominant way of forming part or all of the trap closure. If the trap is structural, was the closure formed by folding, faulting, or fracturing? If the trap is stratigraphic, was the closure formed by depositional, erosional, or diagenetic processes? If the trap is fluidic, was closure formed by pressure, temperature, or chemical processes?
Class	Geometry and/or composition	Geometry—the external shape and size of the trap; may also include geometry of internal trap elements. Composition—the makeup of the reservoir, seal, or fluid that creates or defines the trap boundaries.
Family	Genesis	The way all or part of the trap closure came into being. For example, for an isolated marine carbonate trap, was the closure formed because of the reservoir/seal facies relationships of a reef, an oolite bar, or a tidal channel?

Sublevels

Using one term to classify traps geometrically, compositionally, or genetically is not always adequate. To solve this problem, intermediate groupings such as superfamilies or superclasses can be added where necessary. Trap classes can be subdivided into subclasses and styles if needed, and trap families can be subdivided into subfamilies and varieties. These extra levels allow a fuller description of traps.

Degree of interpretation at different levels

Classification requires different degrees of interpretation at different levels of the proposed scheme. The highest levels require presumably less interpretation than do the lower levels. The higher levels are broader generalizations and reveal broader relationships. Classification at lower levels is more interpretive and therefore more open to disagreement. For example, trap geometries, which establish trap classes, are typically well understood; whereas trap genesis, used to establish trap families, relies on interpretation, is often the subject of considerable disagreement and debate, and may be the last trap element fully understood.

Trap Classification Levels, continued

Trap systems & corresponding regimes

The proposed classification scheme divides traps into the following systems and their corresponding regimes.

- Structural Trap System
  - Fold Regime
  - Fault Regime
  - Fracture Regime
- Stratigraphic Trap System
  - Depositional Regime
  - Erosional Regime
  - Diagenetic Regime
- Fluidic Trap System
  - Pressure Regime
  - Temperature Regime
  - Fluid-Composition Regime

Trap classes and families

As mentioned previously, the various trap regimes can be subdivided into trap classes and trap families, based on geometry, composition, and genesis. Ultimately, every oil accumulation can hopefully be classified correctly at the class and family levels.

Section B

How to Use the Classification Scheme

Introduction

One geologic element may control the existence of a trap. These are pure stratigraphic, structural, or fluidic traps. But many traps are a combination of two or three geologic elements. In these traps, basic trapping elements occur in combination to provide the ultimate trapping mechanism. Classifying combination traps is a matter of deciding which are the primary, secondary, and, in some cases, tertiary controlling elements. This section discusses the classification of simple and combination traps and shows some examples of how to classify them.

In this section

This section contains the following topics.

Classifying Traps

Introduction

Classifying traps is interpretive. As more data become available, the trap classification can change or be modified. Different explorationists may classify a particular trap in completely different categories, depending on their particular viewpoints.

Traps can be classified formally or informally. An informal classification is descriptive; little knowledge is needed to classify a trap beyond learning how to describe it. A formal classification is more rigorous and requires knowing the structure of the scheme proposed in this chapter.

Informal classification

An informal classification is a description that conveys a general or specific impression of a trap. For example, East Anschutz Ranch field, shown in the map and cross section below, could be informally classified as an anticlinal trap. This informal classification conveys a very general impression of the trap. Informal classification can also be more specific. For example, we might classify East Anschutz as an elongated asymmetric anticline with a gently dipping back limb and a steeply to overturned forelimb.

East Anschutz Ranch Field

Structure Contour Map | **Cross Section**

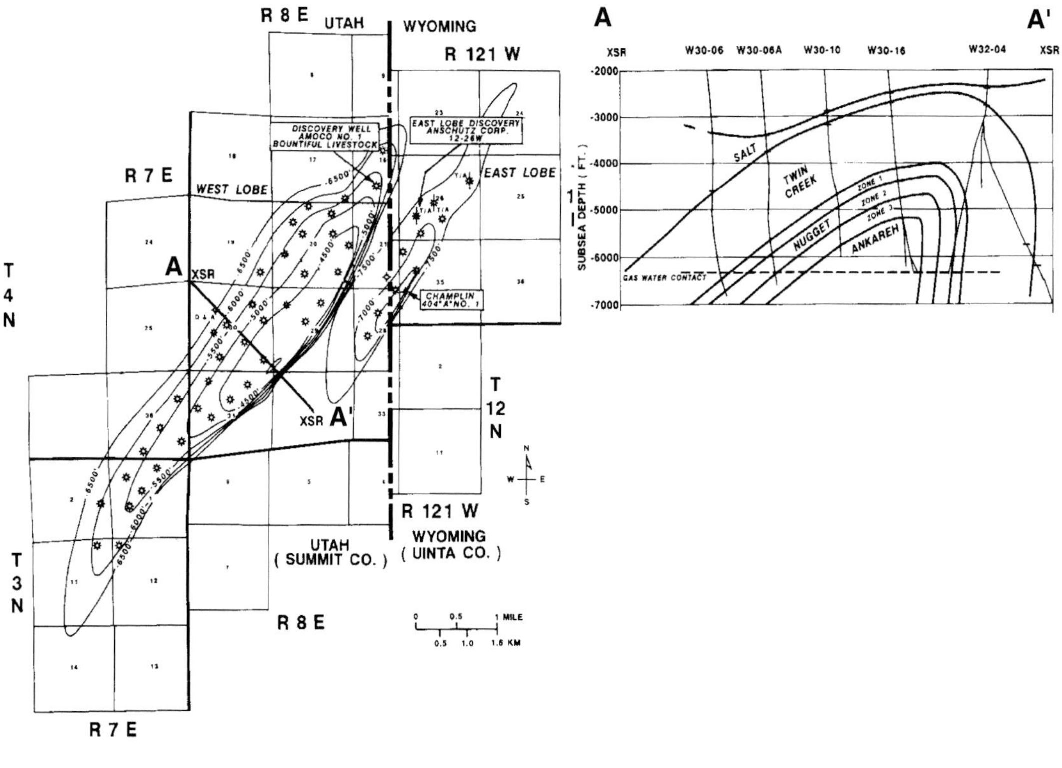

Figure 2–1. From White et al., 1990; courtesy AAPG.

Formal classification

A formal classification conveys more information than an informal classification. It is also more rigorous. The diagram below shows the formal classification for East Anschutz Ranch.

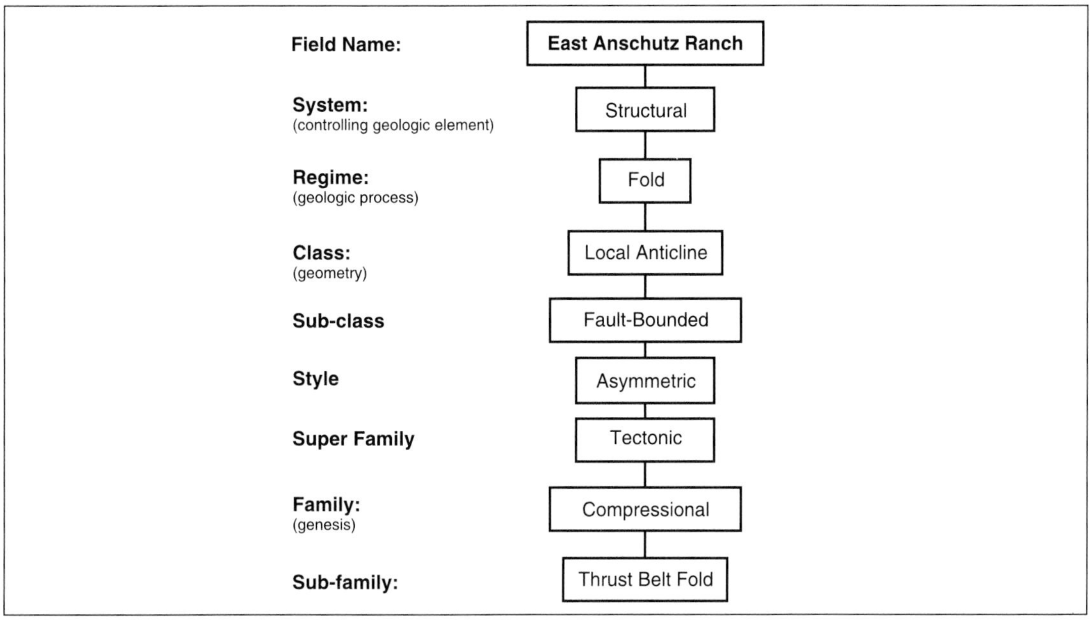

Figure 2–2.

Procedure

The table below lists the procedure for classifying a trap.

<table>
<tr><th>Step</th><th>Action</th></tr>
<tr><td>1</td><td>Determine the trap system: structural, stratigraphic, or fluidic.
<table>
<tr><th>If...</th><th>Then...</th></tr>
<tr><td>More than one element controls the trap</td><td>Go to step 2</td></tr>
<tr><td>Only one element controls the trap</td><td>Go to step 3</td></tr>
</table></td></tr>
<tr><td>2</td><td>Determine the primary, secondary, and (if necessary) tertiary trap system.</td></tr>
<tr><td>3</td><td>Determine the trap regime. What process formed trap closure?</td></tr>
<tr><td>4</td><td>Determine the trap class. Which class best describes trap geometry, or which class describes compositional makeup of the reservoir or seal or fluid that creates or defines trap boundaries?</td></tr>
<tr><td>5</td><td>Determine the trap family. What is the genesis of trap closure?</td></tr>
<tr><td>6</td><td>If necessary, use intermediate groupings (superclasses, superfamilies, subclasses, styles, subfamilies, styles, varieties) to give fuller descriptions.</td></tr>
</table>

Classifying Combination Traps

Introduction

Secondary or even tertiary trapping elements commonly modify the primary trapping agent. Structural traps may have a stratigraphic component or vice versa. Sometimes the distinction whether the trap belongs to one system or another is quite blurred. Traps with two or more trapping elements are called combination traps.

Primary trapping element

To determine what the primary trapping element is, consider each element of the trap and ask, "Would the trap exist if that element were not part of the trap?" We could also ask, "Which element would I look for first if I were exploring for this trap?"

Classifying combination traps informally

To classify a combination trap informally, list the primary trap element first, followed by secondary and tertiary trap elements. You can classify a combination trap informally in at least two different formats. For example, Upper Valley field, Utah, shown in the map and cross section below, could be classified informally as (1) a hydrodynamically modified anticlinal trap or as (2) a hydrodynamic/anticlinal trap.

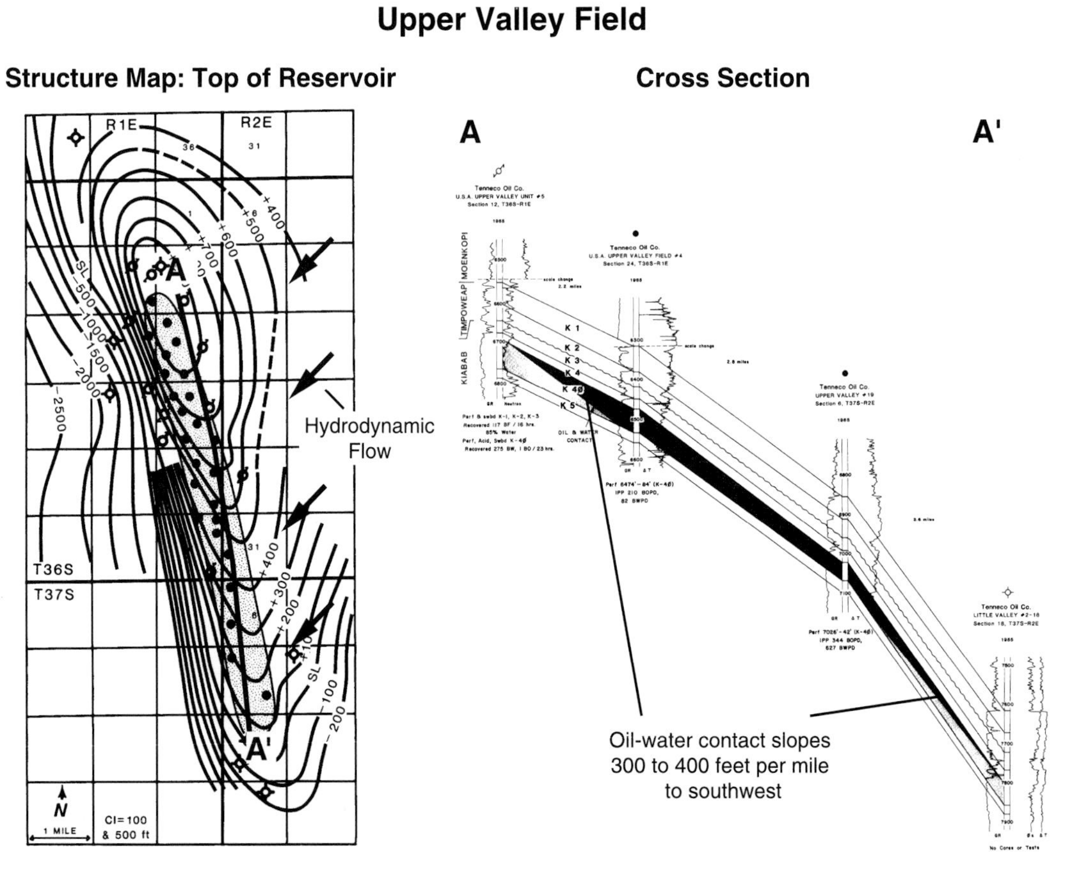

Figure 2–3. Courtesy RMAG.

Classifying Combination Traps, continued

Classifying combination traps formally

We classify a trap formally by listing the regimes, classes, and families for the primary, secondary, and (if necessary) tertiary systems. For example, the diagram below shows the formal classification for Upper Valley field.

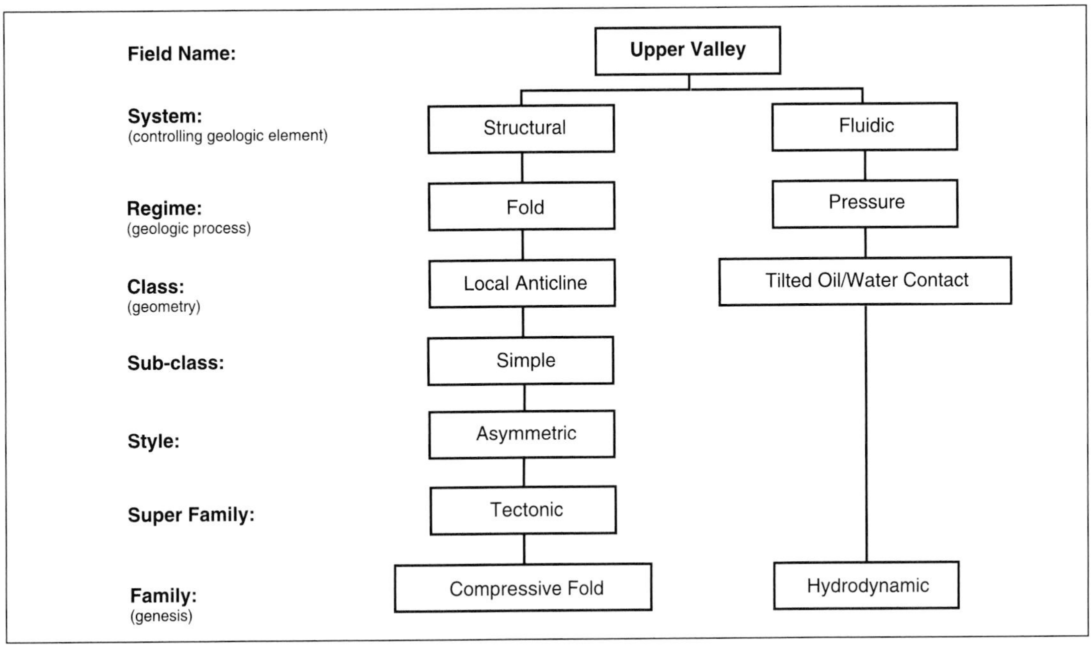

Figure 2–4.

Combination structural traps

Some structural traps are combinations of the three structural trap regimes: fold, fault, and fracture. The Buck Peak field shown below is an example of a combination structural trap.

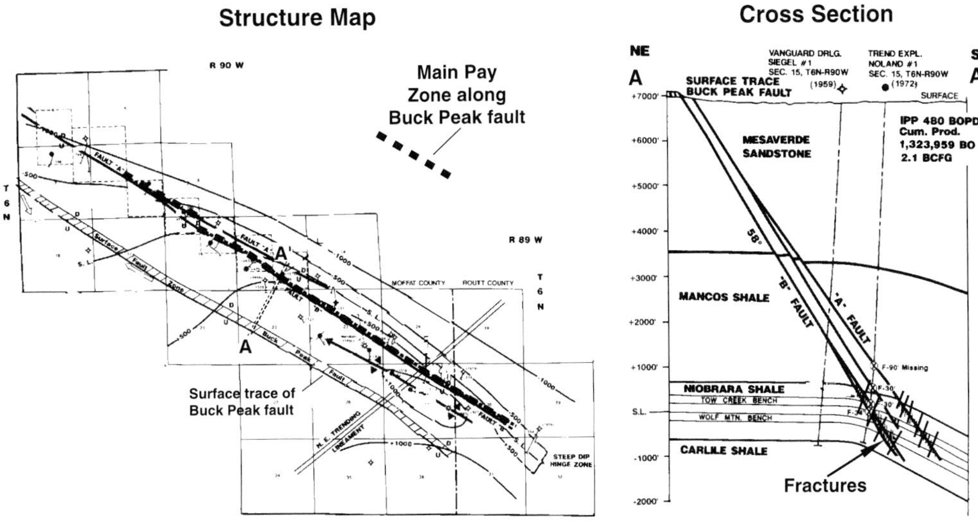

Figure 2–5. Modified from Vincelette and Foster, 1992; courtesy RMAG.

Classifying Combination Traps, continued

Buck Peak formal classification

The diagram below shows the formal classification for the Buck Peak field, which is a combination structural trap.

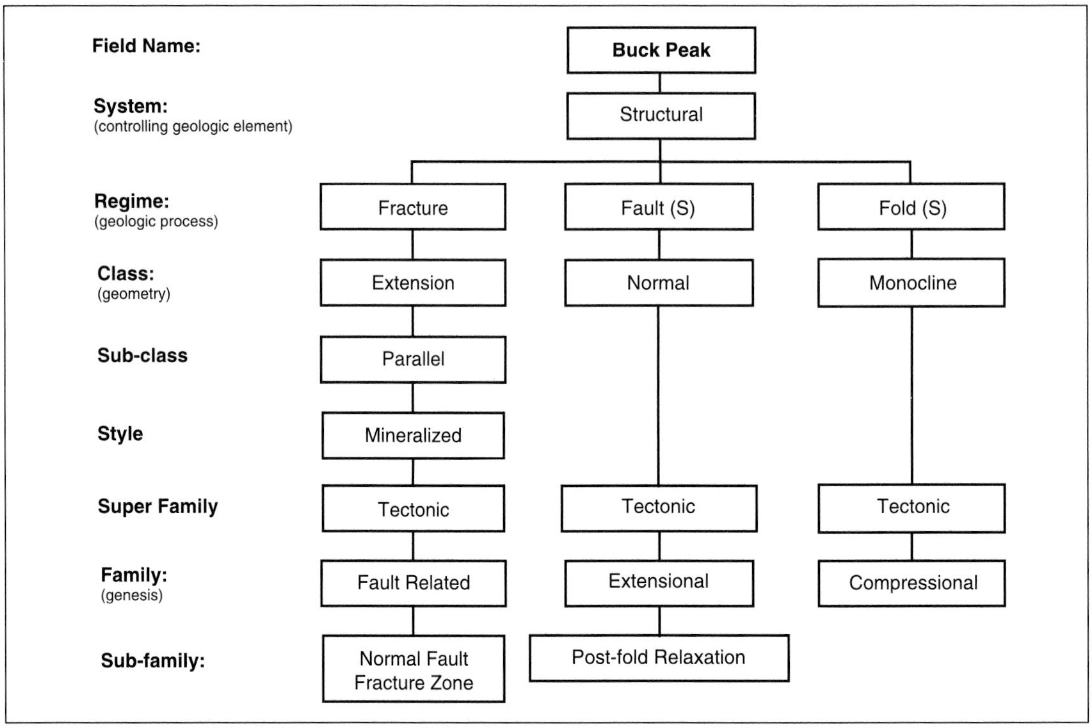

Figure 2–6.

Section C

Details of the Trap Classification Scheme

Introduction

The details of the proposed classification scheme are presented in this section. The scheme should be considered as flexible and subject to further refinement. The authors hope future discussion resulting from analyzing this classification scheme will result in more rigorous and geologically acceptable terminology used to describe trap geometry and similar modification of the proposed families, subfamilies, and varieties used to describe trap genesis. The three subsections of this chapter contain the classification scheme for the three trap systems: structural, stratigraphic, and fluidic.

In this section

The following topics are discussed in this section.

Subsection C1
Structural Trap System

Introduction

The structural system contains three regimes: fold traps, fault traps, and fracture traps. The classification of structural traps at the class level depends primarily on the external geometry of the trap and can be further subdivided into subclasses based on other geometric parameters such as areal extent, vertical relief, structural dip, and internal geometry. The structural classes listed below are not intended to be all inclusive but merely illustrate how the classification scheme is intended to operate.

In this subsection

This subsection discusses the following topics.

Fold Trap Regime

Classes and definitions

The proposed classes in the fold trap regime are monocline, local dome, regional dome, local nose, regional nose, local anticline, regional anticline, and syncline. The following outline shows the classes, some of the subclasses, style, and their definitions. The Subclasses listed are not inclusive but represent the more common types of fold traps and show how the proposed classification scheme can be developed and defined.

Regime: Fold
A fold trap is formed by syn- or postdepositional processes that deform geological surfaces into a curved or nonplanar arrangement (Biddle and Weilchowsky, 1995).

- **Class:** Monocline
  A fold that occurs where strata dip or flex from the horizontal in one direction only and are not a part of a anticline or syncline (*AGI Glossary of Geology,* 1972). A monocline can form only part of the trap closure and must combine with other elements for closure.
- **Class:** Regional nose
  A short plunging anticline without closure. A trap where a nose is a trapping element must combine with other elements to have closure.
- **Class:** Local nose
- **Class:** Regional dome
  Circular or elliptical anticline many miles (km) in diameter.
- **Class:** Local dome
  Circular or elliptical anticline < 20 mi (32 km) in diameter.
- **Class:** Regional anticline
  Elongate convex upward fold.
- **Class:** Local anticline
  - **Subclass:** Simple
  - **Subclass:** Fault bounded or cross faulted
    - **Styles:** Relief, symmetry, internal faulting, internal geometry
- **Class:** Syncline
  Elongate concave upward fold.

Families

Based on their genesis, folds can be divided into two superfamily categories: tectonic and nontectonic. The outline below presents the superfamilies, families, and subfamilies and their definitions for anticlinal fold traps. As with fold classes, the fold families listed below are not inclusive but merely represent the more common fold families.

Regime: Fold

- **Class:** Local anticline
  - **Superfamily:** Tectonic
    Folds resulting from deformation by tectonic processes such as compression or extension.
    - **Family:** Compressional fold
      Formed by compressive tectonic deformation.
      - **Subfamily:** Thrust-belt fold
      - **Subfamily:** Foreland fold
      - **Subfamily:** Cratonic-basin fold
        - **Variety:** Paleostructure
        - **Variety:** Inverted

Families (continued)

Family: Transpressional fold
Subfamily: Single phase
Subfamily: Paleostructure
Subfamily: Inverted structure
Family: Structural drape fold
Form over a deeper structural feature such as a fault block.
Family: Extensional fold
Form by extensional tectonic deformation.
Subfamilies: Rollover anticline
Form as a result of rollover into a listric normal fault.
Family: Basement uplift
Superfamily: Nontectonic
Folds result from deformation by nontectonic processes such as uplift by intrusion or diapirism, differential compaction, salt withdrawal, salt solution, or meteoric impact.
Family: Intrusive core
Dome or anticline form as a result of intrusion.
Subfamilies: Salt dome or anticline
Form as a result of uplift by salt movement.
Subfamilies: Shale dome or anticline
Form as a result of a shale diapir.
Subfamilies: Igneous dome
Form as a result of igneous intrusion.
Family: Differential-compaction (drape) anticline
Form by the differential compaction of sediments over a buried structure such as a reef or horst.
Family: Salt-solution anticline
Form as a result of salt dissolution.
Family: Salt-withdrawal anticline
Form as a result of salt movement out of an area.
Family: Astrobleme
Form as result of the impact of a meteor.

Fault Trap Regime

Classes and definitions

There are four classes in the fault trap regime: normal fault, reverse fault, thrust fault, and wrench fault. The outline below shows definitions and examples for the classes and subclasses of these traps or trapping elements.

Regime: Fault trap
Fault(s) forms part or all of the closure of the trap by sealing the reservoir either laterally and/or from the top (after Biddle and Wielchowsky, 1995).

- **Class:** Normal fault trap
  One or more form all or part of lateral closure by sealing the reservoir.
  - **Subclass:** Tilted fault block
    Block of rock bounded on one or more sides by normal faults. Rotation traps hydrocarbons along edges or in corners.
  - **Subclass:** Horst
    Block of rock bounded on all sides by normal faults.
  - **Subclass:** Listric fault trap
    All or part of closure formed by a fault whose plane curves downward and is concave upward.
- **Class:** Reverse fault trap
  One or more faults form all or part of the closure by sealing the reservoir.
- **Class:** Thrust fault trap
  Forms all or part of the closure by sealing the reservoir either laterally or from the top or bottom.
  - **Subclass:** Overthrust
    Forms all or part of the closure by sealing the reservoir laterally.
  - **Subclass:** Subthrust
    Forms all or part of the closure by sealing the reservoir laterally or from the top.
- **Class:** Wrench fault trap
  Forms all or part of the closure by sealing the reservoir laterally or from the top.
  - **Subclass:** Flower structure
    Opposing reverse faults diverge upward, forming a fan or flower cross section pattern. Develop along wrench fault zones.

Families

Based on the genesis of the bounding faults, traps classified as fault traps can be divided into tectonic and nontectonic superfamilies. The outline below presents examples of trap families for several common fault traps. Similar trap families and subfamilies can be defined for most fault traps when the genesis of the trap is understood fully.

Regime: Fault traps

- **Class:** Normal faults
  - **Subclass:** Tilted fault block
    - **Superfamily:** Tectonic
      Normal fault, resulting from deformation by tectonic processes, forms all or part of the closure.
      - **Family:** Extensional
        Fault, resulting from extensional deformation, forms all or part of the closure.
        - **Subfamily:** Rift basin
        - **Subfamily:** Basin and range
        - **Subfamily:** Growth fault

Fault Trap Regime, continued

Families (continued)

Class: Reverse faults
Subclass: Thrust faults
Superfamily: Tectonic
Thrust fault, resulting from tectonic deformation by tectonic processes, forms all or part of the closure.
Family: Compressional
Fault, resulting from tectonic compressional deformation, forms all or part of the closure.
Subfamily: Regional thrust belt
Subfamily: Foreland fold fault
Subfamily: Forearc basin

Class: Wrench faults
Subclass: Flower structures
Superfamily: Tectonic
Normal fault, resulting from tectonic deformation by tectonic processes, forms all or part of the closure.
Family: Transpressional
Fault, resulting from tectonic transpressional deformation, forms all or part of the closure.
Subfamily: Regional wrench system
Variety: Inverted

Class: Normal faults
Superfamily: Nontectonic
Result from deformation by nontectonic processes such as uplift by intrusion or diapirism, differential compaction, salt withdrawal, salt solution, or meteoric impact.
Family: Extensional
Fault, resulting from nontectonic extensional deformation, forms all or part of the closure.
Family: Vertical uplift
Family: Vertical subsidence
Subfamily: Salt solution
Subfamily: Salt withdrawal

Fracture Traps

Introduction

The reason for including fold traps and fault traps in the structural system may be obvious, but the reason for including fracture traps may not. Some might argue that fractures are just another porosity type and should be thought of as part of the reservoir, not as a trap regime. This classification scheme includes fracture traps in the structural system because fractures are a result of deformation and/or displacement and therefore are structural in nature.

Definitions

The following definitions for fracture, fracture reservoir, and fracture trap are used in the classification scheme.

Fracture—Approximately planar surface along which originally contiguous rocks have broken and separated and along which the relative displacement of originally adjacent points across the fracture is small compared with fracture length (from Pollard and Segall, 1987).

Fracture Reservoir—Reservoir in which most of the permeability and some of the porosity is provided by open fractures.

Fracture Trap—Trap in which lateral boundaries of the trap are provided by change from fractured reservoir to unfractured or less fractured rock or by change from open, permeable fractures to cement-filled or narrow-aperture, low-permeability fractures.

Fracture types

Fractures can be divided into three major groups: extension, shear, and complex.

Extension Fracture—displacement of originally adjacent points across the fracture is perpendicular to the fracture surface. The term "extension" refers only to the opening or extension of the space between the fracture walls, not to the stress system that caused the fracture.

Shear Fracture—displacement of originally adjacent points across the fracture is parallel to the fracture surface.

Complex Fracture—fracture with a complex history of displacement and rejuvenation, and which may have originated as a shear fracture and been rejuvenated as an extension fracture or vice versa.

Fracture Trap Regime

Definitions and examples

Fracture traps are divided into three classes: extension, shear, and complex, based on the internal characteristics and geometry of the fractures that make up the reservoir. The outline below shows the classes, some subclasses, and possible styles into which these traps may be subdivided.

Regime: Fracture trap
Lateral boundaries of the trap are provided by change from fractured reservoir to unfractured or less fractured rock or by change from open, permeable fractures to cement-filled or narrow-aperture, low-permeability fractures.

- **Class:** Extension fracture trap
  Dominant reservoir fractures are extension fractures.
  - **Subclass:** Parallel fractures
    Open fractures in a fractured reservoir, predominantly unidirectional in both strike and dip.
    - **Style:** Mineralized fracture
      Partially or totally mineralized by postfracture cements, typically calcite, gypsum, or silica.
    - **Style:** Nonmineralized fracture
      Contains no postfracture cements or minerals.
  - **Subclass:** Intersecting fractures
    Open fractures in fractured reservoir of several intersecting sets, either along fracture strike or fracture dip.
    - **Style:** Mineralized fracture
    - **Style:** Nonmineralized fracture
- **Class:** Shear fracture trap
  The dominant reservoir fractures are shear fractures.
  - **Subclass:** Parallel fractures
    - **Style:** Mineralized fracture
    - **Style:** Nonmineralized fracture
  - **Subclass:** Intersecting fractures
    - **Style:** Mineralized fracture
    - **Style:** Nonmineralized fracture
- **Class:** Complex fracture trap
  Dominant reservoir fractures are complex fractures.
  - **Subclass:** Parallel fractures
    - **Style:** Mineralized fracture
    - **Style:** Nonmineralized fracture
  - **Subclass:** Intersecting fractures
    - **Style:** Mineralized fracture
    - **Style:** Nonmineralized fracture

Families

Based on the interpretation of the genetic causes of fracture traps, two fracture trap families are recognized: tectonic and nontectonic.

Tectonic fracture trap families

The outline below shows the order of the families of the tectonic fracture trap superfamily and defines some of them.

- **Regime:** Fracture
  - **Superclass:** Extension
  - **Superclass:** Shear
  - **Superclass:** Complex
    - **Class:** Parallel
    - **Class:** Intersecting
      - **Superfamily:** Tectonic fracture trap
        Fractures were generated by crustal tectonic stresses, whether compressional, extensional, or transpressional.
        - **Family:** Fold-related fracture trap
          Fractures are intimately associated with and controlled by tectonic folds.
          - **Subfamily:** Related to zone of maximum curvature.
          - **Subfamily:** Hydrofractures
        - **Family:** Fault-related fracture traps
          Fractures are intimately associated with or controlled by tectonic faults.
          - **Subfamily:** Fractures related to normal faults
          - **Subfamily:** Fractures related to wrench faults
        - **Family:** Regional fracture trap
          Fractures occur over a broad area unrelated to specific folds or faults and in which fractures are thought to have been created by regional tectonic stresses.

Fractures related to folding

Several mechanisms have been proposed to explain the common occurrence of highly fractured zones in various positions along tectonic folds, including bending-induced fractures along zones of maximum curvature, typically along the flanks of monoclines, anticlines, or synclines, as well as along the plunge axis of anticlines. Another cause of fracturing along compressive anticlines could be due to hydrofracturing during compression and squeezing of the folded rocks. Where appropriate, subfamilies can be established, such as maximum-curvature fracture traps and hydrofracture traps.

Fractures related to faulting

Numerous examples exist in which fracture intensity increases with proximity to faults. A number of fracture traps have been attributed to fault-induced or associated fracturing. Subfamilies can be established based on the type of fault with which the fractures are associated, e.g., normal-fault fracture trap or wrench-fault fracture trap.

Fractures related to regional stresses

Within regionally fractured areas, local fracture swarms with enhanced permeability and fracture frequency often occur. The transition from these high-permeability fracture swarms to areas of lower fracture frequency or fracture permeability often provides local lateral trap boundaries within the regional system. These fracture swarms may or may not be related to or associated with local secondary folds or faults.

Fracture Trap Regime, continued

Nontectonic fracture families

A wide variety of nontectonic elements have been interpreted to cause fractures and fracture traps. The more common ones include salt solution, piercement by mobile cores, meteorite impact, compaction drape, shrinkage due to cooling or diagenesis, pore-fluid overpressuring, erosional uplift and unloading, and hydrothermal fracturing. Each of these can be used as nontectonic fracture trap families. Where necessary, subfamilies and varieties can be created for any of these families. The outline below shows the order and some definitions for these traps.

Superclass: Extension fractures
- **Class:** Parallel
- **Class:** Intersecting
  - **Superfamily:** Nontectonic fracture trap
    Fractures generated by nontectonic stresses, e.g., salt solution, piercement, shrinkage, and overpressuring.
    - **Family:** Solution collapse
    - **Family:** Piercement
    - **Family:** Impact
    - **Family:** Compaction drape
    - **Family:** Shrinkage
      - **Subfamily:** Chert diagenesis
      - **Subfamily:** Cooling joints
    - **Family:** Overpressuring
      - **Subfamily:** Source rock maturation
      - **Subfamily:** Geothermal pressuring
      - **Subfamily:** Clay dewatering
    - **Family:** Unloading
    - **Family:** Hydrothermal

Subsection C2

Stratigraphic Trap System

Introduction

The geological controls for stratigraphic system traps are stratigraphic in nature and formed as a result of depositional, erosional, or diagenetic processes. These processes are the basis for the three regimes of the stratigraphic system.

In this section

This section contains the following topics.

Depositional Trap Regime

Introduction

Traps in the depositional regime formed primarily by processes that created facies changes between reservoir and seal-quality rocks. Besides deposition by sedimentary processes, this regime also includes deposition by igneous processes.

Classes

The basis for the three classes of the depositional regime is the geometric arrangement of the facies resulting from depositional processes. The subclasses describe reservoir composition or lithology. Where described, trap styles can be listed based on the lithology or composition of the sealing rocks. The outline below shows the classes and subclasses of the depositional regime.

System: Stratigraphic
- **Regime:** Depositional
  Trap boundaries are created primarily by depositional processes and can involve igneous rocks as well as sedimentary rocks. Three classes are recognized, based on whether the trap involves an isolated reservoir, an updip pinch-out, or depositional relief on top of the reservoir.
  - **Class:** Isolated (local) depositional reservoirs
    Reservoir rock is partially or completely isolated by sealing rocks, which provide top, side, and often bottom seals. These traps are often of limited areal extent, with trap closure defined largely by reservoir distribution.
    - **Subclass:** Sandstone reservoirs
      Partially or completely isolated by seal.
    - **Subclass:** Carbonate reservoirs
      Partially or completely isolated by seal.
    - **Subclass:** Igneous reservoirs
      Partially isolated by seal.
  - **Class:** Depositional pinch-outs
    Depositional processes form an updip pinch-out of permeable rock into impermeable rock. Trap closure is usually created by an updip re-entrant of the pinch-out boundary or by a combination of the pinch-out with other trap elements, such as tectonic nosing or hydrodynamics. Pinch-out boundaries typically involve top, side, and bottom seals.
    - **Subclass:** Regional sandstone pinch-outs
      Regional updip pinch-outs of sandstone into an impermeable facies such as shale or anhydrite.
    - **Subclass:** Local sandstone pinch-outs
      Local updip pinch-outs of sandstone into an impermeable facies such as shale or anhydrite.
    - **Subclass:** Regional carbonate pinch-outs
      Regional updip pinch-outs of carbonate into an impermeable facies such as shale or anhydrite.
    - **Subclass:** Local carbonate pinch-outs
      Local updip pinch-outs of carbonate into an impermeable facies such as shale or anhydrite.

Depositional Trap Regime, continued

Classes (continued)

Class: Depositional relief traps
Process forms positive relief on top of the reservoir; this topographic relief between top seal and reservoir creates the trap closure.

- **Subclass:** Sandstone depositional relief traps
- **Subclass:** Carbonate depositional relief traps
  - **Style:** Carbonate reservoirs sealed by shale
  - **Style:** Carbonate reservoirs sealed by tight carbonate
  - **Style:** Carbonate reservoirs sealed by evaporites

Families

Genetic families for the various depositional trap classes and subclasses have been established based primarily on the genesis of the reservoir. Where desired, trap varieties can be added based on the genesis or origin of the sealing units. Larger superfamilies have been created based on the general depositional environment of the reservoir, i.e., marine, continental, or lacustrine.

Note that the same genetic families and subfamilies can be used for different depositional classes (geometry). This lets cross-correlations be made between different geometric trap classes within similar genetic settings, e.g., isolated reservoirs or pinch-outs within the shallow marine environment. Thus, if desired, trap classes can be combined under similar trap families. Examples of the more common depositional trap superfamilies, families, and subfamilies are given below.

- **Regime:** Depositional reservoirs
  - **Class:** Isolated depositional reservoirs
    - **Subclass:** Isolated carbonate reservoirs
      - **Superfamily:** Marine carbonate reservoirs
        - **Family:** Open-shelf (high-energy) carbonates
          - **Subfamily:** Shoal
            - **Variety:** Oolite
            - **Variety:** Skeletal
        - **Family:** Tidal-zone carbonates
          - **Subfamily:** Tidal channel
    - **Subclass:** Isolated sandstone reservoirs
      - **Superfamily:** Marine sandstone traps
        - **Family:** Shallow-water sandstone reservoirs
          - **Subfamily:** Beach
          - **Subfamily:** Barrier island
          - **Subfamily:** Offshore bar
        - **Family:** Deepwater sandstone reservoirs
          - **Subfamily:** Turbidites
          - **Subfamily:** Turbidite channel
          - **Subfamily:** Submarine fans
      - **Superfamily:** Alluvial sandstone reservoirs
        - **Family:** Fluvial
          - **Subfamily:** Channel
            - **Variety:** Deltaic

Depositional Trap Regime, continued

Families (continued)

Family: Deltaic
Subfamily: Distributary channel
Subclass: Isolated igneous reservoirs
Superfamily: Intrusive igneous bodies
Family: Intrusive sills
Class: Depositional pinch-outs
Subclass: Sandstone pinch-outs
Superfamily: Marine sandstone pinch-outs
Family: Shallow marine
Updip pinch-out of shallow marine sands into lagoonal or basinal shales and silts.
Subfamily: Barrier bar
Variety: Pinch-out into lagoonal shale
Variety: Pinch-out into marine shale
Family: Deep marine
Subfamily: Turbidite
Updip pinch-out of marine turbidite sandstone into marine shale.
Superfamily: Lacustrine sandstone pinch-outs
Family: Lacustrine delta pinch-out
Subclass: Carbonate pinch-outs
Superfamily: Marine carbonate pinch-outs
Family: Tidal zone
Subfamily: Tidal-flat carbonate pinch-out
Variety: Pinch-out into silts and shales
Variety: Pinch-out into tight dolomites and anhydrite
Family: Open shelf (high energy)
Subfamily: Carbonate bank pinch-out
Reservoir variety: Rudistid limestone bank
Seal variety:
Top: Marine shale
Side: Tight shelf limestone
Class: Depositional relief
Subclass: Sandstone
Superfamily: Eolian sandstone reservoirs
Family: Dune
Superfamily: Marine sandstone reservoirs
Family: Deep water
Subfamily: Turbidite fan
Subclass: Carbonate
Superfamily: Marine carbonate reservoirs

Families (continued)

Family: Bioherms
Trap results from depositional relief created by porous organic carbonate buildup sealed by overlying and adjacent tight lithologies. These buildups are commonly referred to as reefs. A wide variety of reef traps have been described and classified based upon both the environment of deposition and geometry of the carbonate reservoir. Oil and gas have been trapped in barrier reefs, fringing reefs, platform reefs, atoll reefs, patch reefs, pinnacle reefs, reef mounds (or mud mounts), and carbonate banks (James and Gelsetzer, 1989). These terms can be used as subfamilies, as noted below. If a more detailed classification is needed, varieties can be established based upon the facies and genesis of the sealing units surrounding the buildups.

Subfamily: Pinnacle reefs
High-relief, circular or ovoid mounds created by upward grown of carbonate frame-building organisms in basinal setting. Reef typically contains a significant amount of high-energy carbonate detritus (grainstones, wackestones) as well as boundstones and framestones. Reef width is less than 10% of height (James and Geldsetzer, 1989).

Subfamily: Platform reefs
Larger reefal carbonate buildup in which lateral dimensions are measured in kilometers and in which reef width is more than 10 times reef height (James and Geldsetzer, 1989).

Subfamily: Patch reefs
Small, low-relief carbonate mounds developed by frame-building organisms on top of a shelf.

Subfamily: Mud mounds
Depositional carbonate mounds consisting largely of clean lime mudstone with relatively little macro-fossil debris.

Class: Supraunconformity traps
- **Subclass:** Onlap pinch-out
  - **Superfamily:** Nonmarine erosion surface
    - **Family:** Sequence-boundary unconformity onlap
      - **Subfamily:** Depositional re-entrant
        - **Reservoir variety:** Deltaic sandstone pinch-out
        - **Seal variety:**
          - **Top:** Deltaic shale
          - **Bottom:** Subunconformity units
- **Subclass:** Buttress pinch-outs
  - **Superfamily:** Nonmarine erosional surface
    - **Family:** Sequence-boundary unconformity buttress
      - **Subfamily:** Pinch-out against erosional ridge
        - **Reservoir variety:** Alluvial sandstone
        - **Seal variety:**
          - **Top:** Nonmarine shale
          - **Side:** Marine shale of subcrop ridge
          - **Bottom:** Marine shale beneath unconformity

Erosional Trap Regime

Definition

Erosional traps are those in which trap boundaries occur along contacts between erosional surfaces and underlying or overlying reservoirs.

Classes and subclasses

Three trap classes have been identified, based on the geometry of the reservoir beds in contact with the unconformity surface. The hierarchical structure and definitions are shown below.

System: Stratigraphic traps
- **Regime:** Erosional traps
  Form as a result of erosional processes
  - **Class:** Truncation traps
    Up-dip reservoir boundary created by truncation of a reservoir beneath an unconformity, followed by deposition of sealing unit on top of an unconformity. The unconformity surface provides top seal, but closure usually requires the presence of depositional or tectonic side and bottom seals beneath the unconformity.
    - **Subclass:** Regional subcrop
      Uniformly or gently dipping reservoir bed beneath an unconformity. Top seal is provided by postunconformity beds; bottom seal is provided by sealing units beneath reservoir.
    - **Subclass:** Paleostructural subcrop
      Folded and/or faulted reservoir beds beneath postdeformation unconformity. Reservoir distribution and trap boundaries are controlled by preunconformity deformation and subsequent erosion.
  - **Class:** Erosional relief traps
    Closure provided by topographic relief beneath an unconformity.
    - **Subclass:** Buried hill
      Top-seal closure created by positive erosional relief of reservoir beneath a sealing unconformity surface.
    - **Subclass:** Truncation edge
      Side seal provided by truncation of a reservoir against later erosional valley, channel, or gorge wall and subsequent deposition of sealing beds in valley, channel, or gorge.

Families

Families of the erosional trap regime have been established based upon the genesis of the unconformity surface that controls the trap boundaries. Two superfamilies are recognized: nonmarine erosion surfaces and marine erosion surfaces. Within these superfamilies, more detailed family classifications can be established. Where desired, trap varieties can be utilized to provide more details of reservoir and seal genesis. The outline below shows the superfamilies, families, and subfamilies of the subclass gorge-edge traps.

Regime: Erosional traps
- **Class:** Truncation traps
  - **Subclass:** Regional subcrop
    - **Superfamily:** Nonmarine erosional surface
      - **Family:** Sequence-boundary unconformity

Erosional Trap Regime, continued

Families (continued)

Reservoir variety: Marine sandstone subcrop
Seal variety:
Top: Marine transgressive shale above unconformity and marine shale above sandstone.
Bottom: Marine shale beneath sandstone
Subclass: Paleostructural subcrop
Style: Complex fold-fault subcrop
Superfamily: Nonmarine erosional surface
Family: Sequence-boundary unconformity
Subfamily: Postcompressional fold-fault unconformity
Reservoir variety: Multiple truncated marine sandstones
Seal variety:
Top: Postunconformity marine shale
Bottom: Underlying marine shale
Class: Erosional relief trap
Subclass: Buried hill
Superfamily: Nonmarine erosion surface
Family: Sequence-boundary unconformity
Subfamily: Local differential erosion
Reservoir variety: Basement igneous complex
Seal variety: Marine shales above unconformity
Subclass: Truncation-edge traps
Superfamily: Marine erosion surface
Family: Submarine canyon or gorge trap
Superfamily: Nonmarine erosional surface
Family: Channel-relief or valley-edge relief traps

Diagenetic Trap Regime

Introduction

Diagenetic traps are those in which the trap boundaries are due to postdepositional diagenetic processes, which can create new reservoirs or new seals.

Classes

The hierarchical structure and definitions for diagenetic traps are shown below.

System: Stratigraphic traps
- **Regime:** Diagenetic traps
  - **Class:** Diagenetic reservoirs
    Form where porosity is created as a result of local diagenetic processes such as dissolution or dolomitization.
    - **Subclass:** Secondary dolomite reservoirs
      Form as a result of localized secondary dolomitization.
    - **Subclass:** Leached (secondary) porosity
      Form as a result of localized leaching of nonreservoir-quality rock to create enhanced porosity and permeability. Common beneath unconformity surfaces.
  - **Class:** Diagenetic seals
    Trap boundaries created by plugging original reservoir porosity and permeability by diagenetic cements or minerals.
    - **Subclass:** Secondary anhydrite barriers
      Form as a result of secondary anhydrite precipitating in original pore spaces.
    - **Subclass:** Secondary clay barriers
      Form as a result of secondary clay, commonly kaolinite, precipitating in original pore space.
      - **Style:** Secondary pore-throat trap
        Caused by a reduction in the size of pore-throat radii of reservoir rocks by depositional or diagenetic processes. These trap types typically have relatively porous units in the sealing facies that are impermeable to oil migration due to capillary restraints but contain producible water.

Discussion of diagenetic trap families

Families of diagenetic traps based on genesis of the diagenetic processes that created or modified either the reservoir or the seal are somewhat difficult to establish because not all diagenetic processes are well understood and disagreements often exist about the cause of specific diagenetic processes that trapped hydrocarbons. Furthermore, almost all reservoirs and seals have undergone some degree of diagenesis since deposition, making diagenesis at least a secondary trapping element in many fields.

The common occurrence of dolomitized reservoirs is a classic case in point. Dolomitized reefs and dolomitized tidal-flat carbonates are common oil and gas reservoirs. Although dolomitization was a critical element in creating commercial porosity and permeability in these reservoirs, exploration efforts usually focus on defining the original depositional fairway of these reservoirs, i.e., reefs or tidal flats. As a consequence, the primary trap classification of these reservoirs occurs under the depositional trap regime. For our purposes, diagenetic traps are those in which trap boundaries are created by diagenetic processes largely independent of the original depositional environment of reservoir or seal.

Families

Below is a suggested classification outline for some of the superfamilies, families, and subfamilies of the Diagenetic Reservoirs and Diagenetic Seals classes.

Regime: Diagenetic traps
- **Class:** Diagenetic reservoirs
  - **Subclass:** Secondary dolomite reservoirs
    - **Family:** Hydrothermal diagenesis
      - **Subfamily:** Ascending hot brines
  - **Subclass:** Leached (secondary) porosity
    - **Family:** Subunconformity diagenesis
      - **Subfamily:** Dissolving
        - **Variety:** Karst and cavern formation
- **Class:** Diagenetic seals
  - **Subclass:** Secondary anhydrite barrier
    - **Family:** Subunconformity diagenesis
      - **Subfamily:** Cementation

Subsection C3
Fluidic Trap System

Introduction

Fluidic traps are oil and gas accumulations in which the trapping element is the physical or chemical condition of the reservoir fluids. There are three regimes in the fluidic system:

1. Pressure traps
2. Temperature traps
3. Fluid-composition traps

This section discusses the regimes, classes, and families of the fluidic trap system.

In this subsection

This subsection discusses the following topics.

Pressure Trap Regime

Introduction

Pressure traps are those in which changes in fluid pressures control or modify trapping elements. Changes from normal pressure gradients to overpressures can create or destroy pressure seals and create isolated pressure compartments that may define trap boundaries. In addition, the presence of a hydrodynamic gradient can cause tilted oil–water and gas–water contacts, which define trap boundaries.

Classes and families

The outline below presents the hierarchy and definitions for pressure traps.

System: Fluidic traps
- **Regime:** Pressure traps
  - **Class:** Overpressure traps
    Limits controlled by change from overpressured reservoir to normally pressured reservoir. Common in some fractured reservoirs in which overpressures were required to generate and support open fractures in the subsurface.
    - **Family:** High-pressure traps
      - **Variety:** Hydrocarbon generation
        Overpressure due to volume increase in conversion of kerogen to oil.
  - **Class:** Tilted oil–water contacts
    Boundary defined by tilted oil–water or gas–water contact.
    - **Family:** Hydrodynamic traps
      Tilted hydrocarbon–water contact in accumulation due to hydrodynamic gradient.

Temperature Trap Regime

Introduction

Temperature traps are those in which trap boundaries are created or controlled by subsurface temperatures. Both low temperatures and high temperatures can create trapping conditions for hydrocarbons.

Classes and families

The classes and families of the temperature trap regime are outlined below.

Regime: Temperature traps
- **Class:** Gas hydrate traps
  - **Family:** Low-temperature traps
    Accumulations in which hydrocarbon gases occur as a solid, ice-like compound of gas and water, formed under conditions of extreme low temperature and high pressure.
- **Class:** Basin-center gas
  Accumulations typically found in deep, hot basin centers in which all available pore space is saturated with gas.
  - **Family:** High-temperature traps
    - **Subfamily:** Generative traps
      High temperatures result in maturation of source rock, which generates and expels sufficient volume of hydrocarbons to saturate pore space of all nearby reservoirs.

Fluid-Composition Trap Regime

Introduction

Fluid-composition traps are controlled by the physical or chemical properties of the trapped fluids themselves. The insolubility, immiscibility, and density contrasts between hydrocarbons and water are major factors that allow hydrocarbons to concentrate into subsurface accumulations. Therefore, in its purest sense, all hydrocarbon accumulations have fluid-composition trapping elements. However, for classification purposes, fluid-composition traps are those in which unique properties of the hydrocarbons provide trapping mechanisms.

Classes and families

The outline below presents the hierarchy and definitions for fluid-composition traps.

Regime: Fluid-composition traps
Result from a chemical property of the trapped oil or gas.

- **Class:** Viscosity traps
  Petroleum can be trapped by the presence of barriers created by highly viscous oil (asphalt, tar) or solid hydrocarbons (albertite, gilsonite, or grahamite).
  - **Subclass:** Tar seals
    - **Family:** Bacterial degradation
      Updip tar seal created by bacteria degradation of the hydrocarbons, preferentially removing the lighter fractions.
  - **Subclass:** Disseminated
    Tar or asphalt fills the pores of shales, sands, or carbonates. These traps are often called tar sands, oil shales, bituminous sandstones, or bituminous limestones.
  - **Subclass:** Veins
    The solid, essentially infusible form of petroleum is called pyrobitumen. It occurs in veins 1 mm to 8 m across and appears to have been injected or is a dead seepage.
- **Class:** Coal-bed methane
  Coal beds trap large volumes of methane, where most is adsorbed onto internal surfaces of micropores or along cleat faces. Coalification generates methane along with water, carbon dioxide, and carbon monoxide.

Section D
References

Biddle, K.T., and C.C. Weilchowsky, 1994, Hydrocarbon traps, *in* L.B. Magoon and W.G. Dow, eds., The Petroleum System—from Source to Trap: AAPG Memoir 60, p. 219–235.

Curtis, Helen, 1983, Biology, 4th Ed.: New York, Worth Publishing, Inc., 1159 p.

Goolsby, S.M., L. Druyff, and M.S. Fryl, 1988, Trapping mechanisms and petrophysical properties of the Permian Kaibab Formation, south-central Utah, *in* S.M. Goolsby and W.M. Longman, eds., Occurrence and Petrophysical Properties of Carbonate Reservoirs in the Rocky Mountain Region: RMAG, p. 193–212.

Jackson, J.A,. ed., 1997, Glossary of Geology, 4th Ed.: American Geological Institute, 769 p.

James, N.P., and H.H.J. Gelsetzer, 1984, Introduction, *in* H.H.J. Geldsetzer, N.P. James, and G.E. Tebbutt, eds., Reefs — Canada and Adjacent Areas: Canadian Society of Petroleum Geologists Memoir 13, p. 1–8.

Leverson, A.I., 1954, Geology of Petroleum: San Francisco, W.H. Freeman and Co., 703 p.

Logan, W.E., 1844, Canada Geological Survey Report of Progress, p. 141.

Milton, N.J., and G.T. Bertram, 1992, Trap styles: a new classification based on sealing surfaces: AAPG Bulletin, vol. 76, p. 983–999.

North, F.K., 1985, Petroleum Geology: Boston, Allen and Unwin, 607 p.

Pollard, D.D., and P. Segall, 1987, Theoretical displacements add stresses near fractures with applications to fault, joints, veins, dikes, and solution surfaces, *in* B.K. Atkinson, ed., Fracture Mechanics of Rock: London, Academic Press, p. 277–349.

Rittenhouse, G., 1972, Stratigraphic-trap classification, *in* R.E. King, ed., Stratigraphic Oil and Gas Fields: AAPG Memoir 16, p. 14–28.

Vincelette, R.R., and N.H. Foster, 1992, Fractured Niobrara of northwestern Colorado, *in* J.W. Schmoker, E.B. Coalson, and C.A. Brown, eds., Geologic Studies Relevant to Horizontal Drilling: Examples from Western North America: RMAG, p. 227–242.

White, R.R., T.J. Alcock, and R.A. Nelson, 1990, Anschutz Ranch East Field, *in* E.A. Beaumont and N.H. Foster, eds., Structural Traps III, Atlas of Oil and Gas Fields: AAPG Treatise of Petroleum Geology, p. 31–56.

White, I.C., 1855, The geology of natural gas: Science, vol. 5, p. 521–522.

Chapter 3

Petroleum Systems

by

Leslie B. Magoon

and

Edward A. Beaumont

Leslie B. Magoon

Leslie B. Magoon graduated from the University of Oregon in Eugene in 1966 with an M.S. degree in geology. Presently, he is a senior research geologist with the U.S. Geological Survey, Menlo Park, California. Prior to that he was with Shell Oil Company for 8 years as an exploration geologist. Over the last 32 years, he has been involved in petroleum geology with emphasis on geochemistry in the Rocky Mountain states, California, Alaska, Colombia, and Malaysia. He has numerous publications on the geology and geochemistry of petroleum provinces in Alaska, the Cook Inlet–Alaska Peninsula, and the North Slope. For the last 15 years he has devoted much of his time to developing and presenting the petroleum system. From 1990–1991, he was an AAPG Distinguished Lecturer. At the 1996 AAPG Annual meeting, Magoon and W.G. Dow, as coeditors, received the R.H. Dott, Sr., Memorial Award for AAPG Memoir 60, *The Petroleum System—From Source to Trap*.

Edward A. Beaumont

Edward A. (Ted) Beaumont is an independent petroleum geologist from Tulsa, Oklahoma. He holds a BS in geology from the University of New Mexico and an MS in geology from the University of Kansas. Currently, he is generating drilling prospects in Texas, Oklahoma, and the Rocky Mountains. His previous professional experience was as a sedimentologist in basin analysis with Cities Service Oil Company and as Science Director for AAPG. Ted is coeditor of the Treatise of Petroleum Geology. He has lectured on creative exploration techniques in the U.S., China, and Australia and has received the Distinguished Service Award and Award of Special Recognition from AAPG.

Overview

Introduction

This chapter discusses the concept and use of petroleum systems. It describes what petroleum systems are and how they can be identified and mapped.

In this chapter

This chapter contains the following sections.

Section A

Defining a Petroleum System

Introduction

The first step in petroleum system analysis is petroleum system definition. This section discusses what the concept of a petroleum system is; how to identify and name a system; how the components relate geographically, stratigraphically, and temporally; and how to map a petroleum system.

In this section

This section contains the following topics.

The Petroleum System Concept

Introduction

The petroleum system is a unifying concept that encompasses all of the disparate elements and processes of petroleum geology. Practical application of petroleum systems can be used in exploration, resource evaluation, and research. This chapter discusses its application to petroleum exploration.

What is a petroleum system?

A petroleum system encompasses a pod of active source rock and all genetically related oil and gas accumulations. It includes all the geologic elements and processes that are essential if an oil and gas accumulation is to exist.

Petroleum describes a compound that includes high concentrations of any of the following substances:

- Thermal and biological hydrocarbon gas found in conventional reservoirs as well as in gas hydrates, tight reservoirs, fractured shale, and coal
- Condensates
- Crude oils
- Natural bitumen in reservoirs, generally in siliciclastic and carbonate rocks

System describes the interdependent elements and processes that form the functional unit that creates hydrocarbon accumulations.

Elements and processes

The essential elements of a petroleum system include the following:

- Source rock
- Reservoir rock
- Seal rock
- Overburden rock

Petroleum systems have two processes:

- Trap formation
- Generation–migration–accumulation of hydrocarbons

These essential elements and processes must be correctly placed in time and space so that organic matter included in a source rock can be converted into a petroleum accumulation. A petroleum system exists wherever all these essential elements and processes are known to occur or are thought to have a reasonable chance or probability to occur.

Petroleum system investigation

A petroleum system investigation identifies, names, determines the level of certainty, and maps the geographic, stratigraphic, and temporal extent of a petroleum system. The investigation includes certain components:

- Petroleum–petroleum geochemical correlation
- Petroleum–source rock geochemical correlation
- Burial history chart
- Petroleum system map
- Petroleum system cross section
- Events chart
- Table of hydrocarbon accumulations
- Determination of generation–accumulation efficiency

Identifying a Petroleum System

Introduction

Before a petroleum system can be investigated, it must be identified as being present.

Petroleum system identification

To identify a petroleum system, the explorationist must find some petroleum. Any quantity of petroleum, no matter how small, is proof of a petroleum system. An oil or gas seep, a show of oil or gas in a well, or an oil or gas accumulation demonstrates the presence of a petroleum system.

Procedure: Identifying a petroleum system

The table below outlines the steps required to identify a petroleum system.

<table>
<tr><th>Step</th><th>Task</th></tr>
<tr><td>1</td><td>Find some indication of the presence of petroleum.</td></tr>
<tr><td>2</td><td>Determine the size of the petroleum system by the following series of steps:</td></tr>
<tr><td></td><td><table>
<tr><th>Step</th><th>Task</th></tr>
<tr><td>a</td><td>Group genetically related occurrences of petroleum by using geochemical characteristics and stratigraphic occurrences.</td></tr>
<tr><td>b</td><td>Identify the source using petroleum–source rock correlations.</td></tr>
<tr><td>c</td><td>Locate the general area of the pod of active source rock responsible for the genetically related petroleum occurrences.</td></tr>
<tr><td>d</td><td>Make a table of accumulations to determine the amount of hydrocarbons in the petroleum system and which reservoir rock contains the most petroleum.</td></tr>
</table></td></tr>
<tr><td>3</td><td>Name the petroleum system.</td></tr>
</table>

Naming a Petroleum System

Introduction

A unique designation or name is important to identify a person, place, item, or idea. As geologists, we name rock units, fossils, uplifts, and basins. The name for a specific petroleum system separates it from other petroleum systems and other geologic names.

Parts of a petroleum system name

The name of a petroleum system contains several parts that name the hydrocarbon fluid system:

1. The source rock in the pod of active source rock
2. The name of the reservoir rock that contains the largest volume of in-place petroleum
3. The symbol expressing the level of certainty

Here is an example of a petroleum system name and its parts.

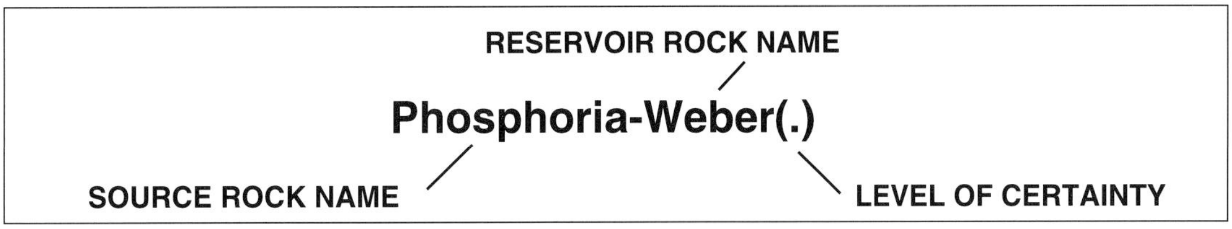

Figure 3–1.

Naming a petroleum system

The figure below shows how a reservoir rock name is selected.

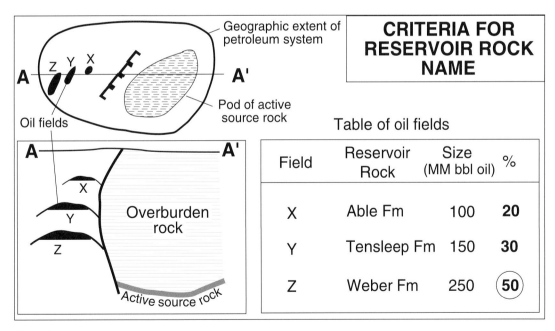

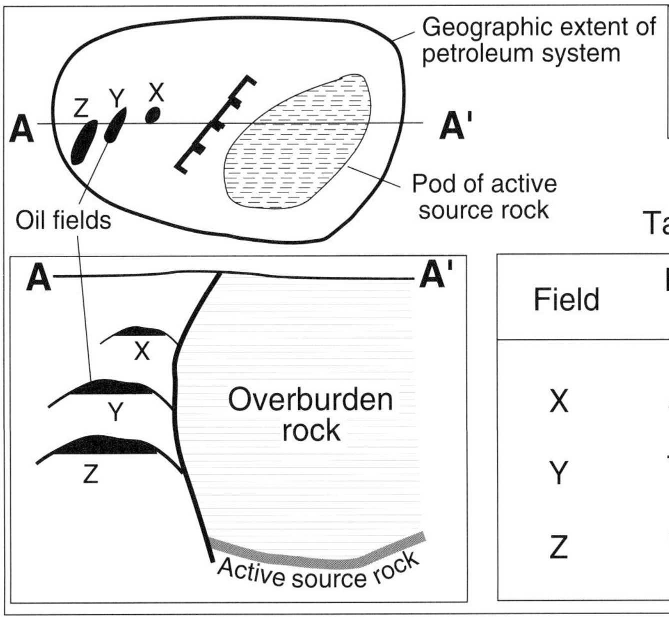

CRITERIA FOR RESERVOIR ROCK NAME

Table of oil fields

Field	Reservoir Rock	Size (MM bbl oil)	%
X	Able Fm	100	**20**
Y	Tensleep Fm	150	**30**
Z	Weber Fm	250	**50**

Figure 3–2.

Naming a Petroleum System, continued

Level of certainty

A petroleum system can be identified at three levels of certainty: known, hypothetical, and speculative. The level of certainty indicates the confidence for which a particular pod of mature source rock has generated the hydrocarbons in an accumulation. At the end of the system's name, the level of certainty is indicated by (!) for known, (.) for hypothetical, and (?) for speculative.

The table below indicates how the level of certainty is determined.

Level of Certainty	Criteria	Symbol
Known	A positive oil–source rock or gas–source rock correlation	(!)
Hypothetical	In the absence of a positive petroleum–source rock correlation, geochemical evidence	(.)
Speculative	Geological or geophysical evidence	(?)

Geographic, Stratigraphic, and Temporal Extent

Introduction

Petroleum systems are limited by time and space. Each system can be described in terms of its own unique temporal and spatial elements and processes.

Temporal aspects

A petroleum system has three important temporal aspects:

- Age
- Critical moment
- Preservation time

The **age** of a system is the time required for the process of generation–migration–accumulation of hydrocarbons.

The **critical moment** is the time that best depicts the generation–migration–accumulation of hydrocarbons in a petroleum system. A map and cross section drawn at the critical moment best show the geographic and stratigraphic extent of the system. The burial history chart below shows the critical moment and the essential elements for the fictitious Deer-Boar(.) petroleum system.

The **preservation time** of the petroleum system begins immediately after the generation–migration–accumulation process occurs and extends to the present day. It encompasses any changes to the petroleum accumulations during this period. During the preservation time, remigration, physical or biological degradation, or complete destruction of the petroleum may take place. During the preservation time, remigrated (tertiary migration) petroleum can accumulate in reservoir rocks deposited after the petroleum system formed. If insignificant tectonic activity occurs during the preservation time, accumulations remain in their original position. Remigration happens during the preservation time only if folding, faulting, uplift, or erosion occurs. If all accumulations are destroyed during preservation time, then the evidence that a petroleum system existed is absent. An incomplete or just completed petroleum system lacks a preservation time.

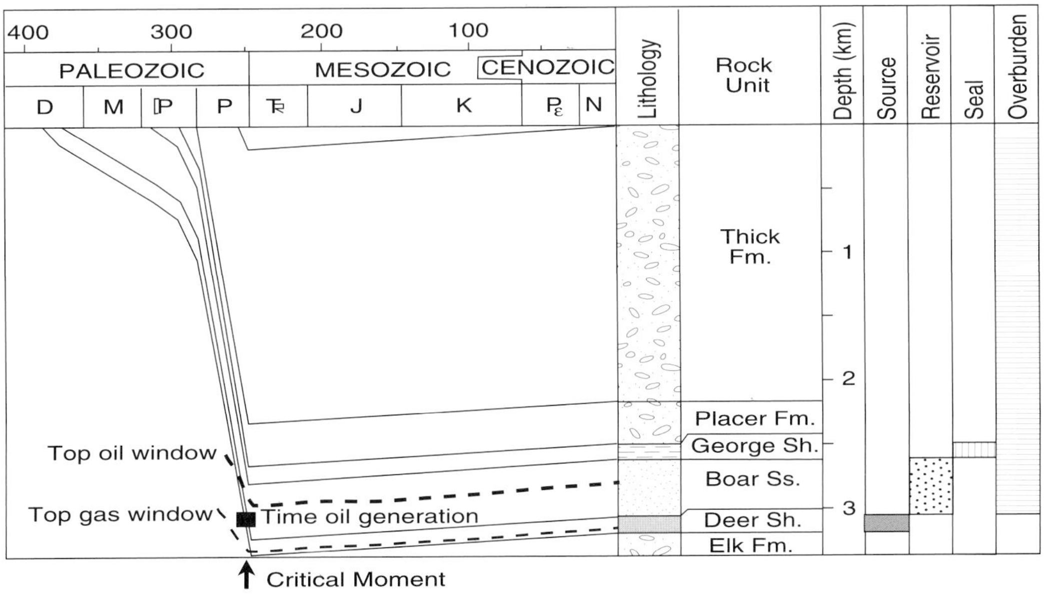

Figure 3–3. From Magoon and Dow, 1994; courtesy AAPG.

Spatial aspects

Each petroleum system can be defined spatially by its geographic and stratigraphic extent.

The **geographic extent** of a petroleum system is determined at the critical moment. It is defined by a line that circumscribes the pod of active source rock and all oil and gas seeps, shows, and accumulations originating from that pod. The map below shows the geographic extent of the fictitious Deer-Boar(.) petroleum system.

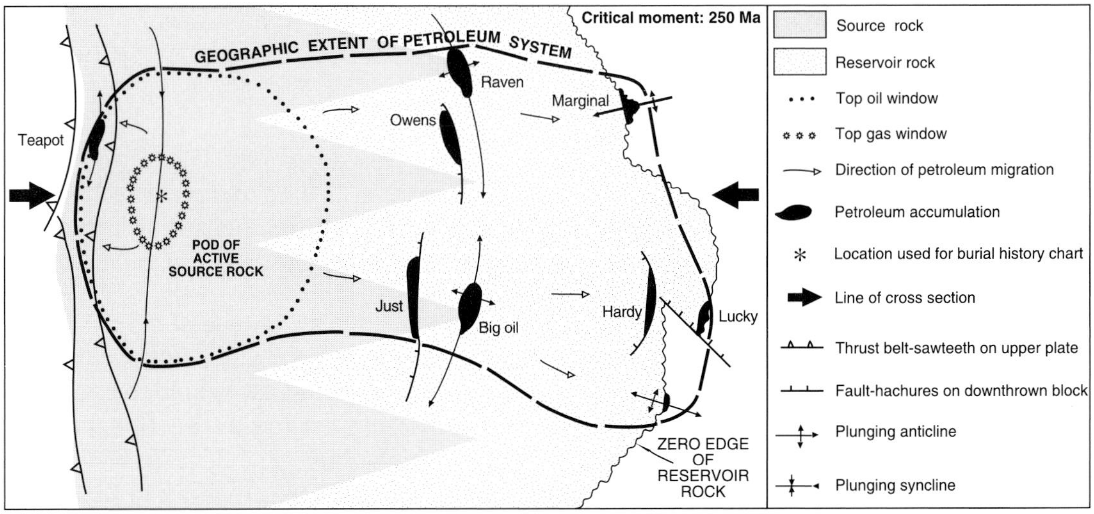

Figure 3–4. From Magoon and Dow, 1994; courtesy AAPG.

The **stratigraphic extent** of a petroleum system is the span of lithological units which encompasses the essential elements within the geographic extent of a petroleum system. The stratigraphic extent can be displayed on the burial history chart and cross section drawn at the critical moment. The cross section below shows the stratigraphic extent of the fictitious Deer-Boar(.) petroleum system at the critical moment.

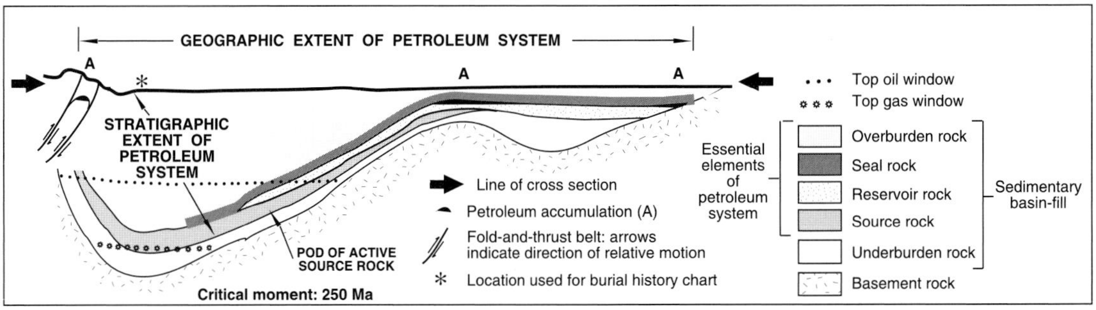

Figure 3–5. From Magoon and Dow, 1994; courtesy AAPG.

What is an events chart?

An events chart shows the temporal relation of the essential elements and processes of a petroleum system. It also shows the preservation time and the critical moment for the system. An events chart can be used to compare the times that the processes occurred with the times that the elements formed.

Events chart example

A petroleum system events chart shows time on one axis and the essential elements and processes on the other. The time required for the generation–migration–accumulation process is the same as the age of the system. The chart also shows the preservation time and critical moment for the system. The events chart for the fictitious Deer-Boar(.) petroleum system is shown below.

The events chart is arranged according to increasing difficulty. For example, mapping and dating the essential elements of a petroleum system are usually easier than mapping and determining the time over which the processes took place. Because the petroleum system deals only with discovered accumulations, there is no question that the elements and processes worked correctly to make oil and gas fields. Later, however, the events chart is transformed into a risk chart to better evaluate a play or prospect.

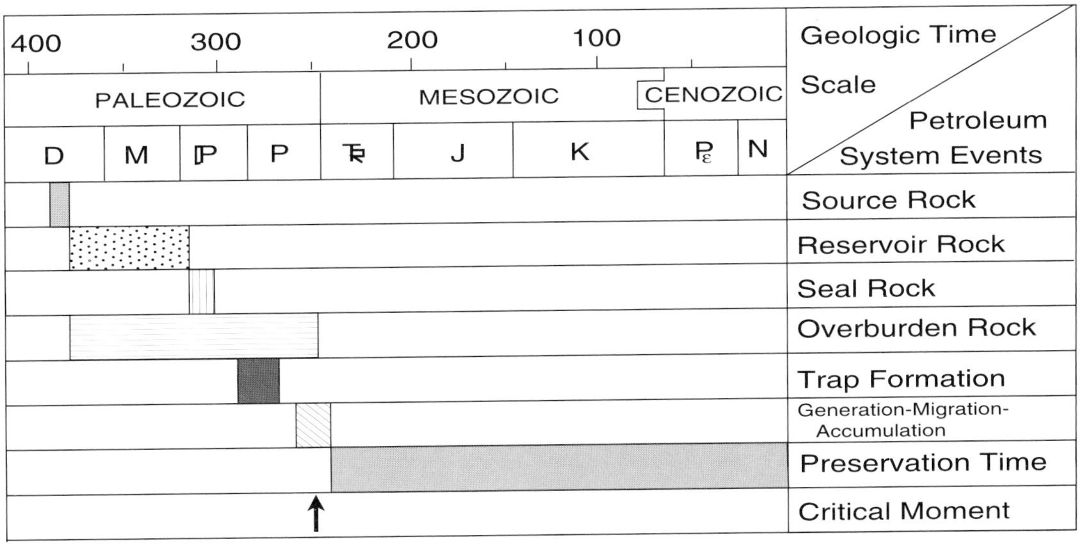

Figure 3–6. From Magoon and Dow, 1994; courtesy AAPG.

Size of a Petroleum System

Introduction

The size of a petroleum system includes the total volume of all recoverable hydrocarbons that originated from a single pod of active source rock. This total volume is used to compare against other petroleum systems and to determine the generation–accumulation efficiency.

Volume of petroleum

The discovered hydrocarbons include shows, seeps, and accumulations of oil and gas. The size of a petroleum system is determined using a table such as the following for the fields in the Deer-Boar(.) system, with reserves of approximately 1.2 billion barrels (bbl).

Field Name	Discovery Date	Reservoir Rock	API Gravity (°API)	Cum. Oil Production ($\times 10^6$ bbl)		Remaining Reserves ($\times 10^6$ bbl)
Big Oil	1954	Boar Ss	32	310		90
Raven	1956	Boar Ss	31	120		12
Owens	1959	Boar Ss	33	110		19
Just	1966	Boar Ss	34	160		36
Hardy	1989	Boar Ss	29	85		89
Lucky	1990	Boar Ss	15	5		70
Marginal	1990	Boar Ss	18	12		65
Teapot	1992	Boar Ss	21	9		34
Total				811	+	415

Generation–accumulation efficiency

Generation–accumulation efficiency is the ratio (expressed as a percentage) of the total volume of trapped (in-place) petroleum in the petroleum system to the total volume of petroleum generated from the pod of active source rock.

Mapping a Petroleum System

Introduction

A petroleum system is mapped by showing the geographic, stratigraphic, and temporal extent of the system.

Mapping the geographic extent

The **geographic extent** is the area over which the petroleum system is known to occur. It is defined in map view by a line on the earth's surface that circumscribes the pod of active source rock as well as all the known petroleum shows, seeps, and accumulations that originated from that pod. The geographic extent is outlined to correspond to the time of the critical moment. It is similar to the known extent, or known geographic extent.

Mapping the stratigraphic extent

The **stratigraphic extent** of a petroleum system is the span of lithological units which encompasses the essential elements within the geographic extent of a petroleum system. The stratigraphic extent can be displayed on the burial history chart and cross section drawn at the critical moment. The stratigraphic extent is from below the pod of active source rock or the petroleum of the discovered accumulations in the system, whichever is deeper, to the top of the overburden rock.

Mapping the temporal extent

The **temporal extent** of the petroleum system is shown on the events chart and includes the age of the essential elements and processes, the preservation time, and the critical moment. By displaying together the time over which these separate events took place, the relation between forming and charging the traps containing the accumulations is easily evaluated.

Section B

Examples of Two Petroleum Systems

Introduction

To better understand how a petroleum system is mapped and described, two examples are presented: the Mandal-Ekofisk(!) and the Ellesmerian(!) petroleum systems (from Cornford, 1994, and Bird, 1994, respectively). The petroleum in the former system migrated across stratigraphic units (or vertically) into many accumulations, whereas the latter migrated along stratigraphic units (or laterally) into a few accumulations. Both oil systems are multibillion barrels in size. These two examples illustrate many of the concepts and principles discussed in section A.

In this section

This section contains the following topics.

Mandal–Ekofisk(!) Petroleum System

Introduction

The Mandal–Ekofisk(!) petroleum system in the Central Graben of the North Sea contains 21.4 billion bbl of oil and 39.4 trillion ft^3 of gas in 39 fields (Cornford, 1994). The age of the reservoir rock ranges from Devonian to Tertiary age with about 85% of the petroleum in rock adjacent to the Cretaceous–Tertiary boundary, specifically the Ekofisk Formation of Late Cretaceous age. Based on geochemical evidence, the Upper Jurassic (Kimmeridgian) to Lower Cretaceous source rock is the Mandal Formation. A positive oil–source rock correlation indicates a known system.

Geologic setting

This petroleum system formed in sedimentary rocks deposited in a failed rift system in the North Sea between Great Britain, Norway, and Denmark. The prerift rocks are mostly underburden rocks and are not involved in this petroleum system except as reservoir rocks for a minor amount of petroleum. The synrift sedimentary section contains the source rock. The reservoir rock, seal rock, and overburden rock were deposited during the postrift period of sedimentation.

Burial history chart

To better determine when the Mandal source rock was actively generating petroleum, a burial history chart (shown below) was constructed. Based on this and other charts, peak generation of petroleum occurred at about 30 Ma, selected as the critical moment.

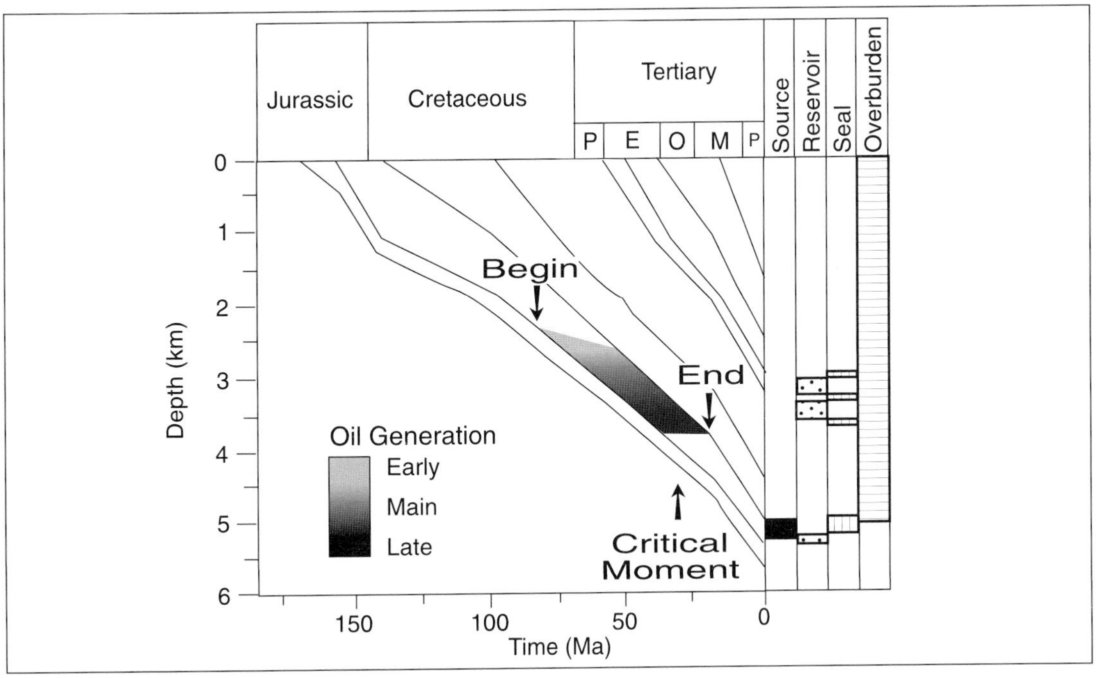

Figure 3–7. From Cornford, 1994; courtesy AAPG.

Petroleum system map

The petroleum system map in Figure 3–8 shows the pod of active source rock and the oil and gas accumulations that were charged by this same pod of active source rock; all are within the geographic or known extent of the system. Most accumulations for the Mandal–Ekofisk(!) overly the active source rock, and the gas/condensate fields overlie the most mature source rock.

Petroleum system cross section

The petroleum system cross section in Figure 3–9 shows migration pathways and the spatial relation of the active source rock to the reservoir rocks. This section trends longitudinally (see Figure 3–8 for location) along the Central Graben and shows the vertical migration path from the active source rock through the Cretaceous rocks and horizontally along the basal Paleogene reservoir rocks until it accumulates in various traps. The underburden rock is pre-Late Jurassic in age and is not involved in the petroleum system except as minor reservoir rocks and where the Permian salt (Zechstein Group) creates diapirs that form petroleum traps and migration paths in fractured chalk.

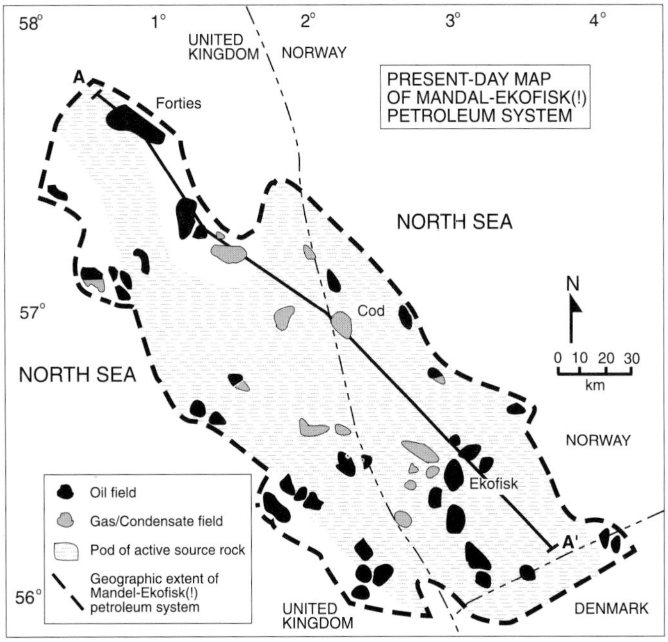

Figure 3–8. Modified from Cornford, 1994; courtesy AAPG.

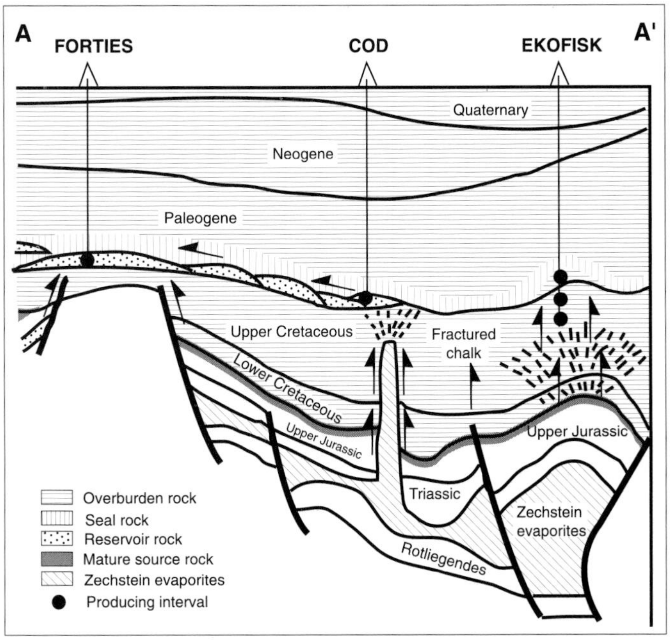

Figure 3–9. Modified from Cornford, 1994; courtesy AAPG.

Oil–source rock correlation

The oil–source rock correlation is a multiparameter geochemical approach; biological markers are one parameter. Biological marker analysis by Mackenzie et al. (1983) and Hughes et al. (1985) from reservoirs in the Greater Ekofisk, Forties, Montrose, and Argyll fields shows that these oils originated from the Mandal Formation source rock, as illustrated in the figure below.

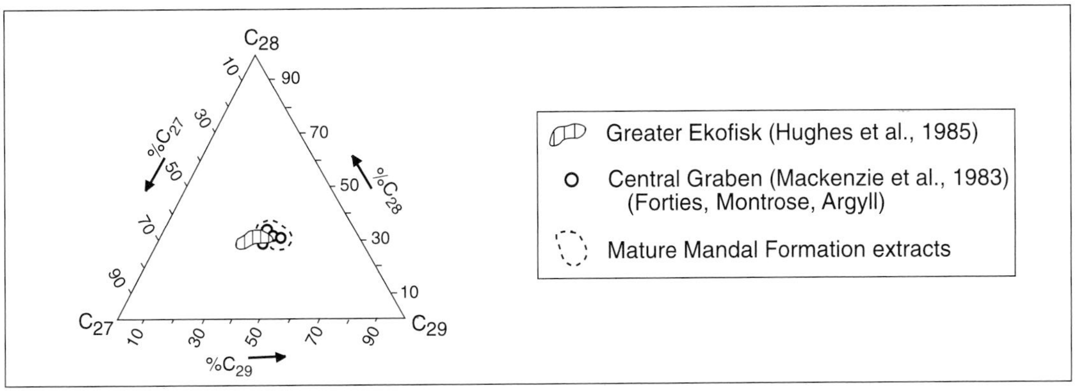

Figure 3–10. From Cornford, 1994; courtesy AAPG.

Petroleum system events chart

An events chart indicates when the essential elements and processes took place to form a petroleum system, the critical moment, and the preservation time. In the chart below, the source rock is the Upper Jurassic to Lower Cretaceous Mandal Formation, which was deposited as the rift formed. Most overburden rock of Cretaceous to Cenozoic age was deposited after the rift formed. The seal rock ranges from Permian to Neogene and consists of halite, shale, and chalk. Based on volume of petroleum, the Permian to Jurassic reservoir rocks are least important; the most important reservoir rocks are Late Cretaceous to early Paleogene in age. Most traps were created as the rift formed and filled through structural movement and halokenesis. Petroleum generation–migration–accumulation occurred from just over 100 Ma to the present day. The critical moment, or peak generation, is at 30 Ma.

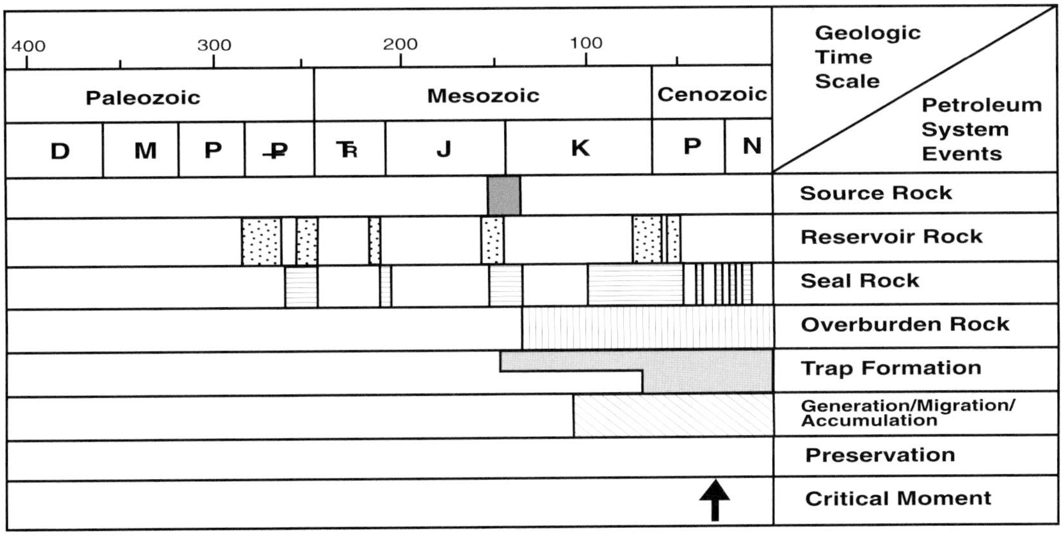

Figure 3–11. Modified from Cornford, 1994; courtesy AAPG.

Mandal–Ekofisk(!) Petroleum System, continued

Size of the petroleum system

The size of the Mandal-Ekofisk(!) petroleum system, as shown in the table below, is determined by the total volume of in-place hydrocarbons that originated from the pod of active Mandal source rock. The in-place hydrocarbons are determined from the recoverable hydrocarbons and, where possible, surface deposits, seeps, and shows.

	In-place petroleum resources					
	Oil		Condensate		Gas	
Field name	($\times 10^6$ bbl)	($\times 10^6$ m^3)	($\times 10^6$ bbl)	($\times 10^6$ m^3)	($\times 10^9$ ft^3)	($\times 10^9$ m^3)
Acorn	—	—	—	—	—	—
Albuskjell	—	—	67	11	848	24
Arbroath	340	54	—	—	83	2
Argyl	218	35	—	—	257	7
Auk	517	82	—	—	98	3
Beechnut	—	—	—	—	—	—
Clyde	405	64	—	—	138	4
Cod	—	—	21	3	489	14
Duncan	49	8	—	—	69	2
Edda	114	18	—	—	353	10
Ekofisk	7,099	1,129	404	64	21,189	600
Eldfisk	1,589	253	—	—	7,249	205
Erskine	—	—	—	—	—	—
Flyndra	—	—	—	—	—	—
Forties	4,333	689	—	—	1,313	37
Fulmar	812	129	—	—	499	14
Gannet	800	127	—	—	1,000	28
Gert	—	—	—	—	—	—
Gyda	—	—	—	—	—	—
Hod	236	38	—	—	207	6
Innes	19	3	—	—	43	1
Joanne	—	—	—	—	—	—
Josephine	—	—	—	—	—	—
Judy	—	—	—	—	—	—
Kittiwake	175	28	—	—	60	2
Lomond	—	—	—	—	—	—
Lulu(Harald)	—	—	—	—	—	—
Marnock	—	—	—	—	—	—
Montrose	327	52	—	—	114	3
N7/11-5	210	33	—	—	236	10
N2/2 Struct.	—	—	—	—	—	—
Sam	—	—	—	—	—	—
Tommeliten	94	15	50	8	330	9
Tor	539	86	—	—	788	71
Ula	825	131	—	—	413	12
Ula Trend	600	95	—	—	450	13
Valhal	1,405	223	66	10	1,823	52
Fiddich	—	—	—	—	—	—
West Ekofisk	—	—	84	13	1,315	37
Sums	**20,706**	**3292**	**692**	**110**	**39,361**	**1167**

Modified from Cornford, 1994; courtesy AAPG.

Ellesmerian(!) Petroleum System

Introduction

The Ellesmerian(!) petroleum system of the North Slope, Alaska, contains approximately 77 billion bbl of oil equivalent (Bird, 1994). The age of the reservoir rock ranges from Mississippian to early Tertiary. Total organic carbon and assumed hydrogen indices from the marine shale source rocks indicate the mass of petroleum generated to be approximately 8 trillion barrels of oil (Bird, 1994). These estimates indicate about 1% of the generated hydrocarbons are contained in known traps. More importantly, the U.S. Geological Survey estimates another 1% is trapped in undiscovered accumulations in the Ellesmerian(!) petroleum system (Bird, 1994).

Geologic setting

The North Slope evolved from a passive continental margin to a foredeep during the Jurassic. Prior to the Jurassic, Paleozoic and Mesozoic strata were deposited on a passive continental margin. They consist of Carboniferous platform carbonate rocks and Permian to Jurassic shelf to basinal siliciclastic rocks. The passive margin converted to a foredeep during the Jurassic and Cretaceous when it collided with an ocean island arc. The foredeep began to fill with sediments in the Middle Jurassic and continues to do so.

The foredeep basin fill consists of orogenic sedimentary materials eroded from the nearby ancestral Brooks Range that were deposited as a northeasterly prograding wedge of nonmarine, shallow marine, basin-slope, and basin conglomerates, sandstones, and mudstones.

Petroleum system map

The map below shows the Ellesmerian(!) petroleum system geographic extent. The limit is determined by the extent of the contiguous active source rock and the related petroleum accumulations.

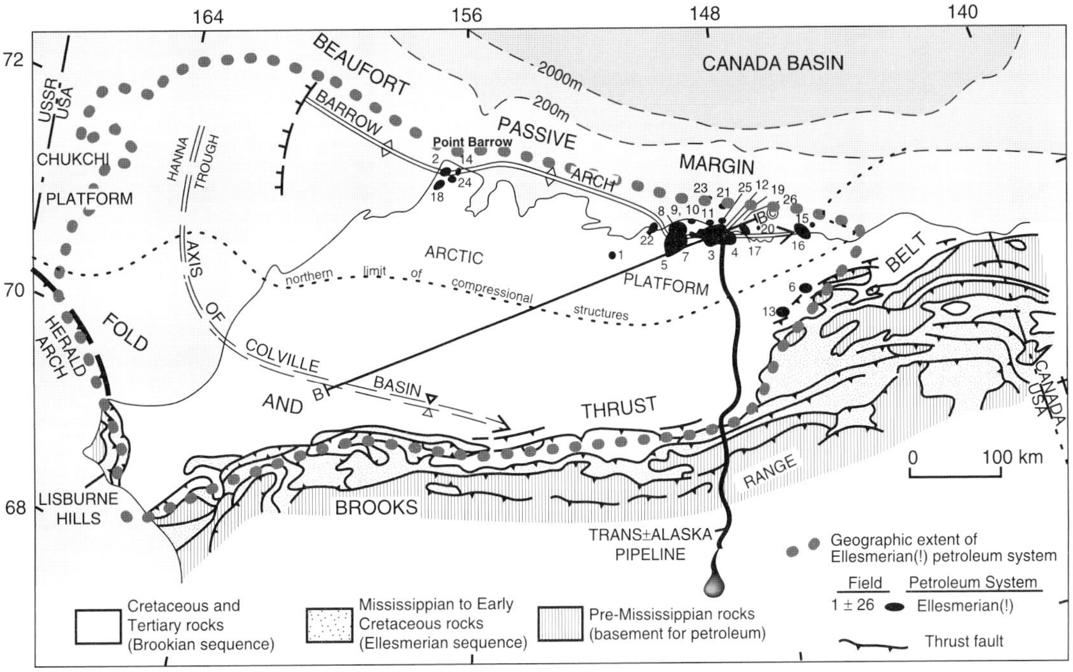

Figure 3–12. From Bird, 1994; courtesy AAPG.

Petroleum system maturity map

The map below shows the thermal maturity of the two main Ellesmerian(!) petroleum system source rocks, the Shublik Formation and the Kingak Shale. Note that Ellesmerian(!) petroleum system traps (shown in Figure 3–12) are mostly located above immature source rocks.

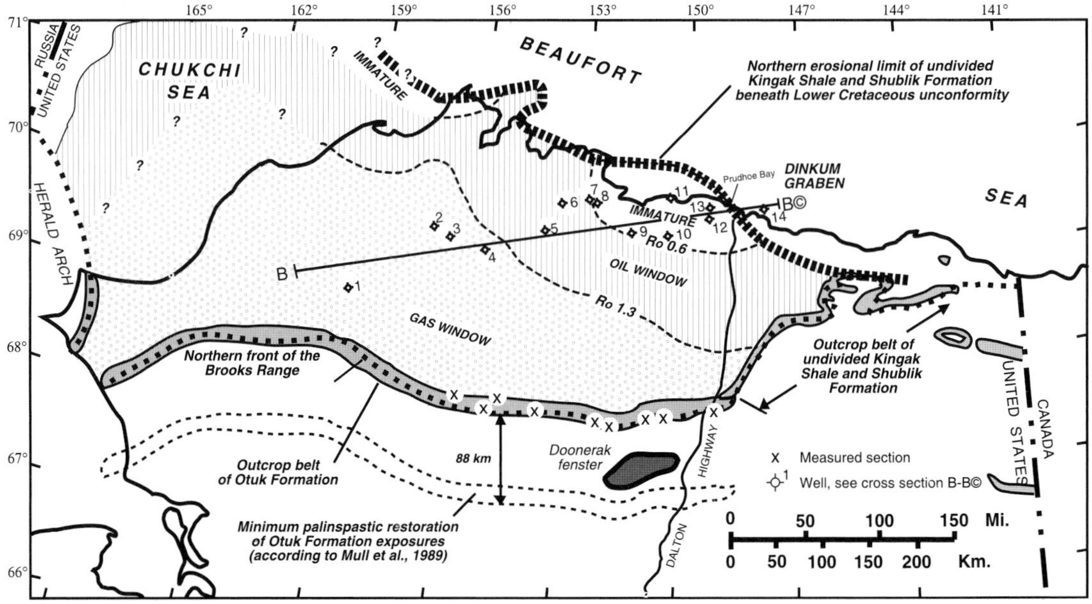

Figure 3–13. From Bird, 1994; courtesy AAPG.

Petroleum system cross section

The cross section of the Ellesmerian(!) petroleum system (below) shows major structural–stratigraphic elements, the occurrence of oil fields, elevation of selected vitrinite reflectance values, and reflectance isograds. For the location, refer to Figure 3–12.

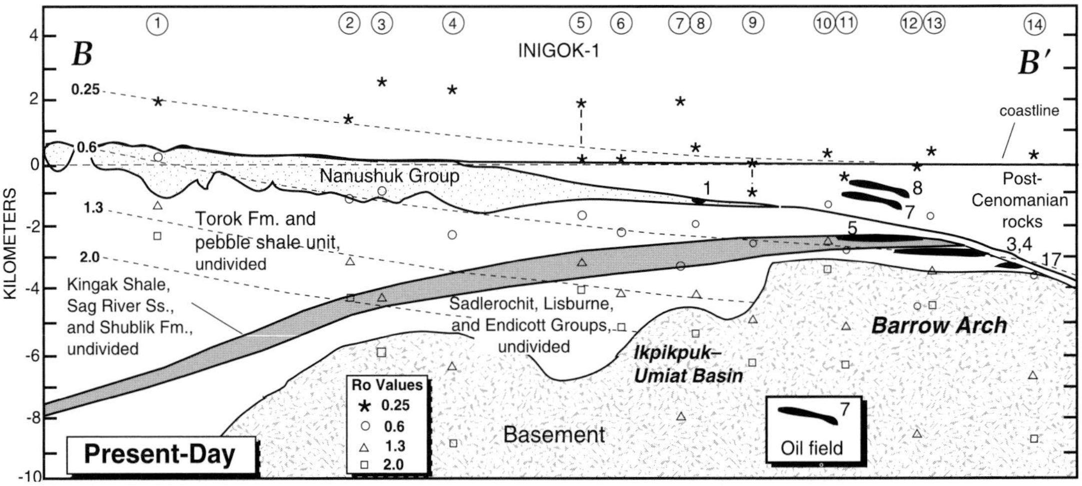

Figure 3–14. From Bird, 1994; courtesy AAPG.

Burial history chart

Analysis of the burial history chart of the Inigok 1 well (below) and other burial history charts indicates peak petroleum generation (the critical moment) probably occurred in Late Cretaceous time (approximately 75 Ma) in the western North Slope and in early Tertiary time (approximately 50 Ma) in the central and eastern part of the North Slope. Also, note the large increase in the rate of sedimentation during the Early Cretaceous.

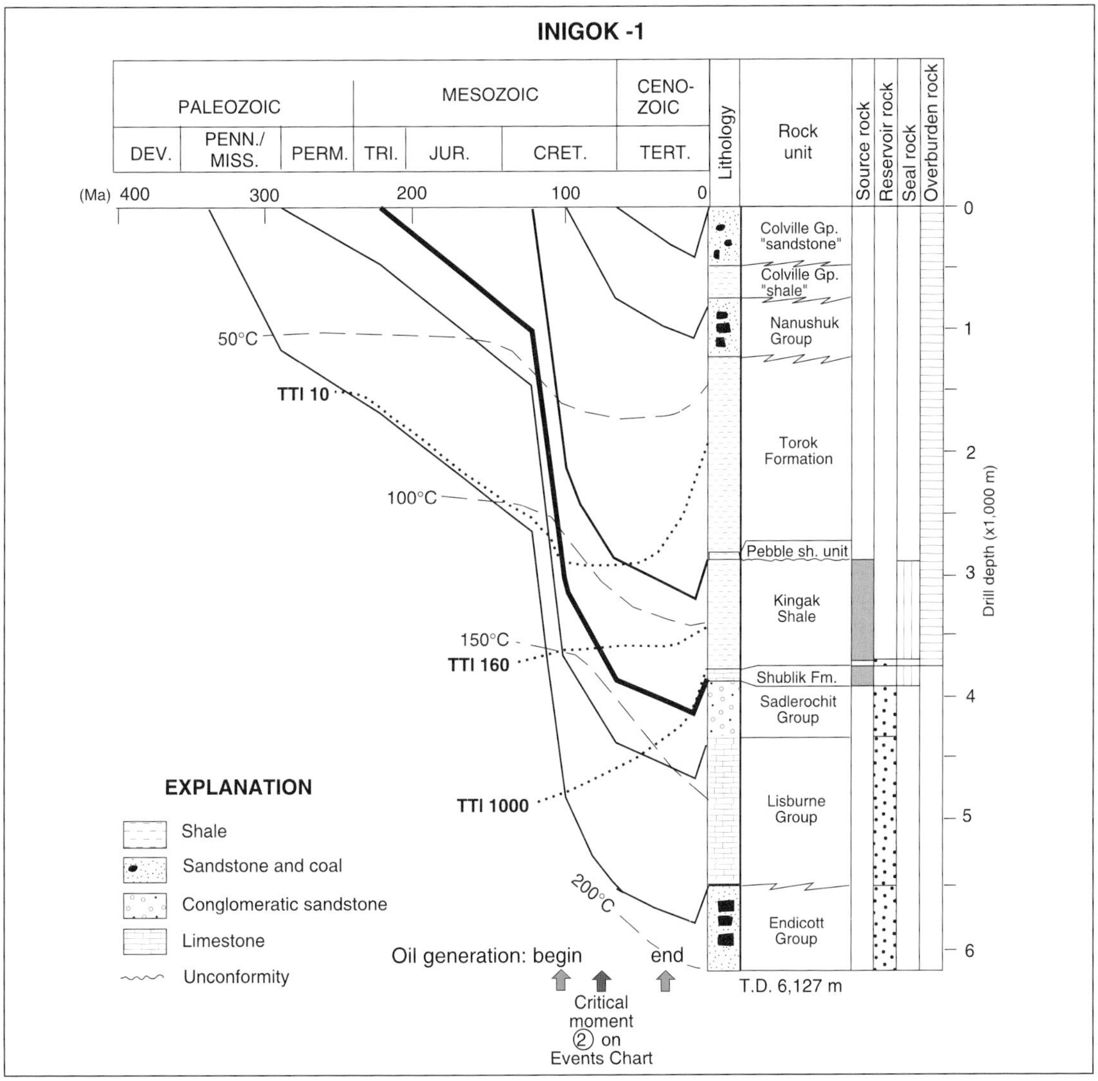

Figure 3–15. From Bird, 1994; courtesy AAPG.

Oil–source rock correlation

Biological marker analysis (below, left) from the main reservoir rock, Sadlerochit Group, of Prudhoe Bay field shows that the oil originated from the Shublik Formation, the Kingak Shale, and the Hue Shale. Carbon isotopic composition comparisons (below, right) indicate that Shublik and Kingak share similar ^{13}C values with oil from the Prudhoe Bay field, whereas the Hue Shale does not.

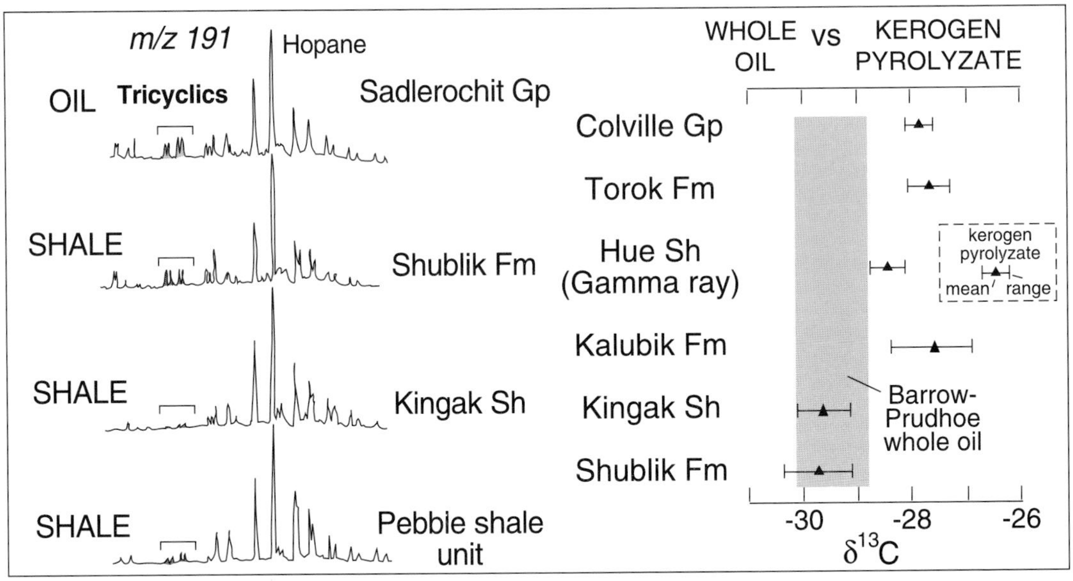

Figure 3–16. (left) From Seifert et al., 1980; courtesy World Petroleum Conference. (right) From Sedivy et al., 1987; courtesy Pacific Section of SEPM.

Petroleum system events chart

The events chart below for the Ellesmerian(!) petroleum system indicates when its elements and processes occurred. The cross-hatched pattern shows the estimated time of the tilting of the Barrow Arch, which resulted in remigration of petroleum from older to younger (early Tertiary) reservoir rocks.

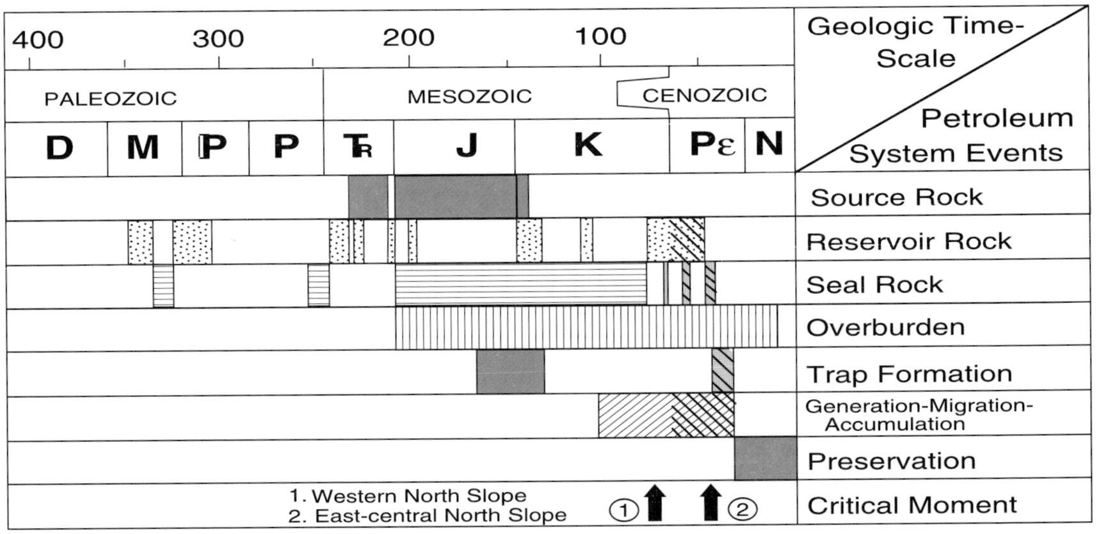

Figure 3–17. From Bird, 1994; courtesy AAPG.

Ellesmerian(!) Petroleum System, continued

Size of the petroleum system

The size of the Ellesmerian(!) petroleum system, shown in the table below, is determined by the total volume of in-place petroleum that originated from the pod of active Ellesmerian(!) petroleum system source rock. The in-place petroleum is determined from the recoverable petroleum and, where possible, surface deposits, seeps, and shows. In the table below, trap type A is structural, B is stratigraphic, and C is combination.

Map ID	Accumulation	Res. Depth (m)	Trap Type	In Place Oil (Bbbl)	In Place Gas (Tcf)	Cum. Prod. Oil (Mbbl)	Cum. Prod. Gas (Bcf)	Reserves Oil (Mbbl)	Reserves Gas (Bcf)
1	Fish Creek	915	B?	<<1	—	—	—	?	?
2	South Barrow	685	A	—	<<1	—	20	—	5
3	Prudhoe Bay	2440	C	23	27	7026	11951	2700	23441
4	Prudhoe Bay	2685	C	3	3	64	382	101	406
5	Kuparuk River	1830	C	-4	-2	723	814	780	634
6	Kavik	1435	A	—	<1	—	—	—	?
7	West Sak		B?	20	<<1	1	—	—	—
8	Ugnu		B?	15	—	—	—	—	—
9	Milne Point		A	<1	<<1	—	—	—	?
10	Milne Point		A	<1	<<1	16	6	84	?
11	Gwydyr Bay		A	<1	<<1	—	—	60	?
12	North Prudhoe		A	<1	<<1	—	—	75	?
13	Kemik	2625	A	—	<1	—	—	—	?
14	East Barrow		A	—	<<1	—	6	—	6
15	Flaxman Island	3810	B?	?	?	—	—	?	?
16	Point Thomson	3960	C	<1	6	—	—	350	5000
17	Endicott		C	1	<2	118	127	272	907
18	Walakpa		B	—	<<1	—	—	—	?
19	Niakuk		C	<1	<<1	—	—	58	30
20	Tern Island		C	?	?	—	—	?	?
21	Seal Island		A	<1	<1	—	—	150	?
22	Colville Delta	1950	C?	?	?	—	—	?	?
23	Sandpiper		A	?	?	—	—	?	?
24	Sikulik		A	—	<<1	—	—	—	?
25	Point McIntyre		C	1	?	—	—	-300	?
26	Sag Delta North		C	<1	<<1	2	2	?	?
	TOTALS			**>67**	**>39**	**7950**	**13308**	**4930**	**30423**

From Bird, 1994; courtesy AAPG.

Section C

Applying the Petroleum System Concept

Introduction

This section discusses how to apply the petroleum system concept to petroleum exploration. It defines petroleum province, basin, system, play, and prospect and it shows how the system relates to the complementary play. It also explains how to use a petroleum system study to reduce exploration risk.

In this section

This section contains the following topics.

Basin, System, Play, and Prospect

Introduction

Words frequently have more than one meaning; nomenclature in this discipline of petroleum geology is no exception. To more clearly separate the petroleum system from the sedimentary basin and the play and prospect, the meaning of these words needs to be clarified with respect to each other and the petroleum province.

Petroleum province

Petroleum province, a geographic term, is an area where petroleum occurs in commercial quantities. **Basin** is sometimes used geographically to mean petroleum province, such as the Williston Basin or Paris Basin. The Zagros fold belt could be a structural province or a petroleum province, not a basin.

A map showing differential thickness of sedimentary rocks is used to determine basins (thick), uplifts (thin), and fold belts (folded). These features are properly named provinces; if they contain petroleum, they are called petroleum provinces. The use of "basin" in this context is improper; it is also inconsistent with the petroleum system concept described below, which defines "basin" as the area into which sedimentary rocks are deposited.

Sedimentary basin

A **sedimentary basin** is a depression filled with sedimentary rocks. The presence of sedimentary rocks is proof that a basin existed.

The depression, formed by any tectonic process, is lined by **basement rock**, which can be igneous, metamorphic, and/or sedimentary rock. The **basin fill** includes the rock matter, organic matter, and water deposited in this depression. In certain cases, such as with coal and some carbonate deposits, the sedimentary material is formed in situ. The essential elements of a petroleum system are deposited in sedimentary basins. Frequently, one or more overlapping sedimentary basins are responsible for the essential elements of a petroleum system. Traps are formed by tectonic processes that act on sedimentary rocks. However, the moment petroleum is generated, biologically or thermally, a petroleum system is formed.

Petroleum system

The **petroleum system** includes the pod of active source rock, the natural distribution network, and the genetically related discovered petroleum occurrences. Presence of petroleum is proof that a system exists.

The pod of active source rock is part of the petroleum system because it is the provenance of these related petroleum occurrences. The distribution network is the migration paths to discovered accumulations, seeps, and shows.

In contrast to the play and prospect, which address undiscovered commercial accumulations, the petroleum system includes only the discovered petroleum occurrences. If an exploratory well encounters any type or amount of petroleum, that petroleum is part of a petroleum system.

Basin, System, Play, and Prospect, continued

Play and prospect

The play and prospect are used by the explorationist to present a geologic argument to justify drilling for undiscovered, commercial petroleum accumulations.

The **play** consists of one or more geologically related prospects, and a **prospect** is a potential trap that must be evaluated by drilling to determine whether it contains commercial quantities of petroleum. Once drilling is complete, the term "prospect" is dropped; the site becomes either a dry hole or a producing field.

The presence of a petroleum charge, a suitable trap, and whether the trap formed before it was charged are usually involved in this evaluation.

These terms are compared in the table below

Item to be Compared	Sedimentary Basin	Petroleum System	Play	Prospect
Investigation	Sedimentary rocks	Petroleum	Traps	Trap
Economics	None	None	Essential	Essential
Geologic time	Time of deposition	Critical moment	Present day	Present day
Existence	Absolute	Absolute	Conditional	Conditional
Cost	Very low	Low	High	Very high
Analysis	Basin	System	Play	Prospect
Modeling	Basin	System	Play	Prospect

Relationship of play to petroleum system

In a play, the petroleum accumulations are commercial and undiscovered. In a petroleum system, the petroleum occurrences are already discovered (Magoon, 1995). Other differences are listed in the table above. Usually, a play is predicated without any particular petroleum system in mind. However, when a play is based on a particular petroleum system, it is called a **complementary play**.

The petroleum system concept is used two ways in exploration. By mapping a petroleum system, an explorationist learns new play concepts to add new oil or gas fields to the petroleum system. This relation is shown in the following equation:

$$PS_{total} = PS_{partial} + CP_1 + CP_2 + CP_3$$

where:

PS_{total} = petroleum system with all accumulations discovered

$PS_{partial}$ = petroleum system with only some of the accumulations discovered

$CP_1, \ldots$ = the complementary play (prospect) concepts used to find the remaining undiscovered commercial accumulations in the petroleum system

The petroleum system is also used as an analog to another less-explored petroleum system. For this approach to work, the explorationist must have a series of petroleum system case studies available for comparison.

Reducing Exploration Risk

Introduction

In exploration, the general question is *Where can we find substantial quantities of hydrocarbons that are economical to produce?* To solve this problem, exploration geologists find and evaluate a prospect. In addition to helping evaluate petroleum charge, trap, and timing, the petroleum system concept can help in the exploration process by determining exploration intensity and assessing risk.

Play

A play is one or more prospects that may define a profitable accumulation of undiscovered petroleum. Traditionally, a play is developed and evaluated without any particular petroleum system in mind. For example, if a prospect (play) is identified near a series of oil fields in anticlinal traps, it could be argued—using geophysics and geochemistry—that the prospect is an anticlinal trap charged with the same oil.

Three independent variables—petroleum charge (fluids), trap (sedimentary rocks), and timing (time)—are usually evaluated. **Petroleum charge** is the volume and characteristics of the oil and gas available to the trap, if it exists. The **trap** includes the reservoir and seal rocks and the trapping geometry formed by the reservoir–seal interface. **Timing** is whether the trap formed before the petroleum charge entered the trap.

Each independent variable has equal weight because if any variable is absent (0), the prospect is a failure; if all variables are present (1.0), the prospect is a commercial success. Therefore, each independent variable can be evaluated on a scale of zero to one (0–1.0). Exploration risk is determined by multiplying the three variables: charge, trap, and timing.

Within each independent variable, a series of subevents (which are also independent) must be evaluated. For example, if a trap is to be evaluated, the reservoir rock must be mapped carefully and its properties predicted using geologic principals. A similar procedure is carried out for the seal and trapping geometry. These subevents must be reduced to a single number between 0 and 1.0 that represents the independent variable, the trap. The subevents that contribute to petroleum charge and timing should also be evaluated in a similar manner.

A practical way to carry out this exercise is to first map the petroleum system so the knowledge about the system can be used to evaluate the complementary play.

Complementary play

The **complementary play** evaluates the exploration risk for finding undiscovered hydrocarbons associated with a particular petroleum system.

First, the petroleum system case study is completed. As the case study develops, an idea(s) or play(s) that involves this petroleum system will occur to the investigator. This play complements the petroleum system because it could add hydrocarbons (if discovered) to the system.

The events chart on the next page shows how the risk chart for the complementary play (prospect) is related to the petroleum system vis-a-vis the three independent variables—trap, petroleum charge, and timing.

Complementary play (continued)

The experience acquired while executing the petroleum system case study provides the measure of difficulty in mapping and determining the age of the essential elements and, more importantly, for the two processes—trap formation and generation–migration–accumulation of petroleum. Obviously, there is no risk or uncertainty related to the discovered accumulations in the petroleum system, but there are varying levels of difficulty in the reconstruction of events that caused these accumulations. This measure of difficulty can be incorporated into the risk chart.

For example, geologic and geophysical information for the producing fields indicates the traps are easily mapped and the time of formation is narrowly constrained. However, this same type of information over the geographic extent of the petroleum system indicates these types of traps have all been tested successfully and the only prospects left are ones that are more difficult to map and date; hence, their relative risk increases.

Using the risk chart in this manner allows the investigator and prospect evaluator an opportunity to separate what is known on the events chart from what is unknown on the risk chart for the prospect.

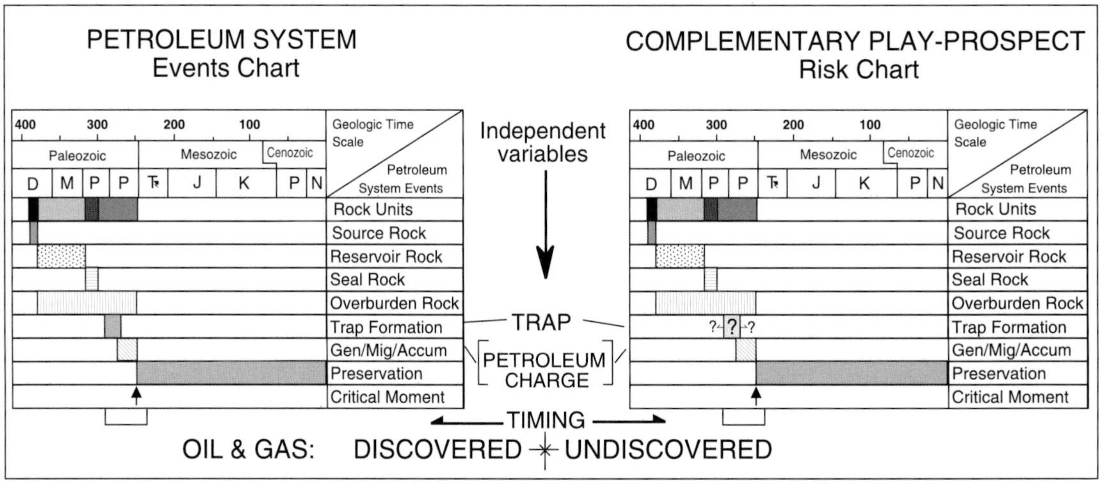

Figure 3–18. From Magoon 1995; courtesy AAPG.

Assigning risk

A petroleum system map can be used to evaluate the time and volume of hydrocarbon charge or to assign risk to a complementary play or prospect by using its position relative to the geographic extent of the system.

Least to most risk

Using the figure below and stipulating that the complementary play is on the migration path for this petroleum system, a play located within or outside the geographic extent of the system has the following level of risk:

1. Least risk; accumulations surround the trap.
2. Some risk; accumulations located on three sides.
3. Riskier; accumulations located on only one side.
4. Most risk; accumulations distant from prospect.

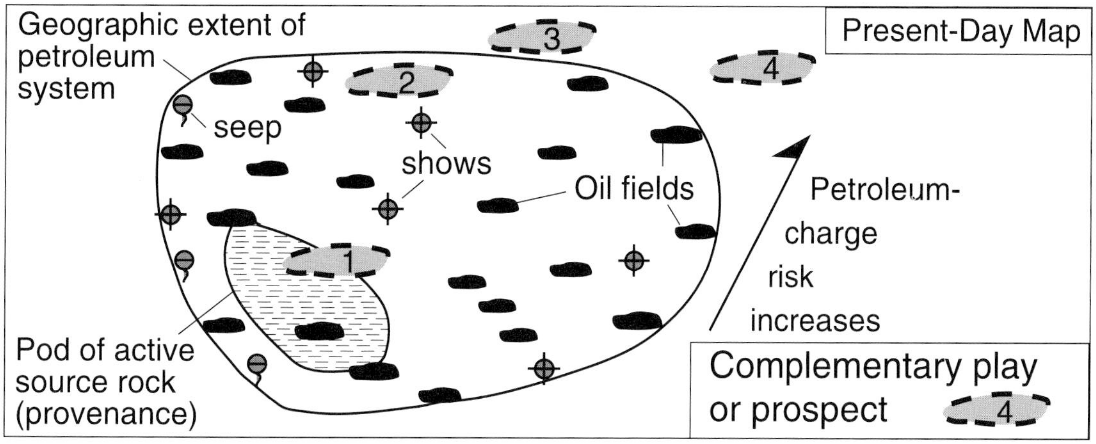

Figure 3–19. From Magoon, 1995; courtesy AAPG.

Studies of the reservoir rock and seal rock as well as trap formation are needed to evaluate migration paths and traps.

Exploration intensity

In a petroleum province, drilling density usually indicates how intensively an area has been explored. Though this is a relative measure, a petroleum province having one exploratory well every square kilometer is well explored compared with a province that has one well every 100 km^2. Exploration intensity by province ranges from lightly to moderately to heavily explored. However, in a petroleum province with overlapping petroleum systems, the shallowest petroleum system may be heavily explored compared with the deeper petroleum systems. To determine level of exploration, each petroleum system in the province of interest should be mapped and the size and location of the commercial accumulations compared with the dry exploratory wells. The dry-hole ratio or success ratio determines exploration intensity and success.

Exploration intensity (continued)

The graphs in the figure below conceptually summarize the exploration process relative to time. The top graph shows that a frontier petroleum province or petroleum system starts with only prospects (1.00 or 100%); with time, some or all (shown here) of those prospects become oil (gas) fields. The bottom graph shows that the highest percentage of the cumulative petroleum reserves are found early in the exploration process. The quicker we determine the size and extent of a petroleum system, the more likely we will be able to decide whether to continue drilling exploratory wells.

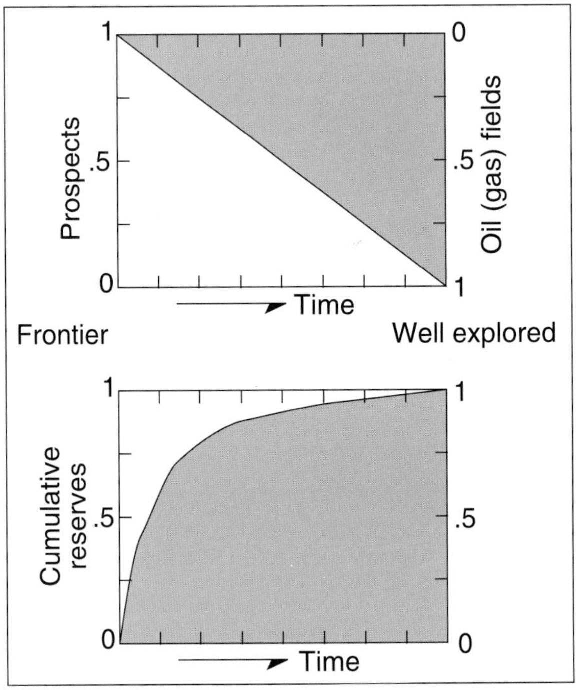

Figure 3–20.

Examples of Applying the Concept

Introduction

Linking the elements (source, reservoir, seal, and overburden) to the processes of petroleum geology (trap formation and hydrocarbon generation–migration–accumulation) is an effective exploration approach. Mapping and studying a petroleum system helps explorationists predict which traps will contain petroleum and which will not. It also helps them focus on that part of a province that will most likely contain accumulations. Below are some examples of how the petroleum system concept can be applied to petroleum exploration at local and regional levels.

Local example

Consider the cross section below from the Papers Wash field from the San Juan Basin, New Mexico. The cross section shows that three separate prospects (traps) were tested (drilled). The deepest trap was filled to the spill point with oil, the middle trap was partially filled, and the shallowest trap was empty. This arrangement suggests that oil migrated to the traps from a mature source rock downdip to the north by filling the traps in sequence.

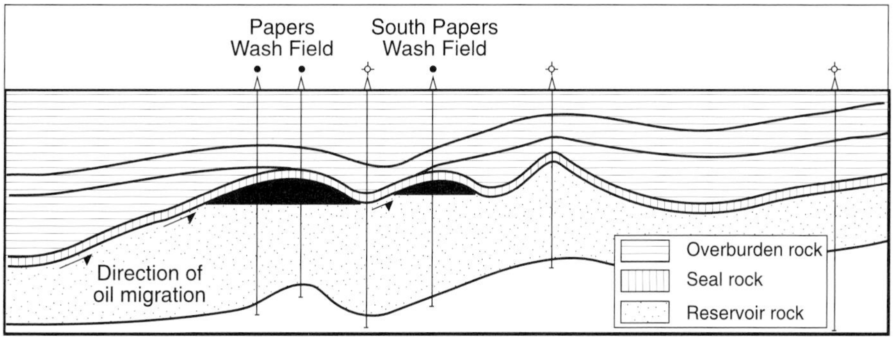

Figure 3–21. From Vincelette and Chittum, 1981; courtesy AAPG.

If these three prospects had not been tested, which would we drill first? With an understanding of the petroleum system that charged these prospects, we could be more confident in recommending which prospect to drill first. If we knew that mature source rock was located directly under the reservoir, then we would expect all traps to be filled an equal amount (below, left). Conversely, if we knew that the source was mature downdip to the north, then we would drill the deepest prospect, not the middle or shallowest prospect to the south (below, right).

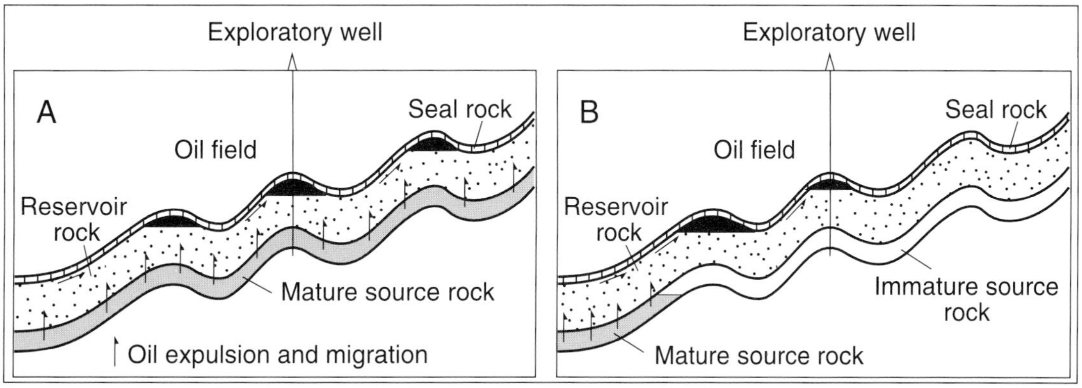

Figure 3–22. From Barker, 1992; courtesy Oklahoma Geological Society.

Examples of Applying the Concept, continued

Regional-scale applications

Petroleum system studies may serve as analogs for undocumented petroleum systems in prospective petroleum provinces. Because a petroleum system study describes both elements and processes, we can use them as look-alike and work-alike analogs. Petroleum systems also can be classified in different ways according to our needs—an example of applying a petroleum system classification scheme to petroleum exploration.

Vertically drained petroleum systems

Demaison and Huizinga (1994) divide petroleum systems into vertically and laterally drained. An earlier section of this chapter describes the Mandal-Ekofisk(!) petroleum system, which is a vertically drained system. Vertically drained systems are generally found in rifts, deltas, wrenches, and overthrust provinces where migration is controlled by faults and fractures. Faults and fractures limit the size of the fetch area available to traps, so a number of small- and medium-sized accumulations abound.

Vertically drained systems have the following characteristics (Demaison and Huizinga, 1994):

- Accumulations occur above or near to the pod of active source rock.
- Lateral migration distances are short.
- Multiple, stacked accumulations usually contain the same genetic oil.
- Surface seepages are common in supercharged systems.
- The largest accumulations are seldom found early in the drilling history; instead, many medium to small accumulations are found.

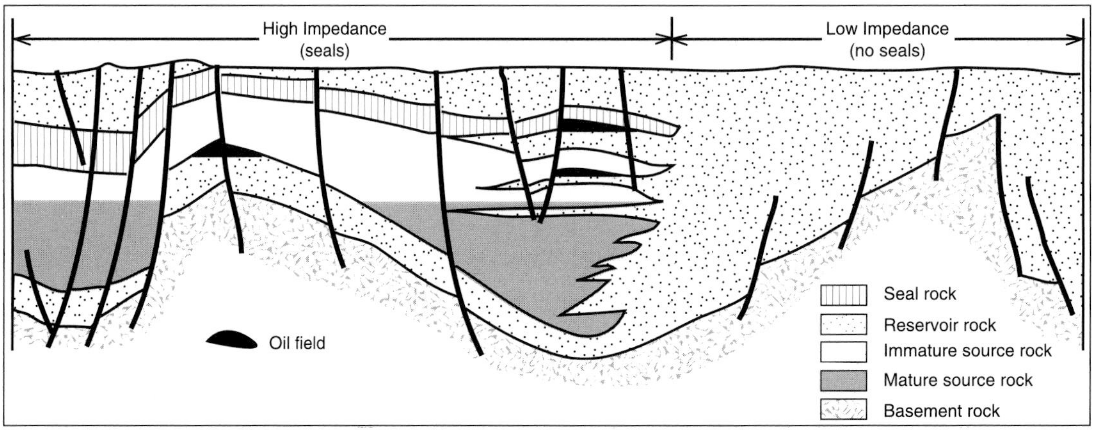

Figure 3–23. From Demaison and Huizinga, 1994; courtesy AAPG.

Examples of Applying the Concept, continued

Laterally drained petroleum systems

According to Demaison and Huizinga (1994), laterally drained petroleum systems have a laterally continuous seal overlying a laterally continuous reservoir. This reservoir/seal couplet is generally contained within a long, uninterrupted ramp. Provinces with these systems have low to moderate structural deformation. Tectonic stability is critical for maintaining seal integrity. Laterally drained systems are most commonly found in foredeep and cratonic sag basins. Plunging low-amplitude arches are necessary for connecting traps to the pod of active source rock. The Ellesmerian(!) petroleum system is an example of a laterally drained system.

Laterally drained systems have the following characteristics:

- Oil accumulations generally occur in thermally immature strata located far from the pod of active source rock.
- Accumulations containing oil that migrated long distances on average account for 50% of the entrapped oil.
- A single reservoir of the same age as the active source rock contains most of the entrapped oil and gas.
- In supercharged systems, large deposits of heavy oil often occur in thermally immature strata near the eroded margin (geographic extent) of the petroleum system.
- The largest accumulation is usually found early in the drilling history of the system. After that, mostly small accumulations are found (J. Armentrout, personal communication, 1997).

The cross section below is an example of a laterally drained petroleum system, patterned after the Eastern Venezuelan Basin.

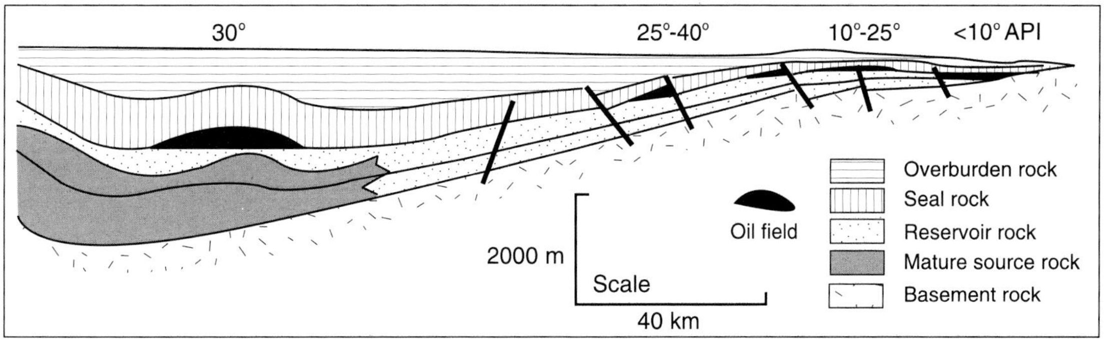

Figure 3–24. From Demaison and Huizinga, 1994; courtesy AAPG.

Section D

References

Barker, C., 1992, The role of source rock studies in petroleum exploration, *in* K.S. Johnson and B.J. Cardott, eds., Source Rocks in the Southern Midcontinent, 1990 Symposium: Oklahoma Geological Survey Circular 93, p. 3–20.

Bird, K.J., 1994, Ellesmerian(!) petroleum system, North Slope, Alaska, USA, *in* L.B. Magoon and W.G. Dow, eds., The Petroleum System—From Source to Trap: AAPG Memoir 60, p. 339–358.

Cornford, C., 1994, The Mandal-Ekofisk(!) petroleum system in the Central Graben of the North Sea, *in* L.B. Magoon and W.G. Dow, eds., The Petroleum System—From Source to Trap: AAPG Memoir 60, p. 537–571.

Demaison, G., and B.J. Huizinga, 1994, Genetic classification of petroleum systems using three factors: charge, migration, and entrapment, *in* L.B. Magoon and W.G. Dow, eds., The Petroleum System—From Source to Trap: AAPG Memoir 60, p. 73–89.

Hughes, W.B., A.G. Holba, D.E. Miller, and J.S. Richardson, 1985, Geochemistry of the greater Ekofisk crude oils, *in* B.M. Thomas et al., eds., Petroleum Geochemistry in the Exploration of the Norwegian Shelf: London, Graham and Trotman, p. 75–92.

Mackenzie, A.S., J.R. Maxwell, and M.L. Coleman, 1983, Biological marker and isotope studies of North Sea crude oils and sediments: Proceedings of the 11th World Petroleum Congress, London, Section PD1(4), p. 45–56.

Magoon, L.B., 1995, The play that complements the petroleum system—a new exploration equation: Oil & Gas Journal, vol. 93, no. 40, p. 85–87.

Magoon, L.B., and W.G. Dow, 1994, The petroleum system, *in* L.B. Magoon and W.G. Dow, eds., The Petroleum System—From Source to Trap: AAPG Memoir 60, p. 3–24.

Sedivy, R.A., I.E. Penfield, H.I. Halpern, R.J. Drozd, G.A. Cole, and R. Burwood, 1987, Investigation of source rock–crude oil relationships in the northern Alaska hydrocarbon habitat, *in* I. Tailleur and P. Weimer, eds., Alaskan North Slope Geology: Pacific Section SEPM Book 50, p. 169–179.

Seifert, W.K., J.M. Moldowan, and R.W. Jones, 1980, Application of biological marker chemistry to petroleum exploration: Proceedings of the 10th World Petroleum Congress, Bucharest, p. 425–440.

Vincelette, R.R., and W.E. Chittum, 1981, Exploration for oil accumulations in Entrada Sandstone, San Juan basin, New Mexico: AAPG Bulletin, vol. 65, p. 2546–2570.

Part II

Critical Elements of the Petroleum System

Introduction

Part II discusses concepts of petroleum geology from a regional perspective. Chapters of Part II cover methods for predicting the condition and development of the geological elements of basin. Chapter 4 discusses the analysis of basin stratigraphy, structure, and fluids. Chapter 5 focuses on fluid pressure and its use in petroleum exploration. Chapters 6, 7, and 8 discuss evaluation of source rock quality, expulsion and migration of hydrocarbons, and correlation of oils to their source.

In this part

Part II contains five chapters.

Chapter 4

Sedimentary Basin Analysis

by

John M. Armentrout

John M. Armentrout

John Armentrout is involved in integrated stratigraphic interpretation at Mobil Oil Corp.'s Dallas Technology Center. He received his BS in biology (1964) and MS in geology (1967) from the University of Oregon. He later attended the University of Washington where he received his Ph.D. in geology. After earning his doctorate, John joined Mobil's Alaskan Exploration Group. Subsequent assignments have included production geology, global basin analysis, deepwater clastics, and new exploration ventures. He is also actively involved in professional societies and has served as vice-president of the Dallas Geological Society, president of the Gulf Coast Section SEPM, president of the Society of Sedimentary Geology, 1991 SEPM technical program chair, and 1997 SEPM vice-chair for the AAPG annual meeting hosted by the Dallas Geological Society. His teaching/lecturing experience includes offering an SEPM course on integrated stratigraphic analysis, being named an AAPG Distinguished Lecturer, and being appointed a National Research Council Post-Doctoral Research Associate with the USGS. John's recent publications include papers on Gulf of Mexico Neogene sequence stratigraphy and hydrocarbon geochemistry; sequence stratigraphy of active margin basins in Oregon, Washington, Trinidad, China, and India; and Neogene biostratigraphy and petroleum systems of the Niger Delta.

Overview

Introduction

Sedimentary basin analysis involves studying the history of sediment accumulation within depocenters and the tectonic processes that create the basin depression, influence the distribution of sediments, and deform the contained rocks. Aspects of basin analysis, as presented in this chapter, focus on several scales:

- Plate tectonic/basin—geographic area of crustal subsidence and its sedimentary fill
- Subbasin depocenter—locus of sediment accumulation
- Depositional sequence—sediment accumulated during one depositional cycle
- Local basins—local structural and stratigraphic compartments within a depocenter

Understanding the local basin—achieved through integrating stratigraphic, structural, biostratigraphic, and geochemical data—is the critical scale of basin analysis for petroleum system identification. Reconstructing a basin's history, from regional tectonic setting to a single local basin, provides the geologic framework for defining exploration plays and prospects.

Example: Gulf of Mexico basin

Throughout this chapter, the Gulf of Mexico (GOM) basin is used as the example of sedimentary basin analysis and the relationship of basin analysis to defining essential elements and processes of the petroleum system. By using only one example, the reader should be better able to focus on the process of data integration, which can be adapted or modified for other basin types. Aspects of plate tectonics and depositional history are used to define several scales of subbasinal entities and their relationship to petroleum source and reservoir rocks. A history of progressive growth faulting and salt mobility controls the formation of potential traps, the locus of sediment transport and accumulation, and potential avenues of hydrocarbon migration and accumulation.

The chapter progresses from largest scale to smallest scale (Figure 4–1). It begins with the entire GOM basin and concludes with a case history of the East Breaks minibasin petroleum system. The East Breaks minibasin is an example of play and prospect definition within the context of a subregional petroleum system within one subprovince of the GOM Tertiary basin.

In this chapter

This chapter contains the following sections.

Index maps for GOM example

The figure below is a series of index maps for the GOM basin analysis example used in this chapter. Each map represents a different scale of sedimentary basin analysis, beginning with the largest (the GOM basin) and progressing to the smallest (the East Breaks minibasin).

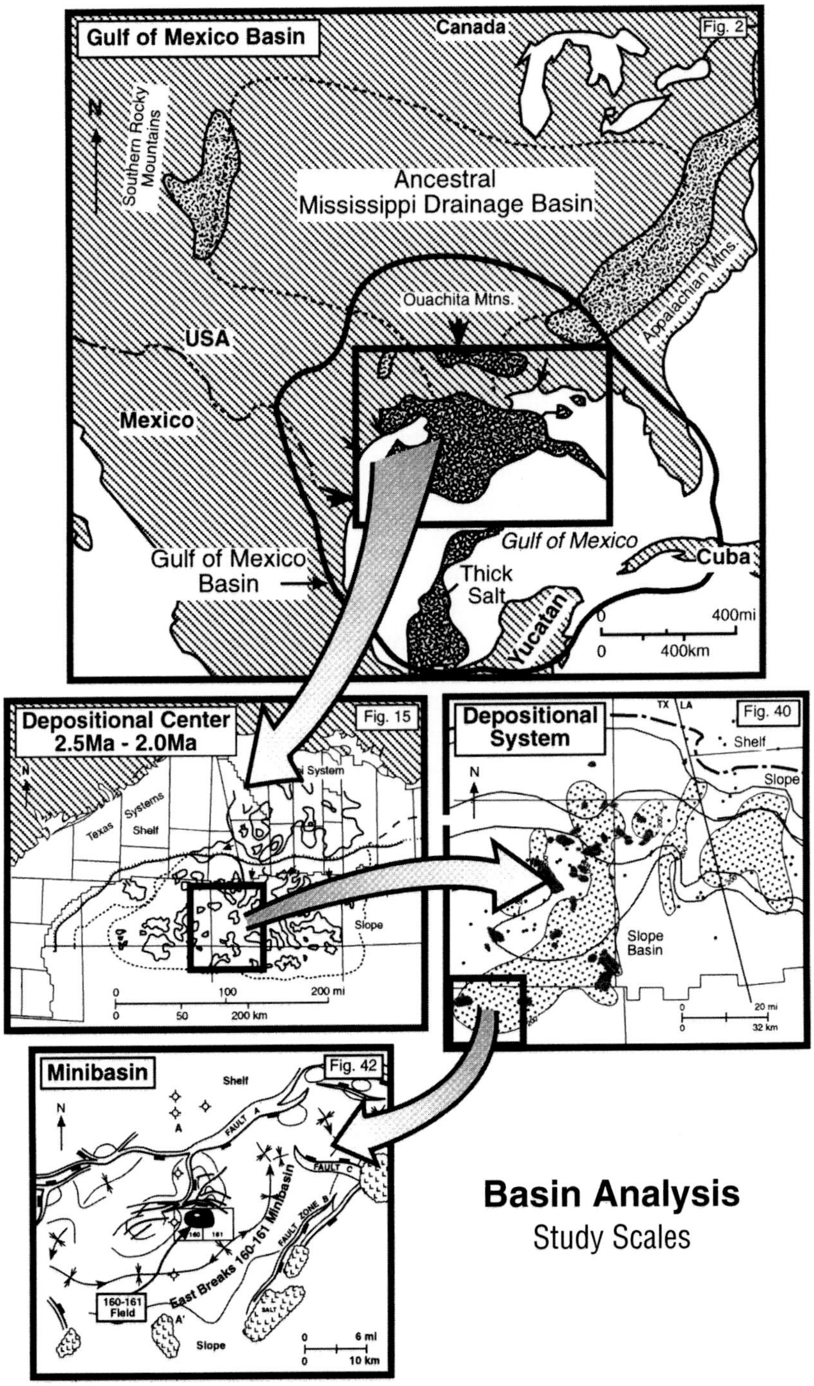

Figure 4–1.

Section A
Basin Framework

Introduction

A sedimentary basin consists of a geographic area of crustal subsidence in which sediment accumulates. A basin may have several episodes of subsidence, sediment accumulation, and deformation, and each episode may have a slightly different geographic extent. Thus, the area of the basin referred to in present-day terms may have a different context at specific times in the geologic past.

This section explains how to analyze the basin from the large-scale perspective. In subsequent sections, the GOM basin will be examined by stepping down through three levels to arrive at individual fields and prospects.

Development of basin history results from integrating bits and pieces of knowledge gathered over decades of study. The GOM basin example presented here evolved along that pathway from the study of local elements gathered together in ever-larger areas of analysis until basinwide and plate tectonic models had been constructed. The presentation of a relatively complete basin interpretation glosses over this historical pathway. In studying this overview of the present-day understanding of the GOM Tertiary basin's history, you may be able to more quickly assemble the essential elements of less-well-understood basins.

In this section

This section contains the following topics.

Subsection A1

Defining the Basin Framework

Introduction

Defining the basin framework is a process that includes the following:

- Outlining a basin's boundaries
- Characterizing its tectonostratigraphic evolution
- Mapping total sediment thickness
- Identifying sand-prone depocenters
- Locating age and location of oil and gas fields
- Establishing their geologic age and hydrocarbon types
- Delineating the occurrence of probable hydrocarbon source rocks

The resulting maps serve as the foundation for subsequent, more detailed analyses of the basin. Depending on the basin in question, this information may be available from the literature, from commercially available petroleum studies, and from oil company files. In some basins the data may be lacking. The first step in basin analysis is to gather all of the information available for the area of study, carefully identifying observation vs. interpretation.

In this subsection

This subsection contains the following topics.

How to Define the Framework of a Basin

The term "basin"

The term "basin" has different meanings in different disciplines. Stratigraphers refer to a basin as the location of sedimentary fill deposited in the geologic past. Structural geologists think of a basin as a container created by tectonic processes, such as rifting. Often the term is used to name and locate a geographic province, such as the Williston basin, which in turn is separate from the genetic use of basin to mean a sedimentary basin—the focus of this chapter.

Defining the basin framework

To define a basin, we follow the steps listed in the table below.

Step	Action
1	Define the outline of the basin and important regional structural features.
2	Map total sediment thickness.
3	Identify subbasins (depocenters and minibasins).
4	Map age and location of oil and gas fields.
5	Map age and location of source rocks.

Basin outline and structural features

The particular study area, whether only a part of a basin or an entire basin itself, should be identified on a large-scale geographic map using total sediment thickness as the primary control. We then map major regional structural features. If postdepositional deformation has resulted in erosion, we construct a paleogeographic restoration to approximate the original depositional basin outline (see section D2, Paleogeography).

Basins, depocenters, and minibasins

The interaction of the eustatic cycles of sediment accumulation within geographically shifting regional depocenters results in a complex stratigraphic architecture later deformed by tectonic movement. This deformation results in the formation of subbasins, depocenters, and minibasins. Minibasins in the GOM basin are relatively small areas of sedimentary thicks bounded by faults and salt-cored highs. We subdivide the basin into depocenters by identifying age-specific sediment thicks. We then subdivide depocenters into minibasins by identifying areas within the depocenter isolated by structure.

Subbasin sediment thickness, location

Each basin consists of a number of subbasin elements that have significant impact on exploration for hydrocarbons within each of these subbasins. We can prepare (or locate) a map showing total sediment thickness and the distribution of hydrocarbon occurrences within each subbasin element.

Source age, location

Hydrocarbon types reflect the composition of the kerogens from which they were generated and provide an estimate of the potential number of source-rock intervals or variations of kerogen facies within a source rock. We can prepare or locate a map showing the distribution of hydrocarbon types.

Example: Defining a Basin Outline

Discussion

The GOM basin includes strata beneath the present-day Gulf of Mexico and extends onshore beneath the Gulf coastal plain of Mexico and the United States. Sediment is supplied primarily by fluvial systems draining the ancestral Mississippi River system and smaller river systems draining the Rocky, Ouachita, and Appalachian mountain ranges. Lesser amounts of carbonate sediments are produced locally by biochemical processes. Critical to the understanding of the GOM basin history and the associated petroleum systems of the northern Gulf of Mexico is the interaction of the Cretaceous–Holocene Mississippi drainage basin and thick salt deposited during the Jurassic.

The figure below shows the geographic distribution of the Neogene Mississippi River drainage basin and distribution of the primary fluvial input systems (arrows). It also shows the interpreted limits of thick Jurassic salt (>1.5 km). The geographic shifts of primary fluvial input have resulted in depocenters of different ages across the GOM Tertiary basin.

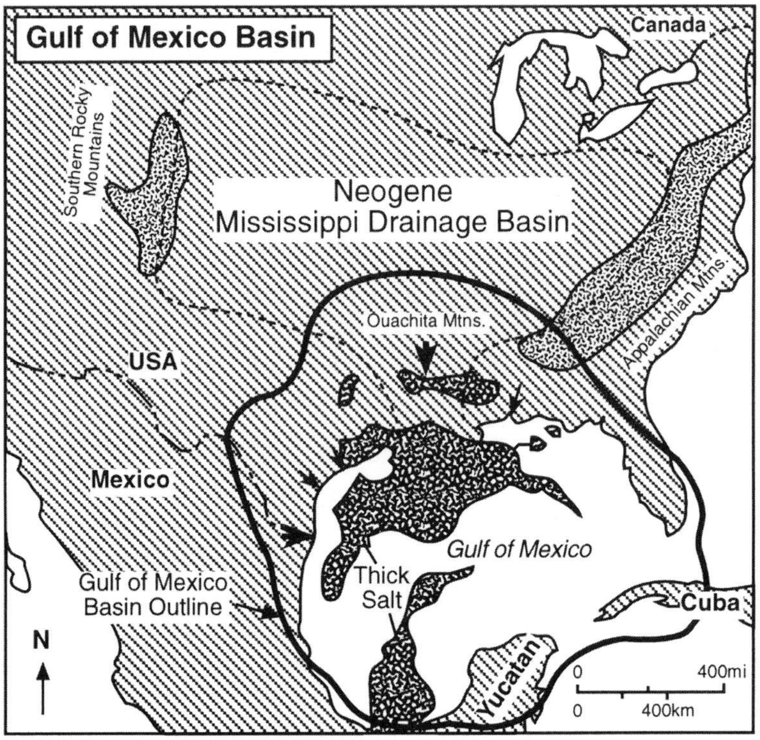

Figure 4–2. Modified after Winker and Buffler (1988); courtesy AAPG.

Example: Mapping Sediment Thickness and Field Location

Discussion

A map of the sediment thickness (isopach) and occurrence of hydrocarbons is an initial step in identifying the petroleum system(s) of a basin. The figure below shows the total Jurassic to Recent sediment thickness and hydrocarbon occurrences in the GOM basin The hydrocarbon occurrences are concentrated in reservoir rocks that range in age from Jurassic to Pleistocene along the northern margin of the basin in the area over transitional crust and thick salt accumulations. Identification of specific subbasinal depocenters within the area of hydrocarbon occurrences is shown in Figure 4–4. Hydrocarbon types reflect the composition of the kerogens from which they were generated and provide an estimate of the potential number of source rocks within the area (see Figure 4–5).

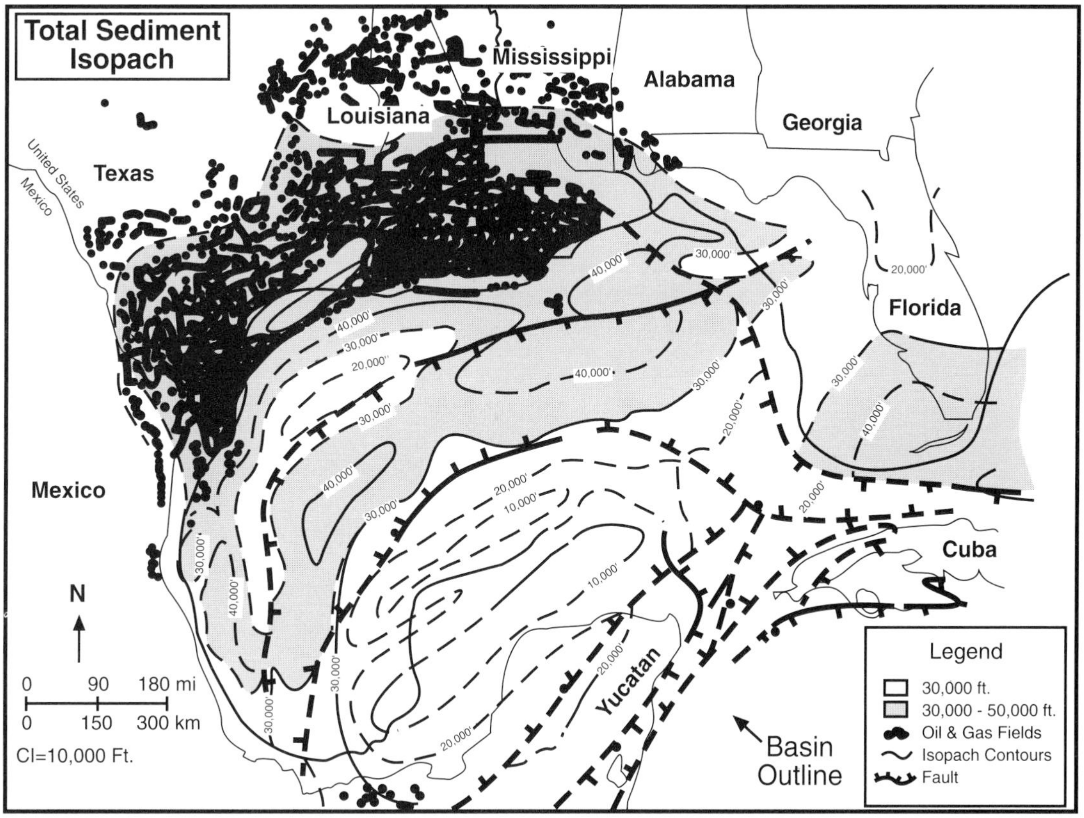

Figure 4–3. From Winker and Buffler (1988); courtesy AAPG.

Map of major sand influxes

Major influxes of sand into the northern GOM margin have shifted laterally from the Late Cretaceous to Recent (Winker, 1982). Each of these depocenters is related to the progressive filling of the basin margin, shifting the accommodation space basinward. Accommodation space refers to the volume of space available for sediment accumulation—the space resulting from the interaction of tectonic subsidence or uplift, sea level change, and compaction of the underlying sediment. Additionally, the lateral shift of the fluvial systems is recorded by sand-prone facies that document both the primary input area and the lateral shift of the depocenter through time.

Many of these lateral shifts result from tectonic events along the basin margin or within the drainage basins themselves (Galloway, 1989a). The lateral shift of the fluvial-deltaic systems is also reflected in the lateral shift of the gravity-flow depositional systems on the slope and basin floor (see Feng and Buffler, 1994).

The map below shows major sand influxes into the northern Gulf of Mexico from Late Cretaceous to Recent. Each area of sand-prone sediment provides age-specific potential reservoirs within these fluvial-deltaic depositional systems.

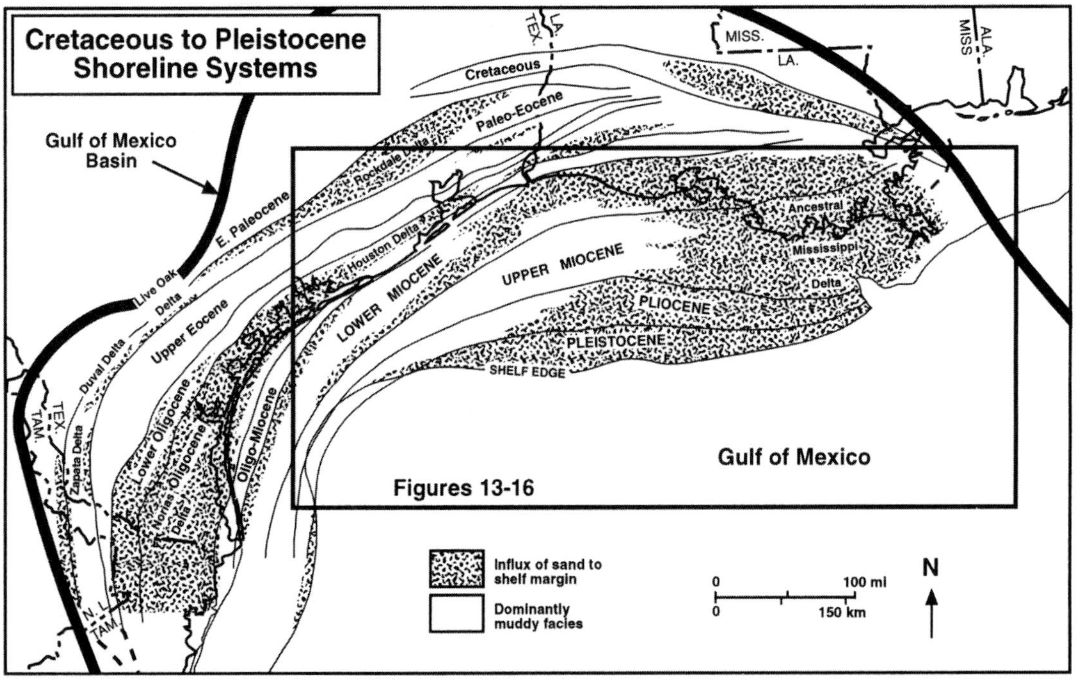

Figure 4–4. After Winker (1982); courtesy Gulf Coast Association of Geological Societies.

Example: Mapping Hydrocarbon Types

Discussion

Hydrocarbon types reflect the composition of the kerogens from which they were generated. Kerogens are the insoluble organic matter in sedimentary rocks. Maps of hydrocarbon types estimate the number and distribution of mature generating source rocks. The following map of hydrocarbon types is based on analyses of more than 2000 oil, 600 gas, and 1200 seep samples correlated to specific source rocks. Nine oil–source-rock families have been identified (labeled 1–9; see table on following page), each having a specific geographic distribution related to mature source-rock location and migration paths. We will focus on the High Island–East Breaks area, where families 1 and 6 overlap (bold arrow).

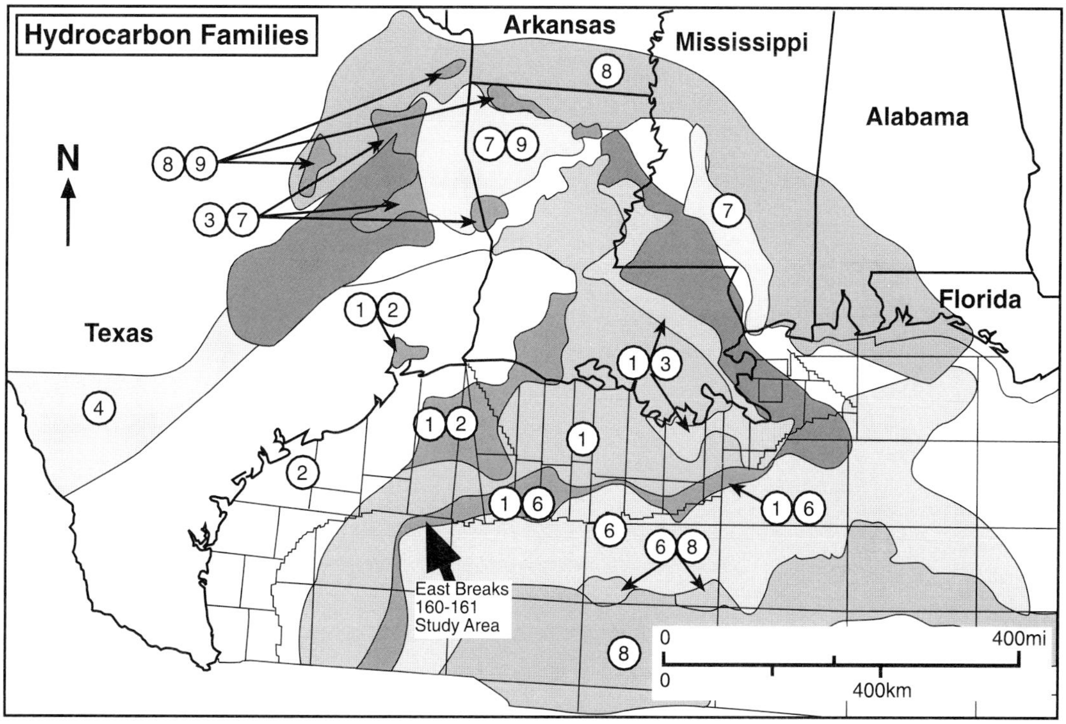

Figure 4–5. Modified from Gross et al. (1995).

Example: Mapping Hydrocarbon Types, continued

Source table

The table below, modified from Gross et al. (1995), lists source-rock ages, oil types, and map numbers for Figure 4–5.

Source-Rock Age	Oil Type	Map #
Lower Tertiary (centered on Eocene, ~50–40 Ma)	Tertiary marine[1] Tertiary intermediate[1] Tertiary terrestrial	① ① ②
Upper Cretaceous (centered on Turonian, ~85–95 Ma)	Marine; low sulfur; no Tertiary influence Calcareous; moderate sulfur; no Tertiary influence[2]	③ ④
Lower Cretaceous (centered on Aptian, ~115–105 Ma)	Carbonate; elevated salinity; Lower Cretaceous Calcareous; moderate sulfur; Lower Cretaceous[2]	⑤ ④
Uppermost Jurassic (centered on Tithonian, ~140–130 Ma)	Marine; high sulfur; Jurassic[3] Marine; moderately high sulfur; Jurassic[3] Marine; moderate sulfur; Jurassic[3] Calcareous; Upper Jurassic or Lower Cretaceous?	⑥ ⑥ ⑥ ⑦
Upper Jurassic (Oxfordian, ~ 152–145 Ma)	Carbonate; elevated salinity; Jurassic[4]	⑧
Triassic (Eagle Mills, > 210 Ma)	Triassic; lacustrine	⑨

[1]Tertiary marine and Tertiary intermediate are mapped together.

[2]Calcareous–Moderate Sulfur–No Tertiary Influence and Calcareous–Moderate Sulfur–Lower Cretaceous are mapped as an undifferentiated unit.

[3]Oil subtypes related to variations in sulfur content and associated geochemical parameters have not been subdivided on Figure 4–5.

[4]Oil subtypes reflecting differences in salinity and clastic input to source facies are known but are not delineated on Figure 4–5.

Summary

By overlaying maps of total overburden thickness above major source-rock intervals, thermally mature source-rock distribution, hydrocarbon occurrences, and major structural features, the regional elements of the petroleum system(s) begin to emerge.

Subsection A2

Assessing the Impact of Tectonics

Introduction

Plate tectonics provides an excellent starting point from which to analyze a basin because plate interactions probably created the basin. Global processes and previous plate positions are understood well enough to place almost any basin into its relative geographic position during the 570 m.y. of the Phanerozoic (Golonka et al., 1993).

Procedure

To unravel tectonostratigraphic phases of a basin, follow the steps listed in the table below and detailed in this section.

Step	Action
1	Assemble a regional tectonic map of the basin and surrounding area.
2	Make regional structure cross sections.
3	Determine plate tectonic evolution and history.
4	Develop a model of tectonostratigraphic phases of the basin that incorporates important tectonic and stratigraphic features.
5	Develop a model of the tectonic history of the basin.
6	Illustrate the tectonostratigraphic phases of the model using a series of cross sections restored to critical stages in the basin's history.
7	Determine the impact of tectonic evolution on petroleum system evolution.

In this subsection

The following topics are covered in this subsection.

Making Regional Tectonic Maps

Introduction

Tectonic maps of a basin and surrounding areas, in combination with regional structure cross sections, give an overall impression of the geologic architecture of the basin and form the base from which other interpretations are made. A large-scale map shows the depth to the basement in the basin and the distribution of crustal types. Always be sure important tectonic elements are shown, such as specific fold belts and major faults.

Tectonic map

The figure below is a tectonic map of the GOM basin. It shows the following:

- Generalized depth to basement (approximately the base of Jurassic sedimentary rock)
- Distribution of four crustal types—continental, thick transitional, thin transitional, and oceanic
- Known distribution of mid-Jurassic evaporites (pre-marine evaporites)
- Several major structural features

The thickest sediments occur over the thin transitional crust, which has subsided beneath the load of more than 14 km (>45,000 ft) of sedimentary rock. (For additional discussion of the structural framework, see Jones and Freed, 1996.)

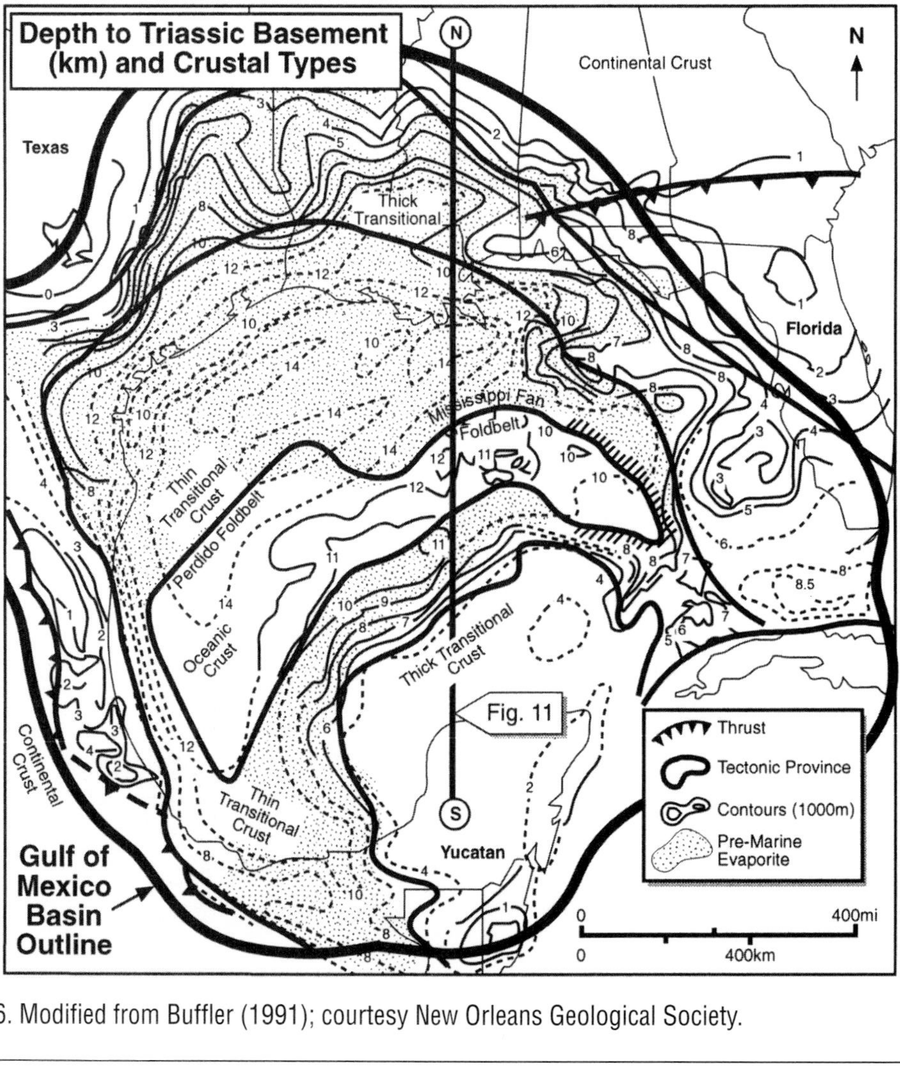

Figure 4–6. Modified from Buffler (1991); courtesy New Orleans Geological Society.

Salt tectonic map

The stratigraphic and tectonic history of the GOM basin is strongly affected by salt tectonics. As a consequence of differential loading of salt by sediment sourced from the North American craton, the distribution of salt-cored structures is oldest in the onshore northern margin of the basin where Late Cretaceous and early Cenozoic progradation resulted in salt-structure growth.

Offshore beneath GOM waters, evacuation of salt structures is oldest in the north and is progressively younger toward the south. However, there are Late Jurassic and Early Cretaceous salt-cored structures along the Sigsbee Escarpment. Pliocene and Pleistocene depositional loading has displaced salt basinward and differentially loaded detached salt sills into salt-cored massifs and salt-cored diapirs.

The salt-withdrawal synclines formed by sediment loading result in bathymetric lows that serve as sediment transport pathways down the slope (Bouma, 1982). The present-day sea-floor bathymetry of the northern Gulf of Mexico slope reflects this transport-pathway lineation of salt-withdrawal synclines bordered by salt-cored anticlines (see Figure 4–41). The distribution of the sediment-thick synclines and salt-core anticlines persists through time, resulting in predictability of sediment transport avenues, depositional areas of potential reservoir sands, and conduits from deeply buried source rocks upward to the hydrocarbon traps (see Figures 4–54 and 4–55).

McGuinness and Hossack (1993) present an excellent discussion of palinspastic reconstruction of the stratigraphic record disrupted by salt tectonics. Jackson et al. (1995) and Simmons et al. (1996) present a good discussion of salt distribution and tectonics.

The figure below shows salt structures in the northwestern Gulf of Mexico and adjacent interior basins.

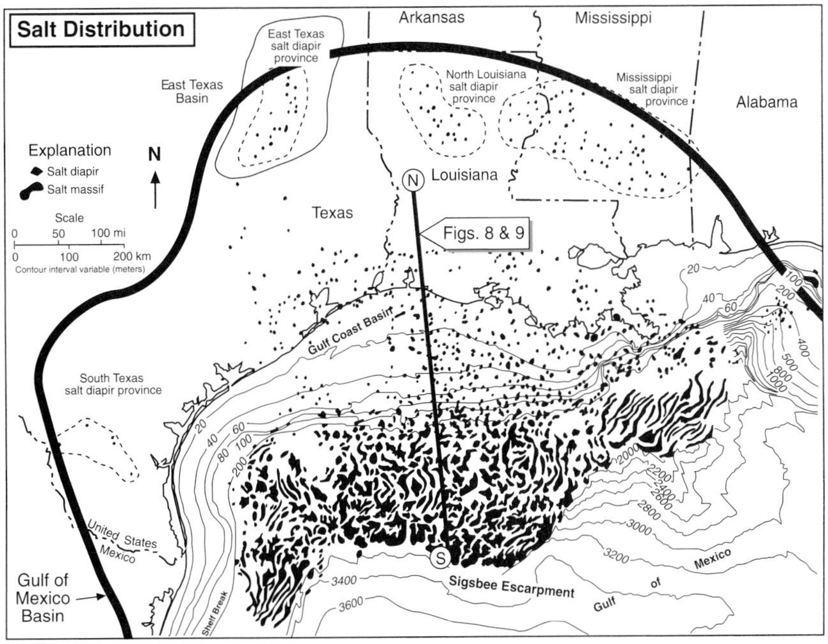

Figure 4–7. Modified from Jackson and Galloway (1984); courtesy AAPG.

Making Regional Structural Cross Sections

Cross section utility

Regional structural cross sections show interpretations of the present-day geology of a basin. They illustrate the relationship between structure and stratigraphy. Modeling the tectonic history and tectonostratigraphic phases begins with regional structural cross sections and works backward, disclosing important events.

Discussion of GOM basin

Much of the petroleum discovered within the northern GOM basin is in Neogene anticlinal and stratigraphic traps developed as a consequence of interaction between Jurassic salt and Cenozoic siliciclastic progradation. The basic model consists of sediment prograding into the basin and differentially loading the plastic salt, causing diapirs and growth faults to develop (Trippet, 1981; Ingram, 1991). Two different interpretations of the present-day geology are presented below in two different structural cross sections. Migration of hydrocarbons from Mesozoic and early Tertiary organic-rich rocks are significantly affected by the selection of either of these two interpretations of salt deformation.

Traditional structure cross section

Traditional regional cross sections, such as in the figure below, have shown highly deformed salt rooted within the in-place Middle Jurassic mother salt. Such cross sections have been used to suggest that successive progradation of siliciclastics loaded and displaced the salt as each sedimentary cycle's depocenter stepped progressively basinward. Differential loading of the salt formed deeply rooted diapirs and shallow growth faults as a result of sediment downbuilding and consequent displacement of salt. Mature source rocks occurring between the deeply rooted diapirs could yield hydrocarbons able to migrate within each salt-walled compartment of each depocenter.

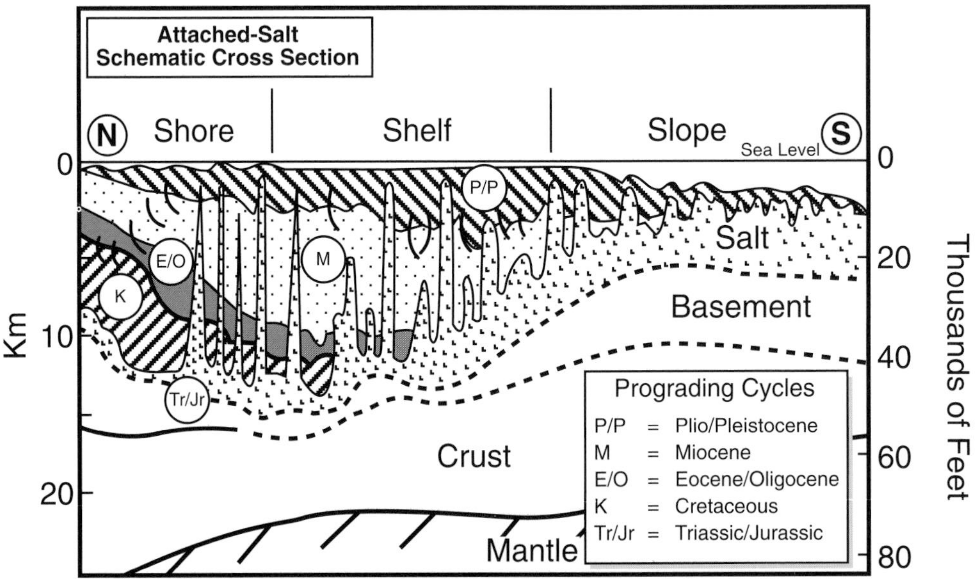

Figure 4–8. Modified after Antoine et al. (1974); courtesy Springer-Verlag.

Recent structure cross section

More recent models of salt deformation recognize both the in-place Middle Jurassic mother salt and displaced sheets of Middle Jurassic salt that have become detached from the mother salt as shown in the figure below. The detached salt is emplaced progressively over younger sediments because of the passive response to differential loading by sediment and gravitational forces. Basinward gravitational slope failure forms major growth fault systems on the upper slope and toe-thrust structures downslope (Bruce, 1973). Each "pulse" of salt displacement evolves through a new generation of deformation (Fiduk et al., 1989; West, 1989; Koyi, 1993; and McGuinness and Hossack, 1993). Maturing source rocks of Mesozoic and early Tertiary age can yield hydrocarbons that may migrate vertically along growth faults and salt walls, through holes in salt canopies, laterally below salt, or within sandstones between salt sheets.

Basin evolution

The contrast between the cross sections of Figures 4–8 and 4–9 illustrate changing concepts of basin evolution. When constructing a basin's history, we must understand the concepts underlying each previous study so we can fully appreciate the subtle changes in geologic models and take into account their consequences as the basin model evolves.

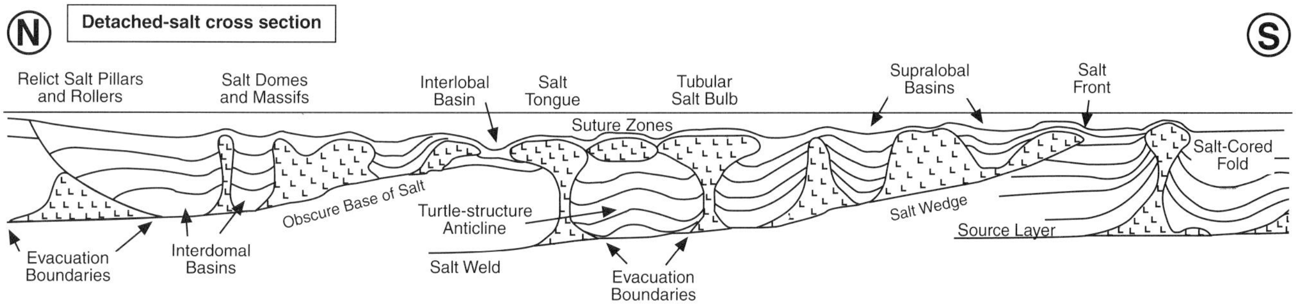

Figure 4–9. From Hall et al. (1993); courtesy Gulf Coast SEPM.

Determining Plate Tectonic Setting and History

Introduction

By understanding the present structural and stratigraphic configuration of a basin, we can interpret its plate tectonic history within the context of global plate reconstructions. Starting with the present configuration of the basin, we can move back in time and map the basin at critical periods in its plate tectonic development. Maps should show features such as spreading centers, contractional areas, extensional areas, crustal types, and mobile belts.

Critical period map

Tectonically, the Gulf of Mexico is a Mesozoic–Cenozoic rift basin formed along a southwest–northeast-spreading center on the southern margin of the North American craton (Buffler, 1991). The basic tectonic architecture developed as a consequence of the Jurassic breakup of Pangea as Africa and South America separated from North America (Pindell, 1993). The GOM basin is underlain by oceanic and transitional crust (Buffler, 1991) deformed along a set of north–northwest-trending faults (Marton and Buffler, 1993).

The figure below shows the Gulf of Mexico region as it looked approximately 130 Ma. Note the spreading and transform fault systems separating the North American, Atlantic, Farallon, and Caribbean plates. Striped areas are cratonic basement; shading is transitional to oceanic basement; and arc-related volcanics are noted by a "^" pattern east of the Farallon/Caribbean trench.

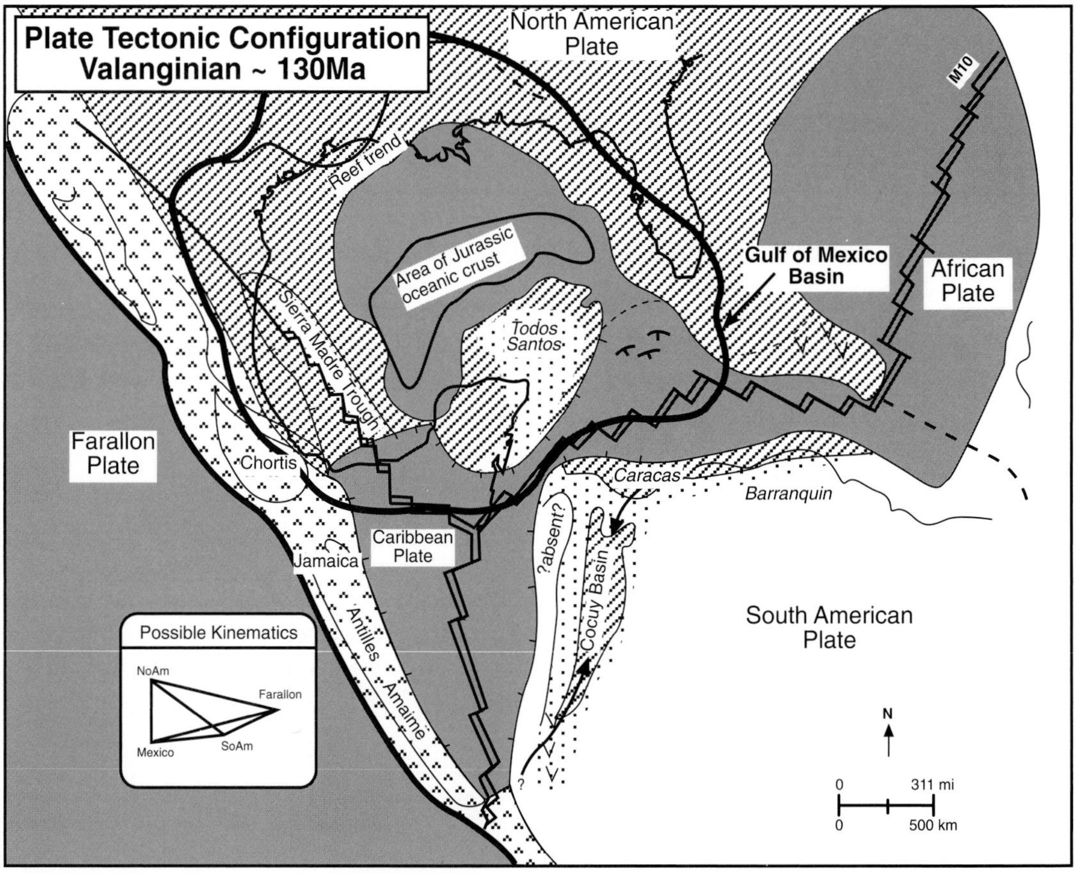

Figure 4–10. Modified from Pindell (1993); courtesy Gulf Coast SEPM.

Determining Tectonostratigraphic History

Introduction

Models of tectonic history provide a framework for understanding the history of each phase of basin development. A tectonostratigraphic phase is a period of basin evolution during which tectonic and stratigraphic elements resulted in a specific configuration of depositional and deformational elements, many of which were critical to the evolution of the basin's petroleum system. The tectonostratigraphic history for a basin is usually portrayed in a time series of cross sections, showing the geologic elements of each phase. Because all basins are three dimensional, care must be taken to assemble enough cross sections to depict basin history accurately.

Tectonostratigraphic phases

Tectonic evolution of the GOM basin has resulted in five primary tectonostratigraphic phases (A–E), each with a different sediment accumulation and deformation history. Figure 4–11 is a schematic diagram showing a series of cross sections representing the four phases of Late Triassic to Early Cretaceous evolution of the GOM basin (see Figure 4–6 for the location).

- **Phase A** (Figure 4–11A) consists of Late Triassic to Early Jurassic rifting along linear zones within brittle crust with deposition of synrift nonmarine sediments and volcanics within half-grabens.
- **Phase B** (Figure 4–11B) of Middle Jurassic age is characterized by rifting and attenuation of the crust, with formation of transitional crust and the associated basement highs and lows that form the basic architecture. The outer periphery of the basin underwent moderate stretching and the crust remained thick, forming broad arches and basins. The central basin underwent considerable stretching and subsidence to form a large area of thin transitional crust over which thick salt was deposited. Nonmarine terrigenous sediments continued to be deposited within the peripheral grabens.
- **Phase C** (Figure 4–11C) of Late Jurassic age consists of emplacement of oceanic crust as mantle upwelling concentrated along the generally east–west-trending weakness in the continental crust. As the crust underlying the basin began to cool, subsidence resulted in the relative rise of sea level. The basin margins were transgressed by broad shallow-to-deep shelfal marine environments with deposition of thick carbonate successions. Locally, thick, terrigenous clastic prisms prograded into the basin. Potential and known reservoirs occur within both the carbonate and clastic depositional systems of this tectonostratigraphic phase. During the Late Jurassic maximum transgression, the deep basin was sediment starved, and thick, organic-rich shales accumulated in low-oxygen environments (source-rock types 6 and 7).
- **Phase D** (Figure 4–11D) of Early Cretaceous age is characterized by broad carbonate platforms rimmed by reef buildups along the margins established at the boundary of differential subsidence between thin and thick crust. Fine-grained carbonates were deposited in the adjacent deep basin. Terrigenous clastics continued to be input at local points along the northern margin. Known and potential reservoirs occur within both carbonate and clastic depositional systems of these early Cretaceous rocks.

Tectonostratigraphic phases (continued)

- **Phase E** (Figure 4–9) began during the mid-Cenomanian with a rapid fall and rise of sea level superimposed on a long-term rise that terminally drowned the outer margins of the carbonate platforms, causing the margins to retreat landward. Widespread submarine erosion created a prominent mid-Cretaceous unconformity. Subsequent deposition was dominated by terrigenous sedimentation as large clastic prisms prograded first from the west and northwest in the Late Cretaceous and early Cenozoic and then from the north (Mississippi River drainage) during the late Cenozoic. Most of the offshore and many onshore reservoirs occur within these Late Cretaceous and Cenozoic siliciclastic deposits. The prograding prisms of siliciclastic sediment differentially loaded the underlying salt, resulting in deformation by both salt mobility and down-to-the-basin growth faulting along the shelf-slope break (Bruce, 1973; Winker and Edwards, 1983).

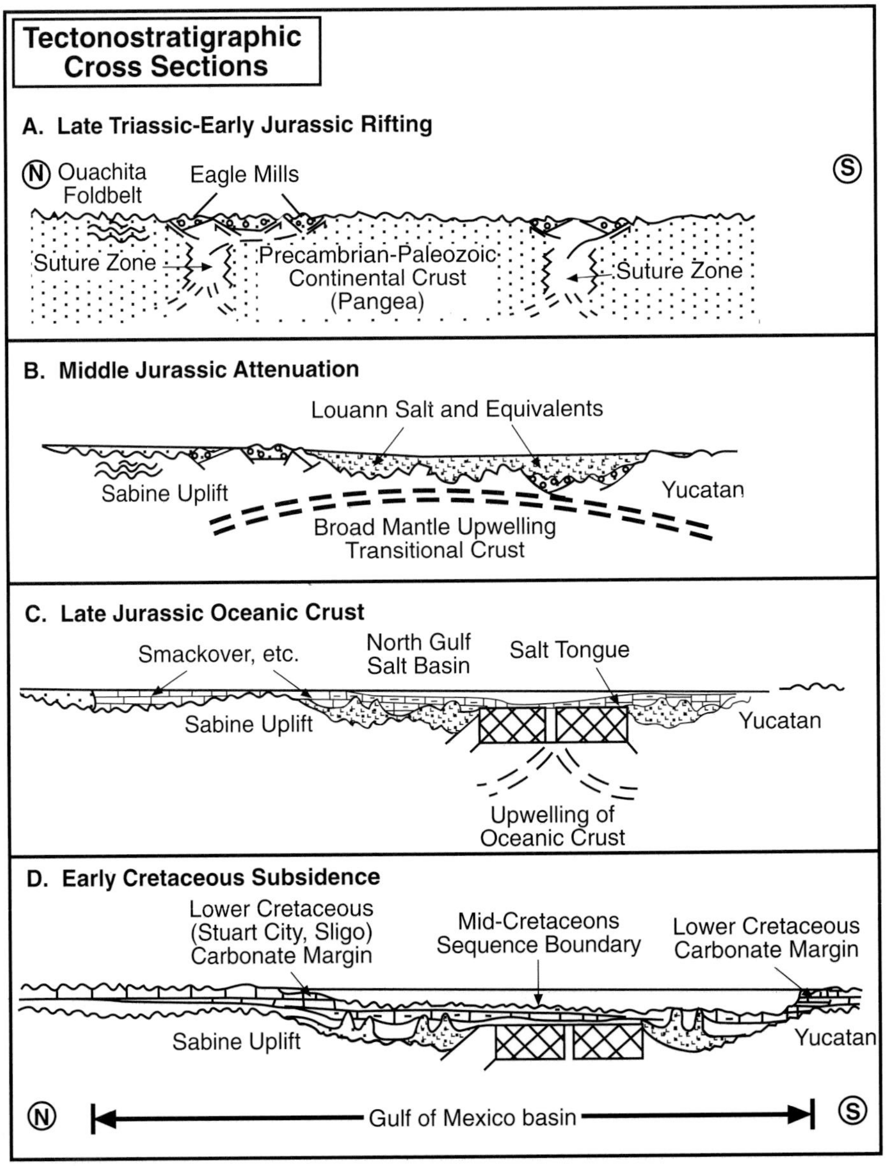

Figure 4–11. Modified from Buffler (1991); courtesy New Orleans Geological Society.

Using a Tectonic History Model for Petroleum System Analysis

Introduction

A model of the tectonic history of a basin provides a regional framework for understanding the development of essential elements and processes of the petroleum systems in a basin. A basin such as the Gulf of Mexico can have more than one petroleum system; therefore, the evolution of elements and processes can have an impact on different petroleum systems at the same time or at different times, depending on the events of each tectonostratigraphic phase.

Example from GOM basin

The tectonic history of the GOM basin provides the regional framework for mapping elements and processes of the petroleum systems within the High Island–East Breaks area. Following is a summary of the tectonic history of the basin.

1. Within the GOM rift basin, major areas of transitional crust formed between continental crust and Late Jurassic oceanic crust. Middle Jurassic crustal attenuation associated with the transitional crust formed sags in which evaporites were deposited.
2. During the Late Jurassic and Early Cretaceous, thermal subsidence of the basin center and relatively high sea level formed extensive carbonate platforms along the basin margin and sediment starvation of the basin center. Organic-rich, oil-prone marine sediments were deposited within low-oxygen environments of this sediment-starved basin. These rocks later became the primary source of oil and gas—some of which migrated to and is stored within porous zones of the carbonate platforms.
3. Late Cretaceous and Cenozoic siliciclastic sedimentation formed thick, prograding prisms over the transitional crust and differentially loaded the Late Jurassic salt. The deformed salt created anticlinal highs bordering sediment-filled synclinal lows, which continued to subside and provide sediment transport pathways downslope. The deformation of the salt and associated sediments formed both structural and stratigraphic traps within the siliciclastic section. Sedimentary burial and salt-thickness/mobility patterns affect hydrocarbon generation due to variations in the thermal conductivity of salt. Intersecting fault trends, one paralleling northwest–southeast-trending basement faults and a second associated with depositional strike-oriented growth faults, provide vertical avenues for migration of hydrocarbons from deeply buried mature Mesozoic source rocks upward into reservoir rocks of Jurassic, Cretaceous, and Cenozoic age.

Areas of maximum sediment accumulation and consequent salt deformation were controlled by areas of maximum sediment input and sea-floor subsidence.

Section B
Depocenters

Introduction

Within a basin, different areas receive different amounts of sediment through time, resulting in numerous depocenters. Each depocenter is an area containing a thick stratigraphic succession. These different depocenters have unique histories of sediment accumulation, compaction, subsidence, deformation, and thermal maturation of potential hydrocarbon source rocks. Delineation of these depocenters is the second step in basin analysis. Subdividing a depocenter into age-significant units and depositional cycles is the topic of section C.

In this section

This section contains the following topics.

Mapping and Analysis of Depocenters

What is a depocenter?

"Depocenter" refers to an area or site of maximum deposition, or the geographic location of the thickest part of any specific geographic unit in a depositional basin (Gary et al., 1974).

Sediment supply rate and facies patterns

Within each depocenter, facies do one of the following:

- Prograde if the rate of sediment supply exceeds the rate of accommodation space formation
- Aggrade if the rate of sediment supply equals the rate of accommodation space formation
- Retrograde if the rate of sediment supply is less than the rate of accommodation space created (Van Wagoner et al., 1988)

Siliciclastic vs. carbonate supply

Most siliciclastic basins have sediment supplied from drainage areas outside of the boundary of the depositional basin. Lateral changes in sediment input locations can result in lateral shifts in the depocenter if enough space exists to accommodate the sediment near each input location. In carbonate basins, organisms near the site of accumulation produce most sediment, and facies tend to extend over large platform areas.

The figure below is a map of the drainage basin of the modern Mississippi River, illustrating the network of rivers feeding into one sediment input point. The Holocene depocenter of the Mississippi River is immediately offshore and west of the river mouth. Smaller drainage basins also supply terrigenous sediment to the western and central Gulf of Mexico, while in situ carbonate factories supply most of the sediment to the Florida peninsula.

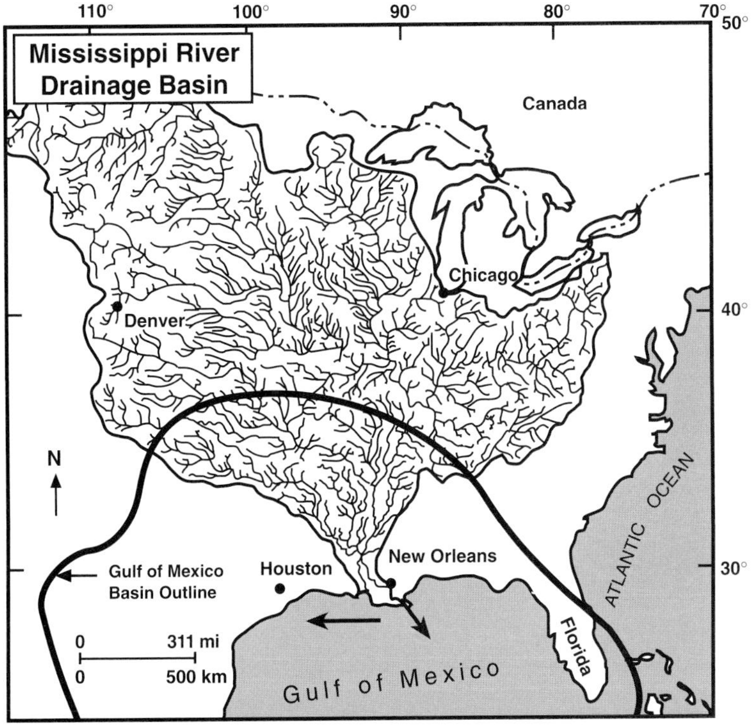

Figure 4–12. Modified from Coleman and Roberts (1991); courtesy New Orleans Geological Society.

Mapping and Analysis of Depocenters, continued

Depocenter complexes

In basins with relatively rapid subsidence and multiple sediment supply systems, a complex set of depocenters occurs. Each depocenter has a unique history of accumulation, based on

- variations in source rock maturation,
- manner and timing of hydrocarbons expulsion and migration, and
- style of fluid entrapment and preservation.

Recognizing the temporal and spatial distribution of each depocenter is critical to understanding basin history and petroleum system formation. Along the basin margin, depocenters may be dominated by deltaic complexes. On the slope and basin floor, depocenters are related to transport systems of gravity-flow processes.

Mapping age of thicks

Mapping age-specific isopach thicks defines laterally shifting sites of maximum deposition along the margin of a basin. Each depocenter has a unique history of accumulation with consequent variations in maturation, migration, and entrapment history of associated petroleum systems.

Mapping depocenters

Follow the procedure detailed in the table below to map depocenters. **Note:** Isopach maps (step 1) are shown in this section. Steps 2–5 are detailed in sections C and D.

Step	Action
1	Make isopach maps of individual depocenters using well data and high-quality seismic profiles calibrated to well data.
2	Establish correlation of surfaces bounding each tectonostratigraphic phase and construct isopach maps or relative thickness maps.
3	Map deltaic/shelf depocenters by mapping net sand distribution from well data.
4	Identify shelf margins using biostratigraphic and seismic facies analysis.
5	Identify deepwater intraslope basins from isochron mapping and calibration to stratigraphy in wells.

Example: Mapping Fluvial Input

Introduction

The late Cretaceous to Recent depositional history of the northern Gulf of Mexico continental margin has been influenced by several factors (Coleman and Roberts, 1991):

- Fluvial supply system and delta formation
- Subsidence
- Diapiric and tectonic movement
- Fluctuation in sea level

Summary of GOM fluvial history

Mesozoic and Cenozoic fluvial systems have filled in the northern margins of the GOM rift basin, prograding the continental margin of one area until sediment input shifts to another area (Figure 4–4). Subsidence is related to basement cooling or differential response of basement types to loading (Figure 4–6). Formation of diapirs and tectonic movement of growth fault systems has already being discussed as it relates to sediment loading. Fluctuation in sea level is discussed in section D.

Example: Mapping Depocenters Through Time

Introduction

Mapping age-specific isopach thicks in the northern GOM basin defines laterally shifting sites of maximum deposition (Figure 4–4). Methods of mapping are clearly presented in Tearpock and Bischke (1991).

GOM basin depocenter time intervals

In the northern GOM basin, depocenters prograde (Figure 4–4) over the transitional crust (Figure 4–6) and deform the underlying salt into a complex network of salt-cored anticlines and salt-withdrawal synclines (Figures 4–8, 9). Late Neogene depocenters of the Mississippi River, the largest source of sediment to the northern Gulf of Mexico, developed during five time periods from the latest Miocene through Holocene (from Piggott and Pulham, 1993; see also Goldthwaite, 1991). Following are the five depocenter intervals and their time periods.

Interval	Time Period, Ma
A	6–4
B	4–3
C	3–2.5
D	2.5–1
E	1–Present

Figures 4–13 to 4–16 are maps of depocenters and paleogeography for intervals A, B, D, and E. These were constructed by correlating wells using fossil extinction events and grids of interpreted seismic reflection profiles. The High Island–East Breaks study area is shown on each map.

Formation of High Island–East Breaks depocenter

Between 2.5 and 2.0 Ma, the major northern GOM basin depocenter was focused offshore of western Louisiana and eastern Texas. The westernmost part of this depocenter appears to have been the input area for the ancestral Mississippi River system. The resulting depocenter, the High Island–East Breaks depocenter, has more than 16,000 ft (4875 m) of late Pliocene and early Pleistocene sediments deposited during a succession of high-amplitude sea level cycles.

Timing of petroleum generation

Each of the isopach maps in this section is annotated with the area of active petroleum generation and migration. These comments are based on the modeling of Piggott and Pulham (1993), illustrated and discussed along with Figures 4–32 and 4–33.

Example: Mapping Depocenters Through Time, continued

Interval A paleogeography

The figure below shows the paleogeography of the Mississippi River depositional system from approximately 6 Ma to 4 Ma (interval A). Deposition consists of net sand isopach thicks on the shelf and intraslope basins that are interpreted to be deepwater "fan" complexes.

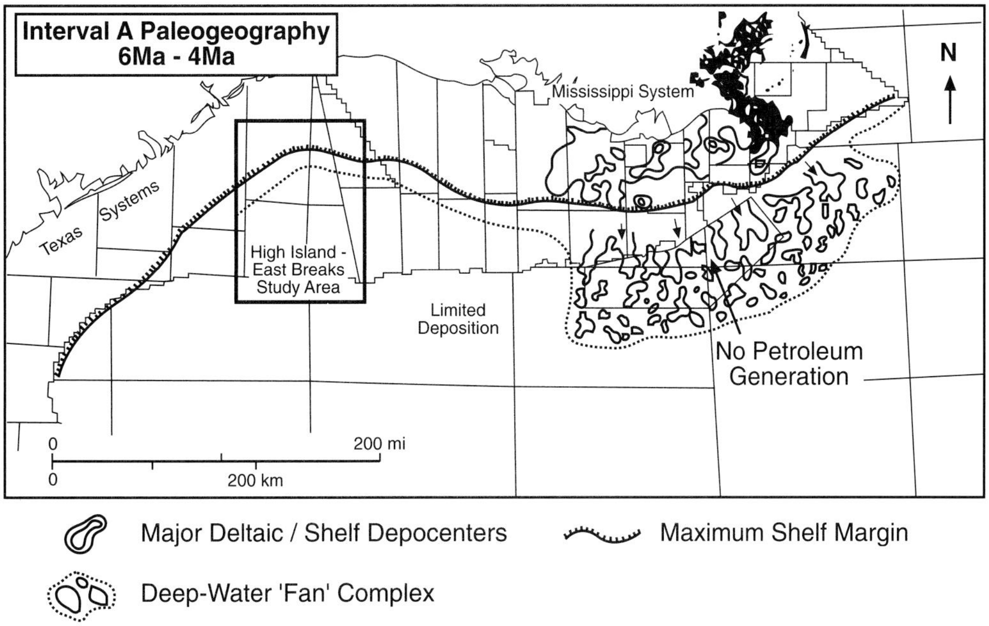

Figure 4–13. After Piggott and Pulham (1993); courtesy Gulf Coast Section SEPM.

Interval B paleogeography

This figure shows paleogeography from approximately 4 Ma to 3 Ma (interval B). Shelf and intraslope basin thicks are potentially sand prone. (Note the shift westward from the previous depocenter location.)

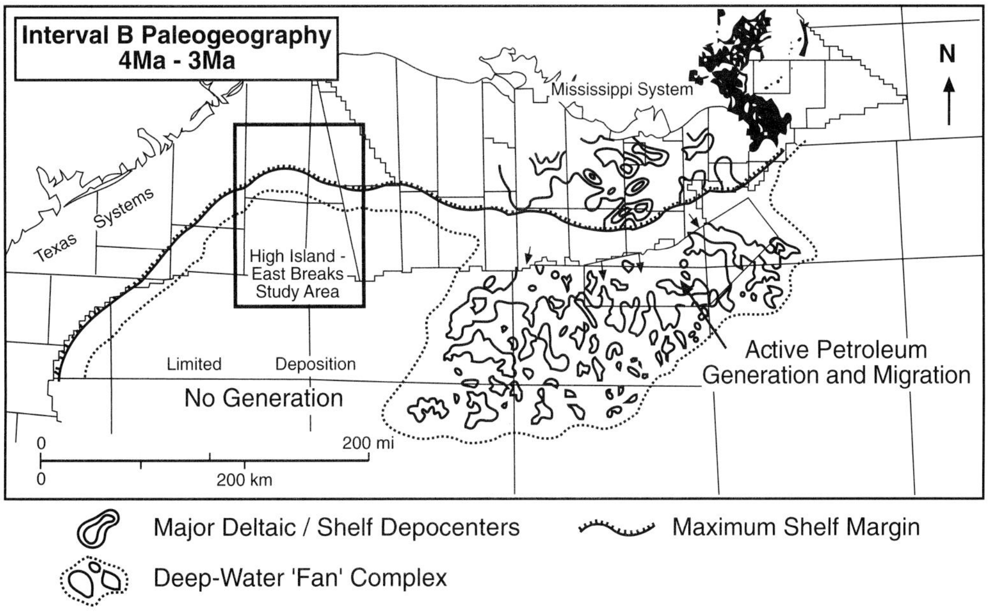

Figure 4–14. After Piggott and Pulham (1993); courtesy Gulf Coast Section SEPM.

Example: Mapping Depocenters Through Time, continued

Interval D paleogeography

The following figure shows paleogeography from approximately 2.5 Ma to 2 Ma (interval D). Again, shelfal net sand thicks and intraslope basin isopach thicks interpreted to be deepwater "fan" complexes are the dominant depositional environments. Note the depocenter has shifted to offshore western Louisiana and Texas. The High Island–East Breaks study area occurs within the western part of this depocenter.

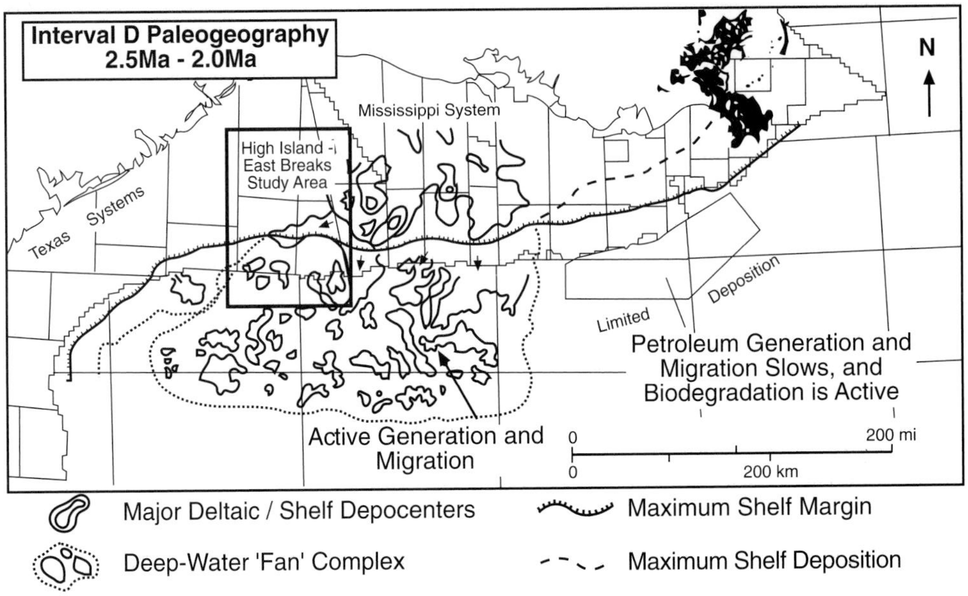

Figure 4–15. After Piggott and Pulham (1993); courtesy Gulf Coast Section SEPM.

Interval E paleogeography

The paleogeographic map below represents time from about 1 Ma to the present (interval E). Canyons are interpreted from incised and back-filled geometries on seismic reflection profiles. Note the depocenter has shifted back to offshore eastern Louisiana from the preceding location offshore eastern Texas/western Louisiana.

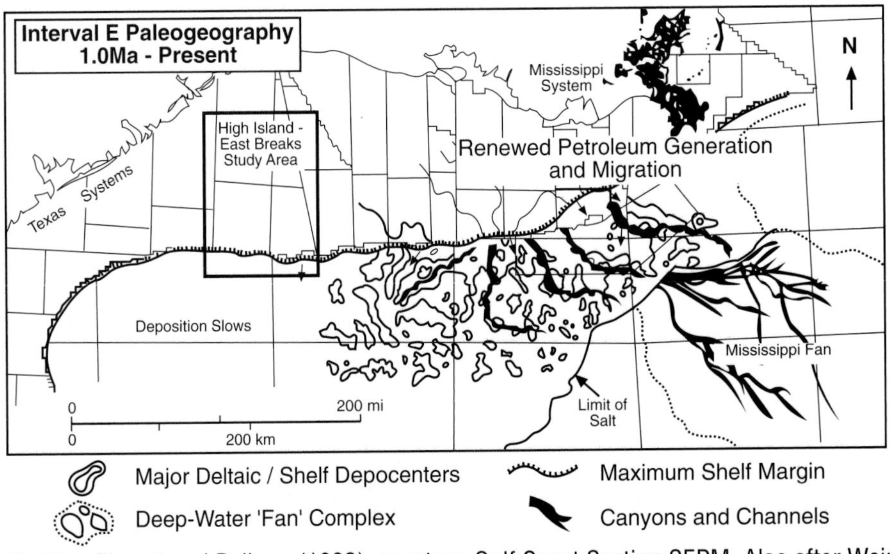

Figure 4–16. After Piggott and Pulham (1993); courtesy Gulf Coast Section SEPM. Also after Weimer (1990); courtesy AAPG.

Example: Mapping Depocenters Through Time, continued

Depocenter summary

Mapping age-specific isopach thicks defines laterally shifting sites of maximum deposition along the margin of the basin. Each of these depocenters has a unique history of accumulation with consequent variations in maturation, migration, and entrapment histories. Evaluation of depocenter maps should include comparison of the results with the larger-scale isopach maps (Figures 4–3, 4–4).

GOM depocenter summary

In the case of the northern Gulf of Mexico, the depocenters prograde over the transitional crust and deform the underlying salt, forming a complex network of salt-cored anticlines and salt-withdrawal synclines. Between 2.5 and 2.0 Ma, the major northern Gulf of Mexico depocenter was focused offshore western Louisiana and eastern Texas. The westernmost part of this depocenter area, the High Island–East Breaks depocenter, appears to have been the input area for the ancestral Mississippi River system. The resulting depocenter has more than 16,000 ft (4875 m) of late Pliocene and early Pleistocene sediments deposited during a succession of high-amplitude sea level cycles (see section C, Depositional Sequences).

Section C
Depositional Sequences

Introduction

Each depocenter has a unique depositional history that reflects the integration of all responses to depositional processes and environmental factors, including tectonics, climate, sediment supply, and sea level variation. These factors result in cycles of deposition: the sediments accumulated during each cycle are the depositional sequence. Integration of multiple data sets, including (1) seismic reflection profiles, (2) biostratigraphic analyses, (3) wireline logs, (4) cores, and (5) detailed measured sections, helps us define the depositional sequences and interpret primary factors affecting formation of each cycle. Precise mapping of each depositional sequence within each depocenter requires careful data integration.

This section discusses the concept of depositional sequences and how to identify them, using a data set from the High Island–East Breaks area. The location of this study area is shown on the depocenter maps of Figures 4–13 through 4–16.

In this section

This section contains the following topics.

Examples in this section

The following figure is a map of the study area, showing the named offshore exploration areas and bathymetry. It also shows the locations of the East Breaks 160-161 field, illustrated seismic profiles and a reference well.

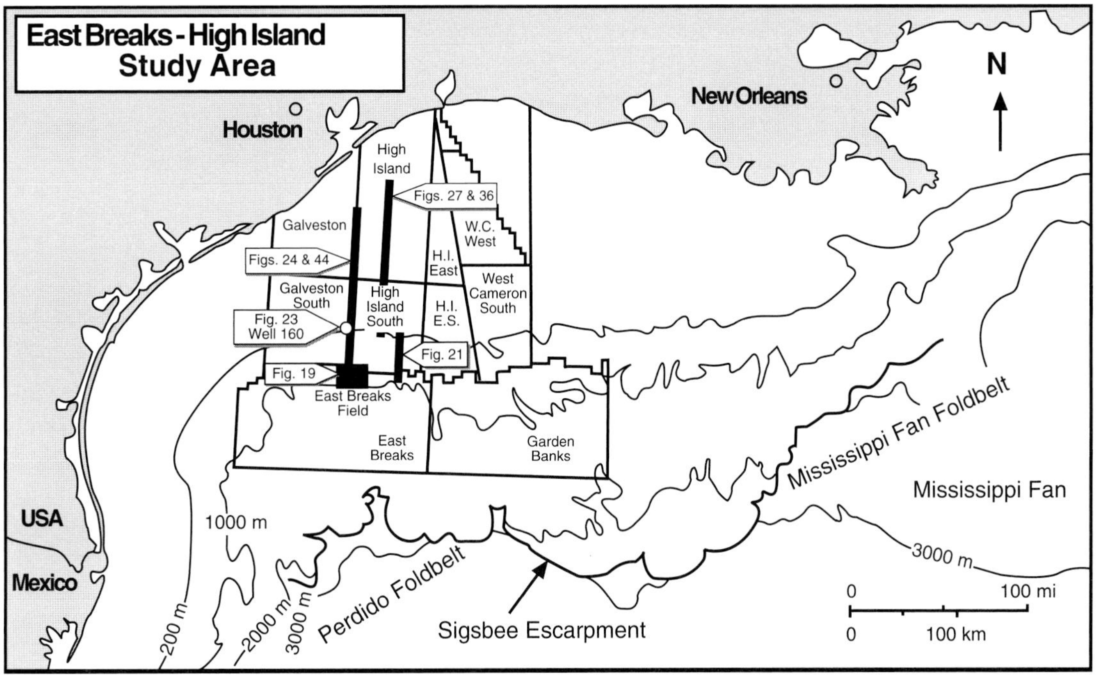

Figure 4–17.

Definitions of Depositional System Elements

Depositional cycle vs. sequence

The term *depositional cycle* refers to time through which one complete cycle of relative sea level change occurs. The sediments deposited during one such cycle are called a *depositional sequence.*

Sequence boundaries

A depositional sequence is bounded by unconformities or the correlative conformities and is subdivided by internal surfaces of transgression and maximum flooding (Mitchum, 1977; see also Vail, 1987; Posamentier et al., 1988; Van Wagoner et al., 1990). Each of these surfaces is chronostratigraphically significant, separating consistently older strata from younger strata.

An alternative concept of defining a depositional sequence is that of Galloway (1989a,b). Galloway uses the maximum flooding surface and correlative condensed section as the bounding surface of the "genetic" depositional sequence. Both sequence concepts use the erosional unconformities, maximum flooding surface, and transgressive surface as interpretation horizons for partitioning each sequence. Sequence surfaces are often best recognized on seismic reflection profiles by stratal terminations called *lapouts,* such as downlap and onlap.

Maximum flooding surface

The maximum flooding surface represents the greatest transgression of shallow marine facies within a sequence (Mitchum, 1977). This is typically associated with a downlap surface formed by the progradation of the overlying highstand systems tract. Not all downlap surfaces are associated with maximum flooding surfaces.

Transgressive surface

The transgressive surface is the first significant marine flooding surface across the shelf (Mitchum, 1977). Above this surface, shallow marine facies shift landward dramatically.

Systems tracts

Systems tracts are composed of all deposits accumulating during one phase of relative sea level cycle, such as lowstand systems tract or highstand systems tract. Attributes of each systems tract are discussed in section D.

Age model

An age model is the chronostratigraphic relationship of different depositional sequences.

Biofacies

A biofacies is an assemblage of organisms (living or fossil) found together because they responded to similar environmental conditions.

Microfossil abundance patterns

Microfossil abundance patterns are relative high and low peaks in the number of microfossils found in a sample or set of samples. They most often indicate sedimentation rates (Armentrout et al., 1990). Intervals with slow rates of sediment accumulation have consequent concentrations of abundant fossils and are associated with maximum flooding and transgressive surfaces. Intervals with high rates of sedimentation usually have low fossil abundances due to dilution and are often associated with sequence boundaries.

Illustration of sequence boundaries

The following figure illustrates the bounding surfaces for sequences. The GOM basin analysis example in this chapter is based primarily on well log and seismic data interpretation using this passive margin sequence stratigraphic model. Different models are necessary for different settings, such as a foreland basin (see Van Wagoner and Bertram, 1995) or a rift basin (Prosser, 1993).

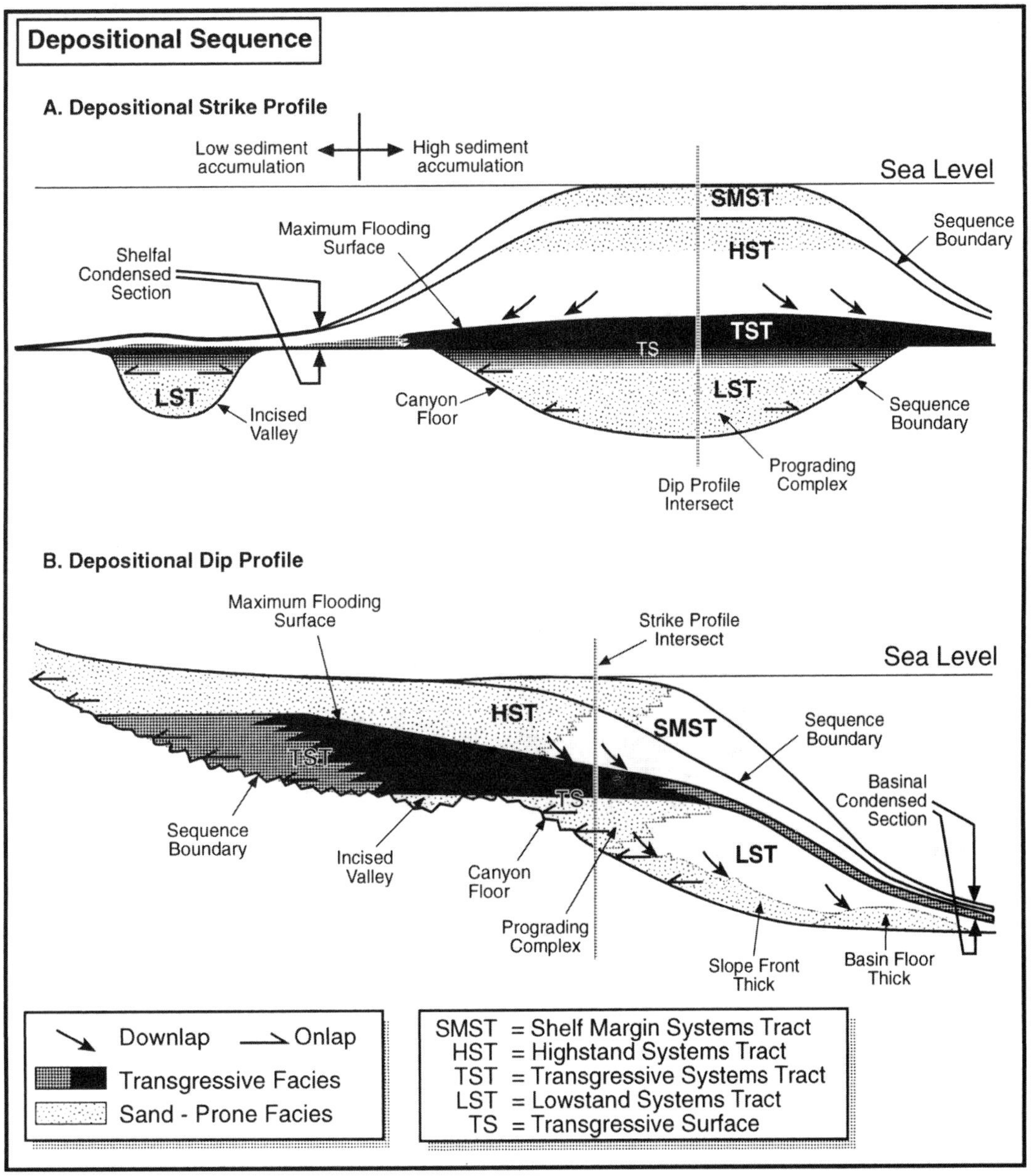

Figure 4–18. After Vail (1987) and Loutit et al. (1988); courtesy AAPG and SEPM.

Identifying Depositional Sequences

Introduction

A depositional sequence is bounded by unconformities or the correlative conformity. It is subdivided by internal surfaces of transgression and maximum flooding (Vail, 1987; Van Wagoner et al., 1990). Each of these surfaces is chronostratigraphically significant, consistently separating older strata from younger strata.

Identifying data

To identify depositional sequences, we use the following:

- Seismic record sections
- Biostratigraphic histograms
- Wireline logs
- Detailed measured stratigraphic sections
- Combinations of the above items

Procedure

Use the table below to identify depositional sequences.

Step	Action
1	Identify depositional sequences in seismic reflection profiles, correlating sequence boundaries throughout a data grid of seismic reflection profiles.
2	Analyze biostratigraphic data for age-significant bioevents and abundance patterns that may suggest depositional sequences.
3	Analyze the depositional patterns from wireline logs, integrate the biostratigraphic data with correlated well log and seismic data, and select candidate depositional sequences.
4	Make regional stratigraphic sections by integrating seismic profile interpretations, biostratigraphic analyses, and regional well log cross sections.
5	Identify depositional sequences based on the fully integrated data set.

Identifying Depositional Sequences in Seismic Sections

Analyzing seismic sections

We identify depositional sequences in seismic sections by finding repetitive patterns of seismic reflections. To test the validity of the sequences identified from seismic reflection profiles, we compare the seismic sequences with sequences identified from biostratigraphic and well log data to see if they make geologic sense. Identifying depositional sequences can be complicated by postdepositional erosion and deformation. It is often helpful to begin a seismic sequence analysis using a grid of relatively few profiles with an area of relatively undeformed rocks.

GOM basin example

In the shelf-margin facies of the East Breaks study area of the GOM basin, a depositional sequence in its simplest form is identified in seismic sections as a couplet consisting of two patterns:

- Sigmoidal clinoform packages
- Regionally extensive parallel reflections

Each clinoform package defines a locally thick progradational unit interpreted as a relative sea level lowstand delta (Sutter and Berryhill, 1985). They are lateral to other clinoform packages and are bounded above and below by regionally extensive, parallel, often uniformly high-amplitude seismic reflections. The regionally extensive parallel reflections correlate across faults and have the same relative thickness on both sides of most outer-shelf and upper-slope faults.

The seismic reflection profile of the figure below, from the East Breaks field area, illustrates both clinoform and parallel reflection patterns in late Pleistocene sediments immediately below the sea floor (between two sets of bold arrows). Three listric growth faults (down arrows) cut through the clinoforms. These growth faults are part of the regional fault system bounding the shelf edge and upper slope salt-withdrawal basins in the High Island and East Breaks areas.

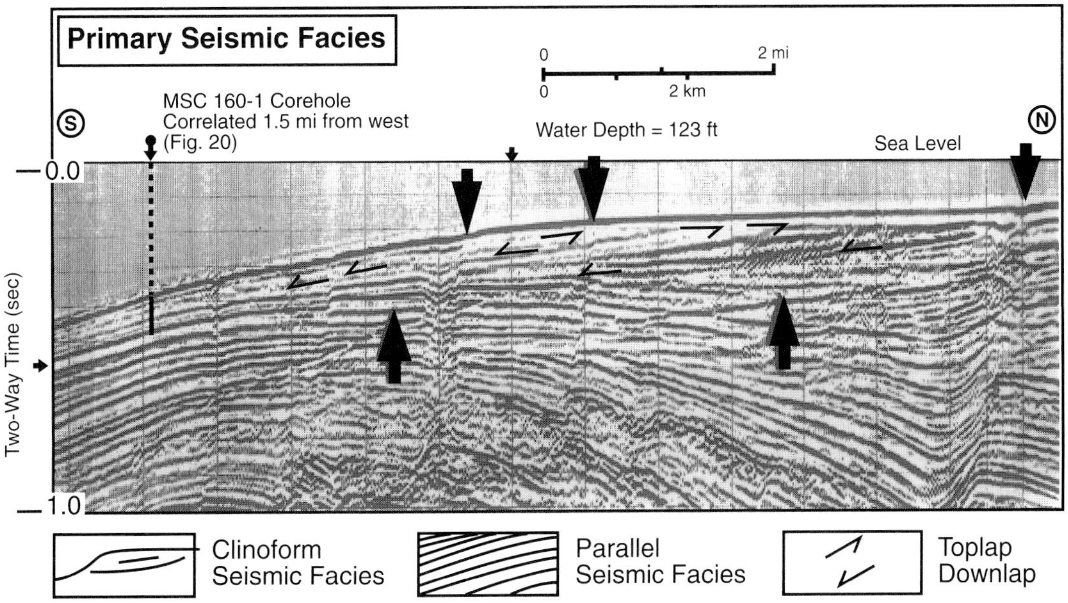

Figure 4–19. Modified from Armentrout (1993); courtesy Gulf Coast SEPM.

GOM basin example (continued)

The arrow at the far left edge of Figure 4–19 marks the trough (white) between parallel, high-amplitude, continuous reflections (black) that underlie the clinoforms (best expressed toward the left side of the figure). Two up arrows show the correlation of this trough across the faults. The clinoforms toplap to the right (north) against the sea floor reflection, defining the overlying transgressive surface above the clinoform tops and below the regionally extensive sea floor reflection. Additionally, the clinoform downlaps basinward, defining a downlap surface. In this case, the downlap surface coincides with the underlying sequence boundary (see Armentrout, 1991).

Depositional cycle

The data from the High Island–East Breaks shelf-margin delta suggest that regionally extensive and uniform layers of mud occur above and below locally shingled clinoform packages. Couplets of these two depositional facies constitute a sequence of one depositional cycle. The position of the sequence at the shelf edge suggests that it is composed of a shelf margin systems tract and a condensed section. For criteria for recognizing depositional cycles in other settings, see Loucks and Sarg (1993), Steel et al. (1995), Van Wagoner and Bertram (1995), and Weimer and Posamentier (1993).

Type 1 vs. type 2 sequences

The sequence stratigraphic model includes type 1 and type 2 sequences (Vail, 1987; Posamentier and Vail, 1988). A type 1 sequence boundary is interpreted to form when the rate of eustatic fall exceeds the rate of subsidence at the depositional break, producing a relative fall in sea level at that position. This usually results in an extensive erosional surface with stream incision landward of the depositional break. In contrast, a type 2 sequence boundary forms when the rate of eustatic fall is slightly less than or equal to the rate of basin subsidence at the depositional break. There is no relative fall in sea level at the depositional break, and erosion and stream incision is less than at type 1 boundaries.

Depositional break

In early publications the depositional break is referred to as the *shelf break,* often uniquely imaged on seismic reflection profiles (Vail and Todd, 1981; Vail et al., 1984). More recently, the depositional break was referred to as the *shoreline break,* a position coincident with the seaward end of a stream-mouth bar in a delta or the upper shoreface in a beach environment (Van Wagoner et al., 1990). Shoreline breaks are well imaged on high-resolution seismic profiles and in well-exposed outcrop belts but are usually below resolution scale of most industry seismic reflection profiles.

Nomenclature problems

These scale differences result in nomenclature problems. The High Island–East Breaks shelf-margin delta (Figures 4–19, 4–21) fits a type 2 sequence criterion of Vail and Todd (1981) because it represents a lowstand prograding complex at the same position as preceding shelf-edge depositional breaks. As such, this lowstand is part of a type 2 depositional sequence and would be called a shelf-margin systems tract. If the criteria of Van Wagoner et al. (1990) are used, the High Island–East Breaks shelf-margin delta would be called a type 1 lowstand prograding complex because the preceding shoreline break is tens of miles further north on the Texas shelf. Clarification of such scale-dependent reference points is critical to effective communication through the careful selection of precise labels for elements of depositional sequences.

Identifying Depositional Sequences from Biostratigraphic Data

Introduction

Biostratigraphic data can aid in identifying individual depositional sequences and stacked depositional sequences, especially when integrated with lithofacies and seismic facies. Biostratigraphic data include the following:

- Microfossil abundance patterns
- Extinction events
- Biofacies

Microfossil abundance patterns

Microfossil abundance patterns derived from examining well cuttings may provide high-resolution observations for identifying depositional sequences. Total microfossil abundance patterns reflect changes in sediment accumulation rates, provided the biogenic productivity varies less than the sediment accumulation rate. For example, during the reduced rate of sediment accumulation associated with transgression, the middle-shelf and deeper transgressive-phase deposits may be characterized by an increase in fossil abundance due to relative terrigenous sediment starvation and consequent concentration of fossil material. If the same conditions of biotic productivity hold during the increased rate of sediment accumulation associated with a prograding system, the accumulated sediments may be characterized by a decrease in fossil abundance due to dilution and environmental stress (Shaffer, 1987a; Armentrout et al., 1990).

Applying abundance patterns

In the Texas offshore Pliocene and Pleistocene depocenter, patterns of fossil abundance are often the most widely applicable observational criteria for identifying the surfaces that define sequences (Armentrout, 1987, 1991, 1996). Sequence boundaries are associated with intervals of few or no in situ fossils and often abundance peaks of reworked fossils in the overlying lowstand systems tract. The transgressive surface is characterized by the stratigraphic upward change from decreasing fossil abundance to increasing abundance. The maximum flooding surface is marked by the maximum fossil abundance interval due to sediment starvation (Loutit et al., 1988; Armentrout et al., 1990).

Example abundance pattern

The figure on the following page is an abundance histogram for the planktonic foraminiferal microfossils *Globorotalia menardii* (s = sinistral) and *Globorotalia inflata* from the MSC 160-1 core hole, East Breaks area (data provided by Gerry Ragan, Mobil Exploration and Producing US). The core hole is 0.3 mi to the west of the seismic reflection profile shown in Figure 4–19. Data on sediment type and biostratigraphy from core hole MSC 160-1 permits geologic characterizations of both the regionally parallel and locally shingled-clinoform seismic facies.

Example abundance pattern (continued)

The figure below contrasts the abundance of sinistral (s) *Globorotalia menardii (G. menardii)* with that of *Globorotalia inflata (G. inflata)* in each sample. Note the alternating pattern of abundance.

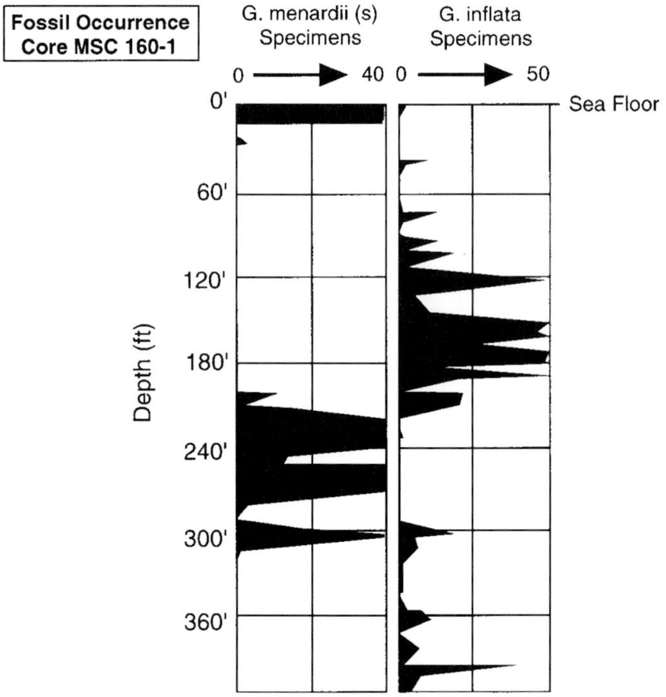

Figure 4–20. From Armentrout (1993, 1996); courtesy Gulf Coast SEPM and Geological Society of London.

Pattern interpretation

The high abundance of *G. menardii* at depths of 0–20 ft (0–7 m) shown in Figure 4–20 correlates with the interval at the sea floor that is part of the regionally extensive transgressive mud of the Holocene. The arrow on the seismic section, shown on Figure 4–19, at about 0.6 sec (two-way time) marks a trough between two high-amplitude continuous reflections that also correlate with the high-abundance interval of *G. menardii* between 190 and 320 ft (58 and 98 m). In contrast, the stratigraphic intervals of *G. menardii* low abundance and *G. inflata* high abundance correlate with the shingled-clinoform seismic facies.

Stratigraphic intervals with abundant *G. menardii* are interpreted to indicate warm-water interglacial conditions, and abundant *G. inflata* are interpreted as temperate-water glacial indicators (Kennett et al., 1985; Martin et al., 1990). The correlation of abundant *G. menardii* with the regionally extensive transgressive mud of the Holocene provides local confirmation of the warm-water interglacial interpretation. The regionally continuous reflections at 0.6 sec also indicate a transgressive interglacial interval. The shingled-clinoform facies correlates with the *G. inflata* abundance peak, suggesting deposition during temperate-water glacial conditions.

Note that the intervals of abundant *G. menardii* are thicker than intervals with abundant *G. inflata.* This suggests that more sediment accumulates associated with glacial lowstand progradation. Deposition of the thick clinoform packages necessitates some fault movement to accommodate the sediment accumulation (Armentrout, 1993).

Recognizing Stacked Depositional Sequences in Seismic Profiles

Introduction

Depositional sequences can stack into successions of sequences if accommodation space permits preservation of successive sequences. Seismically, stacked sequences are expressed as repetitious reflection patterns.

GOM basin example

The seismic reflection profile below is from the High Island South Addition area, GOM basin, 20 mi east of the East Breaks shelf-margin delta. It illustrates the vertical stacking of seven depositional sequences within a fault-bounded salt-withdrawal basin. Down arrows at the inflection point of each clinoform identify the top of the clinoform of each sequence. In general, each cycle consists of (1) a thick basinal package of relatively discontinuous, variable-amplitude, hummocky reflections that grade upward into (2) parallel, continuous, uniform amplitude reflections, overlain by (3) a prograding clinoform that downlaps the underlying facies. Each clinoform is interpreted as a shelf-margin delta prograding into this outer-shelf to upper-slope fault-bounded basin as shown by the present-day sea floor profile. The seven prograding clinoforms are mapped into a nearby well and are correlated with two-cycle charts (Figure 4–25). Cycle 1 of this figure correlates with the clinoform package of Figure 4–19.

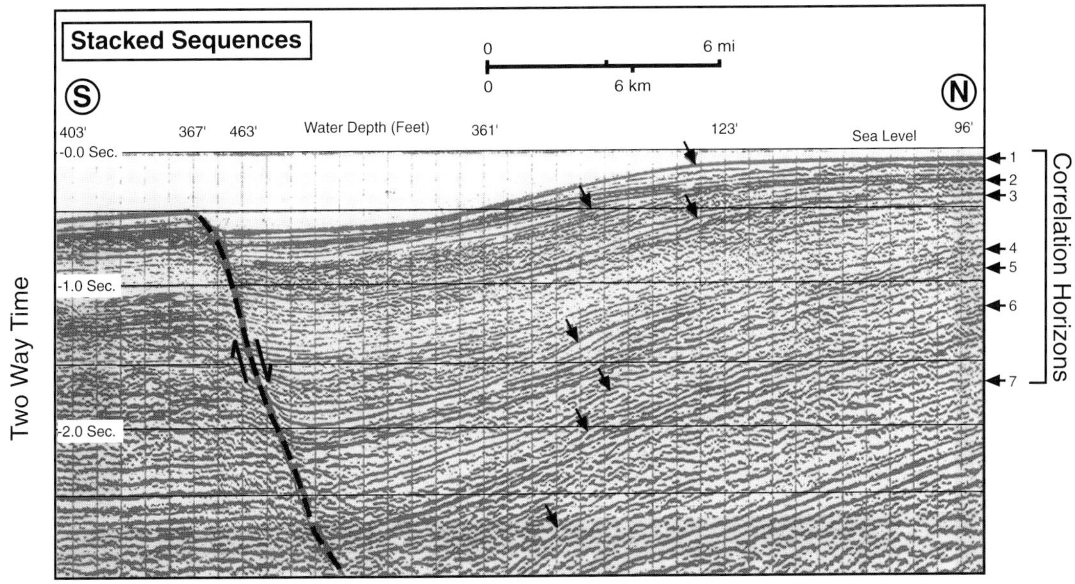

Figure 4–21. From Armentrout (1993, 1996); courtesy Gulf Coast SEPM and Geological Society of London.

Interpretation of example

The nearly vertical stacking of seven shelf-margin clinoforms suggests that accommodation space was created in the same area during seven cycles of progradation. The accommodation space is formed by down-to-the-north movement on the fault. This fault is part of a counter-regional listric growth fault that soles out into salt layers at depth. Movement on the fault occurred at a rate permitting the vertical stacking of shelf-margin clinoforms during each glacial/interglacial sea level cycle rather than progressive basinward progradation of successive clinoforms across a stable shelf-slope profile. This pattern clearly demonstrates the interplay of sediment supply, tectonics, climate, and sea level (see Beard et al., 1982; Anderson et al., 1996).

Recognizing Stacked Depositional Sequences from Well Data

Introduction

Stacked depositional sequences can be recognized in well data using

- variations in well log response
- biostratigraphic data such as microfossil abundance patterns and biofacies distribution

Armentrout (1996) discusses integration of these data sets.

Building regional log cross sections

Regional stratigraphic well-log cross sections form the foundation for many basin studies. They give a regional view of basin stratigraphy and can be integrated with seismic and biostratigraphic data. The table below outlines the steps for building regional well-log cross sections.

Step	Action
1	Build a grid of well-log sections that crosses the entire basin, either along depositional dip or depositional strike. Use as many wells as practical. Where available, add measured sections and core descriptions to the grid.
2	Correlate cross sections. Look for unconformities and flooding surfaces.
3	Tie the correlations from depositional-dip sections to depositional-strike sections.
4	Confirm correlations on seismic reflection profiles.

Biostratigraphic patterns

Using chronostratigraphically significant bioevents as defined by microfossil extinction events and abundance patterns, local cycles of transgression and regression can be correlated from well to well, providing a high-resolution calibration of depositional cyclicity. Patterns of relative dilution vs. concentration of fossils that correlate over a significant geographic area, such as a large portion of a basin margin, can be interpreted as reflecting cycles of regional transgression and regression rather than local lateral shifting of sediment input points.

Stratigraphic intervals rich in calcareous nannoplankton and foraminiferal fossils and having maximum gamma-ray values are interpreted to correlate with condensed depositional intervals deposited during relative sediment starvation related to transgression (Loutit et al., 1988). Intervals devoid of fossils or having low abundance values, often associated with sandy lithofacies, can be interpreted as deposited during relative high rates of accumulation related to progradation of the sediment supply into the area of the well, marking a phase of regression. Biofacies are interpreted using benthic foraminiferal assemblages indicative of water mass conditions (Tipsword et al., 1966; Culver, 1988; Armentrout, 1991).

GOM basin example

In the GOM basin, variations in well-log response and biofacies distribution are analyzed for recognition of stacked depositional sequences. The gamma-ray log display provides a measure of sediment type, with curve deflections to the left suggesting increased sand content while high values to the right indicate increases in clay content. Use of multiple logs, especially spontaneous potential, resistivity, density, and velocity logs calibrated by well-cutting descriptions and formation microscanner displays, provides a data set for reliable rock type identification. The figure below illustrates an interpretation template for log motif analysis.

Patterns of forestepping vs. backstepping log-motif funnels can define transgressive vs. regressive depositional trends and candidate systems tracts and sequences. Vail and Wornardt (1990) and Armentrout et al. (1993) detail the process.

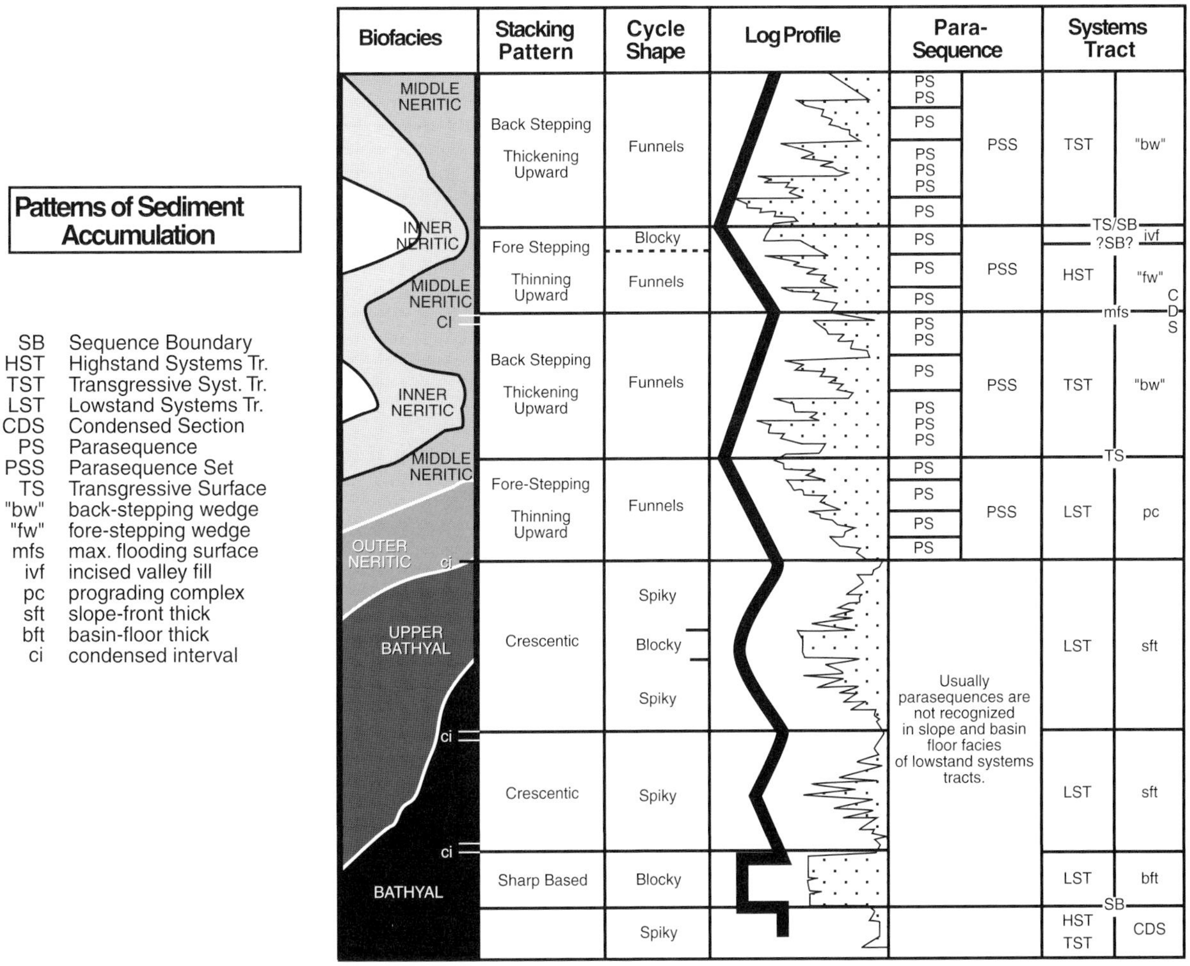

Figure 4–22. From Armentrout et al. (1993); courtesy The Geological Society of London.

GOM basin example chart

The histogram patterns of foraminiferal and calcareous nannoplankton abundance are shown on the next page for the South Galveston Mobil A-158 #3 well. The histogram is based on a detailed checklist of the relative abundance of each species of fossil in each well-cutting sample (Armentrout et al., 1990). Display of this data in two-way time facilitates integration with seismic reflection profiles using the synthetic seismogram to match

GOM basin example chart (continued)

the well data with the seismic reflection profile at the well site. Patterns of shallow vs. deep biofacies and fossil abundance (i.e., concentration vs. dilution) can be correlated with progradation of sandstone vs. mudstone interpreted from wireline log patterns. Bioevents (abbreviated acronyms such as 2B and SG) and faunal discontinuity events (abbreviated FDA-3 and FDA-4) provide correlation horizons between which the abundance patterns provide additional events for correlation (Armentrout, 1991).

In the histogram below (see Figure 4–17 for well location), the foraminiferal abundance scale is 0–1000 specimens and the nannoplankton abundance scale is 0–800 specimens. Biofacies include inner neritic (IN, 0–50 m), middle neritic (MN, 50–100 m), outer neritic (ON, 100–200 m), upper bathyal (UPPB, 200–500 m), middle bathyal (MDLB, 500–1000 m), and lower bathyal (LOWB, 1000–2000 m). This figure is the leftmost (southern) well panel in Figure 4–24. The wireline log (gamma ray) motif patterns (Figure 4–22), biostratigraphic abundance events, and extinction datums provide correlation events.

BIOSTRATIGRAPHIC WELL PANEL

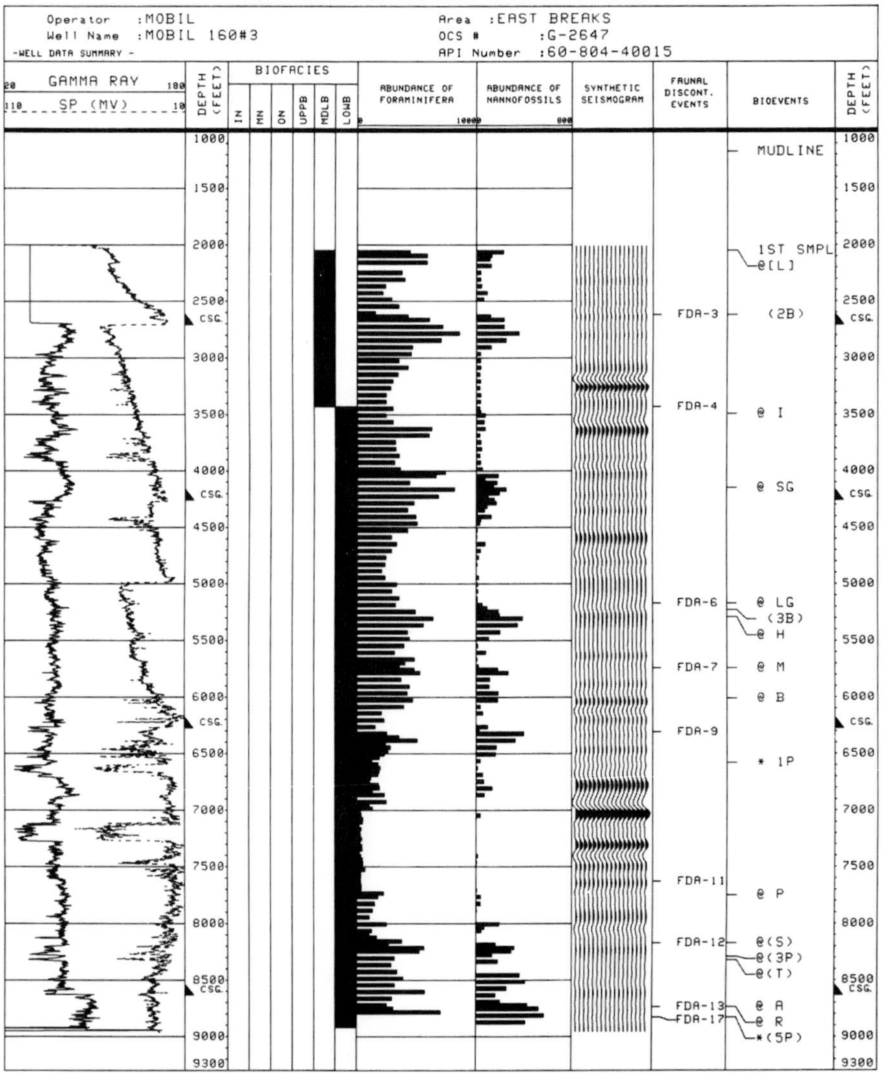

Figure 4–23. From Armentrout (1991, 1996); courtesy Springer-Verlag, Geological Society of London.

Recognizing Stacked Depositional Sequences from Well Data, continued

Biostratigraphic correlation of stacked sequences

The well correlation section on the next page is an example of using high-resolution biostratigraphic correlation to recognize depositional successions within stacked depositional sequences. In some basins containing nondescript fill that lacks unique marker beds, like the Gulf of Mexico, high-resolution biostratigraphic correlation is the best method for subdividing basin fill into sequences and systems tracts (Armentrout, 1987; Galloway, 1989a,b).

The four wells in the cross section are in a depositionally dip-oriented transect (Armentrout, 1996). The correlation horizons, based on seven chronostratigraphically significant bioevents (mostly extinction events), partition the strata into age-correlative intervals (Armentrout and Clement, 1990). Most of the chronostratigraphically significant bioevents occur in association with maximum fossil abundance, resulting in the interpretation of these correlation horizons as maximum flooding surface-condensed section data (Galloway, 1989a,b; Armentrout et al., 1990; Schaffer, 1987a,b, 1990; Armentrout, 1996).

Each well panel is formatted the same as Figure 4–23. The foraminiferal (left histogram) and calcareous nannoplankton (right histogram) abundance patterns of each well are very similar. Biostratigraphic correlation horizons (horizontal lines) provide ties between the wells, facilitating comparison between the abundance patterns and biofacies variations within each chronostratigraphic interval. Each correlation was checked against correlations independently constructed using a regional grid of seismic reflection profiles.

Identifying sequence in the GOB basin example

In Figure 4–24, candidates for maximum flooding surfaces are identified by abundance peaks in both foraminifera and nannoplankton and by extinction events known to be associated with regionally significant maximum transgressions (Armentrout and Clement, 1990; Schaffer, 1987a,b, 1990). Sequence boundary candidates occur between the maximum flooding surfaces and are identified by low abundance of fossils and by wireline log patterns. The northern wells (right) are rich in sand deposited in shallow water (neritic biofacies); sequence boundaries are likely to occur at the top of forestepping parasequence sets. The southern wells (left) are sand-poor shale deposited in deep water (bathyal biofacies); sequence boundaries are likely to occur at or slightly below flat-based blocky sands and at faunal abundance minima.

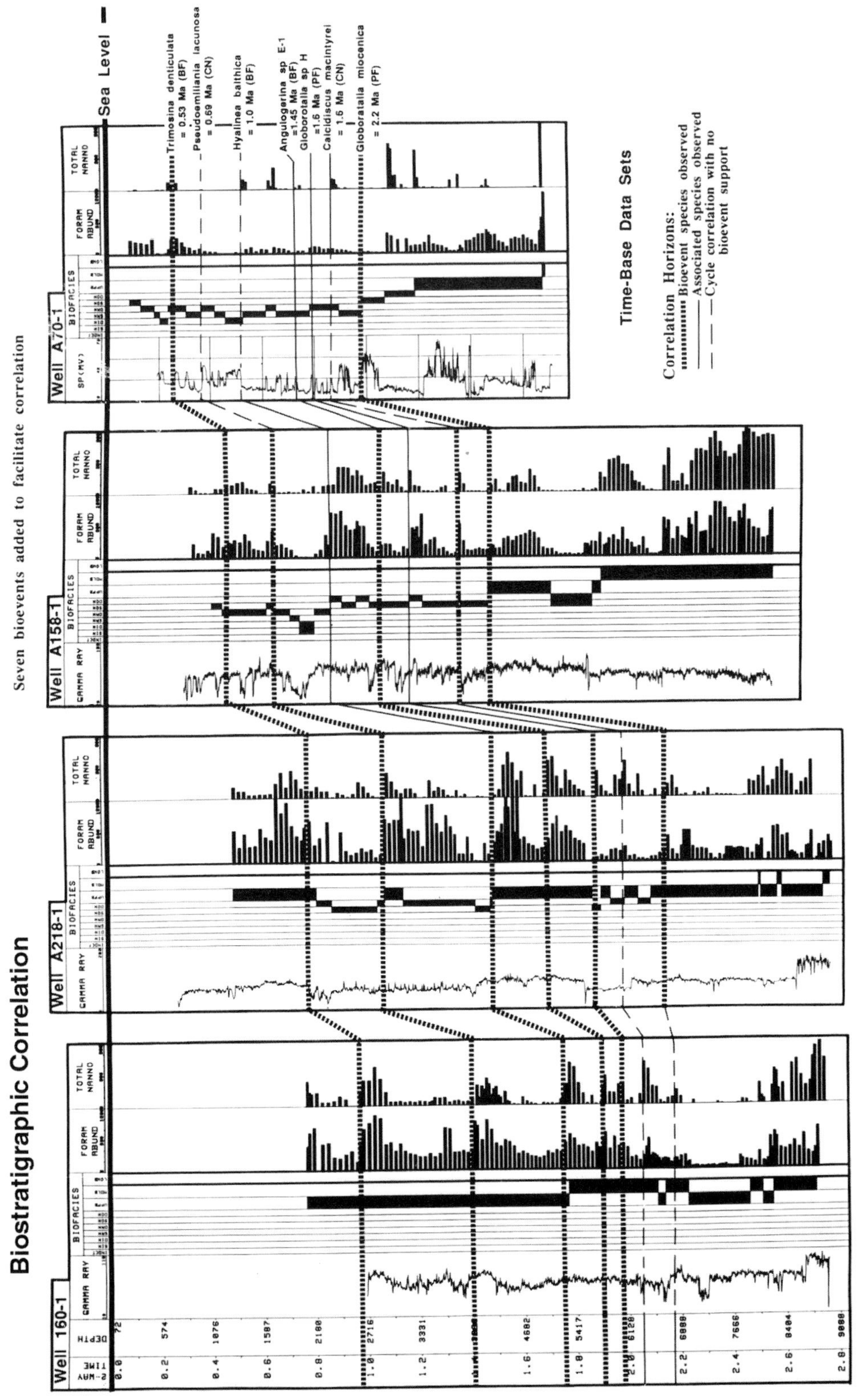

Figure 4–24. From Armentrout (1991, 1996); courtesy Springer-Verlag and The Geological Society of London.

Section D

Depositional Systems Tracts

Introduction

Subdivision of each sea level cycle into its depositional phases helps us construct high-frequency paleogeographic maps, one or more for each depositional systems tract. These maps help us predict reservoir and seal rock as well as delineate probable migration avenues. From integrated data sets, a high-resolution age model can be constructed and used to correlate and calibrate depositional sequences. Using the age model and stratigraphic thicknesses, rock accumulation rates of each cycle can be calculated and the thermal history for each depocenter reconstructed.

Subsection 1 of this section focuses on sea level cycle phase. Subsection 2 focuses on the use of paleogeography in petroleum exploration.

In this section

This section contains the following subsections.

Subsection D1

Sea Level Cycle Phase

Introduction

Depositional cycles can be subdivided into systems tracts, each representing a specific phase of relative sea level, e.g., highstand, falling (regressive), lowstand, and rising (transgressive). Nonmarine systems tracts can be related to rise and fall in lake level or water table level, which may or may not be synchronized with sea level change. [See Wheeler (1964) for a discussion of base level.] Identifying each cycle phase of a depositional sequence and mapping the contained facies provides a paleogeographic map for a relatively short time interval. Such high-resolution maps provide useful predictions for hydrocarbon prospecting. This subsection discusses the concept of sea level cycle phase, identification of cycle phase, construction of a cycle chart, and how sea level cycles of different duration interact.

In this subsection

This subsection contains the following topics.

Determining Sea Level Cycle Order

Introduction

One aspect of basin analysis focuses on mapping specific systems tracts of third-, fourth-, or fifth-order sea level cycles and the relationship that stacked depositional sequences deposited during those cycles have to each other. Knowing the order of a cycle or the phase of a cycle represented by a rock sequence is important for predicting the location and type of reservoir and seal and the location of potential source rocks.

Procedure

To determine cycle order of a sequence of sediments, we use biostratigraphic data, stratigraphic context (i.e., what part of a systems tract the interval is from), oxygen isotope curves, and published sea level curves. The table below suggests a procedure for determining cycle order of a rock sequence.

Step	Action
1	Determine the time span during which the sequence was deposited and compare to age ranges for cycle orders (see table below).
2	Determine the stratigraphic context of the sequence. What are the cycle orders for similar sequences above or below it?
3	Determine the age of the sequence and compare it to published sea level cycle curves (e.g., Haq et al., 1988).

Cycle order from thickness and areal extent

Because rates of sediment accumulation and areas of accommodation space vary, thickness and areal extent are of little use in establishing the order of depositional cycles. Most cycle hierarchies are based on duration. Establishing the duration of a sequence is difficult because of problems in high-resolution dating of rocks. However, with careful work an estimate can be made (see Miall, 1994; Armentrout, 1991, 1996).

Table of cycle order

Use the table below to help assess the sea level cycle order of a rock interval after Van Wagoner et al., 1990.

Cycle Order	Nomenclature	Thickness Range (ft)	Aerial Extent (mi^2)	Duration (Ma)	
				Range	Mode
1st	Megasequence	1000+	Global	50–100+	80
2nd	Supersequence	500–5000+	Regional	5–50	10
3rd	Sequence	500–1500	500–50,000	0.5–5	1
4th	Parasequence Set	20–800	20–2000	0.1–0.5	0.45
5th	Parasequence	10–200	20–2000	0.01–0.1	0.04

GOM basin example

The figure below shows the correlation of the third-order eustatic curve of Haq et al. (1988) and the oxygen isotope curve of Williams and Trainor (1987) with seven prograding clinoform intervals from the High Island South Addition in the GOM basin (see Figure 4–21). The correlations were established using the extinction events of the benthic foraminifera *Hyalinea balthica (Hyal B)* and *Trimosina denticulata (Trim A)* and the present-day sea floor as chronostratigraphic data. Six of the observed depositional cycles occur during the Tejas supersequence B 3.10 (0.8–0.0 Ma) third-order cycle of Haq et al. (1988). This correlation suggests that the local cycles are fourth-order depositional cycles with a duration of approximately 130,000 years each (see Mitchum and Van Wagoner, 1990).

The seven fourth-order cycles occur at approximately the same frequency as the oxygen isotope warm and cold cycles. The oxygen isotope cycles are interpreted as glacial-interglacial cycles corresponding with relative high- and lowstands of sea level (Williams and Trainor, 1987). The clinoforms generally correlate with trends in upward enrichment in isotope values, suggesting progradation during onset of glacial climates as a consequence of lowering sea level as continental ice formed.

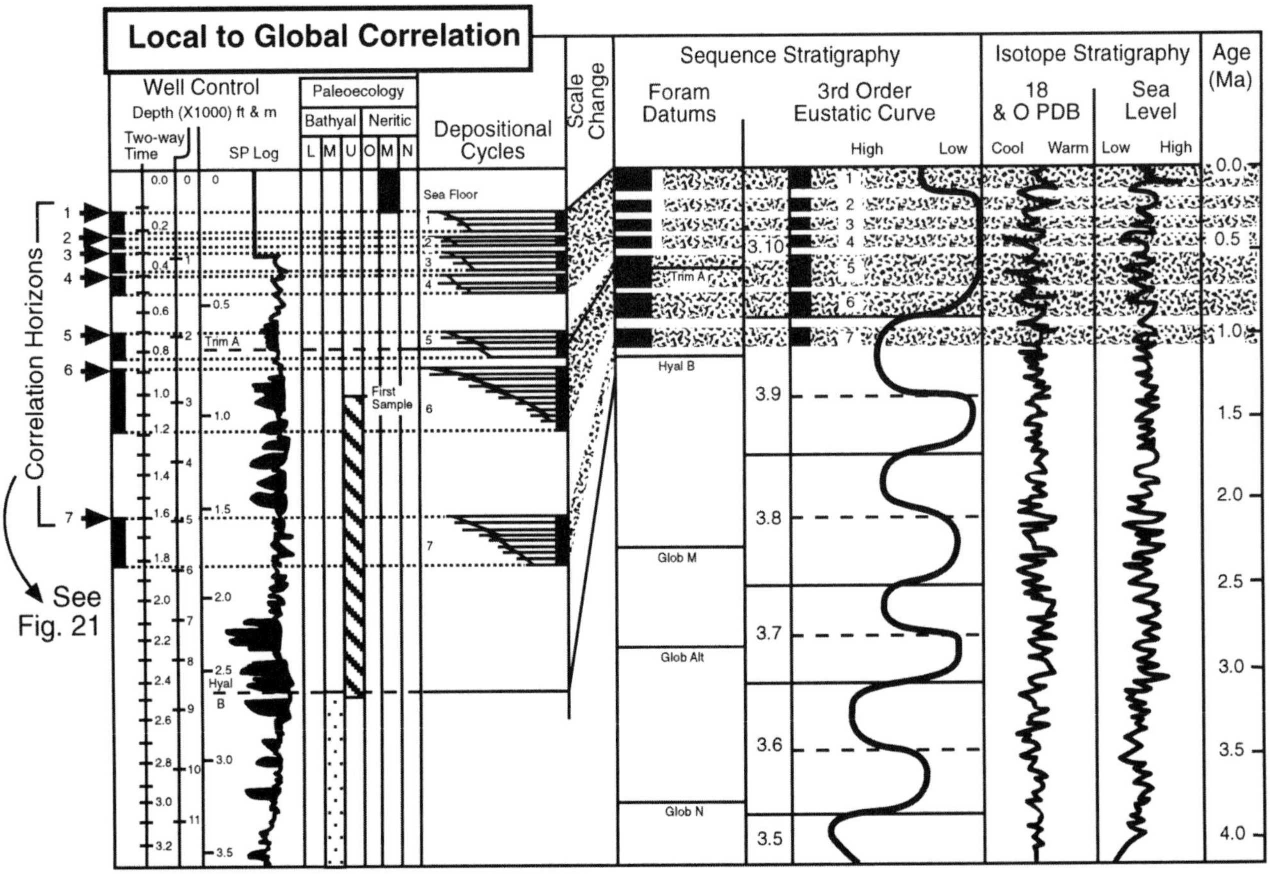

Figure 4–25. From Armentrout (1993); courtesy Gulf Coast SEPM.

Sea Level Cycle Phase and Systems Tracts

Phases of a sea level cycle

Each cycle can be subdivided into four phases of relative sea level change:

- Rising
- Highstand
- Falling
- Lowstand

The interpretation methodology of sequence stratigraphy helps us recognize each cycle phase and provides a nomenclature to describe each element (Vail, 1987; Jervey, 1988; Posamentier and Vail, 1988; Armentrout, 1991, 1996).

Cycle phase & sedimentation

Deposition or erosion of sediments depends on the interaction of cycle phase and the creation of accommodation space. The sediments comprising a depositional sequence are deposited during falling, lowstand, rising, and highstand phases of a sea level cycle. Erosion, which forms a critical element of the boundaries of a depositional sequence, generally occurs during falling sea level and lowstands (Vail, 1987). Within the basin depocenter, the sequence boundary consists of a conformity that correlates with the erosional unconformity along the basin margin.

Systems tracts

Systems tracts are composed of all deposits accumulating during one phase of relative sea level cycle and preserved between specific primary chronostratigraphic surfaces (Brown and Fisher, 1977). Erosion usually dominates the falling phase of a sea level cycle, and the deposited sediments are most often assigned to the lowstand systems tract.

Lowstand systems tracts

The lowstand systems tract occurs between the basal sequence boundary and the transgressive surface. Lowstand systems are thickest toward basin centers because much of the basin margin is undergoing erosion. Lowstand systems with shelf-to-slope geometries may have basin center gravity-flow deposits due to sediment bypass of the slope and thick shelf-edge deltaic systems prograding into deep water. Fluvially dominated depositional systems are common.

Transgressive systems tracts

The transgressive systems tract encompasses those deposits between the transgressive surface and maximum flooding surface. Transgressive systems tracts show landward-stepping depositional patterns and basin margin onlap due to relative rise in sea level, forcing sediment accumulation toward the basin margin. The basin center is likely to become progressively more sediment starved, and coastal depositional systems may show a strong tidal influence.

Highstand systems tracts

The highstand systems tract is between the maximum flooding surface and the overlying sequence boundary. Highstand systems tracts show a progradational stacking pattern due to sediment supply exceeding the accommodation space. Progradation results in basinward downlapping onto the maximum flooding surface. Basin centers may still be sediment starved if shelves are broad. Coastal depositional systems tend to be wave to fluvially dominated, thin, and widespread. Definition and further discussion on identifying characteristics of each of the surface types and systems tracts can be found in Posamentier and Vail (1988), Loutit et al. (1988), Van Wagoner et al. (1990), and Armentrout (1991, 1996).

Identifying Systems Tracts

Introduction

Certain types of hydrocarbon traps are more commonly associated with a particular depositional systems tract. Identifying the highstand, lowstand, or transgressive systems tract and the specific depositional environments within each lets us predict possible reservoir, seal, and charge system for each potential trap.

Methods

Identifying a depositional systems tract can be achieved by analyzing seismic geometries (Figures 4–19 and 4–21), wireline logs motif (Figure 4–22), and biostratigraphic data (Figures 4–20 and 4–23). Carefully integrating multiple data sets increases the probability of a correct interpretation (see Armentrout, 1991, 1996; Armentrout et al., 1993; Vail and Wornardt, 1990).

Stratal pattern simulation

The figure below shows the computer-simulated stacking pattern of stratal units within an unconformity-bound depositional sequence. [For computer modeling, see Jervey (1988).] The simulation forces all sediment to be deposited within the 2-D plain of the diagram. In the natural world, the depositional thicks associated with each systems tract are likely to occur lateral to each other, and their recognition requires a 3-D data set. Additionally, postdepositional deformation and erosion significantly modify the idealized geometry shown in Figures 4–18 and 4–26.

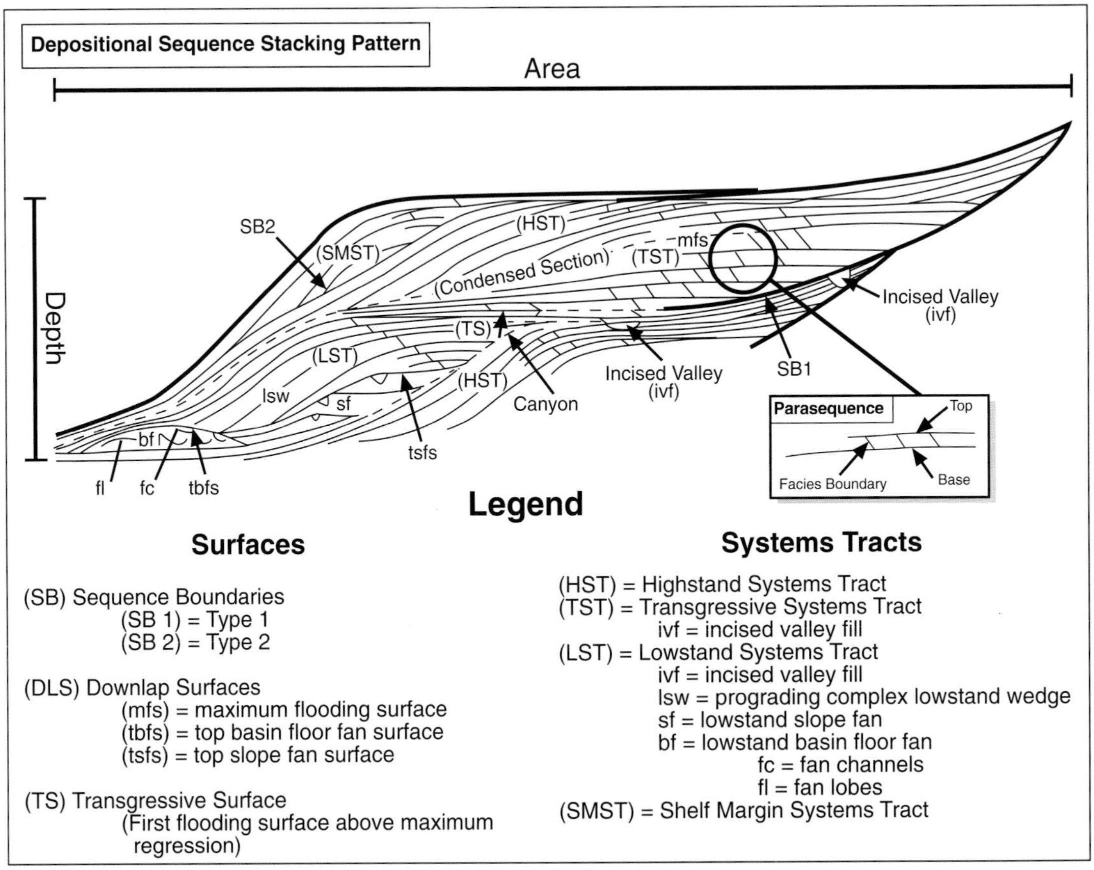

Figure 4–26. Modified from Haq et al. (1988); courtesy SEPM.

Parasequences

For transgressive and regressive shallow-water facies, each of the depositional layers is called a parasequence; they stack into parasequence sets (Van Wagoner et al., 1990). More basinal facies deposited well below wave influence reflect gravity-flow processes and are not called parasequences (Van Wagoner et al., 1990; Vail and Wornardt, 1990). The depositional sequence lithofacies diagram is presented in Posamentier and Vail (1988) for siliciclastics and in Sarg (1988) for carbonate rocks.

Interpreting parasequence sets

Stratal geometries that show parasequences stacked into sets that forestep progressively toward the basin center reflect progradation from the sediment supply exceeding the accommodation space; those that stack into sets that backstep progressively toward the basin margin reflect transgression from an increase in accommodation space that exceeds the sediment supply (Figure 4–22). Progradation of parasequence sets basinward of their age-equivalent shelf edge are, by definition, the lowstand prograding complex; parasequence sets prograding from the basin margin to the age-equivalent shelf margin may be either highstand prograding complexes or shelf margin systems tracts. The absence of a well-defined shelf/slope break complicates recognition of highstand vs. lowstand systems tracts.

Interpretation of stratal patterns example

Relative changes in sea level can also be inferred from detailed analysis of local depositional geometries on seismic reflection profiles. On the seismic reflection profile schematic below (from Armentrout, 1987), clinoforms 1–5 pinch out with toplap against a common horizon, suggesting oblique clinoforms (Mitchum et al., 1977). These oblique clinoforms can be interpreted as forming when sediment supply exceeds the accommodation space and causes shelf-margin progradation; sea level falls at the same rate as subsidence, completely bypassing the shelf with no accumulation of seismic-scale topset beds. Clinoforms 6 and 7 are sigmoidal (Mitchum et al., 1977). These can be interpreted as sediment supply exceeding accommodation space, forcing progradation but with subsidence exceeding the relative change in sea level and consequent accumulation of topset beds. The change from no topset beds to aggradational topset beds indicates a turnaround from apparent still-stand to apparent rise in sea level at the site of deposition.

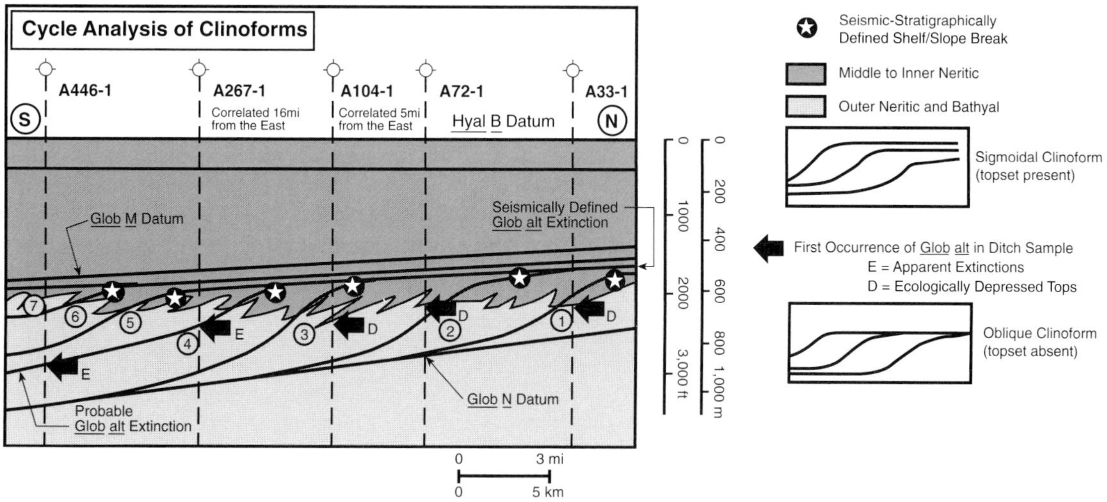

Figure 4–27. From Armentrout (1987); courtesy Gulf Coast SEPM.

Time significance of seismic reflections

Using seismic reflection geometries to suggest relative sea level phase requires confidence in the coeval character of seismic reflections. The first downhole occurrence of *Glob alt* *(Globoquadrina altispira,* bold arrows) in Figure 4–27 suggests a correlation cross-cutting the seismically imaged clinoforms. If the *Glob alt* occurrences are coeval, the seismic reflections are time transgressive.

Note that the first downhole well-cutting sample occurrence of the bioevent *Glob alt* is at the interface of outer neritic and upper bathyal biofacies, except in the two southern wells, A446-1 and A267-1, where the first occurrences occur within stratigraphic intervals containing bathyal biofacies. *Glob alt* is a planktonic foraminifer normally found associated with open marine faunas and floras interpreted as upper bathyal assemblages. The occurrences of *Glob alt* coincident with the first upper bathyal biofacies assemblage suggests a facies-controlled top, depressed below the true extinction top by environmental factors. The two occurrences within upper bathyal biofacies are interpreted as true extinction events. These true extinction events correlate with a seismic reflection, suggesting that specific reflection approximates a time line and can be used to extend the *Glob alt* extinction event datum (2.8 Ma) northward toward the basin margin (see Armentrout and Clement, 1990).

This type of bioevent analysis is essential when identifying chronostratigraphically useful bioevents and demonstrating that seismic reflections approximate time lines (Vail et al., 1977).

Systems Tracts and Trap Types

Introduction

Each systems tract—highstand, lowstand, and transgressive—has a different trapping potential based on the vertical and lateral distribution of lithofacies deposited within specific depositional environments. White (1980) presents an excellent review of trap types within facies-cycle wedges, which are related to transgressive-regressive cycles and can be related most specifically to the transgressive systems tract and the highstand systems tract. In White's classification, prograding lithofacies of the lowstand systems tract might occur as subunconformity traps or might be mistakenly identified as highstand systems tract deposits. Gravity-flow deposits of slope and basin-floor fan systems are most often placed into the lowstand systems tract because they are deposited basinward of the shelf/slope inflection.

White (1980) discusses both siliciclastic and carbonate systems. Sarg (1988) provides an excellent discussion of carbonate systems. Only siliciclastic systems, similar to those of the Cenozoic of the central and western Gulf of Mexico, are discussed here.

Lowstand systems tract traps

Lowstand gravity-flow, sand-prone reservoirs occur in basin-floor and slope systems. They are most often encased within marine hemipelagic mudstones, which serve as seal and sometimes potential source rock. Traps are often stratigraphic, but postdepositional deformation that places the gravity-flow sand deposit in a structurally high position enhances the potential for focused migration of hydrocarbon fluids to the reservoir facies (Mitchum, 1985).

Lowstand prograding complex traps

Siliciclastic lowstand prograding complexes, imaged on seismic reflection profiles as clinoforms, are often fluvial-deltaic complexes with abundant sand in the depositional topsets (Figures 4–19 and 4–21). As the relative sea level cycle turns around from low to rising, the coarse-grained sediment supply decreases. The fine-grained sediments of the transgressive systems tract overlie the lowstand systems tract–prograding complex sand-prone facies, providing excellent top seal to the underlying sandy reservoir. If the transgressive shales are organic rich and buried in the thermal regime for kerogen cracking, hydrocarbons will be generated. If the lithofacies forming the preceding shelf edge can provide lateral seal, the prograding complex reservoir facies may become charged with hydrocarbons even without structural enhancement of the trap (Armentrout et al., 1997).

Transgressive systems tract traps

Transgressive systems tracts step toward the basin margin, with mud-prone facies overlying most of the sand-prone deposits, providing good top seal and often potential source rock to the underlying sands. However, because of the landward-stepping character of this systems tract, the sand-prone depositional facies are not likely to be very thick, resulting in volumetrically smaller reservoirs. Traps can be purely stratigraphic or enhanced with postdepositional structuring that focuses migration (White, 1980). However, the landward-stepping sand-prone facies may prevent adequate lateral seal for stratigraphic traps.

Highstand systems tract traps

Highstand systems tracts step toward the basin center and often prograde at the expense of the preceding parasequence due to erosion during relative fall of sea level. The falling sea level also decreases the space into which the sediment can accumulate, resulting in potentially rapid lateral shifting of the prograding deltaic lobes. This results in relatively thin but widespread sand-prone facies. An effective top seal for such a highstand system would require a very major transgression well landward of the updip end of the sandy facies of the prograding coastal plain (White, 1980). Such a transgression could be eustatic or tectonic in nature, as in a rapidly subsiding foreland basin setting. Postdepositional deformation forming anticlines enhances the potential for entrapping hydrocarbons in sheet-like highstand systems tract reservoirs.

Shelf margin systems tract traps

Shelf-margin systems tracts are the lowstand deposits of a type 2 sequence. Type 2 sequences are deposited when relative sea level falls but not below the preceding depositional inflection. Type 1 sequences are deposited when relative sea level falls below the preceding depositional systems tract (Van Wagoner et al., 1990). The subsequent transgression may provide effective top seal, but the lateral seal of shelf margin systems tracts shares the same limitations as the highstand systems tract.

Early sequence stratigraphic studies, based largely on seismic reflection profiles, used the shelf edge as the depositional inflection reference point (Vail and Todd, 1981; Vail et al., 1984). Subsequent work on outcrops and high-resolution seismic reflection profiles redefined the deposition inflection as the shoreline break (Van Wagoner et al., 1990). The shoreline break is generally coincident with the seaward end of the stream mouth bar in a delta or the upper shoreface in a beach environment. This change in depositional inflection scale results in nearly all seismically recognized lowstand deposits being attributed to type 1 sequences. Because the GOM basin analysis relies largely on seismic reflection profiles, all lowstand deposits are referenced to shelf-edge inflection points.

Systems tracts with greatest trapping potential

White (1980) compiles data on the depositional setting of more than 2000 major oil and gas fields in 200 transgressive and regressive wedges within 80 basins. With clearly stated qualifications, White shows that most hydrocarbons found in siliciclastic reservoirs occur in the base to middle of the wedge in generally lowstand to transgressive depositional facies. This can be attributed to the greater probability of effective top seal in contrast to the highstand systems tract. By using the stratal stacking pattern, supplemented by lithofacies and biofacies data, depositional environments can be properly identified and paleogeographic maps constructed for each systems tract to predict between and beyond data points.

Identifying Sea Level Cycle Phase with Biostratigraphy

Introduction

In basin depocenters, much of the stratigraphic record consists of deposits accumulated during relative lowstand of sea level. These lowstand deposits are separated by condensed intervals containing the distal aspects of the transgressive and highstand systems tracts. Because most of the section is claystone and silty claystone, fossil abundance patterns provide regionally applicable criteria for recognizing systems tracts within a depositional sequence. Upward-increasing fossil abundance suggests rising relative sea level with consequent fossil concentration due to decreasing sediment input. Upward-decreasing fossil abundance suggests falling relative sea level with consequent fossil dilution due to increasing sediment input. Because these strata are largely basinal depocenter deposits of lowstand and condensed section sedimentation, the falling and rising phase of relative sea level changes are correlated to the early phase of lowstand fall and the late phase of lowstand to transgressive rise, respectively.

Example

Within the GOM basin study area, sediment-starved highstand and transgressive deposits merge into the condensed interval. Thick transgressive and highstand deposits occur to the north and in the upper strata of the study area due to the regionally progradational section (Armentrout, 1991). The figure below is a spontaneous potential (SP) well log illustrating the subdivision of the *Glob alt* depositional cycle into the mapping intervals for slope and basin facies. The upper and lower data correlate with locally significant condensed sections at 2.8 and 3.1 Ma (Figure 4–31). The strata between these two condensed sections are divided into presandstone, sandstone, and postsandstone intervals, based on the dominant rock type and the pattern of fossil abundance and biofacies.

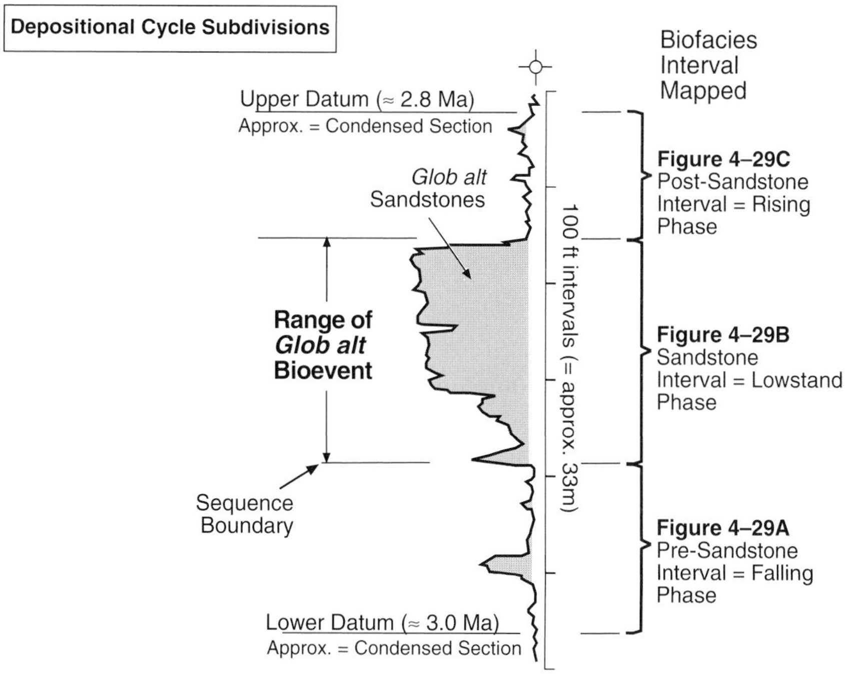

Figure 4–28. After Armentrout (1991, 1996); courtesy Springer-Verlag, Geological Society of London.

Interpretation of example

Because of the basinal location of the *Glob alt* depositional thick, the biofacies are typically bathyal. In this setting, the presandstone interval has upward-decreasing fossil abundance away from the fossil abundance peak in the underlying condensed section. This pattern suggests increased rates of sediment accumulation vs. biotic productivity, interpreted as signals of falling sea level. Conversely, the postsandstone interval typically has upward-increasing fossil abundance toward the overlying condensed section. This pattern suggests decreased rates of sediment accumulation vs. biotic productivity and is interpreted as a signal of rising sea level and consequent sediment starvation at the sample site. The sandstone interval typically has few fossils, and those few may reflect very shallow water depths due to downslope transport of the sand by gravity-flow processes. Data from shelf environments have a different set of interpretation criteria (see Armentrout et al., 1990; Armentrout, 1996).

Example of mapping systems tracts

Patterns of biofacies distribution reinforce other lines of evidence for variations in relative sea level, such as those illustrated by the distribution of clinoforms (Figure 4–27). When overlain on maps of lithofacies and seismic facies, biofacies patterns that complement other environmental interpretations increase confidence in reconstructions of the geologic history of the study area, including depositional cycle definition and subdivision and facies distribution of potential reservoir and seal rocks (see Armentrout et al., 1999).

Biofacies assemblage

Fossil biofacies, calibrated by similarity to modern assemblages, provide information on the type of environment in which specific strata were deposited. Biofacies maps are one type of paleogeographic reconstruction.

Example biofacies maps

The following figure shows biofacies maps of the study area in the Gulf of Mexico. They are based on the subdivision of the *Glob alt* depositional cycle into presandstone, sandstone, and postsandstone intervals. The importance of these maps is their relationship to lithofacies distribution for potential reservoir rock, seal rock, and source rock. Part A is a presandstone interval map, showing a basinward excursion of outer neritic and upper bathyal biofacies forced basinward by falling sea level Part B is a sandstone interval map in which the biofacies excursion is less pronounced, reflecting maximum lowstand at the turnaround from falling to rising sea level. Part C is the postsandstone interval in which the biofacies excursion is absent due to relative rise of sea level.

Example biofacies maps (continued)

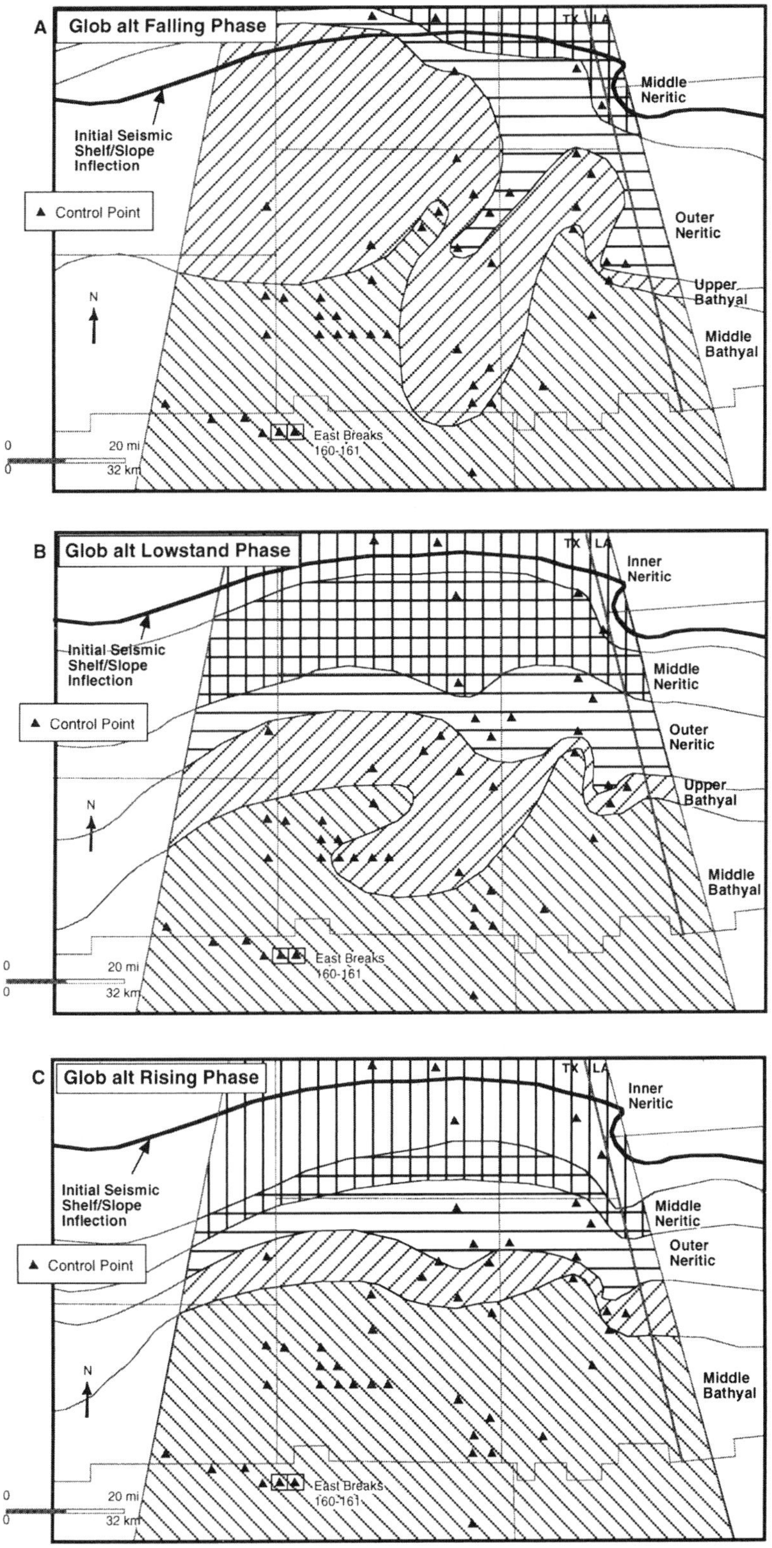

Figure 4–29. After Armentrout (1991, 1996); courtesy Springer-Verlag, Geological Society of London.

Identifying Sea Level Cycle Phase with Biostratigraphy, continued

Interpreting the maps

Biofacies map patterns are defined by distribution of benthic foraminiferal biofacies (Armentrout, 1991, 1996). Figure 4–29 shows the biofacies distribution below, within, and above the *Glob alt* sandstone interval. In upward stratigraphic order, these intervals are interpreted as the sediment accumulated during (1) falling, (2) low, and (3) rising phases of sea level, respectively. A scenario to explain biofacies and sediment patterns in the example is as follows.

1. During the lowering of sea level, the biofacies distributions and sites of maximum sediment accumulation move seaward (Figure 4–29A) where they are deposited on top of the preceding condensed section and associated maximum flooding surface (Figure 4–18). Within the initial lowering phase, the rate of slope and intraslope basin sediment accumulation increases, with fine-grained deposits above the underlying condensed section. As lowering progresses, the river systems bypass sediment across the shelf, depositing it directly on the upper slope. Remobilized sand and sand supplied directly from rivers during floods may be transported downslope by gravity-flow processes, depositing potential reservoirs (Prior et al., 1987). These sands accumulate at changes in the depositional gradient as slope fan and basin-floor fan deposits within the intraslope basins (minibasins) (Bouma, 1982).
2. The biofacies associated with this lowstand depositional phase, the sandstone interval (Figure 4–29B), show similar basinward excursion in outer neritic and upper bathyal biofacies as deposited during the presandstone phase. The inner and middle neritic shallow-water biofacies of the sandstone interval show a seaward shift, relative to the seismic stratigraphically defined shelf/slope break—interpreted as an indication of coastal progradation associated with lowered sea level.
3. Once sea level begins to rise, the supply of sand-rich sediment to the basinal slope area is rapidly cut off. Mud accumulates during this postsandstone interval, culminating with the overlying upper condensed section. These mudstones and those of the presandstone interval provide a seal for the interbedded lowstand sandstones. The biofacies pattern for this postsandstone interval shows a northward shift toward the basin margin as the coastline regresses across the shelf during transgression (Figure 4–29C). The occurrences of neritic biofacies of the postsandstone interval do not shift northward as far as their position during the presandstone interval. This is interpreted as sediment accumulation rate exceeding the rate of accommodation space formation by sea level rise plus basin subsidence. The consequence is coastal progradation, as suggested by comparing the mapped patterns of presandstone and postsandstone biofacies in the High Island–East Addition area just west of the seaward extension of the Texas/Louisiana border.

Biofacies and Changing Sea Level

Introduction

Biofacies are identified by an assemblage of fossils and are interpreted to reflect a specific environment. The mapped distribution of the biofacies assemblage reflects the distribution of the interpreted environment. Biofacies are especially useful in mudstone-dominated facies such as the GOM basin Cenozoic strata.

Traditional biofacies model

The traditional biofacies model is based on the modern distribution of organisms (Hedgpeth, 1957). This is a good model for a relative highstand of sea level (see figure below), in which neritic biofacies occur mostly on the shelf and bathyal biofacies occur mostly on the slope.

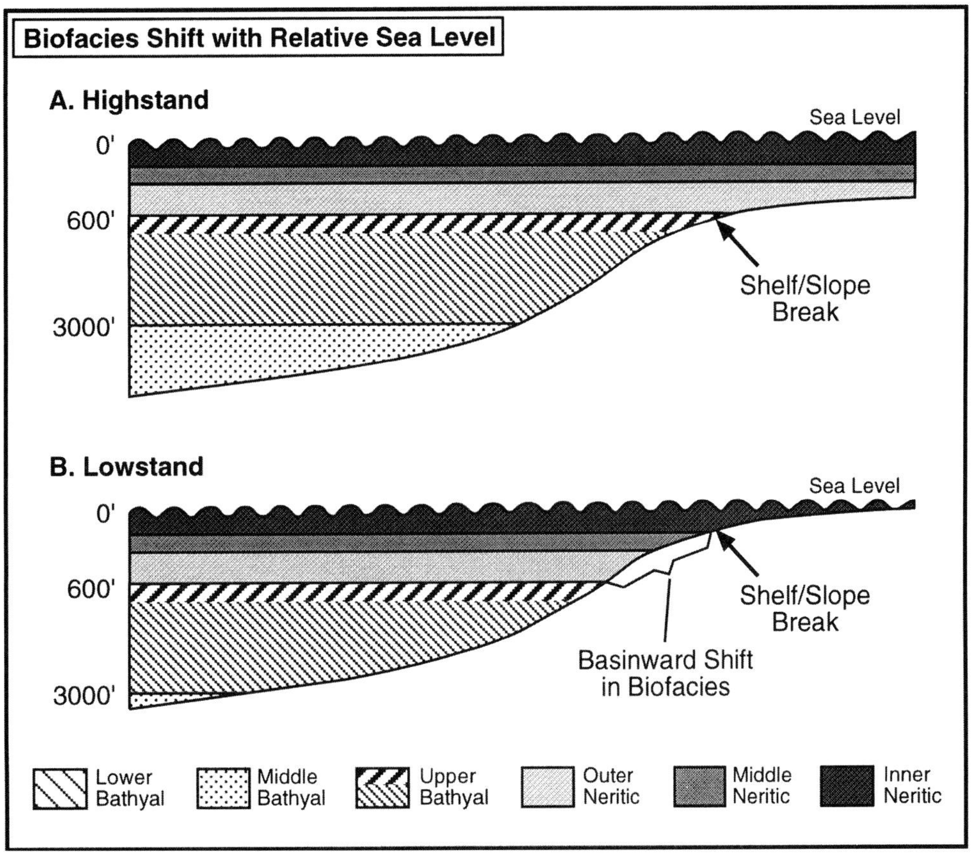

Figure 4–30. After Armentrout (1991, 1996); courtesy Springer-Verlag, Geological Society of London.

Biofacies distribution during lowstand

The lowering of sea level moves the water mass- and substrate-linked biofacies assemblages seaward—possibly far enough to place the inner neritic biofacies at the physiographic shelf/slope break. This movement causes the middle to outer neritic biofacies to shift basinward onto the upper slope of the clinoform (Figure 4–30B). The magnitude of relative sea level fluctuation, as well as the angle of the basin slope, controls how far the biofacies move across the physiographic profile. This pattern of low sea level biofacies distribution is confusing because the commonly used biofacies nomenclature is based on high sea level patterns where, by convention, the neritic biofacies are on the shelf (Figure 4–30A). During a lowstand, neritic biofacies may occur in situ on the physiographic slope.

Holocene GOM basin example

On the Gulf of Mexico shelf, elements of the foraminiferal fauna also move in the seaward direction due to the modification of the environment by the Mississippi River (Poag, 1981). High rates of deltaic sedimentation with coarser sediment grains, abundant terrigenous organic matter, and modified salinity and temperature greatly affect the local environment. Biofacies distribution responds to these environmental modifications. [See Pflum and Freichs (1976) for a discussion of the delta-depressed fauna.]

Lowstand fluvial influence on biofacies

At times of low sea level, when the river systems discharge their sediment load directly on the upper slope, the inclined depositional surface may help sustain downslope transport of the terrigenous material and associated fluids. The modification of the local slope environment near the sediment input point could result in seaward excursions in ecological patterns similar to those caused on the shelf by the modern Mississippi River (Pflum and Freichs, 1976; Poag, 1981). These seaward ecological excursions could extend to bathyal depths where downslope transport is sustained by the inclined surface and gravity-flow processes (see Figure 4–29).

Biofacies mixing

The downslope transport of shallow-water faunas by sediment gravity-flow processes may result in the mixing of biofacies assemblages from different environments (Woodbury et al., 1973). The further mixing of stratigraphically separate assemblages by rotary drilling complicates the identification of mixed assemblages. Such problems can be overcome in three ways:

1. Careful sample analysis, specifically looking for mixed assemblages
2. Use of closely spaced sidewall cores that may sample unmixed in situ assemblages occurring in beds interbedded with displaced assemblages
3. Evaluation of the mapped pattern of age-equivalent interpretations from a large number of wells

Armentrout (1991, 1996) carefully reexamines rapid changes of biofacies and patterns of rapid biofacies variations within age-equivalent intervals between wells. Once these local patterns were reevaluated and accepted as reliable, the interpretations were mapped for each depositional sequence. Figure 4–29 is the results of this analysis and further supports the biofacies models of Figure 4–30.

Constructing Age Model Charts

What is an age model?

Detailed correlation of depositional sequences and the calculation of maturation and timing of generation vs. trap formation requires an age model for the stratigraphy of a study area. An age model is a chart showing the chronostratigraphic relationship of different depositional sequences and associated formations within a study area. Integration of biostratigraphy and depositional sequences and their correlation to a global geologic time scale provides such an age model. Using this age model to calibrate each depositional sequence lets us calculate geologic rates, such as rates of rock accumulation and burial and thermal heating rates of the stratigraphic section.

Procedure

The chart below outlines the procedure for constructing an age model.

Step	Action
1	Construct a depositional sequence chart for the study area. Use all available depositional sequence and biostratigraphic data.
2	Normalize all available sequence charts for the basin, including the study area sequence chart, to the same time scale using the bioevent marker taxa or zonal assemblages.
3	Make a sum of sequences curve by integrating the depositional sequence chart for the study area with the other sequence charts for the basin.
4	Calibrate the sum of sequences curve to a global time scale using global biostratigraphic zones, magnetostratigraphic polarity scales, oxygen isotope chronology, and global sea level cycle charts.

Example

Constructing depositional cycle charts for the GOM basin extends back to at least Kolb and Van Lopik (1958) and Frasier (1974), with Beard et al. (1982) demonstrating the link between depositional sequences and glacial eustasy. The following figure is a composite chronostratigraphic chart that serves as an age model for the GOM basin Pliocene and Pleistocene, summarizing nine studies published between 1982 and 1993. The local cycle charts from each of these studies have been calibrated to the same time scale using the same bioevent marker taxa and are in turn correlated to the global foraminiferal zones and magnetostratigraphic polarity scale as defined by Berggren et al. (1985) and the oxygen isotope chronology of Joyce et al. (1990). The resulting sum of the depositional sequences and their associated condensed sections (Schaffer, 1987a,b, 1990) are illustrated.

The composite of all the local studies appears under the column Sum of Sequences, three of which occur in only one or two studies and are considered to be local and possibly autocyclic events (locally forced redistribution of sediments). The youngest six cycles of the chart occur between the *Pseudoemiliani lacunosa* bioevent (0.8 Ma) and the sea floor (0.0 Ma) and average 130,000 years in duration. The ten older cycles were deposited between *Globigerinoides mitra* (4.15 Ma) and *P. lacunosa* (0.8 Ma) bioevents and average 330,000 years duration. These 16 cycles are interpreted as regionally significant and allocyclic (forced by changes external to the sedimentary unit). They are probably glacioeustatic cycles. (See Figure 4–25 and accompanying discussion.)

Example
(continued)

Age Model, GOM Pliocene–Pleistocene

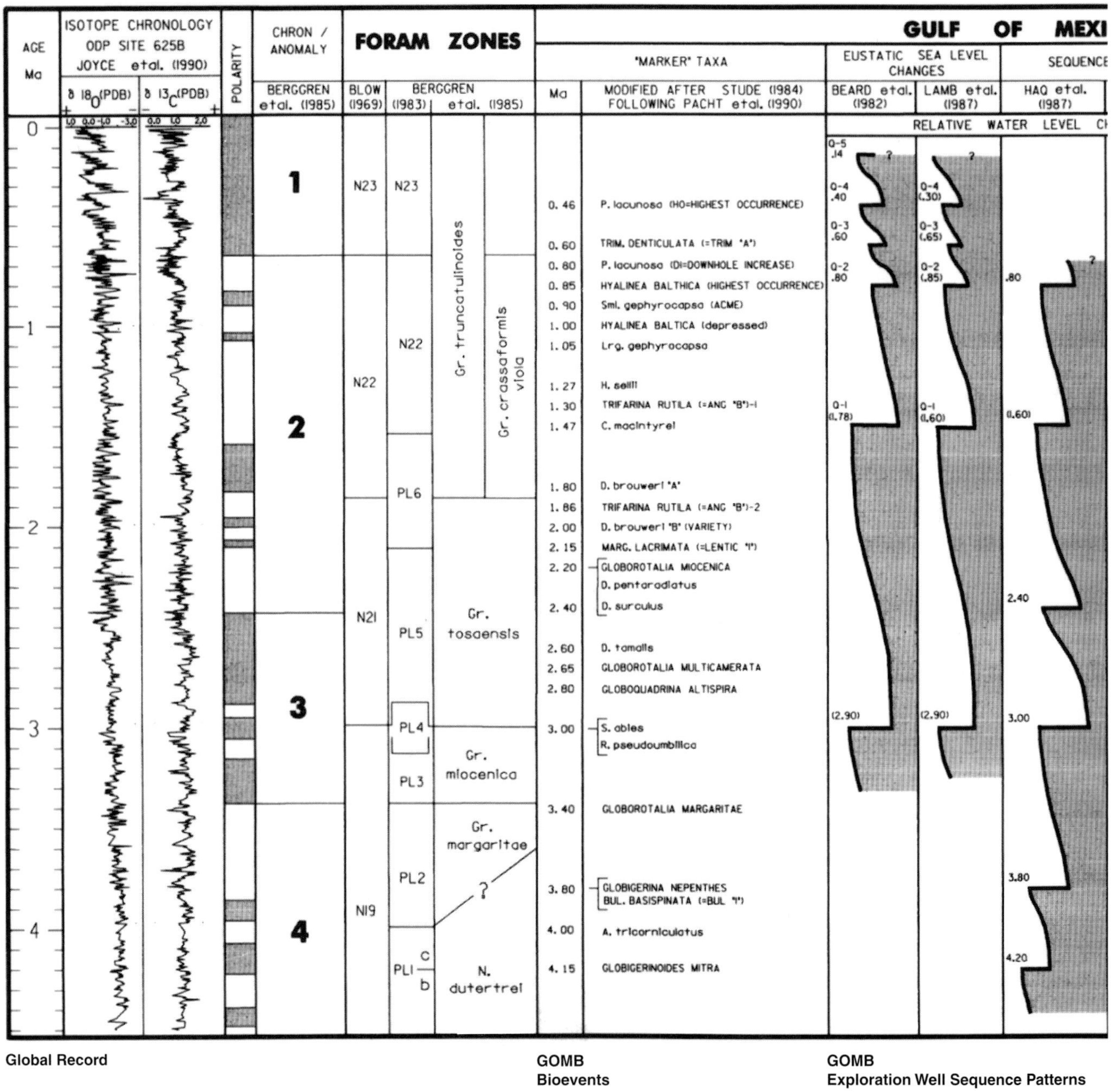

Figure 4–31. From Armentrout (1996); courtesy The Geological Society, London.

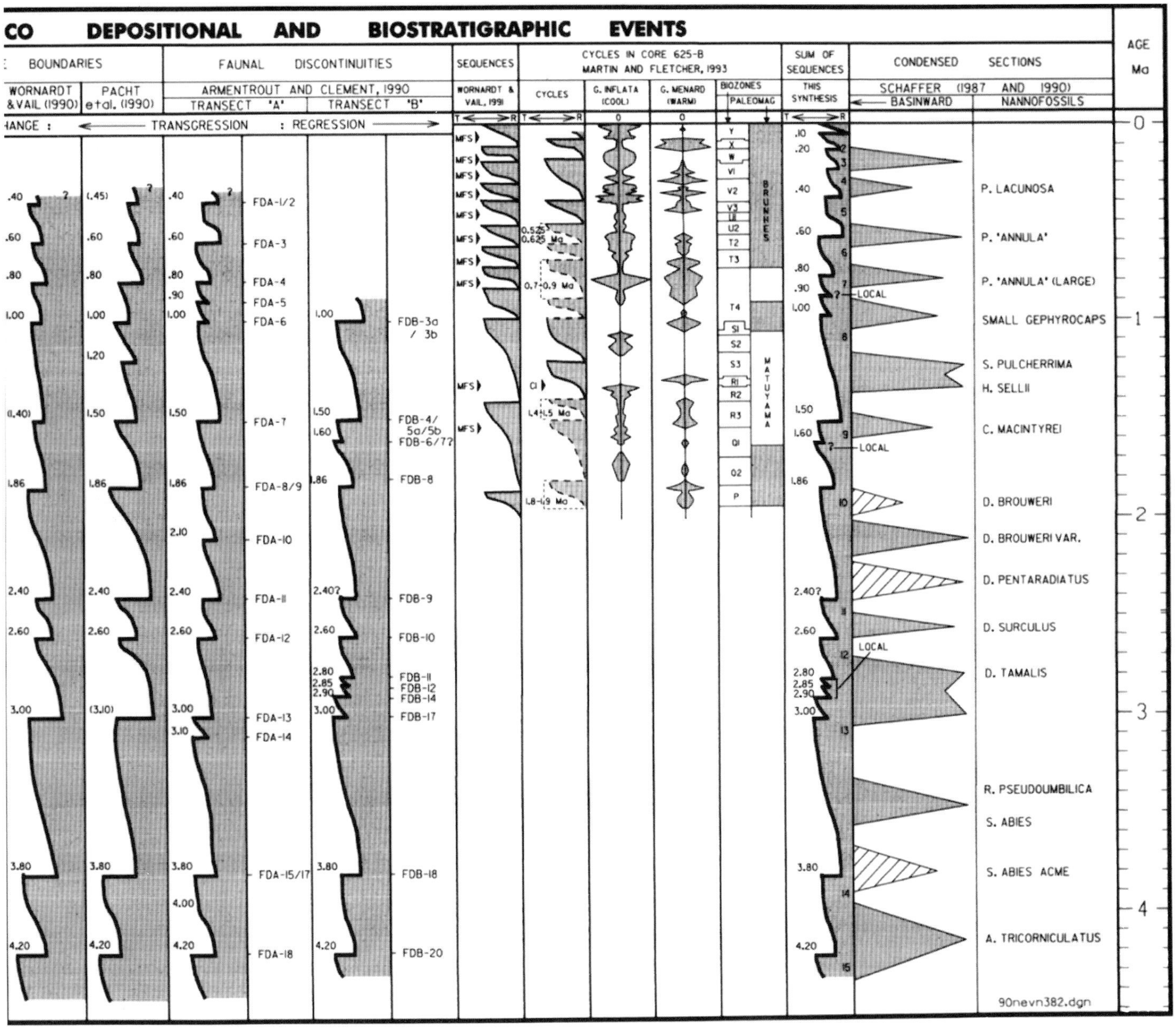

GOMB ODP-Core Sequence Patterns

GOMB "Sum of Sequences"

Example (continued)

Using this age model to calibrate each depositional cycle helps us calculate geologic rates, such as rates of rock accumulation and burial and thermal heating rates of the stratigraphic section.

The following figure shows a rock thickness vs. time plot for nine key wells south of eastern Louisiana within the area of the 6–4 Ma depocenter (Figure 4–13; see also Fiduk and Behrens, 1993). Each major depositional interval is characterized by changes in depositional rates from oldest to youngest, in large part due to the geographic shifting of depositional centers. Dating within the wells is based on key biostratigraphic marker species for the deep-water environments of the GOM basin. Interval B is characterized by high rates of sedimentation associated with abundant gravity-flow sand deposition. It is followed by interval C, characterized by slow sedimentation and deposition of regionally effective top seal.

Burial History Curves

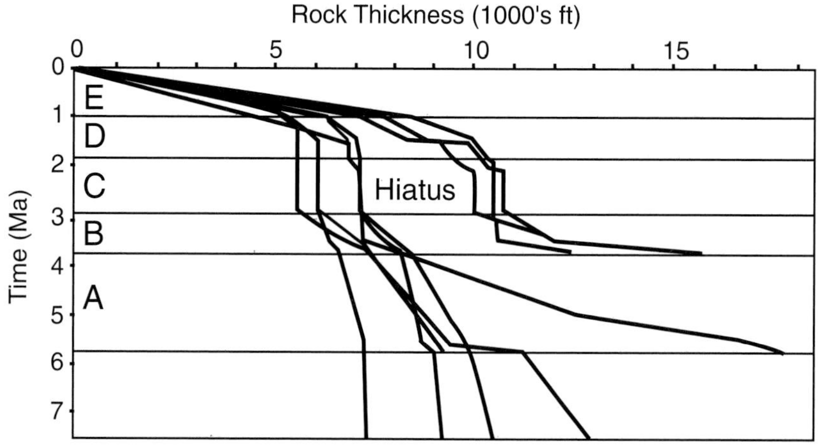

Figure 4–32. After Piggott and Pulham (1993); courtesy Gulf Coast SEPM

Example of modeling oil generation

The figure on the following page shows the rock accumulation rates for the Green Canyon 166 No. 1 well as a histogram (lower graph) and as a set of burial history curves (upper graph). Using temperature data from exploration wells, Piggott and Pulham (1993) calculated temperature thresholds for the accumulated stratigraphic section. Burial of potential marine source rock above a temperature of approximately 100°C could initiate generation of oil.

Example of modeling oil generation (continued)

The dominant hydrocarbon type in the Green Canyon area is associated with hydrocarbon family 6 (Figure 4–5), suggesting a Jurassic source rock. This source rock is indicated by the diamond labeled S and the shaded stratigraphic intervals. Based on the calculation of Piggott and Pulham (1993), using BP Exploration's Theta Modeling, generation of significant oil from a Jurassic source rock may have begun approximately 6 Ma in the Green Canyon 166 No. 1 well area when the Jurassic source rock was buried below 5000 m and above a temperature of 120°C, the threshold for significant oil generation (see "Petroleum Systems").

These calculations of rock accumulation and source rock maturation rates are dependent on good age models. Biostratigraphic data are the primary correlation tools in the GOM basin, as in most basins. Considerable care must be used in correlating basin bioevents to the global geologic time scale. The methodology for and problem of such correlations are discussed in Armentrout and Clement (1990) and Armentrout (1991, 1996).

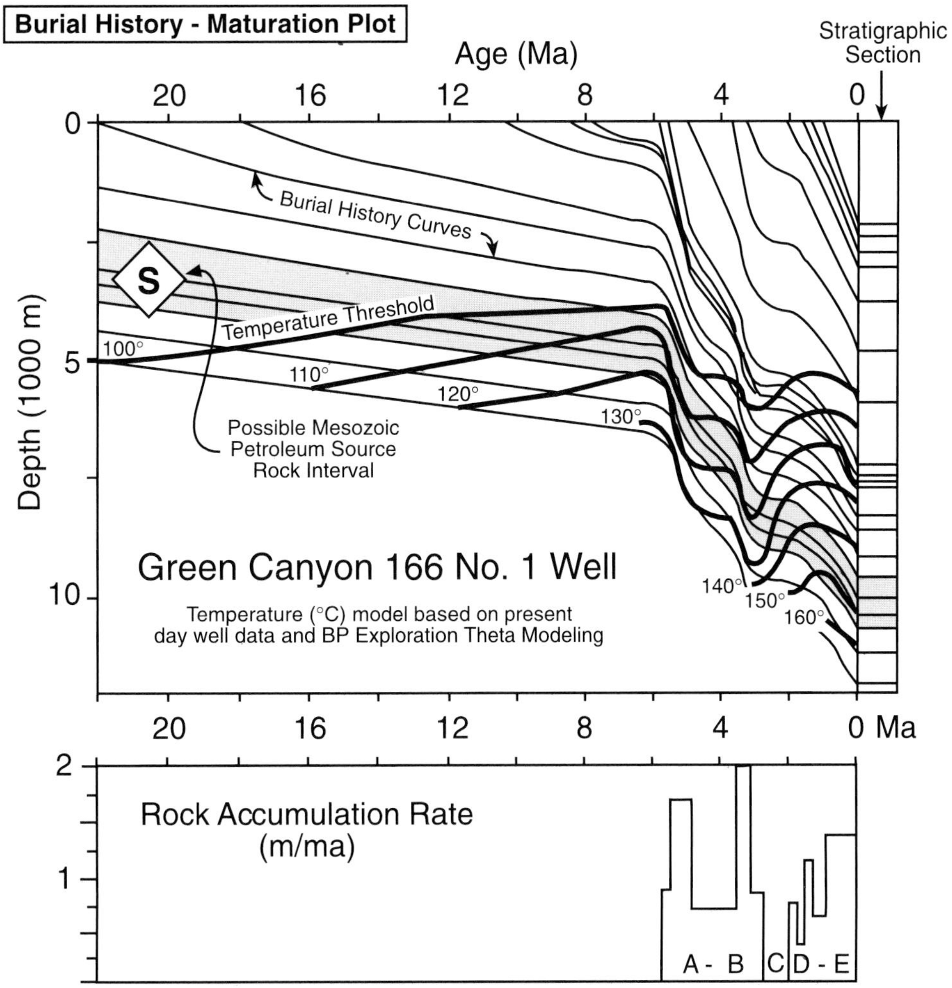

Figure 4–33. After Piggott and Pulham (1993); courtesy Gulf Coast SEPM.

Superimposed Sea Level Cycles

Cycle phase

Cycle phase is the position of relative sea level along a cycle curve at any moment in time. There are at least five or six orders of sea level cycles. Each order can be in phase or out of phase with the other orders. When two successive orders are in phase, i.e., fourth-order transgressions are in phase with third-order transgressions, the impact that each has on deposition or erosion is enhanced (Mitchum and Van Wagoner, 1990). Understanding this phenomenon can help in stratigraphic prediction and lead to the discovery of new fields.

Superimposition of phases

When each scale of cyclicity is convolved with or superimposed onto the next higher order, the patterns of transgression vs. regression either amplify or dampen the transgressions and regressions of the next higher order(s) of cyclicity. The right side of the following schematic illustrates cycle stacking of three orders of symmetrical cyclicity of short (narrow curve), intermediate, and long duration (wide curve), analogous to the fourth, third, and second orders of Haq et al. (1988). Transgressive phases (darker shading) of the short-duration cycles are amplified when coincident with the transgressive phase of the intermediate-duration cycle—even more so if coincident with the transgressive phase of the long-duration cycle.

The same pattern of amplification occurs for coincident regressive cycle phases (lighter shading). When short-duration transgressive phases occur on the regressive phase of the intermediate cycle, the short-duration transgressive phase is dampened and will be even more so if it occurs during the long-duration regressive phase. Regressive phases are similarly dampened if they occur on long-duration transgressions.

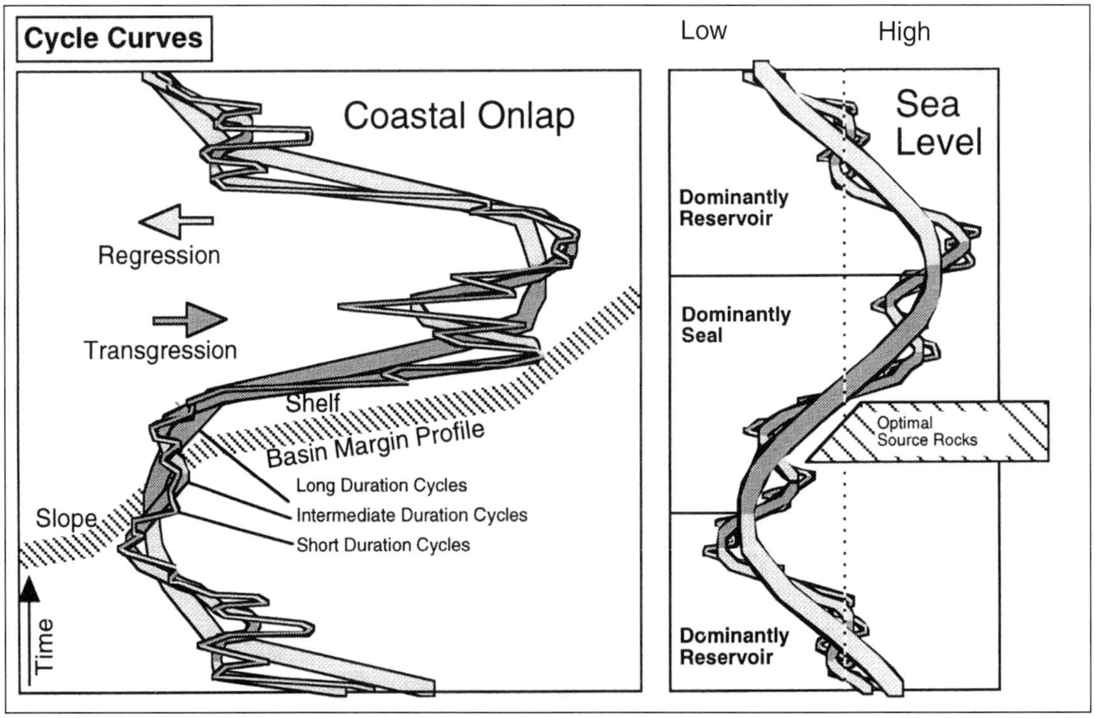

Figure 4–34. From Haq et al. (1988); courtesy SEPM.

Superimposition of phases (continued)

The left side of Figure 4–34 shows the amplification of transgressive and regressive cyclicity when superimposed across a continental margin. Relative sea level rise and fall results in rapid transgressive or regressive deposition across a relatively low-gradient shelf area, slowed and vertically stacked if deposition occurs against a relatively steep gradient slope or basin margin. Regressive phases of siliciclastic deposition are likely to transport significant volumes of sand into the basin, depositing potential reservoir facies. Transgressive phases of siliciclastic deposition are likely to deposit regionally extensive muds, forming potential top seal for underlying regressive sands. During the dominantly transgressive phases of stacked long-to-short transgressive sequences, organic matter can become concentrated in marine muds, forming potential hydrocarbon source rocks (Creaney and Passey, 1993; Herbin et al., 1995).

Depositional geometry of superimposed cycles

The following figure shows the depositional geometry of third-order cycles stacked into a second-order transgressive/regressive cycle. Each third-order cycle is represented by a depositional sequence composed of three phases (Figure 4–18). The lowstand phase may consist of basinal sand-prone mounds (basin-floor fans) and shelf-edge deltas. The transgressive phase is usually dominated by regional mudstones. The highstand most often consists of prograding fluvial and deltaic sediments forming broad coastal plains with potential sandstone reservoir facies.

In carbonate-prone depositional settings, the transgressive-to-highstand phases may be dominated by regionally extensive carbonate platforms. The mudstone-dominated transgressive deposits can provide potential hydrocarbon source rocks, especially in the third-order transgressive phases composited within the second-order transgressive phase. In contrast, the dominance of third-order regressive phases within the second-order regression brings more potential reservoir sand progressively further into the basin. Optimal hydrocarbon traps form where the regressive sandstones are in close proximity to organic-rich transgressive mudstones and are overlain by effective top seal.

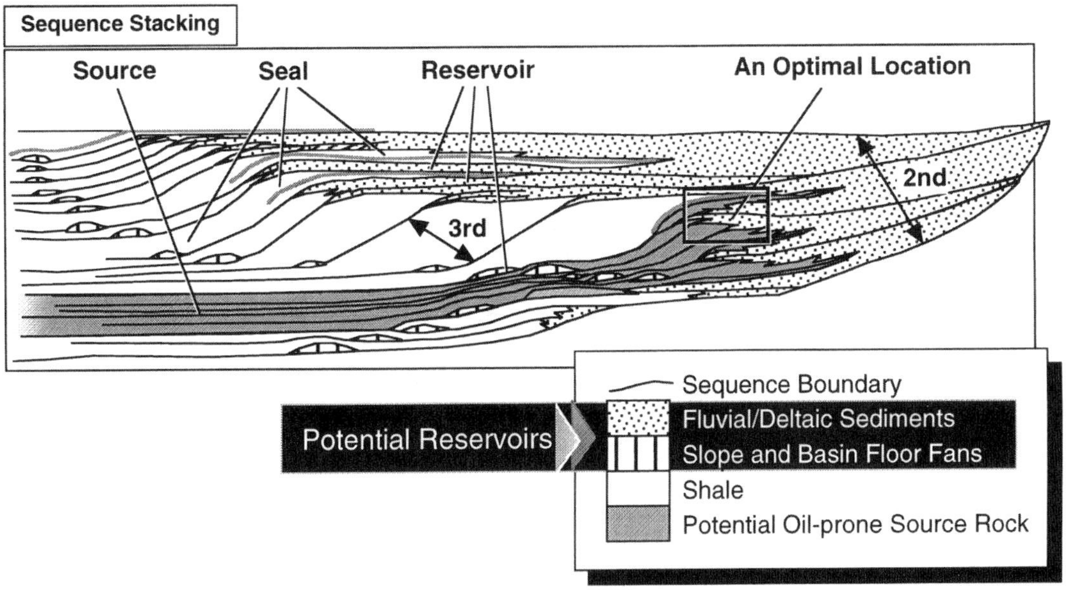

Figure 4–35. After Bartec et al. (1991); courtesy Journal of Geophysical Research.

Effect on reservoir deposition

The lowstand phase of the *Glob alt* depositional sequence is sand prone (Figure 4–29) and produces hydrocarbons from at least 23 fields within the High Island–East Breaks depocenter (Figure 4–40). The sandstone reservoirs were deposited within slope valleys by gravity-flow processes (Armentrout, 1991). The abundance of *Glob alt* sandstone is interpreted to be the consequence of a major fall in relative sea level. The falling sea level resulted in enhanced bypass of sand across the shelf and into the slope basins and deposition of a lowstand systems tract.

The *Glob alt* sequence mapped on Figure 4–29 represents the lowstand depositional phase of the Haq et al. (1988) third-order 3.7 cycle (Figure 4–25). Cycle 3.7 begins with the most significant relative fall in sea level of the Tejas B-3 supersequence after the second-order highstand (cycles 3.4 and 3.5). This significant fall in sea level resulted in transport of large volumes of sand from the paleo-Mississippi River system into the slope basins of the High Island and East Breaks areas of offshore Texas (Figures 4–29 and 4–33), depositing numerous potential reservoirs of gravity-flow sands during maximum amplification of falling sea level. Following lowstand deposition, relative rise in sea level cut off the sand supply and resulted in deposition of hemipelagic mudstones, forming a regional top seal to the *Glob alt* sandstones (Figures 4–29 and 4–33). The top seal is a condensed section that correlates laterally with the transgressive and early highstand systems tracts.

Subsection D2

Paleogeography

Introduction

Basin paleogeographic maps are useful prospecting tools. They help us locate and predict the occurrence of reservoir, seal, or source lithofacies by establishing the location of major geographic features, such as deltas, shorelines, barrier reefs, and slope breaks. Once an isochronous surface or coeval interval is identified, paleogeography can be reconstructed by integrating maps of age-equivalent lithofacies, seismic facies, biofacies, and thickness of reservoir-quality rocks.

In this subsection

This subsection discusses the following topics.

Applying Paleogeography to Prospect Identification

Introduction

Basin paleogeography is defined by picking an isochronous surface or coeval interval and mapping the associated seismic facies and lithofacies. For example, the location of sandy lithofacies vs. clayey lithofacies or mounded vs. tabular seismic reflection configurations may delineate the position of shorelines or reefs. Mapping thickness of reservoir-quality rocks is also useful for establishing paleogeography; thick, linear, dip-oriented trends of sandstone may indicate paleochannel complexes.

Procedure

The table below outlines a suggested procedure for defining paleogeography and applying it to prospect identification.

Step	Action
1	Identify the stratigraphic interval of a single depositional phase that has potential for containing reservoir rocks, i.e., lowstand or highstand, using biostratigraphic markers and regional correlation surfaces.
2	Map depositional facies such as biofacies, net reservoir thickness (lithology or porosity), and seismic facies (i.e., clinoforms, parallel reflections, chaotic reflections within a single depositional phase).
3	Integrate the interpreted seismic facies and biostratigraphic data into a grid of stratigraphic well-log cross sections if wells are available.
4	Map the location of fields producing from reservoirs in the interval of interest with respect to net reservoir thickness; define the type of trap(s) each field contains.
5	Using the seismic interpretations and the geology of the fields mapped in step 4, interpret the deposition of reservoir, seal, and source facies and the formation of stratigraphic or combination traps with respect to sea level cycle phase. Was the reservoir deposited during lowstand, rising, or highstand phases of sea level cycles? What about the seal facies? Is the trap the result of facies relationships that formed during a particular sea level phase or postdepositional deformation?
6	Using information gained in step 5, identify areas that may contain overlooked reservoir, seal, and source rocks in the same isochronous interval or in isochronous intervals with similar character. Also, consider possible migration avenues along which fluids could move from the source rock to the reservoir, from higher to lower pressure regimes. Such avenues might include sand-prone pathways, faults, salt walls, and unconformities.

Constructing a Facies Map

Purpose and procedure

The purpose of a facies map is to reconstruct paleogeography, from which we can predict reservoir, seal, and source-rock distribution. Facies maps are made at an isochronous surface or within a coeval interval (Tearpock and Bischke, 1991; Visher, 1984). We map reservoir system thickness (1) to compare the distribution of reservoir-system thickness and field location and (2) to identify or predict locations with thick reservoirs and trapping conditions that are undrilled. A procedure for mapping facies is outlined in the table below.

Step	Action
1	Identify and correlate significant isochronous surfaces throughout the depocenter, integrating well data, bioevents, and seismic reflection profile grids.
2	Map areas of potential reservoir and seal facies that occur between two isochronous surfaces.
3	Map seismic facies associated with that interval.
4	Plot important physiographic features, such as the shelf-slope break or structurally controlled bathymetric highs.
5	Integrate all data into a depositional facies map.

Seismic facies profile

The figure below is the interpreted seismic facies pattern for part of one seismic reflection profile down the axis of the High Island–East Breaks depocenter (Armentrout, 1991). This is the same seismic profile discussed in Figure 4–27.

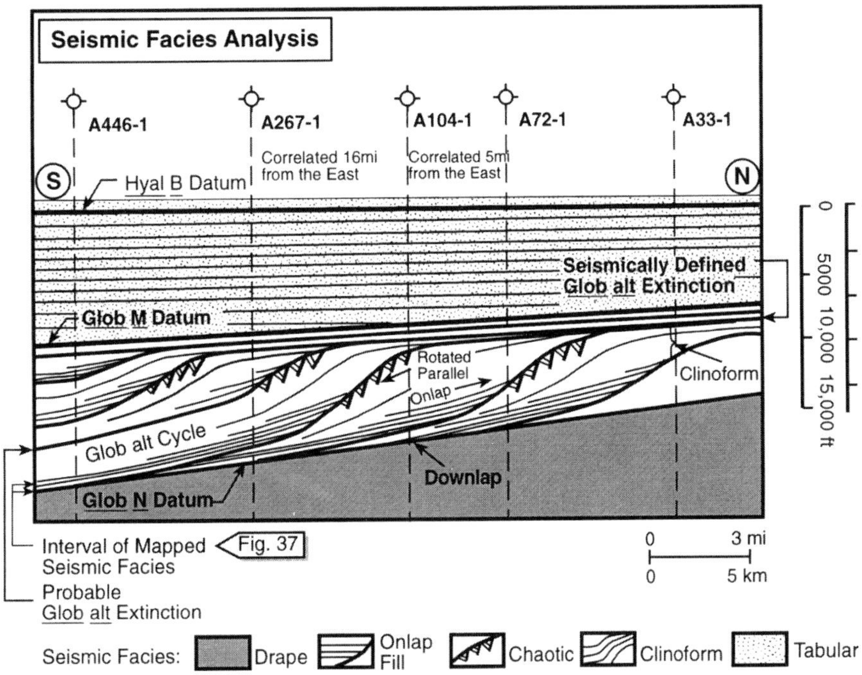

Figure 4–36. After Armentrout (1987); courtesy Gulf Coast SEPM.

Seismic facies profile (continued)

Each prograding clinoform contains a rotated package of chaotic facies within the upper and steepest part of the clinoform facies and basinward of the tabular facies. The clinoform facies is onlapped by parallel, moderate-amplitude, onlapping reflections of the onlap-fill facies, which are subsequently downlapped onto by the next overlying prograding clinoform. In a broader sense, the drape facies below these clinoforms and the *Glob N* datum represent basinal deposits; the clinoform and onlapping-fill facies represent slope deposits; and the overlying tabular facies above the clinoforms and the *Glob M* datum represent shelf deposits—all part of a basin-filling succession.

Associated foraminiferal biofacies shown in Figures 4–27 and 4–29 support this analysis. The *Glob alt* sequence is the fourth clinoform from the right, the fourth-most basinward of five oblique clinoforms that toplap along a common horizon. Superjacent clinoforms show progressively more topset deposition forming sigmoidal clinoforms, suggesting relative rise of sea level (with consistent widespread increase in accommodation space). Observations of seismic facies from a single phase of deposition, such as lowstand or highstand, are recorded on a map and contoured to convey the distribution of each seismic facies (Figures 4–37 and 4–38).

Seismic facies map

Following is a map of the seismic facies of the *Glob alt* lowstand interval (Figures 4–28 and 4–29). The mapped facies are observed in the interval immediately above the sequence boundary at the base of the *Glob alt* sequence in Figure 4–36. In the basin setting, the sequence boundary is, at seismic scale, essentially coincident with the underlying condensed section. The mapped facies are within the lowstand systems tract. Each

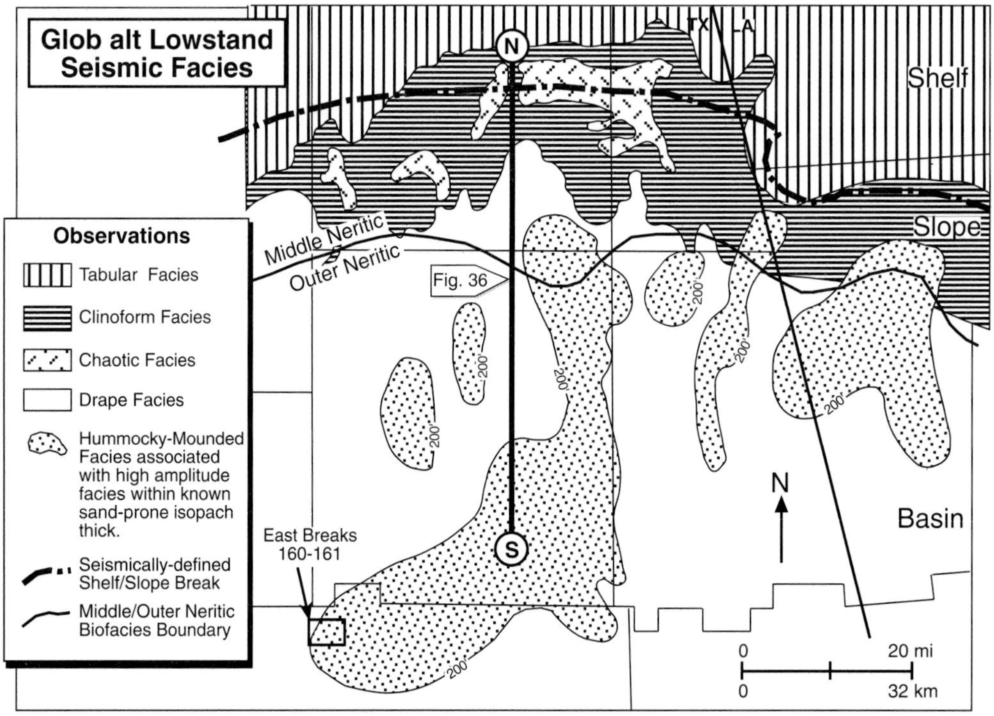

Figure 4–37.

Seismic facies map (continued)

observed facies is plotted along the transect of the seismic reflection profile, profile by profile. The area of shelf/slope inflection is plotted, based on the location of the inflection point between foreset and topset elements of the clinoform. Biofacies information (Figure 4–29) and sediment type (Figure 4–38) can then be overlain on the seismic facies map to provide an integrated data base for interpreting depositional environments (Figure 4–39).

Net sand map

Of the 240 wells used in the study area, 147 penetrated the *Glob alt* interval and provided information on the distribution of the net sand deposited within that interval. Using the net-sand values from the wells, we integrate the data with seismic facies maps within the *Glob alt* lowstand isochron and contour a net-sand isopach map (figure below). Contours are for areas with at least 200 ft (60 m) of net sand. The sandstones occur mostly seaward of the age-equivalent physiographic shelf/slope break identified on the seismic-reflection profiles. Because most of the wells penetrated the *Glob alt* sequence basinward of the *Glob alt* shelf edge, the sandstones penetrated were most likely transported by gravity-flow processes and deposited in environments on the slope and within intraslope basins.

The resulting map shows the net-sand distribution of shelf areas contoured parallel to the shelf edge and slope areas contoured parallel to the depositional dip of the slope valleys down which the sand was transported. The distribution of sand within the depositional dip-oriented isopachs is consistent with the regional pattern of downslope-oriented salt withdrawal valleys bounded by salt-cored anticlines (Figures 4–6 and 4–41). Note the lowstand position of the middle-to-outer neritic biofacies boundary, below which few waves reach the sea floor. This results in downslope sand distribution being controlled by bottom currents alone.

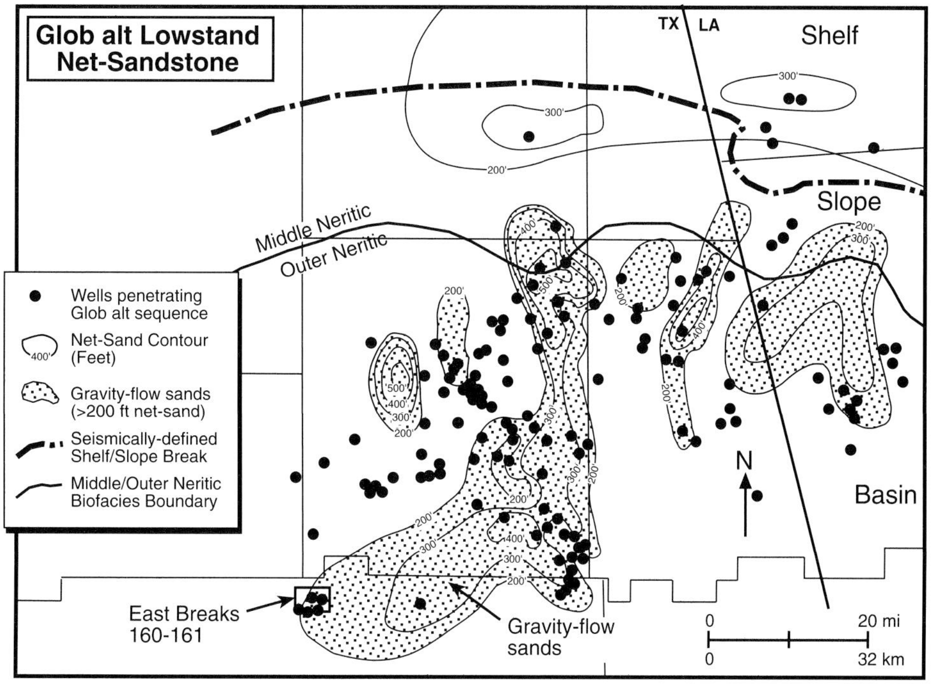

Figure 4–38.

Depositional facies map

The figure below is a depositional facies map for the *Glob alt* interval's basal sequence boundary, constructed by integrating the biofacies map, the net sandstone map, and the seismic facies map (Figures 4–29, 4–38, and 4–37, respectively).

The upper slope deposits consist of the clinoform facies and numerous areas of chaotic facies, including rotated-block packages deposited in middle neritic to upper bathyal water depths (Figures 4–36, 4–37). The shelf facies consist of a thin interval of tabular facies representing a mixed system of inner-to-middle neritic deposits, nonmarine coastal-plain deposits, and the erosional surface at the *Glob alt* sequence boundary. The basinal deposits consist of the drape and onlap-fill facies of bathyal hemipelagic mudstone that encase the sandstone-prone mounded facies of sediment gravity flow origin, indicated here by the > 200 ft (> 60 m) sandstone isopach. The gravity-flow sandstones were deposited within slope valleys basinward of the physiographic shelf/slope break in deep middle neritic and deeper-water environments during falling and lowstand of sea level. The physiographic shelf/slope break is identified by the inflection point between the fore-set and the topset reflections of the clinoform.

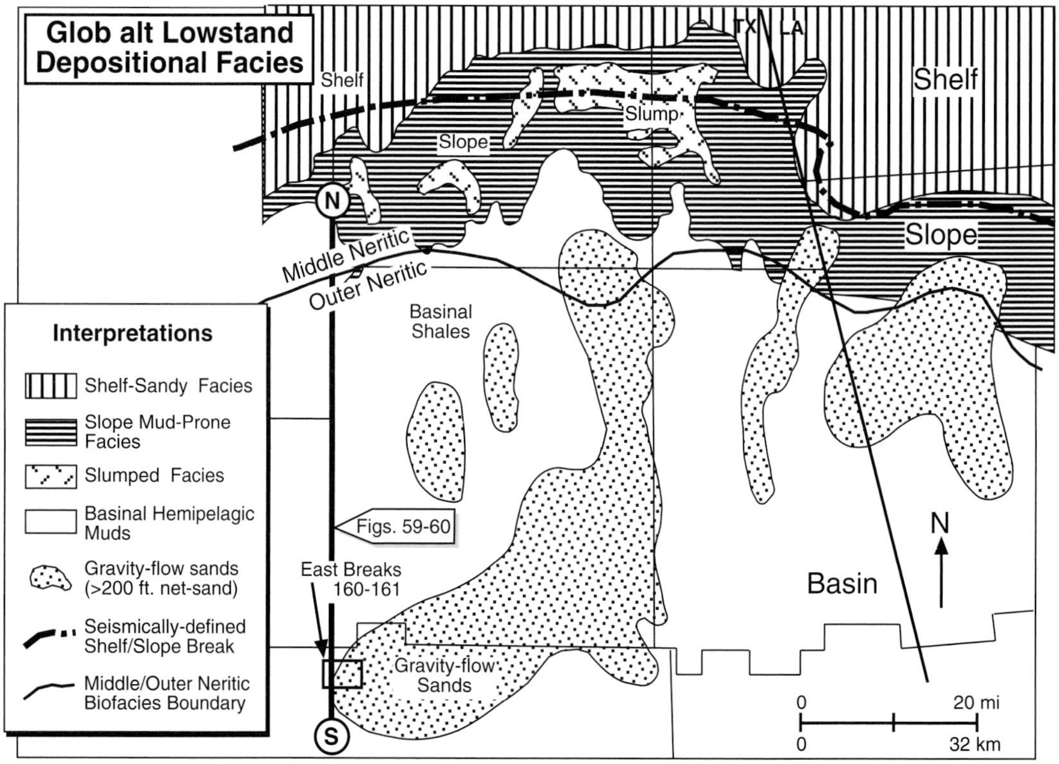

Figure 4–39. After Armentrout (1991); courtesy Springer-Verlag.

Relating Traps to Paleogeography

Introduction

A paleogeography map of a reservoir interval, reservoir thickness, and fields (producing from the same reservoir interval) shows relationships between production and geology that may be used to locate prospects in untested areas.

Procedure

The table below suggests a procedure for relating fields to paleogeography and reservoir thickness.

Step	Action
1	Plot paleogeography, reservoir thickness, and field location on the same map.
2	Relate paleogeographic features (axis of canyons, shelf/slope break, shorelines, etc.), reservoir thickness, and field locations to trap development.

Example

The following figure shows the relationship between 23 fields in the High Island–East Breaks depocenter that produce from the *Glob alt* sandstones and the *Glob alt* sandstone 200-ft (60-m) isopach. Most of the fields with *Glob alt* reservoirs occur around the perimeter of the maximum thickness of net sandstone, near the 200-ft (60-m) isopach. Nearly all of the *Glob alt* reservoirs occur basinward of the lowstand middle-to-outer neritic biofacies boundary [approximately 600 ft (200 m) water depth]. Thus, they are downslope from the shelf/slope inflection and below normal wave base where sedimentation is dominated by gravity-flow processes.

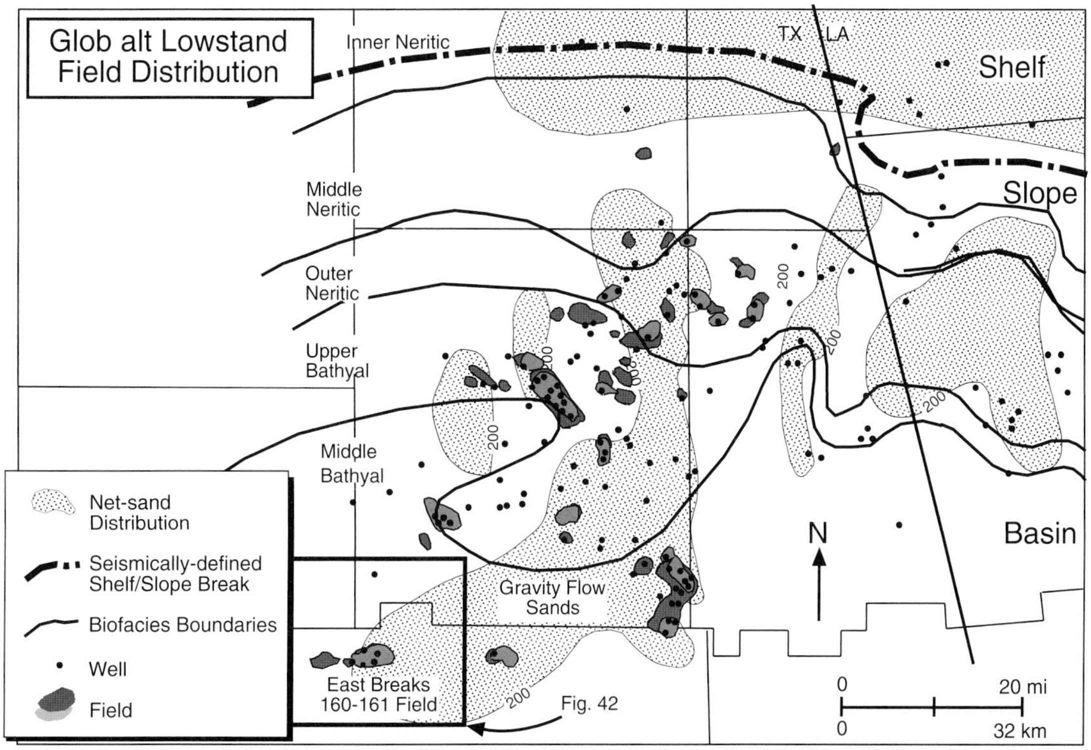

Figure 4–40.

Example (continued)

Deposition by gravity-flow processes occurs within physiographic lows (Kneller, 1995; Kneller and McCaffrey, 1995). Although each field occurs within a local structural high, most have a major stratigraphic component related to their transport through slope channels and deposition as a gravity-flow deposit within the axis of a salt-withdrawal valley (see Figures 4–42, 4–43, and 4–56 for the East Breaks 160-161 field). The sands within these valleys were deposited with a slope-parallel orientation. The trapping structure develops after reservoir deposition as the dip-oriented sand bodies are tilted along the flanks of the salt-cored anticlines (Figure 4–41). The anticlines continue to grow, and the tilt of the sand body becomes progressively more accentuated as each successive cycle of synclinal fill accumulates and displaces the underlying salt.

This process accelerates during relative lowstand of sea level when the river systems discharge their loads near to or into the heads of the slope valleys (Anderson et al., 1996; Winker, 1996).

Explanation of example

In Figure 4–40, producing fields are along the 200-ft (60-m) net sand contour or beyond rather than in the axial thick. This is because of gravity-flow sands accumulating within the synclinal valley axes, which continue to subside through time.

The following figure shows a depositional strike seismic reflection profile across one of these valleys. The high-amplitude, more continuous reflections correlate with condensed-section claystones and often bracket pressure compartments due to their very low perme-

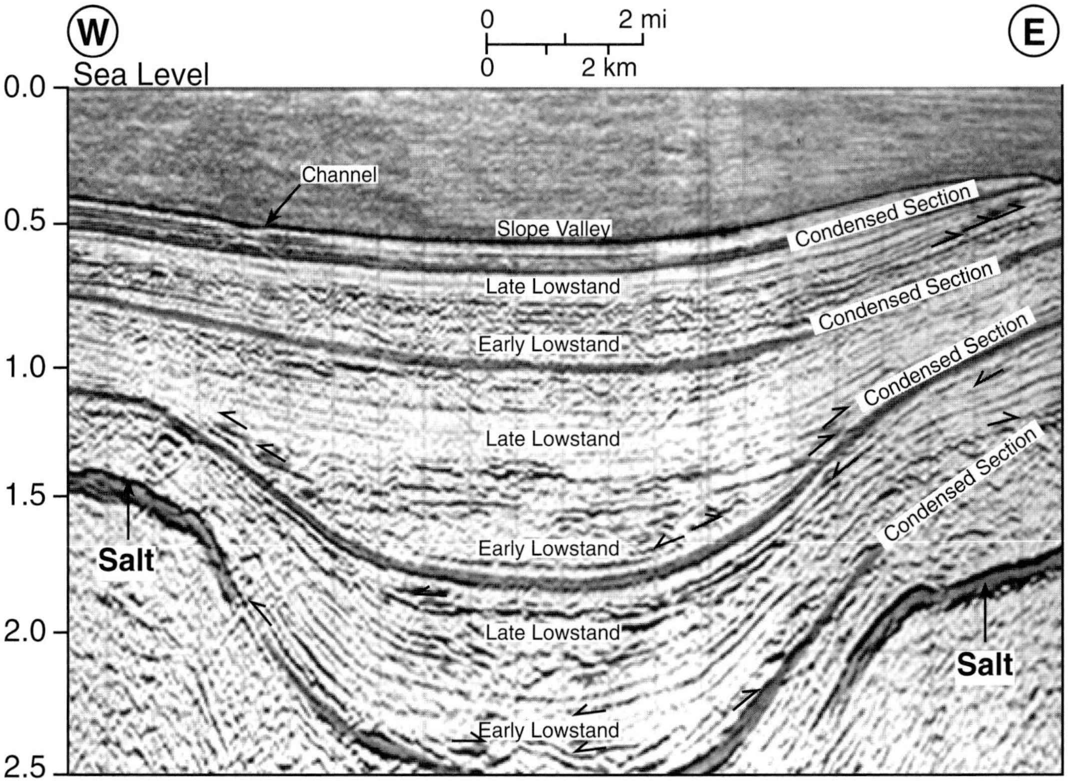

Figure 4–41.

Explanation of example (continued)

ability. Between the condensed sections are the sand-prone early lowstand systems tract, sometimes with hummocky-mounded facies suggesting channel complexes, overlain by silt-prone late lowstand deposits. The differential loading of salt by sediment accumulation along the synclinal valley axis results in differential rotation of each depositional sequence. This rotation along the synclinal flanks results in the early lowstand gravity-flow sands pinching-out structurally upward, providing potential hydrocarbon traps along the valley margins (Armentrout et al., 1996; Bilinski et al, 1995; McGee et al., 1994; *see also* Weimer and Bouma, 1995).

The isochron thick of the *Glob alt* sands in the figure represents the sand-prone slope/valley fill of the *Glob alt* sequence. Understanding the interplay of depositional processes and tectonic deformation is essential to hydrocarbon exploration in GOM minibasins.

Basin slope exploration plays

Gravity-flow events, such as slumps and slides, can initiate transport of sediment downslope. Transport by debris flows and turbidites moving downslope may be confined to narrow valleys or spread outward into the less-confining minibasin of the Gulf of Mexico slope (Kneller, 1995; Kneller and McCaffrey, 1995). These sedimentary systems consist of channel elements through which sediment is transported to lobe-and-sheet depositional elements within the minibasins (Armentrout et al., 1991). Confined flow elements are typically channels with levees resulting from sediment fallout from overbanking turbulent flow. The channel-levee complexes are elongate but may stack into thick successions of potential reservoir facies (Armentrout, 1996). The less-confined lobe-and-sheet facies may spread out within the minibasins, forming large-volume reservoir packages (Bilinski et al., 1995). Winn and Armentrout (1996) have compiled examples of this spectrum of gravity-flow exploration targets, which are critical elements of minibasin petroleum systems.

Section E

Minibasins and Petroleum Systems

Introduction

In the northern Gulf of Mexico, the understanding of minibasins—achieved through the integration of stratigraphic, structural, biostratigraphic, and geochemical data—is the critical scale of basin analysis for petroleum system identification and prospect evaluation. Petroleum system analysis is the identification of the origin of the entrapped oil and the reconstruction of the generation-migration-entrapment history. This information provides a template for further exploration for subtle traps along the migration avenue.

Minibasins are a critical scale for Gulf of Mexico petroleum systems evaluation. Basins of other tectonic styles differ, requiring a somewhat different approach to petroleum systems analysis. For example, stratigraphic entrapment along foreland basin limbs adjacent to foredeep hydrocarbon charge areas is an important aspect of foreland basins (Macqueen and Leckie, 1992: Van Wagoner and Bertram, 1995).

In this section

This section contains the following subsections.

Subsection E1

Minibasins and Petroleum Systems

Introduction

Minibasins are subdivisions of depocenters primarily defined on the basis of structural elements. These elements isolate the petroleum system of a minibasin from the petroleum systems of other minibasins within a depocenter.

In this subsection

This subsection contains the following topics.

Minibasins

Definition

A minibasin is a subdivision of a depocenter that in turn is a subdivision of a basin. Sediment thickness is the primary basis for subdividing basins into depocenters. Structural elements separate one minibasin from another within a depocenter. The figure below shows the structural elements that define the East Breaks 160-161 minibasin, which is bound on the north by fault A, on the east by faults B and C, and on the south by a salt-cored high.

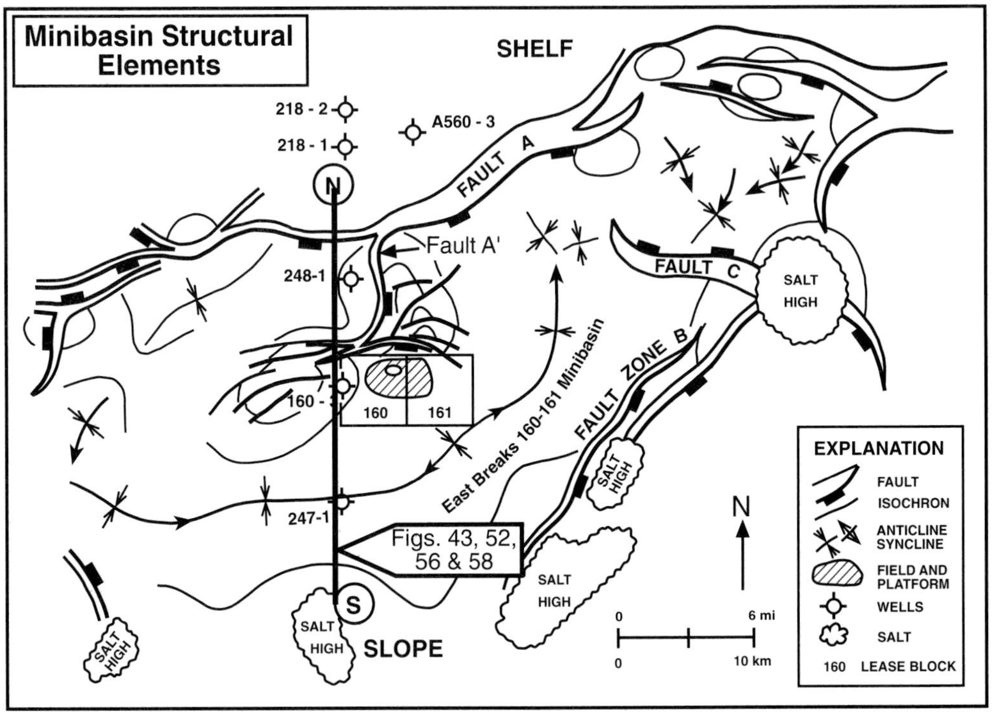

Figure 4–42. From Armentrout et al. (1991); courtesy Springer-Verlag.

Seismic expression

The following figure is a north–south seismic section through the East Breaks 160-161 intraslope minibasin, showing the location of the East Breaks 160-161 field. Production is from the *Trim A* and *Glob alt* reservoirs within the rollover anticline downthrown to the north bounding fault A'. Fault A' splays southwest off regional fault A (Figure 4–42) (see also Schanck et al., 1988; Armentrout et al., 1991).

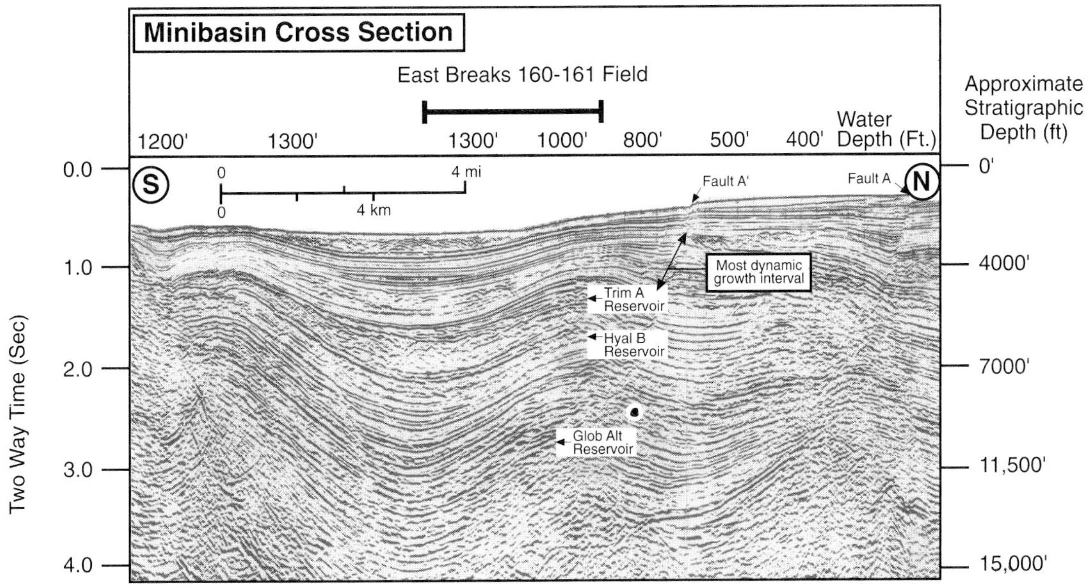

Figure 4–43.

Age of minibasin formation

The age of minibasin formation is determined by looking for relationships between sedimentation and deformation, like faulting or folding. Figure 4–44 is a schematic diagram of the seismic reflection profile along the west side of the East Breaks 160-161 field (Figure 4–42). That reflection profile is nearly coincident with the boundary between the Galveston and High Island exploration areas (Figure 4–17). The diagram depicts salt-cored anticlines and growth faults separating the progradational basin-filling cycles into distinct minibasins. The stratigraphic pattern shows composite depositional sequences, numbered 1 through 4, prograding into and across progressively younger growth-fault and salt-withdrawal basins. The stratigraphic boundaries outline seismic-stratigraphically defined depositional cycles calibrated by bioevents from several wells along the section (Armentrout and Clement, 1990). Scales are approximate.

Age of minibasin formation (continued)

The age of formation of each minibasin can be interpreted from the relative age of expanded sedimentary section downthrown to each major growth fault or salt high. Along the cross section, the expanded section occurs in progressively younger strata. In the northernmost diagrammed minibasin, the expanded section occurs in cycles 1 and 2. In the middle minibasin, the expanded section is in cycles 2 and 3. In the southernmost minibasin (the East Breaks 160-161), the expanded section formed during cycles 3 and 4. A new minibasin has begun to form in cycle 4 sediments basinward of the steep salt-cored upper slope.

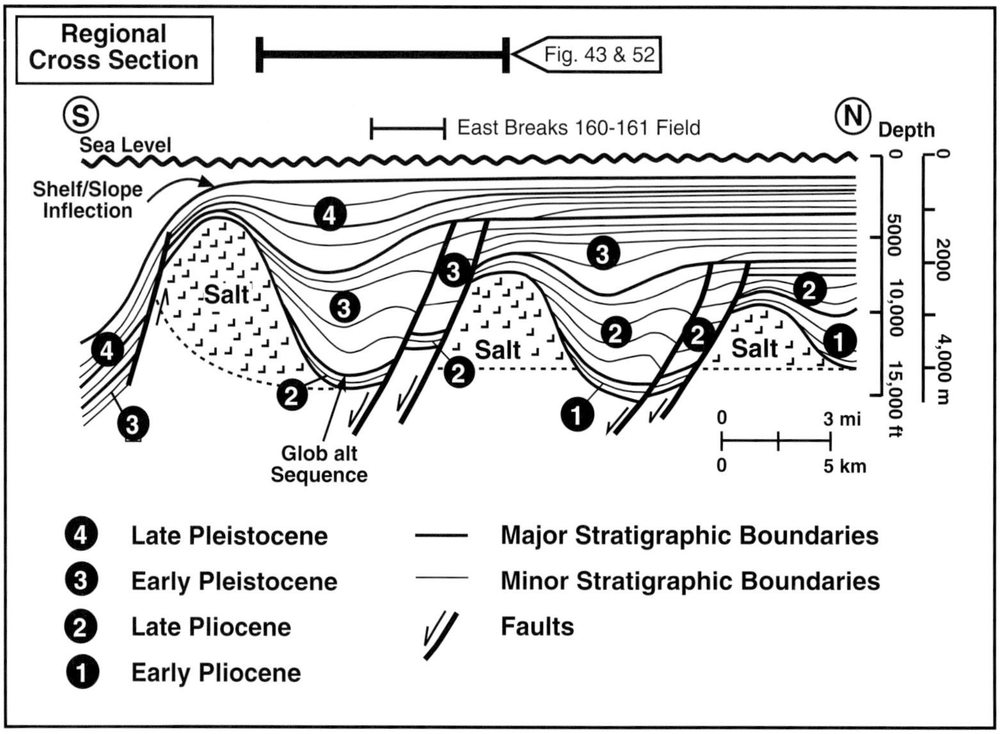

Figure 4–44. From Armentrout and Clement (1990); courtesy Gulf Coast SEPM.

Formation of the East Breaks minibasin

Each of these minibasins formed as sea level fell and the sediment supply system prograded to the shelf edge where it oversteepened and differentially loaded slope muds. Growth faults developed within this unstable sediment prism and displaced mobile salt to accommodate the downbuilding sediment (Winker and Edwards, 1983). This process continued until the salt was completely displaced and the downbuilding sediments welded with the sediments underlying the displaced salt (West, 1989). Once the sediment-on-sediment welding occurred, the fault system either propagated downward or locked up, resulting in the basin filling to the equilibrium profile of the sea floor. The next cycle of minibasin downloading, growth fault development, and salt withdrawal stepped basinward to the next deformable site. That site could be either at the shelf/slope break or within an upper slope valley.

Petroleum Systems

Definitions

Magoon and Dow (1994) define a petroleum system as the essential geologic elements and processes related to those hydrocarbons generated from a single pod of active source rock. The geologic elements are the source rock, reservoir rock, seal rock, and overburden rock. The processes are trap formation, hydrocarbon generation, expulsion, secondary migration, and accumulation. Aspects of preservation, degradation, and destruction of petroleum are omitted as processes because they generally occur after a petroleum system is formed, but these aspects must still be evaluated in assessing the petroleum system potential of a play or prospect.

Events chart

The development of a petroleum system can be summarized using an events chart. The petroleum system events chart plots the timing of each element and process and helps us understand critical moments in the history of the petroleum system under study. Magoon and Dow (1994) define the critical moment as the time that best depicts the generation-migration-accumulation of hydrocarbons in the petroleum system. The critical moment is often an interval of time encompassing the major pulse of hydrocarbon expulsion and accumulation within an existing trap. There can be several critical moments if there is an episodic history for a trap or if there are more than one source rock interval. The figure below is the events chart for the petroleum systems in the East Breaks 160-161 minibasin.

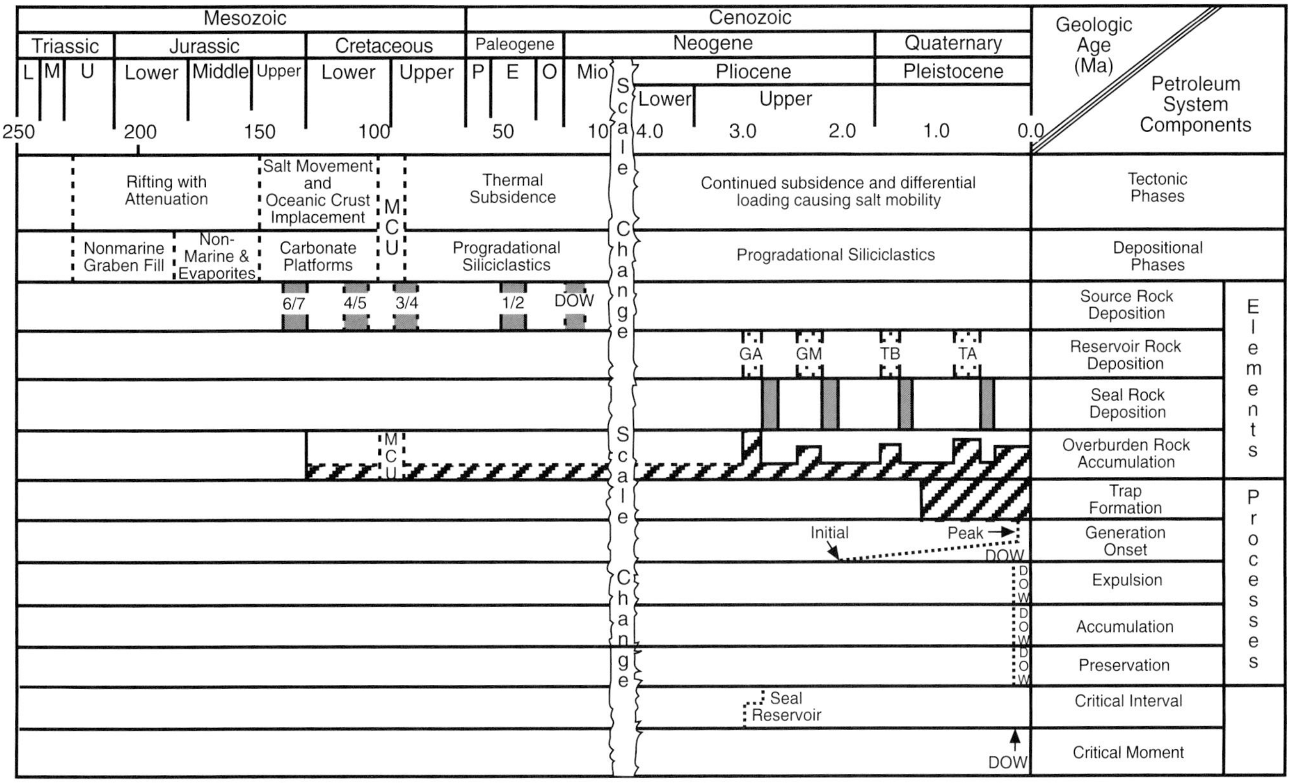

Figure 4–45. Time scale from Haq et al. (1988); DOW represents source rock, generation, and critical moment estimates (Dow et al., 1990).

Events of East Breaks minibasins

Included on the chart for the East Breaks 160-161 minibasin petroleum system is the timing of each tectonic phase and primary facies depositional phase that have had major impact on the local petroleum system. As discussed earlier, the rifting of continental crust formed the proto-GOM basin with local depocenters in which Late Jurassic salt was deposited. As the basin continued to rift, oceanic crust was emplaced and transitional crust became the site of prograding continental margin siliciclastic and carbonate complexes. The prograding sediments differentially loaded the salt, and a progression of salt-withdrawal and growth-fault-bound minibasins formed. It is in the context of these minibasins that petroleum systems developed within the northern GOM basin.

Phases, elements, and processes

As shown in Figure 4–45, twelve critical petroleum system components can be grouped into phases, elements, and processes. Also included are critical interval and critical moment. Other items could be added if needed, such as reservoir diagenesis. The table below summarizes the main components of petroleum system analysis.

Phases	Elements	Processes
• Tectonic • Depositional	• Source • Reservoir • Seal • Overburden	• Trap formation • Hydrocarbon generation • Hydrocarbon expulsion and migration • Hydrocarbon accumulation • Preservation of traps

East Breaks events chart details

Figure 4–45 shows the relationship between the essential elements and processes of the petroleum system of the East Breaks 160-161 minibasin. Also charted are important tectonic phases and primary depositional phases. Numbers on source-rock intervals are for the mapped source rocks of Figure 4–5 and the middle Miocene speculative source interval of Dow et al. (1990). The following abbreviations are used: GA = *Globoquadrina altispira;* GM = *Globorotalia miocenica;* HB = *Hyalinea balthica;* TA = *Trimosina denticulata;* MCU (on overburden accumulation) = *Mid-Cretaceous Unconformity.*

East Breaks source

Magoon and Dow (1994) define a petroleum system as all aspects of hydrocarbons generated from a single pod of active source rock. Five potential source rocks are recognized on Figure 4–45. Dow et al. (1990) consider the middle Miocene as the probable source of East Breaks 160-161 oil. Other workers suggest the East Breaks 160-161 field hydrocarbons are from a mixture of Late Jurassic (numbers 6 and 7) and early Paleogene (numbers 1 and 2) source horizons (see Figure 4–5). Thus, more than one petroleum system is probably active within the East Breaks 160-161 minibasin, and a different critical moment would exist for each system.

Subsection E2

East Breaks Petroleum System Elements

Introduction

The East Breaks 160-161 minibasin is an example of where more than one petroleum system can charge the same trap. It contains all the components required for generation, migration, and accumulation of hydrocarbons. This subsection describes the main elements of the petroleum systems in the East Breaks 160-161 minibasin.

In this subsection

This subsection contains the following topics.

Reservoir Rock

Introduction

Four reservoir intervals are productive in the East Breaks 160-161 minibasin: *Glob alt, Glob M, Hyal B,* and *Trim A* horizons. Reservoir intervals are named for the regionally useful bioevent species stratigraphically above the reservoir. These bioevents most often occur within condensed sections. All four reservoir intervals are interpreted to be gravity-flow sand deposits (Armentrout et al., 1991). Only the *Glob alt* reservoir is considered here.

***Glob alt* sequence deposition**

The *Glob alt* depositional sequence of Late Pliocene age (mapped below) is part of depositional cycle 2 in Figure 4–44. The sequence, deposited on a relatively open slope with only slightly undulating sea-floor topography, thins rapidly basinward due to sediment starvation in the most distal areas of the High Island–East Breaks depocenter (Figure 4–47). Subsequent progradation resulted in differential loading of the allochthonous salt and formation of local depocenters between downloaded growth fault sediment prisms and differentially displaced salt-cored anticlines.

***Glob alt* isochron and seismic facies map**

Glob alt sandstones of the East Breaks 160-161 field occur within an isochron thick where hummocky seismic facies downlap toward and are buried by parallel low-amplitude seismic facies indicative of hemipelagic mudstone drape (Armentrout et al., 1991). The following figure shows an isochron and seismic facies map of the *Glob alt* reservoir interval. The internal reflections of the mounded facies (1) downlap away from the isochron thick and toward the parallel seismic facies (2). Neither the isochron nor the seismic facies is mapped north of the fault due to poor data quality.

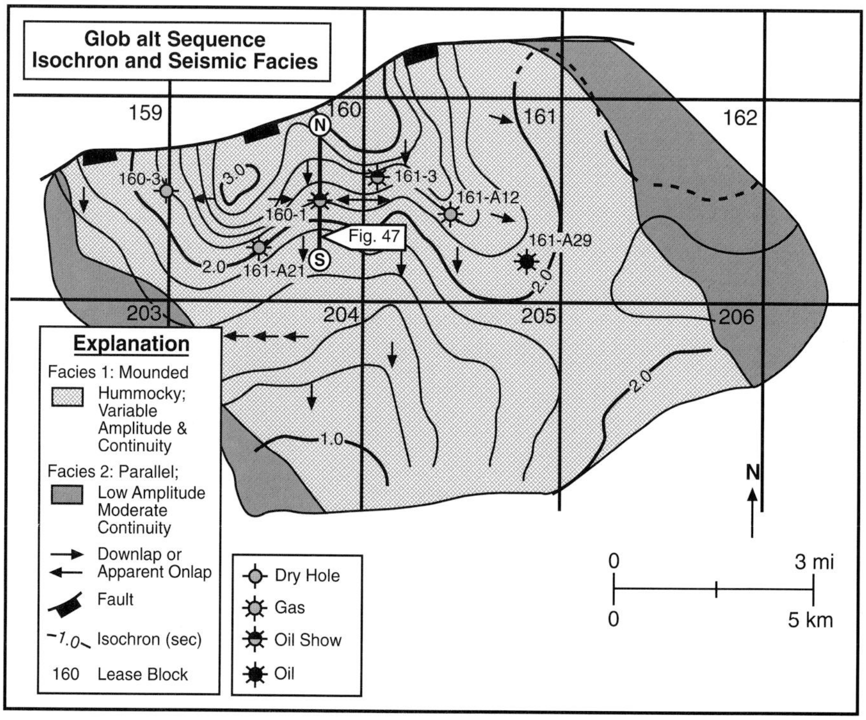

Figure 4–46. After Armentrout et al. (1991); courtesy Springer-Verlag. Original map by Charles R. Beeman, Mobil Oil, 1987.

Seismic profile

The figure below is a seismic reflection profile showing the *Glob alt* reservoir interval. Section A is uninterpreted; section B is interpreted. The reservoir thins southward between the top seal at the *Glob alt* condensed section datum and the underlying, unlabeled datum (thick black lines). The reservoir is penetrated by the 160-1 well in the faulted anticlinal trap formed by the rollover into the growth-fault complex bounding the north side of the minibasin (Figures 4–42 through 4–44). The 160-1 electric log pattern is spontaneous potential.

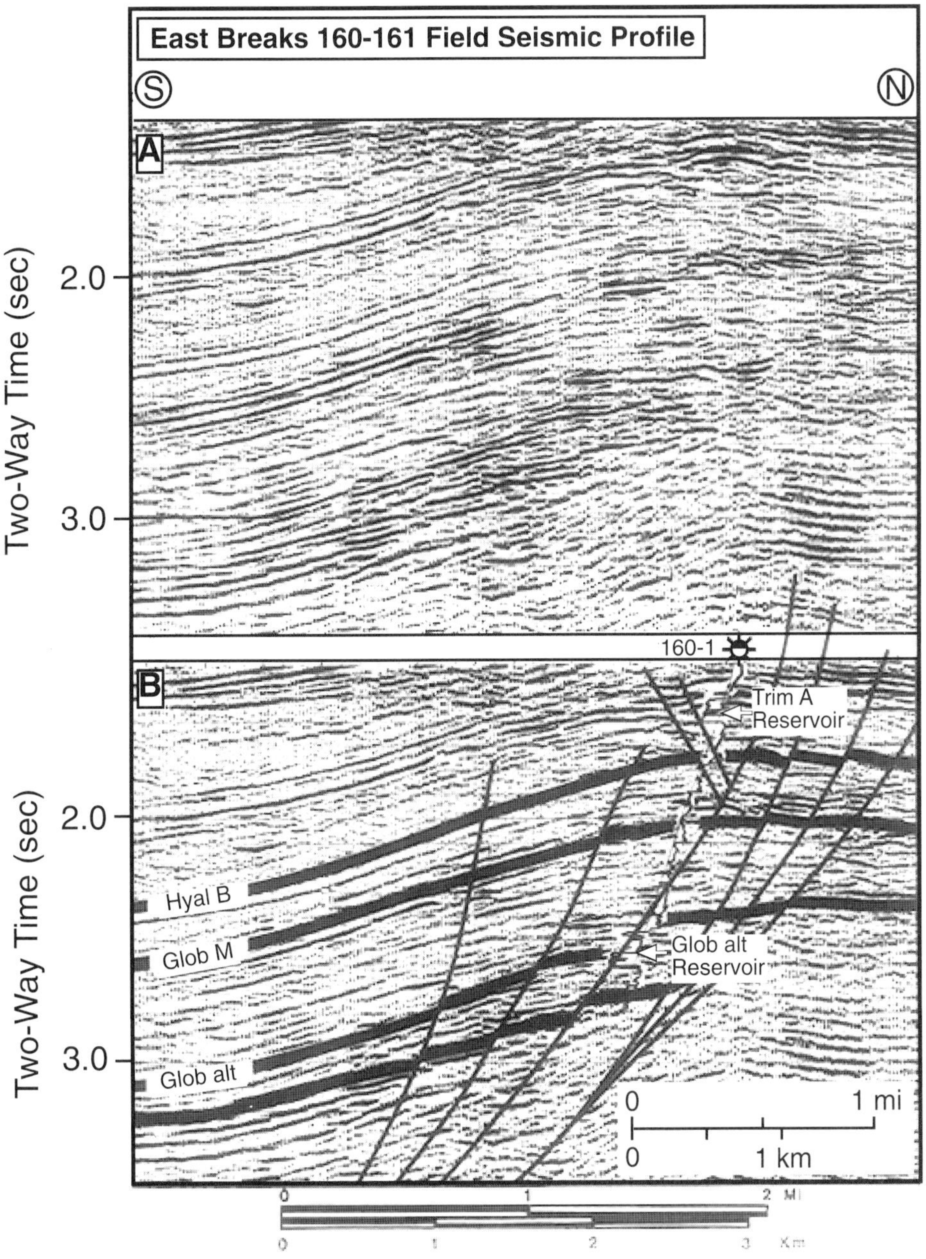

Figure 4–47. After Armentrout et al. (1991); courtesy Springer-Verlag.

Well-log cross section

The following figure is a well-log cross section of the *Glob alt* reservoir interval; datum is a mudstone within the GA-2 sandstone (well locations are shown on Figure 4–46). All logs are spontaneous potential with true vertical depth displays. The GA-4 reservoir sand is below the displayed interval. Log profiles are annotated: arrow C = funnel-shaped, coarsening-upward sandstone; arrow F = bell-shaped, fining-upward sandstone; parallel lines B = blocky profile of relatively thick sandstones and thin mudstone interbeds.

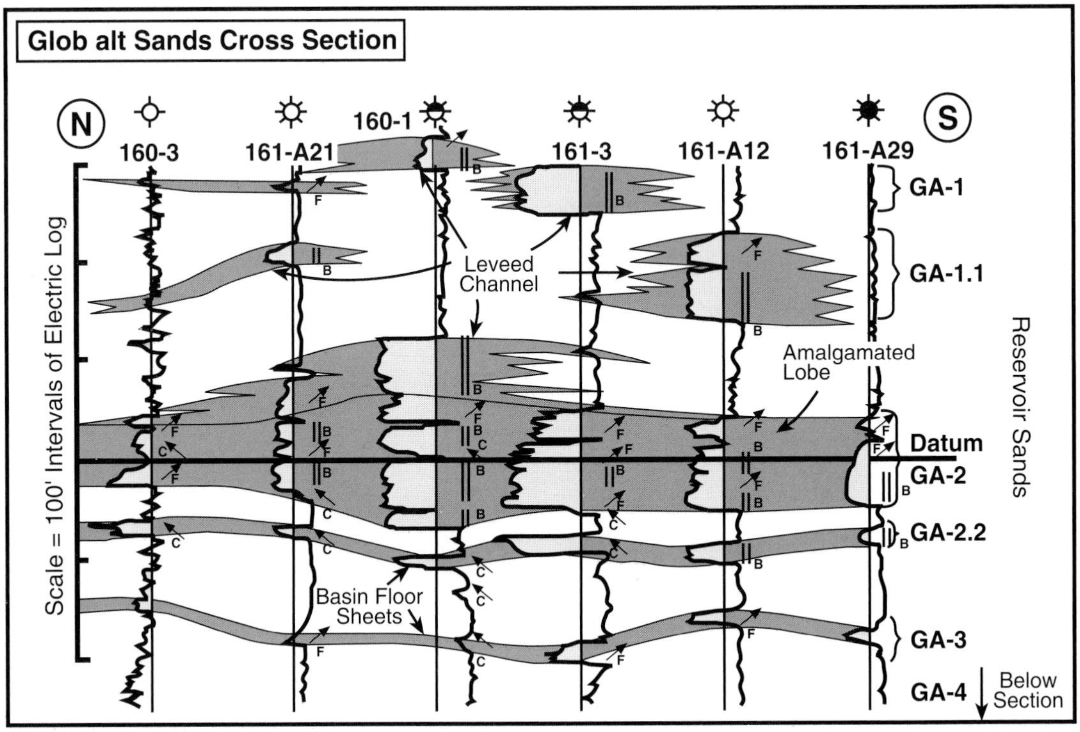

Figure 4–48. After Armentrout et al. (1991); courtesy Springer-Verlag.

Net sandstone isopachs

Well-log correlations within the *Glob alt* isochron thick show a succession of aggrading sandstone bodies (Figure 4–48). Figure 4–49 shows net sandstone isopachs for reservoir units of the *Glob alt* sandstone interval. The stratigraphic succession from top to bottom reservoir sandstone is 1, 1.1, 2, 2.2, 3, and 4. Maps of each sandstone interval document lobate deposition within the minibasin. Individual lobe development shows compensation lobe switching as progressively younger deposits infill the mud-rich/sand-poor intralobe areas of the preceding lobe.

The patterns mapped on the figure suggest lower thin lobate sheets (GA-4, GA-3, and GA-2.2), an intermediate thick lobe of amalgamated blocky sandstones (GA-2), and an upper moderately thick, bilobed leveed-channel system (GA-1.1 and GA-1). Net sandstone isopach contours are 10 ft (3 m); the scale bar is 3000 ft (1000 m).

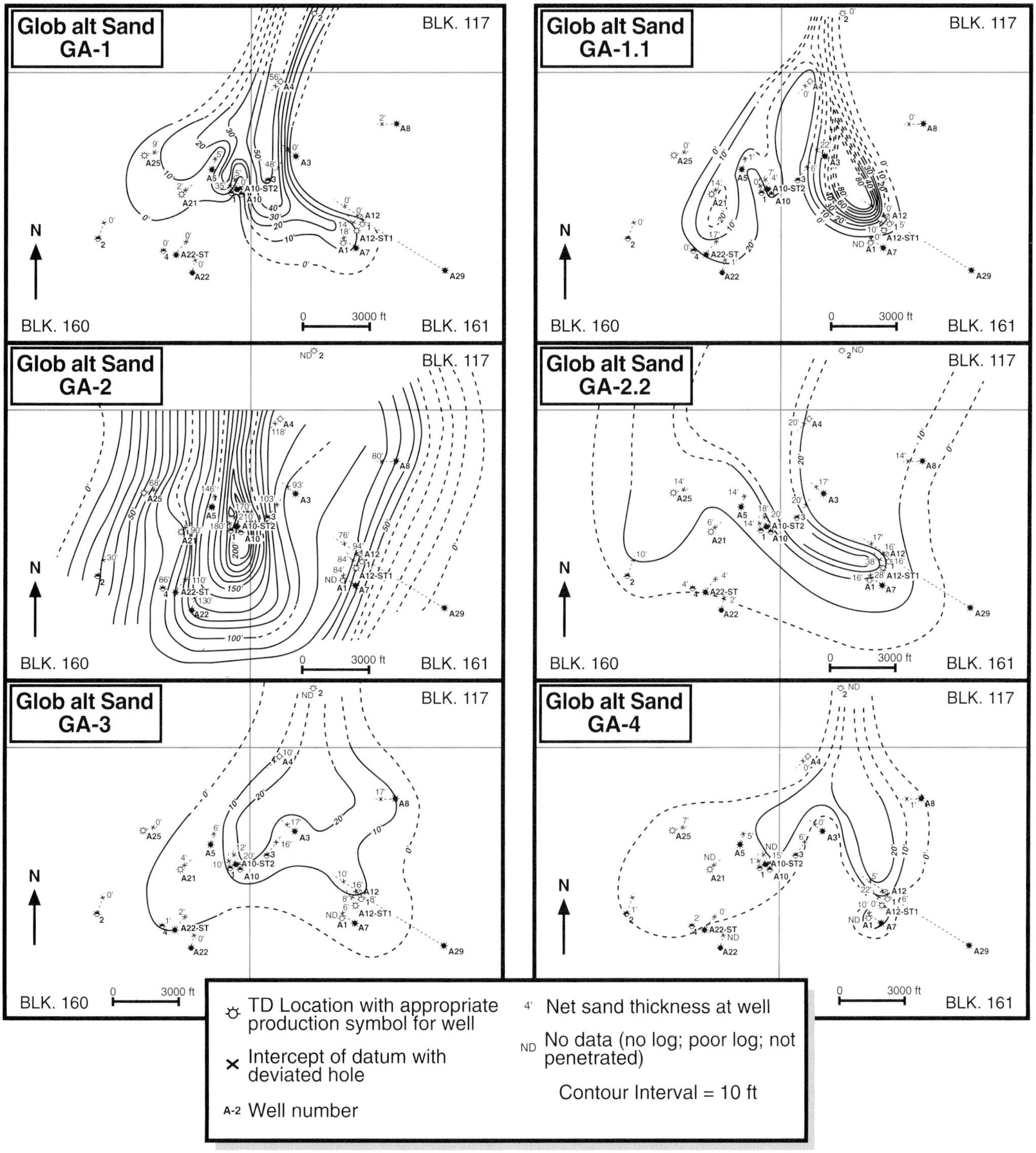

Figure 4–49. From Armentrout et al. (1991); courtesy Springer-Verlag.

Depositional model summary

All the observations made from seismic profiles, isochron maps, seismic facies maps, well-log cross sections, cuttings, biofacies, and cores have been used to construct a depositional model for the *Glob alt* cycle of the High Island–East Breaks 160-161 minibasin. This model incorporates far-traveled gravity-flow sands that accumulated in a depositional thick, filling an upper-slope salt-withdrawal sea-floor low. Laterally shifting fan lobes resulted in a complex architectural framework (Figure 4–48). The profile pattern (Figure 4–47), combined with the mapped isochron and seismic facies pattern of Figure 4–46 and the net sandstone patterns of Figure 4–49, have been interpreted as minibasin basin-floor sheet sandstones, amalgamated-lobe sandstones, and leveed-channel sandstones by Armentrout et al. (1991) (see Figure 4–48).

Depositional model diagram

The following figure is a block diagram of the depositional model for the *Glob alt* reservoir interval. The model shows a 40–50-mi-long (60–80 km) transport system from a shelf-edge delta basinward to the East Breaks 160-161 minibasin. Depositional water depths exceeded 1000 ft (320 m) (upper bathyal), suggesting transport was by gravity-flow processes. Sandstone deposition in the minibasin may have resulted from subtle variations of sea-floor topography, perhaps related to early salt withdrawal (Kneller and McCaffrey, 1995). Mass-wasting processes occurred on the slope well to the north of the field, as shown by slump facies on Figure 4–39. The areal extent of the basin-floor sheet is restricted by the areal extent of the East Breaks 160-161 intraslope minibasin.

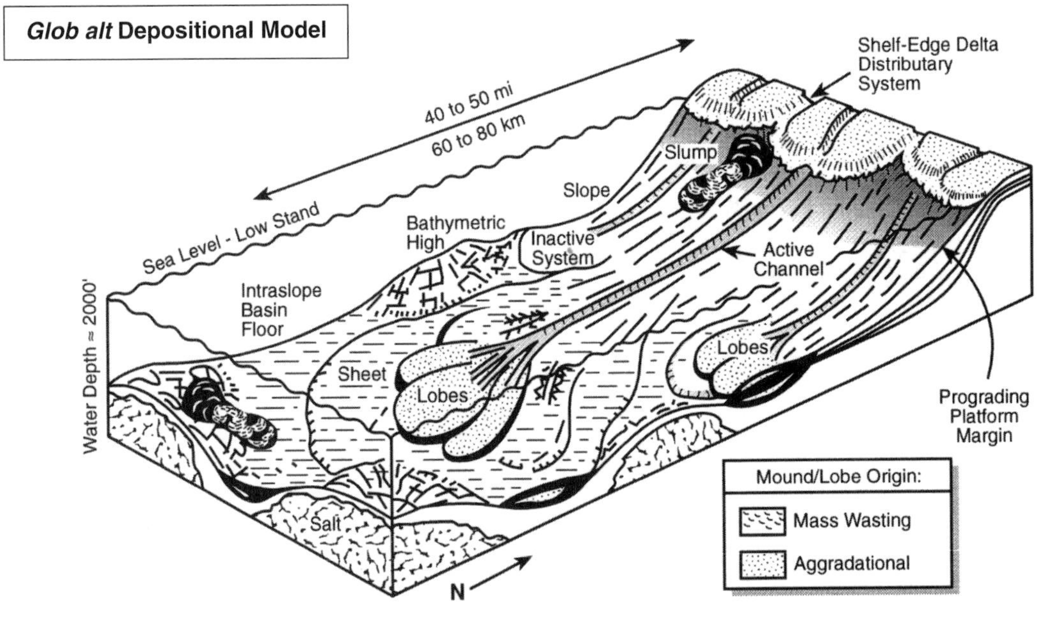

Figure 4–50. From Armentrout et al. (1991); courtesy Springer-Verlag.

Accommodation space

Differential loading of the mobile salt resulted in some syndepositional subsidence and accommodation of the *Glob alt* sand-prone isochron thick. The apparent thickening into the north-bounding growth fault is due to the maximum differential subsidence and isochron thickening being coincident with the fault trace of a much younger growth fault phase. Biostratigraphic calibration of the fault system indicates most, if not all, of the fault offset occurred during middle Pleistocene time, after the *Trifarina rutila bioevent* (= *Ang B*) dated at 1.30 Ma (Figure 4–31). This is more than 1.5 m.y. after deposition of the *Glob alt* sands.

Structural trap formation

Structural trap formation is related to differential rotation of the *Glob alt* sand-prone interval. This rotation occurred between 1.3 Ma and the present. The result was the development of the rollover anticline downthrown to fault A', which is a splay off regional fault A (Figures 4–42 and 4–43). (See Apps et al., 1994; Armentrout et al., 1996; Kneller and McCaffrey, 1995; and Weimer and Bouma, 1995, for discussions on structural control of deepwater deposition.)

Seal Rock

Description

The deepwater sands of the *Glob alt* reservoir are encased in hemipelagic mudstones and have a top seal associated with the condensed section of the *Glob alt* depositional cycle (Armentrout et al., 1991). The well-log cross section in Figure 4–48 shows the correlation of the *Glob alt* sandstones. The top seal, which occurs above the log cross section, is a major mudstone condensed interval coincident with the *Glob alt* datum labeled on Figure 4–47. Precondensed section mudstones encasing the *Glob alt* sandstones provide local top seal and lateral seal.

Effectiveness

The top seal of the *Glob alt* reservoir is especially effective because it is thick and has a regional extent as a consequence of its position at a third-order turnaround from regression to transgression. This turnaround is from regressive cycles 3.4–3.5–3.6 to transgressive cycles 3.7–3.8 on the Haq et al. (1988) cycle chart (see Figure 4–25).

Despite its regional extent and thickness, hydrocarbons have leaked upward into the *Hyal B* and *Trim A* reservoirs, most probably along faults during intervals of fault movement with consequent dilation of fracture networks along the fault

Carrier beds and seal evaluation

Impermeable rocks also affect migration pathways. Porous and permeable beds bounded above and below by impermeable rocks can provide highly effective hydrocarbon carrier beds.

Overburden Rock

Introduction

Overburden rock is the total stratigraphic section above the source rock (Magoon and Dow, 1994). The thickness and age of overburden rock provides a history of the rate of burial of a source rock toward and through the increasing temperature domains of the basin. This includes the range of temperatures necessary for cracking kerogens into hydrocarbons.

Because the depth to the probable source rocks of the East Breaks 160-161 field hydrocarbons is unknown, multiple working hypotheses must be considered. Four intervals of identified source rock are reported by Gross et al. (1995) (Figure 4–5) and are plotted on Figure 4–45. Also plotted is the speculated middle Miocene source rock of Dow et al. (1990). Gross et al. (1995) consider the petroleum of the East Breaks area to have been sourced by Jurassic marine mudstones for the oil and Paleogene marine mudstones for the gas. Alternatively, Dow et al. (1990) suggest middle Miocene marine mudstones as the probable source rock, although Taylor and Armentrout (1990) believe the source rock facies to be older than the Miocene slope mudstones.

Rate of accumulation

Accumulation of overburden above these five potential source rocks is shown by a dashed line on the events chart (Figure 4–45), indicating no specific rate of accumulation until the interval of late Pliocene to Recent sedimentation where rate variation is shown as defined by Piggott and Pulham (1993). Figures 4–32 and 4–33 indicate a major increase in rate of sediment accumulation occurred 6 Ma, which would accelerate burial of potential source rocks into the thermal zone for hydrocarbon generation.

Amount

Drilling has documented that the East Breaks depocenter in the vicinity of the 160-161 field contains at least 15,000 ft (5000 m) of late Miocene to Recent sediment (Figure 4–43). Dow et al. (1990) use this thickness in calculating maturation and generation models. The thickness of overburden rock for any one of the older potential source rock intervals will be greater than 15,000 ft (5000 m), but the exact amount is highly speculative.

Source Rock

Identification problem

Geochemical typing of an oil in a reservoir rock and its correlation to a probable source rock are used to determine the level of certainty or the confidence that an oil originated from a specific source. Oils from the East Breaks 160-161 field have been analyzed by Dow et al. (1990). Those oils, one each from the *Glob alt* GA-3 reservoir and the *Hyal B* HB-2 reservoir, are very similar geochemically and closely resemble continental shelf oils of Louisiana and Texas. The East Breaks 160-161 *Glob alt* and *Hyal B* oils do not correlate with the Type 1-B oils (Thompson et al., 1990) of shelf-edge and continental slope reservoirs (Dow et al., 1990).

Miocene source?

Dow et al. (1990) present a case for a Miocene source rock for the East Breaks 160-161 field, based primarily on the interpretation that the East Breaks 160-161 minibasin is a self-contained petroleum system enclosed by a salt floor and walls, and thus the hydrocarbons must have been generated from within (see Figure 4–8). Those workers present analyses of kerogens from late Miocene gravity-flow-deposited mudstones, suggesting some potential for oil generation, and speculate that more deeply buried, more organic-rich middle Miocene mudstones may be the source of the hydrocarbons. Taylor and Armentrout (1990) analyzed oils and kerogens in turbidite facies at the High Island A-537 field. They speculate that kerogens in Neogene turbidite facies are unlikely to be the source of oils in the A-537 field and further speculate that deeper source rocks with a strong marine algal fingerprint were more likely sources for the oils.

Early Tertiary source?

Gross et al. (1995) suggest that the oil of the East Breaks–High Island area originated from either lower Tertiary mudstones or uppermost Jurassic mudstones (Figure 4–5). Philippi (1974) and Sassen et al. (1988) present evidence for source potential for crude oil in the upper Paleocene to lower Eocene Wilcox Formation. If lower Tertiary Wilcox equivalent or uppermost Jurassic mudstones are the source for hydrocarbons in the East Breaks 160-161 field, then a migration avenue must exist through the salt that underlies the minibasin and generation-migration-accumulation must have been delayed until the trap formed approximately 1.2 Ma. In fact, alternative interpretations of salt distribution at the East Breaks 160-161 field suggest a salt weld with sediment-on-sediment below the minibasin rather than a salt floor (compare Figures 4–8 and 4–9). This suggests migration could have occurred from even older, more deeply buried source rocks.

Migration pathways

Data currently available preclude a precise correlation of the East Breaks 160-161 field oils with a specific source rock. Therefore, the petroleum system(s) charging the *Glob alt* reservoirs is speculative. However, the data do suggest that the hydrocarbons originate from more deeply buried thermally mature rocks than those encasing the reservoir and therefore vertical migration has occurred.

Future work

Detailed biomarker analysis of the East Breaks oils and comparison to detailed analyses of potential source rocks are necessary for a precise correlation and resolution of relatively shallow middle Miocene vs. much deeper lower Tertiary source rocks for the East Breaks 160-161 field hydrocarbons. If this exercise is successful, then the level of certainty for these petroleum systems could be raised to known.

Subsection E3

East Breaks Petroleum System Processes

Introduction

Petroleum system processes include trap formation; source-rock maturation; and generation, expulsion, secondary migration, and accumulation of hydrocarbons within a trap. Modeling of oil generation within the East Breaks 160-161 minibasin suggests that middle Miocene strata would have begun to generate hydrocarbons only 200,000 years ago and would still be active today. If older strata are the source of the petroleum, then generation must have been delayed until the late Pleistocene.

An alternative is that the petroleum has migrated after 1.2 Ma from older traps into the East Breaks 160-161 *Glob alt* through *Trim A* anticlinal traps. Periodic vertical migration of oil probably took place along growth faults between overpressured source beds and more normally pressured reservoirs. Oil accumulated in faulted rollover anticlinal traps with slightly overpressured mudstone seals. Biodegradation of oils reflects shallow accumulation prior to burial of the reservoirs below 140°F (60°C).

This subsection details aspects of this generation-migration-accumulation model.

In this subsection

This subsection contains the following topics.

Trap Formation

Minibasin structural–stratigraphic development

The structural/stratigraphic configuration of the East Breaks 160-161 minibasin formed well after *Glob alt* time. As discussed earlier, the High Island–East Breaks basin was a late Pliocene/early Pleistocene slope basin through which gravity flow sands flowed southward. Progradation overloaded the underlying salt and minibasins formed as a succession of southward-stepping growth-fault/salt-withdrawal sediment thicks (Figure 4–44).

Structural traps

Within these minibasins, structural traps of gravity-flow sandstones formed

- as fault-dependent closure at growth faults,
- as anticlinal closure formed by rollover into growth faults, or
- by postdepositional tilting of sandstones that shale-out upstructure due to syndepositional pinching-out against sea-floor valley margins (Bouma, 1982; Kneller and McCaffrey, 1995).

Stratigraphic traps

Pure stratigraphic traps occur where basinal sandstones completely bypassed updip areas subsequently filled by mud, providing both top seal and updip lateral seal (Bouma, 1982; Galloway and McGilvery, 1995).

Timing of fault movement

Fault movement timing is critical for trap formation timing. Growth-fault rollover anticlines develop by updip expansion and sediment entrapment on the downthrown side of the fault and consequent downdip sediment starvation and continued subsidence within the intraslope basin (see Figure 4–43 for geometries above the *Trim A* interval along fault A'). Thus, the updip trap for gravity-flow sandstone is the rollover into the fault, formed during the dynamic phase of fault movement.

Fault A'

In the East Breaks 160-161 minibasin, the fault splay fault A' forms the northern boundary to the field (Figures 4–42 and 4–43). The dynamic phase of this fault is recorded by the wedge-shaped sediment thickening into the fault, deposited between pre-*Hyal B* (ca. 1.00 Ma) time and late *Trim A* (ca. 0.56 Ma) time (Figure 4–31). Its growth phase began about 1.20 Ma (Armentrout in Dow et al., 1990; Armentrout et al., 1991). Sea-floor expression of this fault clearly indicates offset of Holocene sediments, showing that the fault is currently active (Figure 4–43).

Geochemistry of Two Oils from East Breaks

Introduction

Two oil samples (*Glob alt* = GA-3 and *Hyal B* = HB-2) from two different reservoirs in the East Breaks 160-161 field provide data for modeling the history of hydrocarbon generation and migration within this minibasin. Dow et al. (1990) report that the East Breaks oils are biodegraded and mixed lower molecular weight, thermally mature oil. The C_{10} through C_{30} alkanes of the GA-3 oil are better preserved than those of the HB-2 oil. This is demonstrated by the higher peaks of C_{10} through C_{30} alkanes on the gas chromatograms below, suggesting that the stratigraphically deeper GA-3 oil is less degraded and slightly more mature than the stratigraphically shallower HB-2 oil. Neither oil exhibits evidence of evaporative fractionation reported by Thompson (1987) in over 75% of Gulf Coast Tertiary oils.

Oil preservation pattern

The oil preservation pattern is attributed to the history of generation, expulsion, secondary migration, and accumulation (Dow et al., 1990). The better preserved C_{10} to C_{30} alkanes in the GA-3 oil occur where the reservoir temperature is about 160°F (71°C). The more poorly preserved alkanes in the HB-2 oil occur where the reservoir temperature is about 130°F (Figure 4–52). Microbial activity responsible for biodegradation occurs at temperatures below 140°F (60°C). The earliest migration fluids would have been the least mature and potentially most biodegraded due to the shallow level of accumulation. With increasing burial of the source rock, more mature oil and condensate would have been generated and better preserved in deeper reservoirs below the depth of microbial activity. These observations suggest sequential expulsion and migration of progressively more mature products as the source(s) passed through the oil window. Alternative interpretations are offered in Dow et al. (1990).

The figure below shows whole oil chromatograms of crude oils from two reservoirs in the East Breaks 160-161 field. Oil 1 is from the HB-2 reservoir; oil 2 is from the *Glob alt* GA-3 reservoir. Both are interpreted as biodegraded and mixed with fresh oil, suggesting multiple pulses of accumulation.

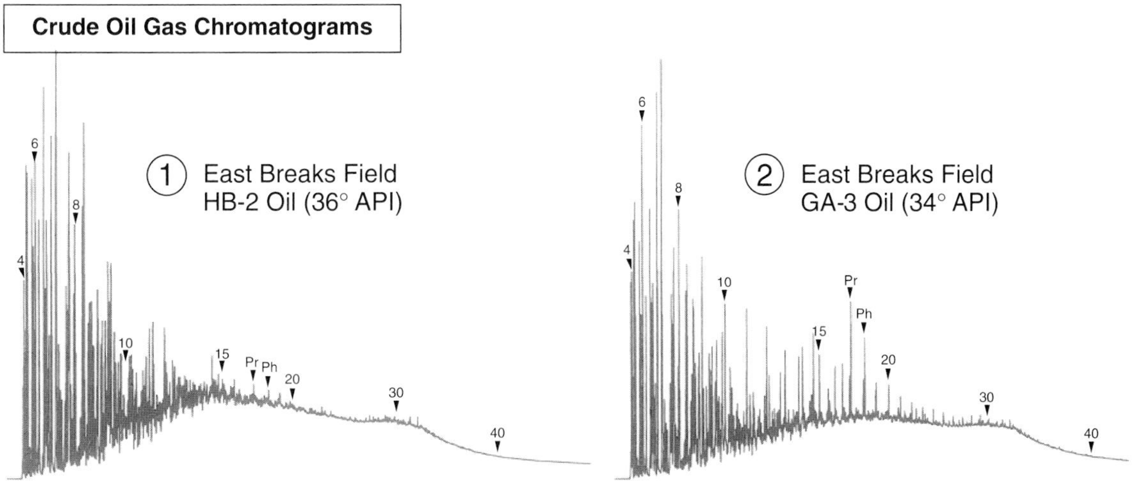

Figure 4–51. From Dow et al. (1990); courtesy Gulf Coast SEPM.

Hydrocarbon Generation Model

Method

A 32-layer, 1-D mathematical model (Figure 4–53) was constructed for the East Breaks 160-161 minibasin. The No. A-29 well in block 160 was used for stratigraphic and thermal control, including borehole temperature surveys and vitrinite reflectance data. Modeling was extended 3,000 ft (1000 m) below true vertical drilling depth (12,000 ft, 4000 m) to evaluate the underlying speculated source potential of the middle and lower Miocene section. The figure is a north–south seismic reflection profile across the East Breaks 160-161 intraslope minibasin (see Figures 4–42 and 4–44). The deviated wellbore of the East Breaks well 160 No. A-29 is marked with a white dashed line. Reservoirs for analyzed oils are indicated for the *Hyal B* HB-2 reservoir and for the *Glob alt* GA-3 reservoir. Rock cutting samples from intervals indicated by A and B were used by Dow et al. (1990) to calibrate kerogen type for kinetic modeling.

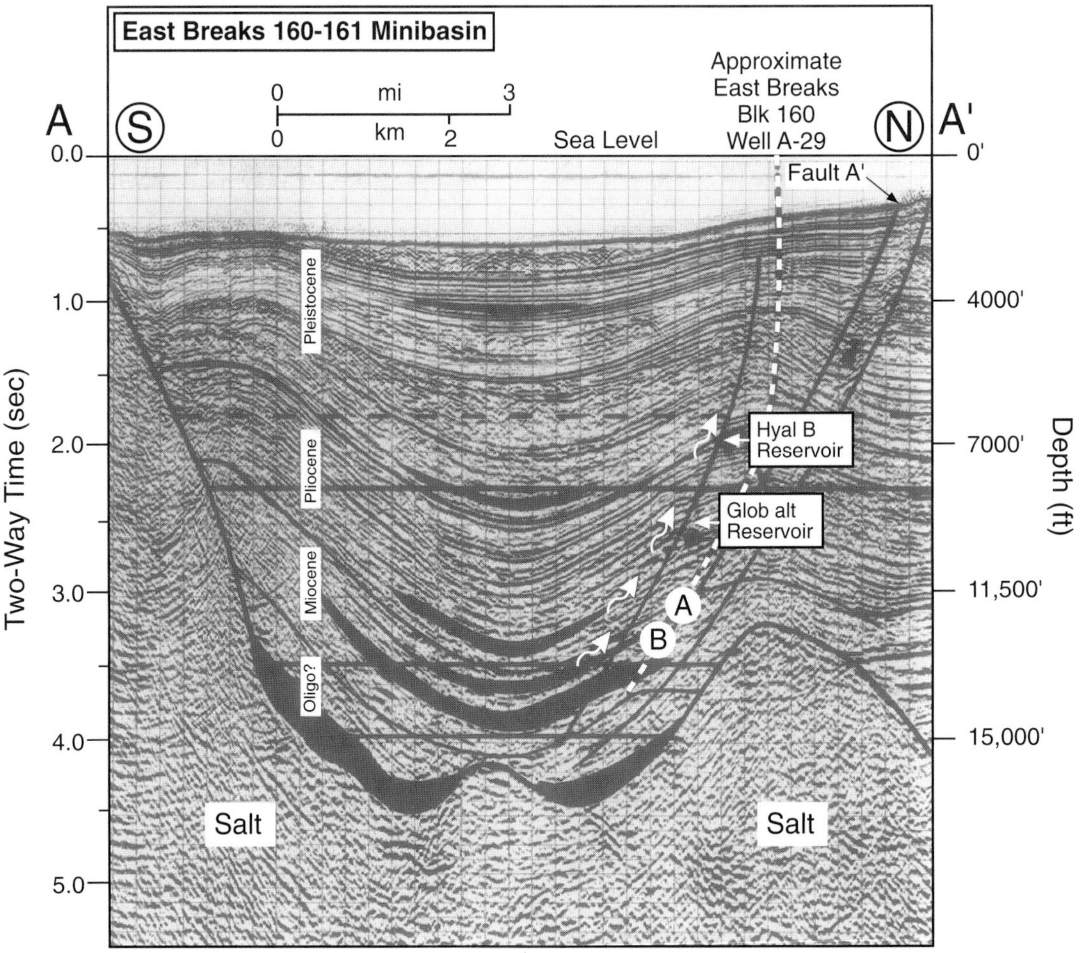

Figure 4–52. After Dow et al. (1990); courtesy Gulf Coast SEPM.

Hydrocarbon Generation Model, continued

Generation and expulsion timing

A burial history plot with computed hydrocarbon generation history shows that peak oil generation in the A-29 well began at the inferred base of the lower Miocene when buried below 11,000 ft (3000 m) about 1.2 Ma, at the base of the inferred middle Miocene when it too passed below 11,000 ft (3000 m) burial about 0.2 Ma.

Miocene source beds, if present, would be actively generating and expelling oil and gas at the present time. Dow et al. (1990) interpret this to account for the biodegraded East Breaks 160-161 field oils being recharged with fresh oil during a later migration phase. The relatively low maturity of the inferred Miocene section should also result in only minor thermogenic gas generation and might explain the absence of evaporative fractionation in the produced crudes of this field in contrast to approximately 75% of Gulf Coast Tertiary crudes (Thompson et al., 1990).

Burial history

The following figure is a 1-D burial history/maturation plot showing the critical moment (2.0 Ma) and the time of oil generation (2.0 Ma to present) for the East Breaks 160-161 minibasin petroleum system, assuming that lower Miocene rocks have sourced the hydrocarbons. Alternative burial history plots could be constructed using the assumed burial depths for each potential source horizon. For these deeply buried potential source horizons, generation must have been delayed until very recently or secondary migration from older, deeper reservoirs provides the hydrocarbons trapped at the East Breaks 160-161 field. Additionally, basins are 3-D entities, and either 2-D models throughout the basin or a 3-D model of the entire basin is essential to understanding the maturation history of a basin.

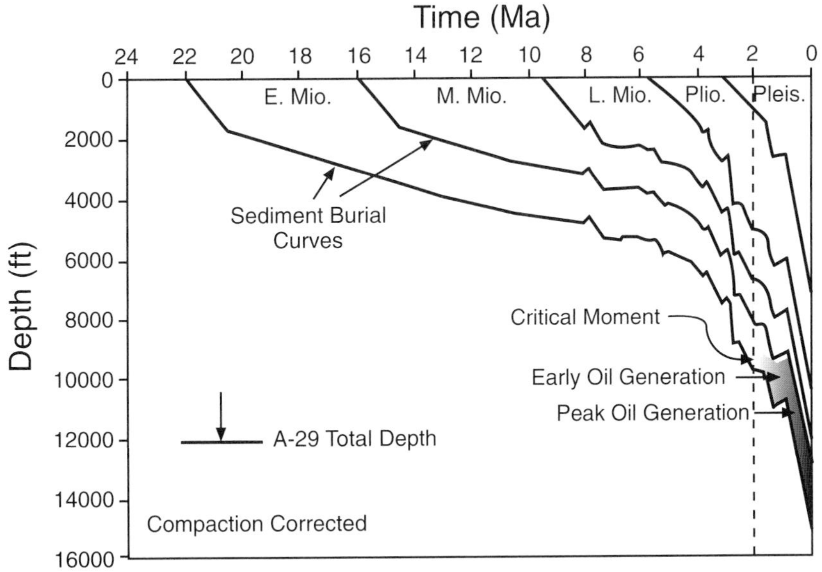

Figure 4–53. After Dow et al. (1990); courtesy Gulf Coast SEPM.

Hydrocarbon Migration Model

Vertical migration path

Petroleum generated at depth, either from the middle Miocene as suggested by Dow et al. (1990) or the lower Tertiary or upper Jurassic as suggested by Gross et al. (1995), had to move vertically within the East Breaks 160-161 minibasin to charge the known gravity-flow sandstone reservoirs. The deepwater lowstand gravity-flow reservoir sandstones are separated by hemipelagic mudstones deposited during condensed sedimentation of each cycle. Migration through matrix porosity of these effective top-seal mudstones is highly unlikely. Thus, vertical migration along faults is the most probable avenue. Episodic movement on the faults would result in multiple phases of migration and could account for the observed mix of oils of different maturities within the same structure (Schanck et al., 1988) and the mix of biodegraded and nonbiodegraded oil in the same reservoir (Dow et al., 1990; see also Anderson, 1993, and Anderson et al., 1994, for migration model).

Lateral migration path

Once the petroleum has migrated up the fault to the porous and permeable sandstone, it could move laterally up-structure within the continuous sand beds until it accumulated within structural closure. The driving force behind the migration is most likely a combination of several factors, including fluid buoyancy, formation pressure trends, and salinity gradients. Similar migration patterns have been suggested by Hanor and Sassen (1990).

Southern Louisiana model

Hanor and Sassen (1990) present data from Cretaceous and Tertiary strata in southern Louisiana for aqueous fluid flow from deep, geopressured sediments vertically upward to normally hydropressured zones. This migration is interpreted to occur through fractures and faults rather than through matrix porosity.

The following figure is a regional cross section summarizing in a qualitative, conceptual way the regional hydraulic flow regimes of the Louisiana Gulf Coast above a depth of 20,000 ft (6096 m). The uppermost regime consists of low-salinity, meteoric water driven gulfward by differences in topographic elevation. The deepest regime consists of moderately saline water driven upward and laterally by excess fluid pressures. In between is a hydraulic regime in which lateral and vertical flow of saline brines is taking place—in part in response to differences in fluid density caused by spatial variations in temperature and salinity. The dissolution of salt plays a critical role in driving fluid flow in this region. Arrows show possible pathways of fluid flow.

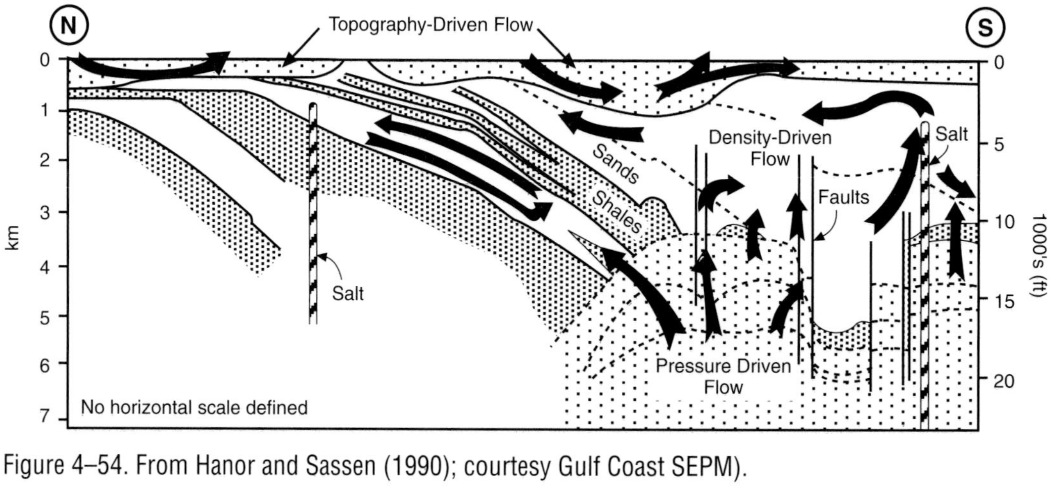

Figure 4–54. From Hanor and Sassen (1990); courtesy Gulf Coast SEPM).

GOM Neogene model

Patterns of migration in the offshore Gulf of Mexico Neogene strata suggest migration avenues similar to the southern Louisiana model. Lovely and Ruggiero (personal communication, 1995) integrated multiple data sets, including geochemical analysis of cores and sea-floor acoustic impedance patterns and orthocontouring of structure maps, and formulated a hypothesis for petroleum migration.

The figure below is a north–south 3-D seismic reflection profile illustrating three possible hydrocarbon migration pathways and related sea-bed features. They concluded that the primary migration pathway involves migration up from geopressured source rocks along the sediment/salt interface with sea-floor seepage forming hydrates and providing nutrients to carbonate producing organisms (1). A secondary pathway involves redirection of some of the petroleum from the sediment/salt interface laterally into sand-rich carrier beds (2). Pathway 3 consists of a fault intersection of either pathway 1 or 2 and the vertical migration along fault-associated fracture conduits with possible formation of fault scarp amplitude halos at intersected reservoirs and sea-floor hydrate/carbonate mounds.

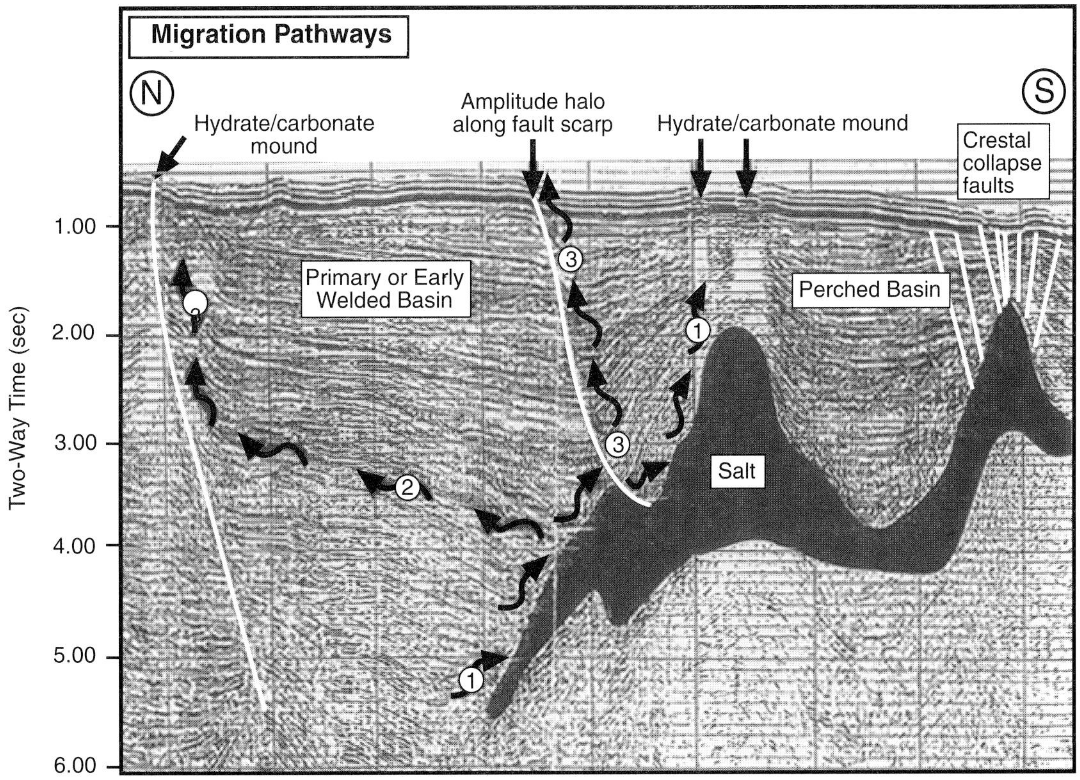

Figure 4–55. Based on data from Lovely and Ruggiero (1995, personal communication).

East Breaks migration model

Using these hypothetical migration avenues, a migration pathway model has been constructed for the East Breaks 160-161 minibasin. Dow et al. (1990) present temperature information, indicating an elevated thermal gradient in the block 160-A-29 well where it is in close proximity to salt. Additionally, the A-29 borehole mud weight of 13.5 lb below 5,000 ft (1524 m) and 15.7 lb below 7,000 ft (2134 m) and mathematical modeling suggest probable overpressure and undercompacted sediments below a depth of 10,000 ft (3048 m). The consequent thermal and geopressure gradient would drive fluid flow from depth up migration pathways into available reservoirs.

The figure below is a north–south seismic section showing the hypothetical model for migration pathways within the East Breaks 160-161 field (see Figure 4–42 for location). Fault conduits allow upward migration from high-pressure, thermally mature probable source rocks into the intersected gravity-flow sandstone reservoirs at the *Glob alt, Hyal B,* and *Trim A* horizons. The *Glob M* horizon between the *Glob alt* and *Hyal B* horizons is productive from sands in the East Breaks 158-159 field 6 mi (about 10 km) to the west within the same minibasin.

The probable fault-plane migration pathway of the East Breaks 160-161 field offsets the sea floor and locally has associated mud volcanoes along the fault scarp. Despite these observations of recent and/or current fault movement and fluid discharge, the absence of hydrates and biogenic carbonate buildups suggests that hydrocarbons are not reaching the shallowest section.

Seal rocks consist of condensed-section mudstones that provide effective top seal for each lowstand gravity-flow sandstone. These condensed-section mudstones are often thick enough to provide effective lateral seal except where faults offset juxtaposed sandstones.

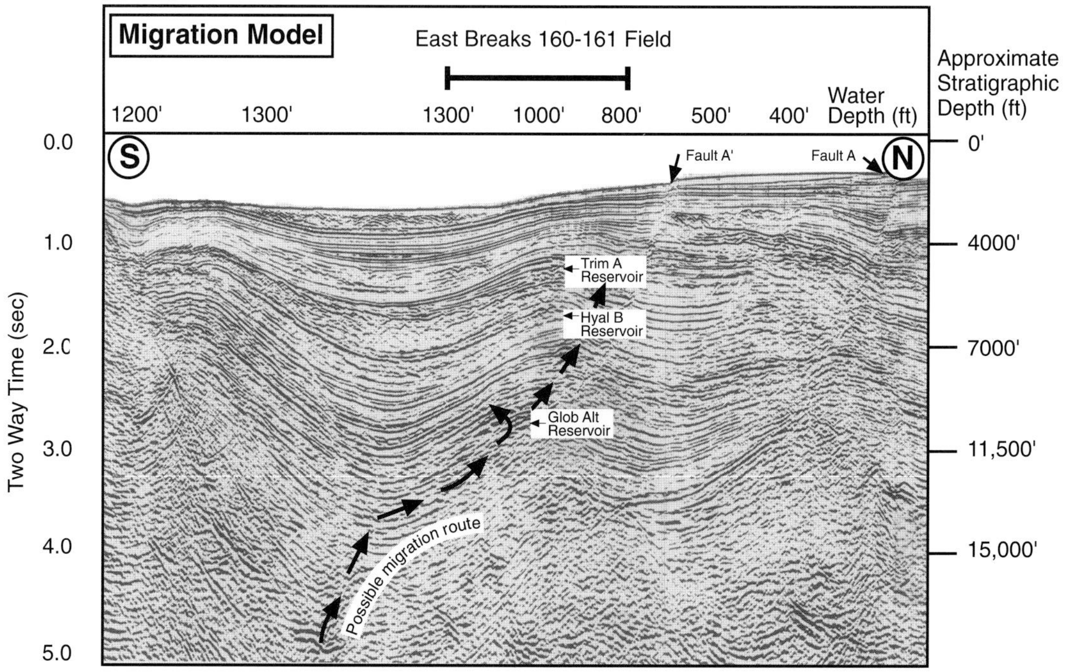

Figure 4–56. From Dow et al. (1990); courtesy Gulf Coast SEPM.

Hydrocarbon Accumulation Model

Impact of growth-fault movement

The multiple phases of petroleum charging the East Breaks 160-161 reservoirs and their accumulation within the anticlinal trap is interpreted to be controlled by the timing of growth-fault movement. Fault movement and fault-associated fracturing in the adjacent rocks could enhance the migration conduit. Migration up the fault would have provided petroleum charge into the intersected reservoir sandstones.

Fault movement and trap formation

Rollover into the growth-fault-initiated trap formation occurred between about 1.2 Ma and the present. Fault movement occurred during each lowstand of sea level when differential loading from shelf-edge deltaic sedimentation and consequent salt withdrawal destabilized the upper slope system (Armentrout, 1993). Given the sea-level fluctuation cycles documented within the East Breaks 160-161 minibasin (Armentrout and Clement, 1990; Armentrout, 1993), at least five and potentially nine lowstand events may have caused episodic movement of the north-bounding growth fault of the East Breaks 160-161 field (Figure 4–31, nine cycles between 1.2 Ma and the present).

Sandbody geometries

The gravity-flow sandstone reservoirs within the field were transported from the north, southward into the East Breaks 160-161 minibasin (Figure 4–40), where the mapped pattern of the *Glob alt* sandstones show elongate and lobate north-to-south geometries (Figure 4–49). These north-to-south depositional geometries are draped over the east–west down-to-the-north rollover anticline, resulting in a seismic reflection amplitude pattern that shows north-to-south flank structural downdip termination (Figure 4–57C). East-to-west reflection amplitude termination is stratigraphically controlled by sand distribution. This petroleum-associated reflection amplitude pattern is in contrast to that for sheet sands that would drape over the entire structure and show four-way downdip structural termination of seismic reflection (Figure 4–57D).

Tying seismic to well data

The figure below is a seismic reflection profile across the East Breaks 160-161 field, showing the 160 No. 1 well SP log and synthetic seismogram and two schematic diagrams for interpreting possible seismic reflection amplitude anomaly maps, which could indicate hydrocarbon-charged sands. Bioevent horizons correlate with the top seal above each reservoir interval. Only the lower *Trim A* and *Glob alt* reservoir sandstones are well developed in this well. The depositional model for a delta-front sheet sand extending over the entire postdepositional anticline is likely to have four-way downdip termination of petroleum-associated seismic reflection amplitude anomalies (view C). The depositional model for a depositional dip-oriented gravity-flow sandstone draped over the postdepositional anticline is likely to have two-way structural termination of a petroleum-associated seismic reflection amplitude anomaly, with stratigraphic termination of reflectors along both depositional-strike directions (view D). The mapped amplitude pattern in both the *Trim A* and *Glob alt* intervals agrees with a channel-fed gravity-flow depositional system.

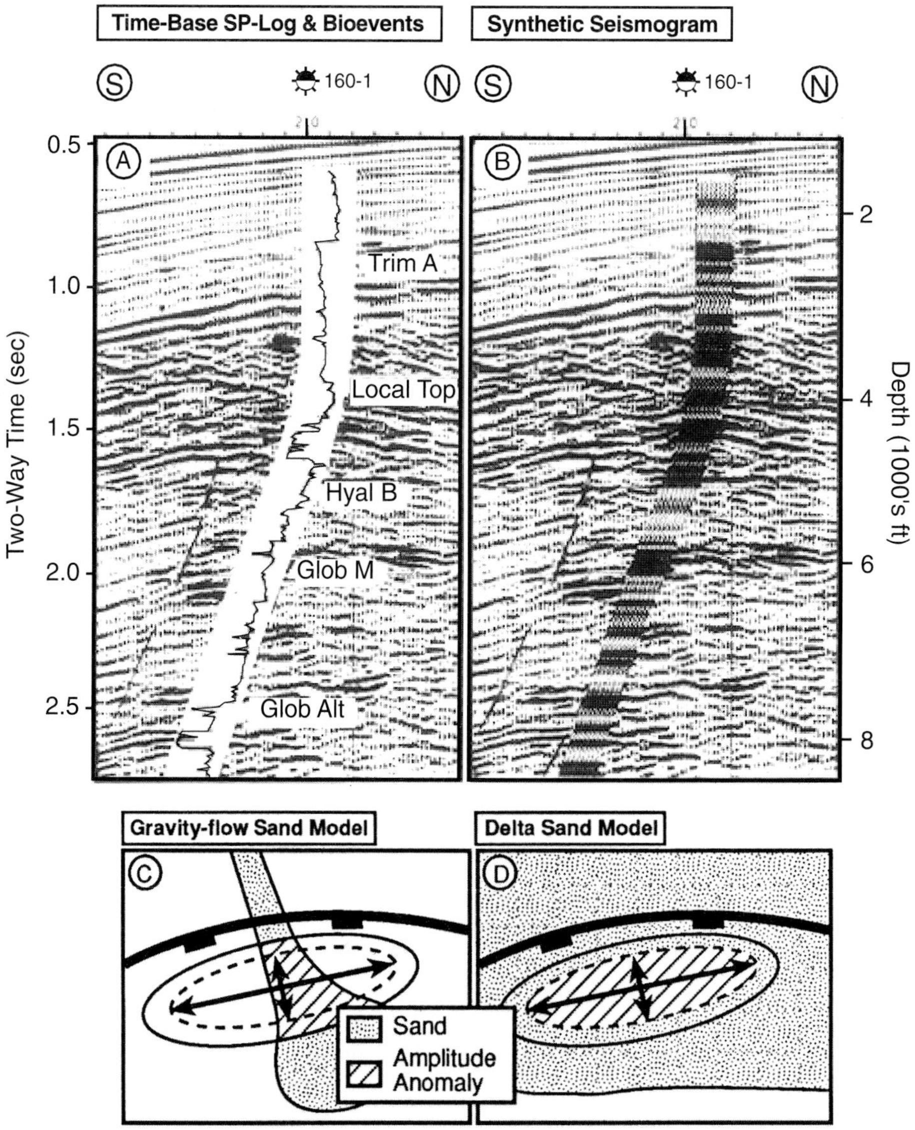

Figure 4–57.

Recharging of reservoirs

Preserving these petroleum resources has been discussed in reference to biodegradation, which has produced much of the gas in the reservoirs—especially at the *Trim A* horizon. Burial of the reservoirs to depths with temperatures in excess of 140°F (60°C) prevents further microbial degradation of the oil. Late episodes of fault movement facilitates recharging the reservoirs with higher maturity oil, migrating upward from the deeply buried active source rock that is not yet specifically identified (see Anderson, 1993; Anderson et al., 1994).

Critical Moment (or Interval)

Introduction

Magoon and Dow (1994) define the critical moment as the time that best depicts the generation-migration-accumulation of most hydrocarbons in a petroleum system. The East Breaks 160-161 field began to accumulate no earlier than 1.2 Ma when the trap began forming, and accumulation is inferred to continue to the present (Dow et al., 1990). The structural configuration has changed little since initial formation, so that the present-day map (Figure 4–42) and cross-sectional geometry (Figure 4–43) accurately depict the trapping aspects of the petroleum system.

Possible critical moments

According to the maturation model for a middle Miocene source rock, peak oil generation would have begun 0.2 Ma (Dow et al., 1990), and the critical moment for the East Breaks 160-161 petroleum system would be 0.20 Ma (Figures 4–45 and 4–53). If a stratigraphically deeper lower Paleocene or upper Jurassic source rock is the origin of the East Breaks oils, an earlier onset of significant generation could have occurred with migration, continuing to today and supplying the petroleum that has charged the field.

Summary

The critical moment will be different for the middle Miocene, lower Paleocene, and lower Tertiary source rock. The critical interval encompasses the composite of all critical moments. The critical interval for the East Breaks 160-161 petroleum system is 2.8 Ma to the present. It is that time period after deposition of the reservoir and seal during which subsequent growth fault movement formed the anticlinal trap and accumulation of migrating hydrocarbons occurred.

Section F

Summary and Exploration Strategy for Deepwater Sands

Introduction

Synthesis of the regional basin analysis, depocenter, and depositional sequence history and the geologic setting of local minibasins provides geologic constraints on petroleum system formation. The East Breaks 160-161 minibasin contains all the elements required for generation, migration, and accumulation of hydrocarbons and is a true petroleum system. Understanding this petroleum system provides a template for exploration of depositionally similar areas.

In this subsection

This section contains the following topics.

Summary of the Petroleum Geology of the East Breaks Minibasin

Introduction	Field development, including step-out drilling, and exploration are enhanced by the understanding of the petroleum system—especially the occurrence of probable source rock, migration pathways, and reservoir.
Generation–migration–accumulation	Reservoired oils in the East Breaks 160-161 field are more thermally mature than the surrounding sediments, demonstrating that the hydrocarbons were contributed from deeper source rocks. Their generation history is controlled by the thermal gradient and overburden rock accumulation history, interpreted from both regional depocenter patterns and local minibasin history. Fault and salt-wall migration pathways provide vertical avenues for migration. Slope basin gravity-flow sands are the principal reservoir target in the High Island–East Breaks area for all except the most shallow stratigraphic intervals, where wave-dominated deposition of shelf sands produced laterally continuous sheet-like reservoirs subsequently draped over anticlinal structure.
Traps	The gravity-flow sands were transported and deposited within sea-floor physiographic lows between the anticlinal structures and within the isochron thicks of the synclinal sediment fill. Petroleum accumulations occur within traps where these synclinal sandstones are folded over postdepositional anticlines (Armentrout et al., 1991) or within structural-stratigraphic traps where synclinal sandstones pinch-out against sea-floor valley margins (McGee et al., 1994) or completely bypassed valley conduits subsequently filled by mudstone plugs (Galloway and McGilvery, 1995).

Exploration Strategy for Deepwater Sands

Introduction

The lateral shifting of depositional lobes within the stacked sandstones of the *Glob alt* reservoir at the East Breaks 160-161 field clearly demonstrates the need to carefully map the internal seismic facies and amplitude patterns within prospects in order to optimize prediction of sandstone occurrence. In concert with detailed fault-pattern maps, the highly compartmentalized reservoir can be delineated and wells optimally located. Additionally, seismic facies maps may suggest downflank or off-structure potential where faulting may not impose development problems. Construction of detailed seismic facies and fault pattern maps, preferably using 3-D seismic reflection volumes, results in a higher success rate of finding the closely spaced but laterally discontinuous reservoirs of gravity-flow intraslope basin plays.

Procedure

Based on the regional basin analysis as previously discussed, an exploration strategy for the East Breaks area and GOM basin deepwater areas can be defined. The table below lists possible steps to take to implement the strategy.

Step	Action
1	Delineate prospective areas by looking for lowstand sand-prone areas. Use trends of isochron thicks basinward of each depositional cycle's shelf edge as a guide.
2	Map seismic facies and structures of sand-prone intervals to locate prospects.
3	Map amplitude patterns within prospects to optimize prediction of sandstone and hydrocarbon occurrence. Calibrate rock/physics models with local well data.
4	Map deep penetrating fault and salt patterns as possible migration avenues for charging reservoirs of potential traps. Take particular note of the timing of active fault movement vs. the modeled timing of hydrocarbon expulsion from active source-rock volumes in communication with the fault.
5	Calculate the risk of trap existence vs. generation-migration timing using burial history and migration avenue models.
6	Locate exploration wells using detailed fault pattern maps overlain by seismic facies maps of sand-prone facies and structural maps showing closure at the top of the sand-prone seismic facies.
7	Use seismic facies maps to identify downflank or off-structure potential where faulting may not impose development problems.
8	As wells are drilled, place each sandstone unit encountered into its regional depositional context as a means of understanding potential reservoir continuity.
9	Use computer simulations based on empirical data to predict the geology—especially petroleum system elements—beyond control points.

Exploration Strategy for Deepwater Sands, continued

Locating sand-prone areas

Trends of isochron thick synclinal fill basinward of each depositional cycle's shelf edge delineate areas in which to map seismic facies, looking for lowstand sand-prone areas partitioned by regionally correlative condensed sections. The slope facies within the lowstand isochron thicks are most likely to be sandy downslope for sand-prone shelf depocenters formed during the preceding relative highstand of sea level.

Finding prospects

Once areas of potentially sand-prone seismic facies are identified, the trapping potential of each can be assessed through both prospect scale seismic facies mapping and structural mapping of the potentially sand-prone interval. In concert with prospect mapping, mapping of deep penetrating fault and salt patterns as potential migration avenues and the calculation of trap vs. generation-migration models helps us assess the risk of specific prospects.

Drilling prospects

Once drilling has commenced, each sandstone unit encountered should be placed into its regional depositional context so that downslope or upslope reservoir potential can be correctly assessed and subsequent wells optimally located.

Potential of *Glob alt* and *Trim A* sandstones

The figure below contrasts the depositional setting of the *Trim A* (A) and *Glob alt* (B) sandstones of the East Breaks 160-161 field. Drilling at the field encountered only channels in the *Trim A* reservoir, with the channel-fed lobes interpreted to occur further down paleoslope in the age-equivalent hummocky-mounded-to-sheet seismic facies. The *Trim A* shelf edge is mapped at the north boundary of the field. Thus, all *Trim A* associated sand-prone facies are restricted to this minibasin. Drilled *Glob alt* facies include channels and channel-fed lobes nearly 50 mi (80 km) from the mapped *Glob alt* shelf edge and probable deltaic sediment source from which the gravity-flow sands were supplied. Exploration potential within the *Glob alt* depositional sequence exists along the entire sediment transport system, as clearly demonstrated by the known occurrence of *Glob alt* reservoirs in the High Island–East Breaks area (Figure 4–40).

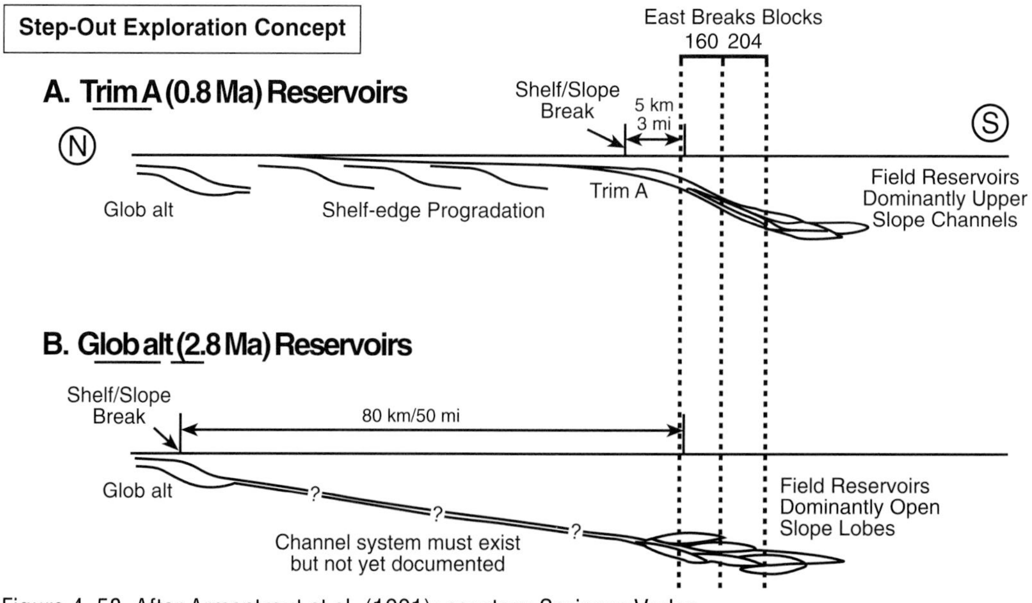

Figure 4–58. After Armentrout et al. (1991); courtesy Springer-Verlag.

Stratigraphic Predictions from Computer Simulation

Introduction

Computer simulation can help us predict lithofacies and hydrocarbon occurrence between and beyond data control. Both 2-D and 3-D simulation programs are available or in development. With high-resolution input of chronostratigraphy, lithofacies, and sedimentary process rates, simulations can be constructed that interpolate and extrapolate distributions of potential organic-rich source rock, seal rock, and reservoir rock.

Sedimentation model

The following figures are from a simulation done by Rouch et al. (1993) for the seismic reflection profile transect in Figure 4–44 (location on Figure 4–39). The detailed calibration of that seismic profile using wireline logs, well-cuttings lithofacies, and biostratigraphic data provides a high-resolution data set.

The data were input in a commercially available simulation package that performs 2-D backstripping and calculates subsidence rates and sediment flux rates across the entire seismic profile. Using a spectrum of input parameters based on regional geology and including those calculated from the backstripping exercise, the simulation fills in each polygon defined by digitized maximum flooding surface horizons with geologically appropriate lithofacies. The digitized horizons and the degree of fit between the simulated sedimentary record and the input data are shown below. Areas where the simulation shows excess sediment accumulation compared to the known record are noted by striped black patterns above the digitized flooding horizon; areas where the simulation shows less sediment accumulation than the known area are noted by solid gray areas below the digitized flooding horizon. The figure is the end result of 24 simulation runs converging toward a best-fit answer (Rouch et al., 1993).

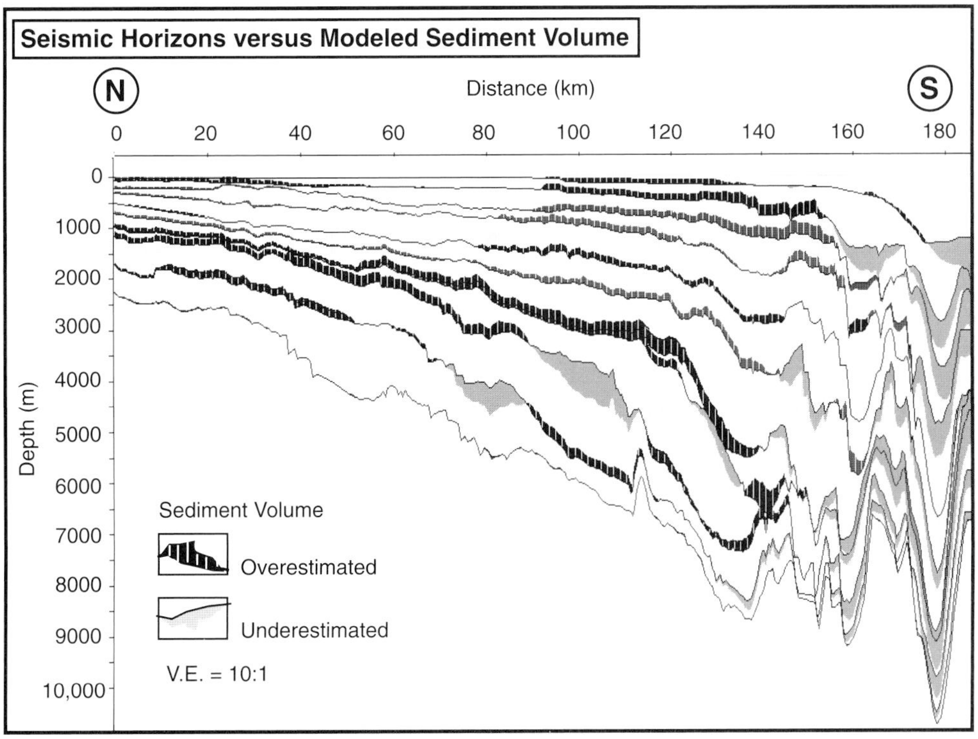

Figure 4–59. After Armentrout (1991); courtesy Springer-Verlag.

Model refinement

The difference between the simulation predictions and the known geology lets us focus on specific areas and processes to refine the model. Analysis of subsidence rates, paleobathymetry, fluvial and coastal gradients, volume of sediment bypassing the area (slope stability factor), slumping, and gravity-flow transport must be considered.

Lithofacies simulation

Once the best-fit simulation for most areas is achieved, lithofacies can be simulated. The resulting simulation displays a spectrum of lithofacies types based on the computer program. These predictions can be tested against the well data lithofacies and further fine-tuning performed. Once the best-fit lithofacies simulation is achieved, it can be used to infer the distribution of source, seal, and reservoir rock between well control and beyond into undrilled areas.

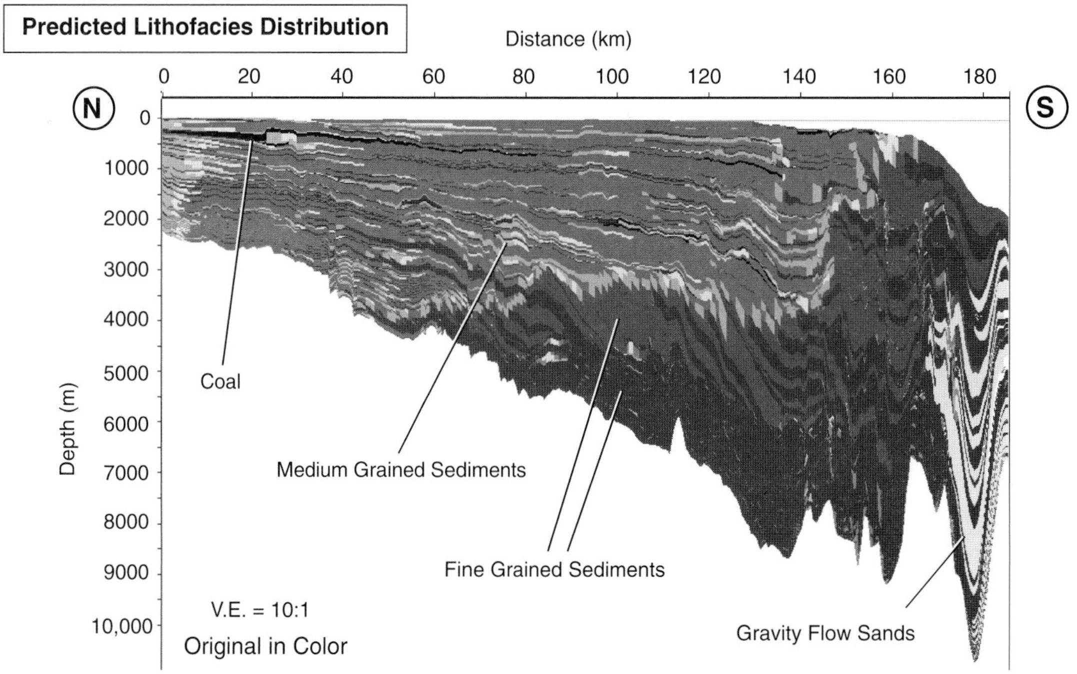

Figure 4–60. After Armentrout (1991); courtesy Springer-Verlag.

Using different computer packages

Continuing development of the simulation package used by Rouch et al. (1993) is focused on predicting organic richness, maturation, porosity, and fluid flow, as well as converting the lithofacies distributions into synthetic seismic reflection profiles that can be compared to profiles generated from field data. Each of the simulations must be checked against available data. Several simulations, each using different computer programs, clarify prediction reproducibility. Development of 3-D simulation programs will further enhance the predictions based on well-constrained data sets.

Integrating basin history

All of these efforts—gathering and integrating empirical data, computer simulation of geologic processes, and prediction of specific lithofacies—must be evaluated within the context of the basin history. The future success of geologic analysis is dependent on our careful and accurate interpretation of basin history from regional to local scales.

Section G
References

Anderson, R.N., 1993, Recovering dynamic Gulf of Mexico reserves and the U.S. energy future: Oil & Gas Journal, 26 April 1993, p. 85–88, 90–92.

______, P. Flemings, S. Losh, J. Austin, and R. Woodhams, 1994, Gulf of Mexico growth fault drilled, seen as oil, gas migration pathway: Oil & Gas Journal, 6 June 1994, p. 97–104.

______, K. Abdulah, S. Sarzalejo, F. Siringan, and M.A. Thomas, 1996, Late Quaternary sedimentation and high-resolution sequence stratigraphy of the East Texas shelf, *in* M. DeBatist and P. Jacobs, eds., Geology of Siliciclastic Shelf Seas: Geological Society of London Special Publication 117, p. 94–124.

Antoine, J.W., R.G. Ray, Jr., T.G. Pyle, and W.R. Bryant, 1974, Continental margins of the Gulf of Mexico, *in* C.A. Burk and C.L. Drake, eds., The Geology of Continental Margins: New York, Springer-Verlag, p. 683–693.

Apps, G.M., F.J. Peel, C.J. Travis, and C.A. Yeilding, 1994, Structural controls on Tertiary deep water deposition in the northern Gulf of Mexico: Proceedings, Gulf Coast Section SEPM 15th Annual Research Conference, p. 1–7.

Armentrout, J.M., 1987, Integration of biostratigraphy and seismic stratigraphy: Pliocene–Pleistocene, Gulf of Mexico: Proceedings, Gulf Coast Section SEPM 8th Annual Research Conference, p. 6–14.

______, 1991, Paleontological constraints on depositional modeling: examples of integration of biostratigraphy and seismic stratigraphy, Pliocene–Pleistocene, Gulf of Mexico, *in* P. Weimer and M.H. Link, eds., Seismic Facies and Sedimentary Processes of Submarine Fans and Turbidite Systems: New York, Springer-Verlag, p. 137–170.

______, 1993, Relative seal-level variations and fault-salt response: offshore Texas examples: Proceedings, Gulf Coast Section SEPM 14th Annual Research Conference, p. 1–7.

______, 1996, High-resolution sequence biostratigraphy: examples from the Gulf of Mexico Plio–Pleistocene, *in* J. Howell and J. Aiken, eds., High Resolution Sequence Stratigraphy: Innovations and Applications: The Geological Society of London Special Publication 104, p. 65–86.

______, and J.F. Clement, 1990, Biostratigraphic calibration of depositional cycles: a case study in High Island–Galveston–East Breaks areas, offshore Texas: Proceedings, Gulf Coast Section SEPM 11th Annual Research Conference, p. 21–51.

______, R.J. Echols, and T.D. Lee, 1990, Patterns of foraminiferal abundance and diversity: implications for sequence stratigraphic analysis: Expanded Abstracts, Gulf Coast Section 11th Annual Research Conference, p. 53–58.

_______, L.B. Fearn, K. Rodgers, S. Root, W.D. Lyle, D.C. Herrick, R.B. Bloch, J.W. Snedden, and B. Nwankwo, 1999, High-resolution sequence stratigraphy of a low-stand prograding deltaic wedge, Oso field (late Miocene), Nigeria, *in* R.W. Jones and M.D. Simmons, eds., Biostratigraphy in Production and Development Geology: Geological Society, London, Special Publication 152, p. 259–290.

_______, S.J. Malacek, P. Braithwaite, and C.R. Beeman, 1991, Seismic facies of slope basin turbidite reservoirs, East Breaks 160-161 field: Pliocene–Pleistocene, northwestern Gulf of Mexico, *in* P. Weimer and M.J. Link, eds., Seismic Facies and Sedimentary Processes of Submarine Fans and Turbidite Systems: New York, Springer-Verlag, p. 223–239.

_______, _______, L.B. Fearn, C.E. Sheppard, P.H. Naylor, A.W. Miles, R.J. Desmarais, and R.E. Dunay, 1993, Log-motif analysis of Paleogene depositional systems tracts, central and northern North Sea: defined by sequence stratigraphic analysis, *in* J.R. Parker, ed., Petroleum Geology of Northwest Europe: Proceeedings of the 4th Conference, The Geological Society of London, p. 45–57.

_______, _______, V.R. Mathur, G.L. Neuder, and G.M. Ragan, 1996, Intraslope basin reservoirs deposited by gravity-driven processes: south Ship Shoal and Ewing Banks areas, offshore Louisiana, *in* J.A. Pacht, R.E. Sheriff, and B.F. Perkins, eds., Stratigraphic Analysis: Utilizing Advanced Geophysical, Wireline, and Borehole Technology for Petroleum Exploration and Production: Proceedings, Gulf Coast Section SEPM 17th Annual Research Conference, p. 7–18.

_______, B.K. Rodgers, L.B. Fearn, R.B. Block, J.W. Snedden, W.D. Lyle, D.C. Herrick, and B. Nwankwo, 1997, Application of high resolution biostratigraphy, Oso field, Nigeria: Proceedings, Gulf Coast Section SEPM 18th Annual Research Conference, p. 13–20.

Bartek, L.R., P.R. Vail, J.B. Anderson, P.A. Emmet, and S. Wu, 1991, The effect of Cenozoic ice sheet fluctuations on the stratigraphic signature of the Neogene, *in* S. Cloetingh, ed., Long Term Sea Level Changes: Journal of Geophysical Research, vol. 96, 6753–6778.

Beard, J.H., J.B. Sangree, and L.A. Smith, 1982, Quaternary chronology, paleoclimate, depositional sequences, and eustatic cycles: AAPG Bulletin, vol. 66, p. 158–169.

Berggren, W.A., D.V. Kent, and J.A. Van Couvering, 1985, The Neogene: part 2. Neogene geochronology and chronostratigraphy, *in* N.J. Snelling, ed., The Chronology of the Geologic Record: Blackwell Scientific Publishing and Geological Society of London Memoir 10, p. 211–260.

Bilinski, P.W., D.T. McGee, D.S. Pfeiffer, and R.S. Shew, 1995, Reservoir characterization of the "S" sand, Auger field, Garden Banks 426, 427, 470, and 471, *in* R.D. Winn, Jr., and J.M. Armentrout, eds., Turbidites and Associated Deep-water Facies: SEPM (Society for Sedimentary Geology) Core Workshop No. 20, p. 75–93.

Blow, W.H., 1969, The late Middle Eocene to Recent Planktonic foraminiferal biostratigraphy: Proceedings, First Planktonic Conference, Geneva, p. 199–422.

Bouma, A.H., 1982, Intraslope basins in northwest Gulf of Mexico: a key to ancient submarine canyons and fans: AAPG Memoir 34, p. 567–581.

Brown, L.F., and W.L. Fisher, 1977, Seismic-stratigraphic interpretation of depositional systems: examples from Brazilian rift and pull-apart basins, *in* C.E. Payton, ed., Seismic Stratigraphy—Applications to Hydrocarbon Exploration: AAPG Memoir 26, p. 213–248.

Bruce, C.H., 1973, Pressured shale and related sediment deformation: mechanism for development of regional contemporaneous faults: AAPG Bulletin, vol. 57, p. 878–886.

Buffler, R.T., 1991, Early evolution of the Gulf of Mexico basin, *in* D. Goldthwaite, ed., An Introduction to Central Gulf Coast Geology: New Orleans Geological Society, p. 1–16.

Coleman, J.M., and H.H. Roberts, 1991, Mississippi River depositional system: model for the Gulf Coast Tertiary, *in* D. Goldthwaite, ed., An Introduction to Central Gulf Coast Geology: New Orleans Geological Society, p. 99–121.

Creaney, S., and Q.R. Passey, 1993, Recurring patterns of total organic carbon and source rock quality within a sequence stratigraphic framework: AAPG Bulletin, vol. 77, p. 386–401.

Culver, S.J., 1988, New foraminiferal depth zonation of the northwestern Gulf of Mexico: Palaios, vol. 3, p. 69–85.

Dow, W.G., M.A. Yukler, J.T. Senftle, M.C. Kennicutt II, and J.M. Armentrout, 1990, Miocene oil source beds in the East Breaks basin, Flex-Trend, offshore Texas: Proceedings, Gulf Coast Section SEPM 9th Annual Research Conference, p. 139–150.

Feng, J.C., and E.W. Behrens, 1993, A comparison of Plio-Pleistocene to Recent sediment accumulation rates in the East Breaks area, northwestern Gulf of Mexico: Proceedings, Gulf Coast Section SEPM 14th Annual Research Conference, p. 115–125.

Fiduk, J.C., and E.W. Behrens, 1993, A comparison of Plio-Pleistocene to Recent sediment accumulation rates in the East Breaks area, northwestern Gulf of Mexico: Proceedings, Gulf Coast Section SEPM 14th Annual Research Conference, p. 41–55.

_______, _______, and R.T. Buffler, 1989, Distribution and movement of salt on the Texas–Louisiana continental slope, Garden Banks and eastern East Breaks areas, Gulf of Mexico: Proceedings, Gulf Coast Section SEPM 10th Annual Research Conference, p. 39–47.

Frasier, D.E., 1974, Depositional episodes: their relationship to the Quaternary stratigraphic framework in the north-western portion of the Gulf basin: University of Texas at Austin, Bureau of Economic Geology Circular 74–1.

Galloway, W.E., 1989a, Genetic stratigraphic sequences in basin analysis I: architecture and genesis of flooding-surface bounded depositional units: AAPG Bulletin, vol. 73, p. 125–142.

_______, 1989b, Genetic stratigraphic sequences in basin analysis II: application to northwest Gulf of Mexico Cenozoic basin: AAPG Bulletin, vol. 73, p. 143–154.

_______, and T.A. McGilvery, 1995, Facies of a submarine canyon fill reservoir complex, lower Wilcox Group (Paleocene), central Texas coastal plain, *in* R.D. Winn, Jr., and J.M. Armentrout, eds., Turbidites and Associated Deep-Water Facies: WEPM Core Workshop 20, p. 1–23.

Gary, M., R. McAfee, Jr., and C.L. Wolf, 1974, Glossary of Geology: AGI, 805 p.

Goldthwaite, D., 1991, Central Gulf Coast stratigraphy, *in* D. Goldthwaite, ed., An Introduction to Central Gulf Coast Geology: New Orleans Geological Society, p. 17–30.

Golonka, J., M.I. Ross, and C.R. Scotese, 1993 , Phanerozoic paleogeographic and paleoclimatic modeling maps, *in* A.F. Embry, B. Beauchamp, and D.J. Glass, eds., Pangea—Global Environments and Resources: Canadian Society of Petroleum Geologists Memoir 17, p. 1–47.

Gross, O.P., K.C. Hood, L.M. Wenger, and S.C. Harrison, 1995, Seismic imaging and analysis of source and migration within an integrated hydrocarbon system study, northern Gulf of Mexico basin: Abstracts, 1st Latin American Geophysical Conference, p. 1–4.

Hall, D.J., B.E. Bowen, R.N. Rosen, S. Wu, and A.W. Bally, 1993, Mesozoic and early Cenozoic development of the Texas margin: a new integrated cross-section from the Cretaceous shelf edge to the Perdido fold belt: Selected Papers, Gulf Coast Section SEPM 13th Annual Research Conference, p. 21–31.

Hanor, J.S., and R. Sassen, 1990, Evidence for large-scale vertical and lateral migration of formation waters, dissolved salt, and crude oil in the Louisiana Gulf Coast: Proceedings, Gulf Coast Section SEPM 9th Annual Research Conference, p. 283–296.

Haq, B., J. Hardenbol, and P.R. Vail, 1988, Mesozoic and Cenozoic chronostratigraphy and cycles of sea-level change: SEPM Special Publication 42, p. 71–108.

Hedgpeth, J.W., 1957, Classification of marine environments: Geological Society of America Memoir 67, p. 17–27.

Herbin, J.P., J.L. Fernandez-Martinez, J.R. Geyssant, A.E. Albani, J.F. Deconinck, J.N. Proust, J.P. Colbeaux, and J.P. Vidier, 1995, Sequence stratigraphy of source rocks applied to the study of the Kimmeridgian/Tithonian in the North-West European shelf (Dorset/UK; Yorkshire/UK; Boulonnais/France): Marine and Petroleum Geology, vol. 12, no. 2, p. 177–194.

Ingram, R.J., 1991, Salt tectonics, *in* D. Goldthwaite, ed., An Introduction to Central Gulf Coast Geology: New Orleans Geological Society, p. 31–60.

Jackson, M.P.A., and W.E. Galloway, 1984, Structural and depositional styles of Gulf Coast Tertiary continental margins: applications to hydrocarbon exploration: AAPG Continuing Education Course Note Series 25, 226 p.

______, D.G. Roberts, and J.S. Snelson, eds., 1995, Salt Tectonics: AAPG Memoir 65, 454 p.

Jervey, M.T., 1988, Quantitative geologic modeling of siliciclastic rock sequences and their seismic expression: SEPM Special Publication 42, p. 47–69.

Jones, J.O., and R.L. Freed, eds., 1996, Structural Framework of the Northern Gulf of Mexico: Gulf Coast Assoc. of Geological Sciences, 112 p.

Joyce, J.E., L.R.C. Tjalsma, and J.M. Prutzman, 1990, High-resolution planktic stable isotope record and spectral analysis for the last 5.35 myr: ODP site 625 northeast Gulf of Mexico: Paleoceanography, vol. 5, p. 507–529.

Kennett, J.P., K. Elmstrom, and N. Penrose, 1985, The last deglaciation in Orca basin, Gulf of Mexico: high-resolution planktonic foraminiferal changes: Palaeogeography, Palaeoclimatology, Palaeoecology, vol. 50, p. 189–216.

Kneller, B., 1995, Beyond the turbidite paradign: physical models for deposition of turbidites and their implications for reservoir prediction, *in* A.J. Hartley and D.J. Prosser, eds., Characterization of Deep Marine Clastic Systems: Geological Society, London, Special Publication 94, p. 31–49.

______ and B. McCaffrey, 1995, Modelling the effects of salt-induced topography on deposition from turbidity currents, *in* C.J. Travis, H. Harrison, M.R. Hudec, B.C. Vendeville, F.J. Peel, and B.F. Perkins, eds., Salt, Sediment and Hydrocarbons: Gulf Coast Section SEPM Sixteenth Annual Research Conference, p. 137–145.

Kolb, C.R., and J.R. Van Lopik, 1958, Geology of the Mississippi River deltaic plain, southeastern Louisiana: U.S. Army Engineer Waterway Experiment Station, Corps of Engineers, Vicksburg, MS, Technical Report 3-483, 120 p.

Koyi, H., 1993, Modeling of segmentation and emplacement of salt sheets in anisotropic overburden: Selected Papers, Gulf Coast Section SEPM 13th Annual Research Conference, p. 135–142.

Lamb, J.L., W.W. Warnardt, T.C. Huang, and T.E. Dube, 1987, Practical application of Pleistocene eustacy in offshore Gulf of Mexico, *in* R.A. Ross and D. Haman, eds., Timing and Depositional History of Eustatic Sequences: Constraints on Seismic Stratigraphy: Cushman Foundation for Foraminiferal Research Special Publication 24, p. 33–39.

Loucks, R.G., and J.F. Sarg, eds., 1993, Carbonate Sequence Stratigraphy: AAPG Memoir 57, 545 p.

Loutit, T.S., J. Hardenbol, P.R. Vail, and G.R. Baum, 1988, Condensed sections: the key to age determination and correlation of continental margin sequences: SEPM Special Publication 42, p. 183–213.

MacQueen, R.W., and D.A. Leckie, eds., 1992, Foreland Basins and Fold Belts: AAPG Memoir 55, 460 p.

Magoon, L.B., and W.G. Dow, 1994, The Petroleum System: AAPG Memoir 60, p. 3–24.

Martin, R.E., and R.R. Fletcher, 1993, Biostratigraphic expression of Plio–Pleistocene sequence boundaries, Gulf of Mexico: Proceedings, Gulf Coast Section SEPM 14th Annual Research Conference, p. 119–126.

_______, E.D. Neff, G.W. Johnson, and D.E. Krantz, 1990, Biostratigraphic expression of sequence boundaries in the Pleistocene: the Ericson and Wollin zonation revisited: Proceedings, Gulf Coast Section SEPM 11th Annual Research Conference, p. 229–236.

Marton, G., and R.T. Buffler, 1993, The southeastern Gulf of Mexico in the framework of the opening of the Gulf of Mexico basin: Selected Papers, Gulf Coast Section SEPM 13th Annual Research Conference, p. 127–139.

McGee, D.T., P.W. Bilinski, P.S. Gary, D.S. Pfeiffer, and J.L. Sheiman, 1994, Geologic models and reservoir geometries of Auger field, deepwater Gulf of Mexico: Proceedings, Gulf Coast Section SEPM 15th Annual Research Conference, p. 245–256.

McGuinness, D.B., and J.R. Hossack, 1993, The development of allochthonous salt sheets as controlled by the rates of extension, sedimentation, and salt supply: Proceedings, Gulf Coast Section SEPM 14th Annual Research Conference, p. 127–139.

Miall, A.D., 1994, Paleocene 16: sequence stratigraphy and chronostratigraphy—problems of definition and precision in correlation, and their implications for global eustasy: Geoscience Canada, vol. 21, no. 1, p. 1–26.

Mitchum, R.M., Jr., 1977, Seismic stratigraphy and global changes in sea level, II: Glossary of terms used in seismic stratigraphy, *in* Seismic Stratigraphy—Applications in Hydrocarbon Exploration: AAPG Memoir 26, p. 205–212.

______, 1985, Seismic stratigraphic expression of submarine fans: AAPG Memoir 39, p. 117–136.

______, and J.C. Van Wagoner, 1990, High-frequency sequences and eustatic cycles in the Gulf of Mexico basin: Proceedings, Gulf Coast Section SEPM 11th Annual Research Conference, p. 257–267.

______, P.R. Vail, and J.B. Sangree, 1977, Stratigraphic interpretation of seismic reflection patterns in depositional sequences, *in* C.E. Payton, ed., Seismic Stratigraphy—Applications to Hydrocarbon Exploration: AAPG Memoir 26, p. 117–143.

Pacht, J.A., B.E. Bowen, J.H. Bearn, and B.L. Schaffer, 1990, Sequence stratigraphy of Plio–Pleistocene depositional facies in the offshore Louisiana south additions: Gulf Coast Assoc. of Geological Societies Transactions, vol. 40, p. 1–18.

Pflum, C.E., and W.E. Freichs, 1976, Gulf of Mexico deep water foraminifers: Cushman Foundation Foraminiferal Research Special Publication 14, 125 p.

Philippi, G.T., 1974, The influence of marine and terrestrial source material on the composition of petroleum: Geochim. Cosmochim. Acta, vol. 38., p. 947–966.

Piggott, N., and A. Pulham, 1993, Sedimentation rate as the control on hydrocarbon sourcing, generation, and migration in the deepwater Gulf of Mexico: Proceedings, Gulf Coast Section SEPM 14th Annual Research Conference, p. 179–191.

Pindell, J.L., 1993, Regional synopsis of Gulf of Mexico and Caribbean evolution: Proceedings, Gulf Coast Section SEPM 13th Annual Research Conference, p. 251–274.

Poag, C.W., 1981, Ecologic Atlas of Benthic Foraminifera of the Gulf of Mexico: Woods Hole Marine Science Institute, 174 p.

Posamentier, H.W., and P. Weimer, 1993, Siliciclastic sequence stratigraphy and petroleum geology: where to from here?: AAPG Bulletin, vol. 77, no. 5, p. 731–742.

______ and P.R. Vail, 1988, Eustatic controls on clastic deposition II—sequence and systems tract models: SEPM Special Publication 42, p. 125–154.

______, M.T. Jervey, and P.R. Vail, 1988, Eustatic controls on clastic deposition I—conceptual framework: an integrated approach: SEPM Special Publication 42, p. 109–124.

Prior, D.B., B.D. Bornhold, W.J. Wiseman, Jr., and D.R. Lowe, 1987, Turbidity current activity in a British Columbia fjord: Science, vol. 237, p. 1330–1333.

Prosser, 1993, Rift-related linked depositional systems and their seismic expression, *in* C.D. Williams and A. Dobb, eds., Tectonic and Seismic Sequence Stratigraphy: Geological Society Special Publication 71, p. 35–66.

Rouch, L.S., J.M. Armentrout, and S.A. Bowman, 1993, Iterative analysis of depositional sequences: computer simulation of seismically defined geometries, south Galveston and East Breaks areas, Gulf of Mexico: Proceedings, Gulf Coast Section SEPM 14th Annual Research Conference, p. 195–207.

Sarg, J.F., 1988, Carbonate sequence stratigraphy: SEPM Special Publication 42, p. 155–181.

Sassen, R., R.S. Tye, E.W. Chinn, and R.C. Lemoine, 1988, Origin of crude oil in the Wilcox Trend of Louisiana and Mississippi: evidence of long range migration: Gulf Coast Assoc. Geological Societies Transactions, vol. 38, p. 27–34.

Schanck, J.W., C.C. Cobb, and M.L. Ivey, Jr., 1988, East Breaks 160 field on the offshore Texas shelf edge: a model for deepwater exploration and development: Proceedings, 20th Annual Offshore Technology Conference, p. 157–162.

Shaffer, B.L., 1987a, The potential of calcareous nannofossils for recognizing Plio–Pleistocene climatic cycles and sequence boundaries on the shelf: Proceedings, Gulf Coast Section SEPM 8th Annual Research Conference, p. 142–145.

_______, 1987b, The nature and significance of condensed sections in Gulf Coast late Neogene sequence stratigraphy: Gulf Coast Assoc. of Geological Societies and Gulf Coast Section SEPM Transactions, vol. 40, p. 767–776.

_______, 1990, The nature and significance of condensed sections in Gulf Coast late Neogene sequence stratigraphy: Gulf Coast Assoc. of Geological Societies Transactions, vol. 40, p. 186–195.

Simmons, G.R., W.R. Bryant, G. Lee, and C. Fiduk, 1996, Regional distribution of salt and basin architecture in the northwestern Gulf of Mexico, *in* J.O. Jones and R.L. Freed, eds., Structural Framework of the Northern Gulf of Mexico: Gulf Coast Assoc. of Geological Societies Special Publication, p. 93–94.

Steel, R.J., V.L. Felt, E.P. Johannessen, and C. Mathiew, eds., 1995, Sequence Stratigraphy on the Northwest European Margin: Elsevier, 608 p.

Sutter, J.S., and H.L. Berryhill, Jr., 1985, Late Quaternary shelf-margin deltas, northwest Gulf of Mexico: AAPG Bulletin, vol. 69, p. 77–91.

Taylor, G.S., and J.M. Armentrout, 1990, Rock geochemistry and relationships to produced oils from upper Pliocene turbidites, High Island area, Gulf of Mexico: Proceedings, Gulf Coast Section SEPM 9th Annual Research Conference, p. 151–161.

Tearpock, D.J., and R.E. Bischke, 1991, Applied Subsurface Geologic Mapping: Prentice-Hall, 648 p.

Thompson, K.F.M., 1987, Fractionated aromatic petroleums and the generation of gas-condensates: Organic Geochemistry, vol. 11, p. 573–590.

______, M.C. Kennicutt II, and J.M. Brooks, 1990, Classification of offshore Gulf of Mexico oils and gas condensates: AAPG Bulletin, vol. 74, p. 187–198.

Tipsword, H.L.J., F.M. Setzer, and F.L. Smith, Jr., 1966, Interpretation of depositional environment in Gulf Coast exploration from paleoecology and related stratigraphy: Gulf Coast Assoc. of Geological Societies Transactions, vol. 16, p. 119–130.

Trippet, A.R., 1981, Characteristics of diapirs on the outer continental shelf–upper continental slope boundary, northwest Gulf of Mexico: Gulf Coast Assoc. of Geological Societies Transactions, vol. 31, p. 391–397.

Vail, P.R., 1987, Seismic stratigraphy interpretation procedure, *in* A.W. Bally, ed., Atlas of Seismic Stratigraphy: AAPG, p. 1–10.

______ and R.G. Todd, 1981, North Sea Jurassic unconformities, chronostratigraphy and seal-level changes from seismic stratigraphy: Proceedings, Petroleum Geology of the Continental Shelf, Northwest Europe, p. 216–235.

______ and W.W. Wornardt, 1990, Well log seismic stratigraphy: a new tool for exploration in the '90s: Proceedings, Gulf Coast Section SEPM 11th Annual Research Conference, p. 379–388.

______, J. Hardenbol, and R.G. Todd, 1984, Jurassic unconformities, chronostratigraphy and sea-level changes from seismic stratigraphy and biostratigraphy, *in* J.S. Schlee, ed., Interregional Unconformities and Hydrocarbon Accumulation: AAPG Memoir 36, p. 129–144.

______, R.G. Todd, and J.B. Sangree, 1977, Chronostratigraphic significance of seismic reflections, *in* C.E. Payton, ed., Seismic Stratigraphy—Applications to Hydrocarbon Exploration: AAPG Memoir 26, p. 99–116.

Van Wagoner, J.C., and G.T. Bertram, eds., 1995, Sequence Stratigraphy of Foreland Basin Deposits: AAPG Memoir 64, 487 p.

______, R.M. Mitchum, P.R. Vail, J.F. Sarg, T.S. Loutit, and J. Hardenbol, 1990, Siliciclastic Sequence Stratigraphy in Well Logs, Cores, and Outcrops: AAPG Methods in Exporation Series 7, 55 p.

______, H.W. Posamentier, R.M. Mitchum, P.R. Vail, J.F. Sarg, T.S. Loutit, and J. Hardenbol, 1988, An overview of the fundamentals of sequence stratigraphy and key definitions: an integrated approach: SEPM Special Publication 42, p. 39–45.

Visher, G.S., 1984, Exploration Stratigraphy: Tulsa, PennWell Books, 334 p.

Weimer, P., A.H. Bouma, and B.F. Perkins, eds., 1994, Submarine Fans and Turbidite Systems: Sequence Stratigraphy, Reservoir Architecture and Production Characteristics, Gulf of Mexico and International: Gulf Coast Section SEPM Foundation Fifteenth Annual Resesarch Conference Proceedings, 440 p.

Weimer, P., 1990, Sequence stratigraphy, facies geometries, and depositional history of the Mississippi fan, Gulf of Mexico: AAPG Bulletin, vol. 74, p. 425–453.

West, D.B., 1989, Model for salt deformation on deep margin of central Gulf of Mexico basin: AAPG Bulletin, vol. 73, p. 1472–1482.

Wheeler, H.E., 1964, Base level, lithosphere surface, and time stratigraphy: GSA Bulletin, vol. 75, p. 599–610.

White, D.A., 1980, Assessing oil and gas plays in facies-cycles wedges: AAPG Bulletin, vol. 64, p. 1158–1178.

Williams, D.F., and D.M. Trainor, 1987, Integrated chemical stratigraphy of deep-water frontier areas of the northern Gulf of Mexico: Proceedings, Gulf Coast Section SEPM 8th Annual Research Conference, p. 151–158.

Winker, C.D., 1982, Cenozoic shelf margins, northwestern Gulf of mexico: Gulf Coast Assoc. of Geological Societies Transactions, vol. 32, p. 427–448.

_______, 1996, High-resolution seismic stratigraphy of a late Pleistocene submarine fan ponded by salt-withdrawl minibasins on the Gulf of Mexico contentental slope: Proceedings, Offshore Technology Conference, no. 38, vol. 1, p. 619–628.

_______ and R.T. Buffler, 1988, Paleogeographic evolution of the early deep-water Gulf of Mexico and its margins, Jurassic to middle Cretaceous (Comanchean): AAPG Bulletin, vol. 72, p. 318–346.

_______ and M.B. Edwards, 1983, Unstable progradational clastic shelf margins: SEPM Special Publication 33, p. 139–157.

Winn, R.D., and J.M. Armentrout, eds., 1995, Turbidites and Associated Deep-water Facies: SEPM Core Workshop 20, 176 p.

Woodbury, H.O., I.B. Murray, P.J. Pickford, and W.H. Akers, 1973, Pliocene and Pleistocene depocenters, outer continental shelf, Louisiana and Texas: AAPG Bulletin, vol. 57, p. 2428–2439.

Wornardt, W.W., Jr., and P.R. Vail, 1990, Revisions of the Plio–Pleistocene cycles and their application to sequence stratigraphy of shelf and slope sediments in the Gulf of Mexico: Proceedings, Gulf Coast Section SEPM 12th Annual Research Conference, p. 391–397.

References, continued

Acknowledgments The author is indebted to several former and present co-workers at Mobil who shared their insight about the Gulf of Mexico. Tom Crutcher and Gil Taylor provided the initial orientation and demonstrated the power of data integration. Tom Lee, Jerry Ragan, Rick Becker, and Ron Echols helped clarify the utility of the fossil record. And George Gail provided astute observations about the petroleum systems. These people, many of the workers cited, all of the papers cited, and the overwhelming number of papers not cited but used over the years provided the basis for this chapter. The use of that information is entirely the responsibility of the author.

Special thanks is due to Ted Beaumont for the invitation to contribute to the volume and for his patience through three rewrites as we adapted a more traditional text to the information mapping format. The initial draft was reviewed and improved thanks to Ron Echols, Vivian Hussey, and George Gail. This final manuscript benefited significantly from reviews by Les Magoon, George Gail, Ron Echols, Ken Tillman, Arlene Anderson, Kris Meisling, Alan Cunningham, and Ted Beaumont. The figures were drafted by Greg Dill and David Helber. Mobil Exploration and Producing Technical Center Inc. approved publication of the paper, and TGS-Calibre Geophysical Company authorized inclusion of the seismic reflection profiles.

Chapter 5

Formation Fluid Pressure and Its Application

by

Edward A. Beaumont

and

Forrest Fiedler

Edward A. Beaumont

Edward A. (Ted) Beaumont is an independent petroleum geologist from Tulsa, Oklahoma. He holds a BS in geology from the University of New Mexico and an MS in geology from the University of Kansas. Currently, he is generating drilling prospects in Texas, Oklahoma, and the Rocky Mountains. His previous professional experience was as a sedimentologist in basin analysis with Cities Service Oil Company and as Science Director for AAPG. Ted is coeditor of the Treatise of Petroleum Geology. He has lectured on creative exploration techniques in the U.S., China, and Australia and has received the Distinguished Service Award and Award of Special Recognition from AAPG.

Forrest Fiedler

Forrest Fiedler earned his Bachelor of Arts and Science degree in geology from Lehigh University in 1957 and his Master of Science in geology from Virginia Polytechnic Institute in 1967. He worked as a mine geologist in Canada and assistant state highway geologist in Virginia before moving to the oil industry. Fiedler's petroleum experience was entirely with Amoco (and its predecessors). Throughout his career, he worked on projects throughout the world in positions ranging from geologist and formation evaluator to research supervisor and regional reservoir engineering supervisor. He retired in 1989 as an engineering associate.

Overview

Introduction

Oil and gas are fluids. Pressure is one the main elements characterizing the physical behavior of fluids in the subsurface. Understanding pressure concepts and their applications is critical to effective petroleum exploration.

This chapter discusses the characteristics and behavior of fluids (liquids and gases) and the pressures manifested by subsurface fluid behavior. It also discusses how an understanding of fluid pressure can be applied to oil and gas exploration.

In this chapter

This chapter contains the following sections.

Section A

Pressure Regimes

Introduction

Pressure is a measure of force per unit area. Pressure in the subsurface is a function of the densities of rocks and fluids. This section discusses different pressure regimes, mainly concentrating on formation fluid pressures.

In this section

This section contains the following topics.

Normal Hydrostatic Pressure

Fluids

A fluid is "a substance (as a liquid or gas) tending to flow or conform to the outline of its container" (Webster, 1991). Thus, the explorationist should think of oil, gas, and water as fluids to understand their behavior in the subsurface. In this chapter, where the fluid state (liquid or gaseous) is important, the state (or phase) is specified.

Fluid pressure

Fluid pressure is that pressure exerted at a given point in a body of fluid.

Hydrostatic pressure

Normal hydrostatic pressure is the sum of the accumulated weight of a column of water that rises uninterrupted directly to the surface of the earth. **Normally pressured** fluids have a great degree of continuity in the subsurface through interconnected pore systems. **Abnormally pressured** fluids can occur where fluids are completely isolated in containers (compartments) that are sealed on all sides.

Hydrostatic mud pressure

The geological definition of "hydrostatic" differs from the engineering definition. Engineers use "hydrostatic" to refer to the pressure exerted by the mud column in a borehole at a given depth. Hydrostatic mud pressures are found on DST (drill-stem test) reports and on scout ticket reports of DSTs.

Properties of hydrostatic pressure

Normal hydrostatic pressure has the following properties (Dahlberg, 1994):

- Amount of pressure increases with depth.
- Rate of pressure change depends only on water density.
- Vector representing the direction of maximum rate of pressure increase is vertical (i.e., the fluid is not flowing laterally).
- The pressure–depth relationship is completely independent of the shape of the fluid container.

Static vs. dynamic fluids

Fluid pressure is nondirectional if the fluid is static. If a pressure imbalance exists in any direction, the fluid moves in the direction of lower fluid pressure. The diagrams below illustrate balanced and unbalanced pressures.

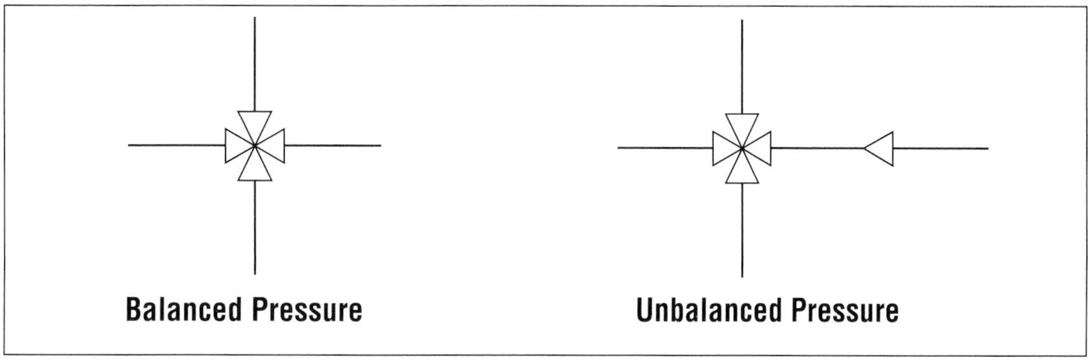

Figure 5–1.

Geostatic and Lithostatic Pressure

Definitions

The **geostatic pressure** at a given depth is the vertical pressure due to the weight of a column of rock and the fluids contained in the rock above that depth. **Lithostatic pressure** is the vertical pressure due to the weight of the rock only.

Geostatic variables

Three variables determine geostatic pressure:

- Densities of formation waters as related to salinities
- Net thickness of different lithologies, e.g., sandstone, shale, limestone
- Porosities of different lithologies

Calculating geostatic pressure

We can calculate geostatic pressure using the formula below:

$$P_G = [\text{weight of rock column}] + [\text{weight of water column}]$$

$$P_G = [\rho_m \times (1 - \phi) \times d\,] + [\rho_w \times \phi \times d]$$

where:

P_G	=	geostatic pressure (psi)
ρ_m	=	weighted average of grain (mineral) density (sandstone and shale = 2.65 g/cm^3, limestone = 2.71 g/cm^3)
ρ_w	=	weighted average of pore-water density (g/cm^3)
ϕ	=	weighted average of rock porosity
d	=	depth (ft)

To calculate weighted averages, use 1000-ft (300-m) increments.

Geostatic gradient

Geostatic gradient is the rate of change of geostatic pressure with depth. A geostatic gradient of 1 psi/ft results from an average density of 2.3 g/cm^3.

How geostatic gradient varies

Geostatic gradients vary with depth and location. The gradient increases with depth for two reasons:

1. Rock bulk density increases with increasing compaction.
2. Formation water density increases because the amount of total dissolved solids (TDS) in the water increases with depth.

For example, in the Cenozoic of Louisiana, the geostatic gradient is 0.85 psi/ft at 1000 ft and 0.95 psi/ft at 14,000 ft.

Normal Hydrostatic Pressure Gradients

Definition

The hydrostatic pressure gradient is the rate of change in formation fluid pressure with depth. Fluid density is the controlling factor in the normal hydrostatic gradient. In the U.S. Rocky Mountains, a formation water gradient of 0.45 psi/ft is common. In the U.S. Gulf Coast, a gradient of 0.465 psi/ft is common.

Factors controlling fluid density

Fluid density changes with depth as a result of changes in the following factors:

- Temperature
- Pressure
- Fluid composition (including dissolved gases and solids)
- Fluid phase—gaseous or liquid

These factors must be taken into account when estimating fluid pressure at depth. The small amount of dissolved gas contributes little to the density and can be ignored in the exploration state.

Factors controlling oil density

Oil density varies greatly because of the large variety of oil compositions and quantity of dissolved gases. Also, oil composition is inherently much more variable than formation water composition.

Factors controlling gas density

Gas density is strongly affected by pressure, temperature, and composition. In the reservoir, gas may be in the liquid phase; if so, we should treat it as a very light oil.

Predicting gas phase can be complicated. Consult an experienced reservoir engineer when making this prediction.

Ranges of fluid density and gradient variation

Oil-field liquids and gases occur in a wide range of compositions. The table below shows typical density ranges and gradients for gas, oil, and water. However, because exceptions occur, have some idea of the type of fluid(s) expected in the area being studied and use appropriate values.

Fluid	Normal density range (g/cm^3)	Gradient range (psi/ft)
Gas (gaseous*)	0.007–0.30	0.003–1.130
Gas (liquid)	0.200–0.40	0.090–0.174
Oil	0.400–1.12	0.174–0.486
Water	1.000–1.15	0.433–0.500

*Varies with pressure, temperature, and composition. The composition used for this table is for an average gas composed of 84.3% methane, 14.4% ethane, 0.5% carbon dioxide, and 0.8% nitrogen (GO Log Interpretation Reference Data Handbook, 1972).

Abnormal Hydrostatic Pressure

Definition

Abnormal hydrostatic pressure is a departure from normal fluid pressure that is caused by geologic factors. The term "geopressure" was introduced originally by Shell Oil Company to refer to overpressured intervals in the U.S. Gulf Coast. "Geopressure" is gradually being replaced by the more descriptive terms "overpressure" and "underpressure."

Causes

Abnormal fluid pressures may be caused by any of the following:

- Uplift
- Burial
- Rock compaction or dilation
- Abnormal heat flow

Abnormal pressures develop when fluid is unable to move into or out of the local pore system fast enough to accommodate to the new environment. Such a pore system must be isolated from the surrounding system by impermeable barriers for abnormal pressure to exist.

The table below shows the generally accepted major causes of abnormal fluid pressure.

Overpressure	**Underpressure**
Uplift	Burial
Heat increase	Heat decrease
Compaction Generation of hydrocarbons	Dilation of pores

Multiple simultaneous causes

More than one mechanism may operate simultaneously or sequentially to create abnormal pressure. For example, burial of a sealed compartment carries a trapped fluid pressure into a deeper environment. The pressure in the compartment compared with the surrounding environment would be abnormally low. The higher temperature at depth would slowly raise the pressure in the compartment to normal.

It may not be possible to predict the existing condition of the pressure system in examples like this because the combined effects of all the variables are often not well known in advance.

Causes of Overpressure

Introduction

When a fluid pressure is higher than estimated from the normal hydrostatic fluid gradient for a given depth, it is called overpressure. For this situation to occur, the fluid must first be trapped within a rock unit (pressure compartment).

Overpressure can be caused by uplift, increased heat, compaction, generation of hydrocarbons, or a combination of these factors.

Uplift

A unit can be uplifted into a regime of lower normal pressure. The encapsulated fluid then is at a pressure higher than that found at the new depth in surrounding formations where the fluid is under normal constraints.

The diagrams below illustrate this situation.

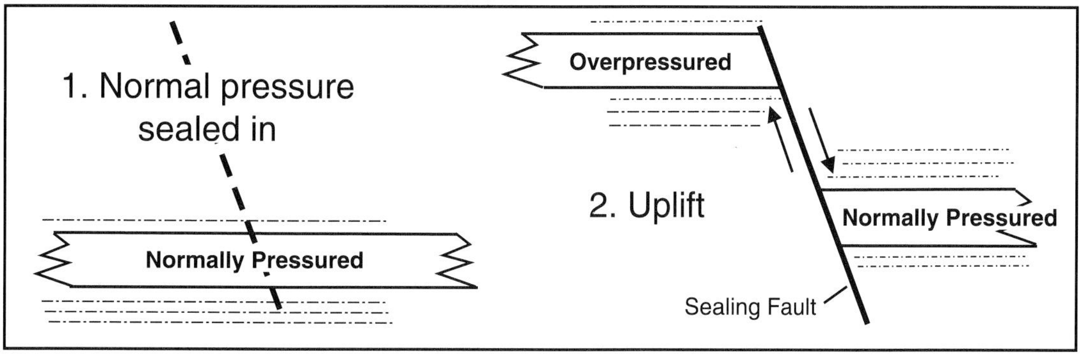

Figure 5–2.

Heat increase

Perhaps the most common way that pressure is increased is for the encapsulated fluid to be heated. The trapped fluid, unable to expand into adjacent pore systems, rises in pressure. Fluids outside the area of trapping are free to adjust to the heating, so they remain at about normal pressure.

Compaction

As an encapsulated rock mass is buried, it tends to compact. Under normal conditions, as the porosity is reduced, the interstitial fluid is expelled. When the fluid cannot escape, the pressure within the encapsulated rock mass rises. This higher fluid pressure takes on some of the overburden load, limiting the amount of compaction. In such cases, the fluid is overpressured and the rock matrix is undercompacted.

Causes of Underpressure

Introduction

Underpressure exists when a fluid pressure is lower than estimated from the normal hydrostatic fluid gradient for that depth at which it occurs. For this situation to exist, the fluid must be trapped within a rock unit.

Underpressure can be caused by burial or heat decrease.

Burial

If the encapsulated unit is buried deeper, its original pressure is carried to a higher pressure environment. If the rock cannot compact, the trapped pressure is abnormally low for the new depth.

As long as a rock unit remains encapsulated by impermeable rocks, it becomes underpressured by burial as faulting or as downwarp occurs.

The diagrams below illustrate this phenomenon.

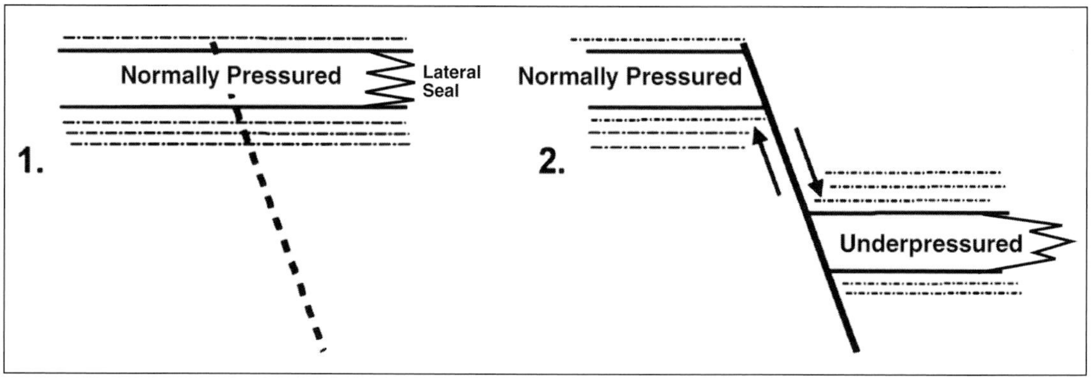

Figure 5–3.

Heat decrease

The major factor causing underpressure is the cooling of pore fluids as they are uplifted and the overburden erodes. For example, drain a bottle filled with hot water and immediately seal the bottle back up by screwing on the cap. The bottle will be underpressured as it cools to room temperature.

This same phenomenon occurs when an encapsulated rock unit is uplifted into a region of lower temperature. However, predicting pressure in uplifted rock units is difficult. Because uplift brings a rock unit from a region of high pressure to a region of low pressure, the uplifted unit may be at a higher-than-expected pressure, a lower-than-expected pressure, or normal pressure, depending on the state of equilibration.

Section B

Using Pressures to Detect Hydrocarbon Presence

Introduction

Buoyancy pressures caused by hydrocarbon columns can be recognized by comparing hydrostatic pressure gradients with formation pressures. Pressures exceeding expected hydrostatic pressures could be due to the presence of hydrocarbon columns.

Two items are critical for detecting buoyancy pressure in a well:

- Accurate static water plot for the well
- Reliable formation fluid pressure measurements

This section discusses how to detect the presence of hydrocarbons using formation fluid pressures.

Procedure

The table below outlines a procedure for using pressures to detect the presence of a hydrocarbon column in a formation.

Step	Action
1	Make a hydrostatic pressure–depth plot through the interval of interest.
2	Plot the pressure(s) measured from the interval of interest.
3	If the measured formation pressures are greater than the hydrostatic pressure, then the formation may contain a hydrocarbon column.
4	Check to see if anomalous pressures make geological sense. **Example:** Measured fluid pressure is 250 psi over the static water pressure. The formation is believed to contain 30°API gravity oil, and the total vertical trap closure is 500 ft. **Solution:** If the 250-psi pressure is due to the presence of a hydrocarbon column, then a column of 2500 ft of 30°API gravity oil would have to be present in the trap (assuming a freshwater gradient). Vertical trap closure is only 500 ft; therefore, the measured formation pressure does not match the geology and is probably wrong.

In this section

This section contains the following subsections.

Subsection B1

Determining Hydrostatic Pressure Gradient

Introduction

A critical element in detecting the presence of hydrocarbons using formation fluid pressures is an accurate hydrostatic pressure gradient for zones of interest. We use the hydrostatic pressure gradient to determine the expected pressures for the zone of interest as if it had no hydrocarbons. Pressures exceeding hydrostatic pressures may be due to the presence of a hydrocarbon column. Most methods for determining hydrostatic pressures are not very precise. Other petrophysical data can help when the estimated hydrostatic pressure gradient is suspect.

In this subsection

This subsection contains the following topics.

Constructing a Hydrostatic Pressure–Depth Plot

Introduction

The goal of constructing a hydrostatic pressure–depth plot is to identify pressures greater than the hydrostatic gradient that may correspond to a hydrocarbon-bearing zone. A hydrostatic pressure–depth plot can be constructed from any of the following:

- Measured pressures
- Regional rule-of-thumb pressure gradients
- Pressures calculated from water density

Calculated pressures are much less accurate than measured pressures but can be used with some effectiveness when they are supplemented with other petrophysical data.

Procedure: Constructing a plot

The table below outlines a procedure for constructing a hydrostatic pressure–depth plot for a single well.

Step	Action
1	Using graph paper with a linear grid, label the X-axis as pressure and the Y-axis as depth. Use as large a scale as possible. Also, make the Y-axis on at least one plot the same scale as on the well logs to aid in interpretation.
2	Plot measured pressure from the aquifers (100% S_w) in the well. If none is available, go to step 3.
3	Plot measured pressure from the aquifers in nearby wells. If none is available, go to step 4.
4	Calculate and plot hydrostatic pressures for a depth above and a depth below the zone of interest. Use the rule-of-thumb pressure gradient for that zone. If it is not available, calculate the gradient from the water density using density measured from the formation water or calculated from R_w. For help, see the following sections.

Calculating pressure gradients from water density

The formation fluid pressure at any depth in a well is a function of the average formation water density (ave. ρ_w) above that depth, not the density of the formation water at any particular depth. Formation water generally becomes more dense with increasing depth.

To calculate water pressure gradient (P_{grad}), use the following formula:

$$P_{grad} = \text{ave. } \rho_w \times 0.433 \text{ psi/ft}$$

where:

$$\text{ave. } \rho_w = \frac{\sum_1^n \rho_w}{n}$$

ρ_w = water density

For example, given ave. $\rho_w = 1.13$, the equation works as follows:

$$P_{grad} = 1.13 \times 0.433 \text{ psi/ft} = 0.489 \text{ psi/ft}$$

Table of water pressure gradients

The table below lists hydrostatic pressure gradients, water density, and salinity in weight percent total dissolved solids (TDS).

Gradient (psi/ft)	Density (g/cc)	TDS (ppm)	TDS (wt %)
04.33	1.000	<7,000	0
0.437	1.010	13,500	13.5
0.441	1.020	27,500	27.5
0.444	1.029	37,000	37.0
0.445	1.030	41,400	41.4
0.451	1.040	55,400	55.4
0.454	1.050	69,400	69.4
0.459	1.060	83,700	83.7
0.463	1.070	98,400	98.4
0.465	1.075	100,000	100.0
0.467	1.080	113,200	113.2
0.471	1.090	128,300	128.3
0.476	1.100	143,500	143.5
0.480	1.110	159,500	159.5
0.485	1.120	175,800	175.8
0.489	1.130	192,400	192.4
0.491	1.135	200,000	200.0
0.493	1.137	210,000	210.0
0.500	1.153	230,000	230.0
0.510	1.176	260,000	260.0

Rules of thumb

Most sedimentary basins have a rule of thumb for average hydrostatic water pressure gradients. For the Gulf Coast basin, it is 0.465 psi/ft. For Rocky Mountain basins, it is 0.45 psi/ft. For fresh water, it is 0.433 psi/ft. If measured hydrostatic pressure is not available for a well, find out the accepted rule-of-thumb average hydrostatic pressure gradient for the depth of the zone of interest where the well is located.

Example of TDS vs. depth

Water density is a function of its TDS concentration. The hydrostatic pressure at any depth is a function of TDS concentration from the surface to that point. The plot below of TDS vs. depth is from southern Arkansas. It shows a gradual increase in TDS from the surface to about 2000 ft, probably due to meteoric effects, and then a linear, more rapid increase in TDS from 2000 to 10,000 ft. Generally, below the depth of meteoric water influence, the increase in TDS in connate brines is linear and ranges from 25,000 to 100,000 mg/l per 1000 ft (80 to 300 mg/l per m) (Dickey, 1969). There are exceptions to this general case.

Such consistent salinity increase with depth is not unique to the East Texas basin but is characteristic of most basins.

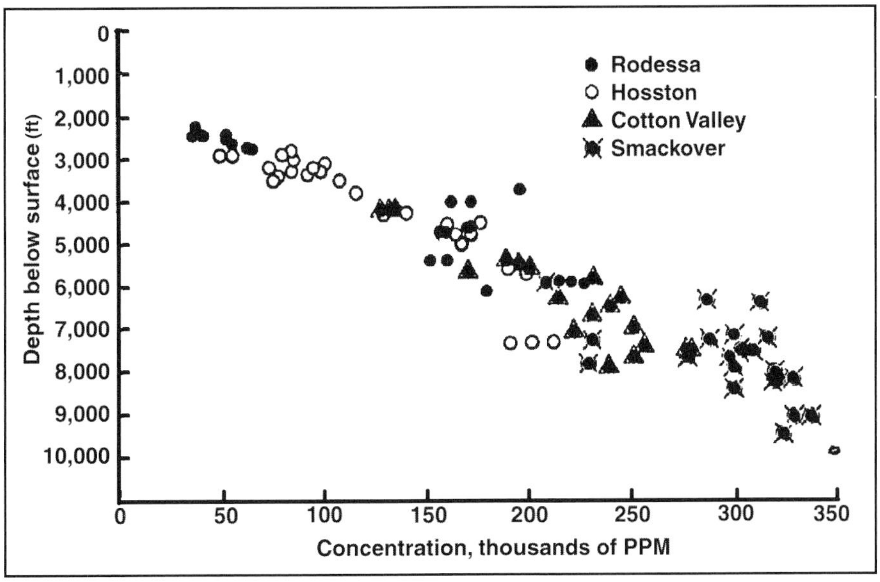

Figure 5–4. From Dickey, 1969; courtesy Chemical Geology.

Estimating Formation Water Density

Introduction

Formation water density is a function of three variables:

- Temperature
- Pressure
- Total dissolved solids (TDS)

It is the mass of the formation water per unit volume of the formation water and is given in metric units (g/cm^3). For reservoir engineering calculations, it is considered equivalent to specific gravity.

Estimating density from TDS

If TDS is known from a chemical analysis of formation water, then the formula below can be used to estimate formation water density (ρ_w) (Collins, 1987):

$$\rho_w = 1 + TDS \times 0.695 \times 10^{-6} \text{ g/cm}^3$$

Procedure: Estimating density from R_w

Use the procedure outlined in the table below to estimate formation water density at reservoir conditions using R_w. The approximate error is ±10% (after Collins, 1987).

Step	Action
1	Gather data: formation temperature (T_f), water resistivity (R_w), and formation pressure. Estimate pressure by multiplying depth by 0.433 psi/ft or other appropriate gradient. Check for T_f errors.
2	Estimate sodium chloride (NaCl) concentration from R_w using Figure 5–5.
3	Estimate density from wt % NaCl and temperature using Figure 5–6.

Step 1: Gather data

To estimate formation water density, collect estimates of the following:

- Formation temperature
- Formation pressure
- Formation water resistivity

Step 1: Gather data (continued)

Step	Action
1	Estimate **formation temperature** (T_f) using the following formula: $$T_f = T_s + D_f\left(BHT - \frac{T_s}{TD}\right)$$ where: T_s = average surface temperature (°F); D_f = depth to the formation (ft); BHT = bottom-hole temperature (found on log header) (°F); TD = total depth (BHT and TD must be from the same log run) (ft)
2	Estimate **formation pressure** (psi) by multiplying 0.433 (freshwater gradient) by formation depth.
3	Obtain **formation water resistivity** (R_w) (ohm-m) in one of three ways: • From a sample of water from the formation of interest measured for R_w • Using a water catalog • Calculating it from an SP log

Step 2: Determine NaCl concentration from R_w

The predominant solute in most formation water is sodium chloride (NaCl). Its concentration determines formation water density and R_w. When only R_w is available, we can use NaCl concentration to determine density.

Use Figure 5–5 below to determine NaCl concentration. At the intersection of formation temperature (from Y-axis) and R_w (from X-axis), find the NaCl concentration (in ppm) by reading diagonal line labels and interpolating.

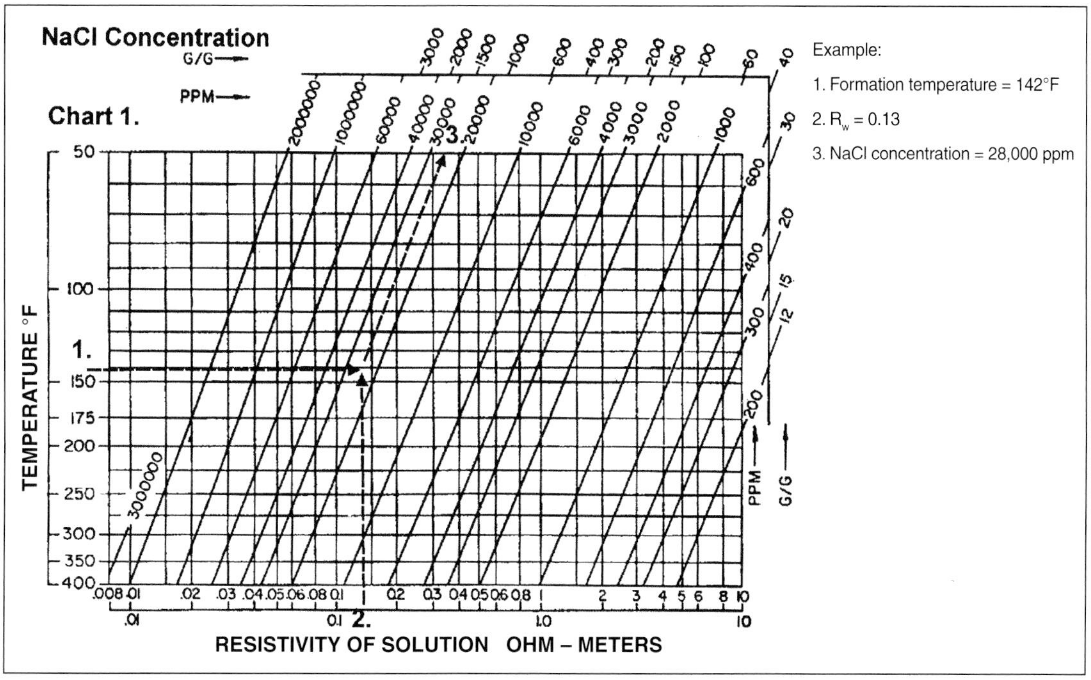

Figure 5–5. Courtesy Schlumberger.

Estimating Formation Water Density, continued

Steps 3 & 4: Estimate density

Estimate formation water density from ppm NaCl and temperature using the chart below. The following table describes the procedure to use with the chart.

Step	Action
1	Enter the chart along the X-axis using formation temperature.
2	Proceed vertically to the appropriate salt concentration expected in the zone.
3	Proceed horizontally to read the liquid density at atmospheric pressure.
4	Using the "Effects of Pressure" segment of the chart, add a density increment to the above-computed density to correct for pressure effects.

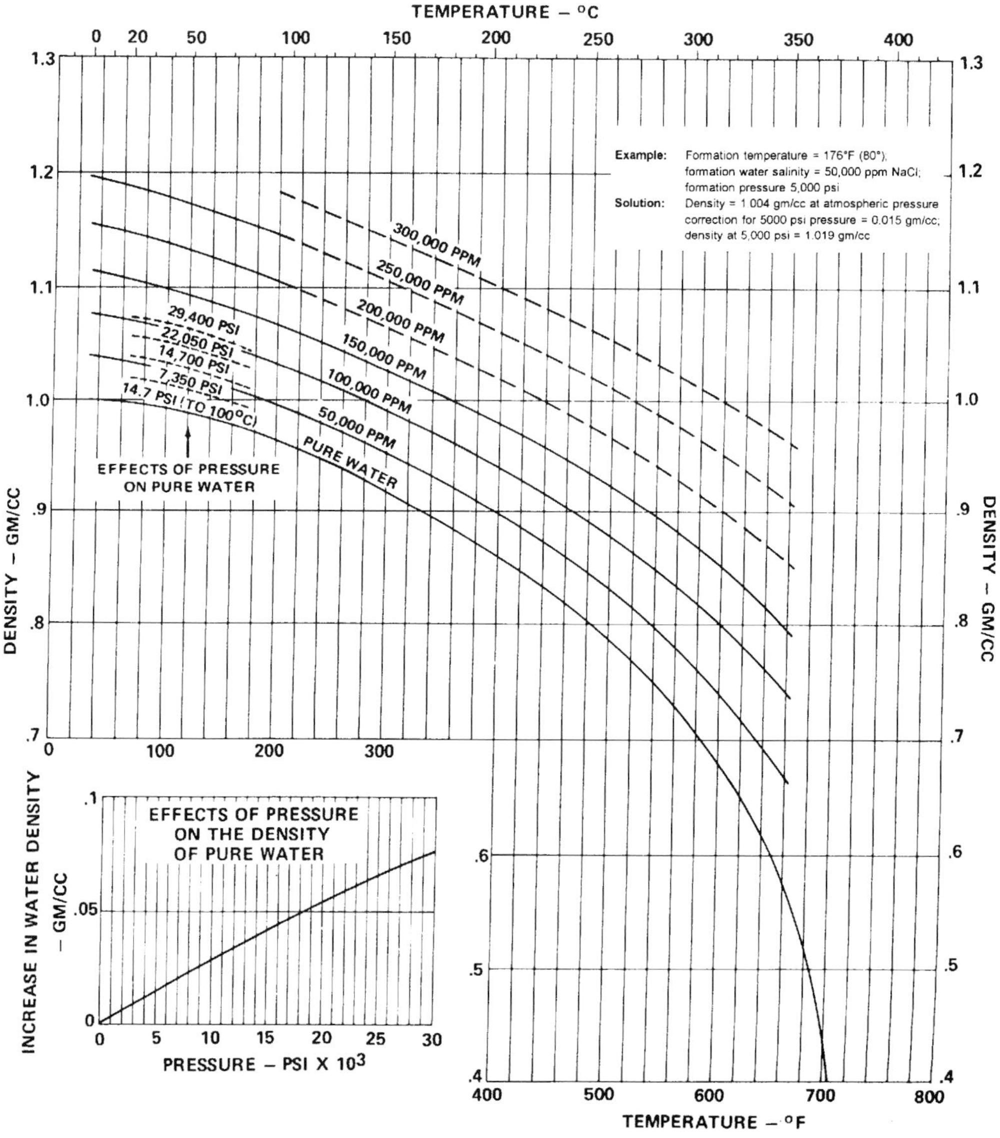

Figure 5–6. Courtesy Gearhart-Owens (1972).

Subsection B2

Static Hydrocarbon Pressure Gradients

Introduction

We can determine the downdip hydrocarbon column length by plotting a reservoir's static hydrocarbon pressure gradient vs. its hydrostatic pressure gradient. Hydrocarbon densities determine static hydrocarbon pressure gradients. The gradient is easily calculated when the density is measured. When density is not measured, charts are available to help estimate density.

This subsection shows how to determine oil and gas pressure gradients, make a plot of hydrocarbon pressure gradient, and determine hydrocarbon column length.

In this subsection

This subsection contains the following topics.

Estimating Static Oil Pressure Gradients

Introduction

The static oil pressure gradient is dependent on oil density. Subsurface density of oil or condensate depends on composition, amount of dissolved gases, temperature, and pressure. Oil or condensate density can be estimated to useful accuracy if stock tank API gravity and solution gas–oil ratio (GOR) are known (Schowalter, 1979).

Estimating oil pressure gradients

Follow the steps listed below to estimate static oil pressure gradient.

Step	Action
1	Estimate oil density using Figure 5–7 below.
2	Estimate oil pressure gradient using the following formula: $$P_{oil\ grad} = \rho_{oil} \times 0.433 \text{ psi/ft}$$ where: $P_{oil\ grad}$ = oil pressure gradient; ρ_{oil} = oil density

Determining oil density

Use the figure below to determine oil density. If the GOR is unknown or if there is no dissolved gas in the oil, use the 0 line.

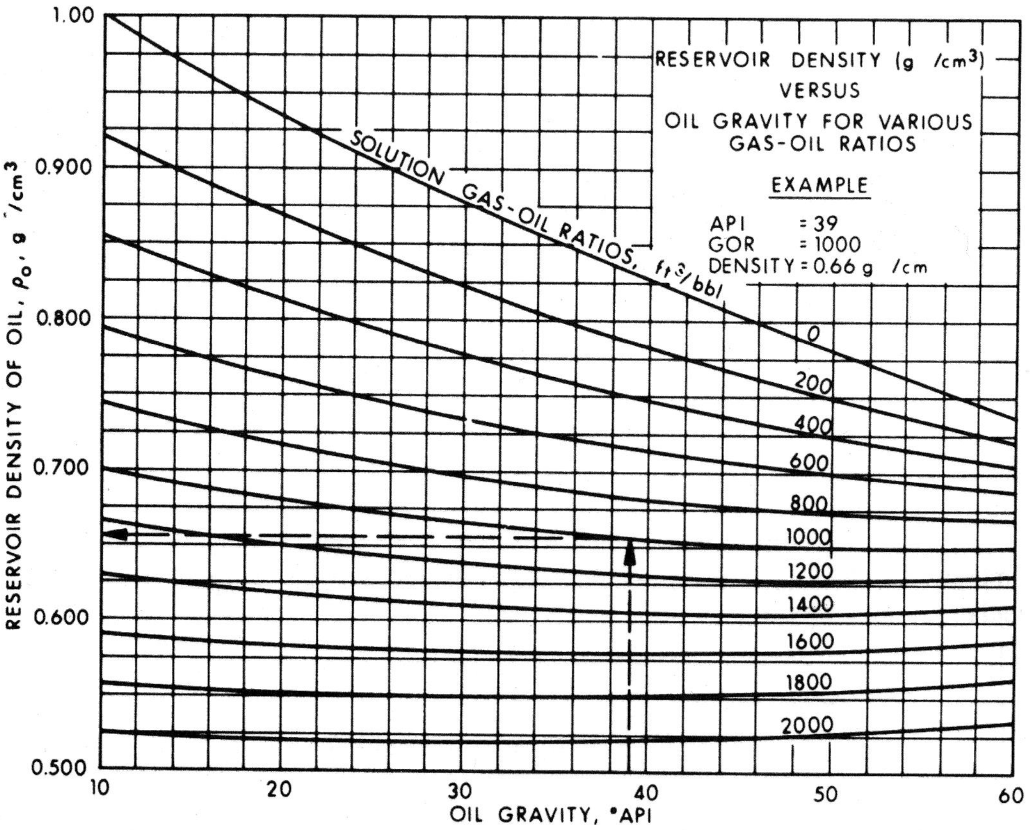

Figure 5–7. From Schowalter, 1979; courtesy AAPG.

Estimating Static Gas Pressure Gradients

Introduction

The static gas pressure of a gas reservoir is a function of gas density. Static gas pressure gradients can be estimated if subsurface gas density is known or has been estimated.

Subsurface gas density is dependent on the ratio of its mass to its volume. Mass is related to the apparent molecular weight of the gas. Volume is related to pressure, temperature, and the apparent molecular weight of the gas.

At atmospheric pressures and temperatures, gas density can be estimated using the Ideal Gas Law. At subsurface temperatures and pressures, gas molecules are so close to one another that they interact enough to change ideal gas behavior. A compressibility factor, z, is added to the Ideal Gas Law to correct for subsurface gas behavioral changes.

Procedure: Estimating gas pressure gradient

Follow this procedure to estimate the gas pressure gradient of a gas reservoir or potential gas reservoir.

Step	Action
1	• If data are available on gas composition and formation temperature go to step 2. • If no data on gas composition or formation temperature are available, estimate gas density from the average gas chart (Figure 5–11) and go to Step 6.
2	Determine the apparent molecular weight of the gas mixture.
3	Read pseudoreduced temperature and pressure from Figure 5–8.
4	If not already known, estimate compressibility factor, z, from Figure 5–9.
5	Using information obtained from steps 2, 3, and 4, estimate gas density from Figure 5–10.
6	Estimate gas pressure gradient using the following formula: $P_{gas\ grad} = \rho_{gas} \times 0.433$ psi/ft where: $P_{gas\ grad}$ = gas pressure gradient ρ_{gas} = gas density

Determining molecular weight

The apparent molecular weight of a gas mixture is equal to

$$MW_{app} = MF_1(MW_1) + MF_2(MW_2) + \ldots MF_x(MW_x)$$

where:

MW_{app} = apparent molecular weight of the gas mixture
MF_x = mole fraction of a component of the mixture
MW_x = molecular weight of a component of the mixture

Determining molecular weight (continued)

To practice, use these values for a gas mixture:

- Composition = 50% methane, 25% ethane, 25% propane
- Molecular weight of carbon (C) = 12
- Molecular weight of hydrogen (H) = 1
- Molecular weight of methane (CH_4) = 12 + 4 = 16
- Molecular weight of ethane (C_2H_6) = 24 + 6 = 30
- Molecular weight of propane (C_3H_8) = 36 + 8 = 44

$$MW_{app} = 0.5(16) + 0.25(30) + 0.25(44) = 8 + 7.5 + 11 = 26.5$$

Determining pseudoreduced temperature and pressure

We can determine the pseudoreduced temperature and pressure from the figure below. In the example, apparent molecular weight is 23, reservoir temperature is 200°F, and reservoir pressure is 2500 lb.

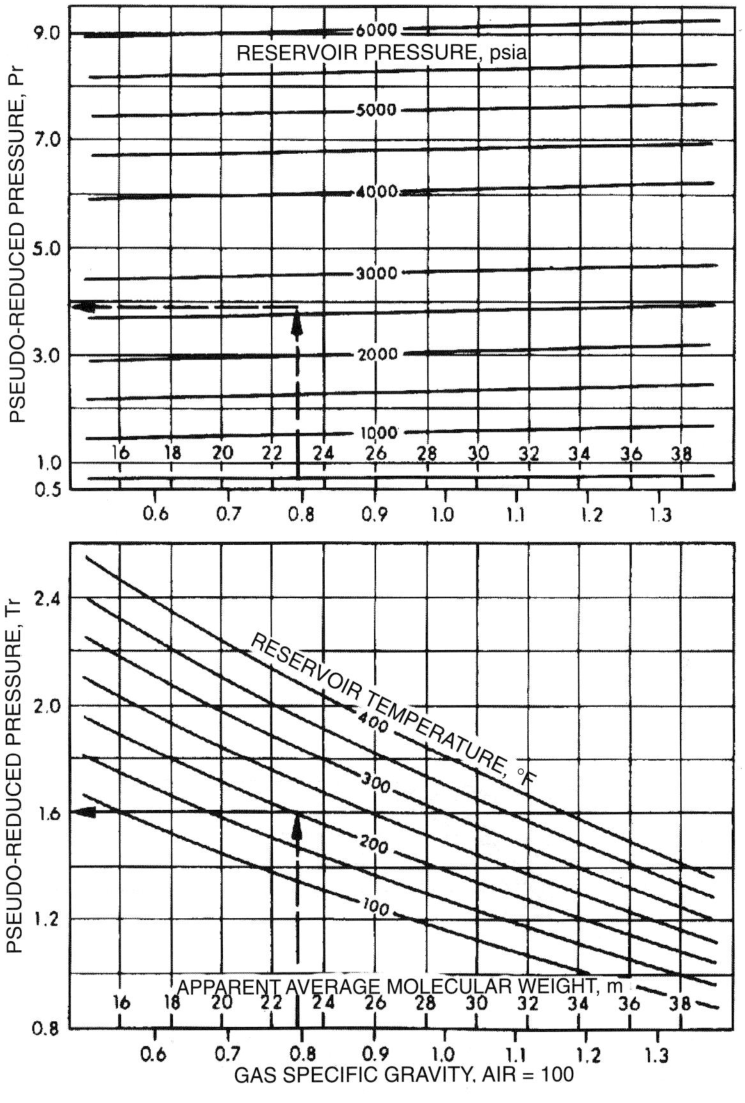

Figure 5–8. From Schowalter, 1979; courtesy AAPG.

Determining *z* The gas compressibility factor, *z*, for the gas reservoir of interest may already be known because it was measured. In this case, use that value. If *z* is not known, use the figure below to determine it from the pseudoreduced temperature and pressure determined from Figure 5–8. Figure 5–9 uses values determined for Figure 5–8.

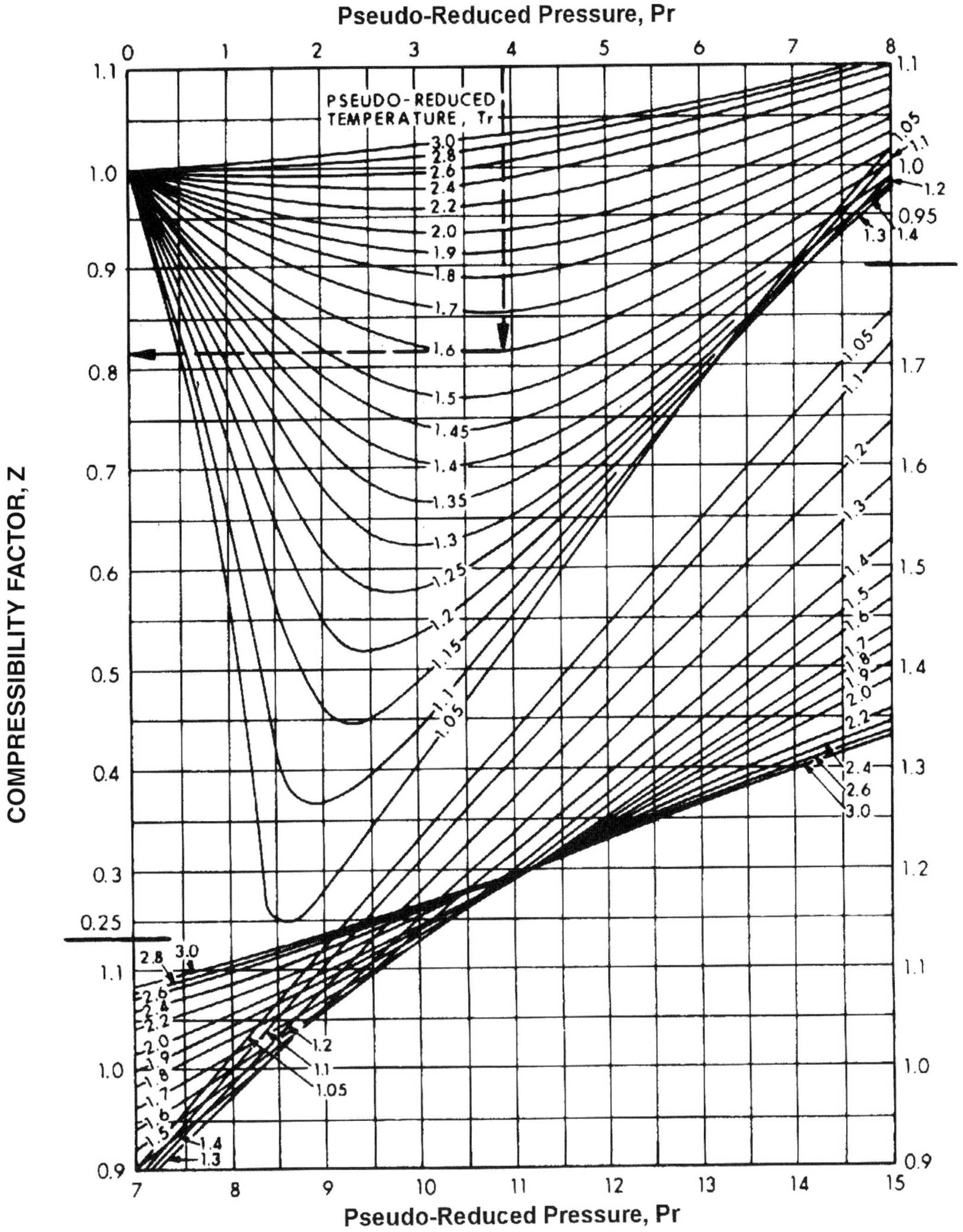

Figure 5–9. From Schowalter, 1979; courtesy AAPG.

Determining subsurface gas density

We can determine gas density from the figure below, knowing reservoir pressure, reservoir temperature, gas compressibility factor, and apparent molecular weight.

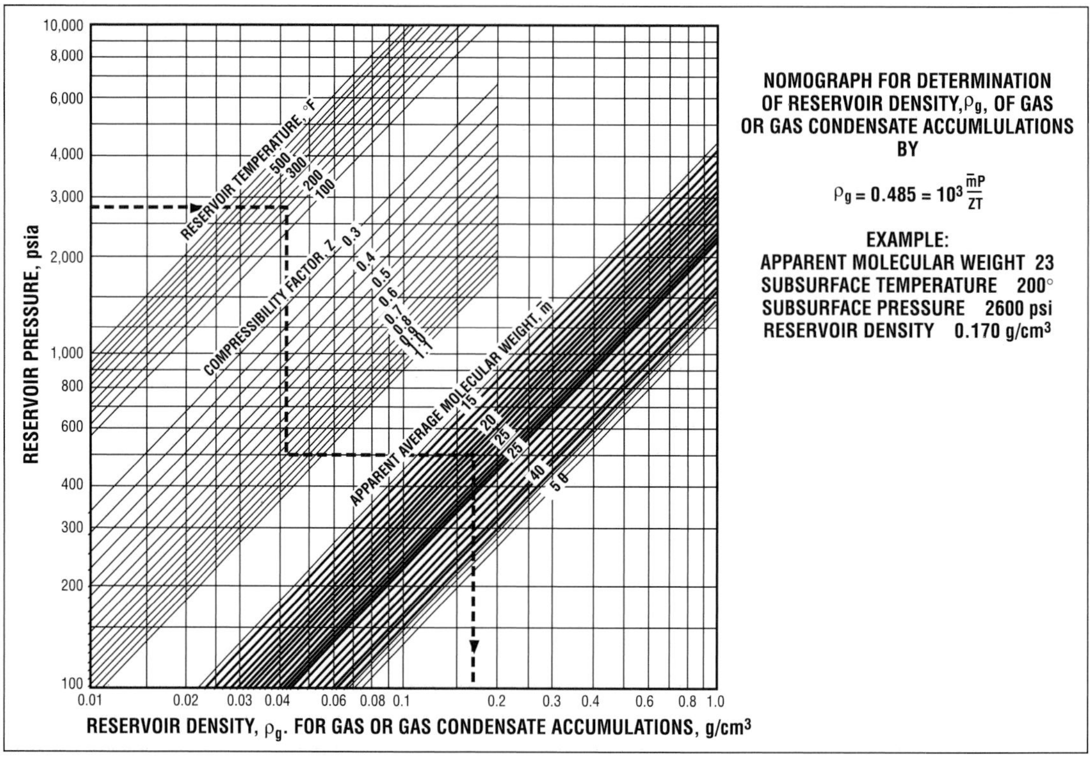

Figure 5–10. From Schowalter, 1979; courtesy AAPG.

Average natural gas

According to Gerhardt-Owens (1970), average natural gas estimated by Stephens and Spencer is considered to be 84.3% methane, 14.4% ethane, 0.5% carbon dioxide, and 0.8% nitrogen. However, many natural gas wells have produced almost pure methane (99%). Others have produced up to 88% ethane, 42% propane, 99% nitrogen, and 91% carbon dioxide. Using the accompanying average gas chart (Figure 5–11) is completely satisfactory is most cases.

Estimating subsurface gas density

We can estimate gas density from Figure 5–11. The chart assumes an average gas composition and was made using the following:

- Formation temperature = 80°F plus 0.8° per 100 ft of depth
- Formation fluid pressure gradient = 0.465 psi per ft of depth
- Supercompressibility factors used from George G. Brown, University of Michigan

Estimating subsurface gas density (continued)

The formula used to determine reduction in volume and the accompanying increase in density of a given gas (because of changes in temperature and pressure) is

$$V = V_1 \times P_{a1}/P_a \times T_a/T_{a1} \times z/z_1$$

where:

V	=	volume, ft^3	T_a	=	absolute temperature, °R
V	=	original volume ft^3	T_{a1}	=	original absolute temperature, °R
P_a	=	pressure, psia	z	=	supercompressibility factor
P_{a1}	=	original pressure, psia	z_1	=	original supercompressibility factor

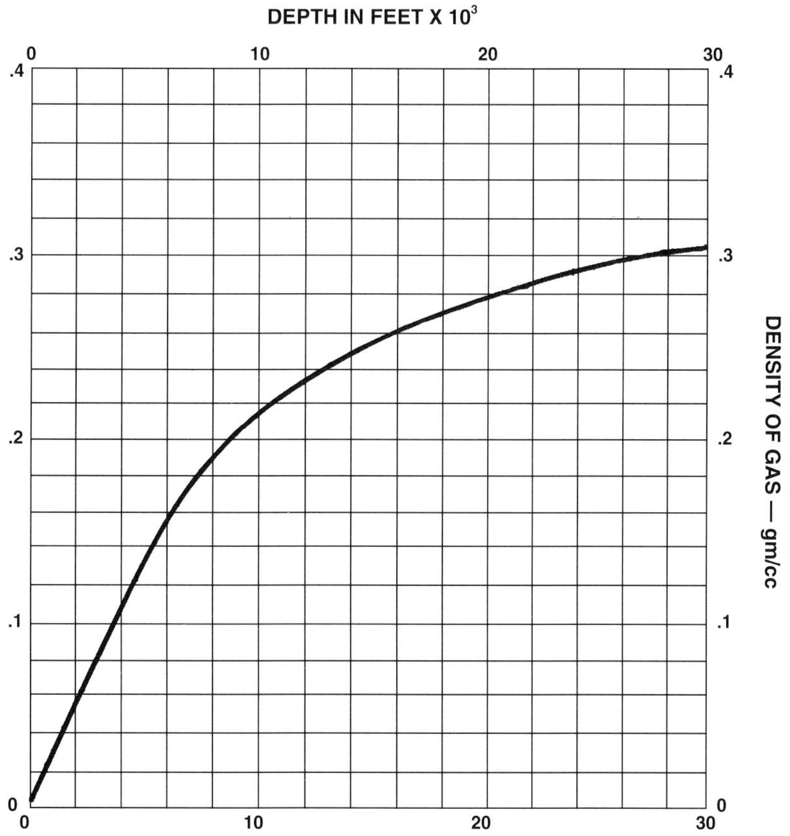

Figure 5–11. Courtesy Gearhart-Owens, 1970.

Plotting the Hydrocarbon Pressure Gradient

Introduction

We can estimate the downdip free-water level from a valid fluid pressure measured within a reservoir.

Plotting gradient

The table below outlines the procedure for plotting a hydrocarbon pressure gradient on a hydrostatic pressure plot when a measured pressure is available from the reservoir.

<table>
<tr><th>Step</th><th>Action</th></tr>
<tr><td>1</td><td>Plot measured fluid pressure on a hydrostatic pressure–depth plot.</td></tr>
<tr><td>2</td><td>Determine the hydrocarbon pressure gradient from one of two ways:
• Measured hydrocarbon density
• Estimates of hydrocarbon density</td></tr>
<tr><td>3</td><td>Determine the buoyancy pressure gradient: static water pressure gradient minus hydrocarbon pressure gradient.</td></tr>
<tr><td>4</td><td>Determine a pressure above or below the measured depth point. The table below lists the steps for determining this number.
<table>
<tr><th>Step</th><th>Action</th></tr>
<tr><td>1</td><td>Pick a depth above or below the measured point.</td></tr>
<tr><td>2</td><td>Multiply the difference in depth by the buoyancy pressure gradient.</td></tr>
<tr><td>3</td><td>Add the number from step 2 to the measured pressure if the depth is deeper; subtract if shallower.</td></tr>
</table>
Example:
Measured pressure at 7607 ft is 3530 psi and buoyancy pressure gradient is 0.076 psi/ft. What is the hydrocarbon pressure at 7507 ft?
Solution:
7607 – 7507 = 100 ft
100 ft × 0.076 psi/ft = 7.6 psi
Hydrocarbon pressure at 7507 ft = 3530 psi – 7.6 psi = 3522.4 psi</td></tr>
<tr><td>5</td><td>Plot the pressure number from step 4 on the pressure–depth plot and draw a line between this point and the measured pressure point. This line is the hydrocarbon pressure gradient.</td></tr>
</table>

Finding Free-Water Level Using Pressure

Introduction

The free-water level occurs where buoyancy pressure is zero in the reservoir–aquifer system. It defines the downdip limits of an accumulation. Pressure data reliability affects the resolution; however, resolution improves when it is supplemented with other petrophysical information.

Procedure: Using RFT data

An easy method for determining free-water level (FWL) is projecting RFT pressure data downward from a reservoir to the aquifer. The figure below illustrates the procedure.

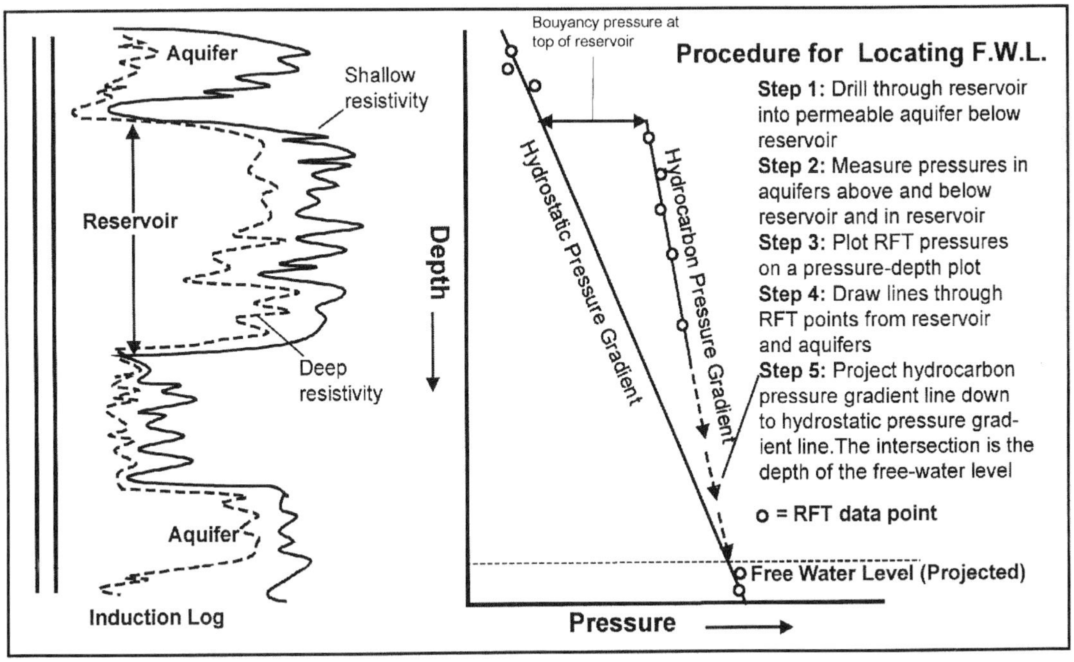

Figure 5–12.

Procedure using a single measurement

The table below outlines the procedure for determining the free-water level using a single pressure buildup point in the reservoir.

Step	Action
1	Determine buoyancy pressure (P_b) at the depth of the measured pressure (P_m) from the measured pressure: $$P_b = P_m - P_{hydrostatic}$$
2	Determine buoyancy pressure gradient (P_{bg}): $$P_{bg} = P_{hydrostatic\ pressure\ gradient} - P_{hydrocarbon\ pressure\ gradient}$$
3	Calculate downdip length of hydrocarbon column (h): $$h = \frac{P_b}{P_{bg}}$$

Procedure using a single measurement (continued)

As an example, let's determine the downdip length of a 30°API oil column with the following givens:

P_m = 3555 psi at 7611 ft
$P_{hydrostatic}$ = 3525 psi
$P_{hydrostatic\ pressure\ gradient}$ = 0.465 psi/ft
$P_{hydrocarbon\ pressure\ gradient}$ = 0.38 psi/ft

Answer (tied back to steps above):

Step 1:

$$P_b = P_m - P_{hydrostatic} = 3555 - 3525 = 30 \text{ psi}$$

Step 2:

$$P_{hydrostatic\ pressure\ gradient} - P_{hydrocarbon\ pressure\ gradient} = 0.465 - 0.38 = 0.085 \text{ psi/ft}$$

Step 3:

$$h = \frac{P_b}{P_{bg}} = \frac{30 \text{ psi}}{0.054 \text{ psi/ft}} = 556 \text{ ft}$$

Therefore, the free-water level is at 8167 ft.

Subsection B3

Methods for Obtaining Formation Fluid Pressures

Methods

Methods for obtaining formation fluid pressures can be divided into two groups: measured and estimated. The table below lists the methods by these two categories.

Measured	Estimated
• Using RFT (repeat formation tester) data • Using reservoir bottom-hole pressure buildup tests • Using DST shut-in pressures	• Calculating hydrostatic pressures from measured water density or salinity • Estimating hydrostatic pressures from fluid density using R_w (formation water resistivity) • Using the weight of drilling mud • Using the rule-of-thumb pressure gradient, 0.465 psi/ft

Accuracy of measured pressures

RFTs, DSTs, and bottom-hole pressure buildup tests measure formation fluid pressures. Pressure gauge accuracy is a critical factor in all three tests, but the BHP measurement is generally more precise due to the greater time taken for the test. Generally, two types of gauges measure pressures: strain and quartz. The table below shows the accuracy and precision of both types.

Gauge Type	Accuracy (% Full Scale)	Precision
Strain Gauge	0.18	< 1 psi
Quartz Gauge	0.025	0.01 psi

In this subsection

This subsection contains the following topics.

Determining Formation Fluid Pressure from DSTs

Introduction

A drill-stem test, or DST, is the most common method to measure reservoir pressure. DSTs are the most reliable reservoir pressure measurement method if sufficient time elapses during the test for the higher formation pressure to equilibrate with the lower borehole pressure. Pressures often must be extrapolated. Irregular boreholes cause tool problems, and assessing the reliability of a DST is often more of an art than a science.

Types of periods during a DST

There are three major types of periods during a typical DST:

- During **run-in or run-out periods**, drilling fluid flows through ports in the tool wall and pressure gauges respond to the weight of the drilling fluid column. The tester valve is closed.
- During **flowing periods,** an interval of the borehole is sealed off from the rest of the borehole by one (bottom hole) or two (straddle) inflatable packers. The tester valve is opened, creating a pressure drop in the tool which sucks fluids into the tool and drillpipe string. Recovered volumes of oil, gas, water, or drilling mud are recorded.
- During **shut-in periods,** the packer(s) is still inflated and the tester valve is closed. Ideally, pressure in the closed tool gradually builds up until it reaches equilibrium with the pressure of the isolated formation.

The figure below shows a typical DST tool, the configurations of the tool during a DST, and the periods of a DST.

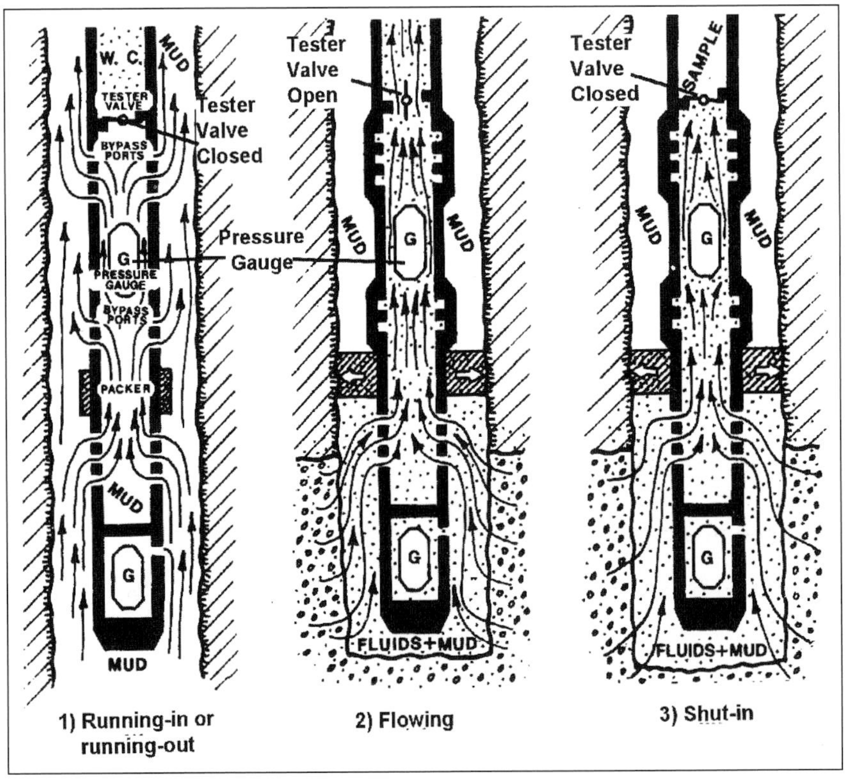

Figure 5–13. Modified from Dalhberg, 1994; courtesy Springer-Verlag.

Determining Formation Fluid Pressure from DSTs, continued

A DST plot

During a DST, pressure is continuously recorded against time. The record begins as the DST tool is lowered down the borehole and ends when the tool returns to the surface. The figure below is a DST plot, showing the various pressures recorded during the different DST periods.

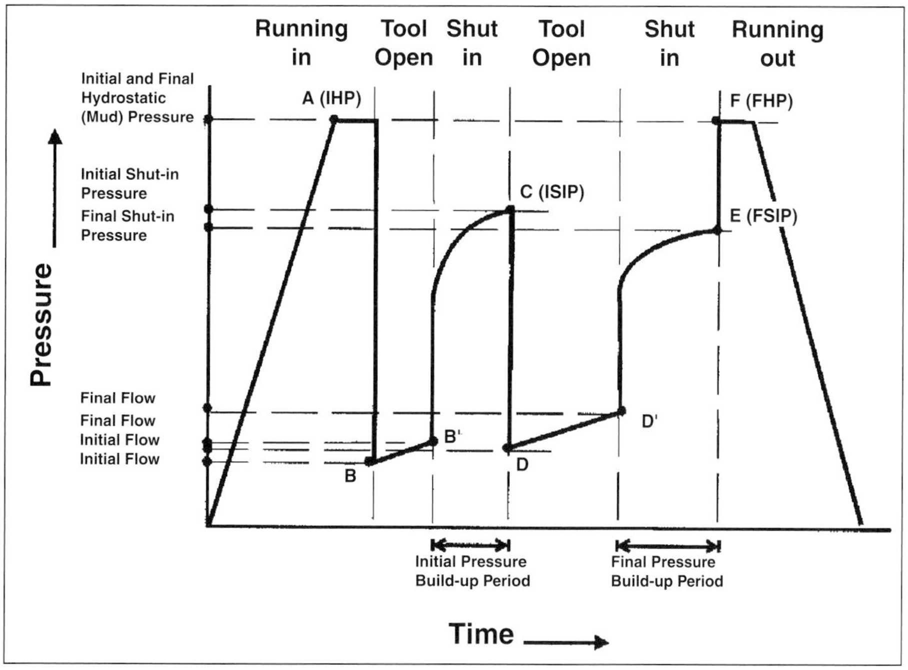

Figure 5–14.

Point A is the initial hydrostatic pressure (IHP), the pressure exerted by the mud column in the borehole at the depth where the recorder is located.

Points B to B′ are the pressures recorded when the tool is opened up to the formation and fluids flow up the drillpipe. B is the initial flowing pressure; B′ is the final flowing pressure.

Point C is the initial shut-in pressure (ISIP). It is measured while the tool is closed. The rapid expulsion of fluid from the reservoir during the preceding flow period causes reservoir pressure to drop near the wellbore. ISIP is the pressure in the reservoir after the first shut-in period. The duration of this shut-in time is determined by the operator and should be planned in advance of the test.

Points D to D′ are the pressures recorded during the next flow period. This flow period (and subsequent flow periods, in some cases) usually lasts longer than the first in order to test the productivity of the reservoir.

Point E is the final shut-in period (FSIP). It records the pressure in the reservoir after the last shut-in period.

Point F is the final hydrostatic pressure (FHP), the pressure of the mud column at the test depth after the test was performed. It should match the IHP within 5 psi as a check of the tool's accuracy (assuming the packers did not leak).

Extrapolating true pressures

DST pressures may not be reliable because the tool is not shut in long enough for pressure to stabilize at final reservoir pressure. A graphical procedure devised by Horner (1951) infers the true reservoir pressure by extrapolating the shut-in periods to infinity.

Below is an example showing how pressure is extrapolated from ISIP and FSIP on a Horner plot (pressure vs. psuedo or Horner time, or $(T + \Delta T)/\Delta T$.

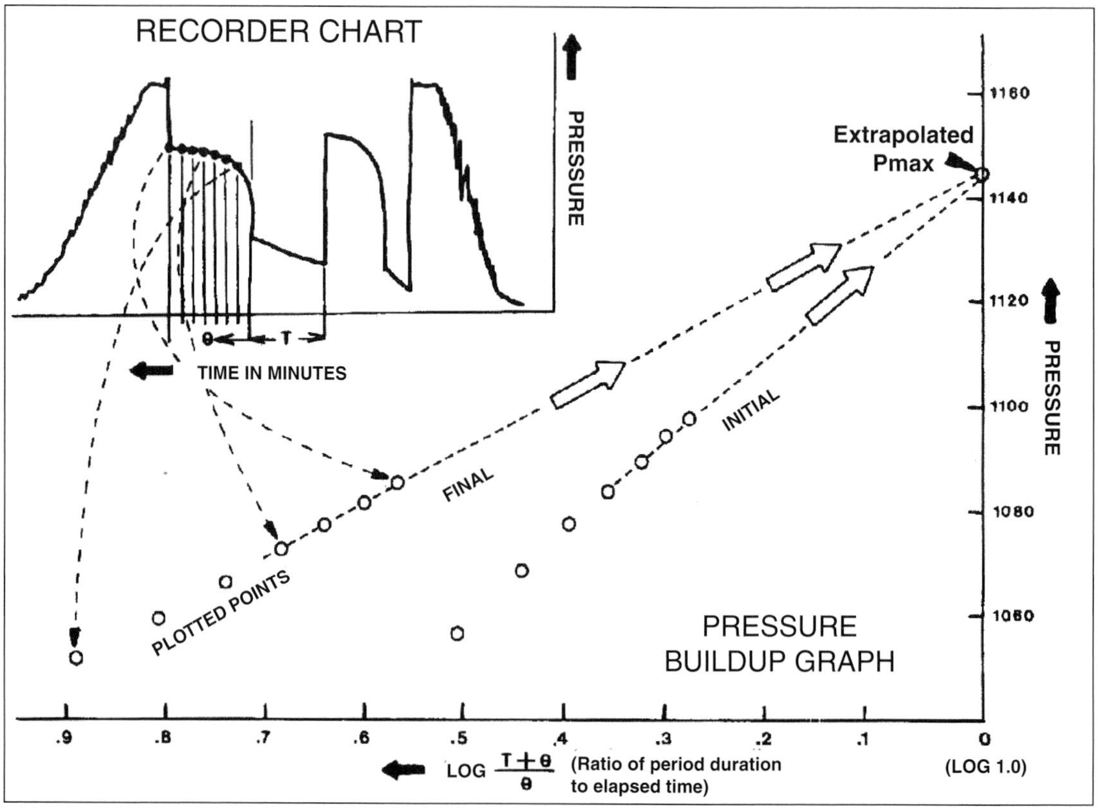

Figure 5–15. From Dahlberg, 1994; courtesy Springer-Verlag.

DST pressures from scout tickets

Scout tickets are a common source of fluid pressure data. They list the duration of various episodes, the pressures measured during the episode, and the amount and types of fluids recovered. How reliable are scout ticket data and which pressure should one use for formation fluid pressure? As an example, Dahlberg (1994) studies 27 DSTs for formation pressure reliability. He extrapolates the reported pressures to true formation pressure using a Horner plot and finds that pressures must be increased an average of 10 psi.

During a DST, two pressures measure the fluid pressure of the formation being tested: the ISIP and the FSIP. The higher is usually closest to true formation fluid pressure. In many cases, it is the ISIP.

Determining Formation Fluid Pressure from RFTs

RFT tool

The repeat formation tester (RFT) tool was designed to measure formation pressure quickly and accurately. It measures pressure at specific points on the borehole wall. The diagram below shows a typical RFT tool. Formation pressure is measured by the formation sampler (see diagram) when it is extended from the tool to contact the formation. Fluid samples from the formation can also be taken with the tool.

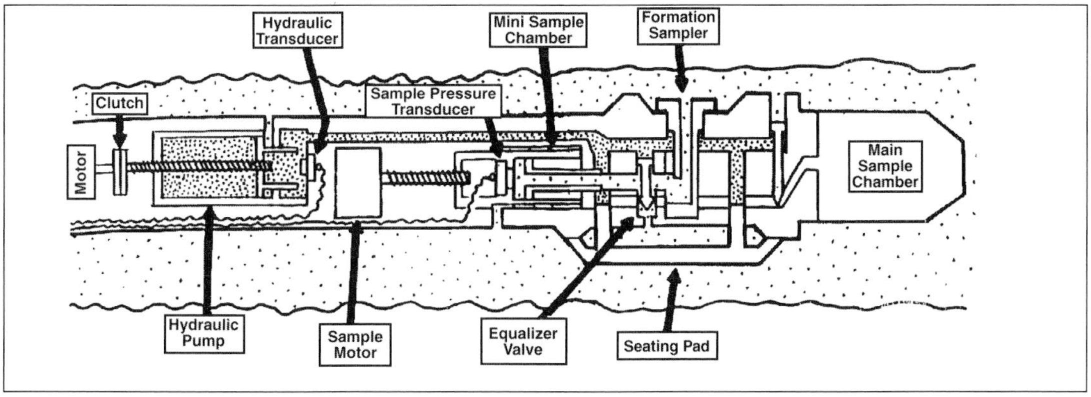

Figure 5–16. Fom Dahlberg, 1994; courtesy Springer-Verlag.

Differences between RFTs and DSTs

An RFT has several important advantages for formation pressure measurement over a DST. The table below lists some considerations.

Consideration	RFTs	DSTs
Time to take one measurement	Less than 5 minutes for permeable formations	More than 90 minutes
Drilling delay to run test	About one logging run (wireline conveyed)	About equal to two trips with drillstring
Sampling interval	Small, < 1 in. (< 2 cm); can test a single flow unit	Several feet or more; generally tests multiple flow units
Samples per run	Many	Few
Expense per test	Small	Large
Purpose of tool	Pressure measurement	Fluid recovery and pressure
Survey problems	• Getting good seat to measure pressure • Screen plugging with material in drilling mud	• Packer failure • Depth determination
Fractured reservoir	May be unreliable	Good if fractures intersect wellbore
Layered reservoir	Not representative	Good if many layers are included in tested interval
Skin damage	Can be major error	Can be measured and corrected for

Example: Comparing RFT to DST

Below is a plot of reservoir pressure vs. depth from a low-permeability chalk reservoir. The RFT data clearly show the hydrostatic gradient, the gas gradient, and the gas–water contact. Making the same interpretation from the DST data in this example is very difficult because data are from a low-permeability chalk reservoir. Reliable pressures are difficult to obtain in low-permeability reservoirs with DSTs. Extrapolated DST shut-in pressures from a partial buildup may not reflect actual fluid pressures. As rock quality increases, extrapolated pore pressure from DST buildup falls more and more closely to actual fluid pressure.

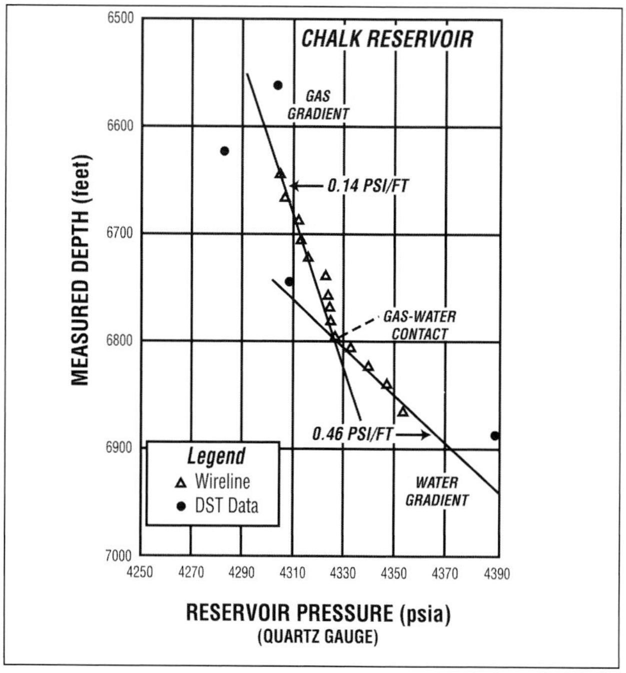

Figure 5–17. From Gunter and Moore, 1987; courtesy JPT.

RFT pressure profile

Below is a typical RFT pressure–time profile. Points are similar to points on a DST pressure profile.

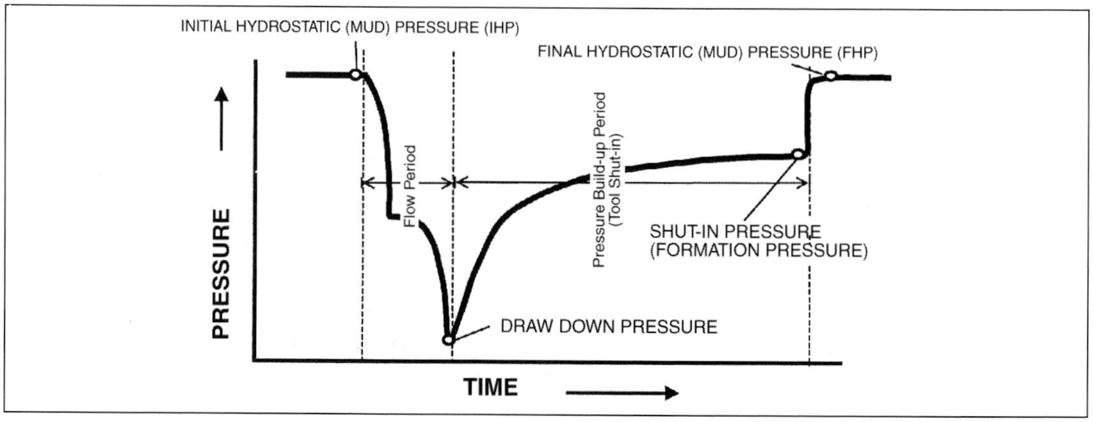

Figure 5–18.

Operating an RFT survey

The table below explains how to operate an RFT survey (see Gunter and Moore, 1987).

Step	Action
1	Use well logs to pick permeable zones for formation pressure measurements. Look for an invasion profile.
2	Plot mud hydrostatic and formation pressure at the well site to recognize anomalies or tool errors and to optimize station coverage.
3	Occasionally repeat formation pressure measurements at the same depth to check for consistency.
4	Repeat at some of the same depths for multiple surveys to help normalize the different surveys.
5	Sample both water- and hydrocarbon-bearing intervals to establish both the water and hydrocarbon pressure gradients.
6	Plot pressures at the same scale as well logs to aid in interpretation.

Controlling RFT quality

The table below describes how to control RFT quality. For details, see Gunter and Moore, 1987.

Step	Action
1	Inspect the tool and check calibration before going in the hole.
2	Run quartz and strain gauges simultaneously. Record both readings independently. Normalize to one another after completing the survey.
3	Maintain a slight overflow of mud to keep the level in the borehole constant during the survey and to prevent mud hydrostatic pressure errors.
4	Take mud hydrostatic pressures while descending into the hole to give the instruments time to equilibrate to changing temperature and pressure and to provide a mud hydrostatic pressure profile.
5	Check for tool errors by calculating mud hydrostatic pressures at different depths from mud weight; check them against measured mud hydrostatic pressures at the same depths.

Section C
Predicting Abnormal Pressures

Introduction

Knowledge of expected subsurface pressure regimes helps us predict the presence of porosity and hydrocarbon charging and promotes safe drilling conditions. When making those predictions, consider the zone of interest in the prospective exploration area in the context of the depositional and tectonic history of the basin where it was deposited. Is the zone of interest in the target area part of a normal progression of deposition, seal formation, and burial? Or were there conditions such as high heat flow, large translations of blocks, and major fault displacements that could produce abnormal pressures?

Besides unraveling the geological history, we can observe the weight of the drilling mud used, cuttings, and well logs to predict formation fluid pressures. This section discusses methods for predicting the presence of abnormal pressures.

In this section

This section contains the following topics.

Reconstructing Burial History

Introduction

Reconstructing the burial history of a play area gives an estimate of vertical displacement by either burial or faulting of at least an order of magnitude of measurement. A pressure–depth plot, using the estimate of vertical displacement and normal fluid gradients, helps reveal the magnitude of the pressure abnormality that might be present if seals were in place at the appropriate time to trap the abnormal pressure.

Procedure: Predicting fluid pressure

To predict the fluid pressure of a sealed container using burial history analysis, use the procedure outlined in the table below.

Step	Action
1	Plot the normal pressure gradient that existed when the container was sealed.
2	Plot the present gradient, adding the new depth of burial.

Example

In the case of a sand body carried deeper by a growth fault, first plot the normal gradients that would have existed prior to burial; then replot the gradients at the existing depth.

The diagrams below illustrate burial stages 1, 2, and 3 and the corresponding pressure–depth relationships.

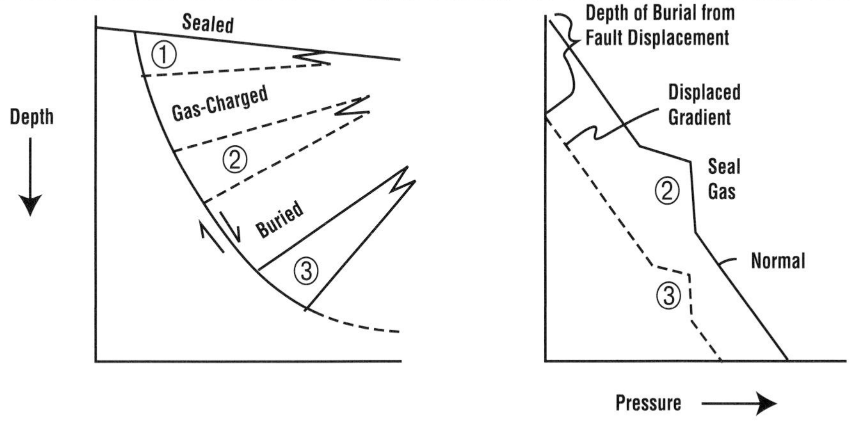

Figure 5–19.

Using normal pressure gradient

Use of normal pressure gradients only gives an approximation for estimating pressure in a burial history analysis. It is difficult, if not impossible, to be more precise because there are so many other unknowns, such as pressure and temperature at the charging stage, molecular composition of the fluids, effectiveness of seals, and original and current temperatures.

Analysis of Mud Weights

Mud weight and pore pressure

The mud weight needed to control a well reflects pore pressure of any permeable formations drilled. To control a well, operators generally use a mud weight that will exert a pressure close to the expected pore pressure. When drilling mud kicks or blows out, the pressure from the mud is less than, but usually close to, pore pressure.

Calculating pressure from mud weight

When the drilling mud kicks or blows out, pore pressure can be calculated by using the following formula:

$$\text{Pore pressure} = 0.052 \times \text{mud weight} \times \text{depth}$$

For example, if a 7500-ft-deep hole contains mud with a weight of 10.5 ppg, then the pore pressure at the bottom of the hole is 4095 psi or more.

Accuracy

This method's accuracy mainly depends on estimates of mud weight. The accuracy of mud weight estimates, measured periodically from the mud pits at the well site, is affected by three factors:

- Formation water and gas cutting of the mud
- Entrapment of air at the surface
- Long circulation periods of the mud

A difference of 0.1 ppg in mud weight can cause an error of 500 psi at 10,000 ft in the estimate of pore pressure.

Problems with interpreting pressure from mud weight

Different operators have different policies about how much margin to allow between formation pressure and mud pressure; the range in margin is quite large. Also, the well bore can penetrate a pressure seal for many hundreds of feet without penetrating a permeable zone, in which case mud weight may not reflect the presence of abnormal pressure below the seal. In general, mud weight should be a clue to be confirmed by other evidence.

Mud weight in overpressured formations

In overpressured formations, normal mud weight will not offset formation pressure. If mud weight is increased, however, it can break down (fracture) the normally pressured formations higher in the hole. High pressure requires higher-than-normal mud weight, but the actual weight used might have been more than necessary (i.e., the formation pressure might not be as high as the mud weight implies).

Mud weight in underpressured formations

If significant underpressure is found, such that the formation breaks down (fractures and takes mud), the condition is noted in the drilling record. In underpressured formations, normal mud weight can fracture the formation. If the weight is decreased, however, fluid can flow into the well bore from uphole formations.

Analysis of Cuttings

Introduction

The physical appearance of drill cuttings may be a clue to subsurface pressure conditions as reflected in the state of compaction or induration of the rock. This applies to cuttings from permeable as well as impermeable rocks.

Evidence of overpressure

When the formation fluid pressure is greater than the mud pressure, the cuttings tend to explode into the well bore. Cuttings are liberated promptly into the mud with a minimum of abrasion by the bit. Consequently, the cuttings have sharp edges and look fresh; they may even be somewhat larger than normal. This case also applies to shale, so we don't have to wait for a mud kick from a permeable zone to anticipate significant overpressure. Cuttings tend to be large and fresh looking when they are from overpressured, low-permeability rocks because the pore pressure cannot readily bleed out of the pore system when permeability is low.

Evidence of underpressure

When mud pressure exceeds formation fluid pressure, the mud tends to plaster the hole (one of the things mud is designed to do). An undesirable byproduct of this attribute is that cuttings are held in place by the pressure differential between the well bore and the formation. Such cuttings, even if broken away from the host rock, are likely to be struck several times by the bit teeth before being carried away in the mud. The cuttings will be further broken (smaller than normal) and may look worn or abraded. This process is more likely to take place in permeable zones where there is a finite flow of mud filtrate into the formation.

Mud properties caveat

Any discussion about cuttings must be tempered with a consideration of the type of mud used. Consult an experienced drilling and mud engineer to determine the specific properties of a given mud system and its effects on cuttings.

Compaction and fluid pressure

Abnormal fluid pressure causes abnormal pressure within the rock matrix; this directly affects compaction. Fluid carries some of the overburden stress. When fluid pressure is abnormally high, the intergranular stress is lower than normal, resulting in undercompaction. Abnormally low fluid pressure increases intergranular stress, allowing overcompaction (unless the framework is exceptionally rigid, as with a coral reef or well-cemented sandstone).

The table below summarizes the relationships of fluid pressure, intergranular stress, and rock matrix appearance.

Pore Pressure	Intergranular Stress	Rock Matrix Appearance	Porosity
Abnormally high	Abnormally low	Evidence of undercompaction	Higher than normal for depth of burial
Abnormally low	Abnormally high	Evidence of overcompaction, i.e., grains may be broken and/or sutured	Lower than normal for depth of burial

Analysis of Cuttings, continued

Density of shale cuttings

Rocks in overpressured sections have lower bulk densities than rocks in normally pressured sections; rocks from underpressured sections have higher bulk densities. Only differences in shale densities, however, can be detected in cuttings for the following reasons. When cuttings enter the mud column, the fluids in the pore space try to equilibrate with the new pressure environment. If the cuttings are permeable, the equilibration takes place continually as the cutting rises in the mud column. If the cuttings are impermeable, however, equilibration is impeded—very strongly, in the case of shale.

Measuring shale cuttings density

Shale cuttings densities are measured at the well site by dropping chips into a glass cylinder containing a stratified sequence of liquids whose density increases downward. Beads of known density are dropped into the cylinder. The level at which the beads settle indicates the density of the liquid at that level, and the different liquid densities are labeled on the cylinder. The level at which the shale chips settle indicates their density.

Unusual authigenic minerals

Side pressure seals, in particular, are thought to be caused by mineralization adjacent to faults. Top seals form by mineralization that cuts across stratigraphic units. Top seals of major overpressured compartments are usually cemented by calcite. When unexpected pore-filling calcite is seen, a pressure seal should be considered a possibility. Any unusual pore-filling minerals seen in cutting samples should alert the geologist to the potential of a pressure seal.

Analysis of Well-Log and Seismic Data

Introduction

Resistivity, sonic, and density logs (as well as some others) can give clues to the presence of over- or underpressure. Shale sections are best for analysis of logs for abnormal pore pressure. Because of their low permeabilities, shales do not equilibrate pressure with the mud column in the well bore. Selecting only the purest shales minimizes the effects of mineral variation, multiple phases, fluid composition, and fluid distribution. That leaves only porosity as the major variable within shale sections. Because porosity is related to compaction, porosity measurements from well logs can be calibrated to fluid pressure in the pore systems.

Log of drilling rate

Drilling time is useful for detecting abnormal pressure. If the variables are limited (weight on bit, rotary speed, mud properties, pump pressure, and bit type), the major remaining variable that affects rate of penetration in shale is porosity.

Drilling time is kept in real time on every drilling rig. It is often the very first indicator of changing downhole conditions.

Procedure: Analyzing well logs

To locate intervals with potentially abnormal fluid pressure, use the following procedure.

Step	Action
1	Find the purest shale intervals on the GR or SP base line. They must be reasonably thick to allow valid responses of the other logs and free of sand or lime stringers. (See points a–e, Figure 5–20.)
2	At the same depth, mark the value of resistivity, conductivity, sonic travel time, or density.
3	Note any series of these best shale values vs. depth. These define a normal shale trend (NST) line for each of the log curves to be used. **Note:** Departure from the NST line indicates abnormal microporosity due to abnormal pore pressure.

Diagram of log response to overpressure

The figure below illustrates how overpressures are interpreted from different types of well logs, as explained in the previous table.

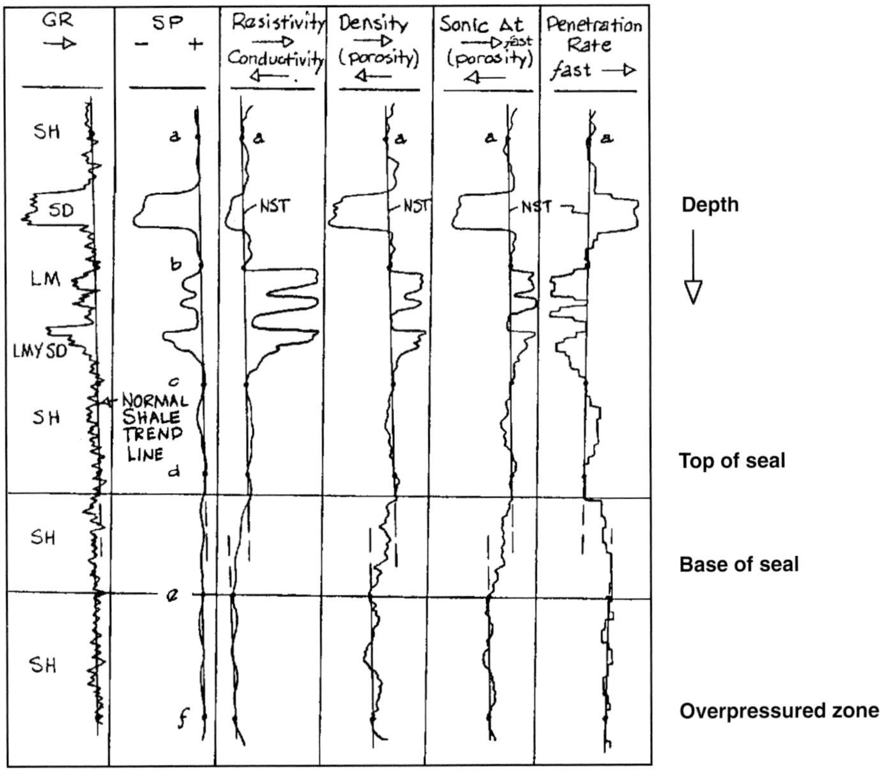

Figure 5–20.

Travel time from sonic logs

In some places, an empirical relation can be established to predict pore pressure from well logs. The figure below shows sonic travel time varying with measured pressure.

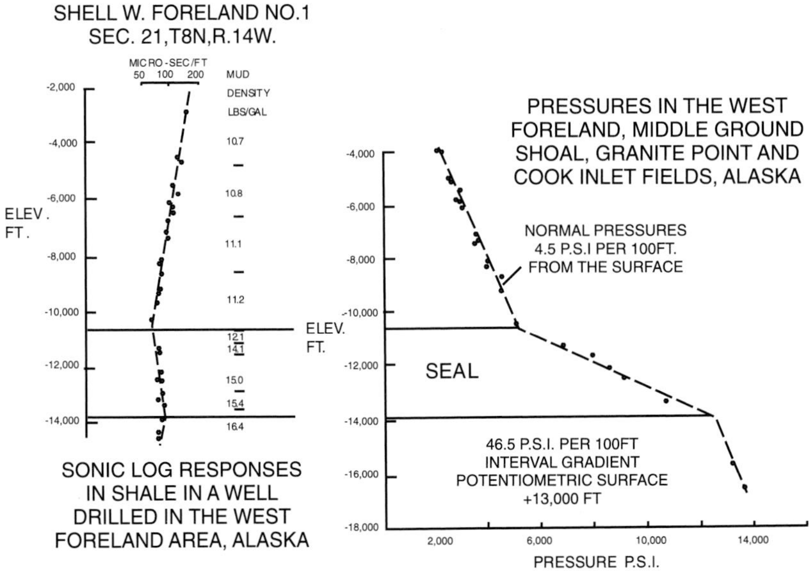

Figure 5–21. From Powley, 1990; courtesy Earth Science Reviews.

Synthetic seismograms

Resistivity, sonic, and density logs can be used to construct synthetic seismograms which, in turn, can be used to calibrate and refine seismic profiles. Hence, there is a tie-in with geophysical modeling (directly in the case of sonic–density transforms, indirectly in the case of resistivity transforms).

Seismic velocity

Seismic velocity is a function of the density and strength modulus of the rocks through which the energy passes. Both density and strength are affected by abnormal pore pressure. Seismic profiles that show unusually slow interval velocity may indicate an undercompacted (overpressured) interval. Unusually fast interval velocity, conversely, may indicate overcompaction (underpressure).

Summary of log and seismic responses

The table below summarizes typical responses in "pure" shales when encountering zones of abnormal pressure, relative to normal responses.

Log Type	Overpressure	Underpressure
Drilling rate	Faster	Slower
SP	May shift to negative	May shift to positive
Gamma ray	May decrease slightly	May increase slightly
Resistivity	Lower	Higher
Conductivity	Higher	Lower
Density	Lower	Higher
Travel time	Slower	Faster
Seismic interval velocity	Low	High

Section D
Pressure Compartments

Introduction

Pressure compartments are found in basins worldwide. A pressure compartment is a volume of rock, all sides of which are sealed such that the fluid within the compartment is isolated from the surrounding normal pressure regime. Pressure compartments affect the movement of fluids that control the migration and accumulation of petroleum and the diagenesis of reservoirs and seals. This section discusses pressure compartments, methods for predicting their presence, and their importance for petroleum exploration.

In this section

This section contains the following topics.

Regional Pressure Compartments

Definition

Most deep sedimentary basins of the world contain a shallow, normally pressured hydraulic system overlying one or more hydraulic compartments whose pressures are above or below the normal static water pressure (Powley, 1990). In this discussion these hydraulic compartments are called **pressure compartments**. They are defined within a basin from pressure measurements.

Seals

Seals isolate fluids within compartments from fluids that are in pressure communication with the surface (normally pressured hydraulic system). The **top seal** is more or less horizontal and usually cuts across stratigraphic units. It forms where authigenic minerals (usually calcite) fill the pore spaces. The **bottom seal** of regional compartments is usually a well defined lithostratigraphic unit. Commonly, the **side seals** are thin, mineralized zones paralleling vertical faults.

Pressure compartment recognition

Pressure compartments develop after the compartment has been sealed, isolating the fluids inside the compartment. Pressure in the compartment can be over, under, or normal. We can map a compartment's top, bottom, and sides from pressure measurements. Since pressure measurements are the main identifying criteria, the normally pressured compartments are usually not recognized.

Schematic of pressure compartment

The following schematic cross section and pressure–depth plot shows how changes in the fluid pressure gradient correlate with the top and bottom seals of a regional pressure compartment in a foreland basin.

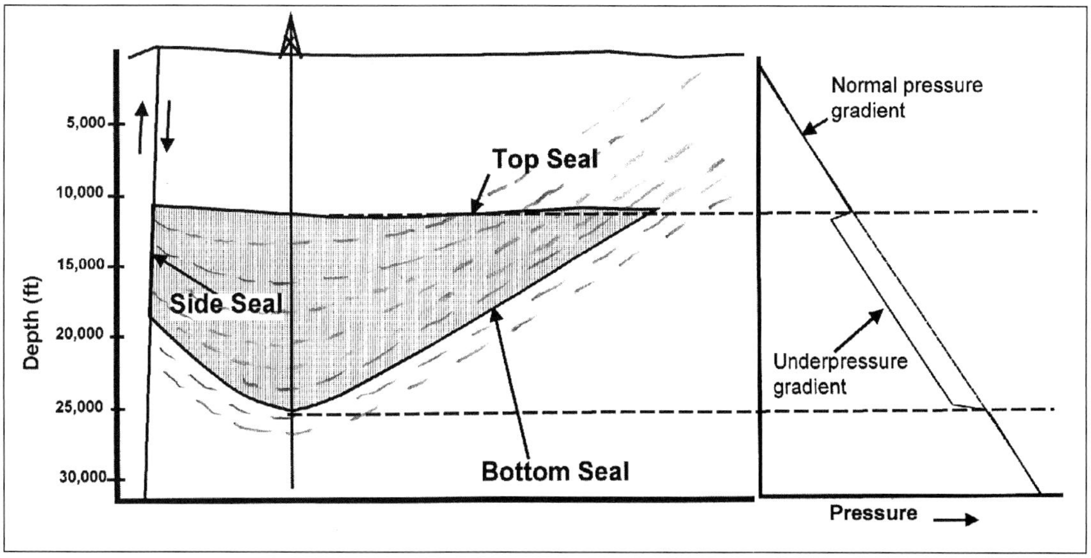

Figure 5–22.

Multiple pressure compartments

Many sedimentary basins contain two or more pressure compartments. The cross section below illustrates the multiple pressure compartments of the Anadarko basin.

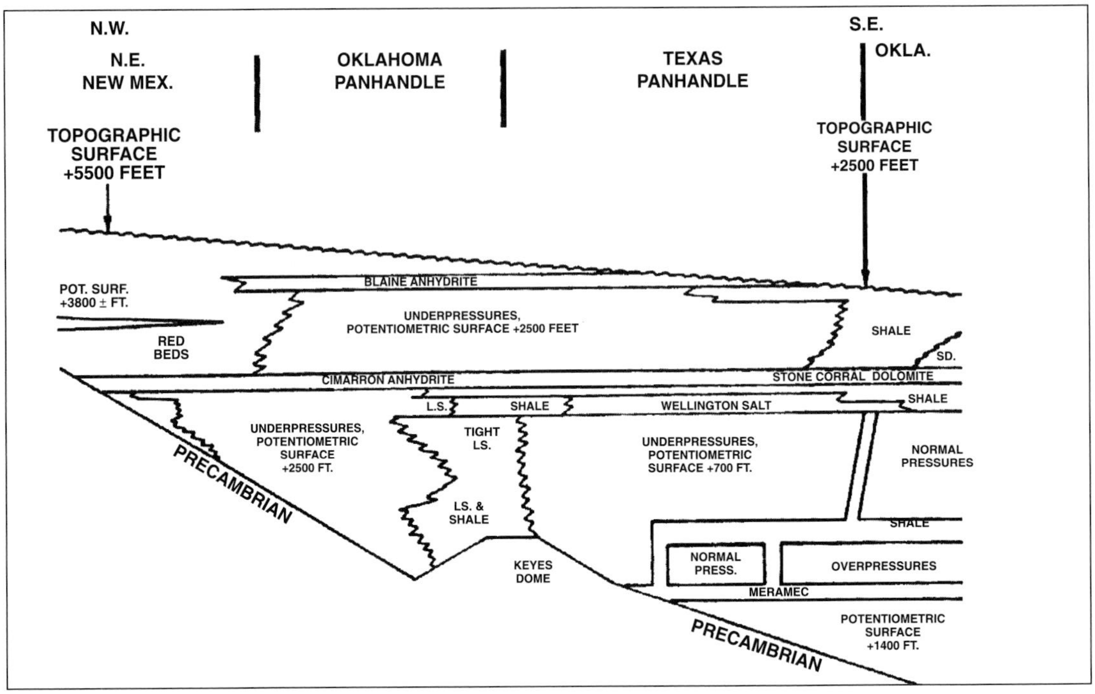

Figure 5–23. From Bradley and Powley, 1995; courtesy AAPG.

Regional pressure compartment

The cross section below illustrates a regional pressure compartment from the Anadarko basin of Oklahoma.

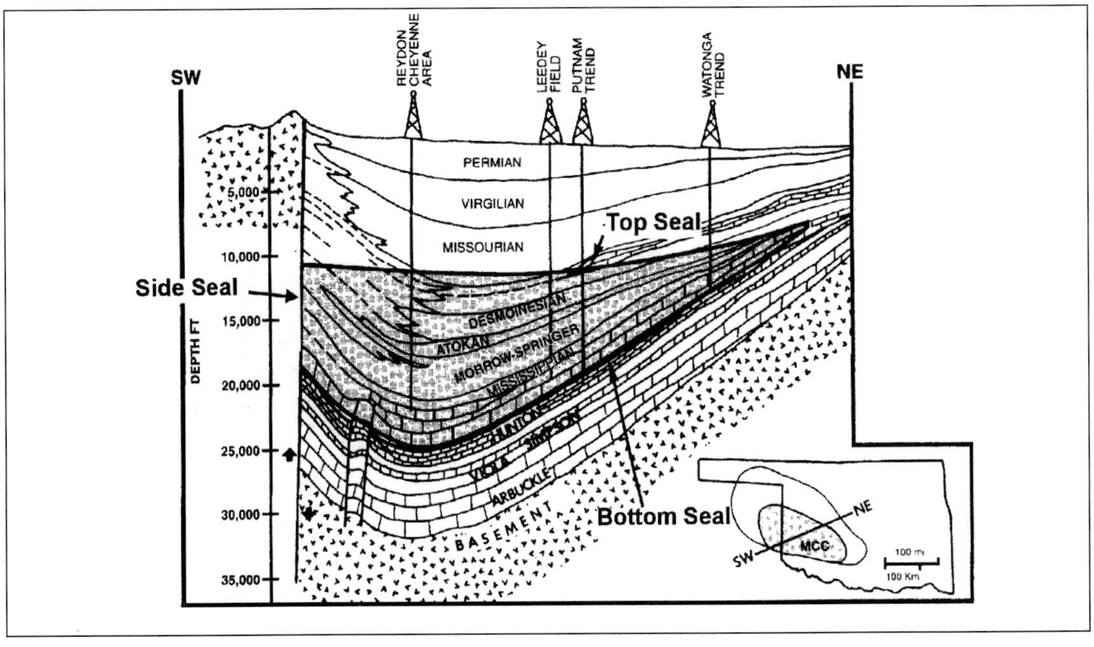

Figure 5–24. From Al-Shaieb et al., 1995a; courtesy AAPG.

Regional Pressure Compartments, continued

Example: Gradient profile

Following is a pressure–depth plot of a well through the Anadarko regional pressure compartment. Fluid pressure goes from normal above the top seal to overpressured within the pressure compartment, then back to normal below the bottom seal. Many regional pressure compartments contain smaller subregional and local pressure compartments. Al-Shaieb et al. (1995b) use the following terms:

- Regional pressure compartments—first-order or mega-compartments
- Subregional compartments—second-order compartments
- Local compartments—third-order compartments

The fluid pressure gradient variations within the pressure compartment on the plot below represent the smaller second- and third-order compartments.

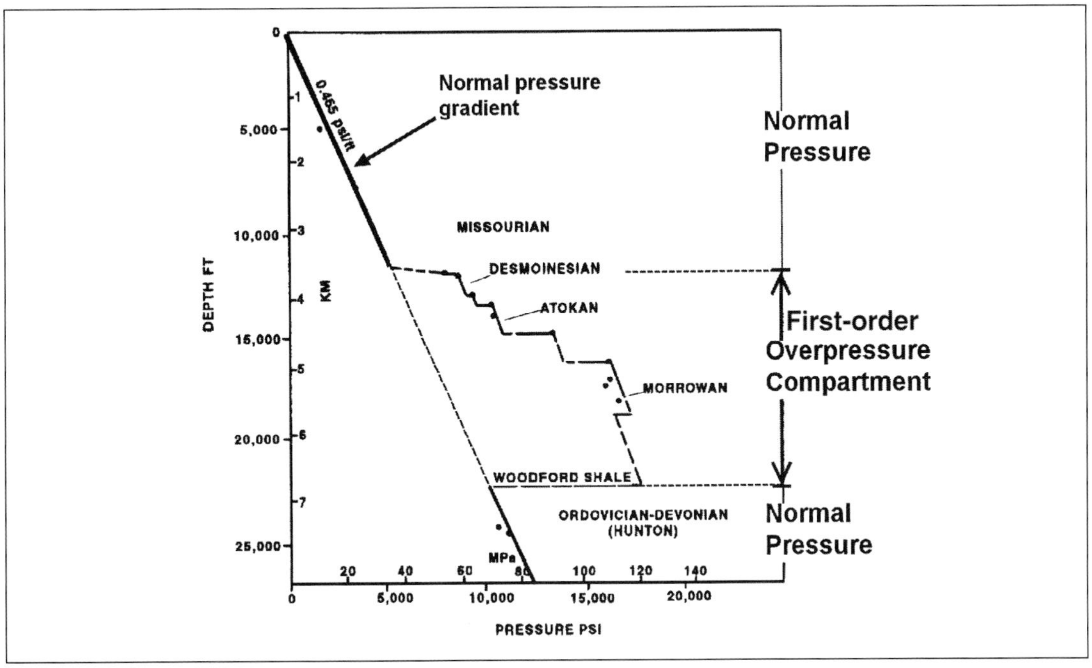

Figure 5–25. Modified from Al-Shaieb et al., 1995a; courtesy AAPG.

Subregional and Local Pressure Compartments

Introduction

Subregional or local (second- and third-order) pressure compartments can be found within normal pressure regimes or regional pressure compartments.

Subregional pressure compartments

Below is an example of a subregional compartment contained within the regional pressure compartment of the Anadarko basin of Figure 5–25.

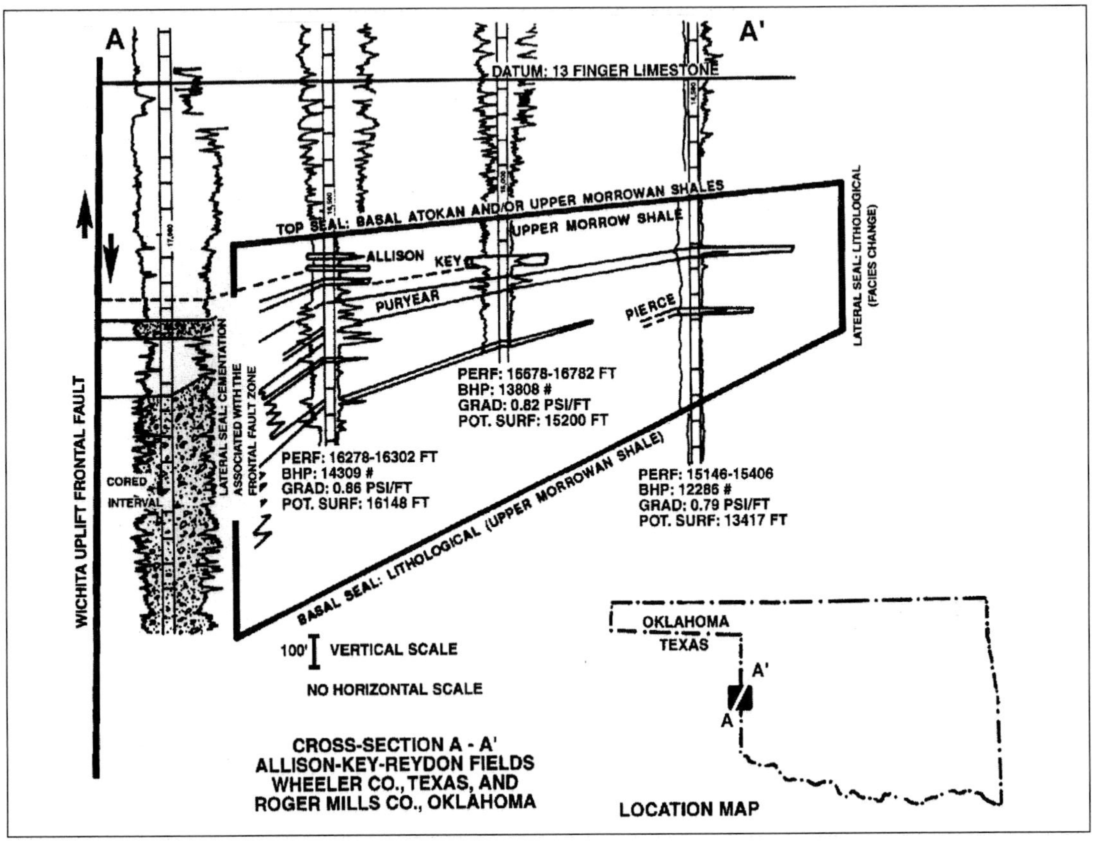

Figure 5–26. From Al-Shaieb et al., 1995b; courtesy AAPG.

Local pressure compartments

The fluids in a porous bioherm completely encased in shale (as shown in the figure below) are virtually isolated from the nearby fluid systems outside the bioherm. The bioherm, then, is a pressure compartment that may or may not be abnormally pressured. Other geological features that may form local pressure compartments are fault blocks, sand lenses, and sand wedges developed in growth faults.

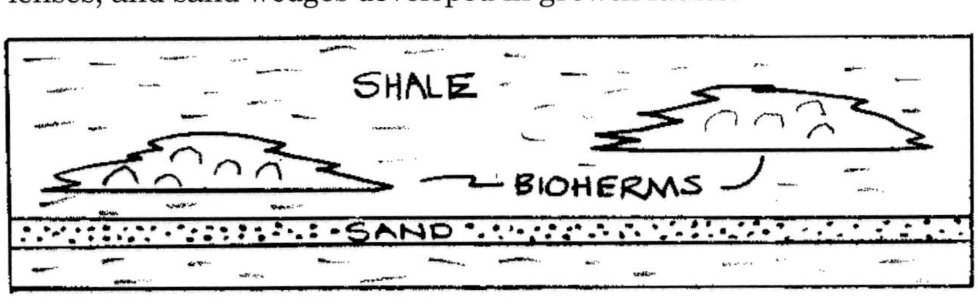

Figure 5–27.

Pressure Compartment Seals

Pressure vs. capillary seals

A seal can be either a pressure seal, a capillary seal, or both. They are defined as follows:

- **Pressure seals** define pressure compartment boundaries. They can also act as capillary seals and define trap boundaries. Pressure seals impede the flow of hydrocarbons and water. They form where pore throats are effectively closed and absolute permeability is near zero.
- **Capillary seals** define trap boundaries. Capillary seals impede the flow of hydrocarbons. They form where capillary pressure across the pore throats of a rock is greater or equal to the buoyancy pressure from a hydrocarbon column. Water can move through an interconnected pore system in a capillary seal.

Pressure compartment top-seal genesis

Commonly, the top seal is at depths where formation temperature is about 200°F (90°C). Evidently, this temperature influences the development of authigenic materials. Quite possibly the zone of mineralization stays near the 200°F isotherm, migrating as the basin subsides or rebounds. Once a seal forms, however, fluid migration through the seal is restricted, so it is more difficult for a seal to dissolve than to form. If so, there may be fossil seals that reflect previous isotherms in the basin.

Side and bottom seals

Bottom seals of regional compartments are usually well-defined lithostratigraphic units. Side or lateral seals can be a lateral convergence of the top and bottom seals; side seals can also be thin, mineralized zones paralleling vertical faults.

Leaky seals

Pressure compartment seals do not usually seal perfectly. If the pressure generation rate within the compartment is greater than the rate of leakage, then pressure will build up in the compartment.

Episodic leakage of hydrocarbons

Regional pressure compartment pressures build as a result of hydrocarbon generation and other mechanisms. Intermittent release of hydrocarbons and other fluids occurs when hydrostatic pressure exceeds the fracture gradient of the top seal. Hydrocarbons released from regional pressure compartments charge formations overlying the top seal of the compartment. Subsequent bleed-down of pressure allows temporary rehealing of the fractures. This cycle undoubtedly repeats many times (David Powley, personal communication).

Episodic leakage of hydrocarbons (continued)

The pressure–depth plot below is from Ernie Dome, Central Transylvania basin, Romania. It shows how pressure and fluids are released from a compartment when pressure in the compartment reaches the top-seal fracture pressure.

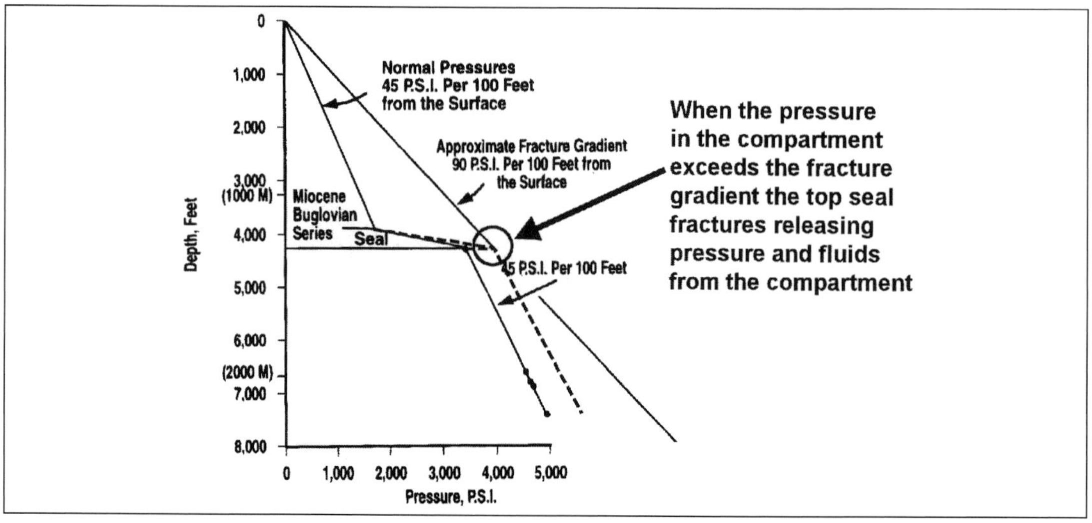

Figure 5–28. After Leonard, 1993; courtesy The Geological Society.

Example of episodic leakage

Below is a plot of rate of pressure generation vs. rate of pressure leakage for a pressure compartment in the Central North Sea graben. It correlates tectonic activity with pressure leakage caused by fault reactivation and hydraulic fracturing of the top seal.

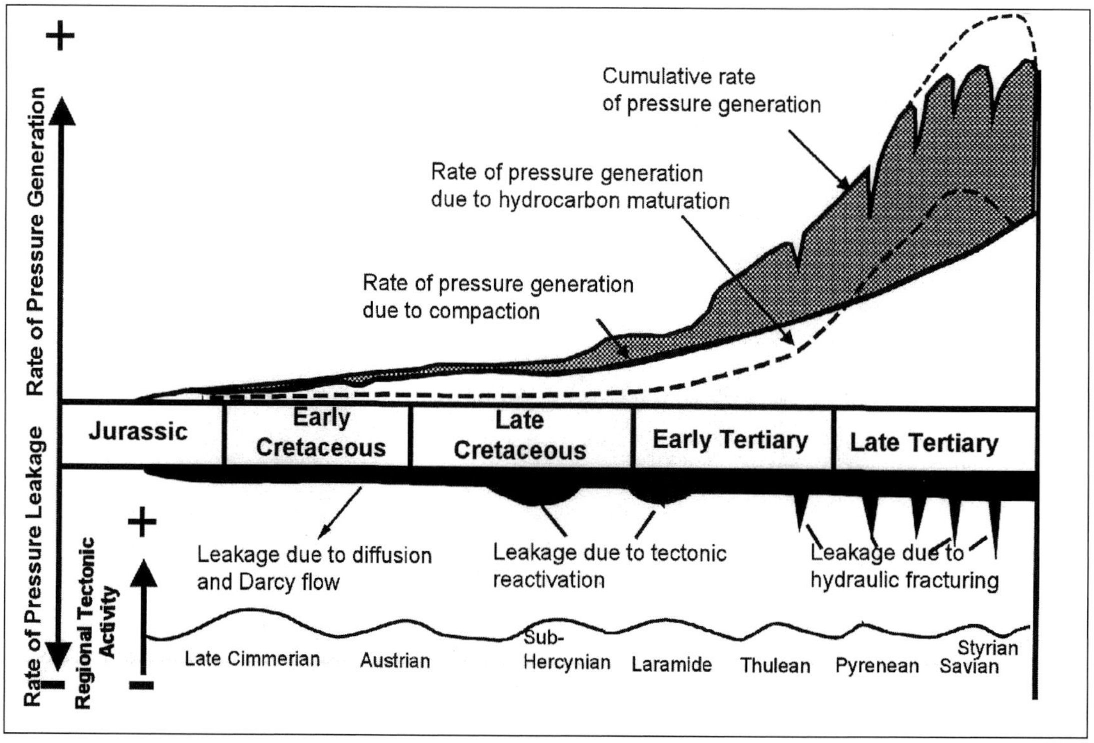

Figure 5–29. After Gaarenstroom et al., 1993; courtesy The Geological Society.

Applying Pressure Compartment Concepts to Exploration

Impact on petroleum geology

Pressure compartments have a significant impact on the distribution of oil and gas within a basin. Leonard (1993) lists ways pressure compartments affect elements of petroleum geology:

- Porosity loss due to compaction is less in overpressured and more in underpressured rocks than in normally pressured rocks.
- Lack of fluid movement in pressure compartments reduces the supply of free ions associated with cementation and secondary porosity formation.
- Temperature increase associated with overpressured compartments decreases the depth of burial for hydrocarbon generation.
- Fracturing of the top seal could be a key to primary and secondary hydrocarbon migration and location of traps.
- Mapping well-to-well pressure variation could identify sealing faults.

Porosity preservation

Overpressured compartments impede porosity loss due to compaction. For example, chalks worldwide begin with porosities greater than 50%. During burial in normally pressured sections, chalk porosities decrease to less than 10% at depths of 1500 m or more. In overpressured compartments of the North Sea, chalks have porosities of 40% or more at depths of 2500 m and 25% or more at depths of 3000 m or more (Leonard, 1993). These porosities are those that would be expected at 700–1200 m in normally pressured rock sections.

The figure below is a porosity–depth plot for chalks worldwide.

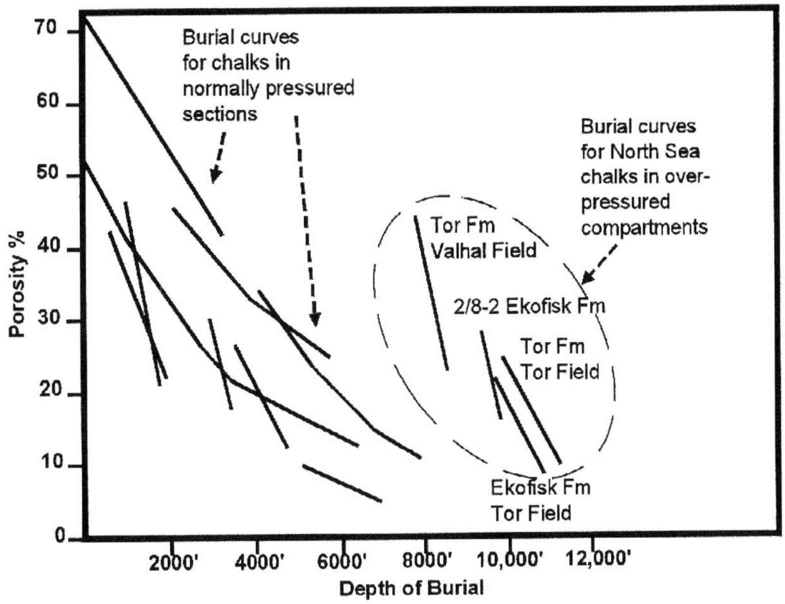

Figure 5–30. After Leonard, 1993; courtesy The Geological Society.

Diagenesis in compartments

Pore fluid movement within pressure compartments is quite limited because compartments are sealed from surrounding beds. Sediments in a pressure compartment may escape both reservoir-destroying cementation and reservoir-enhancing grain dissolution.

Effect on hydrocarbon maturation

The temperature gradient usually increases below the top seal of pressure compartments because the top seal provides a thermal blanket for underlying sediments. This increase in temperature increases the rate of hydrocarbon maturation within the compartment. The figure to the right shows temperature gradient increase below the top seal.

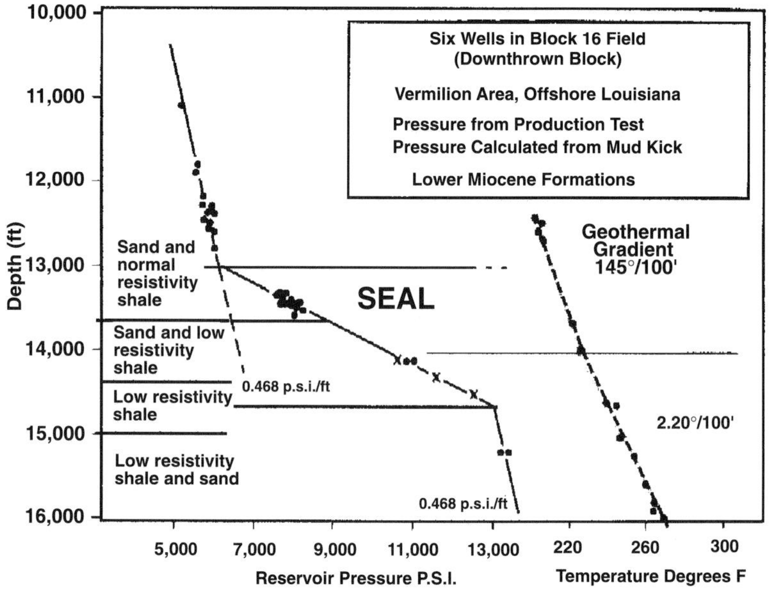

Figure 5–31. From Leonard, 1993; courtesy The Geological Society.

Concentration of traps

In many regional pressure compartments, hydrocarbon generation creates pressures great enough to fracture the top seal. Top-seal fracturing episodically releases pressure and fluids, including oil and gas, from the pressure compartment. Oil and gas tend to be trapped in the first reservoir-quality rock over leak points (Leonard, 1993). Leak points form where the top seal is shallowest because fracture pressure is lowest in the top seal at that point. Leak points also can occur where faults are reactivated during tectonic events (Gaarenstroom et al., 1993).

Compartment-associated traps

The diagram to the right is a schematic cross section of traps associated with pressure compartments.

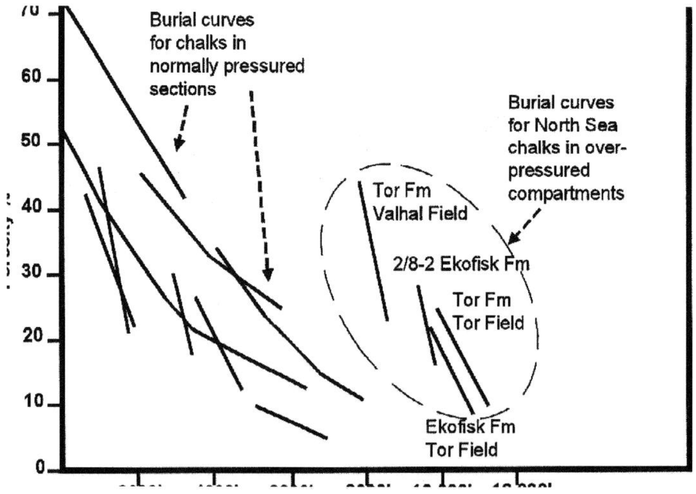

Figure 5–32; after Powley, 1995; courtesy Earth Science Reviews.

Section E

Capillarity and Buoyancy

Introduction

Capillarity and buoyancy are the forces that determine the distribution of oil and gas in the subsurface. This section contains discussions of the concepts of capillarity and buoyancy, and their effect on the amount and distribution of hydrocarbons in a trap.

In this section

This section contains the following topics.

Capillary Pressure

Definitions

The 1987 American Geological Institute's *Glossary of Geology* defines **capillarity** as "the action by which a fluid, such as water, is drawn up (or depressed) in small interstices or tubes as a result of surface tension."

The same glossary defines **capillary pressure** as "the difference in pressure across the interface between two immiscible fluid phases jointly occupying the interstices of a rock. It is due to the tension of the interfacial surface and its value depends on the curvature of that surface." Capillary pressure is represented by P_c.

Discussion

Capillary pressure arises from three phenomena:

1. Interfacial tension (molecular attraction at the boundary of each fluid that causes the fluids to occur as separate phases)
2. Wettability (affinity of fluid to solid)
3. Small pore throats (capillaries)

Interfacial tension

Interfacial tension is a force that exists because the molecules of a liquid attract one another. This attraction causes a drop of liquid to form a spherical shape outside the influence of gravity. Gases have no interfacial tension, so they diffuse instead of form drops. When the difference in interfacial tension between fluids is high (between oil and water, and especially between gas and water), they do not combine; so they are said to be immiscible. Interfacial tension is represented by the Greek letter σ.

Wettability

When two or more immiscible fluids coexist in the pores of a rock, one fluid is likely to have a greater affinity to wet the solid phase (rock surface). This effect causes one fluid to preferentially coat the pore walls and to be drawn into the smallest pores.

Contact angles

In oil-field laboratory testing, the degree of wettability is measured by the contact angle (θ), measured through the more dense phase. In this test, a small drop of oil is inserted in an aqueous bath and is allowed to float up to a polished plate of calcite or quartz. The contact angle is measured several times over a period of several days until it stabilizes.

The diagrams below show how the contact angle is measured for water-wet (left) and oil-wet (right) reservoirs.

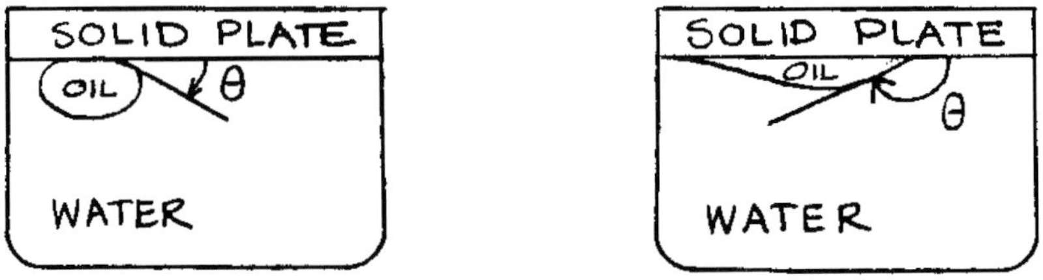

Figure 5–33.

Capillary Pressure, continued

Capillary effect in small tubes

The capillary effect is most pronounced when the effects of wettability and interfacial tension are combined in very small tubes (capillaries), which are analogous to small pore throats. Pores and pore throats all have some similarities with capillary tubes, but a pore system is far more complicated because the pore throats are continuously interrupted in three dimensions by larger pores.

The example below shows how ideal capillary pressure draws a wetting fluid into capillary tubes of different diameters. Note that the direction of movement depends on which fluid is the wetting fluid.

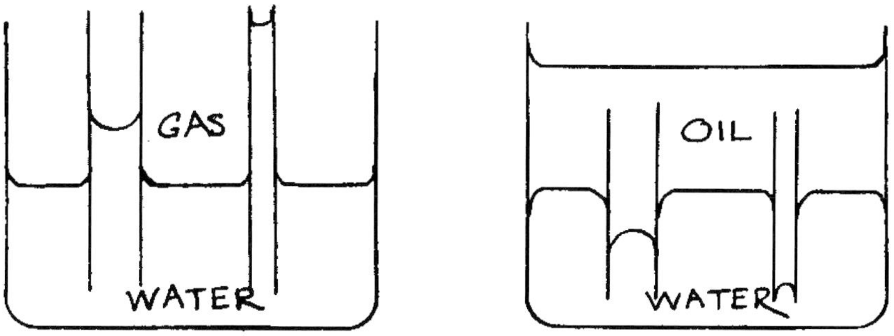

A water-wet gas reservoir — A strongly oil-wet reservoir

Figure 5–34.

Capillary pressure equation

Capillary pressure (P_c) is related to interfacial tension (σ), wetting angle (θ), and radius of capillarity (r) by the following formula:

$$P_c = \frac{2\,\sigma \cos\theta}{r}$$

Capillary pressure is measured in dynes/cc, interfacial tension in dynes/centimeter, wetting angle in degrees, and radius of capillarity in centimeters.

Buoyancy Pressure

Definition

Buoyancy is the tendency for a body (or a drop of immiscible fluid) to float or rise when submerged in a fluid of greater density. Where two immiscible fluids (oil and water) occur together, they create a buoyancy pressure that is a function of the density difference between the two fluids and the length of the less-dense fluid column.

Discussion

If immiscible fluids occur together, they segregate according to their densities: the lightest (least dense) fluid floats to the top, and the heaviest (most dense) sinks to the bottom of the container (or compartment). When they occur in a container free of capillary effects—such as a bottle, lake, or cave—the different fluids exhibit a sharp, flat interface.

Interaction between capillarity and buoyancy

Virtually every reservoir holds its fluids in a porous network. The pores are normally well within the size range where capillary forces are strong. To fill a reservoir with oil or gas, the buoyancy force driving the oil or gas into the pores of the reservoir must overcome the capillary force developed between the original fluid and the displacing fluid. The smaller the pore throats, the greater the capillary pressure associated with them.

Following the path of least capillary resistance, nonwetting fluids (gas or nonwetting oil) first move into the pore system that has the largest pore throats. Later, as the column height of the oil or gas grows and the buoyancy pressure increases, the hydrocarbons begin migrating into pores with smaller and smaller pore throats (in a water-wet system).

Section F
Hydrodynamics

Introduction

This section discusses the concept of dynamic fluid systems and how hydrodynamic aquifers affect the distribution and accumulation of hydrocarbons.

In this section

This section contains the following topics.

Basic Hydrodynamics

Introduction

Hydrodynamics describes lateral fluid movement through aquifers that have generally low dip. The fluids can have a vertical component to their movement but, on a basinwide scale, the lateral flow component is of major concern.

Hydraulic head

Hydraulic head (H_w) is the height or elevation above a given subsurface point at which a column connected to a body of water will equilibrate. It reflects the level of the potential energy possessed by the water (Dahlberg, 1994).

The equation for hydraulic head is

$$H_w = Z + \frac{P}{\rho g}$$

where:

H_w = height above P (ft or m)
Z = height (elevation) of P above a datum (ft or m)
P = measured pressure (lb/ft^2 or kg/cm^2)
ρ = density of fluid (lb/ft^3 or g/cm^3)
g = coefficient of gravity (lb force/lb mass or kg force/kg mass)

The figure below illustrates the relationship of the variables H_w and Z used in the above equation.

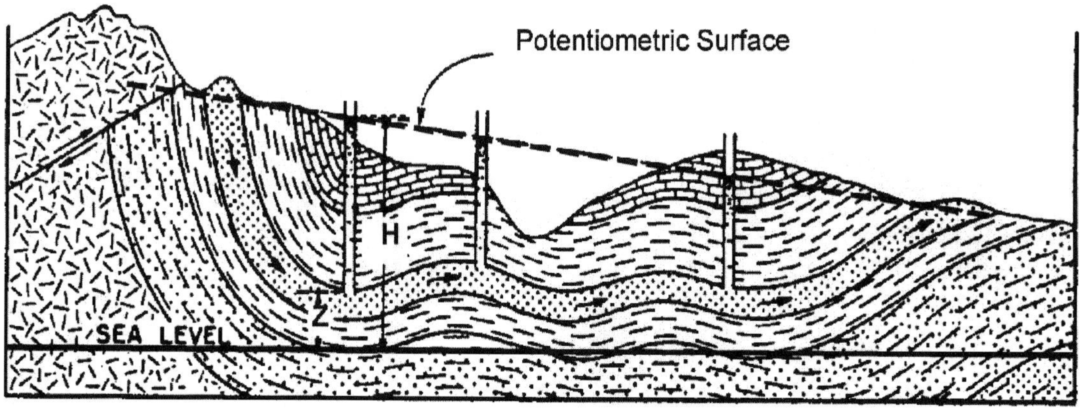

Figure 5–35. From Hubbert, 1953; courtesy AAPG.

Potential energy of fluids

Potential energy (Φ) is the driving force of fluid movement. Its magnitude depends on the hydraulic head (H_w) with respect to sea level and is expressed as

$$\Phi = gH_w = gZ + \frac{P}{\rho}$$

According to Dahlberg (1994), hydraulic head serves as a practical approximation of fluid potential, since the only difference is the coefficient of gravity (g), which is fairly constant.

Potentiometric surface

The potentiometric surface is the surface defined by the hydraulic head (elevation) from a rock unit from several different wells. If the potentiometric surface for a given subsurface rock unit is horizontal, then the potential energy of the water in that formation is constant and the water is at rest (hydrostatic). If the potentiometric surface is sloping, then the water moves (hydrodynamic) in the direction of the greatest downward slope (Hubbert, 1953).

The figure below shows the potentiometric surface for hydrodynamic updip and downdip flow and hydrostatic no flow. The pressure–depth plot shows hypothetical pressure gradients for each condition.

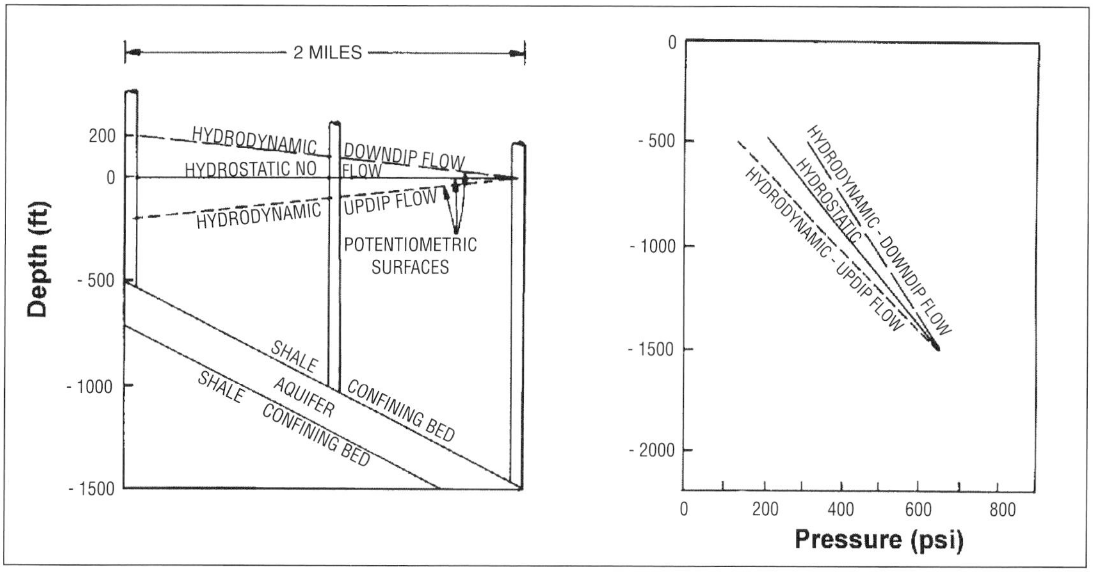

Figure 5–36. From Schowalter, 1979; courtesy AAPG.

Hydrodynamic Influence on Trapping

Potential of water vs. hydrocarbons

Fluid pressure equals ρgH. Under hydrostatic conditions, the buoyant force equals

$$\rho_w gH_w - \rho_h gH_h$$

where:

ρ_w = water density
ρ_h = hydrocarbon density
H_w = water depth
H_h = hydrocarbon column height

Under hydrodynamic conditions, the potential for a hydrocarbon column (Φ_h) is related to the potential of the water by the equation

$$\Phi_h = \rho_h gH_h = \rho_w gH_w - (\rho_w - \rho_h)gZ$$

Dividing through by g $(\rho_w - \rho_h)/\rho_h$ to simplify gives (in a uniformly flat gravity field)

$$\left(\frac{\rho_h}{\rho_w - \rho_h}\right)H_h = \left(\frac{\rho_w}{\rho_w - \rho_h}\right)H_w - Z$$

Constant values for the left-hand side of the equation are equipotential surfaces for hydrocarbons. Hubbert (1953) called this factor U. From the right side, constant values for $\rho_w/(\rho_w - \rho_h)H_w$ are equipotential surfaces for water. Hubbert called this factor V. The elevation factor (Z) is the difference between the equipotential surfaces for hydrocarbons and water.

Substituting U and V in the above equation gives

$$U = V - Z$$

Fluid flow is perpendicular to equipotential surfaces.

Hydrodynamic effect on traps

In a hydrostatic environment, the free-water level of a trap is horizontal. In a hydrodynamic environment, the free-water level of a trap is tilted because the buoyant force (P_b) is interfered with by the hydrodynamic force (P_w). The resultant interference is the vector known as the confining force (P_{cf}). U, an equipotential line, is perpendicular to P_{cf} and is tilted because of the effect of P_w. The diagram below shows these vectors and the equipotential lines for a hydrocarbon accumulation in an anticline in a hydrodynamic environment.

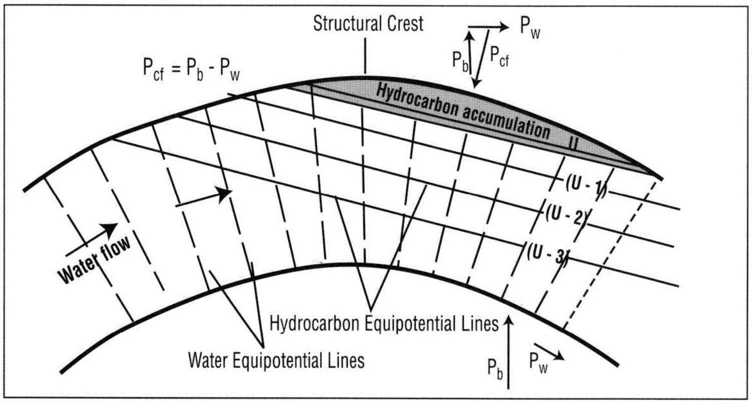

Figure 5–37. Modified from North, 1985; courtesy Allen and Unwin.

Mapping Hydrodynamic Traps

Introduction

Formation fluid pressure data are necessary for mapping prospective hydrodynamic traps. Combining formation fluid pressures with other data, such as density and subsea elevation, produces maps that help outline areas where hydrodynamic gradients may have created, destroyed, or modified traps.

Procedure: Mapping hydrodynamic traps

Follow the steps listed in the table below to map the location of possible hydrodynamic traps.

Step	Action
1	Look for permeability barriers or hydrocarbon–free water levels using pressure–depth plots.
2	Calculate potentiometric values for each well using the formula $H_w = Z + (P/\text{grad } P)$. (See "Calculating H_w" below.)
3	Make a water isopotential map with respect to oil or gas, using the formula for V, $$V = \left(\frac{\rho_w}{\rho_w - \rho_{hc}}\right) H_w$$ **Note**: Use gas density where gas is expected and oil density where oil is expected.
4	Make a gas or oil isopotential contour map using the formula for U where $U = V - Z$. The values for Z, the subsea elevation of the target aquifer, can be determined by simply overlaying a structure contour map on the water isopotential map and subtracting (see "Example" below).
5	Locate possible accumulations of hydrocarbons in hydrodynamic traps by locating the areas of low gas or oil potential. Locations should make sense in context with all other geologic data.

Calculating H_w

A critical step in mapping hydrodynamic traps in a target formation is making a water isopotential map (step 3 above). Before that can be done, however, one must calculate a potentiometric value for each well.

Calculate H_w for each well using the formula

$$H_w = Z + \frac{P}{\text{grad } P}$$

where:

Z = structural elevation of target formation
P = measured fluid pressure in the formation
grad P = static formation water pressure gradient

For grad P, use 0.435 psi/ft for areas where regional water is probably fresh and 0.465 psi/ft for areas where regional water is probably highly saline.

Example: U_0 contours

The map below shows oil in a hydrodynamic trap (shaded area). No oil could be trapped in the structure, represented by solid contours, without the aid of hydrodynamics. The bold contours with long dashes represent the isopotential of oil (labeled U_0). To make U_0 contours, follow this procedure.

Step	Action
1	Subtract the structure of the target formation (Z) from the isopotential of water (V_0).
2	Plot the remainder at the intersection of the two sets of contours.
3	Draw contours of the values.

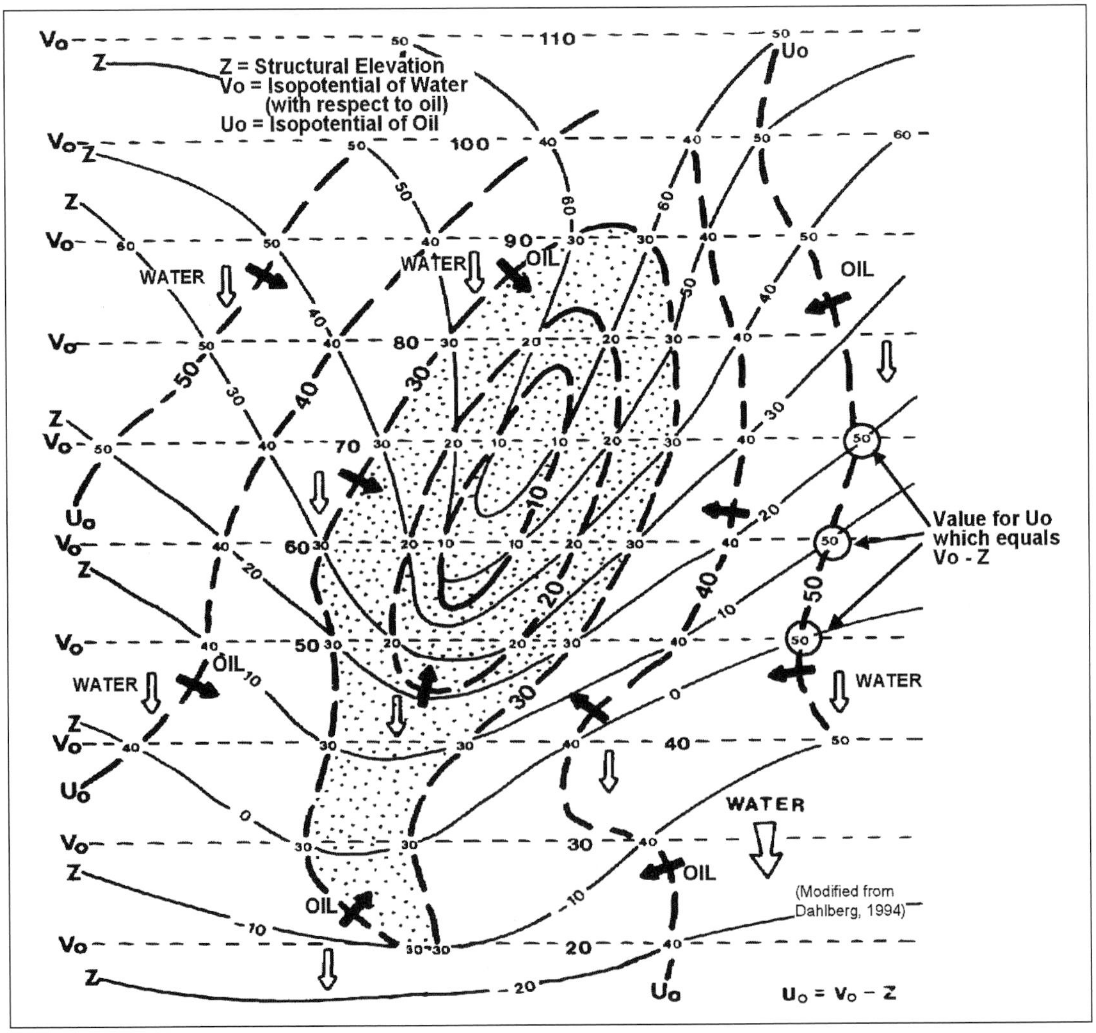

Figure 5–38. From Dahlberg, 1994; courtesy Springer-Verlag.

Section G
Annotated Bibliography

Al-Shaieb, Z., J.O. Puckette, A.A. Abdalla, and P.B. Ely, 1995a, Megacompartment complex in the Anadarko basin, *in* P.J. Ortoleva, ed., Basin Compartments and Seals: AAPG Memoir 61, p. 55–68.

_____, _____, _____, and _____, 1995b, Three levels of compartmentation within the overpressured interval of the Anadarko basin, *in* P.J. Ortoleva, ed., Basin Compartments and Seals: AAPG Memoir 61, p. 69–83.

Bradley, J.S., and D.E. Powley, 1995, Pressure compartments in sedimentary basins, *in* P.J. Ortoleva, ed., Basin Compartments and Seals: AAPG Memoir 61, p. 3–26. *Reviews basin pressure compartment principles and gives examples.*

Collins, A.G., 1987, Properties of produced waters, *in* H.B. Bradley et al., eds., Petroleum Engineering Handbook: Dallas, SPE, p. 24-1–24-23.

Dahlberg, E.C., 1994, Applied Hydrodynamics in Petroleum Exploration, 2nd ed.: New York, Springer-Verlag, 295 p. *Excellent subsurface fluid pressure reference. Covers hydrodynamic and static fluids.*

Dickey, P.A., 1969, Increasing concentration of subsurface brines with depth: Chemical Geology, vol. 4, p. 361–370.

Gaarenstroom, L., R.A.J. Tromp, M.C. de Jong, and A.M. Brandenburg, 1993, Overpressures in the Central North Sea: implications for trap integrity and drilling safety, *in* J.R. Parker, ed., Petroleum Geology of Northwest Europe: Proceedings of the Geological Society's 4th Conference, London, p. 1305–1313.

Gearhart-Owens Industries, 1972, GO Log Interpretation Reference Data Handbook: Fort Worth, Gearhart-Owens Industries Inc., 226 p. *A complete reference containing useful conversion tables, symbols, charts, tables, and nomographs. Each chart is thoroughly explained and documented with references to source material.*

Gunter, J.M., and C.V. Moore, 1987, Improved use of wireline testers for reservoir evaluation: Journal of Petroleum Technology, p. 635–644. *Good explanation of the use and interpretation of wireline pressure testers.*

Horner, D.R., 1951, Pressure build-up in wells: Proceedings of the Third World Petroleum Congress, The Hague, Section II, p. 503–521.

Hubbert, K., 1953, Entrapment of petroleum under hydrodynamic conditions: AAPG Bulletin, vol. 37, no. 8, p. 1954–2026. *The original paper that proposed hydrodynamics as an important trapping mechanism.*

Annotated Bibliography, continued

Leonard, R.C., 1993, Distribution of sub-surface pressure in the Norwegian Central Graben and applications for exploration, *in* J.R. Parker, ed., Petroleum Geology of Northwest Europe: Proceedings of the Geological Society's 4th Conference, London, p. 1305–1313.

North, F.K., 1985, Petroleum Geology: London, Allen & Unwin, 246 p. *Contains many readable discussions of fluid pressure and its application.*

Powley, D.E., 1990, Pressures and hydrogeology in petroleum basins: Earth Science Reviews, vol. 29, p. 215–226.

Schowalter, T.T., 1979, Mechanics of secondary hydrocarbon migration and entrapment: AAPG Bulletin, vol. 63, no. 5, p. 723–760. *Covers many fluid behavior principles, including pressure, with broad application to petroleum exploration.*

Webster's New Twentieth Century Dictionary, Unabridged, 2nd ed., 1979: New York, Simon and Schuster, 2129 p.

Acknowledgment

I (Forrest Fiedler) received valuable help from Dave Powley in various forms. Dave was a mentor at Amoco and inspired me to think things through from basic principles. For this project, Dave counseled me and supplied numerous source documents and examples. I tried to honor all his suggestions, but any errors or omissions are my fault, not my mentor's.

Chapter 6

Evaluating Source Rocks

by

Carol A. Law

Carol A. Law

Carol Law is the Technical Challenge Leader of the Hydrocarbon System Team of BPAmoco. She was the Manager of Geoscience Technology in the Strategic Exploration Organization of Amoco prior to the BP/Amoco merger. Before joining Amoco she was the Manager of Basin Modeling at Geomath Inc., the Houston-based affiliate of the Institute Français du Petrole, where she managed sales and marketing of basin modeling software and acted as a consultant to the petroleum industry. She began her career with Conoco Inc. in the Ponca City-based research organization and moved to the Houston-based Worldwide Exploration Services Division. Law has been involved in basin modeling and geochemistry applications and research since the onset of her career.

Overview

Introduction

To evaluate a play or prospect in an undrilled area, we must first ask, "Is a source rock present?" But this is usually not enough. After determining that a source rock is present, we also need to know its richness, its quality, and its maturity. This chapter covers all of these topics.

In this chapter

This chapter contains the following topics.

Section A
Source Rock Basics

Introduction

The first factor to be assessed in an exploration play in an area yet to be drilled is whether a source rock is present. If so, then we ask, "How good is it? Will it generate oil or gas? Has it generated hydrocarbons already?" To answer these questions, we must know the basics of what constitutes a source rock, how to classify source rocks, and how to estimate potential. This section provides a background in these fundamentals.

In this section

This section contains the following topics.

Types of Source Rocks

Definition of source rock

A source rock is a rock that is capable of generating or that has generated movable quantities of hydrocarbons.

Definitions of source rock types

Source rocks can be divided into at least four major categories:

- Potential
- Effective
- Relic effective
- Spent

These categories and their definitions are shown in the table below.

Type	Definition
Potential source rock	Rock which contains organic matter in sufficient quantity to generate and expel hydrocarbons if subjected to increased thermal maturation.
Effective source rock	Rock which contains organic matter and is presently generating and/or expelling hydrocarbons to form commercial accumulations.
Relic effective source rock	An effective source rock which has ceased generating and expelling hydrocarbons due to a thermal cooling event such as uplift or erosion before exhausting its organic matter supply.
Spent source rock	An active source rock which has exhausted its ability to generate and expel hydrocarbons either through lack of sufficient organic matter or due to reaching an overmature state.

Characterizing Source Rocks

Introduction

To be a source rock, a rock must have three features:

1. Quantity of organic matter
2. Quality capable of yielding moveable hydrocarbons
3. Thermal maturity

The first two components are products of the depositional setting. The third is a function of the structural and tectonic history of the province.

Determining source rock potential

The quantity of organic matter is commonly assessed by a measure of the total organic carbon (TOC) contained in a rock. Quality is measured by determining the types of kerogen contained in the organic matter. Thermal maturity is most often estimated by using vitrinite reflectance measurements and data from pyrolysis analyses.

The table below shows the most common methods used to determine the potential of a source rock.

To determine...	Measure...
Quantity of source rock	Total organic carbon (TOC) present in the source rock
Quality of source rock	• Proportions of individual kerogens • Prevalence of long-chain hydrocarbons
Thermal maturity of source rock	• Vitrinite reflectance • Pyrolysis T_{max}

Section B

Evaluating Source Rock Richness

Introduction

Source rock richness is determined by measuring the total organic carbon (TOC) present in a rock. The two most common techniques of analyzing a rock for TOC are Rock-Eval pyrolysis with TOC and the LECO method. Conventional well logs can also provide information for evaluating interval richness.

This section first discusses what TOC is and then describes these three techniques and the information they yield.

In this section

This section contains the following topics:

Measuring a Rock's Ability to Generate Hydrocarbons

Introduction

How do we determine if an interval of strata can be categorized as a source rock? Measuring the total organic carbon (TOC) present in weight percent (wt %) is the most common method for making this determination. A TOC analysis is a screening analysis used to evaluate the overall organic richness of a rock unit. TOC serves as a guideline for assessing the hydrocarbon generating potential of a unit of rock.

Why use TOC?

Hydrocarbons are 75–95 wt % carbon by molecular weight (Jarvie, 1991) and average 83 wt %. The amount of organic carbon present in a rock is a determining factor in a rock's ability to generate hydrocarbons.

Effect of depositional environment

Depositional environment controls the amount of organic carbon contained in a rock. Source rocks are generally associated with areas where high organic productivity is combined with (1) deposition in poorly oxygenated environments (anoxic to dysaerobic), (2) upwelling, and (3) rapid sedimentation (Chinn, 1991). These processes preserve organic matter.

Average TOCs

The table below (from Chinn, 1991) shows average TOC values for different sedimentary rock types.

Rock Type	TOC Value, %
Average for all shales	0.8
Average for shale source rocks	2.2
Average for calcareous shale source rocks	1.8
Average for carbonate source rocks	0.7
Average for all source rocks	1.8

Caveat

Use the table above only as a guide. TOC average values in the real world are meaningless unless we know how the average was calculated. For example, suppose a potential source rock unit is 100 m thick. What was the average calculated from:

- 1 sample, 1 cm thick
- 10 samples, 10 cm thick, taken every 10 m
- 100 samples, 1 cm thick, taken every 1 m

Was the sampling high-graded, taking only the richest intervals? Without answers to these questions, TOC averages have no value.

Measuring a Rock's Ability to Generate Hydrocarbons, continued

Guidelines for assessing richness

The table below gives guidelines for assessing the richness of source rock intervals.

Generation Potential	Wt % TOC, Shales	Wt % TOC, Carbonates
Poor	0.0–0.5	0.0–0.2
Fair	0.5–1.0	0.2–0.5
Good	1.0–2.0	0.5–1.0
Very Good	2.0–5.0	1.0–2.0
Excellent	> 5.0	> 2.0

Caveat

If a sample being analyzed for richness is not in an immature state, then the present-day maturation level of the interval needs to be determined to establish an initial (prematuration) organic carbon value for the interval. The measured TOC value is not indicative of the sample's source potential.

Using Pyrolysis to Estimate Richness

What is pyrolysis?

Pyrolysis is the decomposition of organic matter by heating in the absence of oxygen. Organic geochemists use pyrolysis to measure richness and maturity of potential source rocks. In a pyrolysis analysis, the organic content is pyrolyzed in the absence of oxygen, then combusted. The amount of hydrocarbons and carbon dioxide released is measured. The most widely used pyrolysis technique is Rock-Eval.

Rock-Eval pyrolysis

In Rock-Eval pyrolysis, a sample is placed in a vessel and is progressively heated to 550°C under an inert atmosphere. During the analysis, the hydrocarbons already present in the sample are volatized at a moderate temperature. The amount of hydrocarbons are measured and recorded as a peak known as S_1. Next pyrolyzed is the kerogen present in the sample, which generates hydrocarbons and hydrocarbon-like compounds (recorded as the S_2 peak), CO_2, and water (Tissot and Welte, 1984). The CO_2 generated is recorded as the S_3 peak. Residual carbon is also measured and is recorded as S_4.

The diagram below shows the cycle of analysis and the corresponding recording.

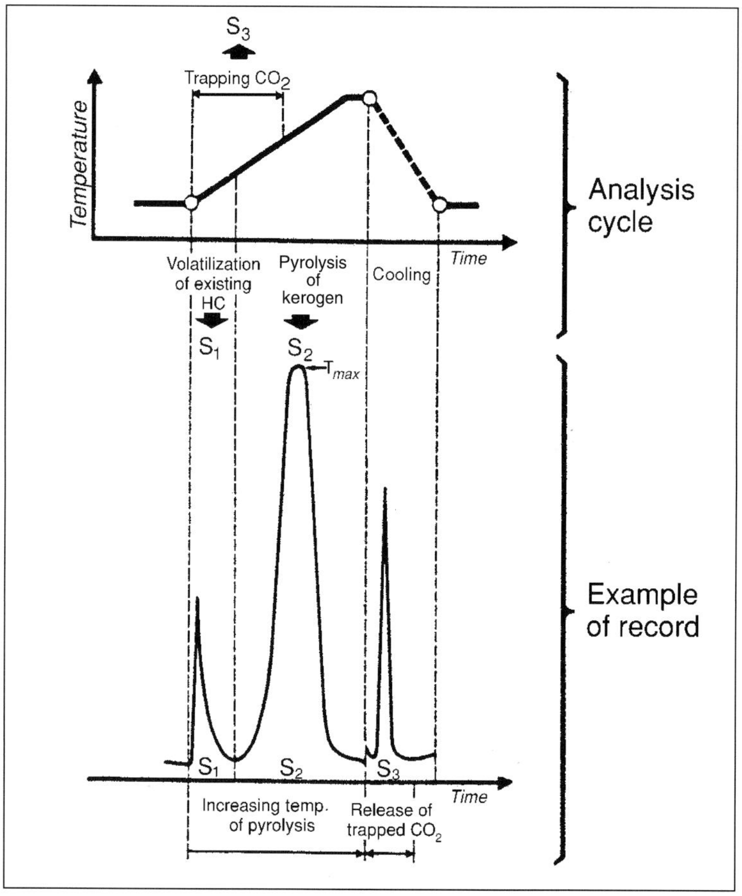

Figure 6–1. From Tissot and Welte, 1984; courtesy Springer-Verlag.

Pyrolysis indices The table below lists the Rock-Eval pyrolysis peaks and explains what they represent.

Peak	Is a measurement of...	Comment
S_1 mg Hc/g rock	The free hydrocarbons present in the sample before the analysis	Can be thought of as a residual hydrocarbon phase. When S_1 is large relative to S_2, an alternative source such as migrated hydrocarbons or contamination should be suspected
S_2 mg Hc/g rock	The volume of hydrocarbons that formed during thermal pyrolysis of the sample	Used to estimate the remaining hydrocarbon generating potential of the sample
S_3 mg Co2/g rock	The CO_2 yield during thermal breakdown of kerogen	Most prevalent in calcareous source rocks.
S_4 mg carbon/g rock	The residual carbon content of the sample	Residual carbon content of sample has little or no potential to generate hydrocarbons due to a lack of hydrogen and the chemical structure of the molecule

Estimating TOC with pyrolysis The percent TOC is actually a value that is calculated, not measured directly, using the following formula:

$$\%TOC = [0.082(S_1 + S_2) + S_4]/10$$

Units are usually given as wt % organic carbon per weight of dry rock (milligrams hydrocarbon per gram of rock).

Using the LECO Method to Estimate Richness

Definition of LECO method

The LECO method of estimating TOC uses an instrument known as a LECO carbon analyzer to measure TOC values by combusting the organic carbon and measuring the resulting carbon dioxide produced. The LECO method has almost totally been replaced by Rock-Eval pyrolysis. However, data may still be available from prior analysis.

Measuring TOC with LECO

Samples are powdered, weighed, and chemically treated prior to analysis to remove the inorganic carbon (carbonate) from the rock. The sample is then combusted in the presence of excess oxygen, allowing carbon dioxide to form from the free (organic) carbon in the rock.

The amount of carbon dioxide is directly proportional to the amount of organic carbon or the TOC of the rock. However, the TOC value can be inflated due to the presence of sulfur compounds, water, and carbonate if they have not been removed prior to analysis.

Comparing TOC values

The TOC measured by the LECO method does not include a measurement of the free hydrocarbons present in the sample. The free hydrocarbons would be volatized when samples are dried after acid treatment is performed to remove the inorganic carbonate minerals. Thus, if a sample has a high free hydrocarbon content, the LECO TOC value will be smaller than a Rock-Eval TOC value, which includes free hydrocarbons (S_1) in the TOC calculation.

Using Conventional Well Logs to Estimate Richness

Introduction

Conventional well logs are useful for estimating source rock richness both qualitatively and quantitatively. Well logs allow a qualitative identification of organic-rich formations and a quantitative analysis of the amount of organic matter. The advantages of using well logs over cuttings are continuous sampling, more accurate depth control, and greater vertical resolution (Herron, 1991).

Using well logs

The use of conventional well logs to predict organic richness of a unit of rock requires calibrating well log intervals to samples measured for TOC using pyrolysis or another suitable measurement technique. Using the calibrated logs, we can extrapolate TOC values to uncalibrated logs to estimate source rock richness over large areas.

Note: Consider changes in depositional environment and maturity when applying these techniques.

Effects of organic matter on well logs

The increasing concentration of organic matter in a rock directly affects its properties by lowering density, slowing sonic velocity, increasing radioactivity, raising resistivity, and raising hydrogen and carbon contents. All of these attributes can be measured using density, sonic, neutron, gamma ray, and resistivity logs. The table below (from Herron, 1991) summarizes log responses to organic matter.

Log/Property	Response/Value for Organic Matter (OM)	Comments
Gamma ray (GR) or uranium (U)	High	High GR caused by U; can be linear with OM; U not always present
Density	Low (approx. 1 g/cm^3)	Similar to pore fluids
Neutron	High	Due to hydrogen in OM
Sonic	High transit time	Estimates vary from 150 to more than 200 μsec/ft
Resistivity	High	May not affect log response unless generated hydrocarbons occupy pores
Pulsed neutron	High carbon–oxygen ratio	Most direct measurement of carbon; needs inorganic correction

Shale response example

The following composite log of Kimmeridge shale, North Sea, is a typical log response to a high concentration of organic matter in a shale section. The underlying Heather Formation is very silty. The source rock interval is indicated by dots with dashes through them. Note the high sonic and gamma ray readings and the low density readings. The resistivity log reads only slightly higher than the overlying shale section.

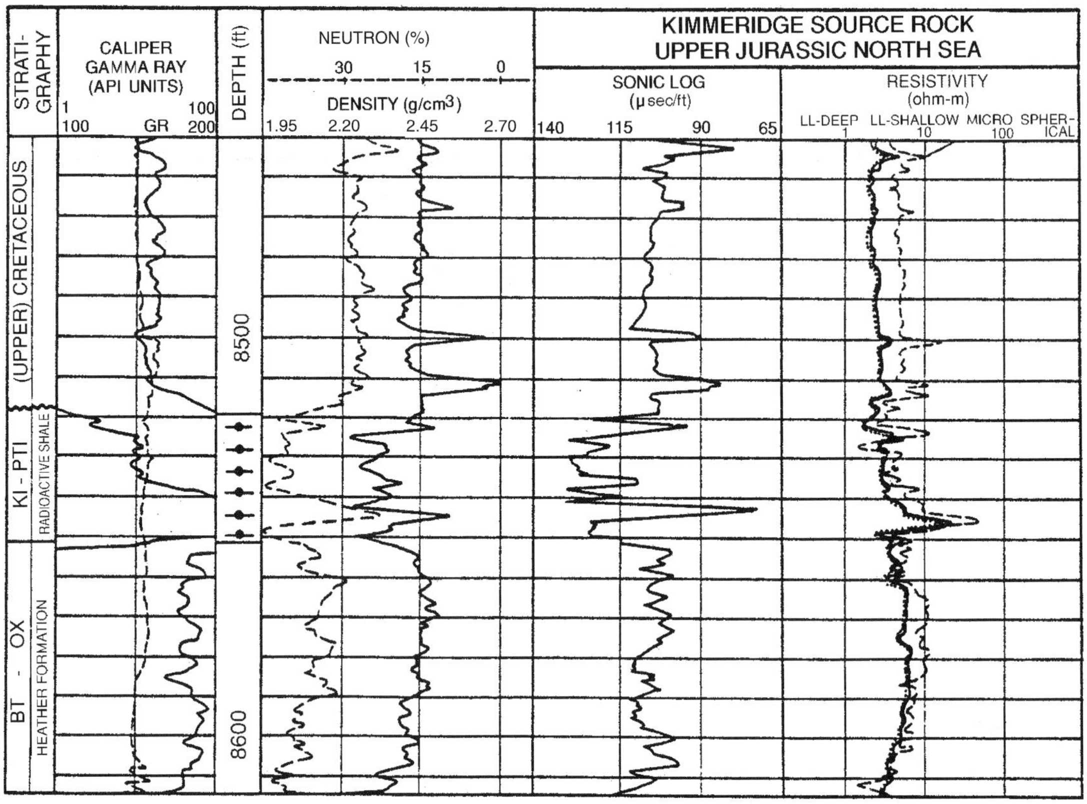

Figure 6–2. From Meyer and Nederlof, 1984; courtesy AAPG.

Using Conventional Well Logs to Estimate Richness, continued

Limestone response example

The following composite log of the Upper Jurassic Hanifa limestone in the Middle East displays a typical response of organic matter in a limestone section. No shale is present in this interval. Note the high gamma ray and resistivity readings. Core analysis of this well indicates the source rock (indicated by dots with dashes through them) is mature and generating oil.

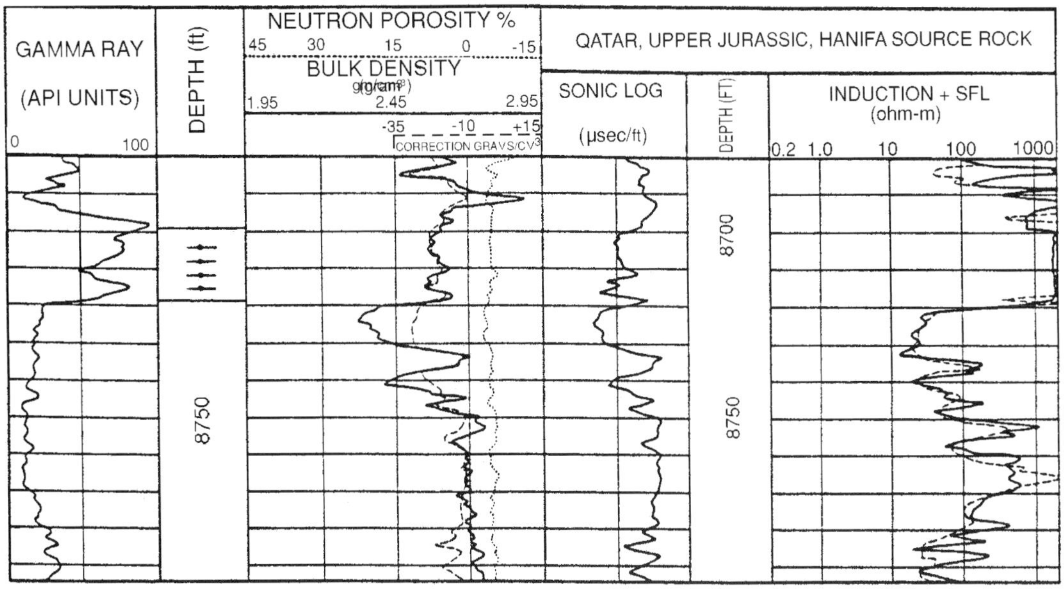

Figure 6–3. From Meyer and Nederlof, 1984; courtesy AAPG.

Limitations

Well-log signals are recorded for an interval thickness, which varies depending on the type of logging tool. Averaged values may not give a true picture of the richness of the source rock.

Section C

Evaluating Source Rock Quality

Introduction

This section discusses types of kerogen and how to estimate the quality of source rocks.

In this section

This sections contains the following topics.

Kerogen Types

Introduction

Depositional environment is the dominant factor in determining the types of organic matter found in a rock. Only two types of organic matter are found in rocks: land derived and aquatic algae derived. Heat and pressure convert organic matter into a substance called **humin** and then into **kerogen**. Time and temperature convert kerogen into petroleum.

What is kerogen?

Geochemists (Durand, 1980; Tissot and Welte, 1984) define kerogen as the fraction of sedimentary organic constituent of sedimentary rocks that is insoluble in the usual organic solvents. Kerogens are composed of a variety of organic materials, including algae, pollen, wood, vitrinite, and structureless material. The types of kerogens present in a rock largely control the type of hydrocarbons generated in that rock. Different types of kerogen contain different amounts of hydrogen relative to carbon and oxygen. The hydrogen content of kerogen is the controlling factor for oil vs. gas yields from the primary hydrocarbon-generating reactions.

Kerogen quality

The type of kerogen present determines source rock quality. The more oil prone a kerogen, the higher its quality. Four basic types of kerogen are found in sedimentary rocks. A single type or a mixture of types may be present in a source rock. The table below lists and defines these four basic kerogen types.

Kerogen Type	Predominant Hydrocarbon Potential	Amount of Hydrogen	Typical Depositional Environment
I	Oil prone	Abundant	Lacustrine
II	Oil and gas prone	Moderate	Marine
III	Gas prone	Small	Terrestrial
IV	Neither (primarily composed of vitrinite) or inert material	None	Terrestrial(?)

Evaluating Quality Using Rock-Eval HI/OI

Introduction

Obviously, the two main elements of hydrocarbons are hydrogen and carbon. Therefore, once we know the amount of organic carbon present in a rock, we then need to know the amount of hydrogen present in order to assess overall source rock quality. The amount of oxygen and hydrogen present in the kerogen defines the kerogen as type I, II, or III and if the rock will be oil or gas prone.

Hydrogen index

The hydrogen index (HI) represents the amount of hydrogen relative to the amount of organic carbon present in a sample. The S_2 curve of a Rock-Eval analysis can help us determine the total amount of hydrogen in milligrams of hydrogen to grams of sample according to the following formula:

$$HI = S_2\ (mg/g)/\%TOC \times 100$$

Oxygen index

The oxygen index (OI) represents the amount of oxygen relative to the amount of organic carbon present in a sample. The S_3 curve of a Rock-Eval analysis can help us determine the total amount of oxygen present in a sample according to the following formula:

$$OI = S_3\ (mg/g)/\%TOC \times 100$$

Determining kerogen quality

The type of kerogen present in a rock determines its quality. Type I kerogen is the highest quality; type III is the lowest. Type I has the highest hydrogen content; type III, the lowest. To determine the kerogen type present in a source rock, plot the hydrogen and oxygen indices on a modified Van Krevlen diagram (at right).

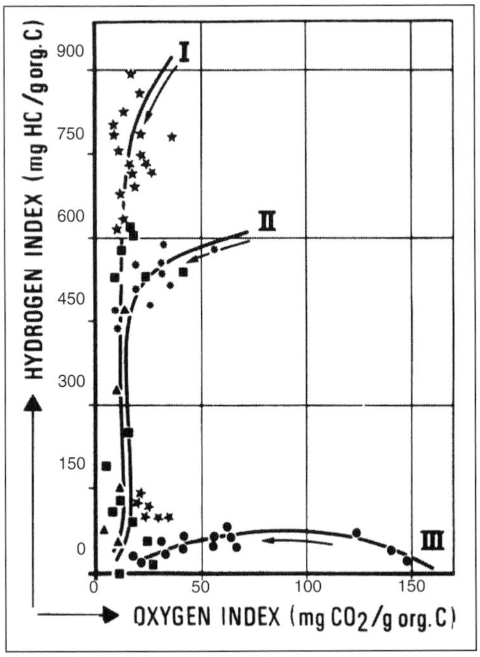

Figure 6–4. From Tissot and Welte, 1984; courtesy Springer-Verlag.

Caveat

Use the HI/OI technique only to determine source rock quality (kerogen type) of immature rocks. HI and OI change as a source rock matures (the amount of hydrogen and oxygen relative to carbon decreases and the HI/OI ratios converge toward the origin of the plot, leading one to a more gas-prone type III interpretation). Therefore, in mature rocks HI and OI are not indicative of the original kerogen quality.

Visually Assessing Quality

The method

To assess kerogen quality visually, we can separate it from the mineral matrix through acidification. We can then examine the kerogen using transmitted light through a microscope to determine its form (structured or amorphous) and origin. Structured kerogens include woody, herbaceous, vitrinite, and inertinite. Amorphous kerogens are by far the most prevalent and include most of the algal material.

Visual kerogen estimates are usually presented in terms of the percentage of each type of kerogen in a sample derived from cuttings composites or core (conventional or sidewall). For example, a visual estimate of kerogen type might be stated as 50% woody, 45% amorphous, 5% inertinite. In general, the more amorphous kerogen present, the more oil prone the rock is.

Visual kerogen types and quality

Visual kerogen types and quality are shown in the table below.

Visual Kerogen Type	Hydrocarbon Potential
Woody	Gas prone
Herbaceous	Oil and gas prone
Vitrinite	Gas prone
Inertinite	No potential
Amorphous (dominantly algal)	Oil and gas prone

Using Pyrolysis Gas Chromatography to Assess Quality

What is Py-GC? Pyrolysis gas chromatography (Py-GC) is anhydrous thermal decomposition of a material that leads to the conversion of kerogen to hydrocarbon compounds. Py-GC can be conducted on whole rock or isolated kerogen samples to obtain a visual signature or "fingerprint" of the organic material present.

How to read gas chromatograms Gas chromatography generally is a qualitative tool. It is not typically used as a quantitative measurement of hydrocarbon molecules. However, the patterns generated in the chromatograms can help us determine if a source rock will be oil or gas prone.

The X-axis of a gas chromatogram is retention time, and the Y-axis is the relative quantity of each compound. Each spike in the chromatogram represents a particular hydrocarbon compound, beginning with lowest number of carbon atoms in the compound on the left and going to higher chains of carbons to the right. The height of the spike represents the relative abundance of the compound pyrolized from the sample's kerogen. Typical gas chromatogram examples for types I, II, and III kerogen are shown below.

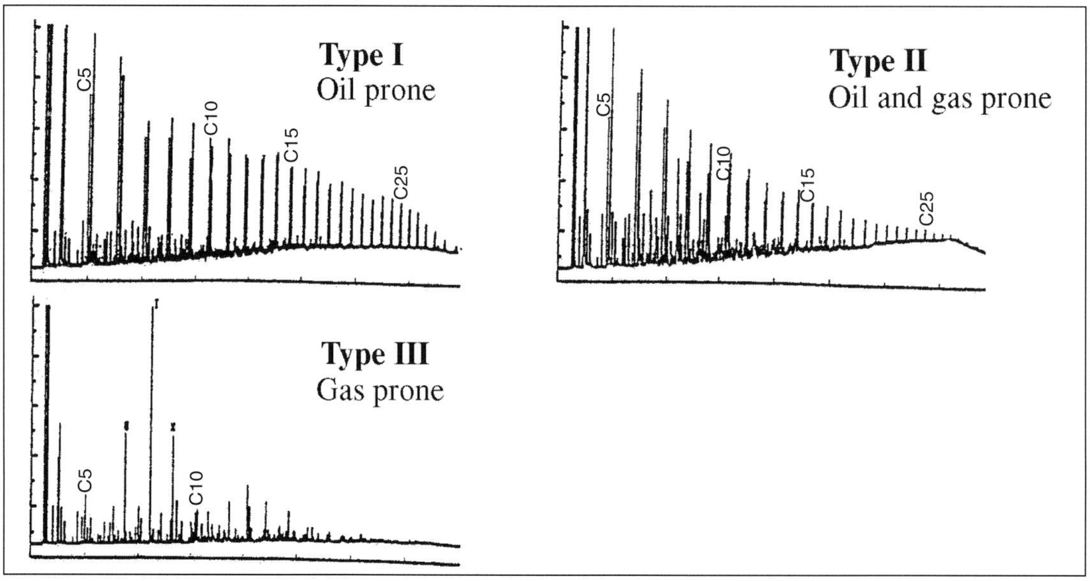

Figure 6–5.

Interpreting gas chromatograms A gas chromatogram is evaluated qualitatively to determine the potential of a rock to generate oil vs. gas. The table below shows how chromatograms for oil- vs. gas-prone rocks are evaluated.

Chromatograms of oil-prone rock	Chromatograms of gas-prone rock
Dominated by long-chain carbon compounds (greater than C_{10})	Dominated by short-chain carbon compounds from C_1-C_4
Contain carbon compounds up to C_{25} or greater	Contain very few carbon compounds above C_{10}

Section D
Evaluating Source Rock Maturity

Introduction

Once the two questions "Is a source rock present?" and "What type of hydrocarbons will it generate?" have been answered to our satisfaction, we must ask, "Has it generated hydrocarbons?" In other words, what is its present-day maturity?

In this section

This section discusses the following topics.

Maturation

Introduction

The chemistry of organic matter contained within a sedimentary rock changes over time, reflecting its temperature and burial history. This change or maturation is measured and can be combined with quality and richness data to gauge the amount of hydrocarbon generated by the organic matter. The present-day maturity level is the product of a number of variables, such as tectonic setting, burial history, and thermal history. A number of variables such as paleolatitude, pressure, fluid flow, rock matrix chemistry, and pore fluid chemistry can affect the thermal history and thus a rock's rate of maturation.

Transformation rate

The rate at which hydrocarbons are generated from organic matter is called the **transformation rate**. Using source rock maturity, we can estimate the transformation rate. Different kerogen types (1) generate hydrocarbons at different maturity levels and (2) have different transformation rates. Maturity measurements can be made on several different components of a rock like vitrinite, kerogen, spores, apatite grains, and biomarkers; each has its own relationship to the kerogen transformation rate.

Caveat

Evaluating the maturation of a geologic section is based on a depth trend from samples in a well or basin. The level of maturity interpreted from most maturation indices is dependent on the type of organic matter or material being analyzed.

For example, T_{max} cutoffs for hydrocarbon-generation zones are greater for type III than for type II kerogen. Therefore, a trend is only valid if based on analysis of samples from a homogeneous organic sequence or if differences in chemistry are accounted for in the interpretation process.

T_{max}

Introduction

T_{max} is the temperature at which the maximum rate of hydrocarbon generation occurs in a kerogen sample during pyrolysis analysis. The S_2 peak represents the rate of hydrocarbon generation (the area under the curve represents the amount). The temperature at the time the S_2 peak is recorded during pyrolysis is T_{max}, given in °C. The diagram below shows output from a pyrolysis analysis and when T_{max} is recorded.

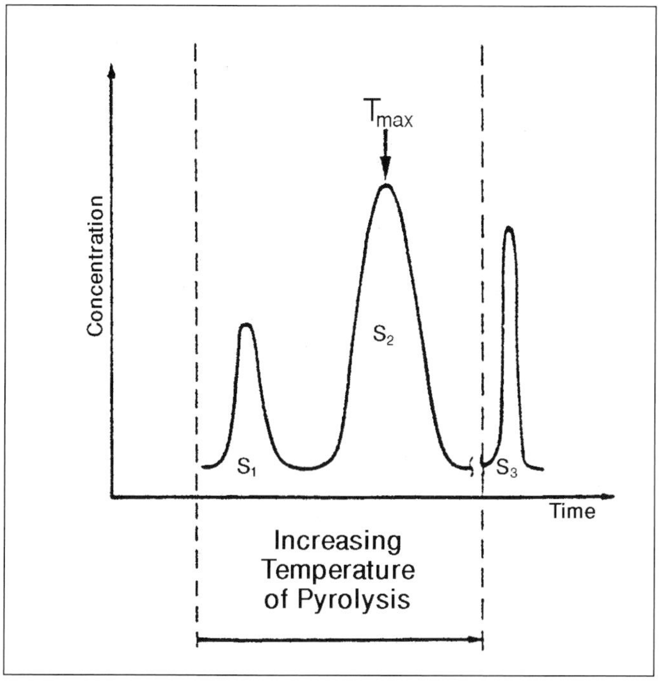

Figure 6–6.

Interpreting T_{max}

We can use the general guidelines for maturation levels given below for Rock-Eval pyrolysis T_{max} for types II and III kerogens. Different pyrolysis techniques have different cutoffs for pyrolysis oil and gas generation zone boundaries. Pyrolysis T_{max} can be significantly different for type I kerogen (Tissot et al., 1987) or kerogen containing high sulfur concentration and is not a reliable indicator of maturity for these kerogen types.

Hydrocarbon Generation Zone	**Rock-Eval Pyrolysis T_{max}, °C**
Immature	< 435
Oil (from type II kerogen)	435–455
Oil (from type III kerogen)	435–465
Gas (from type II kerogen)	> 455
Gas (from type III kerogen)	> 465

Vitrinite Reflectance

Introduction

Vitrinite reflectance is a measure of the percentage of incident light reflected from the surface of vitrinite particles in a sedimentary rock. It is referred to as $\%R_0$. Results are often presented as a mean R_0 value based on all vitrinite particles measured in an individual sample.

Connection between vitrinite and kerogen

The maturation of vitrinite is a kinetic process. The relationship between $\%R_0$ and hydrocarbon generation is dependent on the chemistry of the vitrinite as well as the chemistry of the kerogen.

Oil and gas zones

Oil and gas zone boundaries can be established using vitrinite reflectance data. The boundaries are approximate and vary according to kerogen type. The figure below shows the approximate boundaries for kerogen types I, II, and III. Time–temperature relationships and mixing of various sources of organic matter may alter these boundaries.

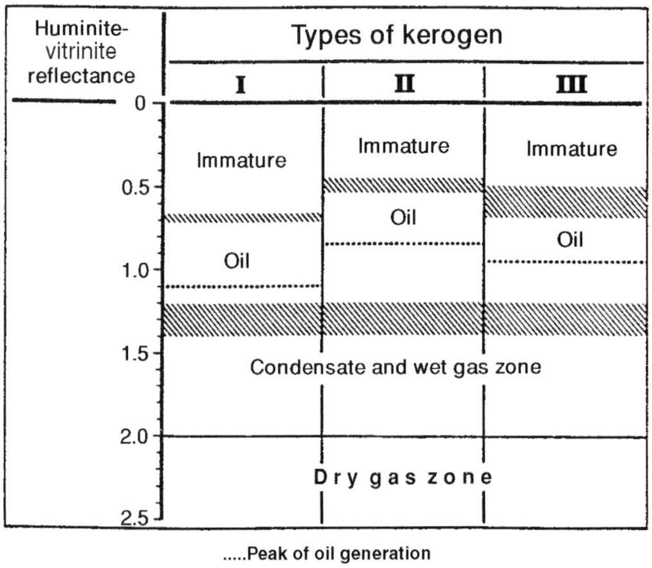

Figure 6–7. From Tissot and Welte, 1984; courtesy Springer-Verlag.

Vitrinite Reflectance, continued

Misleading data, cautions, and recommendations

A bimodal distribution or a large spread in the range of measured values produces a mean R_o value that does not accurately represent the maturity of the rock sample. Variations or errors in vitrinite reflectance measurements may be caused by the following:

- Vitrinite composition
- Incorrect identification of vitrinite particles
- Anisotropy
- Oxidation
- Staining
- Presence of caved vitrinite particles in borehole cuttings
- Reworking of vitrinite in the geologic section
- Drilling mud additives

Therefore, explorationists should always request and examine the raw data as well as the histograms and mean data.

The data below are a perfect example from a sample where the mean value reported is 1.27% R_o, based on 14 measurements. The interpretation of the mean value would place this sample past the oil generation zone. The true reflectance of the indigenous vitrinite in this sample is 0.7% R_o, providing an extremely different interpretation and placing the sample in the early stage of liquid hydrocarbon generation.

A bimodal distribution or a large spread in the range of measured values will produce a mean R_o that does not truly represent the maturity of a rock sample.

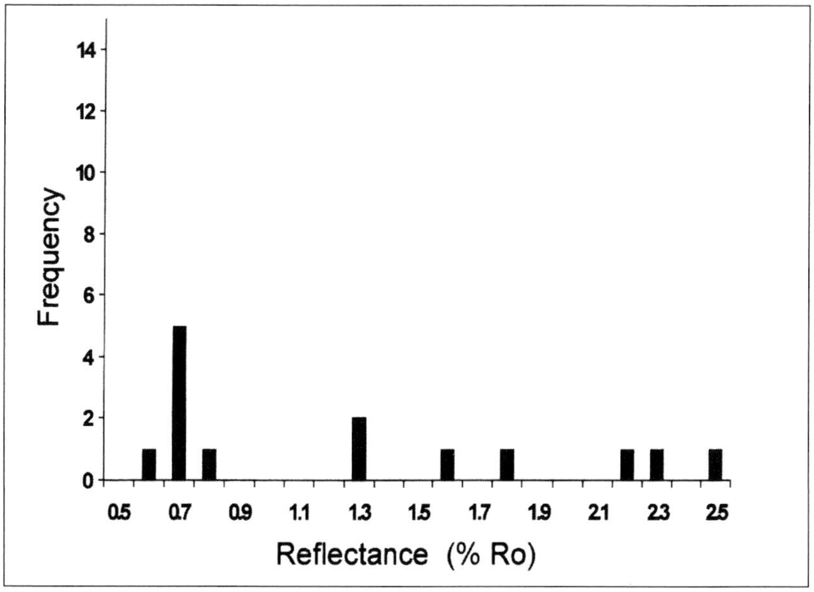

Figure 6–8.

Recognizing good data

An excellent way to recognize high-quality vitrinite reflectance data is to plot it in a histogram. We can have high confidence in the data when a single mode in the distribution curve is tightly clustered about a mean value. The histogram below is a good example.

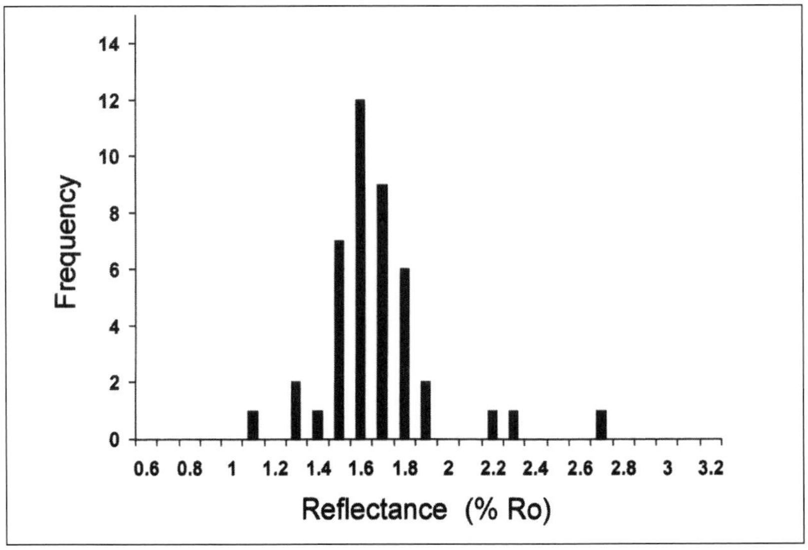

Figure 6–9.

Adequate number of measurements

A histogram profile of vitrinite reflectance used to estimate the maturity level of a sample must have an adequate number of measurements. Make as many reflectance measurements as possible for a valid R_0 determination for a sample. The histogram below is an example of a poor profile due to a lack of data. We should not place a high degree of confidence in an R_0 obtained from this sample. A rule of thumb is 40–50 vitrinite readings per sample.

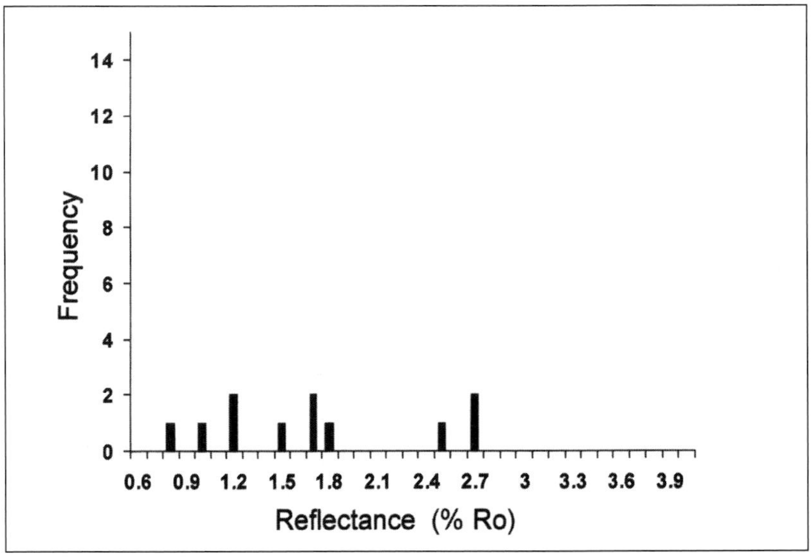

Figure 6–10.

Data contaminated by caving

The histogram below represents poor-quality vitrinite reflectance data due to contamination by caving. As a result of the drilling process, immature kerogen caved into the borehole and mixed with drill cuttings originally containing sparse amounts of vitrinite. The indigenous vitrinite is about 2.5% R_o. Therefore, it is important to know the type of sample used for vitrinite analysis.

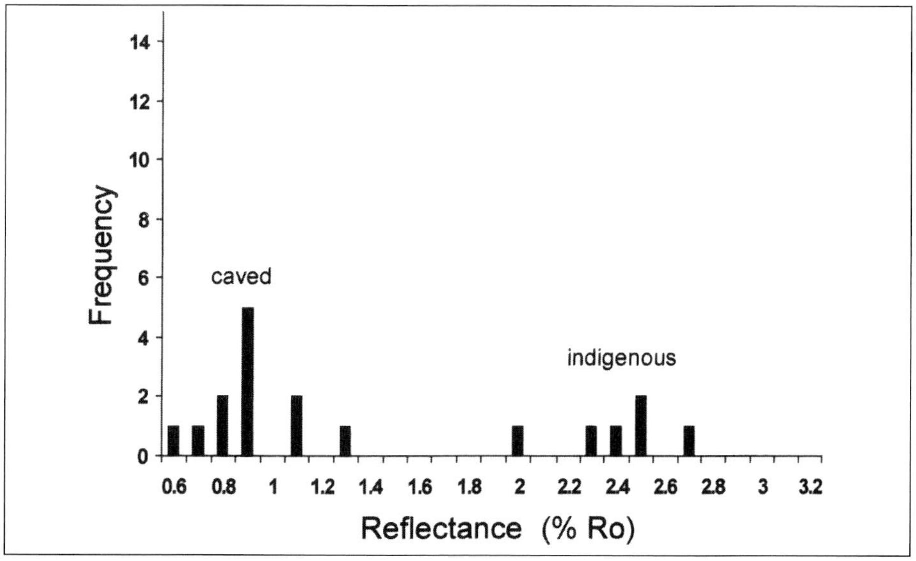

Figure 6–11.

Sample with reworked vitrinite

The bimodal distribution shown in the histogram below represents an indigenous and a reworked population of vitrinite measured in one sample. The reworked population would have been eroded from a more mature provenance and deposited with the indigenous organic matter of this sample.

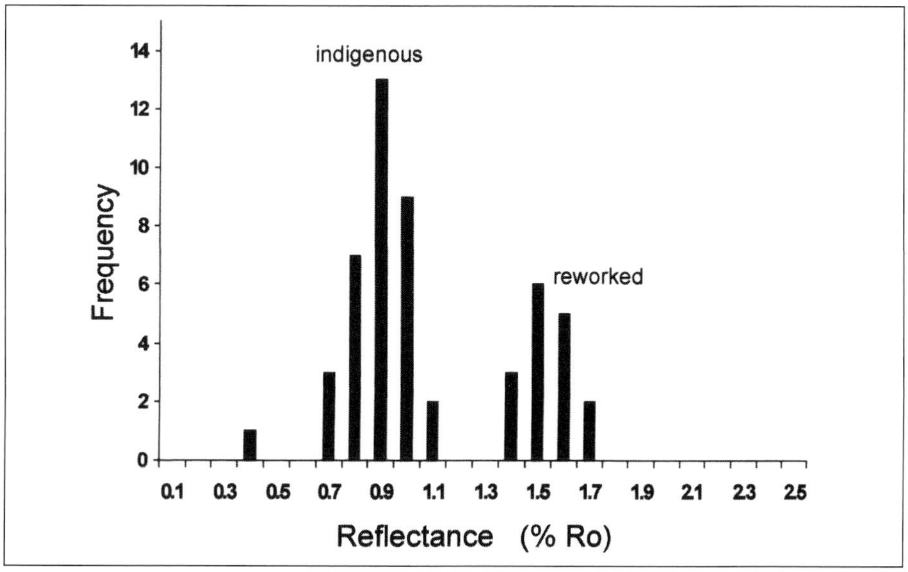

Figure 6–12.

Apatite Fission Track Analysis

What is apatite fission track analysis?

Apatite fission tracks are formed when charged particles are released by the spontaneous nuclear fission of uranium 238 in apatite crystals. The highly charged particles released by the fission reaction damage the lattice of apatite crystals. The damage appears as linear features referred to as **fission tracks**.

The rate of decay of uranium 238 is a time-dependent reaction; therefore, the number of fission tracks in a crystal can be used to measure the time since the formation of the apatite grains. This is the basis for apatite fission track analysis.

Measuring maturity with apatite fission tracks

The continued existence of apatite fission tracks is temperature dependent. At temperatures below 60°C the fission tracks exist as they were formed. However, as the temperature increases from 60–120°C, the length of the fission tracks in apatite crystals will decrease due to thermally induced "healing" of the crystal structure. This process is referred to as **annealing**.

The mean length of a fission track at the time of formation and up to 60°C is 15μ. Fission tracks will completely anneal and disappear at approximately 120°C. Therefore, the length of apatite fission tracks can be used as a measure of the maximum temperature that a rock has been subjected to and provides information related to thermal history.

Using analysis with R_0

Apatite grains are commonly found in sandstones. The amount of information provided from fission track analysis can be significant and is very complementary to vitrinite data in portions of the geologic section that are lean in organic matter. See Duddy et al., 1988, and Gleadow et al., 1986, for a general overview of the interpretation and application of apatite fission track data in petroleum exploration.

Caveat

The chemistry of apatite is variable and can be significant enough to have an effect on the rate of fission track annealing. One should consider this effect when interpreting apatite data. Also, one should make sure caved material has not contaminated a sample of drilling cuttings. This can be a source of erroneous data.

Getting a valid measurement

One reading of fission track length is not enough to make a valid determination of the thermal history of a sample. Instead, many readings need to be made to achieve a high confidence level. A service company's report cites the fission track length as a mean of the total population of fission track lengths measured. Overall, mean track length should decrease as depth and/or temperature increase. We should check the raw data in an apatite fission track analysis report against the known geologic history of an area (and its expected thermal history) to verify or refine a vendor's interpretation.

Effect of uplift on AFTA data

If the mean age distribution of a sample as determined from apatite fission track analysis is less than the geologic age of that sample determined by other means, then that sample is interpreted to have been exposed to temperatures of > 120°C during its burial history. For example, a sample might have been buried to a depth where temperatures were > 120°C. At these high temperatures, all the fission tracks would have annealed. Then the sample might have been subsequently uplifted and exposed to temperatures < 120°C where new fission tracks formed. The number and length of the new fission tracks reflect the latest thermal environment.

This application of fission track data makes the technique extremely useful for evaluating the magnitude and timing of major unconformities in an area of interest.

Example of fission track length interpretation

The length data in itself may not be adequate to evaluate the thermal history. For example, the figure below shows a unimodal distribution of relatively long (unannealed) fission tracks. These data would need to be combined with the fission track age determination to derive thermal history information. If the fission track age of this sample was older than the depositional age, the implication would be that the sample had never been exposed to temperature in the annealing zone and most likely never experienced temperatures greater than 60–70°C. In contrast, if the fission track age was less than the depositional age, the sample would have been subjected to temperatures above 110–120°C, where all of the original tracks would have been annealed. The sample would then have been uplifted rapidly and all of the remaining tracks would have formed since the uplift to a temperature zone less than or equal to the 60–70°C. The fission track age date would provide information on the timing of this rapid uplift event.

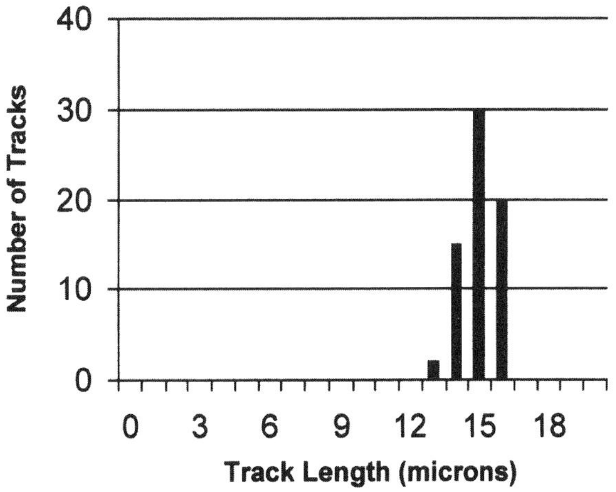

Figure 6–13.

Spore Coloration and Thermal Alteration Indices

How to use SCI and TAI

SCI (spore coloration index) and TAI (thermal alteration index) are maturation indicators that measure the color of palynomorphs. Color changes as a function of maturity.

There are a number of scales for both SCI and TAI within the exploration industry. The SCI and TAI scales have been "standardized" to the vitrinite reflectance maturity scale. Users of SCI and TAI data need to have access to the maturation relationship used by the lab supplying the data, and users should be aware of how the scales compare from one lab to another in order to apply the data correctly. These relationships should be available from the vendor performing the analysis.

Correlation of SCI & TAI with other parameters

The table below shows a very generalized correlation of kerogen maturity parameters with SCI and TAI (after Waples, 1985).

Vitrinite Reflectance (%R_0)	Spore Coloration Index (SCI)	Thermal Alteration Index (TAI)	Pyrolysis T_{max} (°C)	Generalized Hydrocarbon Zone
0.40	4.0	2.0	420	Immature
0.50	5.0	2.3	430	Immature
0.60	6.0	2.6	440	Oil
0.80	7.4	2.8	450	Oil
1.00	8.1	3.0	460	Oil
1.20	8.3	3.2	465	Oil & wet gas
1.35	8.5	3.4	470	Wet gas
1.50	8.7	3.5	480	Wet gas
2.00	9.2	3.8	500	Methane
3.00	10	4.0	500+	Methane
4.00	10+	4.0	500+	Overmature

Hydrogen Index (HI)

Introduction

Gross trends of hydrogen indices (HI) can be used as a maturation indicator. The hydrogen index is calculated from Rock-Eval data using the following formula:

$$HI = S_2 \text{ (mg/g)}/\%TOC \times 100$$

How to apply HI

Hydrocarbon generation zones can be indicated in the HI data for a uniform source section when HI decreases with depth. Inconsistencies due to changes in organic facies or the chemistry of the source rock can produce shifts in the HI data which are not indicative of maturation trends. Therefore, be sure the source is of uniform character when applying this concept.

The figure below shows a decreasing HI trend for a source rock beginning to generate hydrocarbons at a depth of approximately 2200 m.

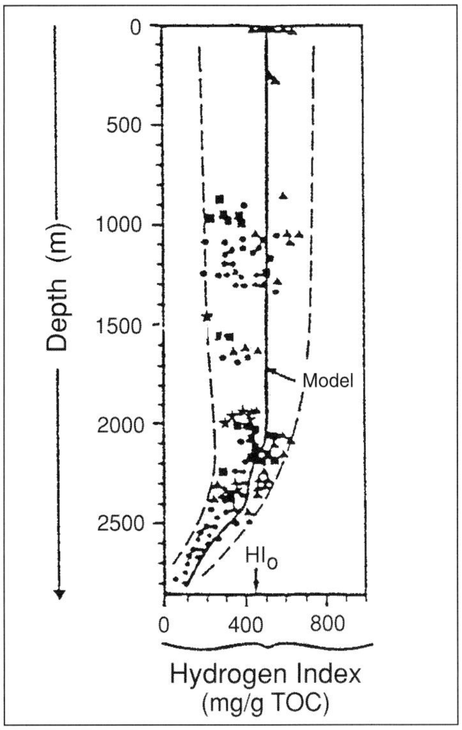

Figure 6–14. From Ungerer et al., 1991; courtesy John Wiley & Sons.

Production Index (PI)

Introduction

Maturity of a homogeneous source section can be accessed from the production index (PI). PI is calculated from Rock-Eval data:

$$PI = S_1/(S_1 + S_2)$$

How to apply PI

PI increases continuously through the oil window up to a value of 0.50. The following cut-offs can generally be applied.

Production Index	Generation Zone
< 0.10	Immature
0.10–0.30	Oil generation
> 0.30	Gas generation/oil cracking

Caveat

PI data are misleading if the S_1 peak includes nonindigenous hydrocarbons, such as drilling additives or migrated hydrocarbons. Expulsion characteristics of a source rock are not considered when looking at PI numbers. If the expulsion saturation threshold of the source rock is high, the PI data will be overestimated. If the expulsion saturation threshold is low, the data will be underestimated.

A trend is valid only if developed over a uniform source internal. If the depositional environment changes significantly, establish a different PI trend for each unique source rock type.

Section E

Relationships Between Maturity and Hydrocarbon Generation

Introduction

Different types of kerogens convert to hydrocarbons at different rates, and they yield different quantities of various hydrocarbon phases. Therefore, one standard relationship between a measured maturity parameter and hydrocarbon generation does not exist. Values such as 0.6% R_0 are generally associated with the onset of oil generation or indicate the top of the oil window. However, this generality applies only if a source rock is composed of pure type II organic matter (marine kerogen).

This section reviews some of the relationships between maturation indicators and hydrocarbon generation from standard kerogen types.

In this section

This section contains the following topics.

Kerogen Type and Hydrocarbon Generation

Introduction

Kerogen consists of many fractions, each converting to hydrocarbons at a specified rate. This rate of conversion to hydrocarbons is defined by a first-order rate equation known as the Arrhenius law:

$$K(+) = A_e^{-E/RT(t)}$$

where:

A = Arrhenius factor
E = activation energy

These are generally referred to as **kinetic parameters**. They can be measured using various pyrolysis techniques and are different for each distinct kerogen analyzed.

Hydrocarbon generation—depth and yield

The depth of hydrocarbon generation and the yield of individual hydrocarbon phases are primarily a function of the kinetics of the kerogen–hydrocarbon conversion. Burial history and catalytic effects, due to source rock matrix chemistry, affect the rate of generation, although these effects are secondary to the kinetic effects.

The following hydrocarbon generation vs. depth plots for types I (left) and III (right) kerogens are based on identical burial and thermal conditions. Thus, they depict the difference in the depth of hydrocarbon generation, based on kerogen type alone. Type I kerogen generally has a shallower liquid hydrocarbon zone and generates significantly larger amounts of hydrocarbons. The onset of generation is indicated by the change in the slope of the curves.

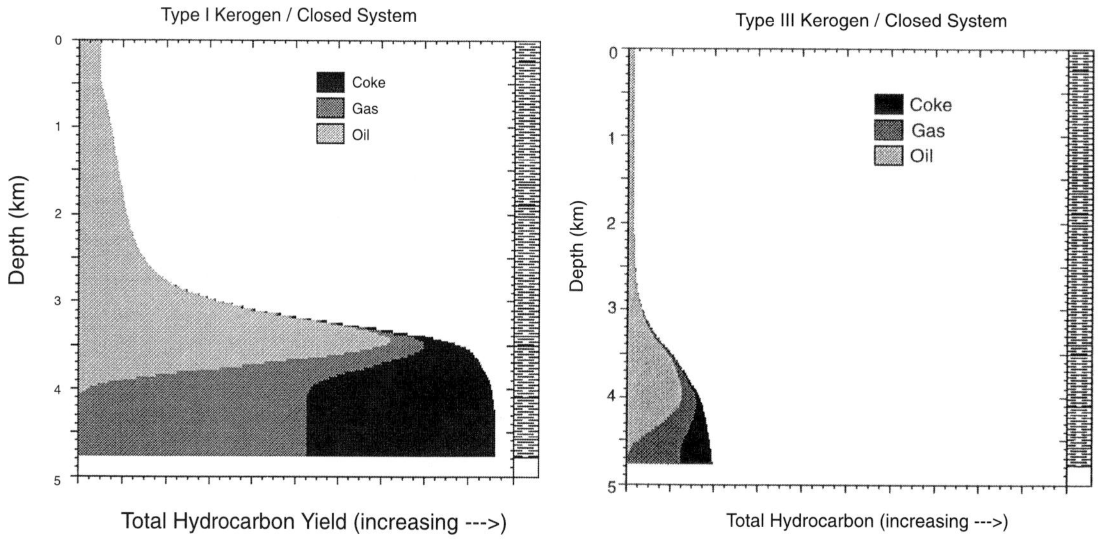

Figure 6–15. From results of Genex 1-D basin modeling software, courtesy Institute Français du Petrole.

Timing hydrocarbon generation

Variations in the kinetic parameters affect predictions of the present-day distribution of hydrocarbon generation zones and also influence when, in geologic time, a potential source interval generates. The figures below compare the timing of hydrocarbon generation from type I kerogen (left) to type III (right). The onset of hydrocarbon generation is indicated by the dramatic change in slope of the curves: 110–100 Ma for type I and 90–80 Ma for type III. The difference in timing shown in this example is based only on the different kinetic parameters of the kerogen types.

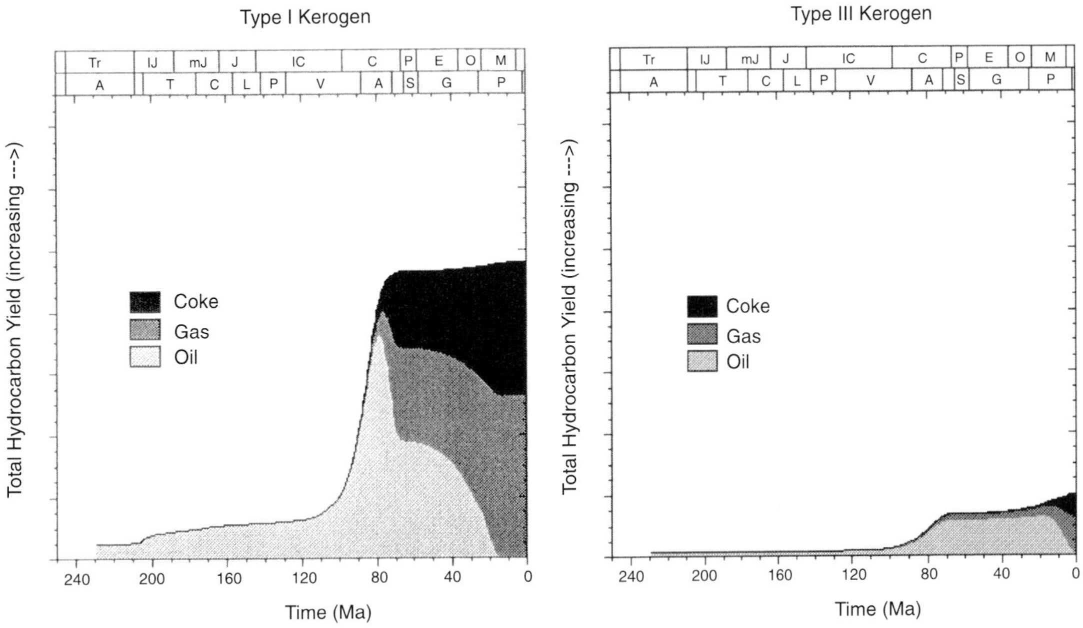

Figure 6–16.

Recommendations

Conduct kerogen kinetic analysis on samples from the basin being modeled. If samples are not available, standard values for types I–III are available from Burnham, 1989; Burnham and Sweeney, 1990; and Tissot and Espitalie, 1975. Apply these values after carefully classifying the kerogen type in terms of the depositional environment of the individual source intervals.

Kerogen Type and Maturity

Introduction

Each kerogen type has its own relationship to maturity parameters. Maturity measurements are made on materials other than kerogen; therefore, they are not a direct measure of the hydrocarbon generation stage of the source intervals. A relationship must be established between maturity of the geologic section and hydrocarbon generation for each kerogen type in a basin. This relationship can be derived using 1-D basin modeling techniques.

Hydrocarbon generation and maturity

The hydrocarbon generation–depth curve shown below indicates where various phases of hydrocarbons would be generated today in the geologic section if a uniform kerogen existed throughout. We would use the following steps to compare the relationships.

Step	Action
1	Define the hydrocarbon generation stage for a calibrated well based on the depth vs. hydrocarbon yield plot (left figure). For example, the onset of oil generation occurs at approximately 2.1 km. Then transfer to the depth versus maturity plot (in this case vitrinite reflectance, right figure) and follow across at 2.1 km until you reach the maturity profile. This vitrinite reflectance value (0.55 $\%R_o$) would indicate the onset of hydrocarbon generation in this well.
2	Apply this relationship to predict the generation zones for this specific kerogen in wells with similar thermal and burial histories in the basin for which maturity data are available.

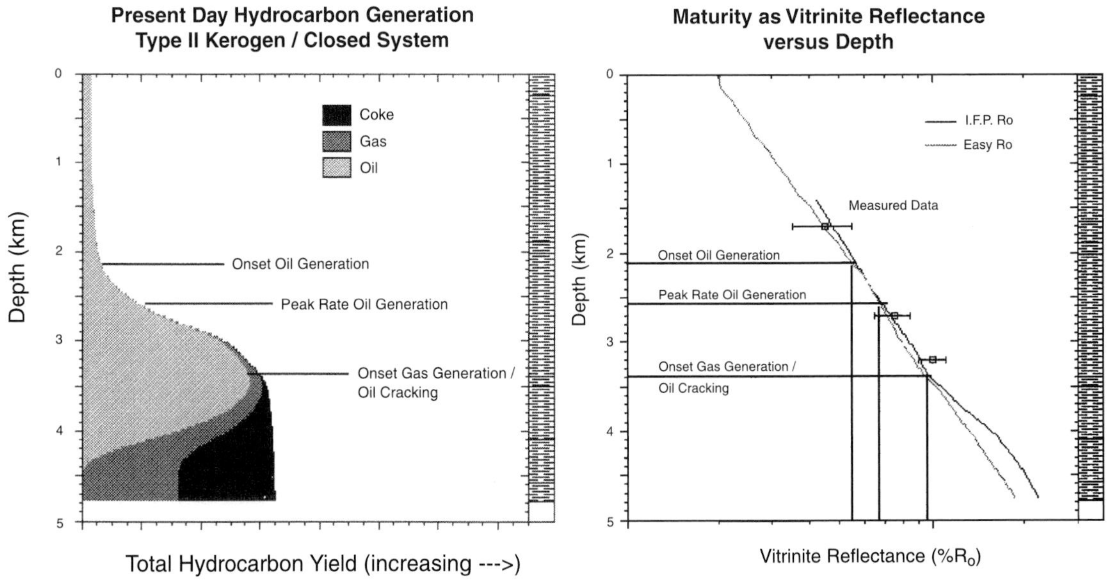

Figure 6–17. From results of Genex 1-D basin modeling software, courtesy Institute Français du Petrole.

Kerogen Type and Transformation Ratio

Introduction

When we compare hydrocarbon generation curves and transformation ratio curves from 1-D models, we can develop a relationship in a way similar to that for generation–maturity. If vitrinite reflectance data are available, the relationship between transformation ratio and maturity can be used to predict (1) percentage of kerogen that has generated hydrocarbons at a given depth and (2) hydrocarbon yields.

Example

Based on the figures below, we determine that at a depth of 2.6 km the modeled well is presently in the oil generation zone and approximately 25% of the kerogen in the source rocks at this depth has generated hydrocarbons. We know from the hydrocarbon generation–maturity relationship that at 2.6 km this well has a vitrinite reflectance of 0.7% R_0. If another well in the basin contains similar source rocks and has a maturity of 0.7% R_0 at 3.7 km, then we can predict that the section at 3.7 km is mature for liquid generation and has generated a liquid hydrocarbons, converting approximately 25% of its kerogen to hydrocarbons.

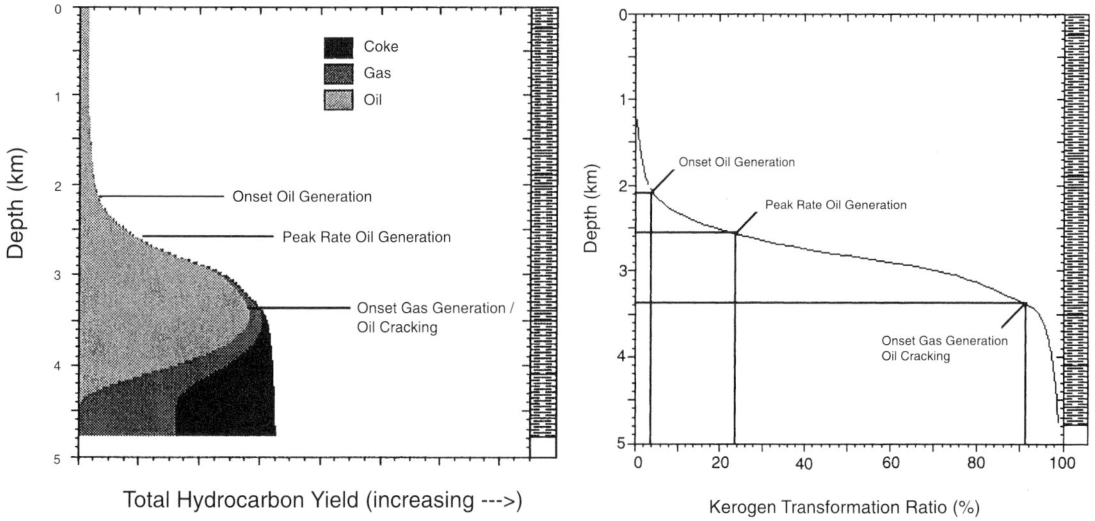

Figure 6–18. From results of Genex 1-D basin modeling software, courtesy Institute Français du Petrole.

Comparison of Kerogen Types

Parameter differences

The table below shows examples of the relationships between hydrocarbon generation zones, maturity, and transformation ratio for standard types II and III kerogens, based on a specific burial and thermal history model. The most significant difference is in the depth to the onset of oil generation, where 1000 m separates the top of the oil windows of these two kerogen types.

Hydrocarbon Generation Zone	Vitrinite Reflectance, % R_o		Transformation Ratio, %		Present-Day Depth, m	
	Type II	Type III	Type II	Type III	Type II	Type III
Onset oil	0.55	0.85	5	12	2200	3200
Onset peak rate generation	0.65	1.00	17	31	2600	3500
Onset gas/cracking liquids	0.95	1.35	88	64	3400	4050

Open- vs. Closed-System Generation Modeling

Introduction

Hydrocarbon generation results from computerized 1-D basin modeling software are typically presented as either open- or closed-system yields. **Open-system** models are based on the assumption that hydrocarbons have been expelled from the source rock, have been transported away, and are no longer subject to the thermal conditions of the 1-D model. **Closed-system** models assume the hydrocarbons have not been expelled from the source rock and that all generated hydrocarbon phases are subject to further cracking to lighter phases.

Implications for yield predictions

Below are examples of yield curves for the same well, based on both open- and closed-system modeling conditions. The open-system model is run with an expulsion efficiency of 70%, meaning 70% of the generated hydrocarbons were expelled before subsequent maturation and were not subjected to secondary cracking to lighter phases. The closed-system model does not incorporate an expulsion component; therefore, the hydrocarbons are subject to cracking to lighter phases. The closed-system model (right) predicts significantly greater quantities of gas at depth than the open-system model (left).

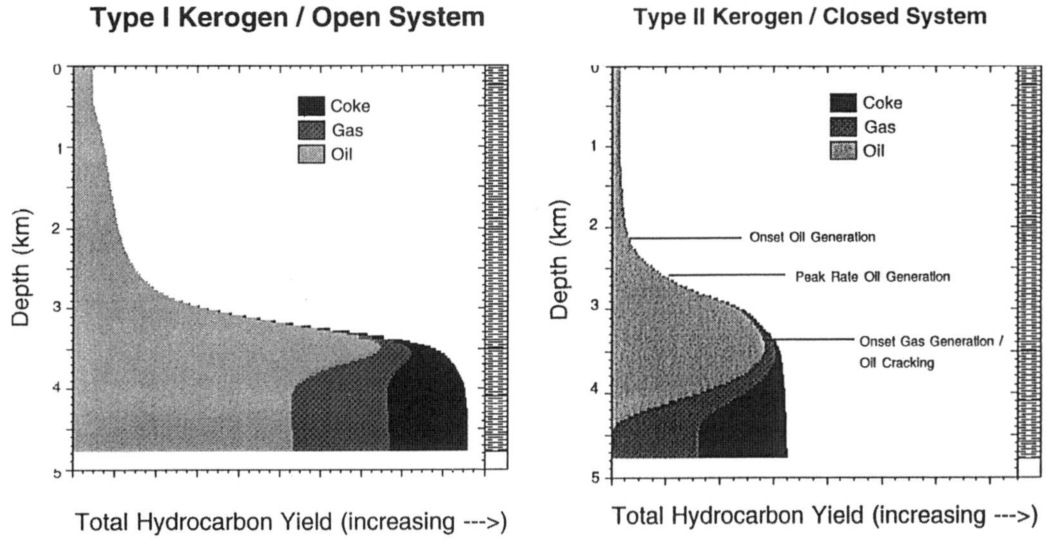

Figure 6–19. From results of Genex 1-D basin modeling software, courtesy Institute Français du Petrole.

Note: In general, open-system models overestimate the quantities of liquids present in a system. Closed-system models overestimate the amount of gas present in the system and are pessimistic in terms of predicting quantities of liquids. Closed-system models typically are not run any more. However, when evaluating older models, consider this effect.

Section F
Annotated Bibliography

Burnham, A.K., 1989, A Simple Model of Petroleum Formation and Cracking: Lawrence Livermore Laboratory report UCID 21665, March 1989. *Basic review of the kinetic conversion of kerogens to hydrocarbons.*

______ and J.J. Sweeney, 1990, Modeling Maturation and Migration of Petroleum: Lawrence Livermore Laboratory report UCRL 102602, rev. 1. *The kinetics of kerogen conversion are presented and discussed relative to the prediction of hydrocarbon generation and occurrence.*

Chinn, E.W., 1991, The role of organic geochemistry in petroleum exploration: Basin Research Institute Bulletin, Louisiana State University, Baton Rouge, LA, p. 15–23. *Short paper that summarizes petroleum geochemistry and its analytical techniques.*

Duddy, I.R., P.F. Green, and G.M. Laslett, 1988, Thermal annealing of fission tracks in apatite—3, variable temperature behaviour: Chemical Geology (Isotopic Geoscience Section), vol. 73, p. 25–38. *Mathematical presentation and discussion of the thermal annealing equations of apatite.*

Durand, B., 1980, Sedimentary organic matter and kerogen: definition and quantitative importance of kerogen, *in* B. Durand, ed., Kerogen: Techniq, p. 13–14.

Gleadow, A.J.W., I.R. Duddy, and J.F. Lovering, 1983, Fission track analysis: a new tool for the evaluation of thermal histories and hydrocarbon potential: APEA Journal, vol. 23, p. 93–102. *Good general overview on theory and application of apatite fission track analysis.*

Herron, S.L., 1991, In situ evaluation of potential source rocks by wireline logs, *in* R.K. Merrill, ed., Source and Migration Processes and Evaluation Techniques: AAPG Treatise of Petroleum Geology, Handbook of Petroleum Geology, p. 127–134.

Jarvie, D.M., 1991, Total organic carbon (TOC) analysis, *in* R.K. Merrill, ed., Source and Migration Processes and Evaluation Techniques: AAPG Treatise of Petroleum Geology, Handbook of Petroleum Geology, p. 113–118. *Good general reference on the LECO and Rock-Eval techniques for measuring TOC.*

Meyer, B.L., and M.H. Nederlof, 1984, Identification of source rocks on wireline logs by density/resistivity and sonic transit time/resistivity crossplots: AAPG Bulletin, vol. 68, no. 2, p. 121–129. *Discusses the principles and application of well log analysis to identify source rocks.*

Peters, K.E., 1986, Guidelines for evaluating petroleum source rock using programmed pyrolysis: AAPG Bulletin, vol. 70, no. 3, p. 318–329. *Reviews pyrolysis in detail and explains how it is applied to petroleum source rock analysis.*

Tissot, B.P., and J. Espitalie, 1975, L'evolution thermique de la latiere organique des sediments: aplications d'une simulation mathematique: Rev. IFP, vol. 30, p. 743–777. *In French. Contains basic IFP kerogen kinetic data.*

______ and D.H. Welte, 1984, Petroleum Formation and Occurrence, 2 ed.: New York, Springer-Verlag, 699 p. *The best overall reference for petroleum geochemistry.*

______, R. Pelet, and P. Ungerer, 1987, Thermal history of sedimentary basins, maturation indices, and kinetics of oil and gas generation: AAPG Bulletin, vol. 71, p. 1445–1466. *Excellent review of the relationships between maturation indicators and hydrocarbon generation from kerogens.*

Ungerer, P., P. Forbes, and J.L. Rudkiewicz, 1991, Computer modeling of the interplay between generation and expulsion of petroleum: a new advance in synthesizing geochemical data: Proceedings of the 13th World Petroleum Congress, Buenos Aires, p. 179–189. *Discusses the relationships between a number of maturation indicators and petroleum generation and migration.*

______, J. Espitalie, F. Behar, and S. Eggen, 1988, Modelisation mathematique des interactions entre craquage thermique et migration lors de la formation du petreole et du gaz: C.R. Acad. Sci. series II, p. 927–934. *In French. Contains discussion of the kerogen-to-hydrocarbon transformation and hydrocarbon cracking reactions.*

Waples, D., 1985, Geochemistry in Petroleum Exploration: Boston, IHRDC, 232 p. *Very basic overview of geochemical principles as applied to petroleum exploration; contains a good general glossary.*

______ and T. Machihara, 1990, Application of sterane and triterpane biomarkers in petroleum exploration: Bulletin of Canadian Petroleum Geology, vol. 38, no. 3, p. 357–380. *Good general discussion of the application of basic biomarkers for correlation of oils and source rocks.*

______ and ______, 1991, Biomarkers for Geologists—A Practical Guide to the Application of Steranes and Triterpanes in Petroleum Geology: AAPG Methods in Exploration no. 9, 91 p. *General guide to interpretation of biomarker data aimed at the exploration geoscientist.*

Chapter 7

Migration of Petroleum

by

Martin D. Matthews

Martin D. Matthews

"Matt" Matthews is a consultant, retired, from Texaco's International Exploration Department and is currently an adjunct professor at Rice University. He holds degrees in geology from Allegheny College (BS), West Virginia University (MS), and Northwestern University (PhD). Matthews has worked in surface and subsurface geochemistry, remote sensing, diagenesis, fractures, fluid flow, basin modeling, depositional systems, and global cyclostratigraphy. Prior to his work at Texaco International, he was a senior scientist for Texaco Exploration and Production Research and held a variety of positions with Gulf R&D Co., including manager of geochemical research and director of geological research. Matthews has also been a professor at Washington State University, has served on the Earth Science Advisory Board at Savannah River Laboratory, and was the director of oil and gas test sites for the Geosat–NASA Test Case study panel. He is listed in *Who's Who in Frontiers of Science & Technology, Who's Who in Optical Science and Engineering, American Men and Women of Science*, and *Who's Who in Technology Today*.

Overview

Introduction

Migration of hydrocarbons is a little-understood but critical process of the petroleum system. This chapter attempts to address the following questions:

- How does oil escape from the source rock?
- Does oil migrate out of the trap?
- Why are there marked differences in oil gravity, wax content, and sulfur content in lateral and stratigraphically successive sands?
- Why are there differences in water salinity for multiple sands in one structural trap?
- What is the role of faults in transporting and trapping hydrocarbons?
- Why are there barren sands within sequences of productive sands?
- How is cross-formational flow of hydrocarbons accomplished?
- Does the form change during migration and, if so, which form is dominant under what conditions?
- How can we estimate the timing, volumes, and compositions of transported hydrocarbons?

In this chapter

This chapter contains the following sections.

Section A
Migration Concepts

Summary of principles

The principles of hydrocarbon migration, discussed in this section, can be summarized as follows:

- Hydrocarbons migrate as a separate phase, primarily due to buoyancy. This force causes them to move vertically at geologically rapid rates.
- Lithologic layers slow or restrict the vertical movement of hydrocarbons. Seals deflect the hydrocarbons laterally updip through underlying beds to a trap or spill point. Lateral migration is also facilitated by meteoric groundwater flow. Flow rates for compaction-driven water generally are too slow to significantly affect hydrocarbon flow.
- The properties of reservoirs and carrier beds (dip, relative permeability, etc.) control the rate of migration and thus the specific direction of the bulk of hydrocarbons under seals.

The broad principles of migration are reviewed in detail in this section.

In this section

This section contains the following topics.

Migration Basics

Introduction

Less is known about migration than any other process involved in the accumulation of hydrocarbons in the subsurface. It is generally described as that unknown process or group of processes that enable petroleum to move from a source to a reservoir.

Observations of migration

Hydrocarbon migration has been observed only rarely and indirectly in the natural environment under atypical conditions. Observation is difficult because it occurs either too rapidly, too slowly, or elsewhere. As such, migration is generally inferred rather than demonstrated. Conclusions about migration are based on snapshots in reservoir and source-rock systems. Laboratory migration experiments are limited in their applications by the time frame and the ability to reproduce subsurface conditions.

Migration studies

The movement of hydrocarbons through an entire stratigraphic section is generally ignored. Geochemists usually focus on migration out of source rocks, and reservoir engineers usually study migration within carrier beds (reservoir-quality rocks). Little is known, though much is inferred, about cross-facies flow required when source rocks and reservoir-quality rocks are not adjacent to one another.

Migration constraints

Physical conditions constraining migration through stratigraphic sections are pressure, temperature, permeability, capillarity, surface tension, molecular size, and density. The main chemical constraint is solubility of migrating hydrocarbons.

Chemistry of migrated hydrocarbons

Detailed chemical correlations made of reservoired hydrocarbons with source rocks strongly indicate that the migration process does not significantly affect the overall geochemistry of the migrated hydrocarbons. However, general differences exist between the chemical composition of oils and the source rocks to which they are chemically correlated. These differences must be explained.

How we observe migration

Materials trapped in diagenetic overgrowths offer snapshots of the migration process. Studies of these materials by microanalytical techniques such as fluid inclusion analysis, microfluorescence, and cathodoluminescence offer potential for great advances in our understanding of the migration process and our ability to recognize and perhaps predict migration pathways and timing.

Migration stages

Hydrocarbon migration consists of four stages: primary, secondary, tertiary, and remigration. The list below contains their definitions.

- **Primary Migration**—The process of loss of hydrocarbons from the source rock.
- **Secondary Migration**—Migration from source to reservoir along a simple or complex carrier system. Includes migration within the reservoir rock itself.
- **Tertiary Migration**—Migration to the surface, either from a reservoir or source rock. Also called dismigration.
- **Remigration**—Migration from one reservoir position through an intervening section into another reservoir position in the same or a different reservoir.

Factors That Cause Migration

Introduction

Hydrocarbons migrate from a position of higher potential energy to one of lower potential energy. The spatial location of these energy differences defines the expected migration path. There are many sources for this energy that causes oil and gas migration.

Sources of energy

Three factors primarily cause hydrocarbon migration. All may be active at the same time during the migration process. Each factor produces energy from one or more sources. The table below lists these factors and their corresponding energy sources.

Factors	Energy Sources
Presence of oil or gas	• Buoyancy • Chemical potential (related to concentration differences) • Expansion due to a phase change (related to maturation) • Volume increase due to maturation • Sediment compaction (squeezing the oil or gas from collapsing pore space)
Indirect effects on oil or gas due to burial	• Thermal expansion • Water motion due to compaction • Topographically driven flow
Decrease in pressure and temperature as a result of the upward migration of oil or gas	• Phase change • Gas expansion

Volume increase due to maturation

As maturation proceeds, solid kerogen is converted to liquid and gaseous hydrocarbons. When the activation energy levels of the kerogen are exceeded, this conversion is very rapid. The change in phase is accompanied by an increase in volume, preferentially overpressuring the pore system within the source-rock unit and resulting in flow from the source-rock unit into the surrounding formations. This factor is of prime importance in source rocks

Buoyancy

A free hydrocarbon phase rises in a water column because its density is less than that of water. This buoyancy force is proportional to the density difference and the height of the hydrocarbon column. It acts vertically. When the rising hydrocarbons encounter a low-permeability (high capillary entry pressure) sloping surface, they are deflected updip and the resultant force is decreased by an amount proportional to the slope of that surface.

Temperature and pressure effects on buoyancy

Rising temperature (T) increases the buoyancy force as the hydrocarbon is buried. The density of hydrocarbons decreases more rapidly than that of water as temperature increases. If the temperature is high enough, liquid hydrocarbons may alter to a gaseous phase. Rising pressure (P) decreases the buoyancy force as the hydrocarbons are buried. The density of hydrocarbons increases more rapidly than that of water as pressure increases. If the pressure is high enough, gaseous hydrocarbons may alter to a liquid phase.

Factors That Cause Migration, continued

Temperature and pressure effects on buoyancy (continued)

The phase diagram below summarizes the competing effects of pressure and temperature changes for a typical volatile oil.

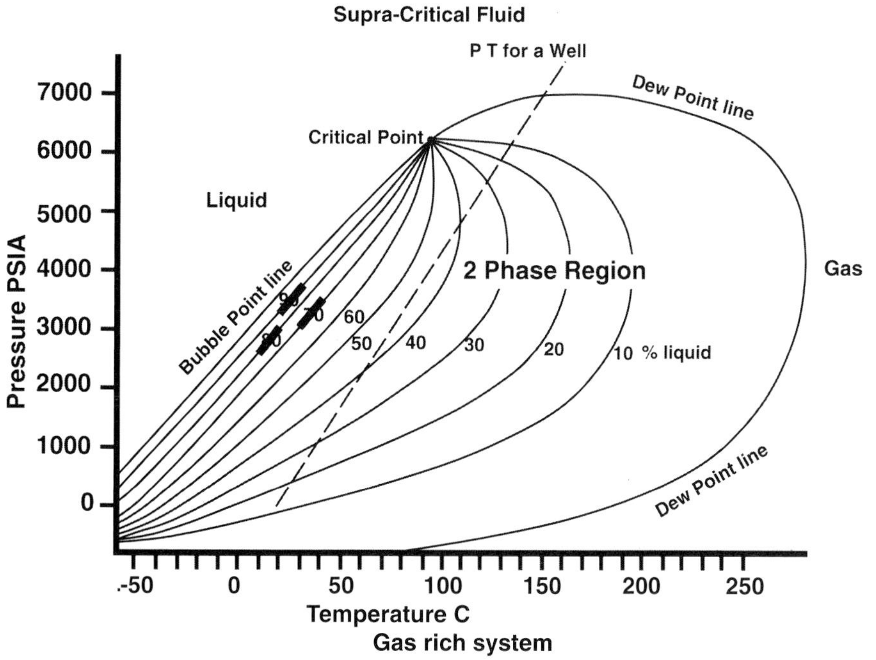

Figure 7–1. After McCain (1990); courtesy PennWell Publishing Co.

Chemical potential

Diffusive forces spontaneously transfer hydrocarbons dissolved in water from areas of higher concentration to adjacent areas of lower concentration. The kilometers-long diffusion gradients of benzene and toluene within reservoirs demonstrate the effectiveness of this process. However, the lack of significant transport of benzene and toluene through barriers or seals indicates diffusion and active aqueous solution transport are minor mechanisms of the accumulation process. The figure below shows the diffusion of gas in water as a function of concentration at origin and distance from origin (free hydrocarbons).

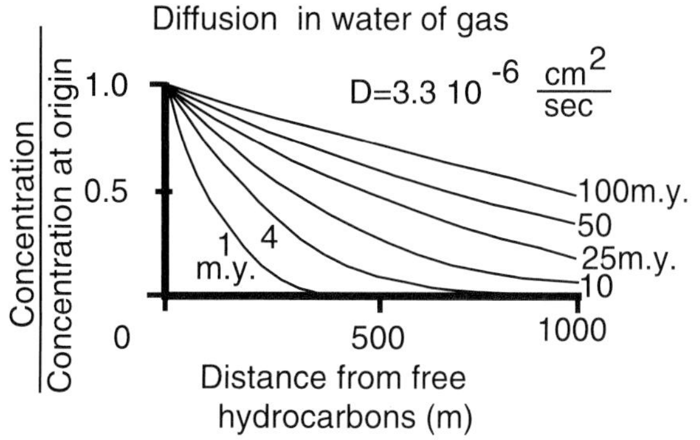

Figure 7–2. After Klimenko (1983); courtesy AGI.

Factors That Cause Migration, continued

Capillary imbibition

Capillary imbibition transfers interconnected free hydrocarbon phases from fine-grained to coarse-grained layers. This force is dominant within source rocks—especially at their contact with coarser beds. If the layer is internal to the source rock (such as a silty streak), it will store these hydrocarbons until a continuous hydrocarbon network connects it with an external coarse-grained layer. If the coarse-grained layer is external, thick, and laterally extensive, it will act as a carrier bed and postexpulsion migration will begin. Capillary imbibition exceeds buoyancy as the force responsible for transferring the hydrocarbon phase to the carrier bed, resulting in downward as well as upward charging from source rocks.

Sediment compaction

Burial results in the downward motion of each sediment package and is accompanied by a decrease in porosity as it compacts. The resultant motion of water is continually upward with respect to the sediment. The water motion with respect to the sediment/water interface, however, is downward because some water is continually trapped as sedimentation continues. In order for compaction-driven fluids to escape the sediment/water interface, they must move laterally into areas of concentrated upward flow.

Factors That Oppose Hydrocarbon Migration

Introduction

The ease with which hydrocarbons move through the stratigraphic section is controlled by the petrophysical properties of the pore system, the mineralogy of the rock, and the properties of the hydrocarbons. These factors determine the preferential pathway of migration from high to low potential energy and are responsible for concentrating or dispersing the hydrocarbons.

Pore throats as sieves

Pore throats act as molecular sieves, allowing particles smaller than the orifice to pass and retaining larger particles. If seals were uniformly composed of the same pore throats, they would be perfect seals for compounds larger than the pore throat apertures.

Hydrocarbon molecular size

Shale pore sizes range over five orders of magnitude and are about the diameter of the individual hydrocarbon molecules. This suggests many pore throats will be able to pass only the smaller hydrocarbon molecules due to physical restrictions (styric effects). Thus, the larger shale pores are supplied with full-spectrum hydrocarbons migrating directly from kerogen in contact with the pores. Larger shale pores are also preferentially supplied with the smaller paraffin and aromatics from the neighboring smaller pores. The figure below compares shale pore size with hydrocarbon molecule size.

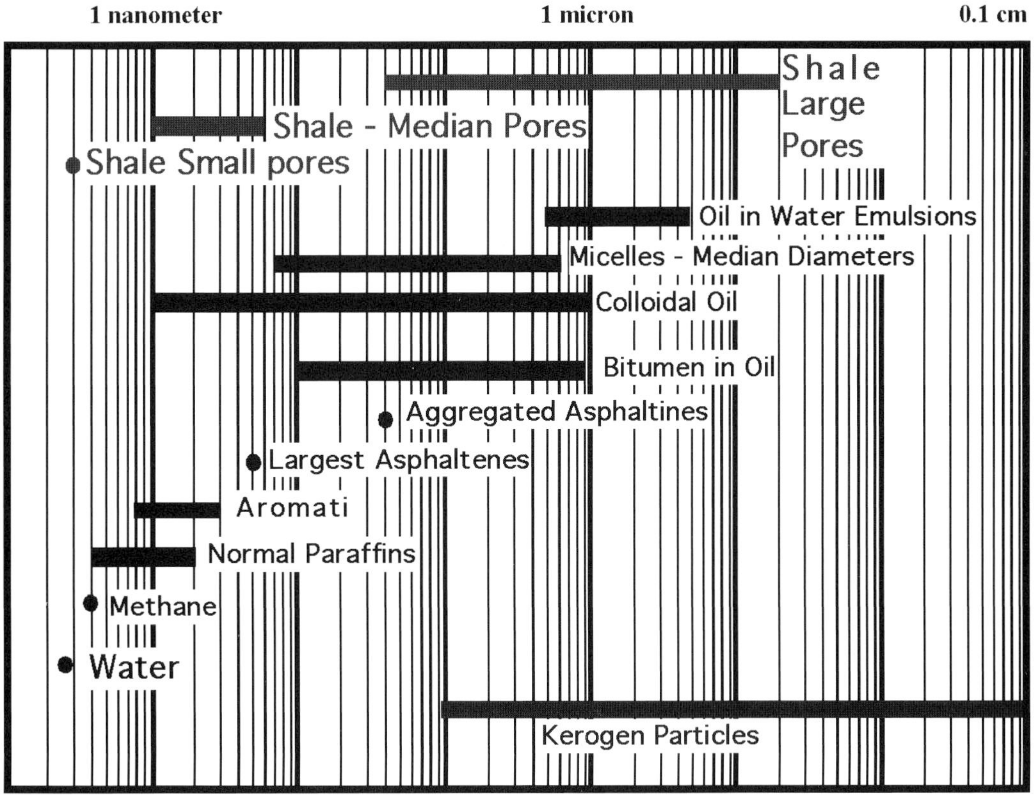

Figure 7–3. From Momper (1978); courtesy AAPG.

Trapping large molecules in shale

Transport of larger molecules, while possible through the large shale pores, becomes increasingly less likely as the path traversed through shale lengthens. This is due to the increased probability of a continuous large pore network terminating into a small pore throat. Indeed, even the flow of the comparatively small water molecule often requires significant pressure gradients to overcome the restrictions to flow common in shales. For water, the problem is generally not one of ability to pass but rather one of rate of passage.

Permeability

Permeability is related to pore throat size, distribution, and interconnectedness. It is a measurement of the rate at which fluids move through a pore system. The properties of the fluids present in the pores also control the rate at which they move through the system. Permeability is inversely related to the viscosity of the fluid moving through the pores. The presence of more than one immiscible phase in the pore system reduces the permeability of each phase below what it would be if it were the only phase present. Permeability measurements are dominantly taken in sands for reservoir engineering purposes and rarely in shales because of difficulties in getting good measurements. Also, permeabilities derived from cores are characteristically lower than those measured during production tests.

Capillary forces

Once a separate phase is formed, capillary forces become effective. Capillary forces arise at the interface between two phases across a restricted opening. Capillary pressure is a function of the interfacial tension between the immiscible fluids and the pore throat size. As the pressure difference across a capillary restriction increases, the interface deforms and eventually the nonwetting phase penetrates the restriction. Capillary effects only arise at the contact of two immiscible phases. Neither solution transport nor continuous phase is affected by capillary effects. The phase that preferentially wets the grain surfaces (usually water) is continuous. The nonwetting phase is generally assumed to form one or more continuous networks through a bed when its concentration exceeds between 4.5% and 17% of the pore volume.

Capillary forces between small pores

For small pores [100 nanometers (nm) or less] and small pore throats (10 nm or less), the concept of surface tension becomes ambiguous. A spherical pore of 100 nm diameter has a pore volume of 5×10^{-16} cm^3. The solubility of methane in water is on the order of 1 g/100 g of water. Therefore 150,000 molecules of methane may be dissolved in the pore water and any excess will be in a free phase. As a bubble of methane deforms to pass through the pore throat, about 75 gas molecules are in the pore throat water. It is unclear what the surface tension of the water is with this number of gas molecules or whether the concept of surface tension is valid for these conditions at all. Due to the decrease in solubility with increasing molecular weight and the increase in molecular size, these questions are even more applicable to the other hydrocarbon species and for smaller pores because the number of molecules in pore and pore throat is even less.

Factors That Oppose Hydrocarbon Migration, continued

Pore pressure

Differences in pore fluid overpressure determine the potential, general direction, and rate of fluid flow. For hydrocarbons, the force of buoyancy must be added. The spatial distribution of pressure differentials interacts with permeability and capillarity to determine the flow rates along multiple migration pathways. Perfect seals—ones that don't leak at all—rarely occur. Pressure minimums are a perfect seal. When all the forces acting on a hydrocarbon mass are resolved and a local minimum in gradient field occurs, the hydrocarbons will remain in the minimum as long as it exists. There is no migration out of that minimum.

Phase changes

The mineralogy of surfaces contacted by migrating hydrocarbons and continually changing chemistry of pore water alters both the phase and chemistry of the hydrocarbons. Hydrocarbons are driven out of solution into a free phase by three things:

- Increasing salinity
- Decreasing pressure
- Decreasing temperature

Sorption

Hydrocarbons can be preferentially sorbed on (wet) mineral surfaces. Sorption can control the rate of transporting different hydrocarbon compounds, acting as a chromatographic column. Sorption of saturated gasoline-range hydrocarbons is greatest for the higher boiling, larger molecules. Aromatic hydrocarbons show a similar relationship but are sorbed to a greater extent. A sorption threshold may need to be exceeded before hydrocarbons can migrate from the source rock. Sorption by kerogen is dominant over that of mineral phases.

Section B
Mechanisms of Migration

Introduction

The mechanisms by which hydrocarbons migrate controls the rate and direction of hydrocarbon motion and places a constraint on its composition. This section summarizes the proposed mechanisms and discusses the consequences of each mechanism to migration. Evidence exists that all mechanisms occur in the subsurface. Most hydrocarbons are believed to be transported as a separate phase in slug flow. The other mechanism may be dominant under special conditions.

In this section

This section contains the following topics.

Migration by Solution in Water

Introduction

Hydrocarbons dissolved in water occur as true solution and micellar solution. Both of these forms enable the hydrocarbons to move one molecule at a time and thus restrict movement minimally. The method of transport is either through direct transport by the water or by diffusion through the water. Reservoirs formed by this type of migration are limited to gas and light condensates. Solution transport is responsible for the loss of gas from many reservoirs and water-washing of oils.

True solution

True solution is a function of pressure, temperature, salinity, molecular weight, and mixtures of components present. The aqueous solubility of normal alkanes and aromatics at 25°C is shown below.

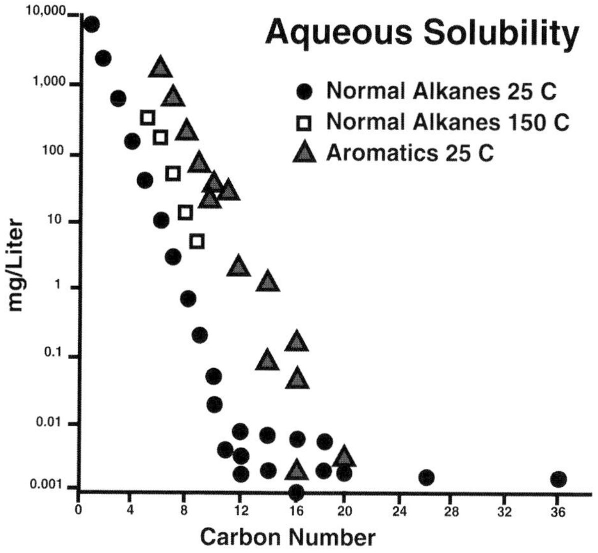

Figure 7–4. After McAuliffe (1980); courtesy AAPG.

Composition of hydrocarbons moved by water

Reservoirs formed by true solution migration are limited to gas and light condensates. This compositional relationship differs significantly from that found in most reservoired oils. However, a few light oils have molecular abundances in agreement with solubility ratios. The occurrence of these light oils as a separate phase demonstrates that solution transport of oils does occur. The infrequent occurrence (less than 10 reported cases) of oils with a compositional signature consistent with solution solubilities suggests this process of migration is an exception rather than the rule.

Exsolution of dissolved hydrocarbons

The movement of water from one location to another transports the associated dissolved gas and oil. As the water mass moves into lower temperature and pressure conditions or its salinity increases, the hydrocarbons exsolve and form a free phase. This should be a relatively continuous process, forming a cloud of bubbles throughout the carrier bed system. A free-phase transport mechanism is then needed to accumulate these bubbles within a reservoir.

Migration by diffusion

Migration by diffusion of light hydrocarbons in a water-filled pore system is extremely slow. Diffusion conveys hydrocarbons from areas of high concentrations to areas of lower concentrations. It is dominantly a dispersive force and is generally responsible for the loss of hydrocarbons, not their accumulation.

Diffusion time vs. distance

The time it takes a light hydrocarbon to diffuse a given distance and reach a concentration level equal to half the concentration of a nondepleted source is shown below.

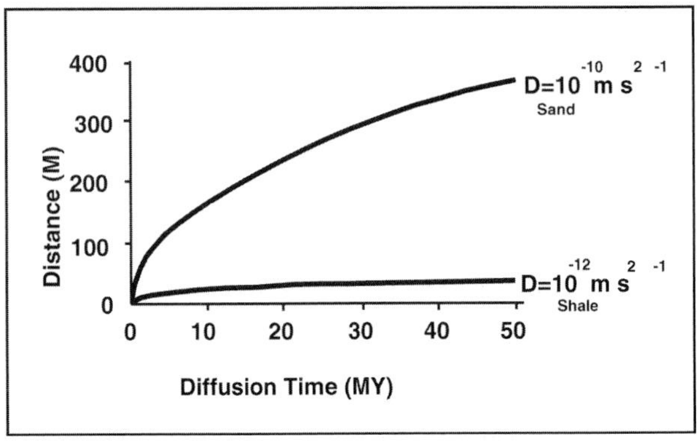

Figure 7–5. From Krooss (1987); courtesy Institute Français du Petrole.

Diffusion in shale vs. sand

In sampled beds, dissolved benzene and toluene can follow a diffusion gradient horizontally for miles in sands but be absent vertically in the over- and underlying sections. This observation suggests diffusion is not a practical transport mechanism in shale. However, even in sands for distances greater than 10–100 m, migration by diffusion is insignificant relative to bulk flow of oil or gas as separate phases.

Selective depletion by diffusion

Studies of source and reservoir contacts show that diffusion of dissolved hydrocarbons selectively depletes the more soluble compounds from the edges of source rocks into adjacent sands. The extracts found in sands resemble condensates or light oils, while the extracts found on the edges of depleted source rocks look less mature and somewhat biodegraded compared to the less depleted center of the source rocks. Diffusion selectively depletes the more soluble compounds in reservoirs. Although light hydrocarbons are expected to be transported only tens of meters into a shale capping a reservoir, significant quantities of light hydrocarbons can diffuse into this section of overlying seal.

Micelles

Micellar solution increases the capacity of water to carry molecular hydrocarbon species by the use of naturally occurring hydrocarbon solubilizers called micelles. Micelles are roughly the size of median shale pores and therefore are only able to travel through the largest shale pore throats without being subject to capillary forces. Natural micelles generally are not present in sufficient concentration to significantly alter the ability of water to contain dissolved hydrocarbons. A major problem with micelles as a transport mechanism is the difficulty of separating the hydrocarbons from them to form an accumulation in a reservoir.

Migration by Separate Phase

Introduction

Continuous, separate-phase migration of hydrocarbons moves high volumes of hydrocarbons during primary, secondary, tertiary, and remigration. Several processes can occur during separate-phase migration: formation of small free hydrocarbon masses, slug flow, cosolution, and compositional changes due to phase changes.

Small free hydrocarbon masses

The existence of small free hydrocarbon masses in the subsurface is inevitable. Each kerogen particle produces such a mass. Small hydrocarbon masses are commonly subdivided by size:

- Colloids—masses the size of median shale pores
- Emulsions—masses the size of large shale pores
- Droplets—masses larger than most shale pores

Of these, only hydrocarbon colloids are able to travel through the largest pore throat network without the limiting effects of capillarity. There is doubt, however, that a small mass of hydrocarbons has sufficient buoyant force to free itself from its attraction to the surface of a kerogen particle.

Slug flow in primary migration

Slug flow (or bulk phase flow) is generally accepted as the dominant mechanism of primary hydrocarbon migration. Within the source rock, the volume of hydrocarbons produced from kerogen increases until a continuous mass forms (a slug) that has enough force to overcome the capillary forces of the largest pore throat network. At that time, the slug moves into the closest coarse-grained bed. Expulsion is preferentially upward because of the hydrocarbons' buoyancy, but it may be downward due to generation and compaction pressure if the pathway is less restrictive. Expulsion probably acts discontinuously, resulting in periodic slugs of migrating hydrocarbons. Broad compositional differences between the slug and those hydrocarbons generated from the kerogen appear to be due to preferential retention of large hydrocarbons by fine pores.

Slug flow in secondary, tertiary, and remigration

Slug flow also dominates secondary, tertiary, and remigration. At each contact between a coarse pore network and a fine pore network, the mass of hydrocarbons accumulates until it reaches a buoyancy pressure great enough to overcome the capillary forces of the fine pore network. Relative permeability effects also aid migration. As hydrocarbons fill a pore network, the ability of a pore network to transport water decreases. This process builds pore pressure, helping push the hydrocarbons through the capillary restrictions.

Slug flow compositional changes

Changes in hydrocarbon composition during secondary, tertiary, and remigration do not appear to be significant. Bulk phase flow minimizes the opportunity of the hydrocarbons to interact with the substrate. Bulk phase flow overloads the adsorption–desorption capability of the substrate due to the quantity and concentration of the migrating hydrocarbons. Broad compositional modifications may be related to physical filtering of the larger hydrocarbons during their passage through a fine pore throat network.

Cosolution

Hydrocarbons have the capability of dissolving other hydrocarbons in them. This process is called cosolution. Methane, for example, which might normally be in a gaseous form, can be dissolved in a liquid oil. Similarly, a small amount of normally liquid oil may be dissolved in gaseous methane and be transported as part of the gas. The properties of the carrying phase are altered by the dissolved component.

Pressure effects

At pressures that exceed the critical point for hydrocarbon mixtures, the terms "gas phase" and "oil phase" become ambiguous. A single phase generally occurs at pressures above 4,000 psi and temperatures above 200°F (93°C). For a hydrostatic gradient, this pressure converts to a little less than 9,000 ft with a geothermal gradient of about 1.5°F/100 ft and a surface temperature of 70°C.

Phase effects on composition

A migrating hydrocarbon mass passes into different pressure and temperature conditions. As this happens, the mass may separate from its original phase into two phases, each containing a different mixture of hydrocarbons. In the following phase diagram, the X-axis shows the phase of the migrating hydrocarbons. The Y-axis on the left side shows pressure in terms of depth. The Y-axis on the right side shows the temperature.

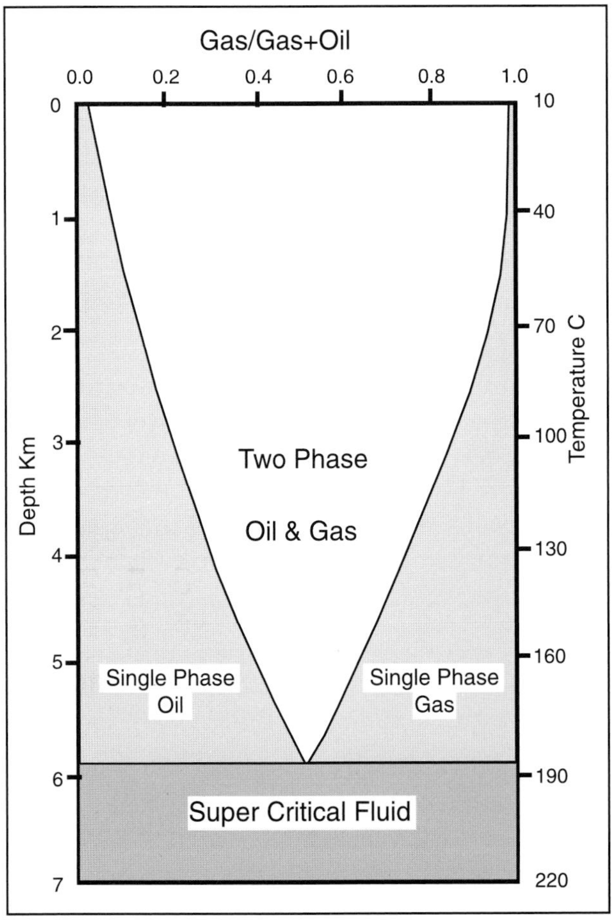

Figure 7–6. After Pepper (1991); courtesy Geological Society.

Migration by Separate Phase, continued

Compositional changes during phase changes

Phase migration occurs when a gas is expelled with oil or migrates through an oil-rich source rock. The figure below shows the gasoline range and heavier hydrocarbons in a single-phase fluid expelled from a source rock at 3000 m. As the fluid migrates upward to lower temperatures and pressures, it undergoes a process called separation migration. At 2500 m, the 100 tons of single phase have separated into 40 tons of gas and 60 tons of oil.

The figure shows the composition of each phase and the mass partitioning of the migrating-gas phase as the liquids are trapped. Note that the migrating-gas phase becomes enriched in the gasoline range and the liquids left behind progressively lose their heavier compounds. Light gas compounds are not shown. Surface geochemical studies indicate the ratios at C^1 to C^5 are little changed by upward migration. Separation–migration can significantly alter the gross composition of the migrated and trapped intervals, while maintaining sufficient detailed similarities so they can be recognized as belonging to the same family and source rock.

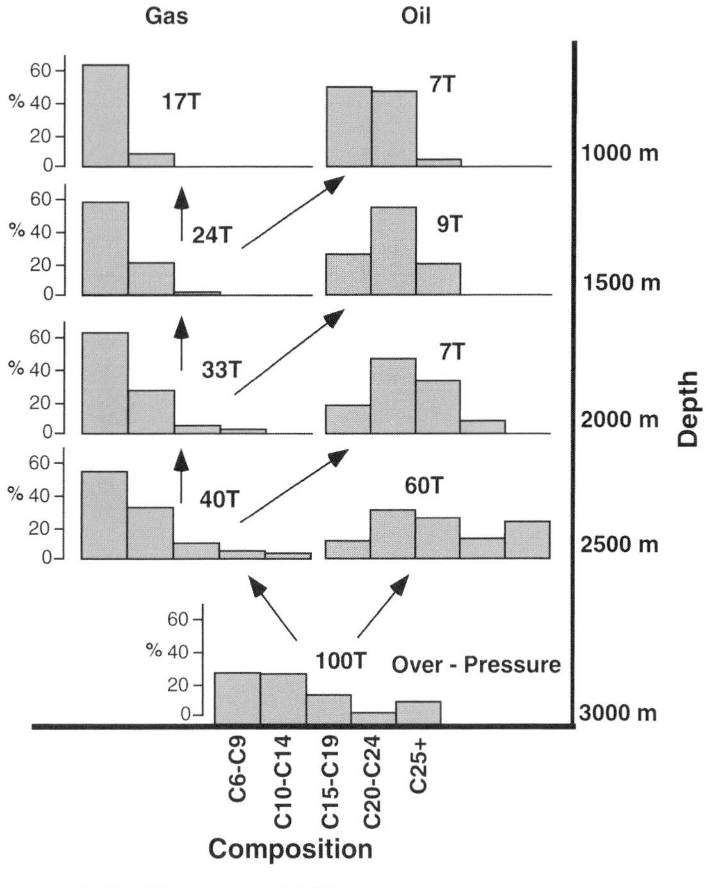

Figure 7–7. After Ungerer et al. (1984); courtesy AAPG.

Kerogen network

Migration along a kerogen network can occur either one molecule at a time or as a separate phase. It is a special case, restricted to rich source rocks where a continuous kerogen network is likely.

Section C

Changes in Hydocarbon Composition During Migration

Introduction

The process of migration alters the chemical characteristics of the hydrocarbons from that which was produced in the source rock. The factors that govern these changes and their effect on hydrocarbon composition are discussed.

In this section

This section contains the following topics.

Compositional Changes During Primary Migration

Introduction

The composition of hydrocarbons expelled from a source rock is a primary control on the composition of reservoired hydrocarbons. In general, the larger-molecular-weight compounds are preferentially retained in the source rock while the smaller compounds are expelled.

Factors favoring oil expulsion

The following factors favor oil expulsion from a source rock:

- Type I or 2 kerogen
- Sufficient time in the oil window
- High levels of TOC
- Concentration of organic matter in lamina
- Low-capillary-pressure conduits

Factors favoring gas expulsion

Five factors favor gas expulsion from a source rock:

- Type 3 kerogen
- Rapid burial through the oil window
- Low TOC
- Dissemination of organic matter
- High-capillary-pressure conduits

Composition of early vs. later generation

Early generation concentrates light products into large pores and fracture networks. Thus, the oil expelled is lighter in composition than the oil retained. However, as maturity continues, the difference between these two disappears and oil–source correlation improves.

Compositional changes and correlation

Expulsion favors light compounds over heavy compounds and saturated hydrocarbons over aromatics. This is due to molecular filtering and adsorption–desorption phenomena, particularly during the early stages. However, because significant quantities of hydrocarbons are retained in the large and medium pore systems within the source rock, the correlation of reservoired oil with its respective source rock is not significantly affected. The effect of continued maturation of the source rock after expulsion is a more significant impediment to correlation.

Compositional Changes During Postprimary Migration

Introduction

During postexpulsion migration, many processes can alter the chemical characteristics of the hydrocarbons expelled from the source rock. The geochemical similarity of reservoired hydrocarbons and hydrocarbons expelled from source rocks, however, indicates there is usually little compositional alteration along the postexpulsion migration routes. An exception to this is the selective trapping of gas- and liquid-rich phases due to the quality of the seal.

Alteration processes

Processes responsible for altering the composition of hydrocarbons during migration include the following:

- Water-washing—selective removal of the more water-soluble components
- Adsorption—selective removal and retardation of hydrocarbon migration rate by mineral and kerogen particles
- Phase partitioning—concentration of different hydrocarbon species into gaseous and liquid phases with changes in pressure and temperature
- Mixing—by (1) including hydrocarbons from post-source-rock kerogen particles along the migration path; (2) mixing migration streams from two or more source rocks; or (3) precipitation of asphaltenes and other high-molecular-weight compounds by the addition of methane
- Biodegradation—biologic alteration of the hydrocarbons

Migration method and alteration

The migration method partly determines the extent of compositional changes that occur during secondary, tertiary, or remigration. If the petroleum moves as a broad front—as would be expected for solution gas or light oil in water and perhaps for dispersed colloids or droplets—there would be a maximum probability of interactions. However, if the petroleum moved as a slug or filament, contact with elements that could alter its composition would be more limited.

Seal leakage from traps with gas caps

In traps with gas caps, the buoyancy of the gas and oil column can exceed the breakthrough pressure of the seal prior to the trap being filled to the spill point. If this happens, the trap will leak through the seal and preferentially lose the gas phase. This situation (deep oil, shallow gas) is observed but is opposite to the expected sequence of entrapment due to maturation (oil migrates first, then gas). The figure below illustrates what happens when seals leak from traps with gas caps.

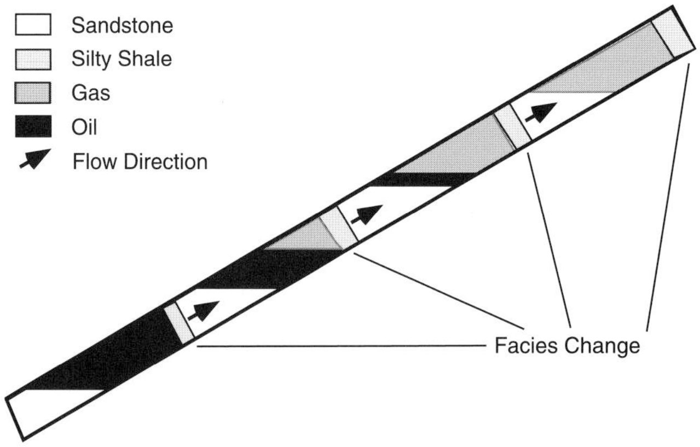

Figure 7–8. After Schowalter (1979); courtesy AAPG.

Compositional Changes During Postprimary Migration, continued

Differential entrapment

The differential entrapment of gas in downdip traps (Gussow, 1954) is achieved by successively filling a sequence of traps in the same formation with oil and gas. As each trap fills to its spill point, the phase that is spilled first is the liquid leg. Thus, the gas is retained in the structurally lower traps and the oil is trapped farther up the migration path. This situation is the expected sequence of entrapment (shallow oil, deep gas) from the maturation sequence. The figure below illustrates what happens when traps preferentially spill oil and retain gas.

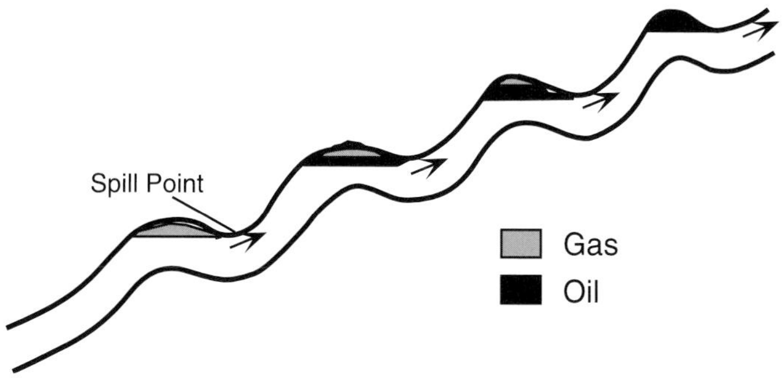

Figure 7–9. From Gussow (1954); courtesy AAPG.

Section D

Migration Pathways

Introduction

Hydrocarbon migration appears to occur in spatially limited areas (always unsampled because of their small size) and in discrete time intervals. It leaves either no trace or a trace that is continually modified or destroyed by later events. Effective hydrocarbon migration occurs along discrete pathways, not along broad, uniform fronts. These pathways are determined by the pore networks, the interaction of these networks between formations, and the stratigraphic variation within the basin. Within the carrier/reservoir bed, the migration pathway is controlled by the structural configuration of the contact with the overlying seal and the continuity of both the carrier permeability network and the overlying seal. This section discusses the general characteristics of these paths and shows several examples.

In this section

This section contains the following topics.

Formation-Scale Migration Pathways

Introduction

Flow of an immiscible phase through a series of beds does not proceed uniformly but occurs preferentially through beds of higher permeability when possible. It is dependent on the capillary properties of individual beds, the proportion of higher- to lower-permeability beds, and spatial relationships of beds to the principal flow directions (bed parallel and bed perpendicular). These factors are similar to the factors reservoir engineers use to characterize reservoir heterogeneity. They are, however, more difficult to assess because of the uncertainty of the characteristics of low-permeability rocks. The knowledge base is currently undergoing rapid change.

Bed orientation control of flow

The effect of bedding geometry on permeability direction and magnitude is significant. The table below shows how bedding orientation controls flow of hydrocarbons during migration.

If bed orientation is...	Then the flow is ...
Parallel to the flow direction	principally controlled by the most permeable units
Perpendicular to the flow direction	principally controlled by the least permeable units
Random alignment to the flow direction	not preferentially focused

Bed-parallel vs. bed-perpendicular flow

The following crossplot shows the difference in relative permeability at varying water saturations for bed-parallel vs. bed-perpendicular muliphase fluid flow in a wavy bedded rock. The water saturations need to be much lower in bed-perpendicular flow to achieve the same relative permeability. The flow within a bed is a function of the proportions of end-member lithologies, their permeability and capillary pressures, and the orientation of the beds to the direction of the flow.

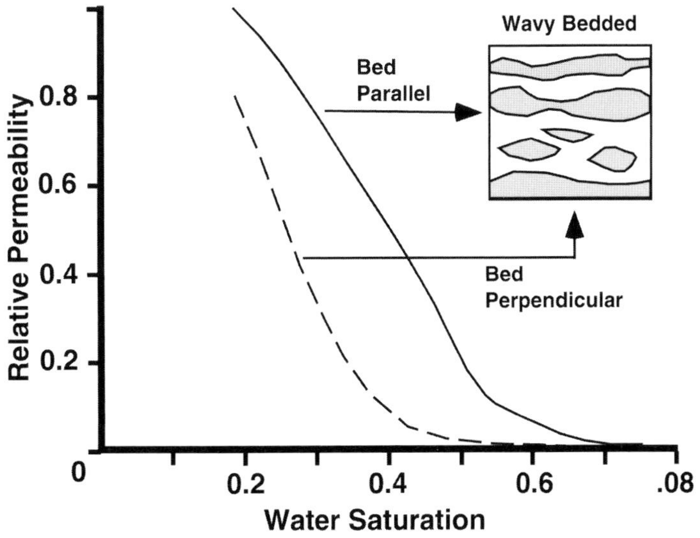

Figure 7–10. After Ringrose and Corbett (1994); courtesy Geological Society.

Defining Migration Pathways from Source to Trap

Introduction

The general flow of petroleum from a mature source rock to a trap can be estimated using a few simple assumptions:

- The dominant force causing petroleum to move is buoyancy.
- Petroleum is deflected laterally through sand-rich sections by overlying shale-rich sections.
- Where there are closed traps along this pathway, petroleum will accumulate until the trap is full and spills, or leaks, any additional migrating petroleum.

The exact flow paths generally require more detailed information about stratigraphic variability, distribution of fractures, and permeability of faults than is generally available to geologists.

Procedure

The table below lists a procedure for defining migration pathways.

Step	Action
1	Identify stratigraphic units with high permeability that could serve as carrier beds.
2	Identify stratigraphic units with low permeability that could serve as regional seals.
3	Make a structure contour map at the top of carrier beds or the base of regional seal. Highs focus flow; lows diffuse flow.
4	Locate source rocks and map the location of the upper boundary of the oil and gas maturation windows.
5	Locate other geologic features that could influence flow pathways, e.g., fault segments, fractures, unconformities, boundaries of intrusions, flanks of salt domes.
6	Draw migration vectors based on the above information.

Data requirements

A map of the structure at the top of the main sand-rich section is required to make a petroleum migration map. Generally, a map showing the present structure is used. However, a much better result can be obtained by using a map showing the structure at the time of main hydrocarbon expulsion. The location of mature source rock is projected vertically onto this map.

Defining Migration Pathways from Source to Trap, continued

Constructing a map

The area of the mature source forms the boundary from which petroleum is considered to migrate. Flow lines showing the expected direction of hydrocarbon migration are constructed on this map using the assumption that migration flow is perpendicular to structural contour lines and moves updip. All closures should be considered as the end of the migration path unless there is a good reason why the trap should spill hydrocarbons. Faults can be considered as either nonsealing (the flow lines go updip right through them) or sealing (they divert the flow of hydrocarbons around them).

Influence of regional seals

The map described above assumes petroleum expelled from the source rock migrates vertically until it reaches a single regionally continuous seal and then migrates laterally into traps, or that any immediate seals have the same structure as the regional seal. Although the latter assumption is often justified, it sometimes may be necessary to make drainage maps on intermediate regional seals and assume the petroleum from the source rock migrates vertically to the first regional seal above it and is deflected laterally as shown by the flow lines interpreted on the base of that seal. At the limit of that seal or at holes in that seal, the petroleum is assumed to migrate vertically until it once again becomes constrained by a seal. In this way, the petroleum is seen to stairstep up the section. It migrates below intermediate regional seals and possibly fills intermediate traps until it is finally constrained below a master sealing section, if one is present.

Example

The figure below is an example of defining migration pathways in the Williston basin. Part A is a structure map at the base of the principal source rock, the Bakken Formation. This simplified map is a reasonable representation of the structural configuration for the basin. Part B shows migration pathways from the Bakken, based on the basin structural configuration only; hydrodynamic effects are not included.

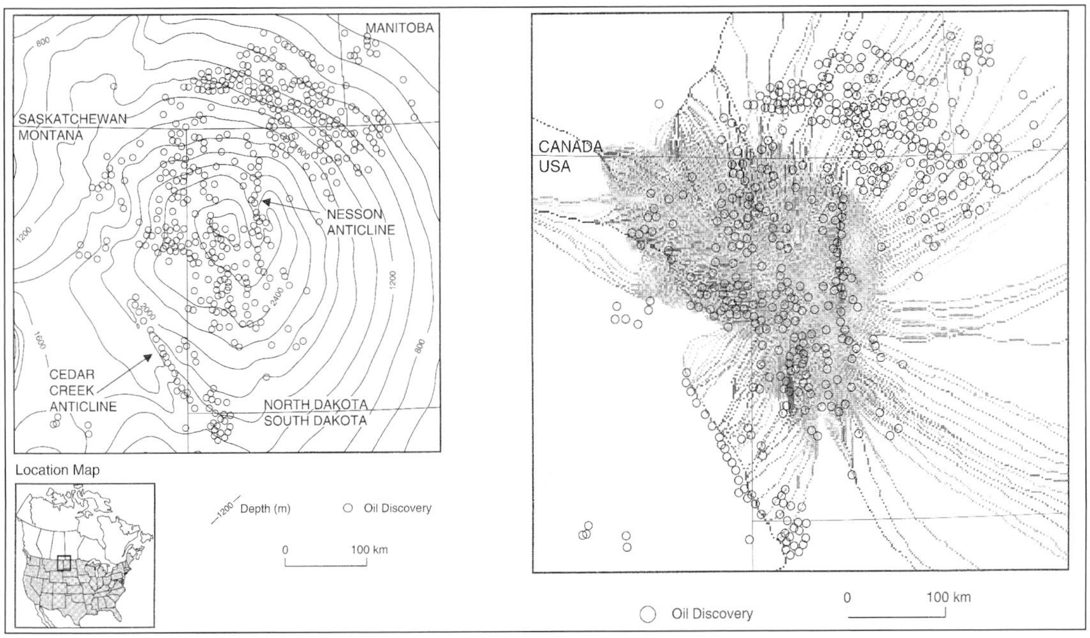

Figure 7–11. From Hindle (1997); courtesy AAPG.

Vertical and Lateral Migration Distance

Introduction

Distance of migration from source to reservoir varies greatly. The rule that the first sealed reservoir in a trapping configuration has the highest probability of containing hydrocarbons has been proven over and over again. Lateral migration distances, established by oil-source geochemical fingerprinting, reach hundreds of kilometers; vertical distances reach tens of kilometers. Estimation of migration distance is based on geochemical observations and inferences. These include maturity of product, geothermal gradients, fingerprint matching between source and reservoir, and geological estimation of the nearest rock unit of source quality.

Vertical migration

A reservoired hydrocarbon is analyzed geochemically to determine the maturity of the source from which it was derived. Using this information and an estimate of the change in maturity, the minimum vertical depth of origin is determined. The change in maturity with depth is estimated from measurement or modeling. Detailed geochemical studies of extracts, including isotopic analysis, often show a smoothly increasing gradient of maturity, suggesting local genesis and short migration distances. Superimposed on this gradient are isolated spikes of hydrocarbons with maturities characteristic of much deeper conditions. These represent migrated product.

Long-distance migration factors

The factors that influence the distance hydrocarbons may travel are complexly interrelated. Such a detailed knowledge of the petroleum system and the stratigraphy of the area is required that prediction of migration distance is next to impossible. It requires source–reservoir correlation, knowledge of the extent of the source rock, and knowledge that there are no other potential sources. The dominant factors favoring long-distance transport of hydrocarbons include the following:

- Large volume of hydrocarbons
- Efficient expulsion
- High-quality carrier beds
- Uninterrupted updip pathways
- High-quality regional seal

Migration Rate

Introduction

From a linear rate standpoint, the least efficient process along the migration path is the rate-limiting step that controls the overall rate of the process. In a sequence of sands and shales, the rate limiter is the least permeable shale and the expulsion rate of hydrocarbons in the source. However, the migration rate of a nonwetting separate phase through barriers like shales is self-adjusting. This is accomplished by enlarging the area through which the process operates. For example, in traps, hydrocarbons are accumulated and spread laterally until the accumulation size causes the rate of migration into the structure to equal that going out of the structure. This accumulation process increases the hydrocarbon flux rate through the overlying shale by increasing the contact area of the hydrocarbons with the shale. Any weaknesses in the shale, such as fractures, will eventually be reached by the accumulating hydrocarbons, increasing the leakage from the trap. Accumulation size is also limited by the spill point.

Parallel and serial processes

The flux rate of hydrocarbon transport in the subsurface is viewed as consisting of both parallel and serial processes. Parallel processes occur simultaneously. They are

- Diffusive transport
- Aqueous transport in solution and as micelles
- Separate phase transport

Serial transport processes are dominant. They occur sequentially along the most effective migration path. Examples of serial processes are

- Expulsion from the source rock
- Capillary restrictions along the migration route to the trap
- Leakage through the seal

Rates for different mechanisms

Hydrocarbons migrate by different mechanisms; each has its own rate. The table below lists the mechanisms and rates.

Migration Mechanism	Migration Rate
Hydrodynamic	0.1 and 100 m/year
Compaction	0.001 and 1 m/year
Buoyancy	Meters per day for gas (oil not measured)
Diffusion	1 to 10 m/m.y.

Hydrodynamics or compaction transport rate

The rate of water movement through pore systems places an upper limit on the rate of hydrocarbon transport by hydrodynamics or compaction. If the hydrocarbons are present as a free phase, buoyant forces may be added to the rate. In practice, however, the additional force supplied by hydrodynamics or compaction is largely counterbalanced by capillary forces and relative permeability effects. Rates vary for hydrodynamic transport, depending on permeability and elevation head. Rates from compaction depend primarily on permeability since pressure can only vary between hydrostatic and geostatic pressure.

Buoyancy transport rate

The rate of transport of hydrocarbons by buoyancy depends on the density contrast of the hydrocarbons with water and hydrocarbon column height. The rate of transport of large hydrocarbon masses is limited by the time it takes the mass to grow to a column height that can overcome capillary forces of barriers to migration. Once a continuous thread of hydrocarbons connects two coarse-grained units through an intermediate fine-grained unit, the transfer of hydrocarbons from the lower unit to the upper is only limited by the permeability of the pathway.

Diffusion transport rate

Hydrocarbon transport by diffusion is very slow. Rates depend on the concentration at the location from which diffusion proceeds. For a free phase this is always a concentration of one; the diffusion coefficient is between 10^{-10} and 10^{-12} m^2/sec.

Rate measurements

Rate measurements of migration are seldom made because of the uncertainty associated with migration length, cross-sectional area, and time interval. Linear rate estimates of gas-phase migration in the upper 200 m of sedimentary basins are as high as tens of meters per day, based on known times of injection of gas into storage reservoirs and subsurface coal burns. Estimates of vertical seepage velocities over larger areas are between 75 and 300 m/year. Oil volume rate estimates of 50 m^3 (300 bbl) per year have been made in the marine environment by collecting bubbles. These rates clearly indicate separate phase migration along multiple narrow migration pathways.

Maximum rates

Maximum rates of separate phase migration are estimated to be much faster than commonly envisioned. Many old fields, particularly gas fields, have produced more hydrocarbons than their original estimates of reserves in place. Initial production rates often decline to a low steady-state value. Discounting the uncertainties involved in these estimates, it appears production may decline until it is balanced by the area integrated charge rate of the field. Many shut-in wells show pressure buildup, indicating transfer of fluids into the field at relatively rapid rates. It is, however, uncertain what portion of the recharge is hydrocarbons and what portion is water.

Section E

Calculating Migration Rate and Charge Volume

Introduction

This section contains the formulas and procedures needed to calculate the expected rates of hydrocarbon migration and the expected volume of hydrocarbons delivered to a trapping configuration.

In this section

This section contains the following topics.

Calculating Migration Rate

Introduction

The rate of migration for oil or gas can be estimated using Darcy's law, the principal formula for calculating permeability. Darcy's law generally holds for rocks with tube-shaped pore systems; however, it is only an approximation for flow in rocks with high percentages of clays, like shales, due to the platey grain shape of the clays. The Kozeny–Carman correction estimates the permeability of rocks with high percentages of clays

Procedure

The procedure for calculating the migration rate of oil or gas is outlined in the table below.

Step	Action
1	Gather data, including permeability of carrier beds, viscosity of oil, fluid density, and pore pressure gradient.
2	Calculate the buoyancy pressure.
3	Calculate the rate of hydrocarbon migration.

Calculating migration rate

Use the version of Darcy's law presented below to calculate the rate of migration for oil or gas:

$$R = -(k \times A/m \times [(P_{grad} + P_c) - \rho_{hc} \times g])$$

where:

- R = rate of migration (m^3/sec)
- k = permeability to oil or gas at a given saturation (m^2)
- A = cross-sectional area (m^2)
- m = dynamic viscosity (Pa-sec) (use 0.01 Pa-sec for oil and 0.0001 for gas at 20°C; 0.001 Pa-sec for oil and 0.00001 for gas at 150°C
- P_{grad} = pore pressure gradient (Pa) (use 4.5 psi/ft if not available)
- P_c = capillary pressure gradient
- ρ_{hc} = hydrocarbon density (kg/m^3)
- g = acceleration of gravity (~9.81 m/sec^2)

Correcting for clay-rich rocks

For rocks with high percentages of clay, use the Kozeny–Carman correction as shown in the table below to obtain a closer approximation of permeability.

Porosity	Use
> 10%	$k = [0.2 \times \phi^3] / s^2 \times (1 - \phi)^2$
< 10%	$k = [20 \times \phi^3] / s^2 \times (1 - \phi)^2$

where:

- ϕ = free porosity
- s = rock surface area (surface area of grains in cross section A)

Calculating Migration Rate, continued

Buoyancy pressure

Buoyancy pressure for a particular hydrocarbon must be calculated for its migration rate. Use the formula below to calculate buoyancy pressure:

$$P_B = g \times z \times (\rho_w - \rho_{hc})$$

where:

P_B = buoyancy pressure
z = height of hydrocarbon stringer
ρ_w = water density
ρ_{hc} = hydrocarbon density

Minimum buoyancy pressure for migration

Migration upslope under a seal occurs when buoyancy is greater than capillary pressure, or

$$g \times l \times \sin Q \times (\rho_w - \rho_{hc}) > 2\gamma$$

where:

l = length of oil stringer
Q = angle with the horizontal
γ = interfacial tension (oil–water), dynes/cm

Each dip reversal in or near a flat hydrocarbon migration path will trap hydrocarbons and make continued hydrocarbon flow updip less likely.

Calculating Charge Volume

Introduction

The volume of hydrocarbons expected to be delivered to a trap is an important risk parameter. This section covers methodology and information to calculate the hydrocarbon charge volume parameter.

Volume constraining factors

Certain factors constrain the amount of hydrocarbon delivered to a trap. These factors can be divided into two groups, as shown below.

Source Rock Factors	Migration Factors
Drainage area	Lateral migration distance
Thickness	Vertical migration distance
Potential ultimate yield	Lateral migration factor*
Yield fraction timing	Vertical migration factor*

* A function of lithology, depth, degree of fracturing, and/or faulting

Procedure

The table below lists a procedure for estimating the volume of migrated hydrocarbons available to fill a trap.

Step	Action
1	Calculate the volume of hydrocarbons generated by the source rock, using the formula $V = A \times T \times Y \times M$ where: V = potential charge volume A = area T = source rock thickness Y = hydrocarbon yield per volume of source from each kerogen facies and maturity class M = migration efficiency
2	Estimate the proportion of the source rock that supplied hydrocarbons to the area in which the trap is located (drainage area). Use a map of the mature source rock.
3	Estimate the efficiency of the migration process. For example, did 20% of the generated hydrocarbons travel from the source rock to the trap?
4	Calculate the volume of migrated hydrocarbons available to fill the trap

Calculating Charge Volume, continued

Estimating drainage area

It is important to make a migration map showing the location of the source rock facies and the drainage areas that feed the areas of interest. The map is best drawn for the time when maturation analysis indicates the hydrocarbons should be migrating. A rougher estimate can be made from a map or the stucture as it exists today. A drainage map is made from the migration map. It should include estimates of maturity and hydrocarbon yield in an appropriate number of area classes. Subareas within these classes are defined by thickness and yield variation within the total drainage area.

Example drainage map

The upper map below is a hypothetical migration pathway map. The lower map shows the thickness of source rock, the top of the oil and gas windows, and the drainage areas for two traps labeled A and B of the same area shown in the upper map. The drainage areas for traps A and B were made using the migration pathway map.

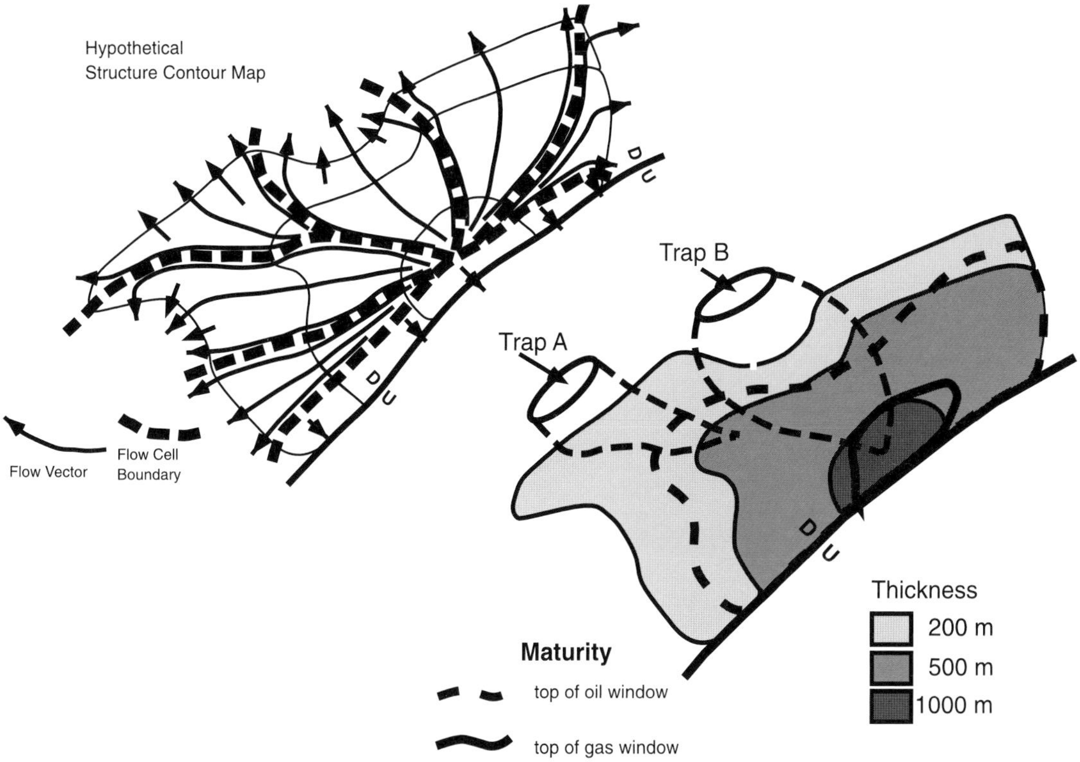

Figure 7–12.

Example of calculating volume

The table below gives an example of calculating hydrocarbon charge volume for traps A and B. The volume of expelled hydrocarbons is calculated using V = A × T × Y × M. Estimation of charge volumes for the two traps (A and B) are made as follows.

Factor	Trap A	Trap B
Area 3 (1000-m-thick mature source rock)	0 km^2	50 km^2
Yield/volume of source in area 1	0.2 bbl/m^3	0.2 bbl/m^3
Total volume generated in area 1	0 bbl	10 billion bbl
Area 2 (500-m-thick mature source rock)	10 km^2	350 km^2
Yield/volume of source in area 2	0.1	0.1
Total volume generated in area 2	0.5 billion bbl	17.5 billion bbl
Area 3 (200-m-thick mature source rock)	40 km^2	10 km^2
Yield/volume of source in area 3	0.02	0.02
Total volume generated in area 3	0.16 billion bbl	0.04 billion bbl
Total generated (areas 1 + 2 + 3)	0.66 billion bbl	27.54 billion bbl
Migration effeciency	10%	10%
Volume available for charge	0.066 billion bbl	2.754 billion bbl

Charge volume classification

Because of the uncertainties in estimating the charge volume, these estimates are often compared to the estimate of reservoir pore volume within the trap. The following classification is suggested.

Overcharged Trap—Charge volume exceeds one order of magnitude of the trap pore volume. It is likely that significant volumes of hydrocarbons have been spilled from the trap.

Fully Charged Trap—Charge volume within plus or minus one order of magnitude of the trap pore volume. It is unlikely that significant volumes of hydrocarbons have been spilled from the trap.

Undercharged Trap—Charge volume is less than one order of magnitude of the trap pore volume. No hydrocarbons are likely to have been spilled from the trap.

Estimating Expulsion Efficiency

Introduction

Efficiencies of expulsion and transport need to be estimated and used to account for inefficiencies in the migration path. Only part of the oil and gas generated by the source rock is actually expelled; of the amount that is expelled, only a small amount is trapped. The diagram below summarizes the efficiencies of the expulsion, migration, and entrapment processes.

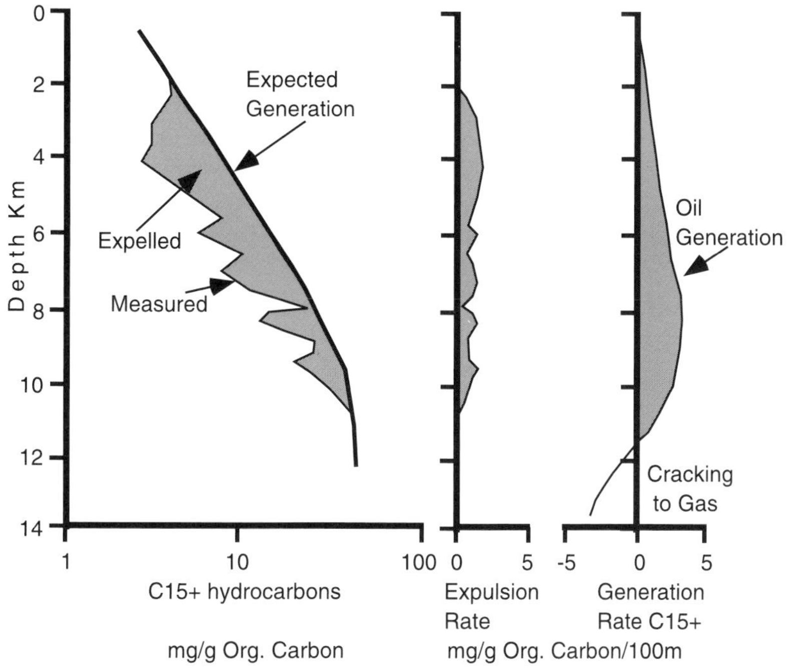

Figure 7–13. After Magara (1980); courtesy AAPG.

Expulsion percentage ranges

Typical oil expulsion efficiencies are estimated to be in the 5–10% range, with values in the 15% range uncommon and 30% rarely demonstrated. This efficiency is low because most of the source rock section contains too low a concentration of organic material to participate in the expulsion process. Efficiencies of gas expulsion are estimated to be 50–90%, with values of 75% common. Unfortunately, much of this is gas lost due to solution and does not participate in reservoir charging. For both oil and gas, expulsion efficiencies tend to increase with increasing TOC. Expulsion efficiencies for oil and gas can be as high as 70–80% for very rich, effective source rocks near preferential migration pathways.

Procedure

In migration volumetrics, it is important to estimate the original petroleum potential of the source rock—not just its present measured potential (with increasing maturation, a portion of the original potential will have been realized and is therefore unmeasurable). Estimates of expelled hydrocarbons may be derived by measuring the amount remaining in a source and subtracting that value from the amount that should have been generated from the original assumed kerogen content.

Estimating Expulsion Efficiency, continued

Procedure (continued)

Below is a procedure for estimating expulsion efficiency.

Step	Action
1	Estimate the original kerogen content of the rock using TOC values measured from source rock samples.
2	Model the original hydrocarbon generation potential of the source rock using the estimated original kerogen content.
3	Measure the volume of hydrocarbons expelled during pyrolosis (S_2.)
4	Estimate the actual expelled hydrocarbon volume by subtracting the S_2 value from the original hydrocarbon generation potential of the source rock.
5	Calculate efficiency by dividing the expected volume of expelled hydrocarbons from the actual volume of hydrocarbons generated.

Expulsion diagram

The following figure summarizes the procedure for estimating expulsion efficiency.

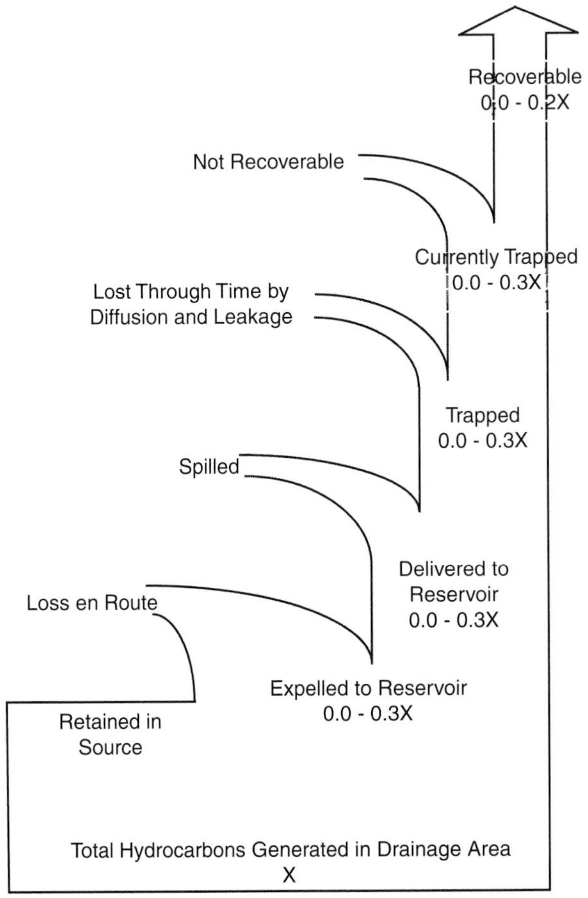

Figure 7–14. From McDowell (1975); courtesy Oil & Gas Journal.

Section F
References

References cited

Gussow, W.C., 1954, Differential entrapment of gas and oil: a fundamental principle: AAPG Bulletin, vol. 38, p. 816–853.

Hindle, A.D., 1997, Petroleum migration pathways and charge concentration: a three dimensional model: AAPG Bulletin, vol. 81, p. 1451–1481.

Klimenko, A.P., 1983, Diffusion of gasses from hydrocarbon deposits, *in* Petroleum Geochemistry, Genesis, and Migration: AGI Reprint Series, vol. 1, p. 117–122.

Krooss, B.M., 1987, Experimental investigation of the diffusion of low-molicular weight hydrocarbons in sedimentary rocks, *in* B. Doligez, ed., Migration of Hydrocarbons in Sedimentary Basins: 2nd IFP Expl. Res. Conference Proceedings, p. 329–351.

Magara, K., 1980, Evidences of primary migration: AAPG Bulletin, vol. 64, p. 2108–2117.

McAuliffe, C.D., 1980, Oil and gas migration: chemical and physical constraints, *in* W.H. Roberts and R.J. Cordell, eds., AAPG Studies in Geology no. 10, p. 89–107.

McCain, W.D., Jr., 1990, The Properties of Petroleum Fluids: Tulsa, PennWell Books, 548 p.

McDowell, A.N., 1975, What are the problems in estimating the oil potential of a basin? Oil & Gas Journal, June 9, p. 85–90.

Momper, J.A., 1978, Oil migration limitations suggested by geological and geochemical considerations, *in* W.H. Roberts and R.J. Cordel, eds., Physical and Chemical Constraints on Petroleum Migration: AAPG Continuing Education Course Notes Series no. 8, p. B1–B60.

Pepper, A.S., 1991, Estimating the petroleum expulsion behavior of source rocks: a novel quantitative approach, *in* W.A. England and E.J. Fleet, eds., Petroleum Migration: Geological Society Special Publication no. 59, p. 9–31.

Ringrose, S.P., and P.W.M. Corbett, 1994, Controls in two phase fluid flow in heterogeneous sandstones, geofluids, *in* J. Parnell, ed., Origin, Migration, and Evolutions of Fluids in Sedimentary Basins: Geological Society Special Publication no. 78, p. 141–150.

Schowalter, T.T., 1979, Mechanics of secondary hydrocarbon migration and entrapment: AAPG Bulletin, vol. 63, p. 723–760.

Ungerer, P., F. Behar, P.Y. Chenet, B. Durand, E. Nogaret, A. Chiarelli, J.L. Oudin, and J.F. Perrin, 1984, Geological and Geochemical models in oil exploration, principles and practical examples, *in* G. Demaison and R.J. Murris, eds., Petroleum Geochemistry and Basin Evaluation: AAPG Memoir no. 35, p. 53–77.

References, continued

Additional references

Brace, W.F., 1980, Permeability of crystalline and argillaceous rocks: International Journal of Mechanics and Mineral Sciences and Geomechanical Abstracts, vol. 17, p. 241–251.

Cooles, G.P., A.S. Mackenzie, and T.M. Quigley, 1986, Calculations of petroleum masses generated and expelled from source rocks: Organic Geochemistry, vol. 10, p. 235–245.

Dahlberg, E.C., 1982, Aplied Hydrodynamics in Petroleum Exploration: New York, Springer-Verlag, 161 p.

Hermannrud, C., S. Eggen, T. Jacobsen, E.M. Carlsen, and S. Pallesen, 1990, On the accuracy of modeling hydrocarbon generation and migration: the Egersund basin oil field, Norway: Organic Geochemistry, vol. 16, p. 389–399.

Hunt, J.M., 1979, Petroleum Geochemistry and Geology: San Francisco, W.H. Freeman Company, 617 p.

Lerch, I., and R.O. Thomsen, 1994, Hydrodynamics of Oil and Gas: New York, Plenum Press, 308 p.

Mann, U., 1994, An integrated approach to the study of primary petroleum migration, *in* J. Parnell, ed., Origin and Evolution of Fluids in Sedimentary Basins: Geological Society Special Publication 78, p. 233–260.

Matthews, M.D., 1996, Hydrocarbon migration—a view from the top, *in* D. Schumacher and M.A. Abrams, eds., Hydrocarbon Migration and Its Near Surface Expression: AAPG Memoir 66, p. 139–156.

Perrodon, A., 1983, Dynamics of oil and gas accumulations: Bulletin des Centres de Recherches Exploration-Production Elf-Aquitaine, Memoir 5, 368 p.

Rhea, L., M. Person, G. de Marsily, E. Ledous, and A. Galli, 1994, Geostatistical models of secondary oil migration within heterogeneous carrier bed: a theoretical example: AAPG Bulletin, vol. 78, p. 1679–1691.

Tissot, B.P., and D.H. Welte, 1984, Petroleum Formation and Occurrence: Berlin: Springer-Verlag, 699 p.

Vandenbroucke, M., 1993, Migration of hydrocarbons, *in* M.L. Bordenave, ed., Applied Petroleum Geochemistry: Paris, Technip, p. 123–148.

Acknowledgment

The author thanks Texaco for permission to publish this manuscript. He is particularly indebted to Vic Jones, Ted Weisman, the late Bill Roberts, and Hollis Hedberg for their guidance as well as to co-workers throughout the industry for their stimulating discussions.

Chapter 8

Oil–Oil and Oil–Source Rock Correlations

by

Douglas W. Waples

and

Joseph A. Curiale

Douglas W. Waples

Doug Waples has spent more than twenty-five years developing and applying geochemical techniques in oil exploration. He has lived in the U.S., Japan, Chile, and Germany during his career and has worked for Chevron and Mobil. He also was a professor at the Colorado School of Mines and continues his interest in education through short-course teaching. He participated on two legs of the Deep Sea Drilling Project. Doug is presently a consultant in geochemistry, modeling, and worldwide exploration, based in Evergreen, Colorado. He has published about 80 papers, including three books, on a wide range of topics in geochemistry. He holds a Ph.D. in physical organic chemistry from Stanford University.

Joseph A. Curiale

Since 1981, Joe Curiale has been a geochemist with Unocal. Before joining Unocal, he received a bachelor's degree in chemistry (with an earth science specialization) from the University of California at San Diego and a Ph.D. in geology from the University of Oklahoma. He has conducted source rock and petroleum geochemical studies for Unocal throughout North America and in several basins of Europe, Asia, Africa, and South America. He is the author or coauthor of more than 70 publications, has served on several industry and professional society committees, and is presently a co-chief editor of *Organic Geochemistry*. He received the 1992 Best Paper Award from the Canadian Society of Petroleum Geologists and past chairman of the Organic Chemistry Division of the Geochemical Society. His research interests include the application of molecular markers to the understanding of geological processes and the interpretation of organism-specific biomarker distributions in ancient marine and lacustrine settings.

Overview

Introduction

Correlations are comparisons of (1) oils with other oils or (2) oils with source rock extracts to determine whether a genetic relationship exists. Correlations are accomplished by comparing elemental, molecular, and isotopic parameters using techniques such as gas chromatography (GC), gas chromatography with mass spectrometry (GC/MS), and carbon isotope ratio determination.

Objectives of correlation studies include the following:

- Classifying oils into genetic families
- Establishing oil–source rock relationships
- Addressing problems of reservoir continuity

Exploration applications of correlation studies include the following:

- Determining how many effective source rocks exist in a given area
- Proposing migration pathways from kitchen areas to new prospects or plays
- Providing input data for volumetric calculations
- Providing data for development geology

All good correlations require full integration of geochemical data with geology. The final interpretation must fit all available geologic and geochemical data, as well as local and global geologic and geochemical concepts.

Correlations represent a powerful but underutilized capability within petroleum geochemistry, largely because many geologists are unfamiliar with both the technology and the value of correlations. Future applications of geochemistry should place more emphasis on correlations, and geologists should become more conversant with correlation technology and philosophy. Geochemists alone are seldom able to extract full value from correlation studies because they often do not have the necessary geologic information or the expertise to integrate geologic concepts with the geochemical data. Therefore, the participation of geologists in correlation studies is essential.

In this chapter

This chapter contains the following sections.

Section A
Introduction to Correlations

Introduction

In this section we first discuss the basic principles that should govern the planning and execution of any correlation study. We then briefly mention the potential applications of statistical methods in interpreting the data used in correlations. The limitations inherent in all correlation studies are discussed in detail, since they strongly affect the analytical techniques we choose and the confidence we have in our final conclusions. Finally, we include some practical suggestions to facilitate correlation studies and improve the quality of the work.

In this section

This section contains the following topics.

Basic Principles

What are correlations?

Correlations are comparisons of two or more samples based on the physical and chemical properties of those samples.

Purpose of correlation studies

The purpose of any correlation study is to determine whether a genetic relationship exists among a group of oil samples or between an oil and a proposed source rock. Positive correlations are always useful because they confirm some proposed concept; but negative correlations can be of even greater value in developing new exploration ideas.

Objectives of correlation studies

Objectives of correlation studies include the following:

- Classifying oils in genetic families
- Establishing oil–source rock relationships
- Addressing problems of reservoir continuity

Applications of correlation studies

Exploration applications of correlation studies include the following:

- Determining how many effective source rocks exist in a given area
- Proposing migration pathways from kitchen areas to new prospects or plays
- Providing input data for volumetric calculations
- Providing data for development geology

Determining data reliability

In any correlation study, we must decide which data are most reliable for answering the questions about genetic relationships and which data have been affected by postgenetic transformations, such as expulsion, migration, biodegradation, water washing, and thermal cracking. In addition, we must resolve other complicating issues, such as differences in maturity of the samples being compared, facies variations in source rocks, possible mixing of oils from different sources in a single reservoir, and the intrinsic differences between oils and source rock bitumens. These topics are discussed in more detail in Curiale (1993, 1994).

Positive correlations

A positive correlation between two or more samples occurs when all pieces of evidence are compatible with the existence of a genetic relationship among the samples. Since some differences inevitably exist between any two samples, the key to achieving a positive correlation is not to find samples that are identical but rather to find samples in which the differences are explainable by normal transformation processes, maturity differences, intrinsic differences between oils and source rock bitumens, natural variation (e.g., facies), or analytical uncertainty.

Correlation processes

To increase the quality of and your confidence in positive correlations, use the following table.

To increase confidence in your correlation . . .	Because . . .
Measure as many different properties as possible	All positive correlations are based on circumstantial evidence. Therefore, measuring more properties means acquiring more evidence.
Use detailed molecular and isotopic comparisons (e.g., GC/MS or compound-specific isotope analyses)	Molecular and isotopic techniques are very sensitive and provide much "fingerprint" detail about sample compositions.
Analyze as many samples as possible	A large number of samples provides background information on natural variation that could otherwise be confused with genetic differences.
Use samples that have suffered as little postgenetic transformation as possible	Postgenetic transformations—especially biodegradation, cracking, and gas stripping of oils—can make positive correlations very difficult. Also, all oil–source rock correlations are complicated by the fact that significant compositional changes occur as the oil is expelled from the source rock and migrates.
Use source rock samples that are mature, not postmature	Since many source rock samples are immature, a comparison with mature oils can be difficult—not only because physical appearances and molecular distributions are different, but also because extracts from immature rocks are sometimes genetically unrelated and compositionally dissimilar to mature extracts and oils (Kohnen et al., 1992).

Negative correlations

If we can find even one major difference between two samples that cannot be explained by either natural variation or postgenetic transformation, the correlation is considered to be negative and we should conclude that the samples are not genetically related. In some cases, the discrepancy may consist of a single major difference (e.g., presence of an important source-related biomarker in one sample and not in the other). In other cases, the discrepancy may represent the sum of numerous minor differences between the samples. It is crucial in evaluating possible negative correlations that postgenetic effects (e.g., cracking, biodegradation) not be interpreted as genetic characteristics. Moreover, intrinsic differences between immature extracts and mature extracts or oils should not necessarily be interpreted as negative correlations.

Positive vs. negative correlations

Positive correlations tend to reinforce and refine existing exploration concepts, whereas negative correlations often refute existing ideas and offer new opportunities for creative thinkers. Both types of correlation have obvious value to explorationists.

A positive correlation is seldom 100% certain. Our confidence level in any positive correlation increases with the amount and quality of the data and samples used in the correlation. Curiale (1994) discusses the problem of inadequate numbers of samples and overreliance on data of questionable validity. Moreover, some samples are quite easy to correlate positively because they share an unusual characteristic (e.g., the presence of an unusual biomarker). Samples that have no unusual or distinguishing features can often be correlated positively with many other samples, and at least some of those apparent correlations are likely to be in error.

A negative correlation, in contrast, can be quite definitive if the differences are large and if they clearly are not the result of postgenetic transformations. Probably the most difficult negative correlations are those based on numerous small differences, each of which in and of itself would not be conclusive. In such cases, we should ascertain that the differences are not related to variations or differences in facies, maturity, or migration.

Statistical Analysis

Statistical methods

In studies involving large numbers of samples, many different analyses, and a huge variety of ratios and quantities to be evaluated, it is easy to become bogged down in an overabundance of data. To speed up the process of evaluating correlation data and to make the process less subjective, statistical methods have been used (e.g., Sofer et al., 1986; Telnæs and Dahl, 1986; Curiale, 1987). These techniques include both cluster analysis and multivariate statistical analysis (principal components analysis).

Application of cluster analysis

The figure below shows the application of cluster analysis in using data on trace-element concentrations to correlate eleven crude oils from northern Alaska. Although the concentrations of elements in an oil may vary due to alteration episodes (such as biodegradation), the relative distribution of these elements often remains constant and source distinctive. The concentrations of copper, iron, manganese, nickel, and vanadium in each oil were used to construct this cluster. The Bray–Curtis distance shows the degree of dissimilarity from oil to oil. Here eight oils of type A and three oils of type B are indicated. Other geochemical evidence supports this subdivision.

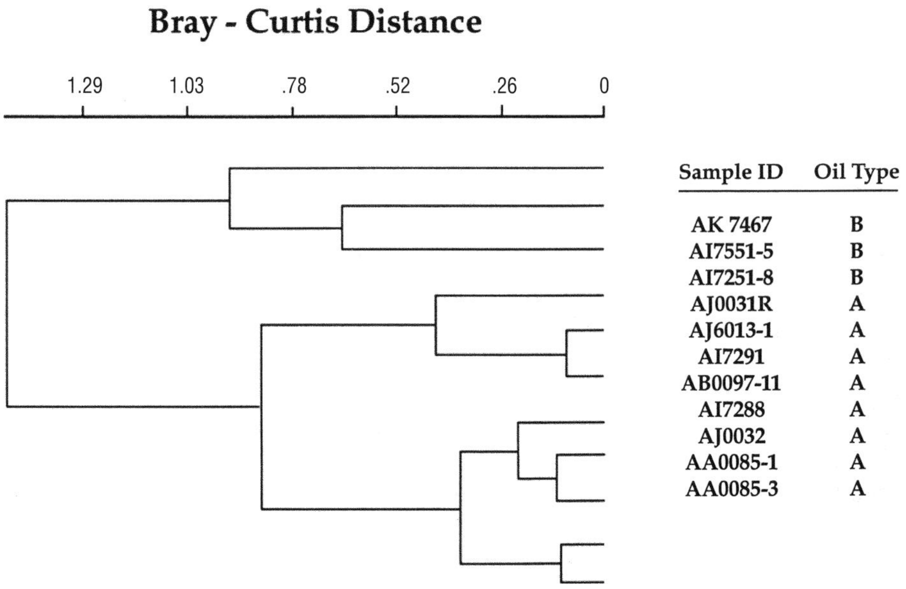

Figure 8–1. From Curiale (1987); reprinted with permission of the American Chemical Society.

Integrate with geology and geochemistry

Unfortunately, many of the applications of such statistical methods fail to emphasize either the chemistry or the geology of the system. Future applications should attempt to integrate the purely statistical analysis with geochemical and geological knowledge to achieve the most useful and realistic interpretation possible.

Limitations of Correlations

Introduction

What happens to oils and rocks at depth and over time can alter the geochemical parameters measured in correlation studies. Geologists need to be aware of how those changes may limit correlation accuracy. Six main problems limit the utility, accuracy, and confidence of correlations:

- Differing thermal maturities of samples
- Solution-exsolution at different depths
- Biodegradation
- Natural variation among samples
- Multiple sources for oil in a trap
- Lack of distinguishing characteristics

Differing thermal maturities of samples

Oil–oil and oil–source rock correlations are most successful when the samples being compared are at the same or similar thermal maturities. Except in cases of extreme overmaturity of one or more of the samples, these problems can usually be overcome by an experienced interpreter. However, for highly mature samples some information and confidence are inevitably lost. Inexperienced interpreters can easily confuse maturity effects with genetic differences.

Solution-exsolution at different depths

A further limitation in oil–oil correlations exists when migrating gas dissolves part of a crude oil at depth (i.e., at high pressure) and exsolves a portion of its oil components at shallower depths (i.e., at reduced pressure). Because each component of petroleum is soluble to a different degree in natural gas, this solution-exsolution process can radically alter the oil composition and the appearance of gas chromatograms.

Biodegradation

Although biodegradation affects gas chromatograms very strongly, steranes, triterpanes, and isotopes are much less affected. Modern correlation technology can usually overcome differences caused by biodegradation.

Natural variation among samples

Any group of oils will inevitably exhibit variations among the members. This "natural variation" can stem from true differences, sample handling, analytical error, or differences in technique between laboratories. The amount of acceptable or "normal" difference varies greatly, depending on the range of maturities, biodegradation, expulsion and migration (the effects of which are especially large when comparing oils with source rock extracts), and variations in source rock facies. Correlations become increasingly difficult and tenuous as distances between samples increase.

Vertical and lateral rates of change in source rock facies are highly variable but are generally highest in nearshore and nonmarine environments. Katz (in press), for example, documents the extreme variability in source facies in the lacustrine Pematang Formation of central Sumatra and the consequent variability in oil properties. As he notes, correlations in such settings are very difficult and depend critically upon sample coverage of the source facies.

Limitations of Correlations, continued

Natural variation among samples (continued)

A major part of the art of correlation is deciding whether an observed difference is significant or is better considered to be the result of natural variation. The differences between the various members of a family of oils are often more subtle than the discussions in this chapter suggest. In fact, sometimes the variations within a single family (especially those that cover wide geographic areas or those from nonmarine sources) are as large as the variations between families.

Multiple sources for oil in a trap

Many sedimentary basins contain more than one oil source unit. If two or more source rocks are thermally mature, oils from both may become commingled within a single trap, preventing straightforward oil–source rock correlations. A good example is found in Seifert et al. (1979).

Lack of distinguishing characteristics

Some correlation efforts inevitably yield ambiguous results. Some oils are difficult to correlate definitively because they lack distinguishing characteristics. Furthermore, in some basins several source rocks may have very similar geochemical signatures, making it difficult to determine precisely which unit is the actual source for a given oil. In such cases, we often try to acquire additional data in an effort to uncover some unique characteristic that will be the key to a successful correlation.

Practical Suggestions

Use many analytical tools

The importance of a diversified set of analytical tools cannot be overemphasized. We have noted that many published correlation efforts often rely unduly on biomarker analyses, often to the exclusion of elemental data and even stable carbon isotope ratios. This reliance on biomarkers undoubtedly arises because of the widespread and rapid availability of molecular data through GC/MS analysis and is promoted by the existence of a large database of molecular analyses of crude oils. Nevertheless, excessive reliance on a single analytical technique can lead to erroneous correlation conclusions, especially since many of the biomarkers used in correlations are present only in concentrations of a few parts per million.

Because oils are susceptible to many transformations during expulsion and migration and in the reservoir—including cracking, phase separation, and biodegradation—correlation techniques and parameters must be selected to minimize complications due to postgenetic transformations. In general, oil–source rock correlations are more difficult than oil–oil correlations, largely because we seldom have samples from the effective (mature) source rocks themselves. Problems arise from variations in facies between the basin center and the sampling point as well as from potentially large maturity differences. Condensates can be difficult to correlate because they have lost much of their valuable information during cracking, phase separation, or both.

Integrate geochemistry with geology

It has been all too common to base correlations entirely or mainly on geochemical considerations without proper regard for the geological content. While it is true that geochemical and geological considerations should be separated in the initial stages of a correlation study to ensure the geochemical conclusions are truly independent, the final story should fully integrate the geochemical model within the geologic framework. Although geochemical data can often give new insights, all geochemical conclusions must ultimately be consistent with the geologic facts. Failure to properly integrate geologic and geochemical data can lead to geochemically based correlations that are difficult or impossible to justify geologically.

One of the best examples of such a discrepancy is in an early study of oils of the Michigan basin (Vogler et al., 1981) in which Devonian oils above the thick regional Silurian salt were correlated positively with Ordovician oils below the salt, without regard for the geologic problems involved in the proposed migration. Subsequent studies using more sensitive technology and larger numbers of samples show that the positive correlation was in fact fortuitous (Illich and Grizzle, 1983; Pruitt, 1983; Waples, 1985; Rullkötter et al., 1986) and that migration through the salt had not occurred.

Section B

Data Used in Correlations

Correlation compares parameters

Correlation studies compare the parameters of an oil with those of another oil or with a source rock extract. These parameters are of three types:

- Elemental—the bulk composition of a sample
- Isotopic—ratios of one stable isotope to another in a sample
- Molecular—the presence and relative or absolute abundance of certain specific molecules in a sample

Molecular parameters are the most important because they provide the most specific data, including data that can sometimes be used for estimating ages of oils or source rocks.

Selection of correlation parameters

As noted in the previous section, as wide a range of data types as possible should be used in correlations. Particular emphasis should be placed on molecular and isotopic parameters because they carry much more information than do elemental parameters.

In this section

This section contains the following subsections.

Subsection B1
Elemental Parameter Data

What are elemental parameters?

Elemental parameters refer to the bulk composition of the samples. These parameters include sulfur and (less commonly) nitrogen, nickel, and vanadium content. In rare cases, we may have data on other trace elements. Data on the gross composition of the oil are also included in this category.

Sulfur

High-sulfur and low-sulfur oils have fundamentally different origins. Most high-sulfur oils come from nonclastic source rocks. Although some extremely rich clastic source rocks like the Kimmeridge Clay of the North Sea also yield moderately high-sulfur oils, most clastic source rocks yield oils with less than 0.5% sulfur by weight. However, sulfur content is also a function of maturity.

Maturity effects

The trend in sulfur content within a single megafamily of high-sulfur oils is a function of API gravity, which normally increases with increasing maturity. Thus, highly mature oils that were originally high in sulfur (e.g., from a carbonate source) can have low sulfur content, as evidenced in the figure below. Therefore, unless the maturity levels of all samples are similar, or unless some correction for maturity is made, sulfur content can be misleading as a correlation parameter. Sulfur content decreases with increasing maturity (API gravity) in low-sulfur oils as well, although the range of variation is usually too small to be of much practical value.

Illustrated below is a set of southern California oils showing wide variation in both gravity and sulfur content. Several workers attribute this relationship to factors such as migration and maturity differences, as well as to source variations (e.g., Orr, 1986).

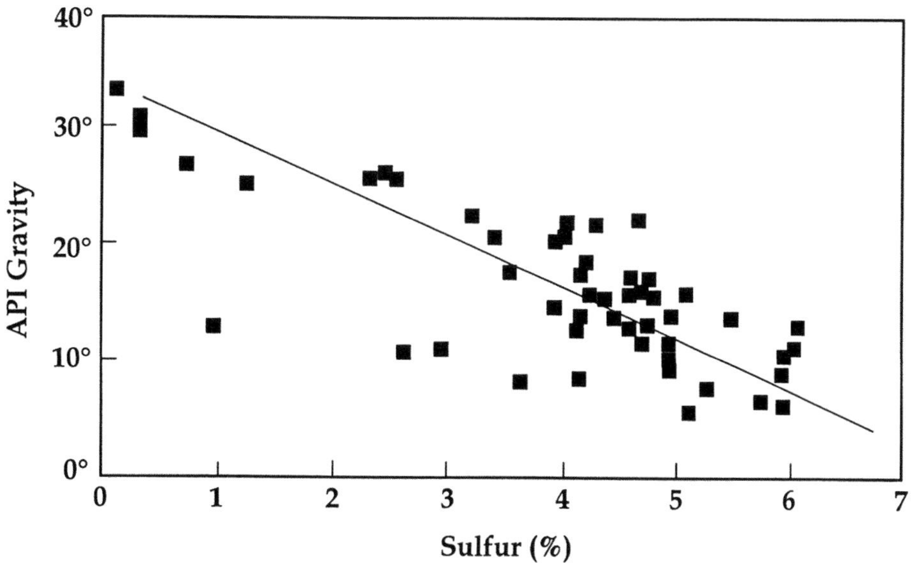

Figure 8–2. Data from Kennicutt and Brooks (1988); courtesy Oil & Gas Journal.

Elemental Parameter Data, continued

Gross composition

Most common is the breakdown of the heavier (C_{15+}) fraction into saturated hydrocarbons (saturates), aromatic hydrocarbons (aromatics), lighter nonhydrocarbons (NSOs, polars, or resins), and heavier nonhydrocarbons (asphaltenes). Oils with terrestrial input often have high saturate/aromatic ratios, whereas those from carbonate sources have low saturate/aromatic ratios and high content of nonhydrocarbons. Saturate–aromatic ratios probably increase slightly with increasing maturity and decrease with biodegradation.

Other parameters

Other parameters included in this category are API gravity (or density), color, wax content, pour point, and viscosity. Most of these parameters are of little value, however, because they are highly susceptible to transformation processes.

Subsection B2
Isotopic Parameter Data

Definition

Isotopic parameters are measurements of the ratio of one stable isotope to that of another stable isotope of the same element. Stable isotope ratios are usually measured on carbon but sometimes are measured on sulfur or hydrogen.

Carbon isotope ratios

Carbon isotope ratios are commonly measured on whole oils, kerogens, and whole extracts (bitumens) from rocks. In many cases they are also measured on the C_{15+} saturate and aromatic fractions and are often displayed on a Sofer (1984) diagram (e.g., the figure on the right, below). Less commonly, carbon isotope ratios are measured on the distillate and/or chromatographic fractions. For oil–source rock correlations, isotope ratios can also be measured on kerogen. Results of isotope analyses are often presented in a so-called Galimov diagram (left, below). Carbon isotope ratios can be characteristic of geologic age and environment (e.g., Chung et al., 1992, 1994).

The figures below show carbon isotope ratios for fractions of six oils comprising two families from the Zagros orogenic belt. The "Galimov" plot (left) and the Sofer diagram (right) show the $\delta^{13}C$ values. Oils 3 and 4 are from the Ahwaz field, whereas oils 13, 14, and 16 are from the northeastern Dezful area. The midrange position of oil 18 suggests that it could be a mixture of these two main oil types. These conclusions are also supported by molecular and elemental data.

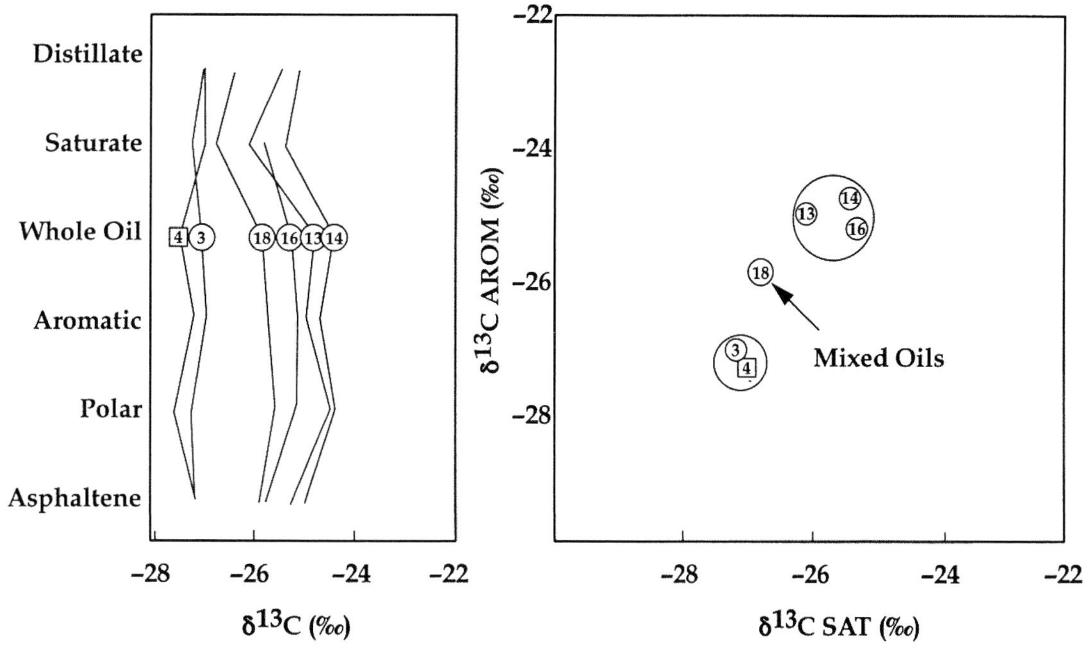

Figure 8–3. From Bordenave and Burwood (1990); reprinted with permission from Elsevier.

Compound-specific isotope analysis

Over the last decade, much interest has developed in compound-specific isotope analysis, in which carbon isotope ratios are measured for numerous individual compounds in a sample and then plotted to give a fingerprint.

In addition to *n*-alkanes, isotope ratios have been measured for pristane, phytane, and other biomarkers (Bjorøy et al., 1991; Clayton and Bjorøy, 1994). Although this technique is highly promising for correlations, initial attempts to interpret the data suggest that additional research to identify causes for isotopic variations will be necessary before the technique can be applied routinely and with confidence.

The figure below shows an example of a correlation between an oil and a condensate using $\delta^{13}C$ values for individual $C_{10} - C_{27}$ *n*-alkanes. These two samples are from a single oil field on the U.S. Gulf Coast. The condensate does not contain measurable *n*-alkanes beyond *n*-C_{18}, rendering biomarker techniques of little value. The similarity in *n*-alkane $\delta^{13}C$ values for these two samples supports the conclusion that they are sourced from similar organic facies.

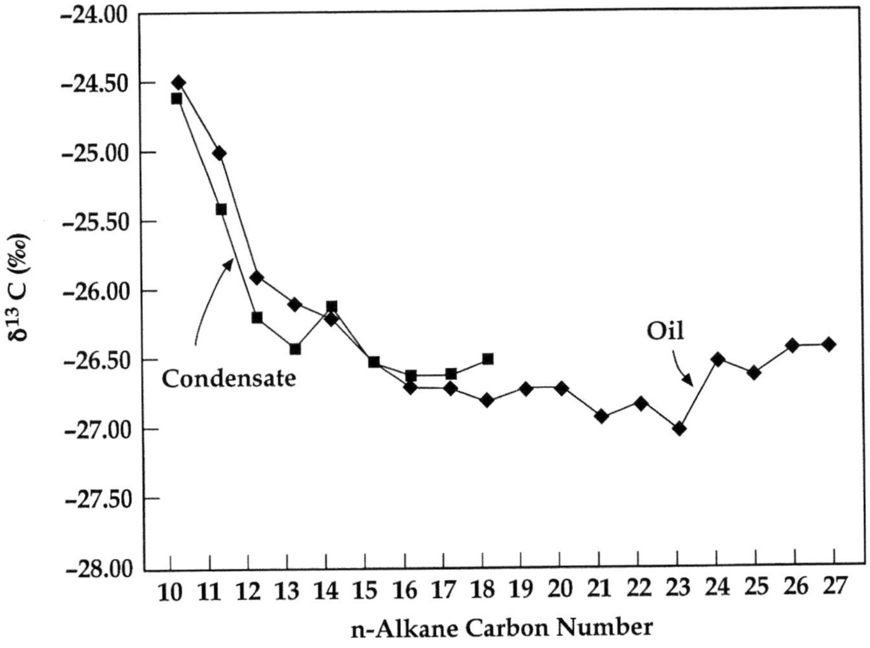

Figure 8–4. Courtesy Unocal.

Sulfur and hydrogen isotopes

Sulfur isotopes are frequently measured for high-sulfur oils and related kerogens. They are useful primarily in distinguishing among various types of anoxic environments (Orr, 1986). Hydrogen isotopes are used occasionally, particularly for gases. Interpretation of hydrogen isotopes for oils is difficult (Schoell, 1982).

Subsection B3
Molecular Parameter Data

What are molecular parameters?

Molecular parameters are based on the presence or on the relative or absolute abundance of specific molecules in an oil or a source rock extract.

Molecular parameters are the most powerful of all correlation tools because of the precision of the information they convey and the large amount of data that can be obtained. In addition to correlating an oil directly to another oil or to a source rock extract, certain molecular parameters can be used to estimate ages of oils. This capability is valuable in initiating the search for a source rock to correlate with a particular oil.

Geochemical techniques

Data about molecular parameters are obtained by the following geochemical techniques:

- Gas chromatography (GC)
- Gas chromatography/mass spectrometry (GC/MS)
- Pyrolysis–Gas chromatography (Py–GC)
- High-performance liquid chromatography (HPLC)

GC/MS is the most important technique because it provides abundant, highly specific data.

In this subsection

This subsection contains the following topics.

Data Obtained by Gas Chromatography

Applications

In gas chromatography the distributions of *n*-alkanes and isoprenoids are usually most useful. Of particular significance for correlations are the wax content (C_{23+}), the Carbon Preference Index (CPI) (Bray and Evans, 1961), and the pristane–phytane (Pr/Ph) ratio. The following figures show gas chromatograms of the saturate fractions of several oils, illustrating the differences that can be observed in these compound classes as a result of differences in the source material.

Example: Oil of terrestrial origin

The figure below is a gas chromatogram of a high-wax oil of terrestrial origin with an odd-carbon preference in the wax region and a high pristane–phytane ratio typical of coaly or certain nearshore aquatic environments. Significant input of terrigenous organic matter is indicated by a bimodal *n*-alkane distribution (a second mode in the wax region, from *n*-C_{23} to *n*-C_{31}), a pristane–phytane ratio greater than 2.0, and a strong odd-carbon *n*-alkane dominance from *n*-C_{25} to *n*-C_{31}. These features are characteristic of deltaic or lacustrine-sourced oils (in this case, from Indonesia).

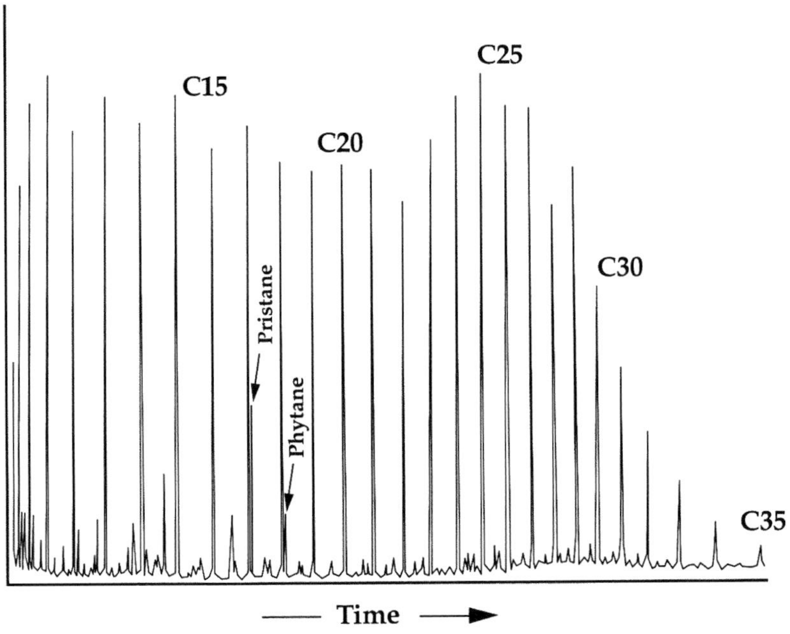

Figure 8–5. From Robinson (1987); reprinted with permission from the Indonesian Petroleum Association.

Example: Oil of marine origin

The figure below is a gas chromatogram of an extremely waxy oil from the Paradox basin, Utah. It was sourced from a marine anoxic evaporitic carbonate. Here the waxes, which are not derived from terrestrial plants, show an even-carbon preference, and the pristane–phytane ratio is very low (<1.0). Low pristane–phytane ratios and the even-carbon predominances serve to distinguish nonterrigenous waxy oils from terrigenous ones.

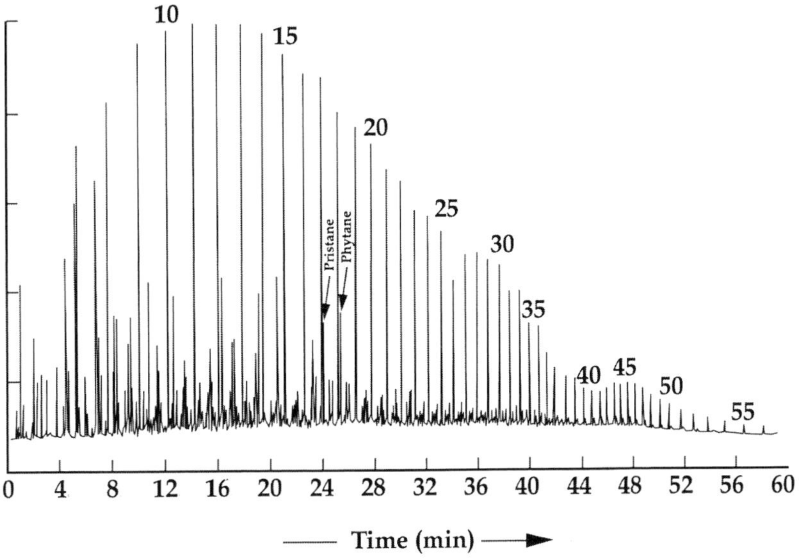

Figure 8–6. Courtesy Unocal.

Example: Oil of marine algal origin

The figure below shows a gas chromatogram of a low-wax oil derived from typical marine algae. Pristane–phytane ratios for such oils tend to be slightly above 1.0. This Alaskan oil was derived from a source rock containing predominantly marine algal organic matter.

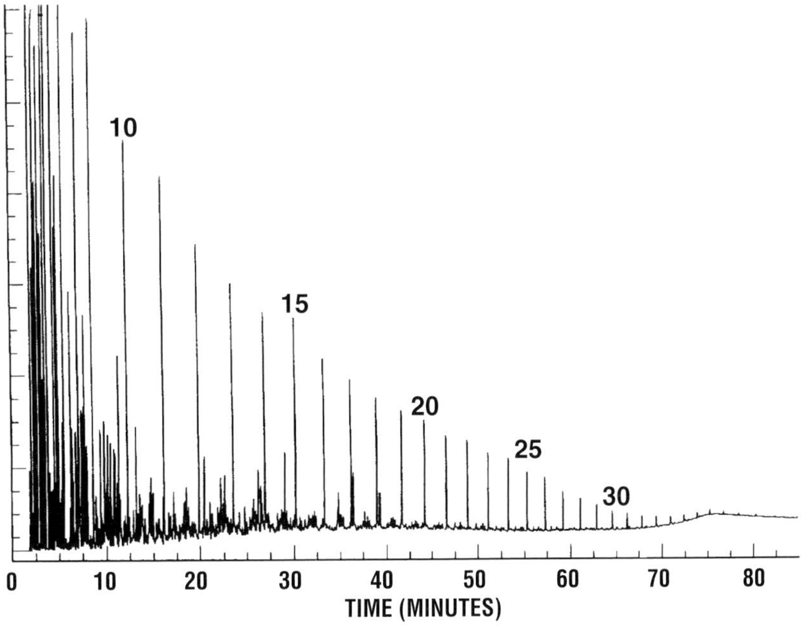

Figure 8–7. Courtesy Unocal.

Data Obtained by Gas Chromatography, continued

Example: Oil derived from *G. prisca*

The figure below is a gas chromatogram of saturates from an Ordovician-sourced oil from the Illinois basin. It shows a low-wax oil derived primarily from the primitive organism *Gloeocapsamorpha prisca.* Samples derived from *G. prisca* show strong odd-carbon preferences up to *n*-C_{19}, and have very low concentrations of both pristane and phytane (Reed et al., 1986; Longman and Palmer, 1987; Hatch et al., 1990; Guthrie and Pratt, 1995).

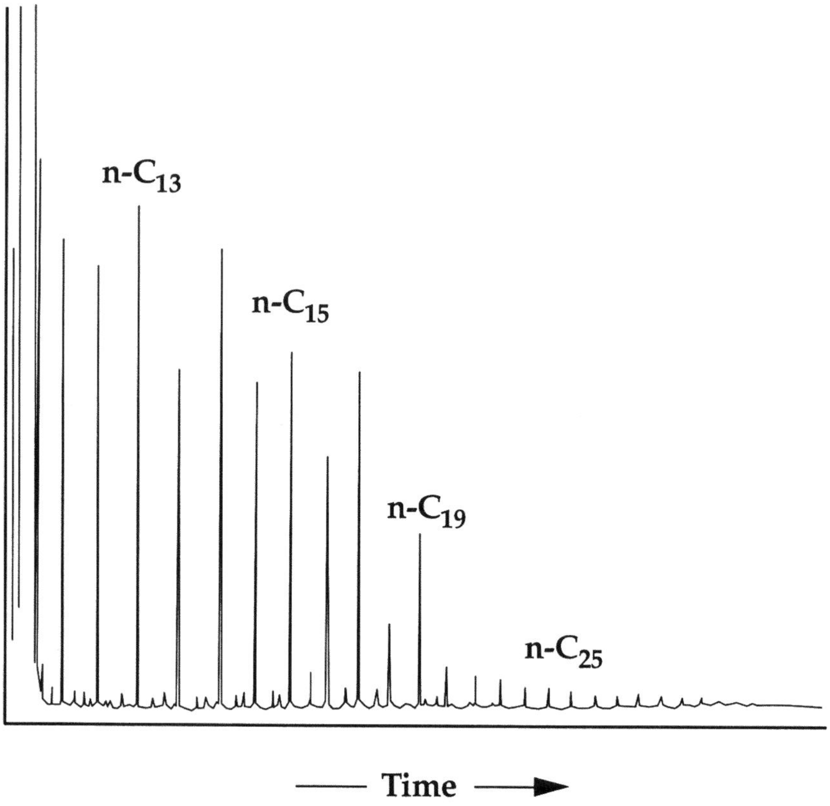

Figure 8–8. From Hatch et al. (1990); reprinted with permission from AAPG.

G. prisca

G. prisca is well known from the Ordovician (and is thus a useful age marker), but the gas chromatographic characteristics of *G. prisca* or its descendants have been seen in rocks as young as Devonian. In some studies of the Michigan basin, a few of which predated the recognition of the geochemical peculiarities of *G. prisca*, several workers mistook the presence of *G. prisca*-like chromatographic characteristics in the Devonian oils as absolute indicators of an Ordovician source. In fact, some of the Devonian source rocks themselves show the same characteristics (D. Waples, unpublished data).

Data Obtained by Gas Chromatography, continued

X-compounds

The figure below shows an example of an unusual group of alkanes called X-compounds. They contain one or more methyl branches near the middle of a long-chain hydrocarbon. These compounds originate from primitive cyanobacteria (blue-green algae) and are diagnostic of Precambrian sources.

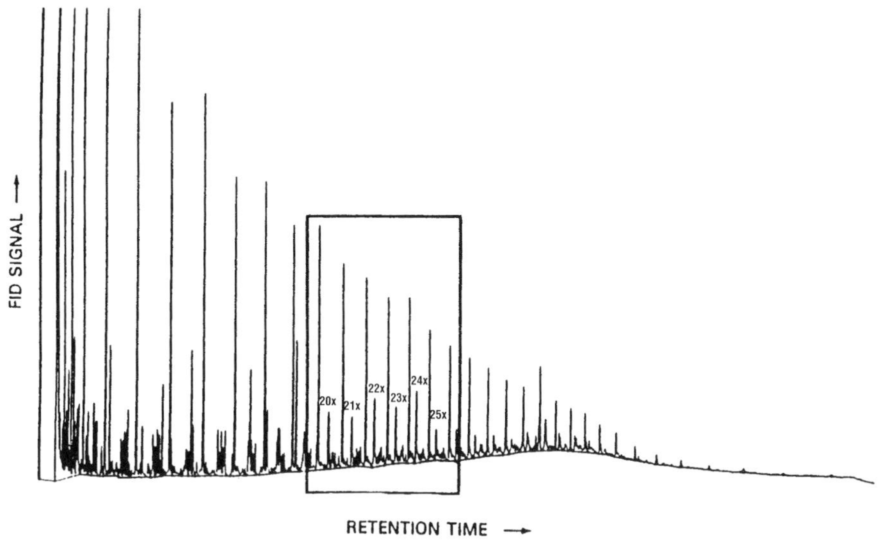

Figure 8–9. From Klomp (1986); reprinted with permission from Elsevier.

Resin-derived terpanes

Sesquiterpanes and diterpanes, derived principally from the resin in terrestrial plants of the Late Cretaceous and Cenozoic, are often abundant in younger samples with terrestrial plant input. In such cases, they usually can be seen (although not interpreted in detail) using gas chromatography. The chromatogram below of the saturated hydrocarbons from a rock extract shows minor amounts of sesquiterpanes (the cluster of peaks eluting near n-C_{15}) and large amounts of diterpanes (the small cluster of peaks eluting near n-C_{20}). Samples containing sesqui- and diterpanes often display other characteristics of terrestrially influenced samples, such as odd-carbon preferences, high wax contents, and high pristane–phytane ratios. To analyze the resin-derived terpanes in detail, however, we should use GC/MS.

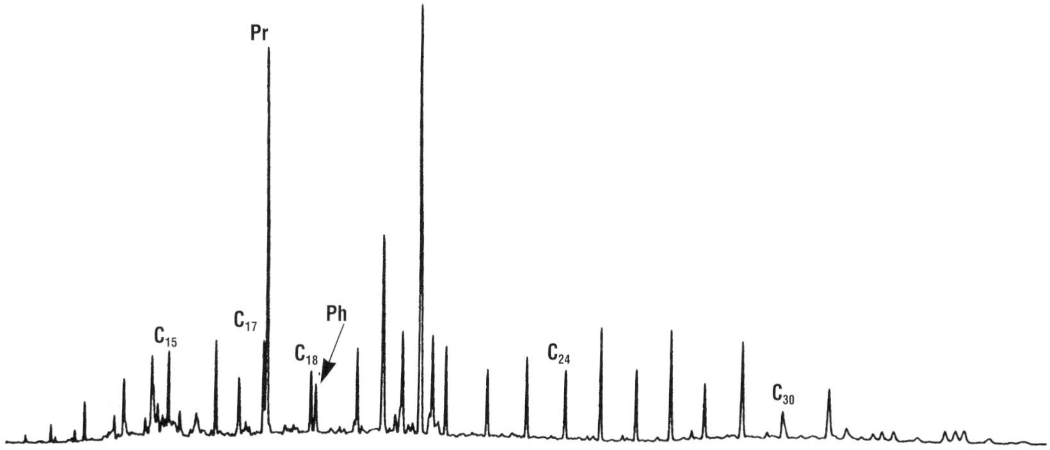

Figure 8–10. Courtesy Unocal.

Bisnorhopane

An unusual biomarker is 28,30-bisnorhopane, which can be extremely abundant in those few samples where it is present. The figure below shows gas chromatograms of two extracts of immature source rock candidates in southern California (Monterey Formation, Santa Maria basin). They contain bisnorhopane as well as a series of monoaromatic steroid hydrocarbons. These two biomarker types, together with the low pristane–phytane ratios shown here, are characteristic of Monterey oils. These distinctive characteristics provide a fairly confident correlation to Monterey oils, despite the very low maturity of the source rocks.

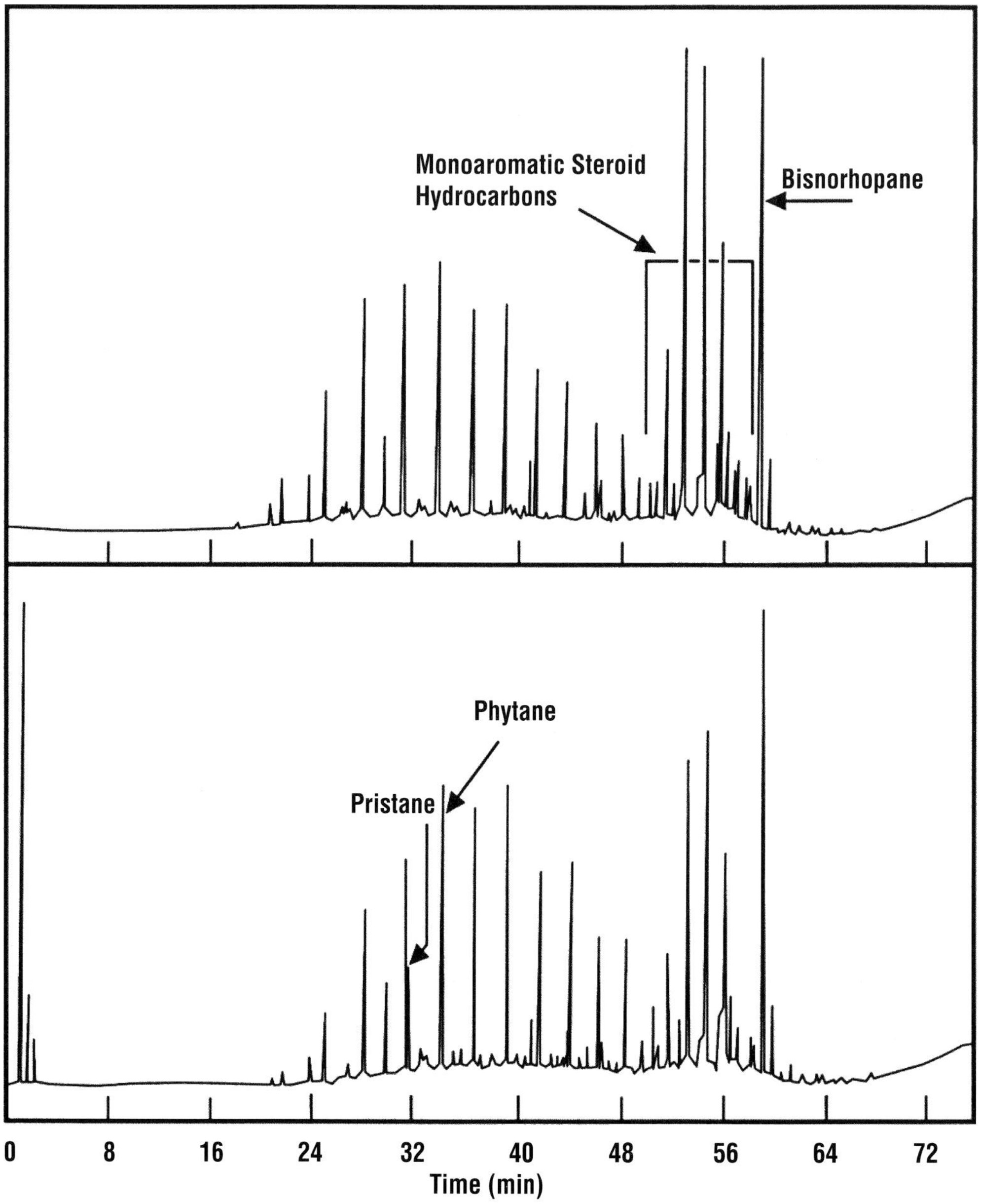

Figure 8–11. From Curiale et al. (1985); reprinted with permission from Elsevier.

Data Obtained by Gas Chromatography, continued

Other minor components

Other minor components present in gas chromatograms can be used for correlations, even when compound identities are not known. However, one should always treat unidentified compounds with caution, since they may represent contaminants, or their concentrations may be affected by maturity or alteration effects.

The figure below shows gas chromatograms of two oils from Texas and Oklahoma. Full-scale chromatograms on the left show the oils are not degraded, a condition necessary for this type of correlation. The shaded areas indicate the regions expanded on the right. Based on the many similarities in the expanded-scale chromatograms and on other geochemical similarities, it was concluded that these two oils were derived from the same Lower Paleozoic source facies.

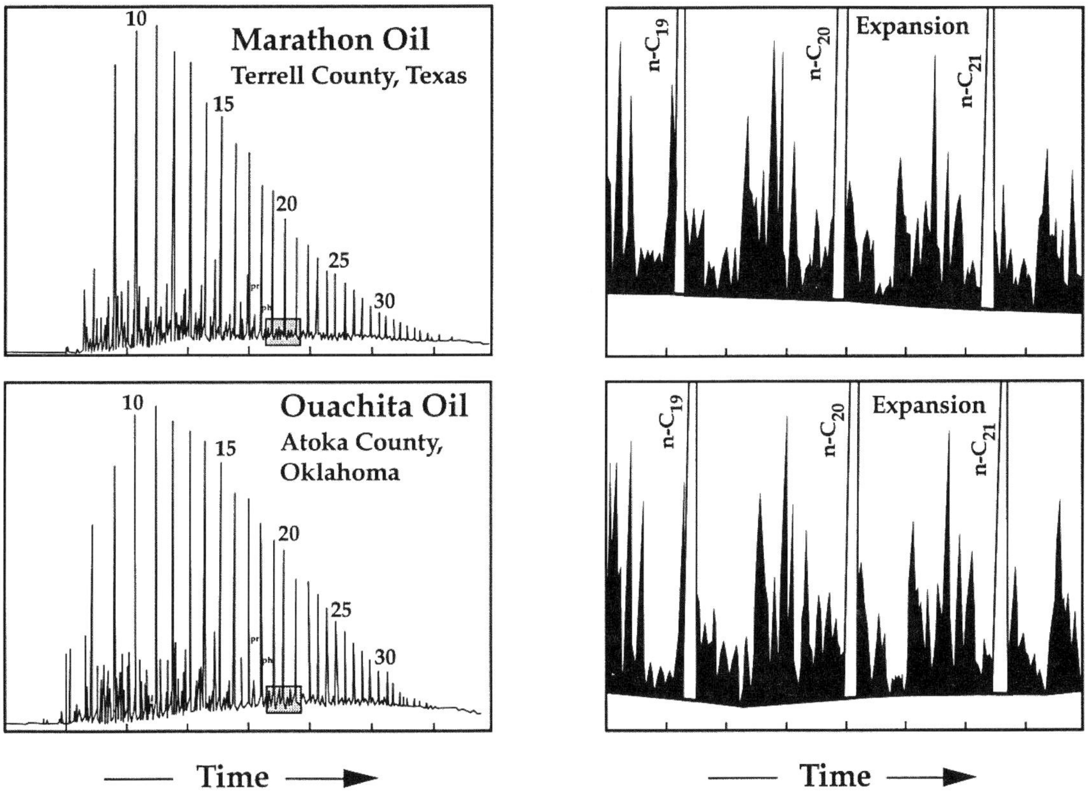

Figure 8–12. From Curiale (1992); reprinted with permission from Elsevier.

Data Obtained by Gas Chromatography, continued

Star diagrams

Star diagrams (polar plots) are sometimes used to display the relative amounts of a series of peaks in a chromatogram. See, for example, Kaufman et al. (1987).

Limitations due to maturity differences

Maturity-related differences are often observed when comparing oils with each other and with source rock extracts. High-wax oils are affected most strongly by maturity. Maturity differences involving source rocks can present particular difficulties when source rock samples are extremely immature.

For these reasons, and also because of the possibility of fortuitous similarities between unrelated samples, gas chromatography seldom provides definitive positive correlations. It may, however, provide fairly definitive negative correlations. When used in conjunction with other correlation parameters, it can often be valuable for positive correlations as well, as demonstrated in the following two examples.

Maturity difference example

The figure below shows gas chromatograms of two oils from Wyoming. Both were sourced from the Permian Phosphoria Formation, but are reservoired in different fields. The bimodal distribution of *n*-alkanes in the top oil is consistent with a lower level of maturity than that of the unimodal oil at the bottom. Comparison of these oils using gas chromatography for the purpose of oil–oil correlation must be done with caution because of the maturity differences.

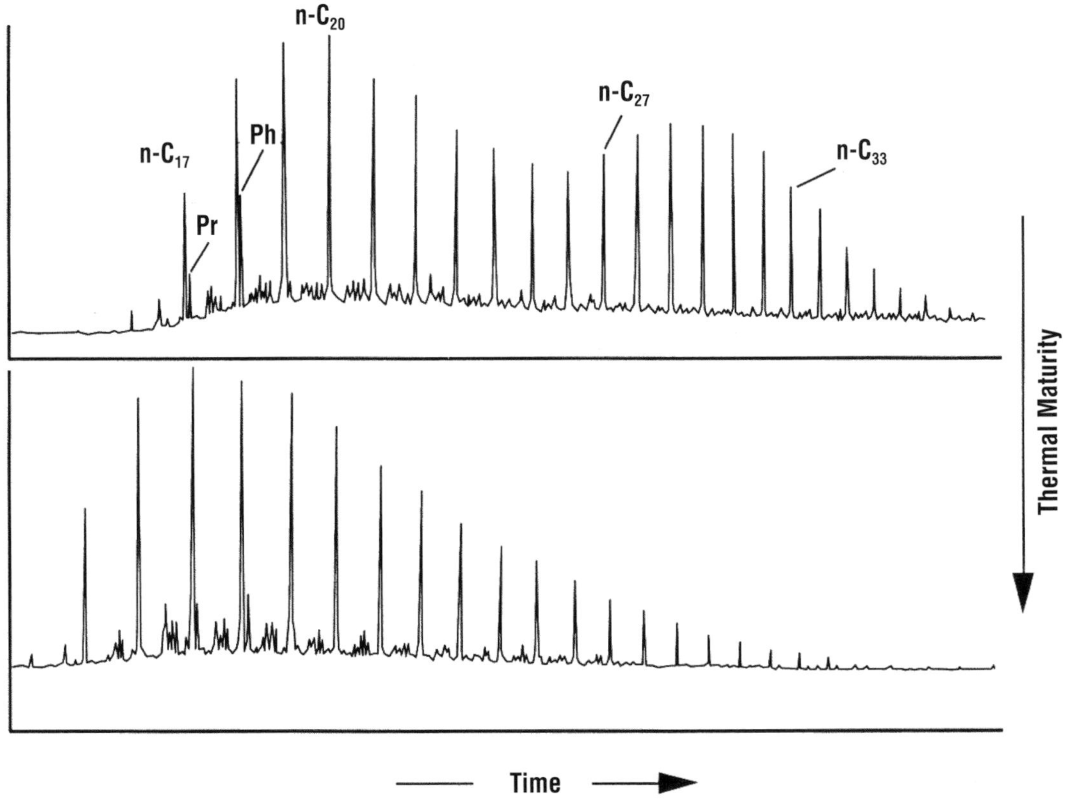

Figure 8–13. From Peters and Moldowan (1993); reprinted with permission from Prentice-Hall.

Data Obtained by Gas Chromatography, continued

Examples of maturity differences

The figure below shows gas chromatograms of saturated hydrocarbons from an immature extract of coaly organic matter (top) and an oil with a fairly high wax content believed to have been sourced from a similar facies (bottom). Both show many of the same characteristics—high wax content, odd-carbon preference in the wax range, high pristane–phytane ratio—but maturity effects have changed many of the details.

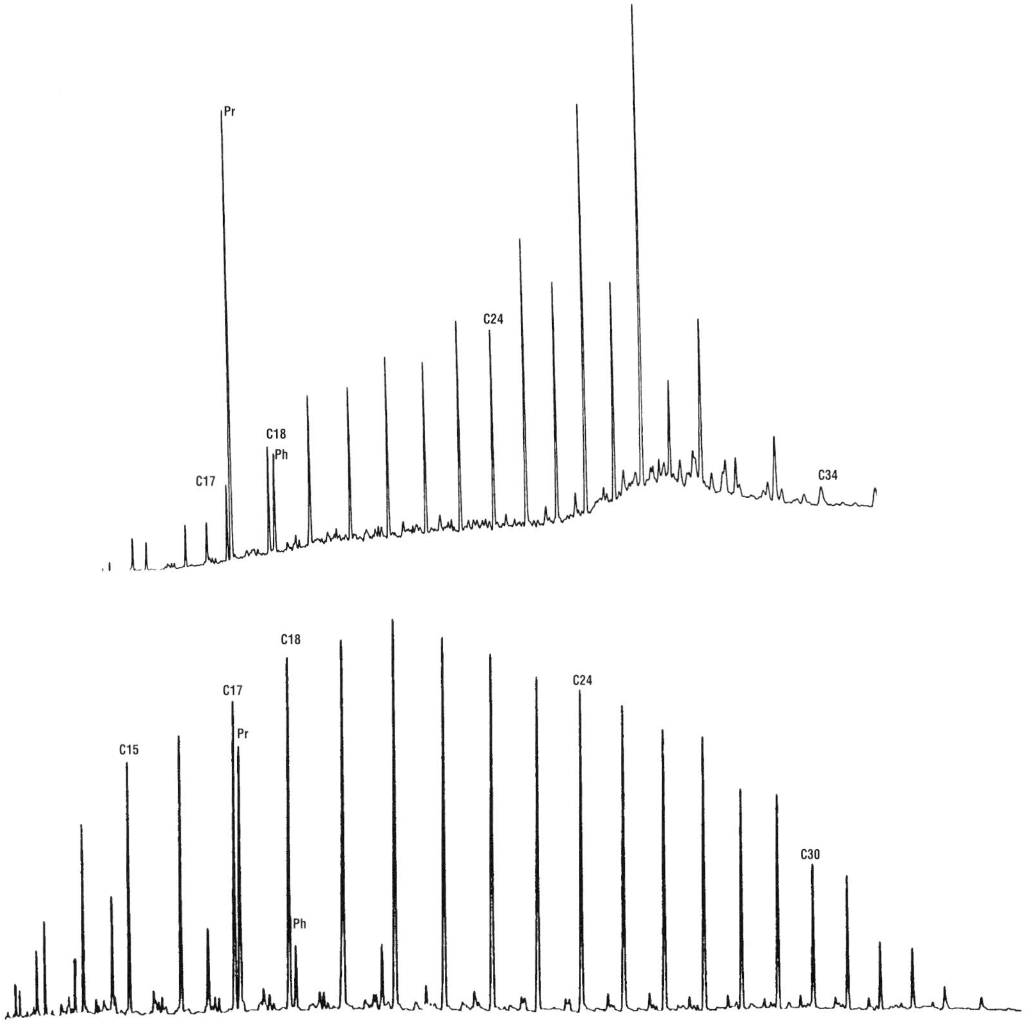

Figure 8–14. Courtesy Unocal.

Limitations due to evaporative loss

Evaporative loss can affect the appearance of gas chromatograms. When the solvent is removed too fast during recovery of source rock extracts, selective loss of some of the C_{15+} components can occur. This loss not only alters the appearance of the gas chromatograms but may also change compound ratios (for example, the pristane–phytane ratio through selective loss of pristane). In some instances, gas stripping in the reservoir can selectively remove lighter components, leaving an oil or residue that looks lightly biodegraded or, in some instances, waxy.

Example of loss of C_{15+} fraction

The figure below shows a gas chromatogram of saturated hydrocarbons in a source rock extract from which the extracting solvent was evaporated too vigorously, leading to loss of some of the C_{15+} fraction. This problem can be recognized by looking at the n-C_{17} and n-C_{18} peaks. Normally they are almost the same size, but in this case the n-C_{17} peak is much smaller. Pristane has also been depleted relative to phytane, leading to an erroneous pristane–phytane ratio unless some correction is made.

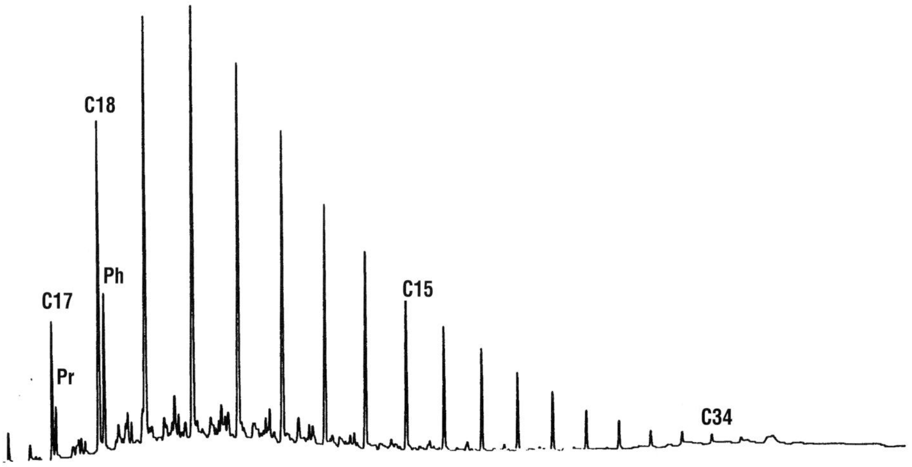

Figure 8–15. Courtesy Unocal.

Example of loss of light ends

The figure below shows a gas chromatogram of an oil whose light ends were partially removed during gas stripping in the reservoir. Oils like this one are often observed in deep reservoirs in Tertiary deltaic sequences.

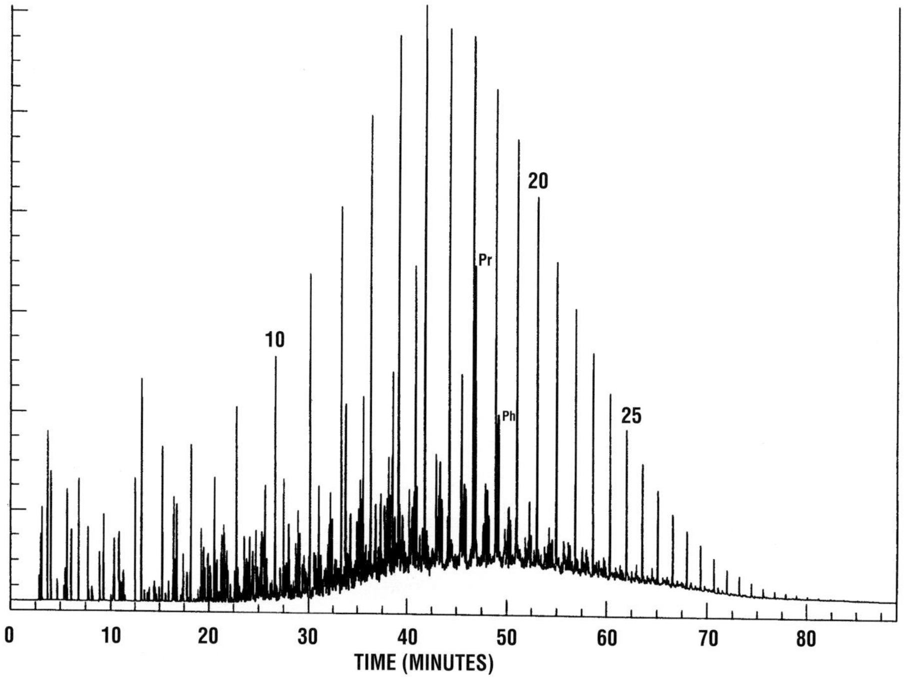

Figure 8–16. Courtesy Unocal.

Limitations due to internal standards

An internal standard is commonly coinjected with the sample to aid in quantification during gas chromatography. If this internal standard is not clearly labeled on the chromatogram, it may be confused with an indigenous compound and erroneously used in correlation.

Examples of problems with internal standards

The figure below shows gas chromatograms of the saturated hydrocarbons from two seep oils from Papua New Guinea. Both samples contain an internal standard that elutes just before n-C_{27}. Because the left oil is biodegraded, the detector sensitivity was set very high to record the trace amounts of remaining n-alkanes. Consequently, the internal standard peak is very tall. In contrast, the right oil (undegraded) shows a much smaller internal standard peak because the detector sensitivity was lower.

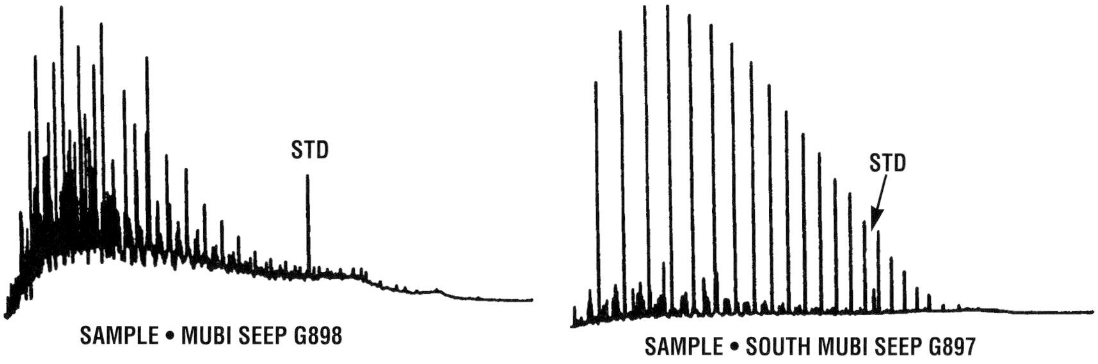

Figure 8–17.

The figure below shows a gas chromatogram of the saturated hydrocarbons from the Lufa seep oil, another seep oil from Papua New Guinea. Because this work was carried out by a different laboratory than the analyses in the previous figure, the internal standard used here is different. This standard elutes just before n-C_{22}. The pristane–n-C_{17} ratio suggests that this oil is different from those in Figure 8–17, a fact confirmed by other geochemical evidence.

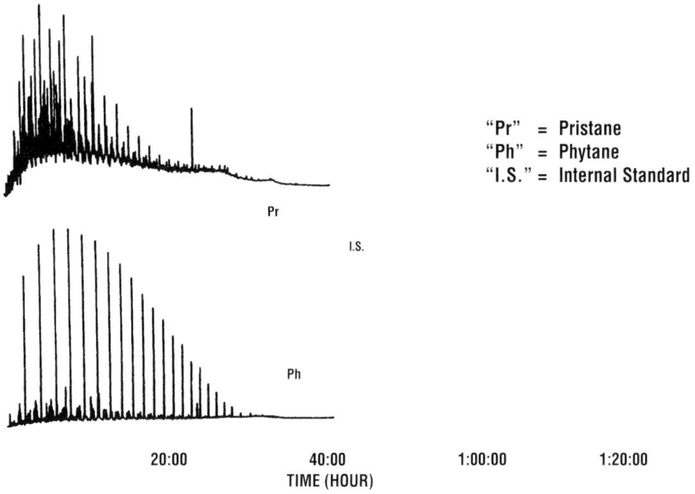

Figure 8–18. From Murray et al. (1993); courtesy Australian Geological Survey Organization.

Data Obtained by Gas Chromatography, continued

Limitations due to contaminated samples

In other cases, particularly in rock extracts, the sample may be contaminated. Plasticizers, for example, are common but are usually easy to recognize. The figure below shows a gas chromatogram of saturated hydrocarbons from a source rock sample contaminated with bits of plastic. The largest peak is dioctylphthalate, derived from contact with the plastic.

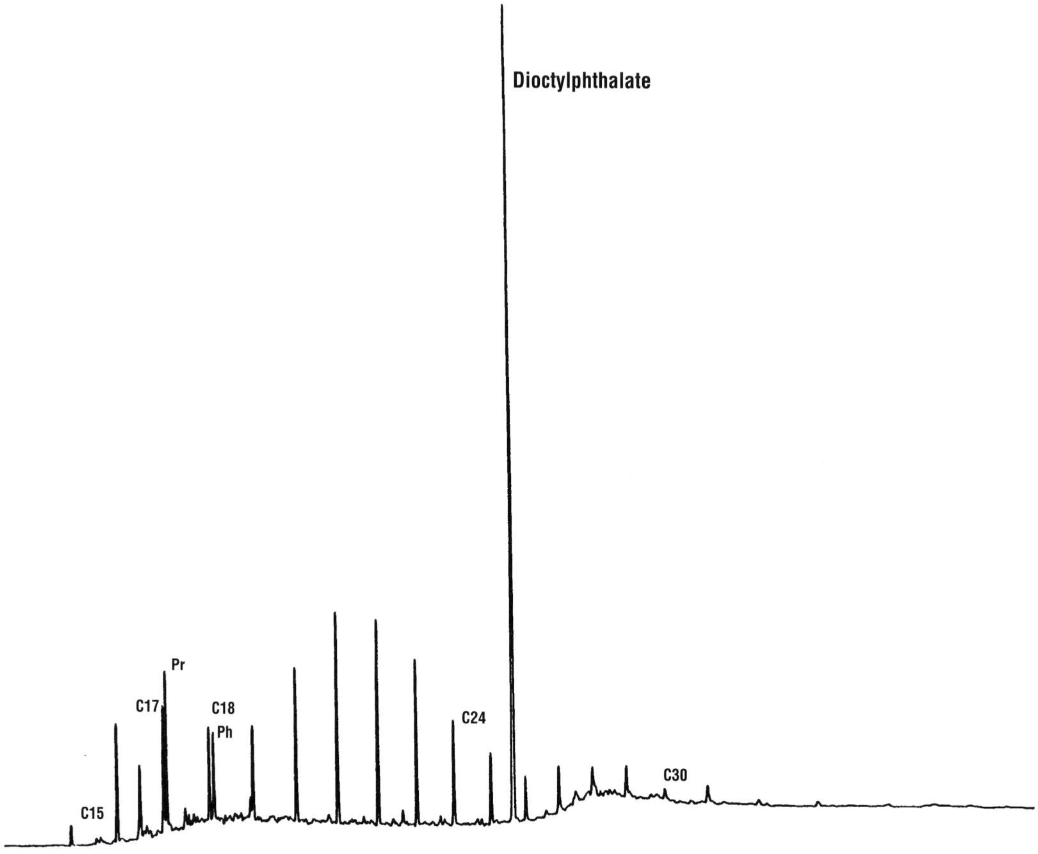

Figure 8–19.

Biodegradation limitations

Biodegradation can severely alter gas chromatograms. In the earliest stages of biodegradation, n-alkanes are removed selectively, leading to significant loss of information.

Examples of biodegradation

The figure below (left) shows gas chromatograms of three oils from a common source in central Myanmar. A waxy oil (top) is sequentially converted into an extremely biodegraded remnant oil (bottom). The API gravity of the oil decreases and sulfur content increases substantially with increasing biodegradation.

Pristane–phytane ratios may also be affected slightly at low stages of biodegradation. At moderate levels these compounds are removed completely (left figure). The right figure below shows whole-oil gas chromatograms of three oils from the offshore Mackenzie Delta, northwestern Canada, showing a modest decrease in the pristane–phytane ratio, apparently as the result of minor biodegradation.

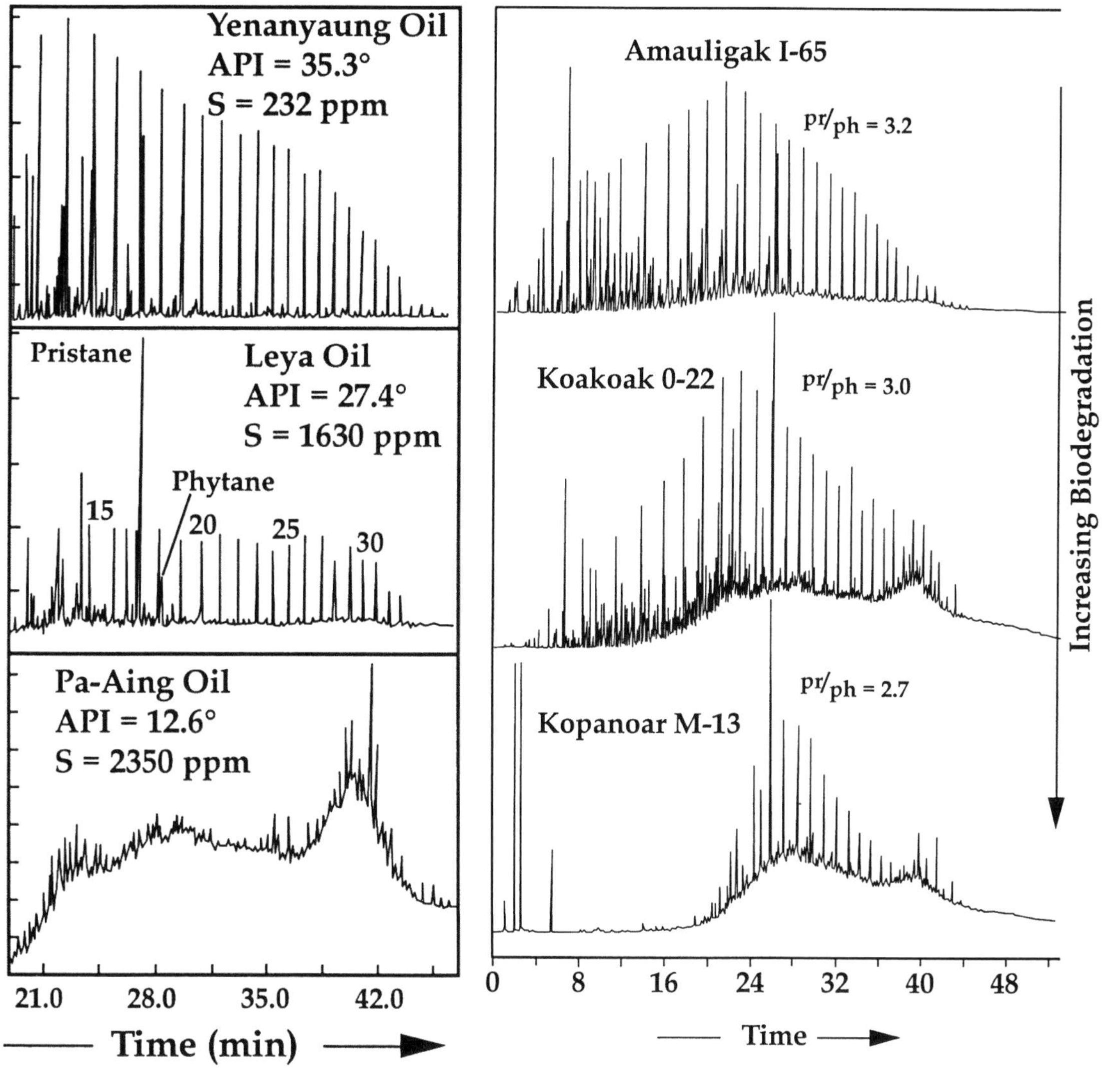

Figure 8–20. From Curiale et al. (1994) and Curiale (1991); reprinted with permission from Elsevier.

How is GC/MS Done?

What is GC/MS?

GC/MS is a technique used to identify and quantify those compounds present in small concentrations that cannot be adequately separated, identified, and quantified using gas chromatography.

Selected ion monitoring (SIM)

Traditionally, the most common application of GC/MS in exploration has been selected ion monitoring (SIM). In this technique, a single ion is monitored at a time, permitting one class of compound to be separated and analyzed apart from all others. In a single run several different ions can be monitored, allowing analysis of many classes of compounds.

Example of SIM

The figure below shows three SIM mass chromatograms for a single oil sample. The top left chromatogram show the m/z 191 chromatogram, in which the only compounds are those having a fragment ion with a mass of 191 daltons. (The value m/z is the mass of the ion divided by its charge.) The bottom left chromatogram shows the compounds yielding an m/z 217 fragment in the mass spectrometer, while the top right chromatogram shows those compounds that give an m/z 218 fragment. The 217 and 218 mass chromatograms are very similar because both are derived mainly from steranes. The differences in relative intensity reflect the tendency of some types of steranes to give more 217 daughter ions and others to give more 218. These tendencies are due to structural differences among different families of steranes and are useful in themselves.

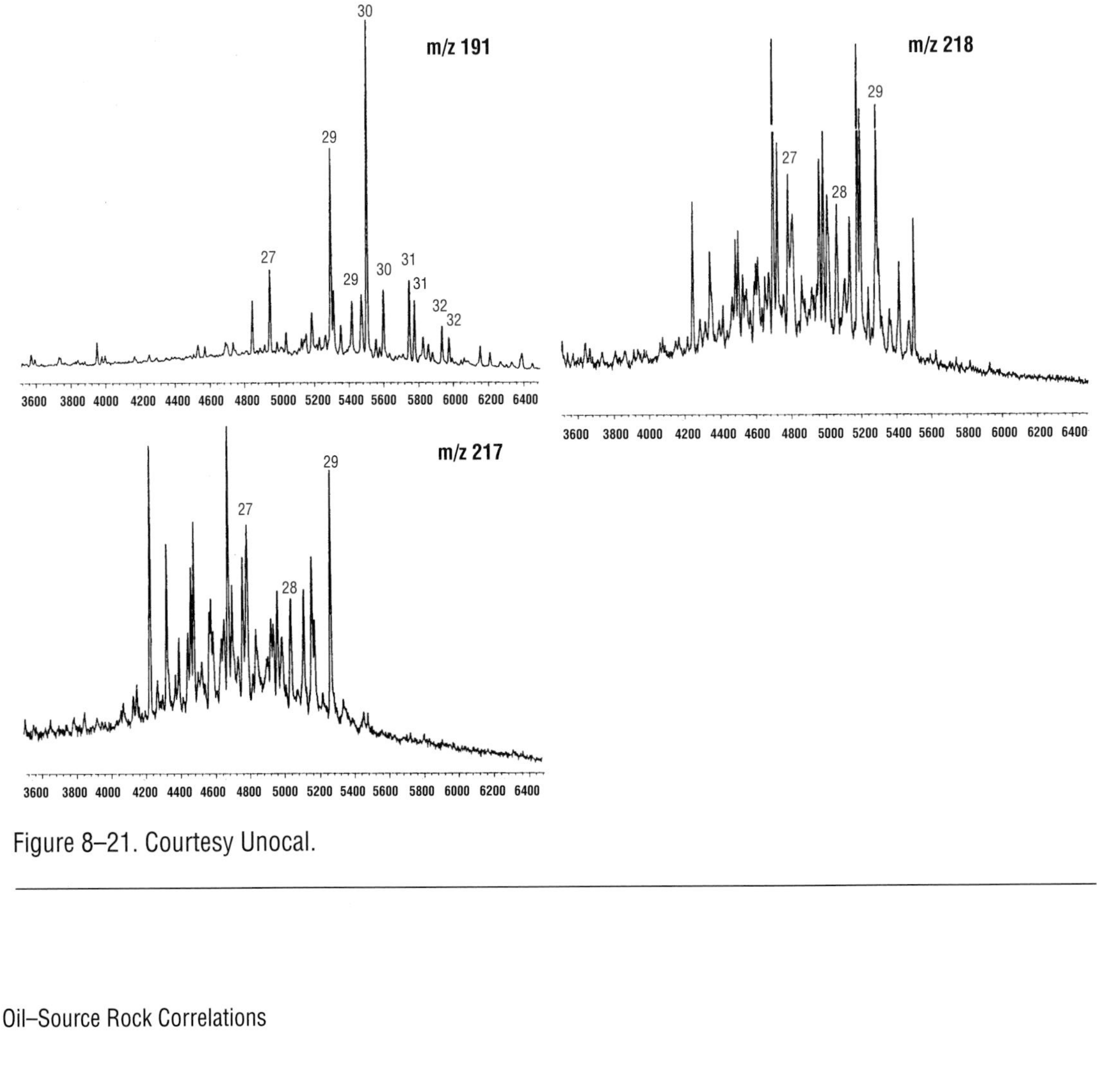

Figure 8–21. Courtesy Unocal.

Common ions

The table below lists common ions and the aliphatic hydrocarbon compound classes for which they are most commonly used.

Ion (m/z)	Compound class monitored
123	Diterpanes, sesquiterpanes
125	Carotanes
177	Demethylated triterpanes
191	Triterpanes, bicadinanes, tricyclic diterpanes (cheilanthanes)
217	Steranes, bicadinanes
218	ββ steranes
231	4-methylsteranes
259	Diasteranes

Metastable reaction monitoring (MRM)

Although SIM has a long and valuable history in analyzing complex mixtures of biomarkers, it is not always able to separate all the compounds we would wish. To achieve a more detailed separation and more accurate identification and quantification, particularly of steranes, different kinds of mass spectrometers can be used, resulting in methods such as GC/MS/MS and metastable reaction monitoring (MRM). In these techniques we look at the products of each molecule separately so that we know not only the mass of the fragment ion but also the parent from which it came.

For example, in data on steranes obtained from MRM, instead of a single trace that includes all the steranes, there is a series of traces, each dedicated to a single precursor compound. Thus, one trace monitors all the steranes with 29 carbon atoms, another those with 28 carbons, and so on.

Example of MRM

Figure 8–22 shows MRM output for steranes from the Lufa oil seep in Papua New Guinea. The same sample was also discussed on page 8–27. Each fragmentogram monitors the transformation of a particular molecular ion to the designated daughter ion. The top four traces monitor conversion to the m/z 217 fragment ion from four different sizes of original sterane molecules. The top chromatogram represents the decomposition of methylsteranes (molecular weight = 414 daltons), and through its very low relative intensity at 100% scale (1.7) shows these compounds to be present in minor amounts. The next three chromatograms are for the C_{29}, C_{28}, and C_{27} steranes, respectively. From the relative concentrations (24.4, 10.6, and 15.8) of these fragments, we see the C_{29} species is dominant. The fifth chromatogram monitors 4-methylsteranes, which in this sample represent only minor components. The last two fragmentograms, in contrast, monitor two different bicadinane species.

Example of MRM (continued)

The presence of bicadinanes in this sample further limits the source rock age for this oleanane-bearing oil.

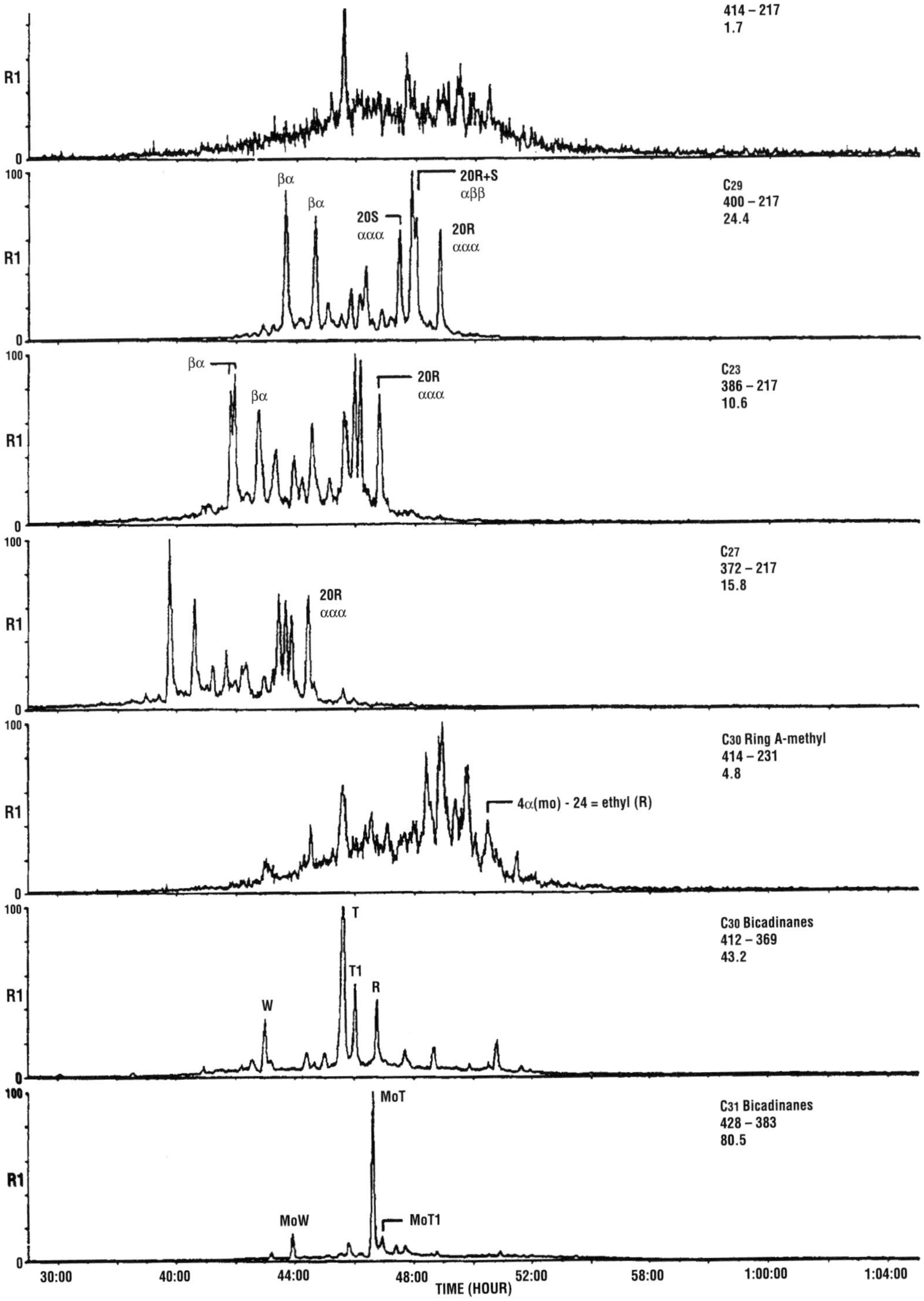

Figure 8–22. From Murray et al. (1993); courtesy Australian Geological Survey Organization.

Environments Indicated by Specific Compounds

Environments indicated by steranes

The relative amounts of C_{27}, C_{28} and C_{29} steranes in oils are controlled by the types of photosynthetic organisms that contributed to the organic matter. A dominance of C_{27} steranes is almost always associated with marine organisms. Most nonmarine organic matter has a dominance of the C_{29} sterane precursors, but C_{29} steranes can dominate in marine systems as well. The abundance of C_{28} steranes in marine systems may depend primarily on geologic age (Grantham and Wakefield, 1988), but this idea is controversial. In nonmarine systems, there is no proposed relationship between C_{28} sterane abundance and age. C_{30} steranes (*n*-propylcholestanes) are usually less abundant than the other regular steranes and occur only in samples deposited where marine organisms lived (Moldowan et al., 1985).

Example of steranes

The figure below shows m/z 217 mass fragmentograms from two oils showing quite different distributions of regular steranes. The top example is dominated by C_{29} steranes with only moderate amounts of C_{27} and C_{28}. The bottom sample, in contrast, shows similar amounts of all three homologs plus moderate amounts of the C_{30} steranes (four unlabeled peaks to the far right).

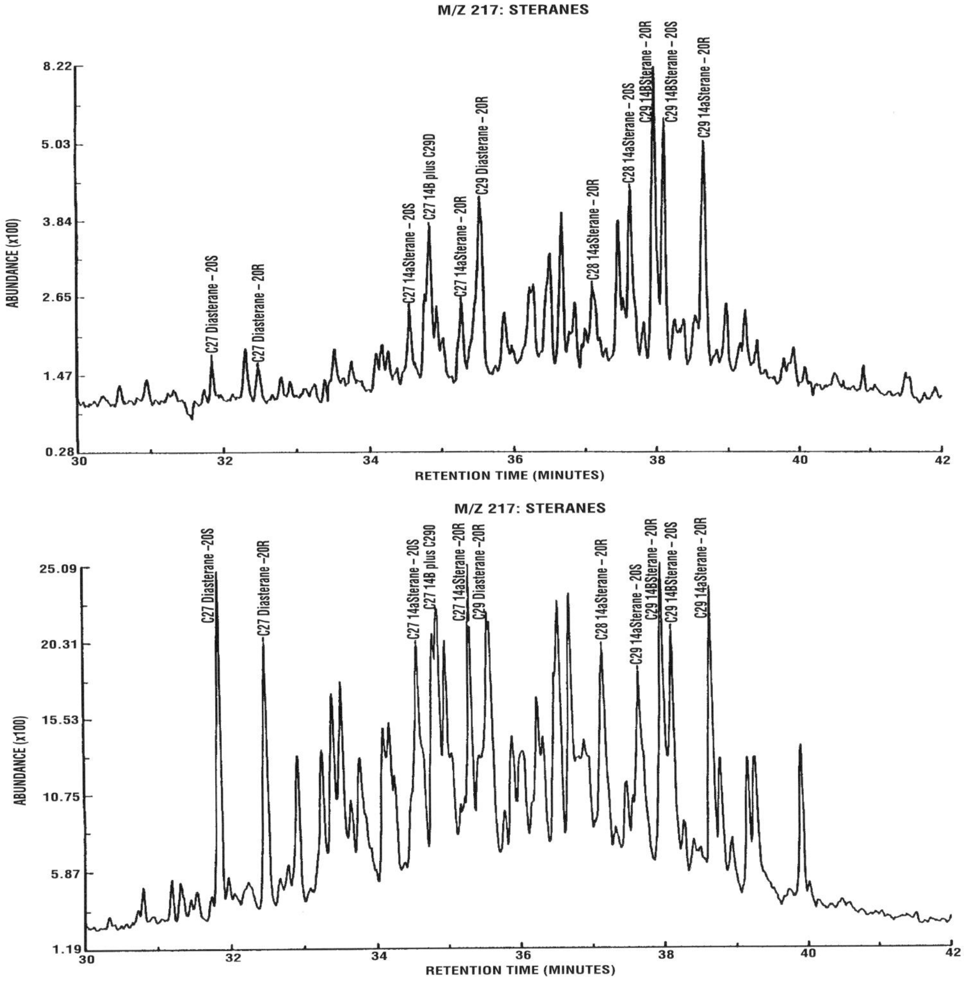

Figure 8–23.

Environments Indicated by Specific Compounds, continued

Example of steranes (continued)

The figure below shows a ternary diagram, a convenient and common way of displaying basic data on sterane distributions. This example shows the relative proportions of the C_{27}, C_{28}, and C_{29} regular steranes for several extracts from two distinct facies within the nonmarine Elko Formation (Eocene/Oligocene) of Nevada. The lignitic siltstones are dominated by terrestrial plant material, whereas the oil shales are made up of lacustrine algae.

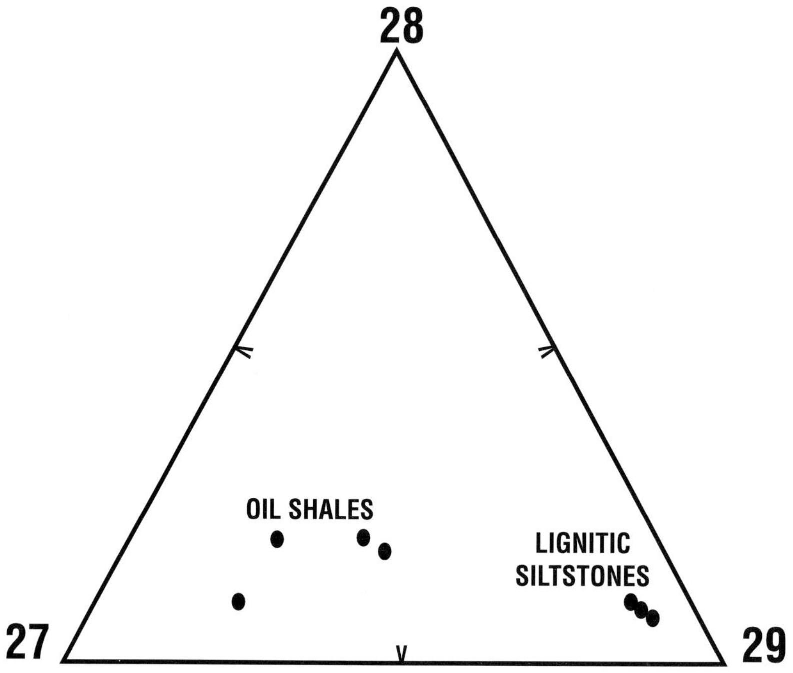

Figure 8–24. From Palmer (1984); reprinted with permission from Rocky Mountain Assoc. of Geologists.

4-methyl-steranes

MRM analysis is useful in distinguishing *n*-propylcholestanes from 4-methylsteranes and in assigning identities to different types of 4-methylsteranes. This sophisticated GC/MS analysis method will probably become commonplace because of its specificity in oil–oil and oil–source rock correlation efforts.

Example of distribution of 4-methylsteranes

The figure below shows the distribution of 4-methylsteranes in selected rock extracts. The 414 → 231 metastable ion transition shows C_{30} steranes methylated on the A-ring. Two major families are shown here. The dinosteranes (derived from dinoflagellates) are designated "dino," whereas another group of 4-methylsteranes with an ethyl group at the 24 position are designated "24(Et)."

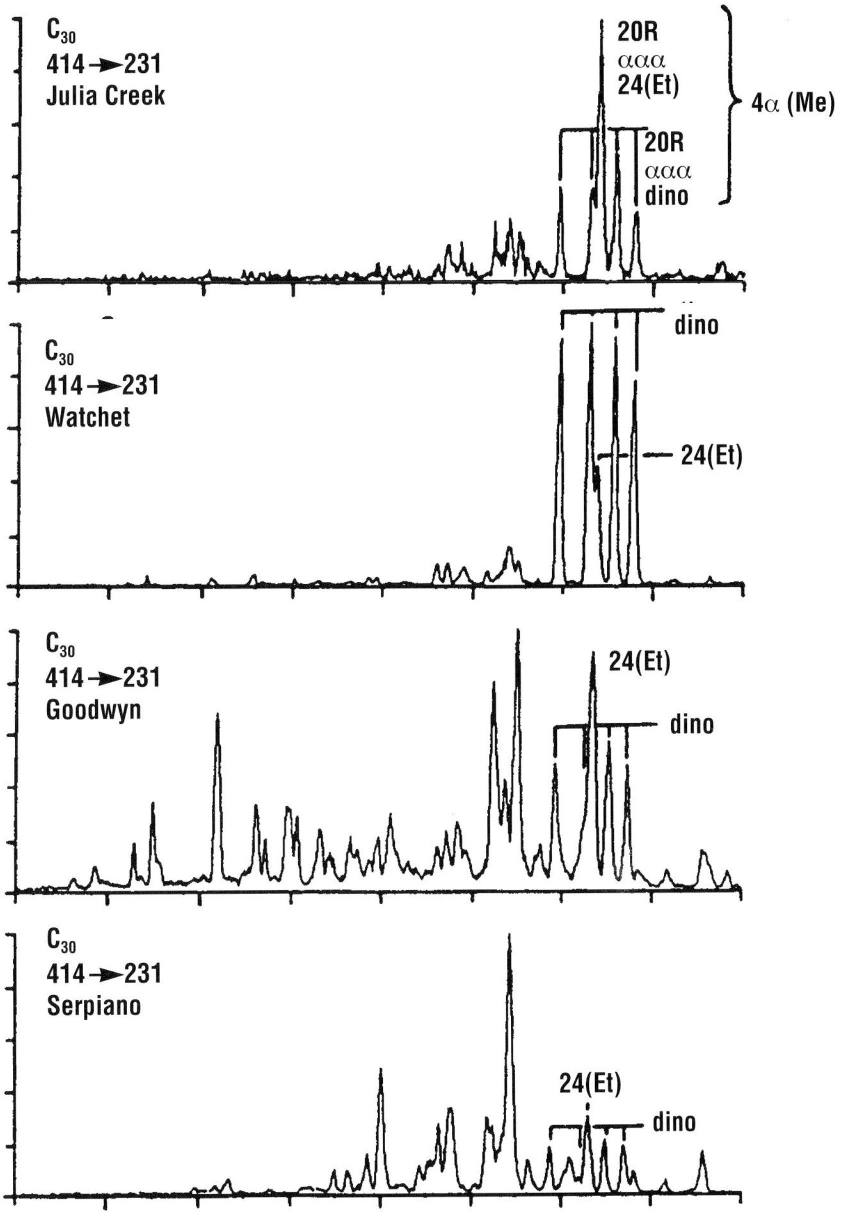

Figure 8–25. Modified from Summons et al. (1992); reprinted with permission from Elsevier.

Environments indicated by diasteranes

Diasteranes are mainly associated with clastic environments, and they increase in relative abundance with increasing maturity. However, they are also known from nonclastic samples and can, in some cases, be abundant even in low-maturity samples.

Figure 8–23 shows two distinct distributions of diasteranes. The top oil has very few diasteranes, indicating a possible lack of clay in the source rock. The bottom oil, in contrast, has similar amounts of diasteranes and regular steranes and probably comes from a clastic source.

Environments indicated by hopanes

Hopanes, which originate from bacteria, are the most abundant triterpanes. A distribution with a regular decrease of homohopanes from C_{31} to C_{35} is thought to be associated with clastic environments (Waples and Machihara, 1991) and/or more oxidizing conditions (Peters and Moldowan, 1993).

Example of homohopanes

The figure below shows the m/z 191 mass fragmentogram of an oil displaying the most common type of homohopane distribution.

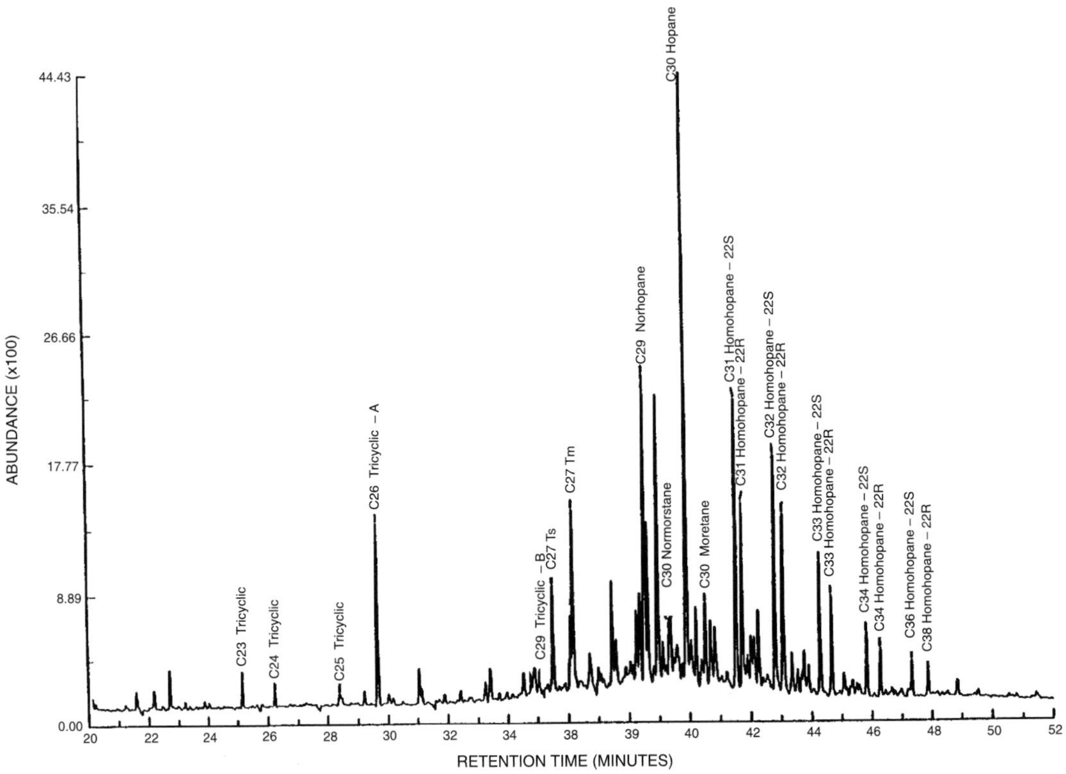

Figure 8–26.

Environments Indicated by Specific Compounds, continued

Irregular homohopane distributions

Irregular distributions of the C_{32}–C_{35} homohopanes are associated with carbonates (Waples and Machihara, 1991) and/or more reducing conditions (Peters and Moldowan, 1993). Unusually large amounts of the C_{31} homohopanes are sometimes associated with coals and coaly material (Waples and Machihara, 1991).

Example of irregular homohopane distribution

The figure below shows m/z 191 mass chromatograms for two sediment extracts from the Brac-1 well (Croatia) showing irregular homohopane distributions [relative enhancement of the C_{35} species (left) and C_{34} species (right)]. We would expect the oils sourced from these sediments to show these same characteristics.

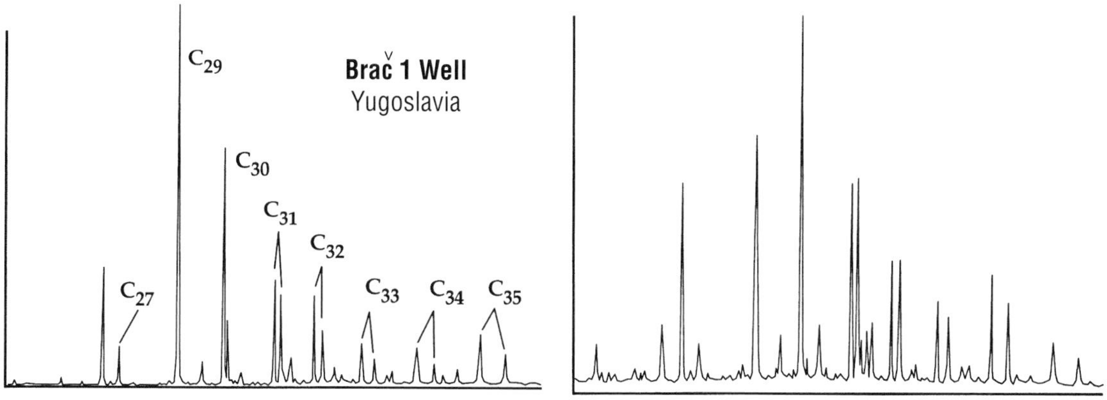

Figure 8–27. From Moldowan et al. (1992); reprinted with permission from Prentice-Hall.

Environment indicated by gammacerane

In addition to the hopane family, several other types of triterpanes that are occasionally encountered can be very useful in correlations. Gammacerane is often found in sediments deposited under abnormal salinites, including lacustrine facies. Identification of gammacerane can be difficult, however, both because it is usually only a minor component and because it elutes at different places with different chromatographic columns.

Examples of gammacerane

Figure 8–28 shows gammacerane in the m/z 191 mass chromatograms of two genetically related oils from southern Sicily. In this example, gammacerane elutes after the C_{31} homohopanes. Note also the relative increase in the C_{34} and C_{35} homohopanes. The presence of gammacerane and the homohopane distribution suggest a strongly reducing, possibly carbonate or hypersaline depositional setting for the source rock of these oils.

Figure 8–29 also shows samples with gammacerane, but in this case gammacerane essentially coelutes with the C_{31}-22R epimer. This example shows an oil from the Perla-1 well in southern Sicily and a source rock extract from the Noto Formation that correlates with it almost exactly.

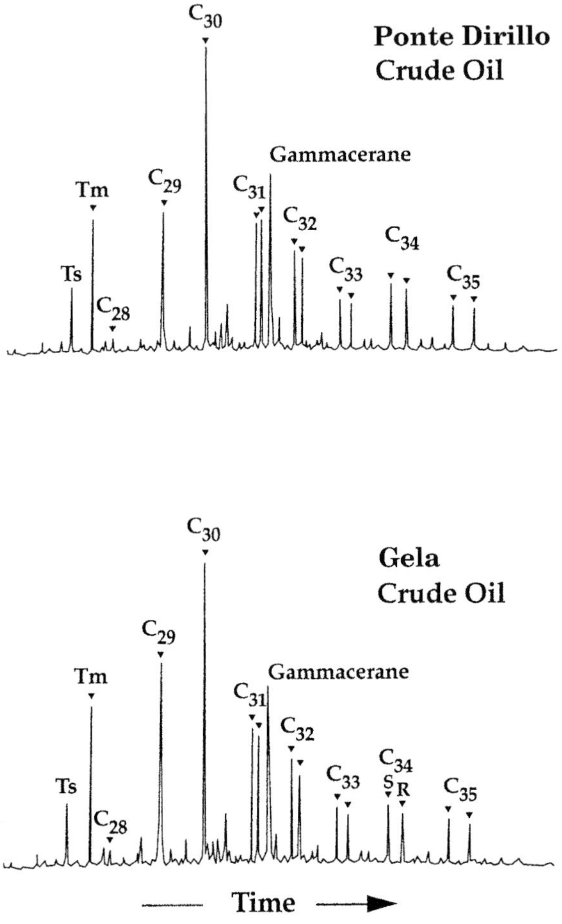

Figure 8–28. From Ocampo et al. (1993); reprinted with permission from American Chemical Society.

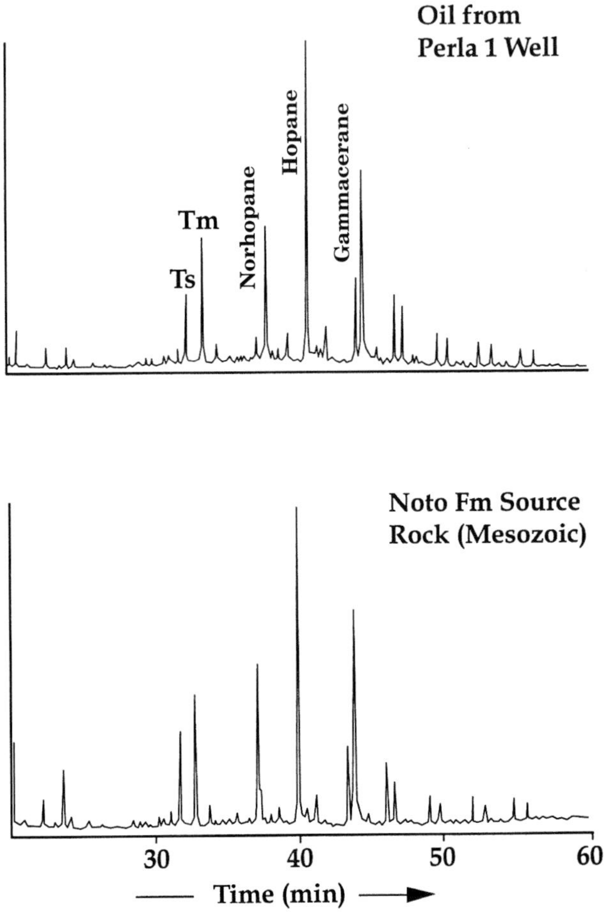

Figure 8–29. From Mattavelli and Novelli (1990); reprinted with permission from AAPG.

Environment and age indicated by oleananes

Oleanane (two major isomers exist) originates from terrestrial flowering plants of Late Cretaceous or, more commonly, Tertiary age and as such is very valuable in correlation problems when deciding whether an oil comes from a source rock that is young or old (Riva et al., 1988).

Example of oleanane

The figure below shows three mass chromatograms (m/z 191.18, 177.16, and 217.20, from top to bottom) for an oil from central Myanmar. The peak marked "o" is a combination of 18α(H) and 18β(H) oleanane. The tallest peak in the m/z 191 mass chromatogram is hopane, and the peaks indicated by solid dots are bicadinanes.

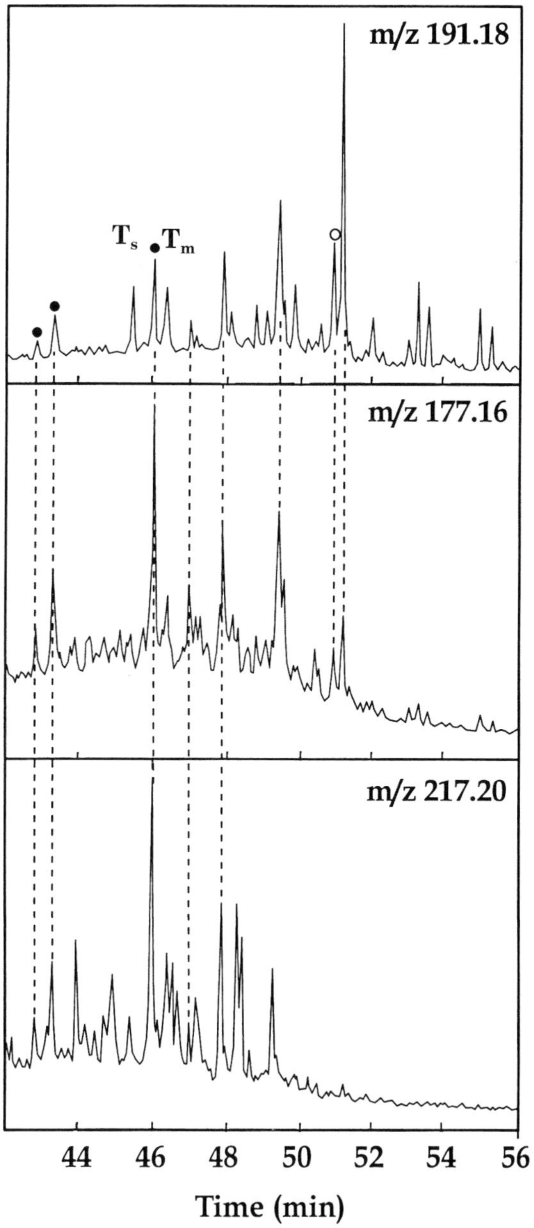

Figure 8–30. From Curiale (1994); reprinted with permission from AAPG.

Environment indicated by bicadinanes

Bicadinanes are among the very few compounds that give substantial peaks in both the m/z 191 and 217 fragment ions. Bicadinane resins are derived from terrestrial plants that evolved in the Tertiary. The primary source plants, dipterocarps, spread slowly through Southeast Asia during the middle to late Tertiary. Bicadinanes are rare in other places and at other times, except from the Tertiary of New Zealand and Australia, where they probably originated from other species (Murray et al., 1993). Bicadinanes are often found together with oleanane.

Figure 8–30 shows bicadinanes in an oil sample from Myanmar. Note that the bicadinane peaks (indicated by solid dots) appear in all three fragment ions.

Environment indicated by C_X and C_Z triterpanes

Two triterpanes, often called "C_Z" and "C_X," are also empirically associated with terrestrial organic matter, but their origin is unknown. They can be seen in Figure 8–26. C_Z has also been called compound X (Philp and Gilbert, 1986) and has been shown to be a diahopane (e.g., Peters and Moldowan, 1993). C_X is probably a neohopane. They often co-occur with other terrestrial markers, such as high C_{29} steranes, oleanane, and bicadinanes, but they can also occur alone.

Example of C_X and C_Z triterpanes

Figure 8–31 shows m/z 191 mass chromatograms of three oils from the Cooper/Eromanga basin of Australia. The highest relative concentrations of C_Z and C_X occur in the oil that appears to have the lowest absolute concentration of other triterpanes (Karmona), as judged by the greatest amount of noise in the baseline. C_Z and C_X (unlabelled but visible to the left of peak "b" in the Karmona sample) are probably more resistant to thermal destruction, and thus increase in relative concentration as other triterpanes are destroyed at high levels of maturity (Waples and Machihara, 1991). C_X often coelutes with T_m (peak "b" in this figure).

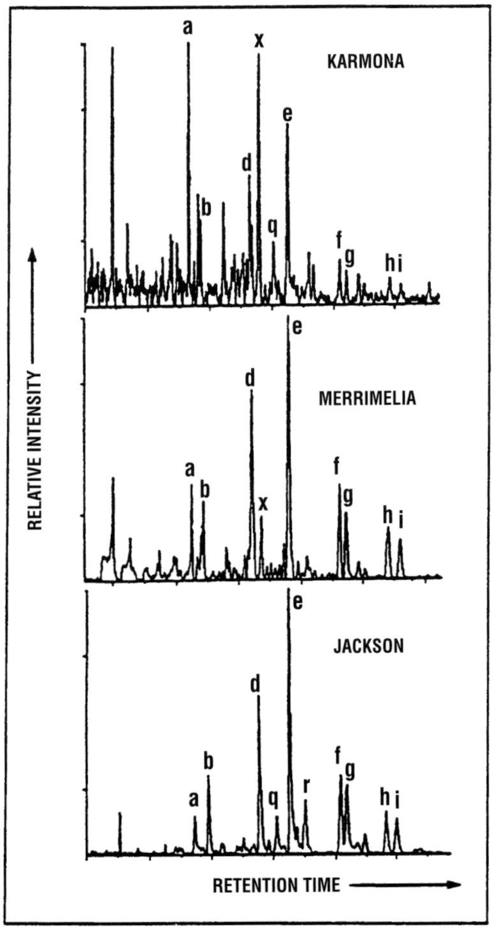

Figure 8–31. From Philp and Gilbert (1986); reprinted with permission from Elsevier.

Environment indicated by 28,30-bisnorhopane

Sometimes in great abundance, 28,30-bisnorhopane has been found in a few important source rocks and related oils (Monterey Formation, Kimmeridge Clay). It is probably of microbial origin. Because bisnorhopane is most common in sulfur-rich environments, its origin may have to do with bacteria that participate in the sulfur cycle. Denis Miiller (personal communication, 1994) notes that in the Monterey oils of southern California, bisnorhopane contents are proportional to sulfur contents.

Example of 28,30-bisnorhopane

The figure below shows the m/z 191 mass fragmentogram of an oil with a high relative concentration of 28,30-bisnorhopane, eluting to the left of norhopane (C_{29} hopane).

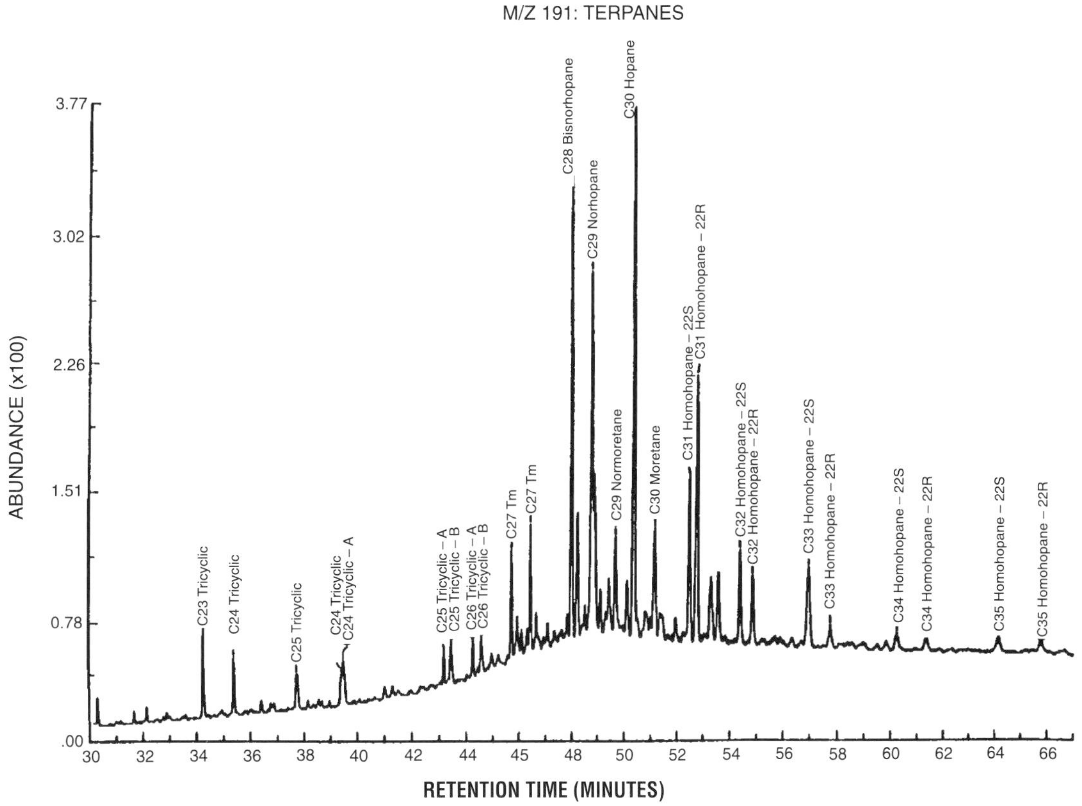

Figure 8–32.

Environments Indicated by Specific Compounds, continued

Environments indicated by tricyclic terpanes

Certain tricyclic terpanes, probably derived from bacteria, *Tasmanites*, or both, are ubiquitous. In most facies they are less abundant than pentacyclic triterpanes such as hopanes but in some cases are dominant. However, because these tricyclics appear to be more stable, tricyclic/pentacyclic ratios also seem to be influenced by maturity, and thus may not always be reliable for correlations. The distribution of individual tricyclics and tetracyclics may also be used for correlation—especially for carbonates, where the tetracyclics are most abundant.

Example of tricyclic terpanes

The figure below shows the m/z 191 fragmentogram for an unusual oil in which the tricyclic terpanes (left side of the chromatogram) strongly dominate the pentacyclics.

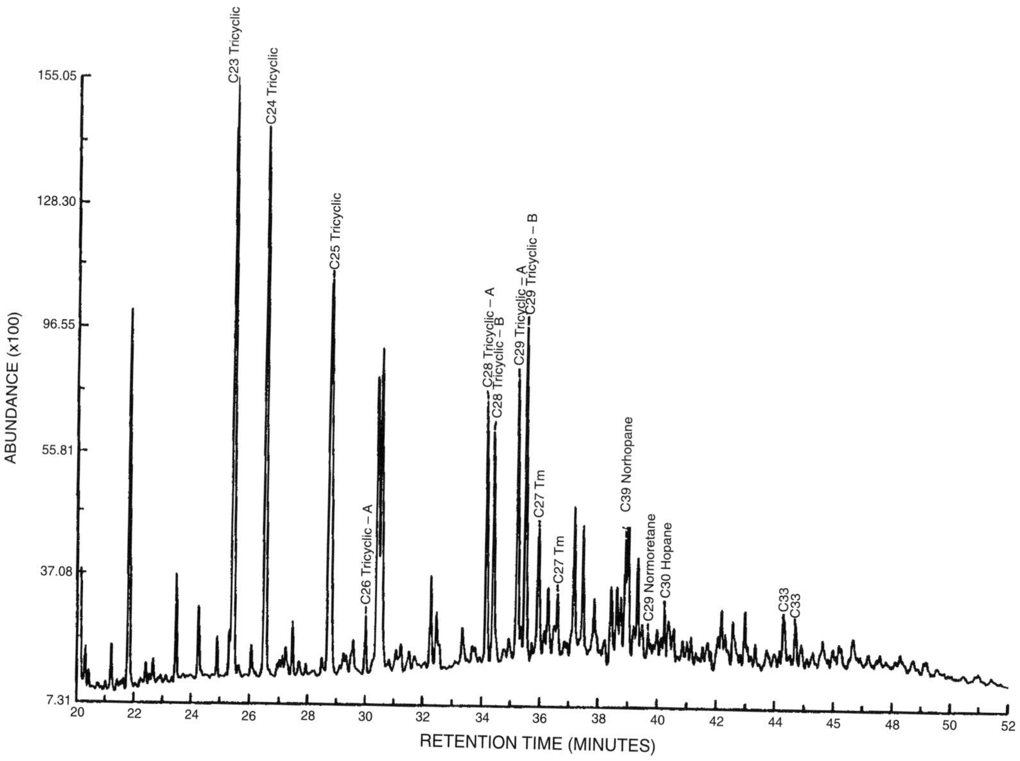

Figure 8–33.

Environments indicated by diterpanes

Other diterpane and sesquiterpane distributions are also used for correlations. Most diterpanes originate from terrestrial resins, but microbial sources are also known (Peters and Moldowan, 1993). Sesquiterpanes derive primarily from terrestrial plant resins. Most resin-derived compounds are of Tertiary or possibly Late Cretaceous age.

Example of diterpanes

The figure below shows m/z 123 mass chromatograms of two oils from northeast China. The differing sesquiterpane distributions show that the oils are not derived from the same source rock facies.

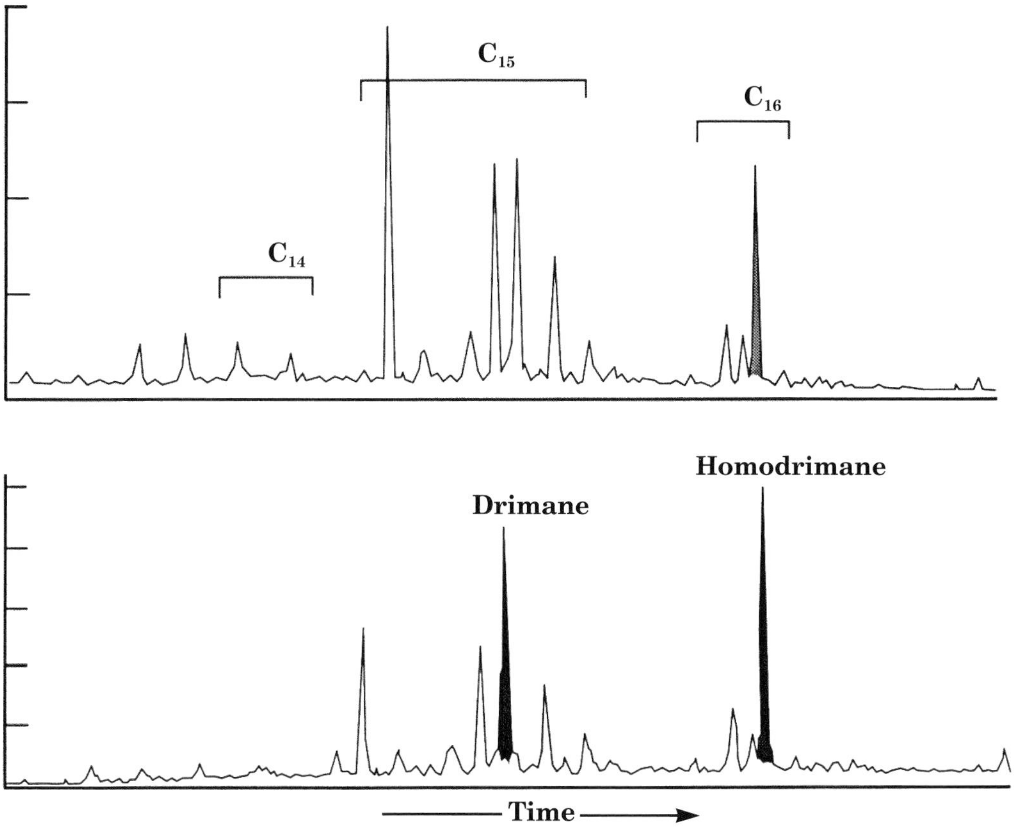

Figure 8–34. From Huang et al. (1992); reprinted with permission from Elsevier.

Environments indicated by carotanes

Carotanes—hydrocarbons derived from photosynthetic organisms and associated with anoxic marine and lacustrine facies—are also used as oil–oil and oil–source rock correlation parameters. Peters et al. (1989) used the occurrence of β-carotane in Devonian rocks (of the U.K. offshore) to suggest a Devonian input to the source composition of the Beatrice oil. These compounds are particularly useful in hypersaline settings. Lacustrine and marine facies containing carotanes can often be distinguished by other indicators, such as the presence of 4-methylsteranes and pristane–phytane ratios less than 1.0 for lacustrine facies.

Carotanes often not analyzed

Unfortunately, many analyses overlook carotanes because these high-molecular-weight compounds elute very late on gas chromatograph columns. To obtain this information, you may have to make special arrangements prior to analysis. Thus, the absence of carotanes in chromatograms may simply indicate that they were not looked for, rather than that they are truly absent.

Environments Indicated by Specific Compounds, continued

Example of carotanes

The figure below shows that carotanes are sometimes so abundant that they can be analyzed using gas chromatography. (More definitive identification and analysis of samples in which carotanes are less abundant can be done using GC/MS.) The gas chromatograms are of the Beatrice Field oil in the Moray Firth (U.K.) and of the extract of a Devonian rock believed to be one of the source contributors.

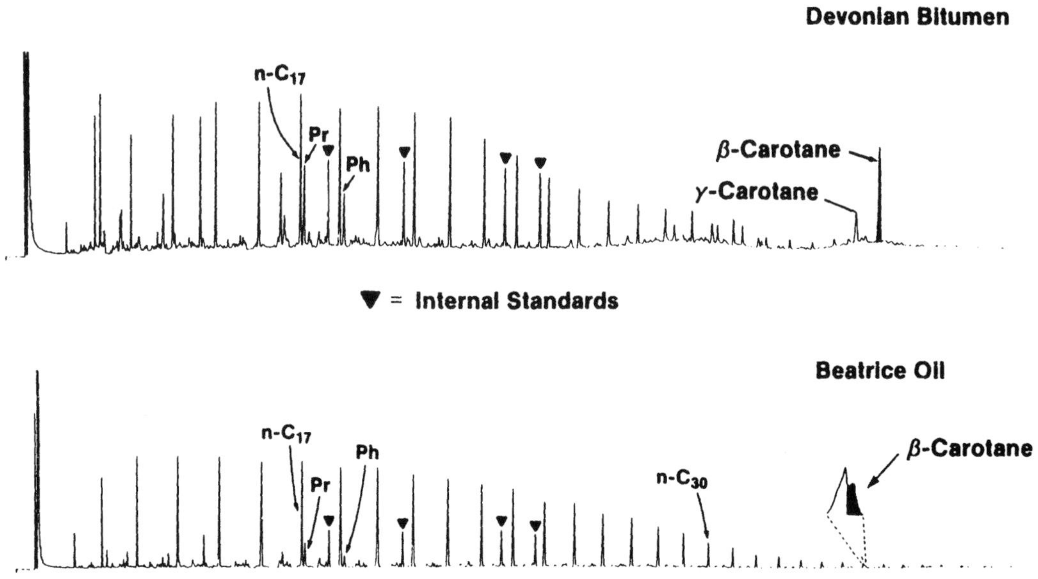

Figure 8–35. Modified from Peters and Moldowan (1993); courtesy Prentice-Hall.

Summary of application of GC/MS to correlation studies

The following table summarizes the application of GC/MS to correlation studies.

This class of compound . . .	May indicate an origin of . . .
C_{27} steranes	Marine organisms (minor amounts occur in nonmarine organisms)
C_{29} steranes	Marine or nonmarine organic matter
C_{30} steranes	Marine or lacustrine organisms
Diasteranes	Clastic environment
Hopanes	Bacteria
Gammacerane	Abnormal salinites
Oleanane	Late Cretaceous or Tertiary terrestrial flowering plants
Bicadinanes	Tertiary terrestrial plants
C_Z and C_X triterpanes	Terrestrial organic matter or environment
28,30-bisnorhopane	Microbes
Tricyclic terpanes	Bacteria or *Tasmanites*
Diterpanes	Terrestrial resins or microbes
Sesquiterpanes	Terrestrial plant resins
Carotanes	Anoxic marine or lacustrine environment

Examples of Correlations Using GC/MS

Example from the North Sea

The figure below demonstrates a typical biomarker-based oil–source correlation from the Central Graben of the North Sea. The oil is reservoired in Upper Cretaceous rocks, whereas the source rock is from the Upper Jurassic. In this case, the sterane ratios indicate that the particular source rock sample analyzed may actually be more mature than the oil. Because of the similarity in maturities, the correlation is easier than for many less mature source rocks. The similarity in distributions of both triterpanes and steranes strongly supports a positive oil–source rock correlation in this instance.

Numbered peaks are hopanes. T_s and T_m are, respectively, 18α(H)-22,29,30-trisnorneohopane and 17α(H)-22,29,30-trisnorhopane. Rearranged and regular steranes are indicated.

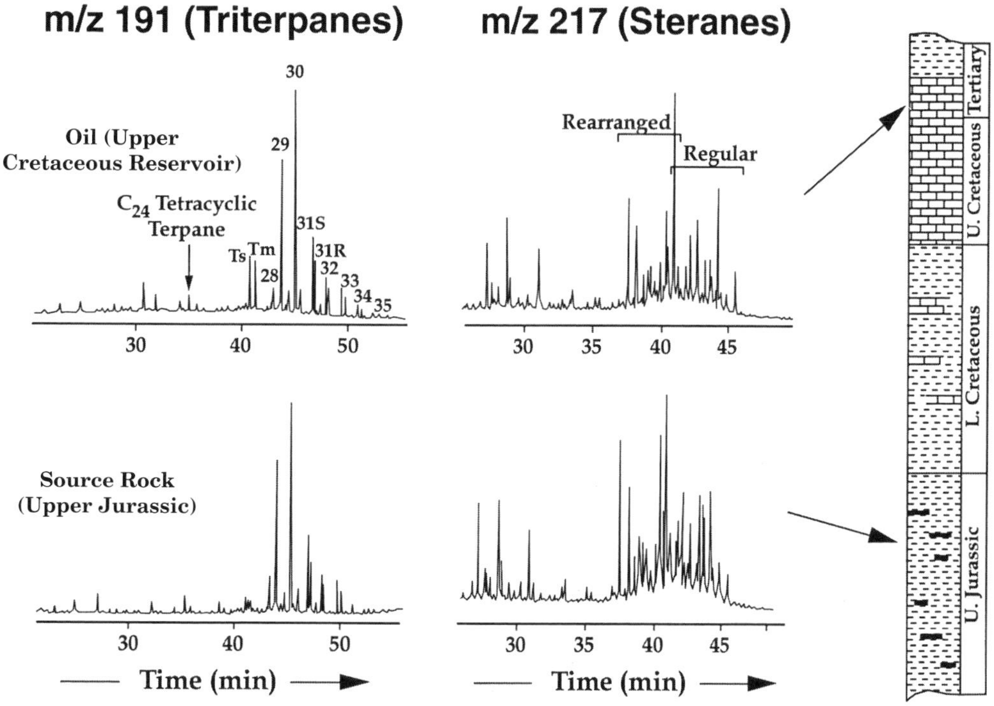

Figure 8–36. From Telnæs and Cooper (1991); reprinted with permission from Elsevier.

Example from the Gulf of Mexico

The figure below (left) shows the sterane distribution for a typical oil from the northern Gulf of Mexico. In this case, the distribution of 5α(H),14α(H),17α(H),20R-cholestanes, -methylcholestanes, and -ethylcholestanes (that is, the C_{27}, C_{28}, and C_{29} regular steranes, respectively) is used as a correlation parameter because it generally remains constant throughout the thermal generation of oil. Oils from this area all have essentially identical sterane distributions (right), suggesting they are related.

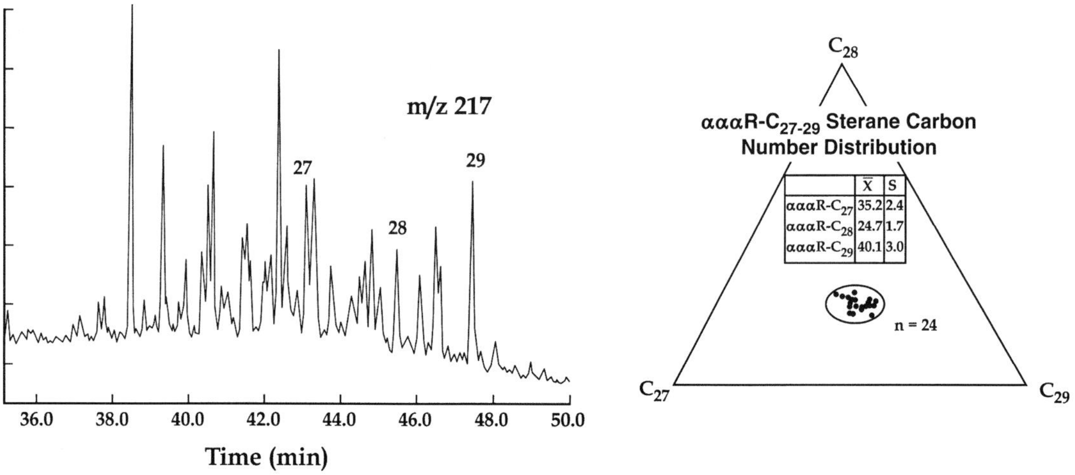

Figure 8–37. Courtesy Unocal.

Example from Oman

Two families of oils sourced from Precambrian rocks in Oman have been identified by Grantham (1986). Figure 8–38 shows the sterane and triterpane fragmentograms for representatives of the two families. Triterpane distributions look very different (bottom figures) but in fact differ mostly in the tricyclic/pentacyclic ratio. This ratio is believed to be affected by maturity as well as by source, so this difference alone does not prove the families are different. The steranes, however, are very different. One family is dominated by the C_{29} regular steranes (top left, peaks E, F, G, H) while the other contains almost exclusively C_{27} regular steranes (top right, peaks A, B, C).

Examples of Correlations Using GC/MS, continued

Example from Oman (continued)

Gas chromatograms (not shown) reveal the presence of a series of X-compounds in both families, diagnostic of Precambrian sources.

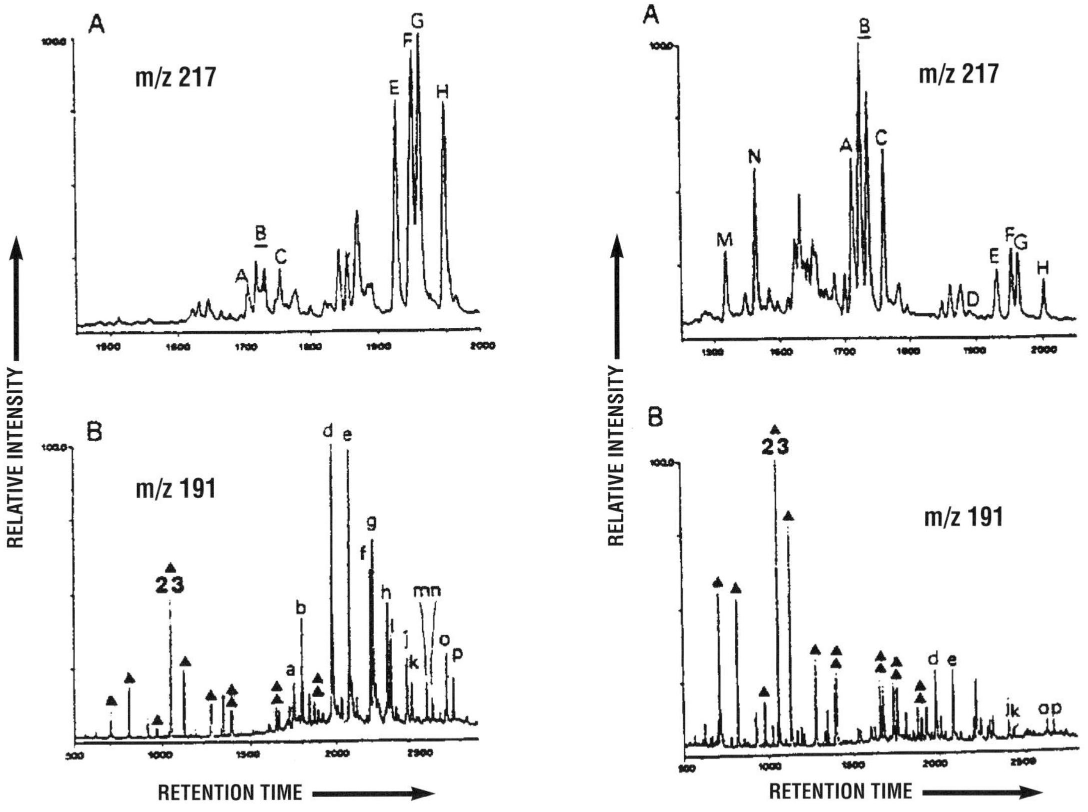

Figure 8–38. From Grantham, (1986); reprinted with permission from Elsevier.

Sterane proportions

This ternary diagram shows relative proportions of $C_{27} - C_{29}$ regular steranes in numerous oils from the two families (A and B). The many oil samples analyzed are very consistent, showing clearly that two distinct families exist. Unfortunately, most correlation problems do not have such clean and neat solutions.

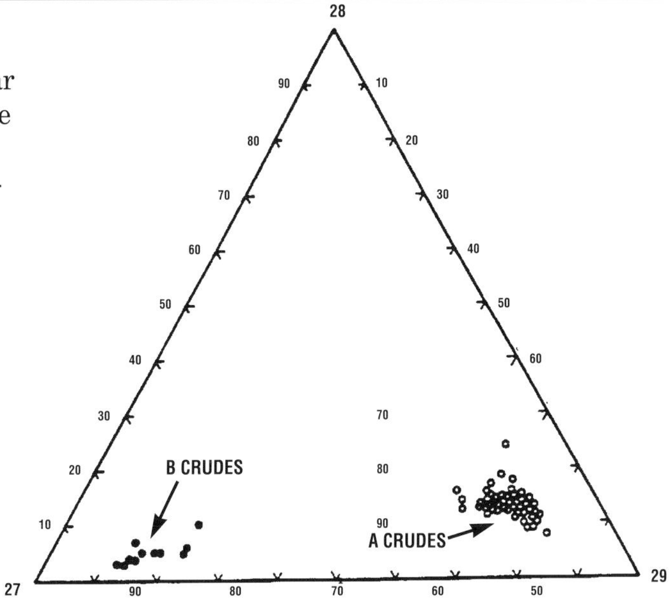

Figure 8–39. From Grantham (1986); reprinted with permission from Elsevier.

Limitations of GC/MS

Effects of maturation and migration

Sterane and triterpane concentrations decrease greatly during oil cracking. Therefore, thermal condensates (light oils) do not normally contain large amounts of steranes and triterpanes. Consequently, steranes and triterpanes are usually of little value in high-maturity oils and condensates. Furthermore, some condensates that do contain steranes and triterpanes may have picked up all or most of them during migration by extraction from the rocks through which they passed (see Waples and Machihara, 1991, for examples and references). Finally, because triterpane and particularly sterane distributions change greatly during maturation, correlations of those biomarkers between an immature source rock and an oil can be very difficult. In such cases a strictly numerical approach, working with peak ratios and relative proportions, can be better than a visual one, since the eye can be unduly influenced by maturity-related differences instead of genetic characteristics.

Biodegradation and sterane distributions

Biodegradation, where severe, can also cause major changes in sterane and triterpane distributions. The ααα-20R steranes (regular steranes with the 20R configuration) are lost selectively during the early stages of severe biodegradation, followed by loss of all ααα steranes. The figure below illustrates this trend. It shows the m/z 217.2 mass chromatograms of three oils from central Myanmar in successive stages of biodegradation, ranging from not degraded (top) to extremely degraded (bottom). The severely degraded oil has lost almost all of its regular steranes, with greater loss of 20R than 20S. Gas chromatograms of these three oils are shown in Figure 8–20.

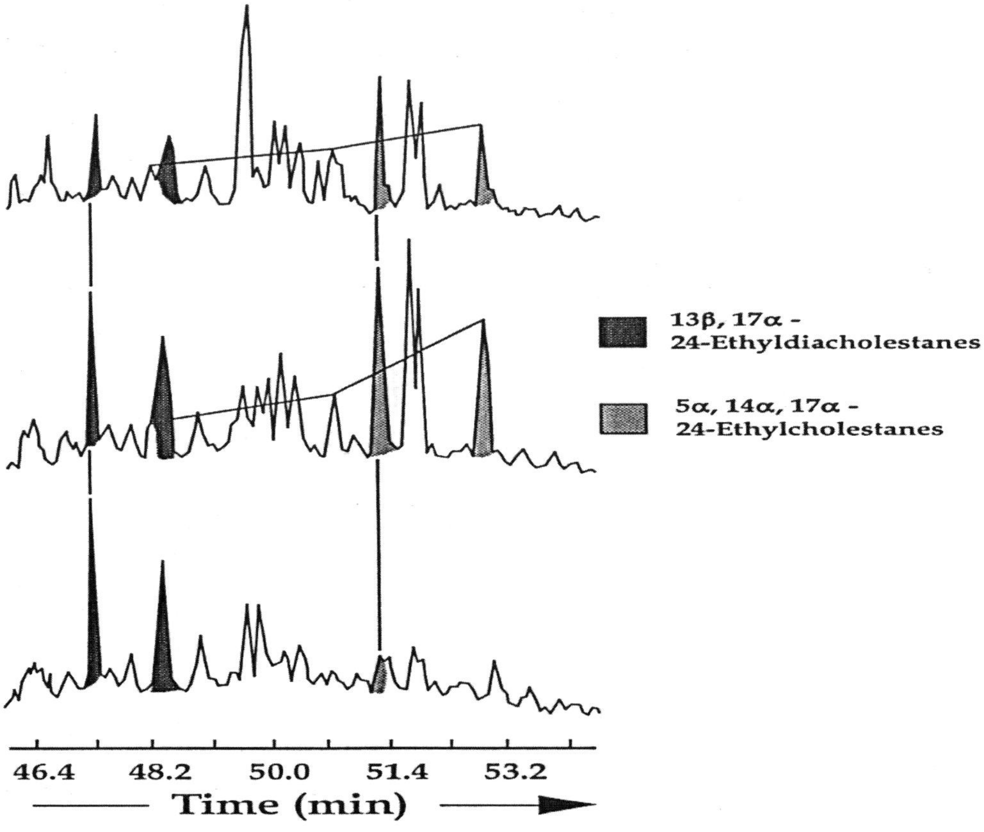

Figure 8–40. From Curiale (1994); reprinted with permission from AAPG.

Biodegradation and hopane distribution

Although hopane distributions are well known to change during extreme biodegradation, the causes for these changes are controversial and poorly understood. At very high levels of biodegradation, hopanes and moretanes disappear. In their place appear series of demethylated hopanes and moretanes (25-norhopanes and 25-normoretanes). Although workers originally believed the regular hopanes and moretanes were converted to their demethylated forms by bacterial removal of a single methyl group, that explanation has been disputed. Some workers today believe that the hopanes and moretanes simply disappear, and their disappearance merely reveals pre-existing series of less abundant demethylated species that could not be seen in the presence of regular hopanes and moretanes.

The figure below shows an example of the regular hopane and moretane series in a non-degraded oil (top), as shown in the m/z 191 mass chromatogram, compared to the series of demethylated hopanes and moretanes in a heavily biodegraded oil (bottom), revealed in the m/z 177 mass chromatogram.

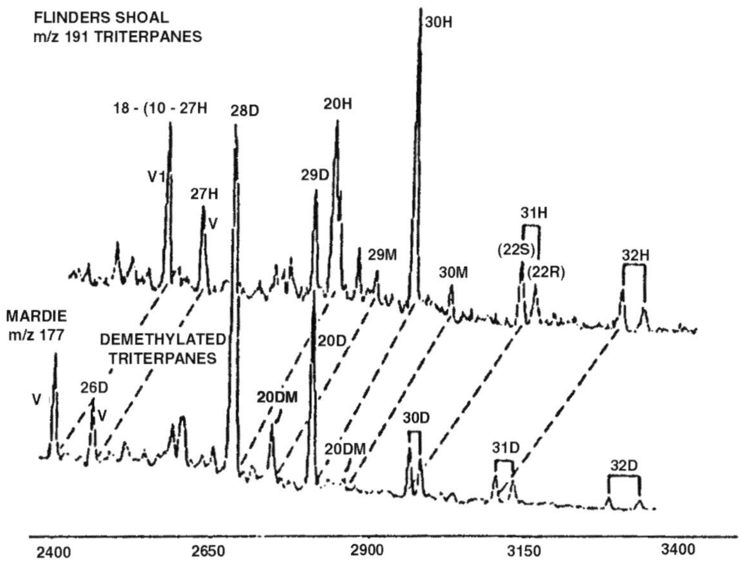

Figure 8–41. From Volkman et al. (1983); reprinted with permission from Elsevier.

Another hopane distribution example

The figure below, which shows m/z 191 mass chromatograms of two genetically related oils from Papua New Guinea, gives another example of a major difference in hopane distribution. This difference could erroneously be considered genetic but is actually an unusual result of severe biodegradation. The top oil, recovered from a drill-stem test and not biodegraded, contains a full suite of triterpanes. The bottom seep oil, in contrast, is heavily biodegraded (gravity <15° API), resulting in selective loss of the C_{30} hopane and homohopanes. The C_{29} hopane is either unaffected or only slightly reduced in concentration. T_m, T_s, moretanes, and C_Z (indicated with *) also appear unaffected at this level of biodegradation.

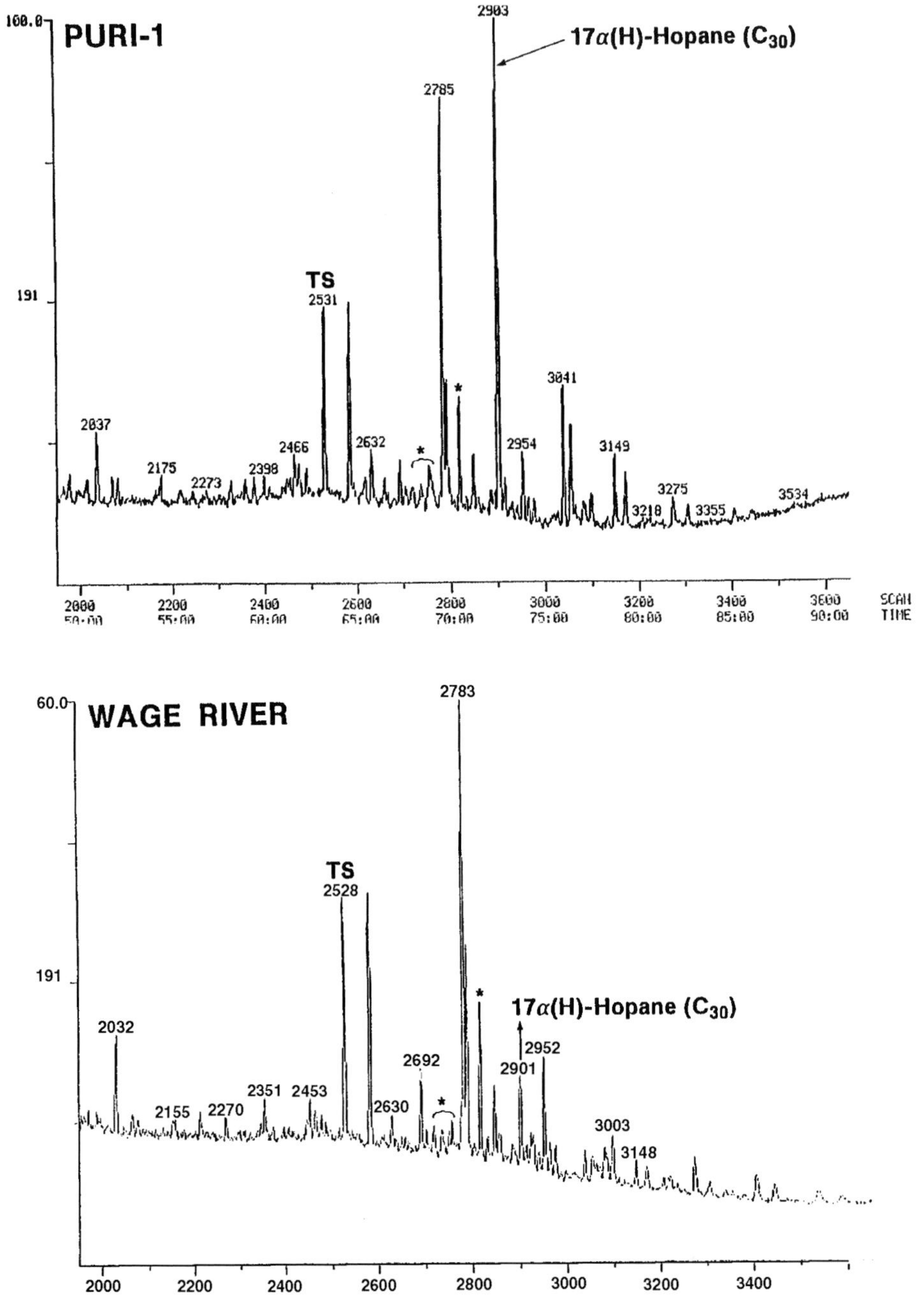

Figure 8–42.

Limitations of GC/MS, continued

Internal standards

Internal standards can appear in GC/MS data as well as in gas chromatograms. The figure below shows m/z 191 (top) and 217 (bottom) mass chromatograms for a seep oil from Papua New Guinea. The three peaks in the top chromatogram to the left of T_s come from the internal standard, which was supposed to be a single compound but is actually a mixture (probably of various isomers of the same compound). The internal standard was unlabelled on this mass chromatogram and, as such, poses a serious risk even for experienced interpreters since the internal standard peaks might be thought to represent indigenous compounds.

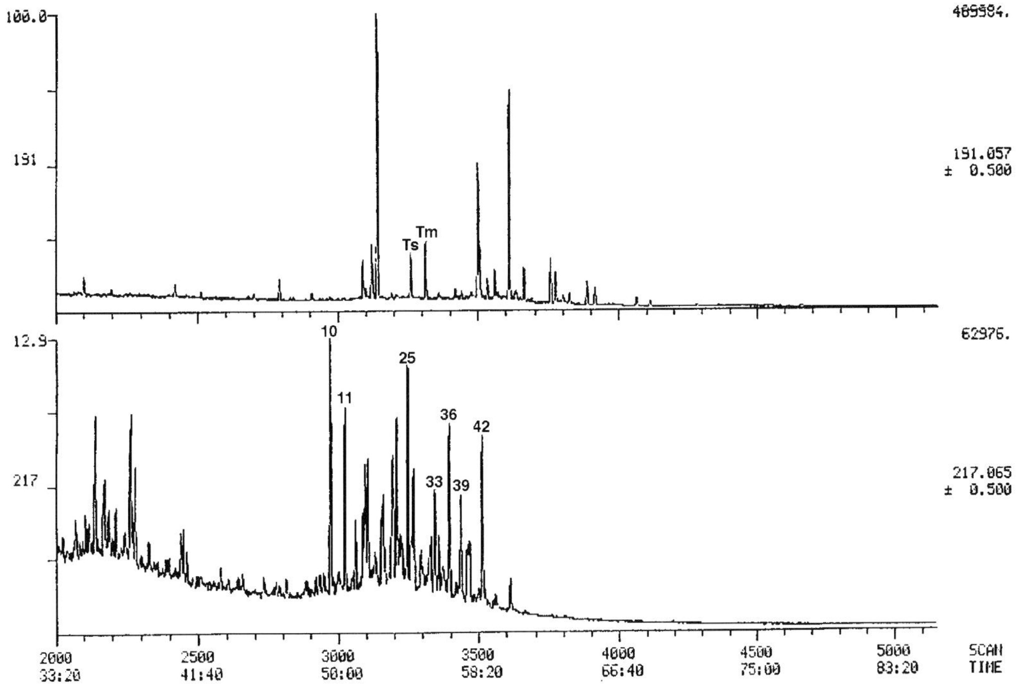

Figure 8–43.

For additional information

Additional technical information on GC/MS techniques is available in Waples and Machihara (1991) and Peters and Moldowan (1993).

Pyrolysis–Gas Chromatography

What is pyrolysis–gas chromatography (Py-GC)?

When kerogen is pyrolyzed and the products are analyzed by gas chromatography, those products can be similar to those present in oils. One can compare the pyrolysis products either with the products of natural generation (oil) or with the products of laboratory pyrolysis of the asphaltenes from oils. Both comparisons are useful for oil–source rock correlations. Oil–oil correlations can also be carried out by comparing products of asphaltene pyrolysis from the various oils.

Dry pyrolysis is simpler

Two different pyrolysis techniques can be employed. Dry Rock-Eval pyrolysis is technically simpler but yields products rather different from those in natural systems. It is therefore more difficult and risky to use as a detailed correlation tool.

Hydrous pyrolysis is better

In contrast, hydrous pyrolysis techniques, where source rock candidates are artificially matured at relatively high temperatures in the presence of liquid water, can be very helpful in correlating oils to source rocks since it yields products that are fairly similar to those obtained by natural maturation. Hydrous pyrolysis experiments are also particularly helpful when only immature source rock candidates are available. These source rocks can be "matured" experimentally, and the resulting expelled "oil" can be compared to other oils.

Example

The figure below shows sterane m/z 217 mass fragmentograms of an immature rock extract (bottom left), a hydrous pyrolyzate (top right), and the correlatable oil (bottom right). The carbon-number distribution changes during pyrolysis, indicating a fundamental difference in composition between the immature extract and the kerogen. The pyrolyzate, however, is molecularly very similar to the oil.

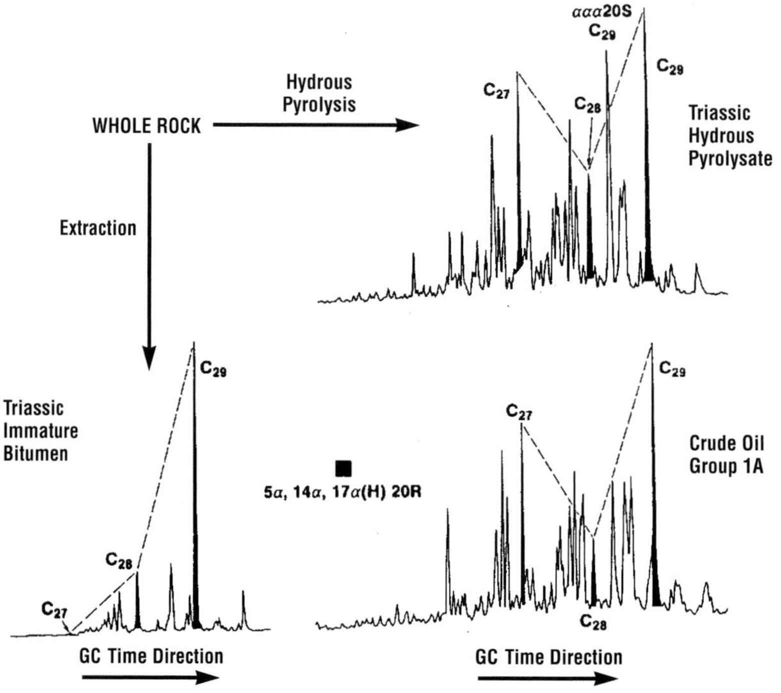

Figure 8–44. Modified from Moldowan et al. (1992); courtesy AAPG.

Data Obtained by High-Performance Liquid Chromatography

What is HPLC? Porphyrins in crude oil are large, complex molecules derived primarily from chlorophyll and related compounds. They are found in virtually all oils and rock extracts, with the exception of condensates that have lost their heavy ends. Porphyrins are separated by HPLC and can be analyzed by several different methods.

Example The figure below shows a comparison of nickel porphyrin distributions for a source rock extract (top) and an oil (bottom) from southern Sicily. The similar porphyrin distributions for the oil and the source rock extract suggest a plausible positive correlation, which in this case was supported by other geochemical data.

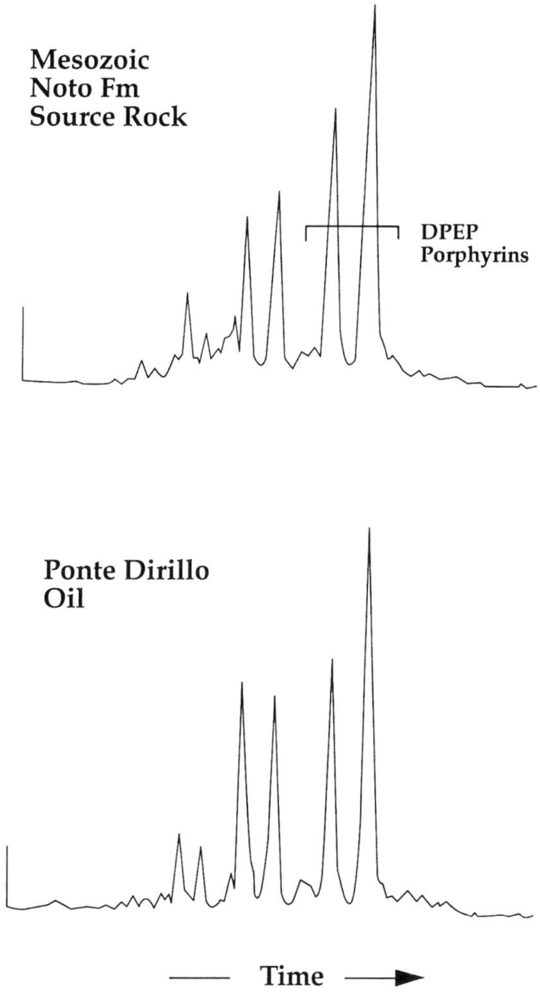

Figure 8–45. From Ocampo et al. (1993); reprinted by permission from American Chemical Society.

Section C
Case Histories

Introduction

The techniques discussed and illustrated in the previous sections have been used by many workers in many basins around the world. In this section, we illustrate two case histories each of oil–oil and oil–source rock correlation, again emphasizing two critical features of successful correlations.

1. Use genetic correlative features, that is, features that result from original source rock input and not from secondary processes such as maturation, migration, or biodegradation.
2. Use a diverse set of correlation criteria from among the arsenal of available tools to avoid misinterpretations arising from the use of a single parameter.

The four case histories in this section are from published literature of the past fifteen years. Only selected aspects of the full studies are discussed here; refer to the original literature for details.

In this section

There are four case histories in this section.

Case History 1: Oil–Oil Correlation in the Norwegian Sector, North Sea

Introduction

Commercial oil reserves were discovered in the Norwegian sector of the North Sea more than twenty years ago. Oil–oil and oil–source rock correlations are now reasonably well known and constrained for this region. Early efforts at correlating oils in this area were documented by Phillips Petroleum Co. workers (Hughes et al., 1985) following examination of 30 oils from eight fields. In addition to performing conventional compound-fraction separations and GC and GC/MS analyses, those workers also examined sulfur compound distributions, sulfur and nitrogen contents, and carbon isotope ratios. Their integrated study provides a good example of a modern oil–oil correlation.

Initial evidence suggests several oil families

The eight fields are in the Central Graben of the North Sea, where the oils occur in Cretaceous and Jurassic reservoirs at 2800–3500 m true vertical depth. The source is presumed to be Upper Jurassic mudstones, based on a correlation of Ekofisk oil to Kimmeridgian source rocks (van den Bark and Thomas, 1980). Initial examination of bulk geochemical parameters in the 30 oils indicated wide compositional variation, as illustrated in the percent sulfur vs. API gravity plot below. Similar variability exists in the nitrogen concentrations and in the distribution of saturated hydrocarbons, aromatic hydrocarbons, NSO, and asphaltene fractions (not shown). Using these data alone, we might conclude that several source-distinctive families exist.

The figure shows data for a set of oils from eight fields in the Norwegian sector of the North Sea. The left figure is concentration of sulfur in oil plotted against API gravity, showing a trend of decreasing sulfur content with increasing gravity. Note that the Ekofisk and Eldfisk field oils show only small ranges in sulfur content and gravity. The right figure shows $\alpha\alpha\alpha$-20S/(20S+20R) ratios plotted for each of the eight fields. This wide range extends from a decidedly marginally mature oil (in Hod field) to oils in which this parameter has reached equilibrium.

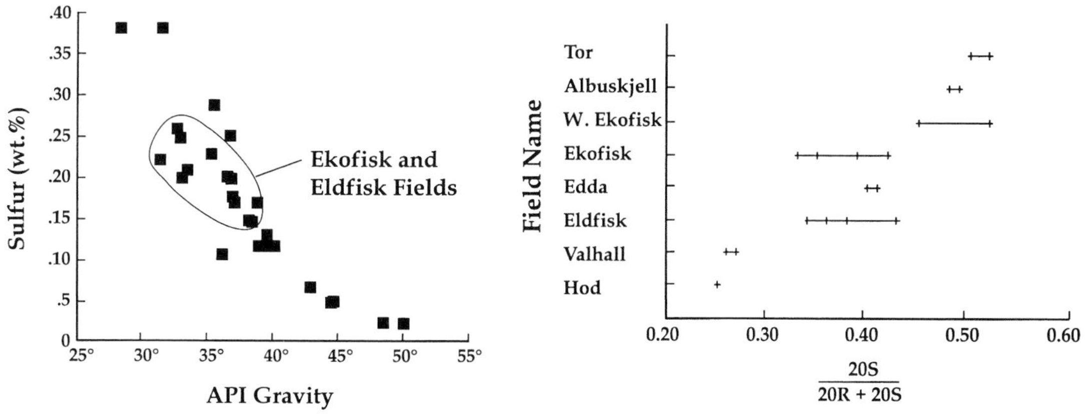

Figure 8–46. From Hughes et al. (1985); reprinted with permission from Graham and Trotman.

Oil–Oil Correlation in the Norwegian Sector, North Sea, continued

Further evidence shows oils are similar

Examination of correlation parameters that are more specifically source distinctive, however, suggests that the variations within the set of oils are actually minor. The distribution of C_{27}-C_{29} regular steranes shows that most of the oils cluster rather tightly, with approximately equal concentrations of each homolog (top figure, below). Furthermore, Hughes et al. (1985) report that $\delta^{13}C$ values for the oils range from –28.7 ‰ to –26.8 ‰, with 28 of the 30 oils falling in the –28.3 ‰ to –27.1 ‰ range. Finally, terpane distributions show that many of the oils are very similar to one another (bottom figure, below).

The ternary diagram (top) shows the distribution of ααα-20R-steranes by carbon number. The oval encloses all of the samples. The small range for most of the samples within the oval suggests that a single organic source facies could be responsible for most of the oils. In the m/z 191 mass chromatograms (bottom) for a typical Ekofisk and Eldfisk oil, note the peak-to-peak similarity of these oils of similar maturity.

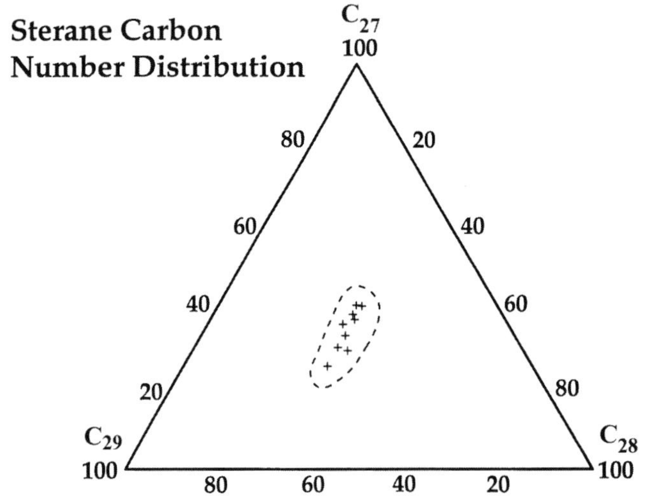

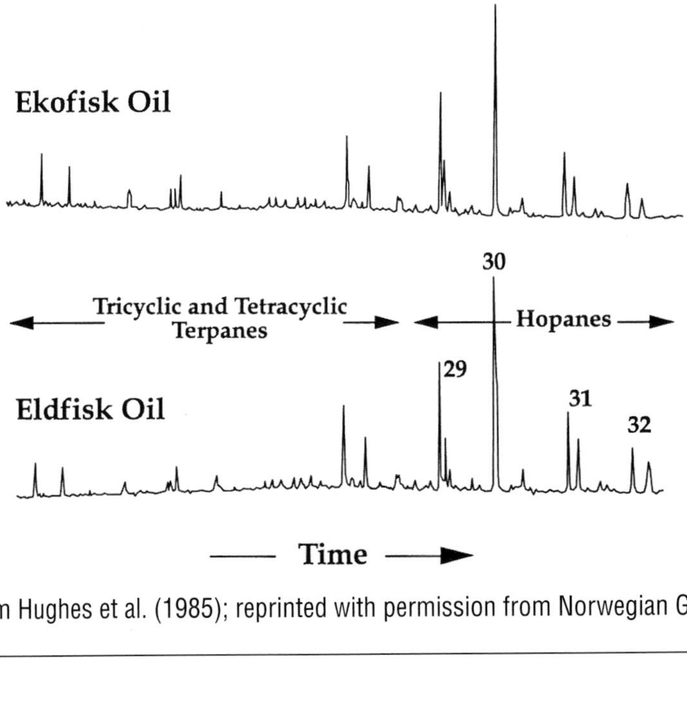

Figure 8–47. From Hughes et al. (1985); reprinted with permission from Norwegian Geological Society.

Conclusions drawn from the correlation study

The wide variation in bulk parameters, in contrast to the similarity in certain source-distinctive parameters, suggested to Hughes et al. (1985) that nongenetic effects could be controlling the bulk geochemical data. Detailed molecular analyses were then used to establish that the variation in bulk parameters arises from differences in thermal maturity among these samples. Figure 8–46 shows that the $\alpha\alpha\alpha$-20R/(20R+20S)-24-ethylcholestane ratio ranges from 0.25 to equilibrium values of 0.50–0.55 for the oils from these eight fields but is reasonably constant within any single field. This finding is geologically significant since oil maturity increases from south to north in the Norwegian sector of the North Sea. This observation in turn suggests northward migration of oil from a progressively maturing source rock to the south.

The maturity ordering proposed by Hughes et al. (1985) in Figure 8–46 is supported by numerous other molecular indices and helps explain the wide variability in bulk parameters. For example, the percent sulfur vs. API gravity trend may exist because the most mature oils have low sulfur contents and high gravities. Indeed, comparing the molecular data with these bulk parameters indicates the maturity trend in the figure is reflected in the sulfur-gravity trend, although some minor source-related differences are present in the sample set. The authors provide further evidence of their conclusions through the use of principal components analysis, which discriminates between source- and maturity-dependent parameters.

What this case study illustrates

This case study illustrates the importance of emphasizing source-distinctive correlation parameters as well as the value of using many types of geochemical data. Without this wide range of applicable geochemical parameters, the source-related similarities in these oils might have been unappreciated and the various oils interpreted as arising from entirely different source units.

Case History 2: Oil–Oil Correlation in the Brazilian Offshore Basins

Introduction

The data generated when conducting a fully integrated oil–oil correlation also help determine the depositional setting of the source(s) for the oil(s). It is often possible to predict the source of an oil from its chemical composition, as illustrated by this case study. In addition, this example also presents an early approach to the use of compound concentrations (instead of biomarker ratios) as correlation parameters.

Geological setting

The offshore margin of Brazil contains oil reserves in Cretaceous and lower Tertiary reservoirs within several large basins. These basins, the product of rifting of Africa from South America in the Early Cretaceous, contain several source units representing depositional settings ranging from lacustrine to deltaic to marine.

The figure below is a generalized west–east cross section from the Brazilian continental margin, with the coastline approximately at the western margin. Note the wide range of depositional settings, corresponding to the wide range of potential source rocks for the five source-distinctive groups of oils in these marginal basins.

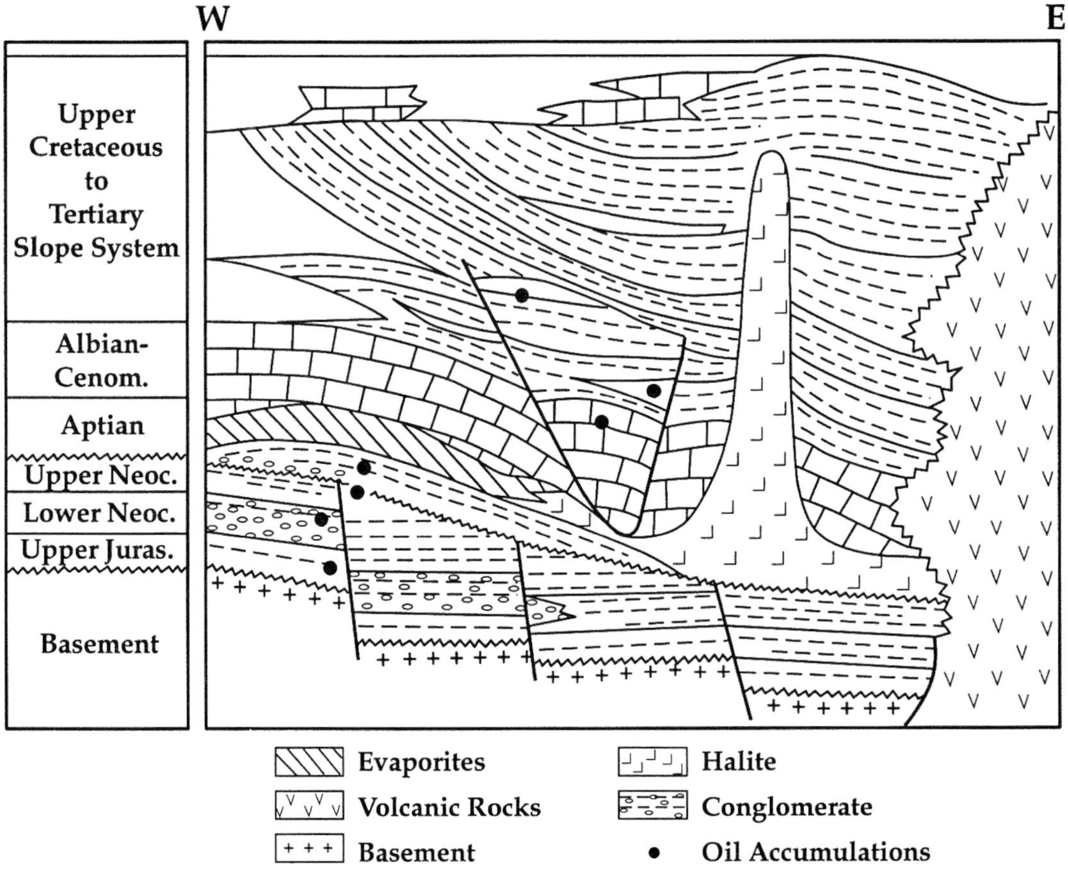

Figure 8–48. From Mello et al. (1988a); reprinted with permission from Marine and Petroleum Geology.

Oil–Oil Correlation in the Brazilian Offshore Basins, continued

Parameters measured

To understand the source families responsible for the oils on the Brazilian margin, Mello et al. (1988a) measured numerous elemental, isotopic, and molecular characteristics for about 50 oils; 16 of these were examined using techniques of semiquantitative biomarker analysis. Their study is an excellent example of the importance of using diversified analytical methods. A partial list of the parameters measured includes $\delta^{13}C$ of the whole oil; sulfur content; vanadium–nickel ratio; compound-class distribution; pristane–phytane ratio; various biomarker ratios involving diasteranes, methylsteranes, tricyclic terpanes, bisnorhopane, and gammacerane; and semiquantitative concentration data for various isoprenoids, β-carotane, selected steranes, hopanes, and oleanane. This set of parameters was then used to classify the oils into five source-distinctive groups. No one or two correlative parameters could establish these groupings—only through the combined use of several elemental, isotopic, and molecular parameters could the correlations be made and depositional settings inferred.

Group I oils, freshwater lacustrine setting

For illustrative purposes, we discuss here differences in the characteristics of group I and group IV oils (Mello et al., 1988a). The group I oils are very low in sulfur (<0.01%) and vanadium–nickel ratio (<0.06) and have $\delta^{13}C$ values more negative than –28.0 ‰. Concentrations of diasteranes, steranes, 4-methylsteranes, and gammacerane are low; *n*-propylcholestanes (C_{30} steranes) are absent. A distinctive odd-carbon *n*-alkane dominance and a waxy appearance to the gas chromatogram of these oils is evident. These and other features suggest a freshwater lacustrine depositional setting.

The figures below are typical gas chromatograms of saturated hydrocarbons for group I (left) and group IV (right) oils from the Brazilian continental margin. Note the many source-distinctive differences, including pristane–phytane ratio and the dominance of waxy *n*-alkanes in the group I oil. Supplemental numerical data indicate these differences extend to the sulfur concentration, the vanadium–nickel ratio, and the $\delta^{13}C$ value.

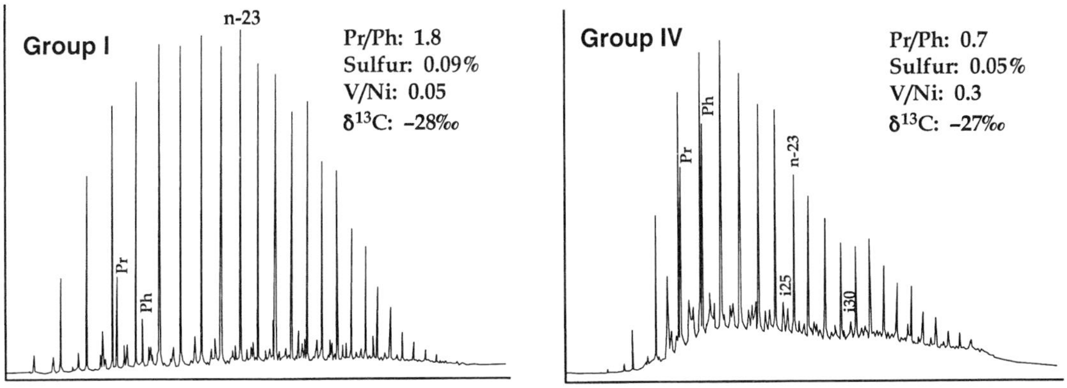

Figure 8–49. From Mello et al. (1988a); reprinted with permission from Marine and Petroleum Geology.

Group I and group IV oils contrasted

In contrast to group I oil, group IV oils contain significantly higher levels of sulfur, higher vanadium–nickel, less negative $\delta^{13}C$ ratios, and lower wax contents (see Figure 8–49). Sterane concentrations are high, as are concentrations of *n*-propylcholestanes. In addition, tricyclic and tetracyclic terpanes are present in relatively higher concentration in group IV oils, and the homohopane distribution is irregular, with high C_{33}.

The figures below are typical m/z 191 mass chromatograms for group I (top) and group IV (bottom) oils from the Brazilian continental margin, showing the differences in terpane distributions. A marine carbonate depositional setting for the source of group IV oils is reflected in the high abundance of tricyclic and tetracyclic terpanes, in the high C_{33} homohopane concentration, and in the low wax content.

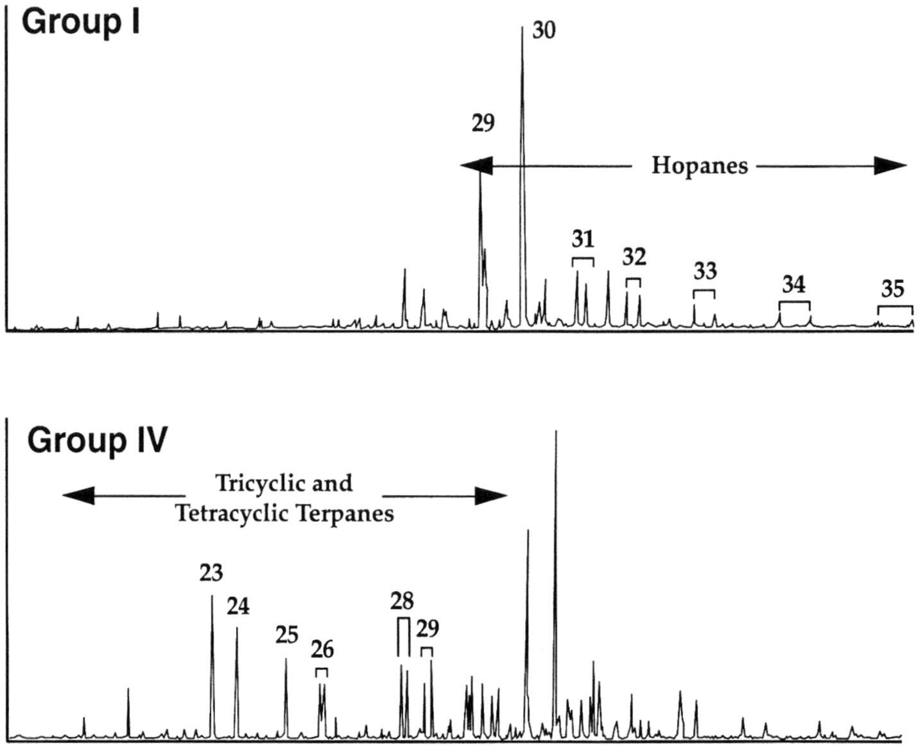

Figure 8–50. From Mello et al. (1988a); reprinted with permission from Marine and Petroleum Geology.

Geological conclusions

These source-distinctive correlational groupings are supported by geographical and geological considerations. The group I oils occur in the central Brazilian basins in sandstone reservoirs of mid-Cretaceous age juxtaposed with coeval lacustrine source rocks. In contrast, group IV oils occur in the northernmost basins in Upper Cretaceous and lower Tertiary reservoirs.

What this case study illustrates

This case study demonstrates the utility of compound concentration data and emphasizes the use of routine oil–oil correlation data in predicting the depositional setting of oils. Later efforts have confirmed several of these predictions using similar correlation tools on prospective source rocks in the region (Mello et al., 1988b). The resulting oil–source rock correlations are supported by a similarly wide range of analytical approaches.

Case History 3: Oil–Source Rock Correlation in the Zala Basin, Hungary

Introduction

The Zala basin, part of the Pannonian basin system in western Hungary, contains oils reservoired in Triassic through Miocene rocks. Clayton and Koncz (1994) examined 21 oil samples and 26 core samples from this basin to determine the number of oil families and the presence of source rocks, and to propose oil-source correlations. In this case study we discuss one of those correlations.

Geological setting

The Zala basin consists of various Eocene fault blocks, unconformably overlain by a Middle and Upper Miocene section and underlain by Upper Cretaceous and Triassic rocks.

The figure below includes a stratigraphic section (left) of the Zala basin. The Nagylengyel oils are reservoired in Upper Cretaceous and underlying Upper Triassic rocks. A generalized west-to-east stratigraphic section across the Zala basin is shown on the right. Vertical lines are well-bore ties, beginning with the Re-1 well on the west and including three wells of the Szilvágy field and three wells of the Nagylengyel field.

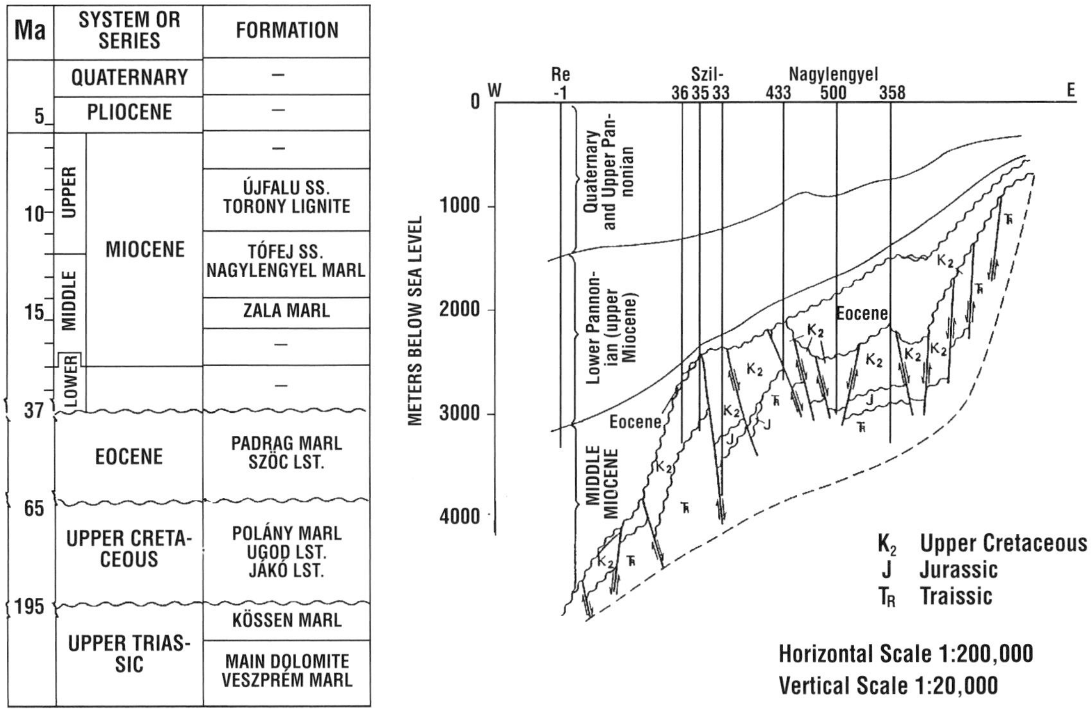

Figure 8–51. Modified from Clayton and Koncz (1994); reprinted with permission from AAPG.

Oil–Source Rock Correlation in the Zala Basin, Hungary, continued

Characteristics of NL oils

The 21 oils can be grouped into at least three families, corresponding roughly to existing fields: the Nagylengyel (NL), Szentgyörgyvölgy (Szen), and Szilvágy (Szil). Our discussion concerns the characteristics and source of the NL oils, which, on the basis of isotopic and molecular criteria (e.g., lack of oleananes), are distinct from the Szen and Szil families. The NL family, reservoired in Upper Cretaceous and Triassic rocks, is characterized by a low pristane–phytane ratio, significant amounts of at least one C_{24} tetracyclic terpane, and high concentrations of vanadium and nickel. In general, these characteristics suggest a carbonate-rich source rock. Its age, inferred from the absence of oleanane in the oils, may be older than Late Cretaceous, although oleanane is often absent in carbonates due to lack of terrestrial input.

After establishing the NL oils as a single type, Clayton and Koncz (1994) determined the source potential for the available sedimentary section using 26 core samples and attempted to correlate the NL oils to each of the possible sources. Just as the first screening step for the oil–oil correlation involved $\delta^{13}C$ values of the aliphatic and aromatic hydrocarbons, the first screening step for the oil–source rock correlation effort involved comparing $\delta^{13}C$ of the whole oils and bitumens from the source candidates. Their results indicate that two potential sources [the Upper Triassic Kössen Marl and the Sarmatian (middle Miocene) shales] have very similar $\delta^{13}C$ values. When these carbon isotope data are combined with oleanane–hopane ratios and C_{27}–C_{29} sterane distributions, cluster analysis comparison supports a dominantly Upper Triassic source for the NL oils, with possibly a minor contribution from the Sarmatian (middle Miocene) shales.

The figures below show isotope data used to support oil–oil and oil–source rock correlations for the NL oils of the Zala basin. The Sofer plot (left) distinguishes the NL oils from the Szil and Szen types, since the NL oils are significantly lighter isotopically. The data on the right (including data compiled by Koncz, 1990) show that only the Upper Triassic and Sarmatian (middle Miocene) units are isotopically similar to the NL oils.

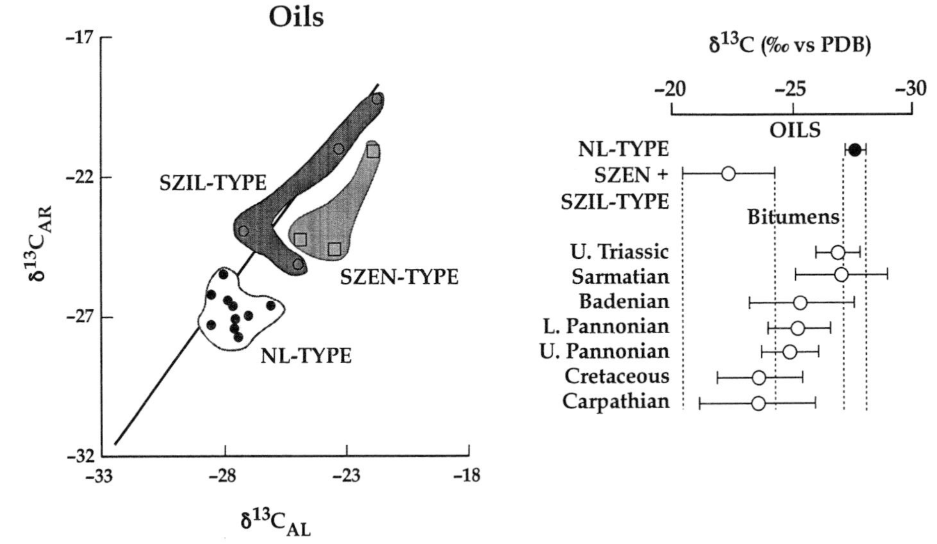

Figure 8–52. From Clayton & Koncz (1994); reprinted with permission from AAPG.

Oil–Source Rock Correlation in the Zala Basin, Hungary, continued

Using geological data to refine the correlation

The geological data may refine this oil–source rock correlation still further. As indicated in Figure 8–52, an Upper Triassic (Kössen Marl) source for the NL oil family is consistent with the occurrence of NL oils in Triassic and Upper Cretaceous reservoirs. In contrast, down-section (and, in some cases, down-structure) migration from a middle Miocene source into an Upper Triassic reservoir, as would be necessary to justify a significant middle Miocene contribution to the NL oil family, is clearly difficult. Furthermore, total organic carbon values and hydrogen indices of the Kössen Marl are greater than those of the Sarmatian (middle Miocene) shales by factors of six and three, respectively, indicating the marl is a much better source unit. Finally, the characteristics of the NL oils are consistent with a source from marlstone, and modeling results presented by Clayton and Koncz (1994) suggest that maturation and timing of migration of Kössen-sourced oil is most consistent with placement in Upper Triassic reservoirs.

What this case study illustrates

From this case study, we see that any valid oil–source rock correlation must satisfy the following requirements:

1 Be preceded by a successful oil–oil correlation.
2. A prior study to establish which sedimentary units in the basin are oil source rocks or possess source rock potential.
3. Have at least two of the three major groups of geochemical parameters (elemental, isotopic, molecular) support the positive correlation before it can be considered valid. (In the case of the NL oils, isotopic and molecular data both support the correlation.)
4. Be geologically reasonable, with a migration pathway available between source and reservoir at the time migration occurred.

Case History 4: Oil–Source Rock Correlation in the West Siberian Basin

Introduction

Several Russian geoscientists as well as geochemists in the United States and Europe have addressed the question of the source(s) of oils in the prolific West Siberian basin. Peters et al. (1994) present the results of a fully integrated oil–oil and oil–source rock correlation study involving numerous oils and possible source rocks in the basin. This case study examines the relationship between one of the West Siberian Basin oil families and its suggested source rock.

Geological setting

The West Siberian basin, located in central Russia, is approximately bisected north–south by the Ob River. The figure below is a stratigraphic section of the basin. Oils are reservoired throughout the section but are concentrated in the Lower Cretaceous and Upper Jurassic.

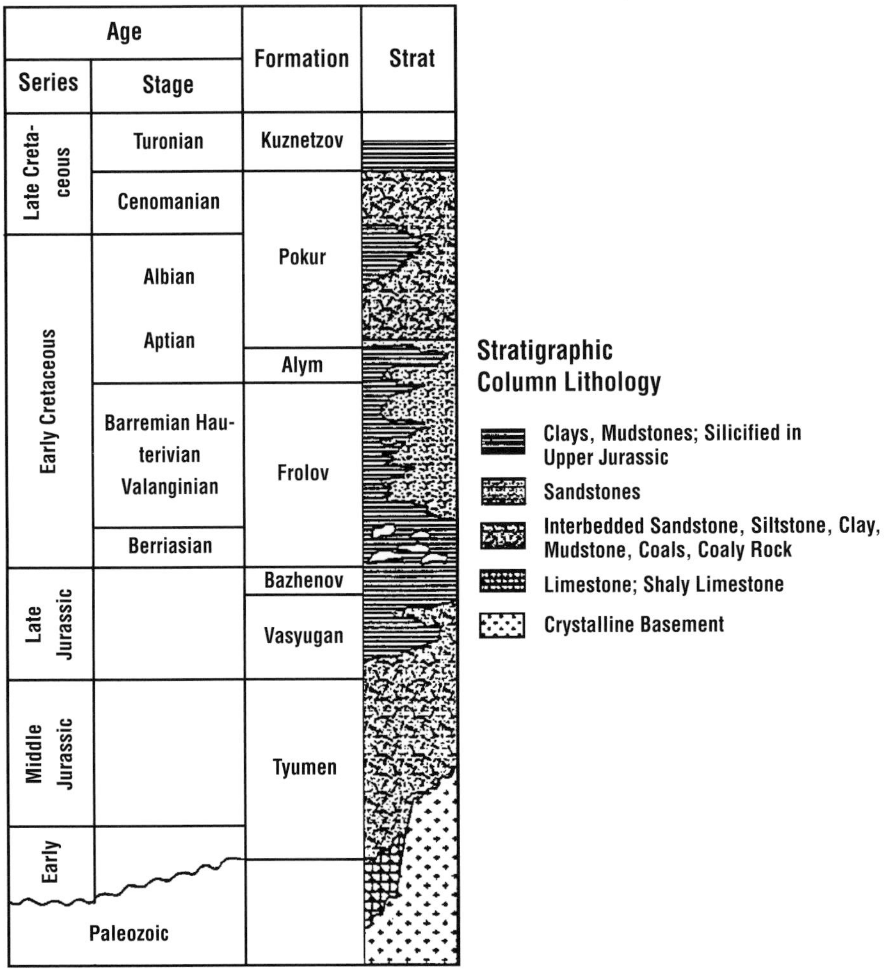

Figure 8–53. From Peters et al. (1994); courtesy AAPG.

Correlation process

Peters et al. (1994) examined 32 oil samples from this region, using a full assortment of elemental (sulfur), isotopic ($\delta^{13}C$ of whole oil), and molecular data (biomarkers). In addition, source-based cluster analysis using sterane and diasterane distributions, tricyclic terpane distributions, and carbon isotope ratios was used to group the oils and prospective source rocks.

Peters et al. (1994) approached both the oil–oil and oil–source rock correlation aspects together, relying upon molecular and isotopic data accompanied by cluster analysis results. The distributions of regular steranes and monoaromatic steroid hydrocarbons (C_{27} – C_{29}) provided an excellent framework for the correlation. The oils (shown as solid circles in the figure below) form two distinct families according to these criteria: 26 oils fall in a group relatively depleted in the C_{29} homolog, while six oils form a group relatively enriched in C_{29}. This two-family oil–oil classification is also consistent with whole-oil carbon isotope ratios as well as with other biomarker data.

The ternary diagrams below show the distribution of the C_{27}–C_{29} regular steranes (left) and monoaromatic steroid hydrocarbons (right) for oils in the West Siberian basin. Two oil families can be distinguished on the basis of their relative amounts of the C_{29} homologs. The bitumens from all the Bazhenov Formation rock samples plot together with a single oil family. Molecular structures are shown for the compounds used in the ternary diagrams.

Several possible source rocks in the basin show steroid carbon-number distributions similar to those of one of the oil families in Figure 8–54. In particular, all the Bazhenov Formation samples (uppermost Jurassic) plot adjacent to the oil family that is relatively lean in the C_{29} homolog. Other rock samples that also plot with this family in these ternary diagrams do not show valid oil-source correlations using other biomarker and isotope parameters.

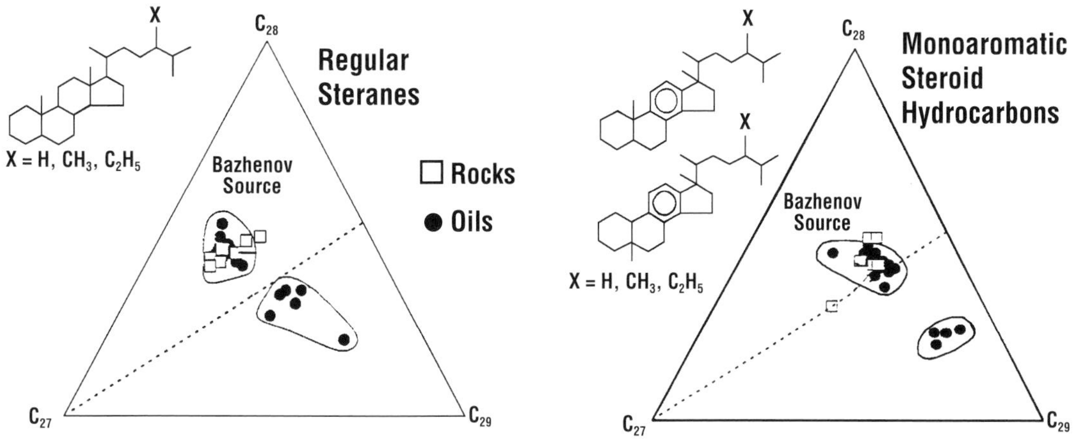

Figure 8–54. From Peters et al. (1994); courtesy AAPG.

Correlation process (continued)

Further support for a Bazhenov source is provided by the distribution of extended hopanes. As indicated in the figure below, the "Bazhenov" oils have extended hopane distributions virtually identical with the Bazhenov source rock extracts (indicated as bitumens in the figure). This positive correlation is strengthened because the homohopane distributions are somewhat unusual; thus, the similarity is unlikely to be fortuitous.

The figure below shows that distributions of homohopanes by carbon number (C_{31}–C_{35}) for bitumens from the Bazhenov Formation are essentially identical to those for the low-C_{29}-sterane oil family.

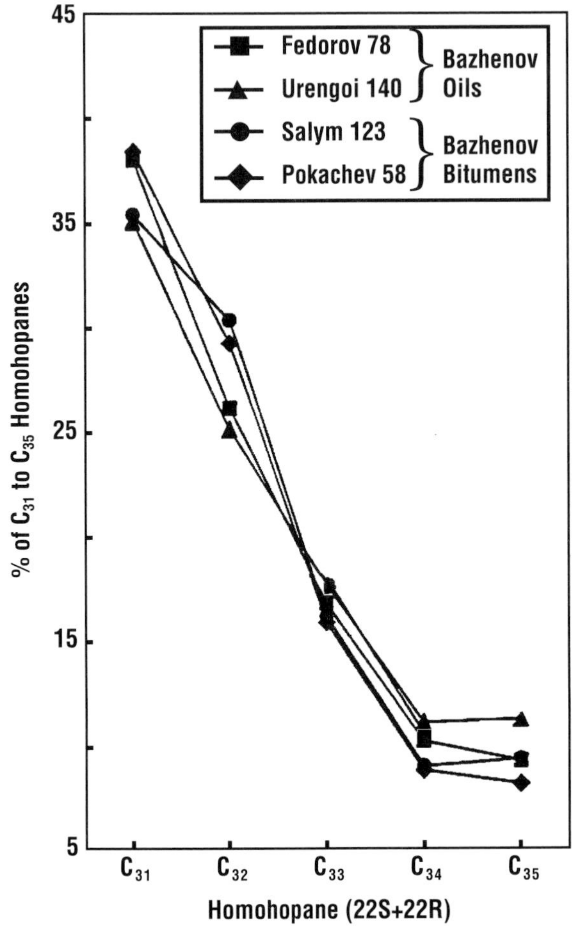

Figure 8–55. Modified from Peters et al. (1994); courtesy AAPG.

What this case study indicates

The conclusion of Peters et al. (1994) that the "low-C_{29}" oils are most likely sourced from the Bazhenov Formation is based upon isotopic and molecular data that are unaffected by maturity and alteration differences that the oils suffered after leaving the Bazhenov source rock. These changes caused variations in sulfur concentrations from less than 0.5% to greater than 2.0%. This case study emphasizes the importance of using source-distinctive biomarker and isotopic data to see through the changes wrought by differences in oil maturity and in-reservoir alteration.

Section D
References

Bjorøy, M., K. Hall, P. Gillyon, and J. Jumeau, 1991, Carbon isotope variations in n-alkanes and isoprenoids of whole oils: Chemical Geology, vol. 93, p. 13–20.

Bordenave, M.L., and R. Burwood, 1990, Source rock distribution and maturation in the Zagros orogenic belt: provenance of the Asmari and Bangestan reservoir oil accumulations: Organic Geochemistry, vol. 16, p. 369–387.

Bray, E.E., and E.D. Evans, 1961, Distribution of n-paraffins as a clue to recognition of source beds; Geochimica et Cosmochimica Acta, vol. 22, p. 2–15.

Chung, H.M., M.A. Rooney, M.B. Toon, and G.E. Claypool, 1992, Carbon isotopic composition of marine crude oils: AAPG Bulletin, vol. 76, p. 1000–1007.

———, G.E. Claypool, M.A. Rooney, and R.M. Squires, 1994, Source characteristics of marine oils as indicated by carbon isotopic ratios of volatile hydrocarbons: AAPG Bulletin, vol. 78, p. 396–408.

Clayton, C.J., and M. Bjorøy, 1994, Effect of maturity on $^{13}C/^{12}C$ ratios of individual compounds in North Sea oils: Organic Geochemistry, vol. 21, p. 737–750.

Clayton, J.L., and I. Koncz, 1994, Petroleum geochemistry of the Zala basin, Hungary: AAPG Bulletin, vol. 78, p. 1–22.

Curiale, J.A., 1987, Distribution of transition metals in North Alaskan oils, *in* R.H. Filby and J.F. Branthaver, eds., Metal complexes in fossil fuels: American Chemical Society Symposium Series 344, p. 135–145.

———, 1991, The petroleum geochemistry of Canadian Beaufort Tertiary "non-marine" oils: Chemical Geology, vol. 93, p. 21–45.

———, 1992, Petroleum geochemistry of Texas and Oklahoma oils from the Marathon/Ouachita foldbelt: Chemical Geology, vol. 98, p. 151–173.

———, 1993, Oil to source rock correlation. Concepts and case studies, *in* M.H. Engel and S.A. Macko, eds., Organic Geochemistry: New York, Plenum Press, p. 473–490.

———, 1994, Correlation of oils and source rocks—a conceptual and historical perspective, *in* L.B. Magoon and W.G. Dow, eds., The Petroleum System—From Source to Trap: AAPG Memoir 60, p. 251–260.

———, D. Cameron, and D.V. Davis, 1985, Biological marker distribution and significance in oils and rocks of the Monterey Formation, California: Geochimica et Cosmochimica Acta, vol. 49, p. 271–288.

———, U. Pe Kyi, I.D. Collins, U. Aung Din, U. Kyaw Nyein, U. Maung Nyunt, and C.J. Stewart, 1994, The central Myanmar oil family—composition and implications for source: Organic Geochemistry, vol. 22, p. 237–255.

Grantham, P.J., 1986, The occurrence of unusual C_{27} and C_{29} sterane predominances in two types of Oman crude oil: Organic Geochemistry, vol. 9, p. 1–10.

______ and L.L. Wakefield, 1988, Variations in the sterane carbon number distributions of marine source rock derived crude oils through geological time: Organic Geochemistry, vol. 19, p. 61–73.

Guthrie, J.M., and L.M. Pratt, 1995, Geochemical character and origin of oils in Ordovician reservoir rock, Illinois and Indiana: AAPG Bulletin, vol. 79, p. 1631–1649.

Hatch, J.R., J.B. Risatti, and J.D. King, 1990, Geochemistry of Illinois basin oils and hydrocarbon source rocks, *in* M.W. Leighton, D.R. Kolata, D.F. Oltz and J.J. Eidel, eds., Interior cratonic basins: AAPG Memoir 51, p. 403–423.

Huang, Y., G. Ansong, F. Jiamo, S. Guoying, Z. Biqiang, C. Yixian, and L. Maofen, 1992, The investigation of characteristics of biomarker assemblages and their precursors in Damintun ultra-high wax oils and related source rocks: Organic Geochemistry, vol. 19, p. 29–39.

Hughes, W.B., A.G. Holba, D.E. Miller, and J.S. Richardson, 1985, Geochemistry of greater Ekofisk crude oils, *in* B.M. Thomas et al., eds., Petroleum geochemistry in exploration of the Norwegian Shelf: London, Graham & Trotman, p. 75–92.

Illich, H.A., and P.L. Grizzle, 1983, Comment on "Comparison of Michigan basin crude oils" by Vogler et al.: Geochimica et Cosmochimica Acta, vol. 47, p. 1151–1155.

Katz, B.J., in press, Stratigraphic and lateral variations of source rock attributes of the Pematang Formation, Central Sumatra, *in* G.H. Teh, ed., Proceedings volume Kuala Lumpur 1994 AAPG international conference—Southeast Asian basins: oil and gas for the 21st century: Geological Society of Malaysia.

Kaufman, R.L., A.S. Ahmad, and W.B. Hempkins, 1987, A new technique for the analysis of commingled oils and its application to production allocation calculations, *in* Proceedings of the 16th Annual Convention of the Indonesian Petroleum Association: p. 247–268.

Kennicutt, M.C., and J.M. Brooks, 1988, Surface geochemical exploration studies predict API gravity off California: Oil & Gas Journal, September 12, p. 101–106.

Klomp, U., 1986, The chemical structure of a pronounced series of iso-alkanes in south Oman crudes: Organic Geochemistry, vol. 10, p. 807–814.

Kohnen, M.E.L., S. Schouten, J.S. Sinninghe Damste, J.W. de Leeuw, D. Merrit, and J.M. Hayes, 1992, The combined application of organic sulphur and isotope geochemistry to assess multiple sources of palaeobiochemicals with identical carbon skeletons: Organic Geochemistry, vol. 19, p. 403–419.

Koncz, I., 1990, The origin of the oil at the Nagylengyel and nearby fields [in Hungarian]: Általános Földtani Szemk, vol. 25, p. 55–82.

Longman, M.W., and S.E. Palmer, 1987, Organic geochemistry of mid-continent middle and late Ordovician oils: AAPG Bulletin, vol. 71, p. 938–950.

Mattavelli, L., and L. Novelli, 1990, Geochemistry and habitat of the oils in Italy: AAPG Bulletin, vol. 74, p. 1623–1639.

Mello, M.R., P.C. Gaglianone, S.C. Brassell, and J.R. Maxwell, 1988a, Geochemical and biological marker assessment of depositional environments using Brazilian offshore oils: Marine and Petroleum Geology, vol. 5, p. 205–223.

———, N. Telnæs, P.C. Gaglianone, M.I. Chicarelli, S.C. Brassell, and J.R. Maxwell, 1988b, Organic geochemical characterisation of depositional palaeoenvironments of source rocks and oils in Brazilian marginal basins: Organic Geochemistry, vol. 13, p. 31–45.

Moldowan, J.M., W.K. Seifert, and E.J. Gallegos, 1985, Relationship between petroleum composition and depositional environment of petroleum source rocks: AAPG Bulletin, vol. 569, p. 1255–1268.

———, C.Y. Lee, P. Sundararaman, T. Salvatori, A. Alajbeg, B. Gjukic, G.J. Demaison, N.-E. Slougue, and D.S. Watt, 1992, Source correlation and maturity assessment of select oils and rocks from the central Adriatic Basin (Italy and Yugoslavia), *in* J.M. Moldowan, P. Albrecht, and R.P. Philp, eds., Biological markers in sediments and petroleum: Englewood Cliffs, New Jersey, Prentice-Hall, 411 p.

Murray, A.P., R.E. Summons, J. Bradshaw, and B. Pawih, 1993, Cenozoic oil in Papua New Guinea—evidence from geochemical analysis of two newly discovered seeps, *in* G.J. Carman and Z. Carman, eds., Petroleum Exploration and Development in Papua New Guinea: Proceedings of the Second PNG Petroleum Convention, Australian Geological Survey, p. 489–498.

Ocampo, R., A. Riva, J.M. Trendel, J. Riolo, H.J. Callot, and P. Albrecht, 1993, Petroporphyrins as biomarkers in oil-oil and oil-source rock correlations: Energy & Fuels, vol. 7, p. 191–193.

Orr, W.L., 1986, Kerogen/asphaltene/sulfur relationships in sulfur-rich Monterey oils: Organic Geochemistry, vol. 10, p. 499–516.

Palacas, J.G., D.E. Anders, and J.D. King, 1984, South Florida basin—prime example of carbonate source rocks of petroleum, *in* J.G. Palacas, ed., Petroleum Geochemistry and Source Rock Potential of Carbonate Rocks: Tulsa, AAPG, p. 71–96.

Palmer, S.E., 1984, Hydrocarbon source potential of organic facies of the lacustrine Elko Formation (Eocene/Oligocene), northeast Nevada, *in* J. Woodward, F.F. Meissner, and J.L. Clayton, eds., Hydrocarbon source rocks of the greater Rocky Mountain region: Denver, Rocky Mountain Association of Geologists, p. 491–511.

Peters, K.E., and J.M. Moldowan, 1993, The Biomarker Guide—Interpreting Molecular Fossils in Petroleum and Ancient Sediments: Englewood Cliffs, New Jersey, Prentice-Hall, 363 p.

______, ______, A.R. Driscole, and G.J. Demaison, 1989, Origin of Beatrice oil by co-sourcing from Devonian and Middle Jurassic source rocks, Inner Moray Firth, U.K.: AAPG Bulletin, vol. 73, p. 454–471.

______, A.E. Kontorovich, B.J. Huizinga, J.M. Moldowan, and C.Y. Lee, 1994, Multiple oil families in the West Siberian basin: AAPG Bulletin, vol. 78, p. 893–909.

Philp, R.P., and T.D. Gilbert, 1986, Biomarker distributions in oils predominantly derived from terrigenous source material, *in* D. Leythaeuser and J. Rullkötter, eds., Advances in Organic Geochemistry 1985: New York, Elsevier, p. 73–84.

Pruitt, J., 1983, Comment on "Comparison of Michigan basin crude oils" by Vogler et al.: Geochimica et Cosmochimica Acta, vol. 47, p. 1157–1159.

Reed, J.D., H.A. Illich, and B. Horsfield, 1986, Biochemical evolutionary significance of Ordovician oils and their sources: Organic Geochemistry, vol. 10, p. 347–358.

Riva, A., P.G. Caccialanza, and F. Quagliaroli, 1988, Recognition of 18β(H)-oleanane in several crudes and Cainozoic-Upper Cretaceous sediments. Definition of a new maturity parameter: Organic Geochemistry, vol. 13, p. 671–675.

Robinson, K.M., 1987, An overview of source rocks and oils in Indonesia: Proceedings, Indonesian Petroleum Association 16th Annual Convention, p. 97–122.

Rullkötter, J., P.A. Meyers, R.G. Schaefer, and K.W. Dunham, 1986, Oil generation in the Michigan basin: a biological marker and carbon isotope approach, *in* D. Leythaeuser and J. Rullkötter, eds., Advances in Organic Geochemistry 1985: Oxford, Pergamon, p. 359–376.

Schoell, M., 1982, Application of isotopic analyses in oil and natural-gas research: Spectra, vol. 8, no. 2 & 3, p. 32–41.

Seifert, W.K., J.M. Moldowan, and R.W. Jones, 1979, Application of biological marker chemistry to petroleum exploration, *in* Proceedings of the Tenth World Petroleum Congress: London, Heyden & Son, p. 425–440.

Sofer, Z., 1984, Stable carbon isotope compositions of crude oils: application to source depositional environments and petroleum alteration: AAPG Bulletin, vol. 68, p. 31–49.

______, J.E. Zumberge, and V. Lay, 1986, Stable carbon isotopes and biomarkers as tools in understanding genetic relationship, maturation, biodegradation and migration of crude oils in the northern Peruvian Oriente (Maranon) basin: Organic Geochemistry, v. 10, p. 377–389.

Summons, R.E., J. Thomas, J.R. Maxwell, and C.J. Boreham, 1992, Secular and environmental constraints on the occurrence of dinosteranes in sediments: Geochimica et Cosmochimica Acta, vol. 56, p. 2437–2444.

Telnæs, N., and B.S. Cooper, 1991, Oil-source rock correlation using biological markers, Norwegian continental shelf: Marine and Petroleum Geology, vol. 8, p. 302–310.

______ and B. Dahl, 1986, Oil-oil correlation using multivariate techniques: Organic Geochemistry, vol. 10, p. 425–432.

van den Bark, E., and O.D. Thomas, 1980, Ekofisk: first of the giant oil fields in western Europe, *in* M.T. Halbouty, ed., Giant Oil and Gas Fields of the Decade 1968–1978: AAPG Memoir 30, p. 195–224.

Vogler, E.A., P.A. Meyers, and W.A. Moore, 1981, Comparison of Michigan basin crude oils: Geochimica et Cosmochimica Acta, vol. 45, p. 2287–2293.

Volkman, J.K., R. Alexander, R.I. Kagi, and G.W. Woodhouse, 1983, Demethylated hopanes in crude oils and their applications in petroleum geochemistry: Geochimica et Cosmochimica Acta, vol. 47, p. 785–794.

Waples, D.W., 1985, Geochemistry in Petroleum Exploration: Boston, IHRDC, 232 p.

——— and T. Machihara, 1991, Biomarkers for geologists: Tulsa, AAPG, 91 p.

Part III

Critical Elements of the Trap

Introduction

There are three critical elements of a trap:
- The size and quality of the reservoir system
- The quality and intergrity of the seals
- Its preservation over time

Predicting all of these elements is critical to the success of any play or prospect. Part III addresses methods for predicting the performance of the reservoir, the presence of seals, and the preservation of traps.

In this part

Part III contains three chapters.

Chapter 9

Predicting Reservoir System Quality and Performance

by

Dan J. Hartmann

and

Edward A. Beaumont

Dan J. Hartmann

Dan J. Hartmann received his B.S. degree in geology from New Mexico Tech. in 1963. He then joined Pan American Petroleum (now BP-Amoco) where he worked in various capacities ranging from exploration geologist through supervisor of exploration and exploitation for the western United States and Alaska. From 1981 through 1985, Hartmann served as vice-president/general manager for Mitchell Energy Company and was responsible for the western United States and Canada. In 1985, he formed DJH Energy Consulting, which specializes in exploration/exploitation consultation and education for the oil industry. Hartmann has extensive international and domestic experience that includes projects involving complex S_w models of shaly sandstones and carbonates. He has published some of his work and taught short courses on a wide variety of reservoir type and quality issues.

Edward A. Beaumont

Edward A. (Ted) Beaumont is an independent petroleum geologist from Tulsa, Oklahoma. He holds a BS in geology from the University of New Mexico and an MS in geology from the University of Kansas. Currently, he is generating drilling prospects in Texas, Oklahoma, and the Rocky Mountains. His previous professional experience was as a sedimentologist in basin analysis with Cities Service Oil Company and as Science Director for AAPG. Ted is coeditor of the Treatise of Petroleum Geology. He has lectured on creative exploration techniques in the U.S., China, and Australia and has received the Distinguished Service Award and Award of Special Recognition from AAPG.

Overview

Introduction

The economic success of any prospect ultimately depends on reservoir system performance. The reservoir system controls two critical economic elements of a prospect: (1) the rate and (2) the amount of hydrocarbons recovered. In geologic terms, pore type and pore–fluid interaction are the most important elements determining reservoir system performance.

This chapter discusses concepts and simple evaluation techniques for evaluating pore types and pore–fluid interaction. Understanding how reservoir systems behave on a petrophysical basis helps us predict reservoir system behavior in wildcat situations. Examples, written by Edward B. Coalson and included in section F, illustrate many of the techniques and principles discussed in the chapter.

In this chapter

This chapter contains the following sections.

Section A
Reservoir System Basics

Introduction

Ultimately, the quality of a reservoir system determines the economic viability of a field. Reservoir system quality and reservoir drive, together with fluid properties and producing horizon geometry, determine reservoir performance. Reservoir systems can be subdivided into containers and flow units to help us predict and assess reservoir system quality. Mapping the potential reservoir system of a prospect and comparing it with reservoir systems in analog fields help us predict reservoir drive.

This section discusses basic reservoir system concepts—containers, flow units, and drive mechanisms—and the techniques for analyzing them.

In this section

This section contains the following topics.

What is a Reservoir System?

Introduction

The term "reservoir" creates confusion between different disciplines. Explorationists apply the term to mean a porous and permeable rock regardless of the fluid it contains. Reservoir engineers apply the term to mean a rock that contains hydrocarbons and associated fluids. This difference in meanings can cause problems for multidisciplinary teams unless the terminology is clear.

Reservoir system components

In this discussion, a reservoir system is a water–hydrocarbon system contained within the pores of a rock unit. A reservoir system has three main components: a reservoir, an aquifer, and a transition zone (interface) between the two.

- A **reservoir** is a porous and permeable rock saturated with oil or gas in buoyancy pressure equilibrium with a free water level (zero buoyancy pressure). It has one or more containers and is located below a seal.
- A **transition zone** is the interval of rock separating the reservoir from the aquifer; it is less than 100% saturated with water.
- An **aquifer** is a porous and permeable rock 100% saturated with water. It has one or more containers that may or may not be shared with a reservoir.

The diagram below illustrates the major components of a conventional reservoir system.

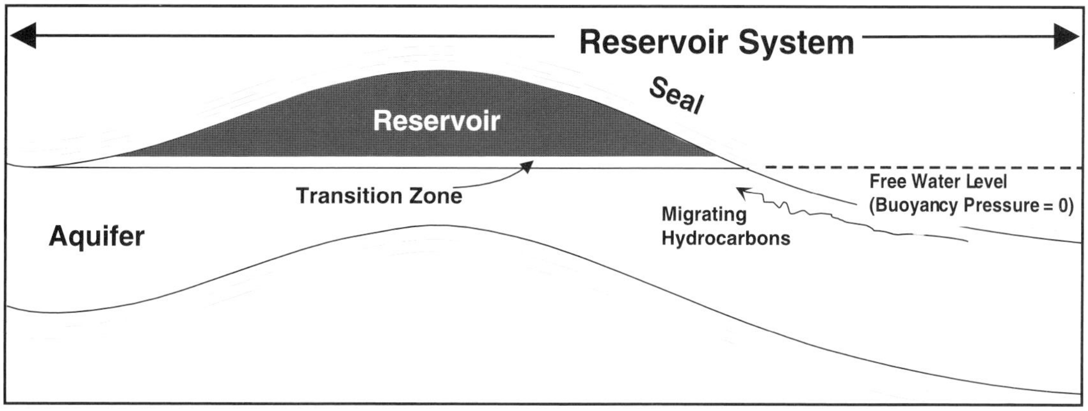

Figure 9–1.

Waste and transition zones

A **waste zone** may be found at the top of a reservoir, just below the seal, if there is a decrease in the size of the pore throat radii of the reservoir. It generally produces hydrocarbon and water on a production test (Showalter, 1979).

A **transition zone** is located at the base of a reservoir and forms as a result of a loss of buoyancy pressure in the hydrocarbon phase. Pore throat diameter and fluid densities determine its thickness. It generally produces hydrocarbon and water on a production test.

Free water level

The **free water level** is located at the base of a hydrocarbon column and the transition zone. Above this level, the reservoir produces water alone, hydrocarbon and water, or hydrocarbon alone on a production test. Below this level lies the aquifer of a water-drive reservoir system. It produces water only. Zero buoyancy pressure exists at this level or below.

Analyzing a Reservoir System

Reservoir performance

The fundamental goal of the explorationist is to predict the performance that a reservoir will have over the production life of the field. Reservoir performance affects the economic viability of a play or prospect and is a function of reservoir system quality. Performance is expressed by

- Initial production rate and production rate decline over time
- The percentage of hydrocarbon recovered from the hydrocarbon originally in place (recovery factor)

Reservoir system quality

Reservoir system quality is the capacity of a reservoir to store and transmit oil or gas. The quality of a reservoir system is determined by its

- Pore throat size distribution and pore geometry (including natural fractures)
- Pore volume
- Permeabilities to hydrocarbon
- Water saturation (hydrocarbon pore volume)
- Lateral continuity, number, and position of flow units and containers
- Reservoir pressure and drive mechanism

Procedure for reservoir system analysis

Below is a suggested procedure for reservoir system analysis.

Step	Action
1	Select a key well(s) for detailed petrophysical analysis.
2	Subdivide the reservoir in the key well(s) into flow units.
3	Determine pore type for each flow unit in the key well using core descriptions, thin section and SEM analysis, porosity/permeability–r_{35} analysis, S_w–depth plot, Buckles plot, etc.
4	Construct stratigraphic strike and dip cross sections that include the key well. Use a region/fieldwide time marker at the top of the reservoir as the datum.
5	Subdivide the reservoir interval of each well into flow units.
6	Correlate flow units between wells and subdivide the reservoir into containers by determining which flow units interact during drainage.
7	Determine hydrocarbon volume by computing the volume of pay by flow unit for each container.
8	Predict performance in terms of recovery amount and time by incorporating the above analysis with expected fluid properties and drive mechanism. Predictions should compare well with performance of analog reservoir systems.

Selecting a key well

The key well is most representative of the reservoir and has the best data. In some cases, such as in complex reservoirs, more than one key well may be necessary. A detailed petrophysical analysis of the key well can be compared to and calibrated with other wells in the reservoir that have less data.

Defining Flow Units and Containers

Introduction

To understand reservoir rock–fluid interaction and to predict performance, reservoir systems can be subdivided into **flow units** and **containers**. Wellbore hydrocarbon inflow rate is a function of the pore throat size, pore geometry, number, and location of the various flow units exposed to the wellbore; the fluid properties; and the pressure differential between the flow units and the wellbore. Reservoir performance is a function of the number, quality, geometry, and location of containers within a reservoir system; drive mechanism; and fluid properties. When performance does not match predictions, many variables could be responsible; however, the number, quality, and location of containers is often incorrect.

What is a flow unit?

A flow unit is a *reservoir subdivision* defined on the basis of similar pore type. Petrophysical characteristics, such as distinctive log character and/or porosity–permeability relationships, define individual flow units. Inflow performance for a flow unit can be predicted from its inferred pore system properties, such as pore type and geometry. They help us correlate and map containers and ultimately help predict reservoir performance.

What is a container?

A container is a *reservoir system subdivision* consisting of a pore system, made up of one or more flow units, that responds as a unit when fluid is withdrawn. Containers are defined by correlating flow units between wells. Boundaries between containers are where flow diverges within a flow unit shared by two containers (see Figure 9–4). They define and map reservoir geology to help us predict reservoir performance.

Defining flow units

To delineate reservoir flow units, subdivide the wellbore into intervals of uniform petrophysical characteristics using one or more of the following:

- Well log curve character
- Water saturation (S_w–depth plots)
- Capillary pressure data (type curves)
- Porosity–permeability cross plots (r_{35}—defined later)

The diagram below shows how flow units are differentiated on the basis of the parameters listed above.

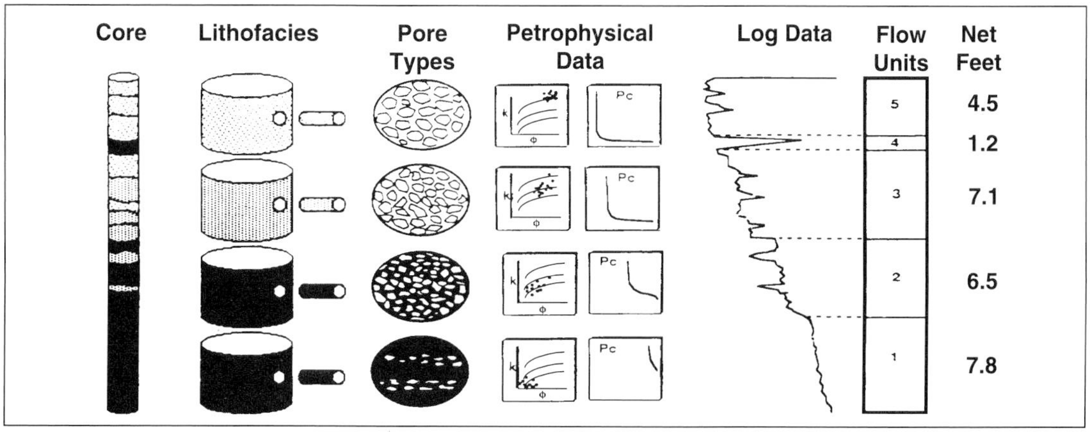

Figure 9–2. From Ebanks et al., 1993; courtesy AAPG.

Example

The example below from the Morrow Sandstone of southeastern Colorado illustrates flow unit definition using water saturation, log analysis, lithology, and mean pore throat size (port size).

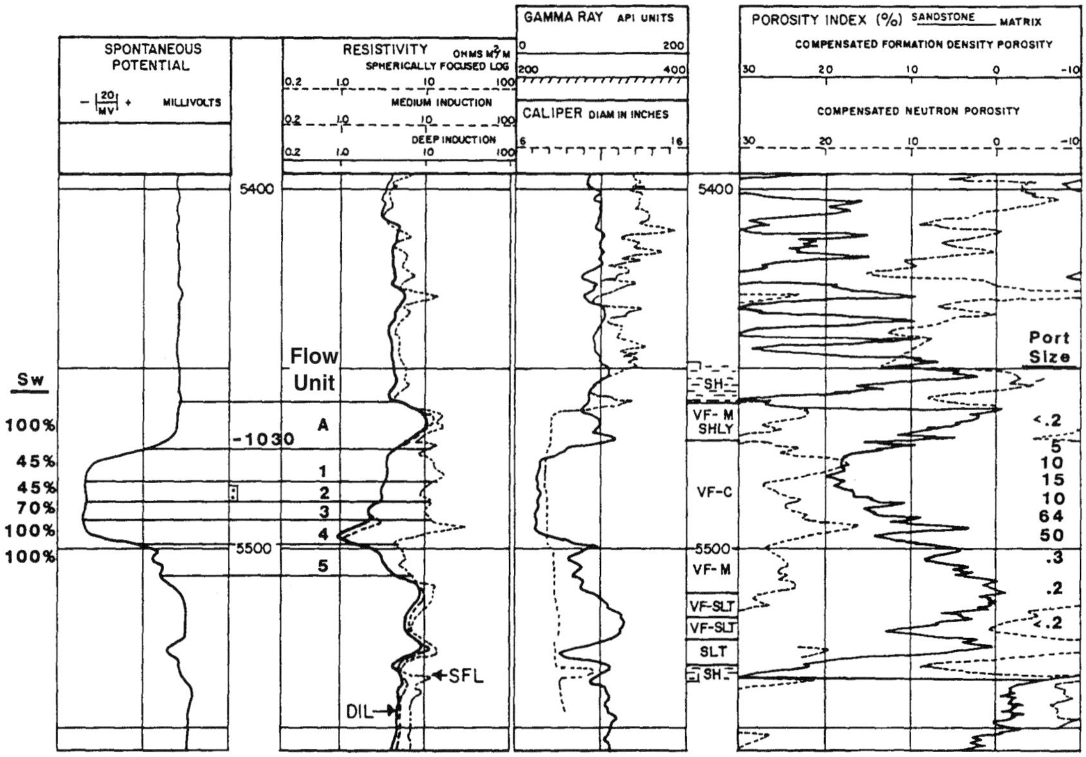

Figure 9–3. From Hartmann and Coalson, 1990; courtesy RMAG.

Procedure: Defining containers

Defining containers within a reservoir system is relative to the flow quality of the rock. Flow units with the largest connected pore throats dominate flow within a reservoir system. Follow the steps listed in the table below as a method for defining containers.

Step	Action
1	Correlate flow units between wells in strike and dip-oriented structural and stratigraphic cross sections.
2	Identify the high-quality flow units from rock and log data.
3	Draw boundaries between containers by identifying flow barriers or by interpreting where flow lines diverge within flow units common to both containers.

Defining Flow Units and Containers, continued

Impact of container quality and drive

The diagram below is a cross section of a reservoir system in an unconformity truncation trap. The reservoir system contains two different containers characterized by pore systems of different quality. Flow units 1 and 3 are microporous; flow units 2 and 5 are mesoporous; and flow unit 4 is macroporous. Container 1 is comprised of flow units 4 and 5 and part of 3. It has a strong water drive. Container 2 is comprised of flow units 1, 2, and part of 3. It has a partial water drive. The boundary between containers 1 and 2 is where fluid flow diverges in flow unit 3. Container 1 is of higher quality in terms of performance capability.

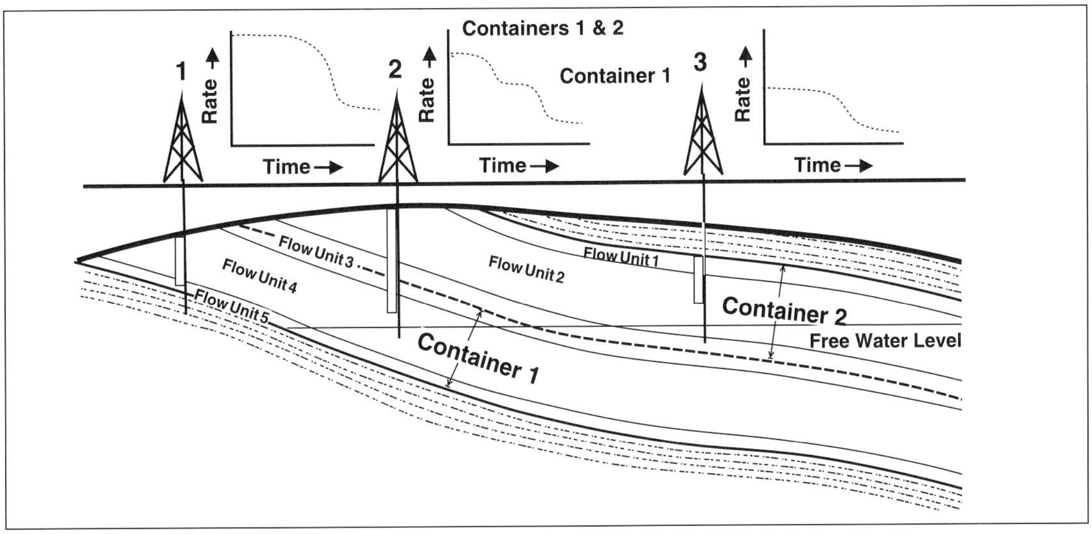

Figure 9–4.

Three wells in the figure drain the reservoir. Next to each well is a decline curve. We can consider how container quality and drive affect well performance:

- Well 1 has the highest performance because it drains the reservoir portion of container 1, which has the highest quality in terms of its pore system and aquifer support.
- Well 2 drains the reservoir portion of containers 1 and 2. Initial flow is relatively high but falls rapidly as it drains its portion of container 1. It flattens as it continues to drain container 2.
- Well 3 drains container 2. Initial flow is lowest because of the poor quality of its pore system and aquifer support. It has the poorest performance.

Flow units, facies, and containers

The stratigraphic cross section below shows the facies and flow units present in the Hartzog Draw field of Wyoming. The producing formation is the Upper Cretaceous Shannon Sandstone, composed of fine- to medium-grained clayey and glauconitic sandstones deposited as marine shelf bars. Notice how facies and flow units do not always correspond, especially within the central bar facies. The flow units in this section of Hartzog Draw behave as a unit; therefore, only one container is present.

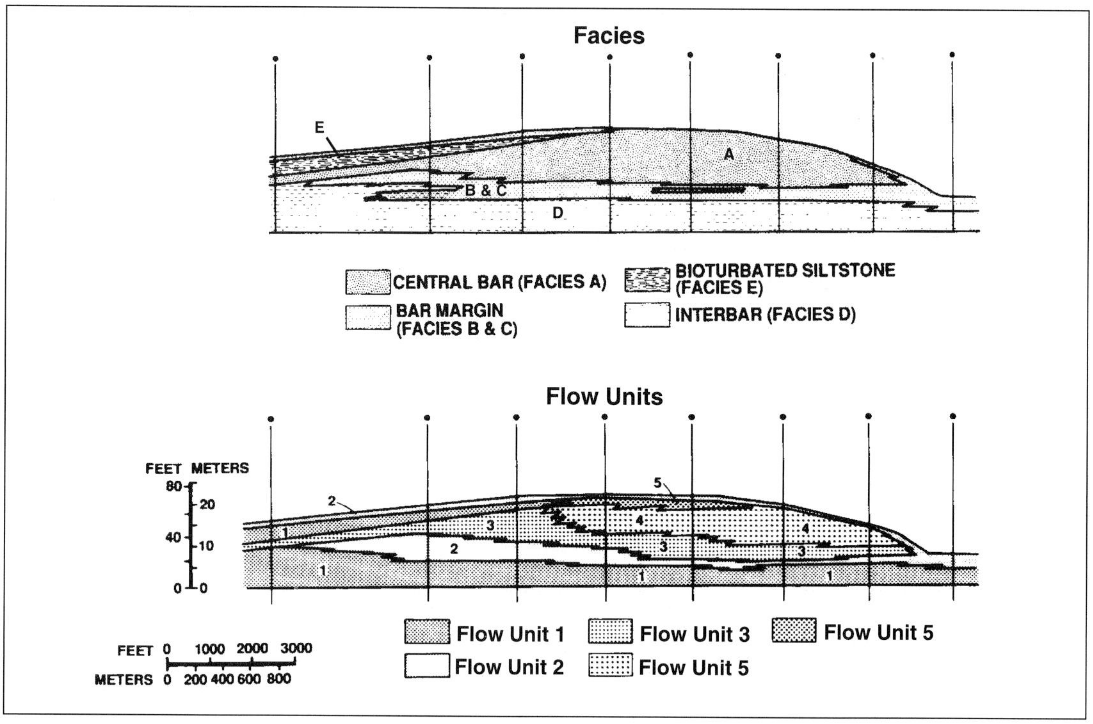

Figure 9–5. From Ebanks et al., 1993; courtesy AAPG.

Flow unit and container upscaling

In many cases, the reservoir system model must be oversimplified because of lack of time or data. For example, a reservoir system with thick sections of thin, interbedded sands and shale can theoretically be subdivided into thousands of flow units. Instead, we settle for averaging that section into one flow unit because the time to correlate each flow unit throughout the reservoir system is not available or because only log data are available and the thin beds are beyond the resolution of the tool. When only seismic data are available, we may only be able to define containers by the resolution of the seismic data.

Reservoir Drive Mechanisms

Introduction

The reservoir drive mechanism supplies the energy that moves the hydrocarbon located in a reservoir container toward the wellbore as fluid is removed near the wellbore. There are five common drive mechanisms:

- Water drive
- Gas expansion
- Solution gas
- Rock or compaction drive
- Gravity drainage

One type usually dominates, but drive types can occur in combination. Depending on the drive mechanism, characteristic recovery efficiencies can be expected for a given reservoir.

Water drive

A strong water drive provides very good pressure support from the aquifer (100% voidage replacement) with minimal pressure drop at the wellbore. The aquifer water expands slightly, displacing the oil or gas from the reservoir toward the borehole as pressure drops around the borehole. This mechanism exists only where the aquifer is of equal or better quality than the reservoir and has a much larger volume than the reservoir (about 10 times) or is in communication with surface recharge. A strong water drive is more effective in oil reservoirs than in gas reservoirs. On a semi-log plot of production decline, the curve tends to be flat.

In fields where the aquifer is smaller and/or has lower quality, there is limited expansion of water into the reservoir as oil or gas is withdrawn. This is a partial water drive.

The figure below depicts typical decline curves for a wellbore draining a reservoir system with a strong water drive (A) and a partial water drive (B).

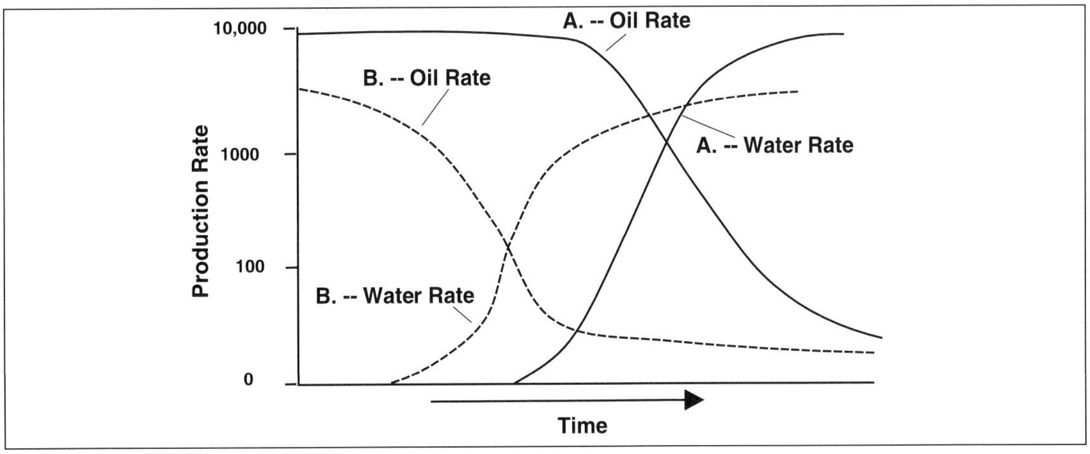

Figure 9–6.

Partial water drive

A partial water drive results where an aquifer has poorer quality in terms of pore geometry or has limited volume. When the water support diminishes, the hydrocarbon production rate drops more rapidly than in a reservoir with a strong water drive and recovery is reduced. Its production decline curve trends more concave upward on a semi-log plot than a decline curve for a strong water drive.

Gas expansion

In reservoir systems with little or no water drive, gas expansion often provides the energy necessary to move hydrocarbons to the wellbore. Free gas in a gas reservoir or in the gas cap of an oil reservoir expands to replace produced hydrocarbons. In an oil system, this expansion slows the rate of fluid pressure drop in the reservoir and supports hydrocarbon production. Pressure drops in proportion to the volume of hydrocarbon removed from the reservoir and the quality of the reservoir. Reservoirs with gas expansion drives have, at most, a limited aquifer.

Solution gas

Crude oil under high pressure can contain large amounts of dissolved gas. The more gas there is in solution, the more compressible the oil. In oil reservoirs with little or no water drive, reservoir energy to drive the oil toward the wellbore can be supplied by expansion of the oil due to gas expanding in solution. This is a solution gas (or dissolved gas or depletion) drive. When pressure drops below the bubble point in the reservoir, small, disconnected gas bubbles form in pores, also pushing the oil toward the wellbore. At about 5–10% free gas in the reservoir, the bubbles coalesce and the gas moves toward the wellbore as a separate flowing phase. When this happens, oil production drops and gas production increases rapidly because of the increased relative permeability to gas.

Rock drive

As reservoir fluid pressure declines, the pressure on the solids, or **net confining pressure** (P_{nc}), increases because pore fluid pressure carries less of the weight of the overburden. Some reservoirs respond to the increase in P_{nc} by the collapse of the pore space. This can be an efficient way to expel hydrocarbons. Rock drive is common in shallow reservoirs or in reservoirs with unconsolidated sediments. It can also be expected to occur where porosity has been held open by high fluid pressures. Good examples of high pressure and unconsolidated reservoirs are some Danian Chalk reservoirs of the North Sea.

Gravity drainage

In gravity drainage, oil drains downward through a reservoir under the influence of gravity. This requires high vertical permeability or steeply dipping beds and thus is common in fractured reservoirs. Efficiency can be surprisingly high (75%+), especially where beds have steep dip, the oil has low viscosity, and the oil draining from the top of the column is replaced by exsolved gas.

Combination

Drive mechanisms can occur in combination. For instance, a gas expansion drive is commonly accompanied by a partial water drive. Water drives can be enhanced by imbibition effects, a minor drive type. Undersaturated oil reservoirs can begin producing by solution gas drive, then change to partial water drive when the energy from the dissolved gas is reduced to the point where it no longer is effective.

We sometimes can recognize combined drives from production decline curves, especially when oil, gas, and water are all plotted by rate. All plots of individual wells from a field should have common horizontal and vertical scales so they can be compared from well to well.

Reservoir Drive Mechanisms, continued

Decline curves for drive types

Analysis of production decline curve shape can provide a good indication of the dominant drive mechanism. The figure below compares typical production decline curves for the different drive mechanisms described above for a reservoir with approximately the same pore volume. It assumes all other factors are normalized.

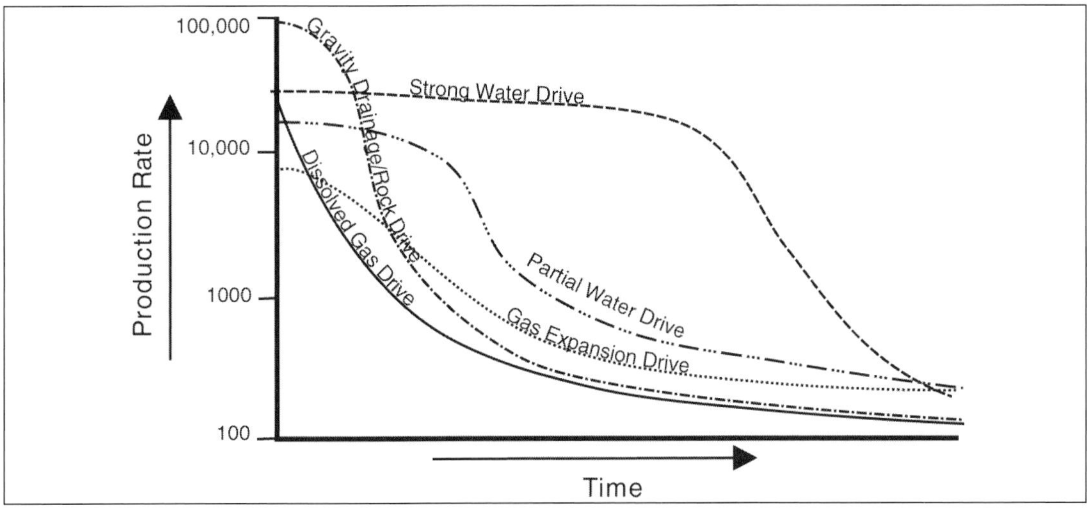

Figure 9–7.

Predicting Reservoir Drive Mechanism

Introduction

One can predict drive type by analyzing (1) the reservoir system of a prospect and (2) the production history characteristics of similar nearby reservoirs.

Predicting drive type

Reservoir analysis includes making cross sections, structural maps, and isopach maps. Analyzing nearby producing fields yields the best set of inferential data. This includes (1) making plots of historical oil, gas, condensate, and water production and pressure decline and (2) making cumulative production maps. When all available information has been assembled, find the drive type that best fits the prospective reservoir system. The table below summarizes typical characteristics of primary drive types.

Drive	Characteristics
Water	• Quality of aquifer pore geometry comparable to reservoir pore geometry • Aquifer volume at least 10 times greater than reservoir volume • Flat to gradual production and pressure declines • Gradually to rapidly increasing water production late in life of reservoir • Early increasing water production from downdip wells • GOR (gas–oil ratio) relatively constant • High recovery factor (50% or more)
Gas expansion	• Moderate drop in reservoir pressure • Moderate production decline • Water-free production (or relatively minor) • GOR flat for first 50% of production, then increases • GOR increases rapidly in structurally high wells • Moderate recovery factor (typically 30%)
Solution gas	• Rapid drop in reservoir pressure early in production history • Exponential production decline • Water-free production (or relatively minor) • Increasing GOR early, decreasing later as gas is exhausted • Low recovery factor (20% or less)
Rock drive	• Unconsolidated reservoir such as sandstone, chalk, or diatomite • Reservoir in overpressure section • No decline while reservoir compacts, then rapid production decline
Gravity	• Steeply dipping beds or vertical permeability greater than horizontal • Fractured reservoir • Low-viscosity oil (in general) • Rapid production decline • High recovery rate (75% or more), but often with low recovery volume

Production history characteristics for drives

The graphs below show oil reservoir production history characteristics for water, gas expansion, and gas solution drives. To predict reservoir drive type, if possible, plot the production history of nearby fields with analogous reservoir systems and compare with these graphs.

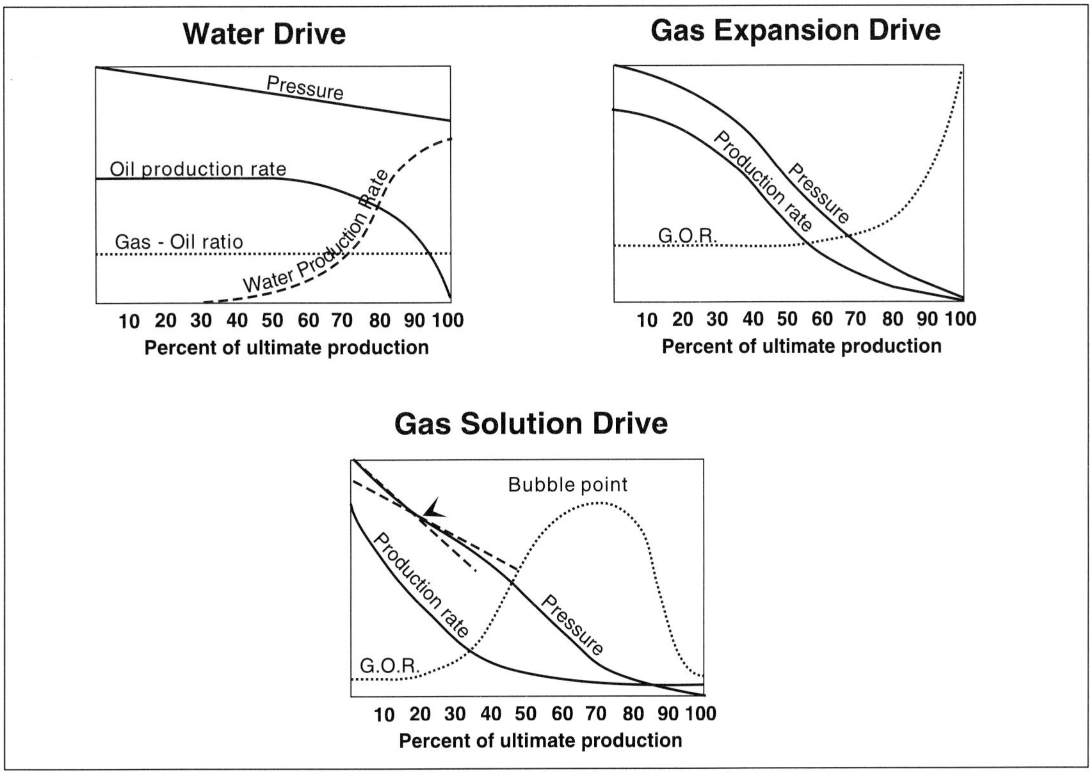

Figure 9–8. Modified from Levorsen, 1954; courtesy W.H. Freeman and Co.

Recoveries of oil vs. gas reservoirs

The table below shows typical recovery rates for oil vs. gas reservoir systems for different reservoir drive mechanisms with mega and macro port type systems (John Farina, personal communication, 1998; Garb and Smith, 1987). Recoveries would be lower for meso to micro port systems. Use this table to project the recoveries for your prospects.

Reservoir Drive Mechanism	Percent Ultimate Recovery	
	Gas	Oil
Strong water	30–40	45–60
Partial water	40–50	30–45
Gas expansion	50–70	20–30
Solution gas	N/A	15–25
Rock	60–80	10–60
Gravity drainage	N/A	50–70

Recoveries for sandstone vs. carbonate reservoirs

The American Petroleum Institute conducted a study to determine recovery amounts and efficiencies for water vs. solution gas drives for sandstone and carbonate reservoirs, summarized in the table below (Arps, 1967). Use the table to project recoveries for your prospects.

Drive	Units	Sandstone			Carbonate		
		Min.	Ave.	Max.	Min.	Ave.	Max.
Water	bbl/acre-ft	155	571	1,641	6	172	1,422
	m^3/h-m	199	735	2,113	8	221	1,831
	%*	28	51	87	6	44	80
Solution gas	bbl/acre-ft	47	154	534	20	88	187
	m^3/h-m	60	198	688	26	113	241
	%*	9	21	46	15	18	21

*Percent stock tank barrels originally in place

Section B
Classifying Pore Systems

Introduction

Rocks can be classified on the basis of their pore geometry into four major pore categories that can be divided into ten subcategories. Extensive experience and laboratory analysis show that these pore type categories have a particular behavior when interacting with fluids that can be used to predict the behavior of reservoir systems over time. This section shows how to classify pore types and explains how pores and fluids interact.

In this section

This section contains the following topics.

Pore System Fundamentals

Introduction

Porosity consists of relatively large voids, or pores, distributed among smaller passages called pore throats. A pore system is an aggregate of pores and pore throats that shares a similar morphology. These elements play a role in determining reservoir and seal petrophysics (the characteristic way that oil, gas, and water move through rocks). The figure below shows typical 3-D pore system geometries found in intergranular, intercrystalline, vuggy, or fractured rocks.

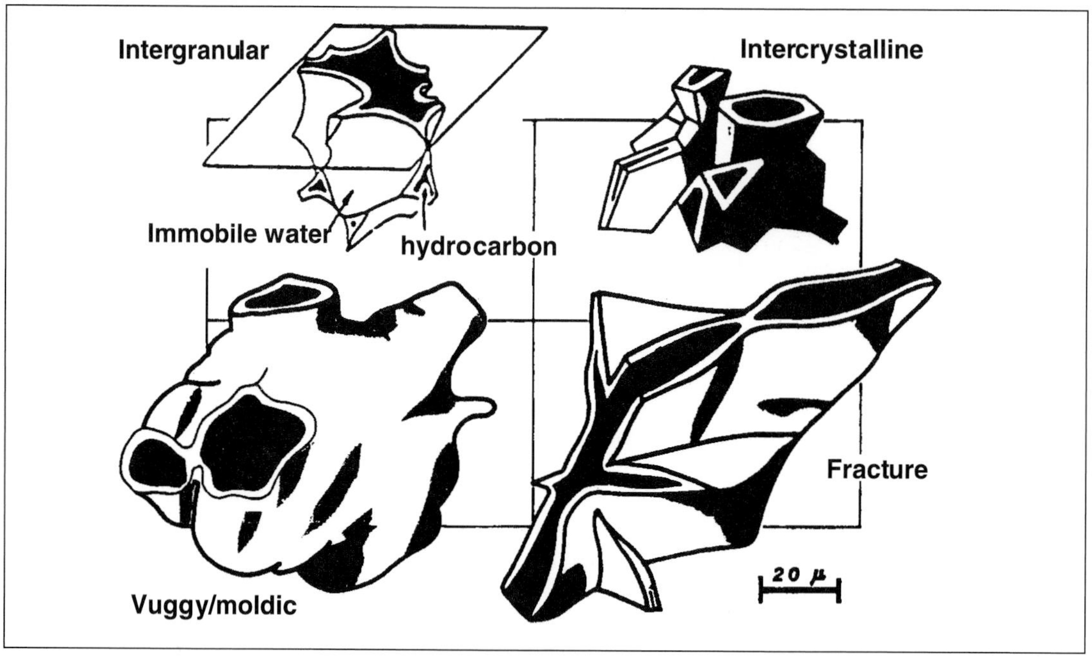

Figure 9–9. From Coalson et al., 1994; courtesy RMAG.

Critical elements of pore-system geometry

The pores of a rock occur between grains or crystals, in fractures, or in vugs. A rock's storage capacity is controlled by the size and number of pores. A rock's permeability (flow capacity) is controlled by the size, shape, and number of the pore throats (connections) per pore. Four critical elements of the geometry of a rock's pore system are

- Pore system shapes
- Pore and pore throat sizes
- Pore connectivity
- Ratio of pore throats to pores

Pore System Shapes

Archie and non-Archie rocks

Choquette and Pray's (1970) porosity types include two different groups of pore system shapes: petrophysically simple **Archie porosity** and petrophysically complex **non-Archie porosity**. In most cases, water saturation (S_w) of rocks with Archie porosity can be predicted from log analysis using the Archie equation

$$S_w = \left(\frac{1}{\Phi^m} \times \frac{R_w}{R_t} \right)^{1/n}$$

without modification. To predict water saturation in rocks with non-Archie porosity, we modify the Archie equation.

Table of characteristics

The table below describes pore system shapes and other important characteristics of Archie and non-Archie rocks (after Coalson et al., 1994).

Feature	Archie	Non-Archie
Pore system shapes	Intergranular (found between rounded particles); interparticle	Mold-like • Intraparticle • Moldic • Shelter
	Intercrystalline (found between angular particles)	Vug-like • Boring/burrow • Growth-framework • Fenestral • Vug/channel/cavern
		Fracture-like • Fracture • Shrinkage
Relationship of pore shape to rock particles	Negative image of particles making up matrix	Relates only indirectly to particles making up matrix
Pore connectivity	Pore throats connect pores into regular networks	Pores are irregularly distributed and can be either poorly or very well connected
Porosity reduction processes	Grain coating or pore filling by calcite, silica, or dolomite	Pore or pore throat filling by clays or other minerals

Pore and Pore Throat Sizes

Introduction

Pore and pore throat sizes have two defining parameters
- Absolute size
- Aspect ratio

Absolute size

Absolute size of a pore throat is the radius of a circle drawn perpendicular to fluid flow and fitting within its narrowest point. Absolute size of a pore is the radius of the largest sphere that will fit inside it. The cross-sectional shape of fluids moving through intergranular porosity is roughly circular. Both pores and pore throats can be divided into petrophysically significant size ranges.

Measuring pore and pore throat sizes

The figure below illustrates the concepts of pore size and pore throat size determined by measuring the radius of a sphere in the pore and the radius of a disk in the pore throat. Pore size can be estimated visually by using an SEM (scanning electron microscope), for example. Pore throat sizes for a rock can be measured using capillary pressure–mercury injection tests, which can be converted to a distribution or profile of pore throat sizes for a sample (see later sections in this chapter for more detailed discussions of pore throat size measurement). Erlich et al. (1991) describe a procedure for estimating pore and pore throat size from thin section image analysis.

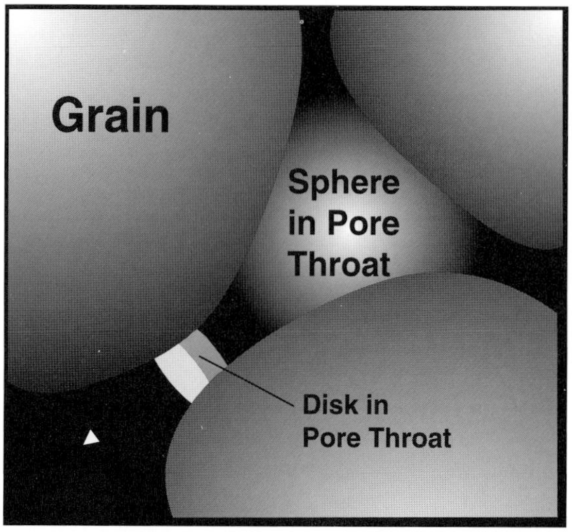

Figure 9–10. From Coalson et al., 1994; courtesy RMAG.

Aspect ratio

Aspect ratio is the ratio of pore size to pore throat size. Geometrical reasoning and limited experimental data suggest that aspect ratios have small ranges in intergranular and intercrystalline pore systems. Disparate Archie rock types such as quartz-cemented sandstones, bioturbated sandstones, and sucrosic dolomites have aspect ratios that range between 5:1 and 10:1. Non-Archie rock types have even larger variations in aspect ratios.

Connectivity and Pore Throat Size

Connectivity

Even very large pores contribute nothing to fluid flow unless they connect to other pores. Connectivity increases with the size of pore throats and with increasing number of pore throats surrounding each pore. The number of pore throats that connect with each pore is the **coordination number** (Wardlaw and Cassan, 1978).

Pore shape, throat size, and throat abundance

How do pore shape, pore throat size, and pore throat abundance affect the flow dynamics of a reservoir? Visualize a room with a door in each wall. The number of people who can fit into the room is a product of the size and shape of the room. The movement of people into or out of that room is a product of the size, shape, and number of doors. A large cube-shaped room with many small doors allows the people to leave the room at a given rate relative to a smaller tubular-shaped room with a few large doors.

A particular pore type has similar entrance/exit dynamics. Pore throats are the doors (**ports**) to the pore. Along with S_w, pore throats control permeability to hydrocarbons in reservoir rocks.

Characterizing pore systems by size

How does one characterize the size of a pore system: by pore size or by pore throat size? Characterizing the size of a pore system by pore size presents problems. For example, how do we accurately measure and average pore size in rocks with poorly sorted pore sizes?

Pore systems are easily characterized by size using pore throat size. Pore throat sizes can be measured using capillary pressure curves. A capillary pressure curve is converted to a distribution profile of pore throat size, and a pore throat size that characterizes the rock is determined by picking a certain saturation level.

Which saturation level should we use? Work by Dale Winland and Ed Pittman (Pittman, 1992) shows a statistical correlation between optimal flow through rocks and the radius of the pore throats when 35% of the pore space of a rock is saturated by a nonwetting phase during a capillary pressure test. They call the size of pore throats at 35% nonwetting phase saturation $\mathbf{r_{35}}$, also called **port size**. Port size is convenient for characterizing the size of a pore system. Pore systems can be subdivided into "port types" by port size. (See "Characterizing Rock Quality" in section C for a discussion of port size.) The table below shows port types and size ranges for those port types.

Port Category	Port Size Range (r_{35}), μ
Mega	> 10
Macro	2–10
Meso	0.5–2
Micro	0.1–0.5
Nano	<0.1

Classifying Pore Systems

Combining pore shape and size into classes

Pore geometry is categorized as intergranular, intercrystalline, vuggy/moldic, or fracture. Pore throat sizes are categorized into mega-, macro-, meso-, and micro-port types. Combining both pore geometry and port type into a classification scheme is an effective method of describing pore systems. For example, a very fine-grained sandstone might be classified as having intergranular mesoporosity or a limestone as having vuggy macroporosity.

Typical rock types by pore class

The table below describes a typical rock type for each pore type in the classification.

Pore Geometry/ Port Type	Archie			Non-Archie	
	Intergranular/ Interparticle	**Intercrystalline**	**Clay Cemented**	**Vuggy**	**Fracture**
Mega/ Macro	Clean, coarse sandstone or carbonate grainstone	• Coarsely crystalline carbonate • Quartz- or carbonate-cemented coarse sandstone	Chlorite or illite cemented (pore lining) coarse sandstone	Connected vugs or vugs in a crystalline matrix	Fracture width >50μ
Meso	Clean, coarse silt to very fine sandstone or carbonate grainstone	• Very fine to medium crystalline carbonate • Quartz- or carbonate-cemented fine to medium sandstone	• Chlorite or illite cemented (pore lining) fine to medium sandstone • Kaolinite cemented (pore filling) coarse sandstone	Poorly connected vugs or vugs/oomolds in a fine to medium crystalline matrix	Fracture width 5–50μ
Micro	Clean clay-size to fine siltstone or clay-size carbonate	• Silt-size crystalline carbonate • Quartz- or carbonate-cemented silt to very fine sandstone	Sandstone with clay in pore throats	Disbursed vugs in microcrystalline matrix	Fracture width < 5μ

Determining Pore Throat Size from P_c Curves

Introduction

Capillary pressure (P_c) curves are a rock property measurement that relates the volume of pore space controlled by pore throats of a given size (usually given in microns) to a given capillary pressure.

What is capillary pressure?

P_c is the resistant force to hydrocarbon migration. It is a function of the interfacial tension (γ), the wettability (Θ), and pore throat radius (r). P_c increases with decreasing pore throat size, increasing interfacial tension, and increasing contact angle (greater oil wetting). It can be expressed as follows:

$$P_c = \frac{2\gamma \cos\Theta}{r}$$

This expression assumes the capillary phenomenon occurs within a tube with a circular cross section. Real pores only approximate this, and then only if they are intergranular or intercrystalline (Coalson, personal communication, 1997).

Capillary test procedure

In a mercury capillary pressure test, a rock with a measured porosity is immersed in a mercury pressure cell. The pressure in the cell is raised to a predetermined pressure level (P1, figure below). When the cell comes to equilibrium, the volume of injected mercury is measured (V2). Since the porosity of the test sample is known prior to the test, the volume of injected mercury can be converted to the percent of the total pore volume filled with mercury (for example, 10% at 10 psi for point M1). All the pores filled with mercury at this point in the test have at least one 10μ pore throat radius or larger and represent 10% of the sample's pore volume. This procedure is repeated several more times at different pressures (for example, points M2 through M5).

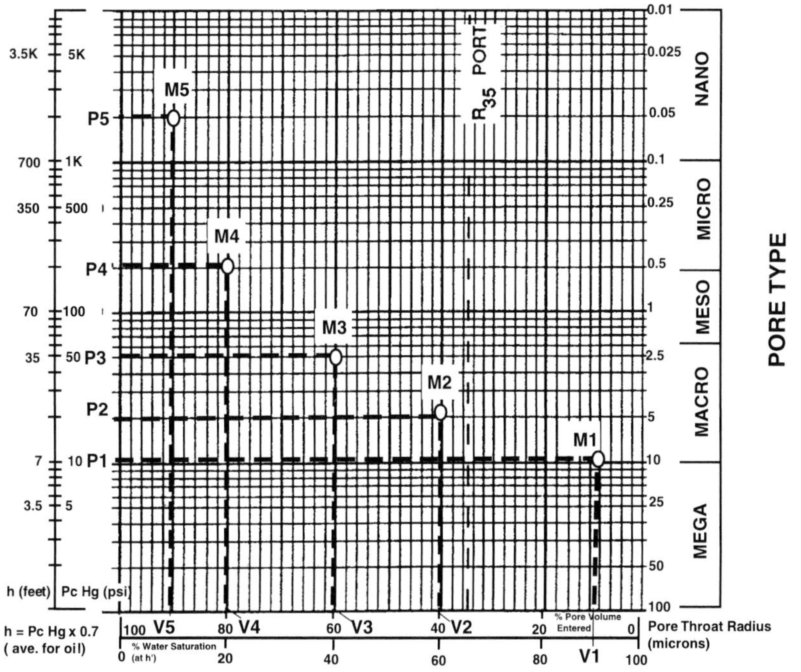

Figure 9–11.

Pore throat profiles

A curve is drawn through the measured points at test completion. This capillary pressure curve also represents a pore throat size profile for the tested sample. It relates a given pore throat size to its capillary resistance (P_c). The diagram below shows the curve drawn through the points in Figure 9–11.

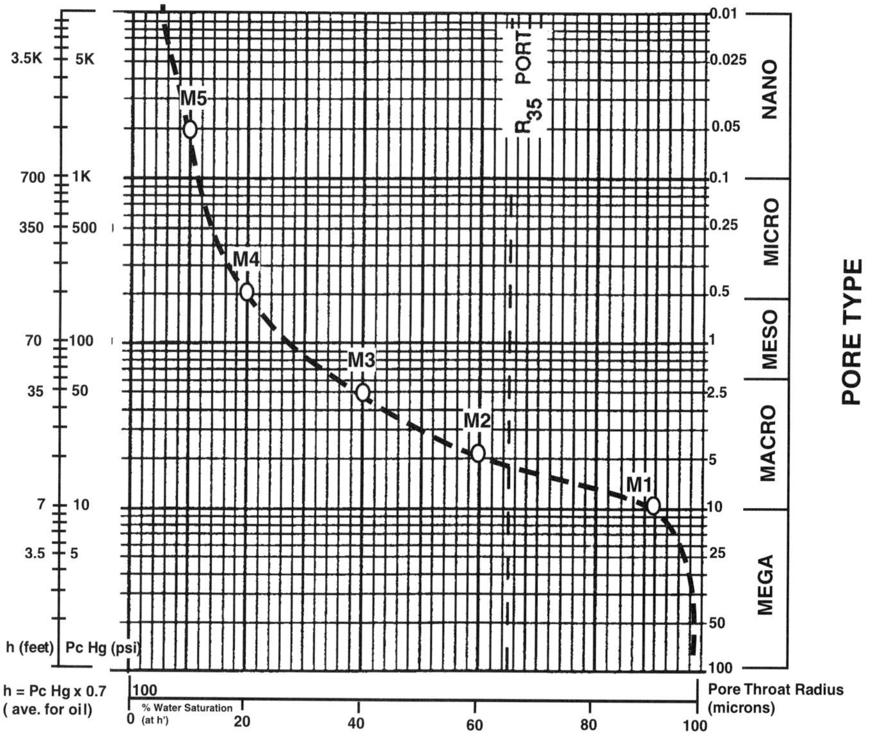

Figure 9–12.

Converting capillary pressure to pore throat size

Capillary pressure curves are converted to profiles of pore throat size by solving the previous equation for *r*:

$$r = \frac{2\gamma \cos \Theta}{P_c}$$

Capillary pressure for a given S_w can also be converted to an approximation of height above free water (*h*) within a reservoir system. From a capillary pressure curve at a given S_w, we read the capillary pressure and multiply it by a factor that converts P_c to buoyancy pressure (P_b). If the conversion factor is not known, we use 0.4 for gas and 0.7 for oil.

Using P_c to estimate *h* and *r*

Use the table below to estimate height above free water (*h*) and pore throat radius (*r*) from a mercury capillary pressure curve.

To estimate	Step	Action
Pore throat size (*r*) from S_w	1	Enter the X-axis at percent pore volume (S_w value).
	2	At the intersectionof grid line and P_c curve, read the corresponding value for *r* on the Y-axis
Height above free water level (*h*) from S_w	1	Enter the X-axis at percent pore volume (S_w value).
	2	At the intersection of grid line and P_c curve, read the corresponding value for P_c on the left Y-axis.
	3	Multiply P_c by the appropriate gradient (as a rule of thumb, use 0.7 for oil, 0.4 for gas).

Example

Using the curve in the diagram below, if S_w = 20% (point 1), then the mercury capillary pressure (P_c) that must be overcome to enter pore throats at that point on the curve is 200 psi (point 2). Converting mercury P_c to hydrocarbon column height (*h*):

$$h = 200 \text{ psi} \times 0.7 = 140 \text{ ft of oil column}$$
$$= 200 \text{ psi} \times 0.4 = 50 \text{ ft of gas column}$$

The minimum pore throat radius entered when S_w is 20% and P_c is 200 psi is 0.5μ.

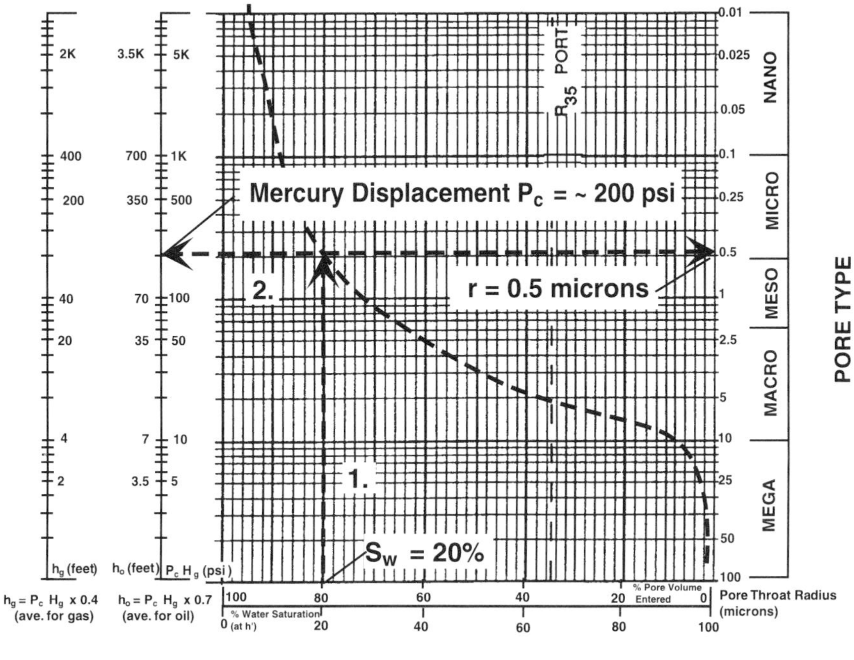

Figure 9–13.

Section C
Pore–Fluid Interaction

Introduction

Pore–fluid interaction determines the amount and rate of hydrocarbon recovery. Reservoir pore throat radius, buoyancy pressure, and fluid properties are the main elements controlling pore–fluid interaction. Since direct observation of pore–fluid interaction in the reservoir is impossible at present, capillary pressure and relative permeability analysis of rocks yields the most insight into the behavior of fluids in a particular pore system.

This section discusses pore–fluid interaction and techniques for predicting the behavior of fluid within a pore system.

In this section

This section contains the following topics.

Hydrocarbon Expulsion, Migration, and Accumulation

Introduction

The pores and fluids of a reservoir system interact during the processes of expulsion, migration, accumulation, and flow to a wellbore. Differential pressure (ΔP) in the fluid continuum of the petroleum system, caused by properties of fluids and pores, controls these processes.

Expulsion

Hydrocarbon generation causes pressure build-up in the source rock, exceeding the pore pressure of the adjacent aquifer. Oil or gas is expelled or "squeezed" into the aquifer due to the differential pressures between source rock and aquifer fluid.

Migration

Hydrocarbon migrates through an aquifer when it is "buoyed" upward due to ΔP caused by the density differential of the hydrocarbons and the formation water. The oil or gas migrates in filaments through the pore system of the aquifer as long as the buoyancy pressure (P_b) exceeds the capillary resistance of the water in the pore throats. This relationship is illustrated in the diagram below.

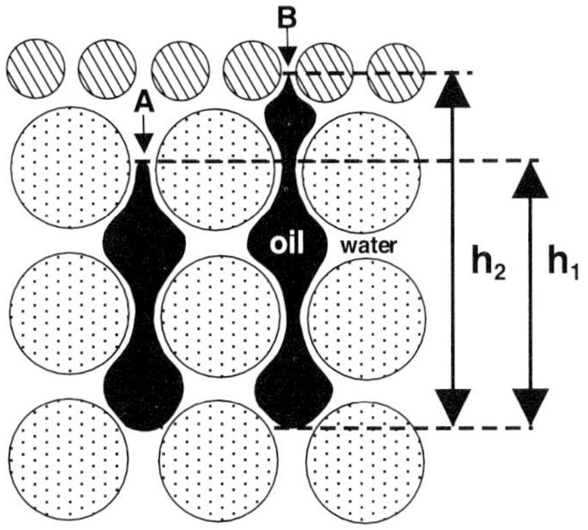

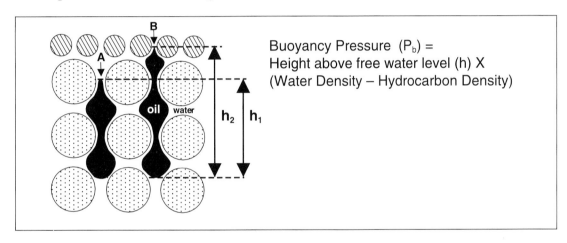

Figure 9–14. After Berg, 1975; courtesy AAPG.

For migration to continue as pore throat size decreases from one site to the next (points A and B in Figure 9–14), the length of the filament (h) must increase until an adequate P_b exists across the pore throat to initiate breakthrough.

Accumulation

A hydrocarbon accumulation forms when migrating hydrocarbon filaments encounter a zone (the seal), either laterally or vertically, with pore throat sizes smaller than the carrier bed. The seal pore throat breakthrough pressure or the distance to the spill point of the trap, whichever is less, determines the hydrocarbon accumulation column height.

Buoyancy pressure profile

When a reservoir has formed in a trap and has come to pressure equilibrium with the water in the aquifer, the pore pressure of the hydrocarbons at different depths in the reservoir plot along a steeper gradient than the water gradient. The figure below shows this relationship.

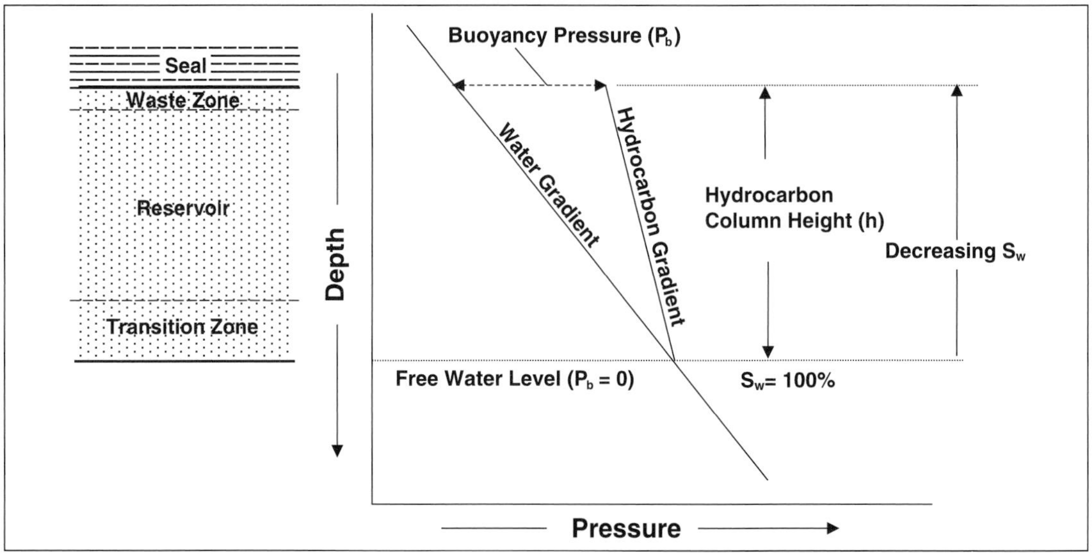

Figure 9–15. From Coalson et al., 1994; courtesy RMAG.

The pressure contrast between the hydrocarbon gradient and the water gradient at a given depth in the reservoir (height above free water) is the buoyancy pressure (P_b). The longer the column, the higher the P_b at the top of the column.

Water saturation

The water remaining on the surfaces of the pores and pore throats of a rock after hydrocarbon has driven (drained) out the rest of the water is called the **residual water saturation** (S_{wr}). P_b provides the energy needed to overcome the capillary resistance of the water in the pore throat and drive down S_{wr} in the pore. The higher a portion of the reservoir (with a given capillary pressure profile–pore type) occurs above the zero (0 psi) P_b position, the lower its S_{wr} will become. Consequently, an S_{wr} model can be developed from capillary pressure profiles because S_{wr} is a function of the profile of pore throat sizes and height above P_b = 0 psi.

Characterizing Rock Quality

Methods

Analyzing air permeability (K_a) and porosity (Φ) data separately to characterize rock quality can be deceiving. Analyzing K_a and Φ data using the K_a/Φ ratio or the r_{35} method (Pittman, 1992) is much more effective for determining quality. The K_a/Φ ratio or the r_{35} method yields information about the fluid flow and storage quality of a rock.

Which is better rock?

Using K_a and Φ data separately to characterize reservoir rock quality is misleading. Consider the rocks shown in the SEM microphotographs in the figure below. Flow unit 1 is a mesoporous, sucrosic dolomite. Its average Φ is 30% and average K_a is 10 md. Flow unit 2 is a macroporous, oolitic limestone. Its average Φ is 10% and average K_a is 10 md.

Initially, we might think that flow unit 1 is higher quality because it has three times more porosity and the same permeability as flow unit 2. However, in terms of fluid flow efficiency and storage, as shown by the K_a/Φ ratio or r_{35}, flow unit 2 is actually the better rock.

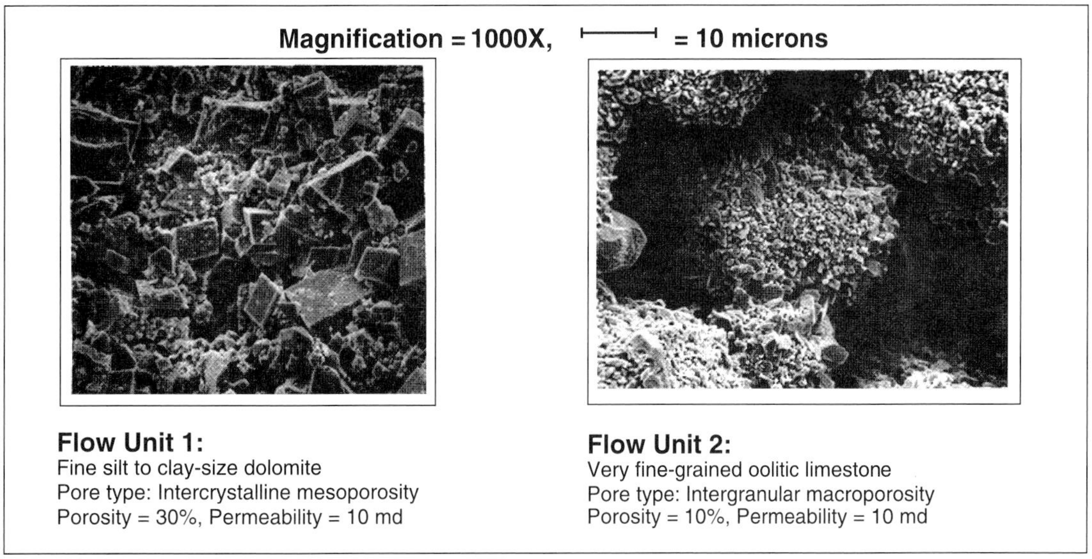

Magnification = 1000X, = 10 microns
Flow Unit 1:
Fine silt to clay-size dolomite
Pore type: Intercrystalline mesoporosity
Porosity = 30%, Permeability = 10 md
Flow Unit 2:
Very fine-grained oolitic limestone
Pore type: Intergranular macroporosity
Porosity = 10%, Permeability = 10 md

Figure 9–16.

In a reservoir section, increasing Φ and constant K_a indicate pores are becoming more numerous and smaller and pore surface area is increasing. Immobile water saturation for a reservoir (S_w) becomes greater as more surface is available to the wetting fluid. Higher immobile S_w decreases the available pore storage space for hydrocarbons. Also, as the pore size decreases, so does the pore throat size. Flow unit 2 above is the better reservoir rock because it has larger pore throats and lower immobile S_w. K_a/Φ ratio or r_{35} accounts for the interrelationship of K_a and Φ, making them effective methods for comparing rock quality.

What is the K_a/Φ ratio?

K_a and Φ are standard components of many reservoir engineering wellbore flow performance equations. The K_a/Φ ratio reflects rock quality in terms of flow efficiency of a reservoir sample. When clastics and carbonates are deposited, they have a close correlation of particle size to the K_a/Φ ratio. Mean pore throat radius increases as grain or crystal size increases, but modification to grain shape and size tends to "smear" the distribution.

In the example on the preceding page, flow unit 1 has a K_a/Φ value of 33 and flow unit 2 has a K_a/Φ value of 100. Even though Φ is greater and K_a is the same for flow unit 1, the lower K_a/Φ value indicates its quality is lower than flow unit 2.

K_a/Φ plot

On the plot below, the contours represent a constant K_a/Φ ratio and divide the plot into areas of similar pore types. Data points that plot along a constant ratio have similar flow quality across a large range of porosity and/or permeability. The clusters of points on the plot below represent hypothetical K_a/Φ values for flow units 1 and 2 presented in Figure 9–16. The position of the clusters relative to the K_a/Φ contours indicates flow unit 2 has higher quality in terms of K_a/Φ ratio than flow unit 1.

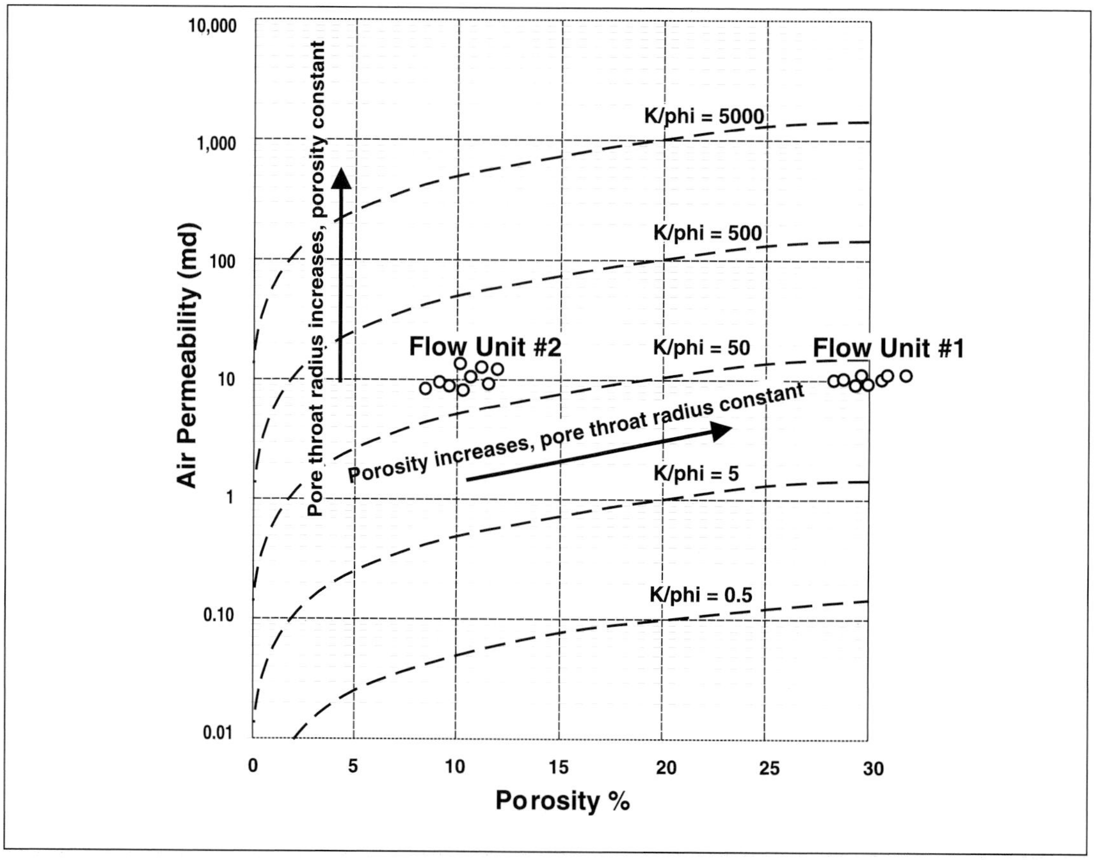

Figure 9–17.

What is r_{35}?

H.D. Winland of Amoco used mercury injection–capillary pressure curves to develop an empirical relationship among Φ, K_a, and pore throat radius (r). He tested 312 different water-wet samples. The data set included 82 samples (56 sandstone and 26 carbonate) with low permeability corrected for gas slippage and 240 other uncorrected samples. Winland found that the effective pore system that dominates flow through a rock corresponds to a mercury saturation of 35%. That pore system has pore throat radii (called port size, or r_{35}) equal to or smaller than the pore throats entered when a rock is saturated 35% with a nonwetting phase. After 35% of the pore system fills with a non-wetting phase fluid, the remaining pore system does not contribute to flow. Instead, it contributes to storage.

Pittman (1992) speculates, "Perhaps Winland found the best correlation to be r_{35} because that is where the average modal pore aperture occurs and where the pore network is developed to the point of serving as an effective pore system that dominates flow." The capillary pressure curve and pore throat size histogram below illustrate Pittman's point.

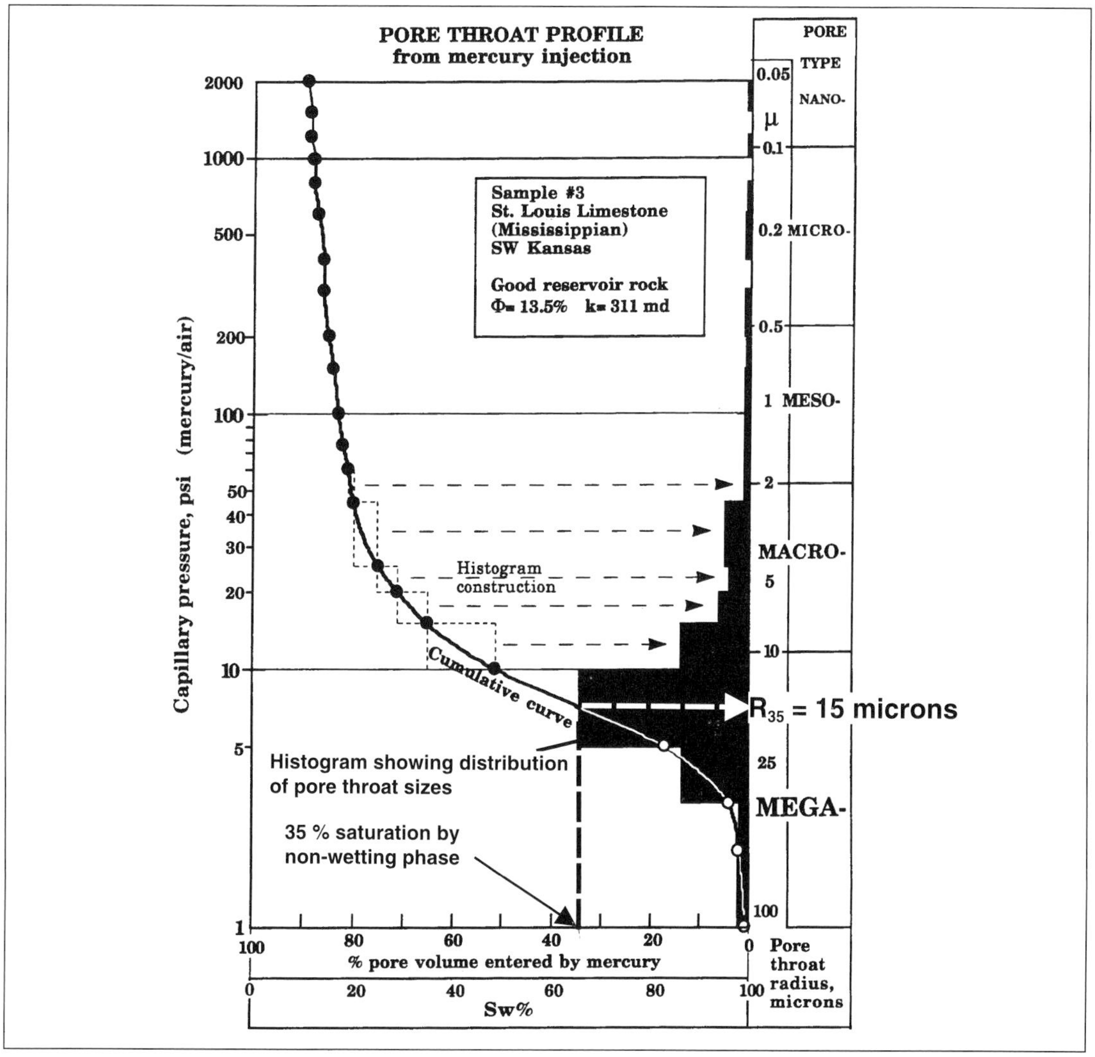

Figure 9–18. Modified from Doveton, 1995.

Characterizing Rock Quality, continued

The Winland r_{35} equation

Winland (1972, 1976) developed the following equation to calculate r_{35} for samples with intergranular or intercrystalline porosity:

$$\log r_{35} = 0.732 + 0.588 \log K_a - 0.864 \log \Phi$$

where:

K_a = air permeability, md
Φ = porosity, % (not decimals)

Solving for r:

$$r_{35} = 10^{\,0.732 + 0.588 \log K_a - 0.864 \log \Phi}$$

Characterizing rock quality with r_{35}

Rock quality is easily characterized using r_{35}. Consider the clusters of points representing flow units 1 and 2 (Figure 9–16) on the K_a/Φ plot below. The diagonal curved lines represent equal r_{35} values. Points plotting along the same lines represent rocks with similar r_{35} values and have similar quality. By interpolation, r_{35} for flow unit 1 is approximately 1.1μ, and r_{35} for flow unit 2 is approximately 3μ. The r_{35} in flow unit 2 is almost three times as large as flow unit 1. Therefore, flow unit 2 has better flow quality.

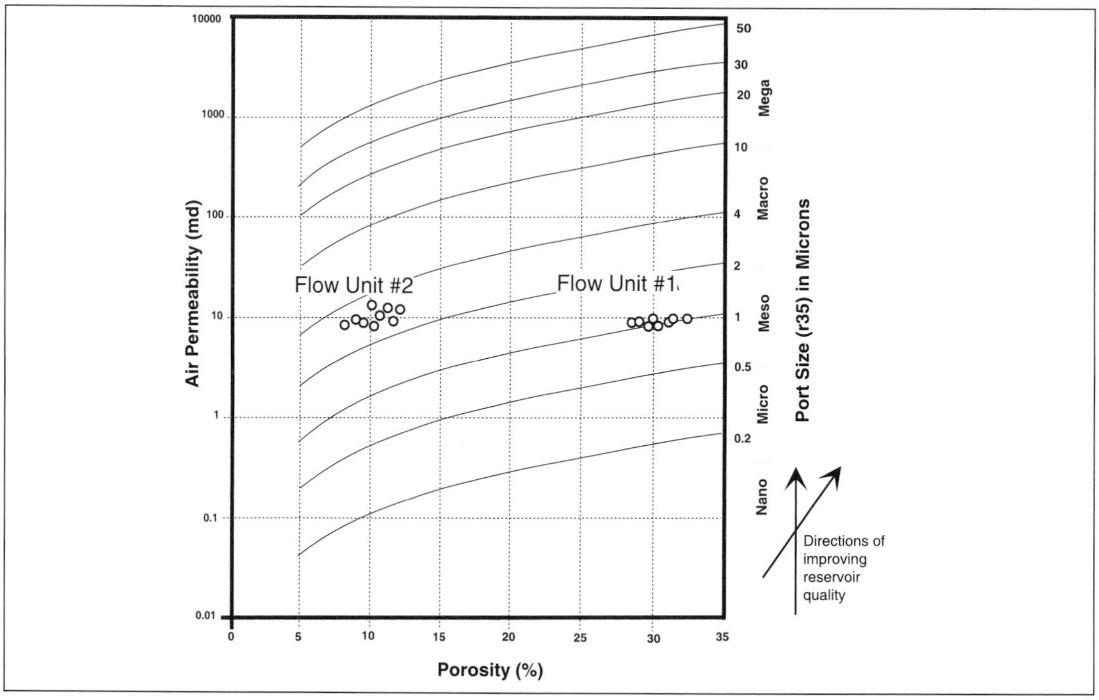

Figure 9–19.

Advantages of r_{35} over K_a/Φ ratio

Using r_{35} instead of the K_a/Φ ratio for characterizing rock quality of water-wet rocks has advantages:

- r_{35} is an understandable number; K_a/Φ ratio is a dimensionless number
- r_{35} can be determined from capillary pressure analysis and related to K_a/Φ values
- If two variables are known (K_a, Φ, or r_{35}), then the other variable can be calculated using Winland's equation or estimated from a K_a/Φ plot with r_{35} contours

Example capillary pressure curves

Hypothetical capillary pressure curves can be drawn by using r_{35} as a point on the curve. The capillary pressure curves below are hypothetical curves for the example presented in Figure 9–19. The curves demonstrate that entry pressures for flow unit 2 are less than those for flow unit 1; therefore, fluid flow in flow unit 2 is more efficient. In the figure below, it takes 28 ft of oil column for oil to enter 35% of pore space of flow unit 2 and 70 ft to enter 35% of pore space of flow unit 1.

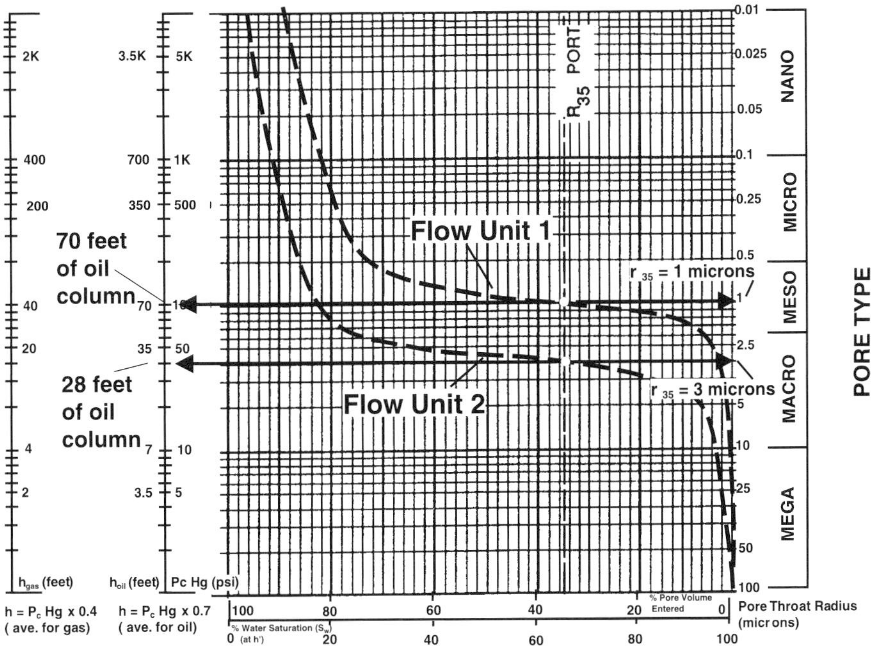

Figure 9–20.

Example relative permeability curves

Below are hypothetical drainage relative permeability curves to represent flow units 1 and 2.

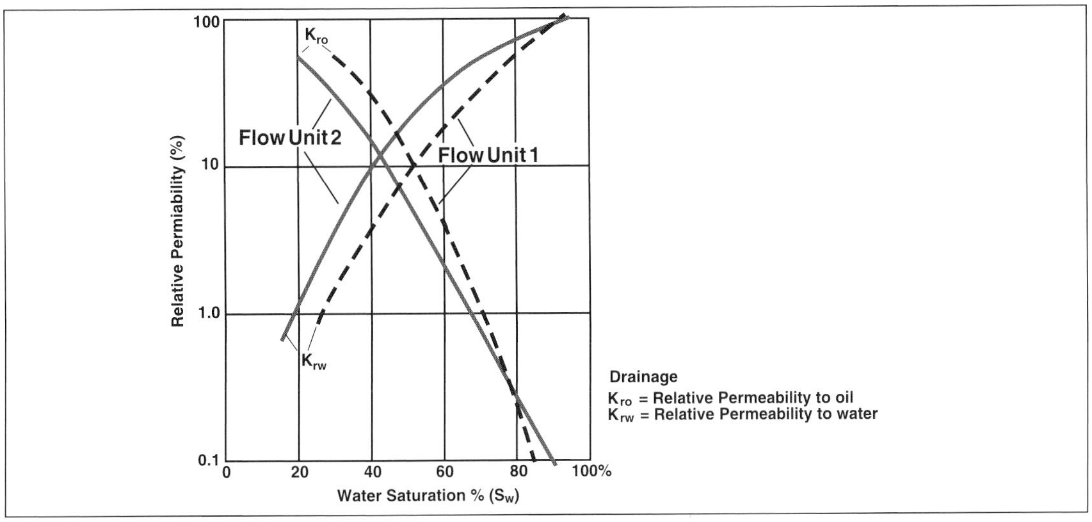

Figure 9–21.

P_c Curves and Saturation Profiles

Introduction

Water–hydrocarbon saturation profiles for a reservoir can be approximated using the capillary pressure (P_c) curves for the flow units it contains. The data in a P_c curve can be converted to give the following:

- An estimate of buoyancy pressures required to enter the pore throats of flow units.
- The radius of pore throats entered at a given buoyancy pressure.
- The water–hydrocarbon saturation of a flow unit at different buoyancy pressures.

Placing flow units into structural cross sections shows their position with respect to the free water level and buoyancy pressure profile. Using the structure sections, saturation profiles can be made for each flow unit, their corresponding containers, and the reservoir as a whole.

Pore throat size and saturation profiles

Water in the pore throats of rocks with macroporosity offers little capillary resistance to migrating hydrocarbons compared with the pore throats of rocks with microporosity. As a result, oil and gas migrate through a rock with macroporosity with minimal buoyancy pressure, i.e., hydrocarbon column. Macropore reservoirs have little or no saturation transition zone.

In rocks with microporosity, capillary forces hold water tightly to rock surfaces, decreasing the effective size of the already small pore throats. Therefore, a greater buoyancy pressure is required for oil or gas to migrate. Micropore reservoirs have longer saturation transition zones than macro- or mesoporous reservoirs; immobile water saturation is lower in macroporous rocks.

In the example reservoir cross section below, the rock in container 1 is mesoporous; the rock in container 2 is macroporous. Container 1 has a longer transition zone than container 2 because of this. Both containers have the same buoyancy pressure and free water level because the two containers are in pressure communication.

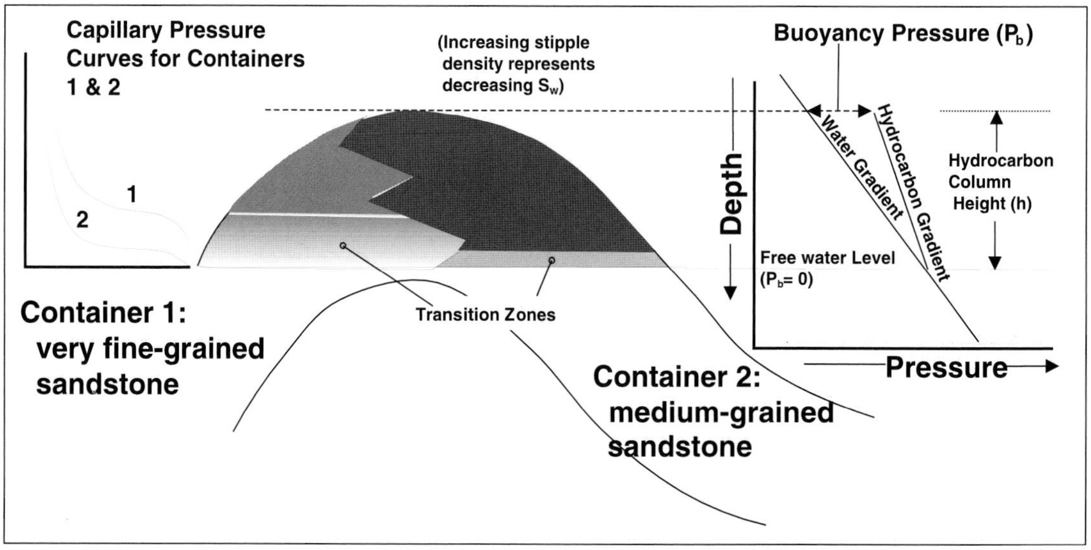

Figure 9–22.

P_c Curves and Saturation Profiles, continued

Pore throat size sorting

The graph below shows hypothetical examples of P_c curves for rocks with varying pore throat size sorting. The r_{35} value is the same for each sample; therefore, all three curves pass through the same point. The curves labeled A illustrate different pore throat size sorting. If the pore throats of the sample have a narrow range of sizes (i.e., are well sorted), the P_c curve will be flat as the pressure in the mercury reaches the entry pressure for those pore throats. If the range of pore throat sizes is wide, the curve will steepen.

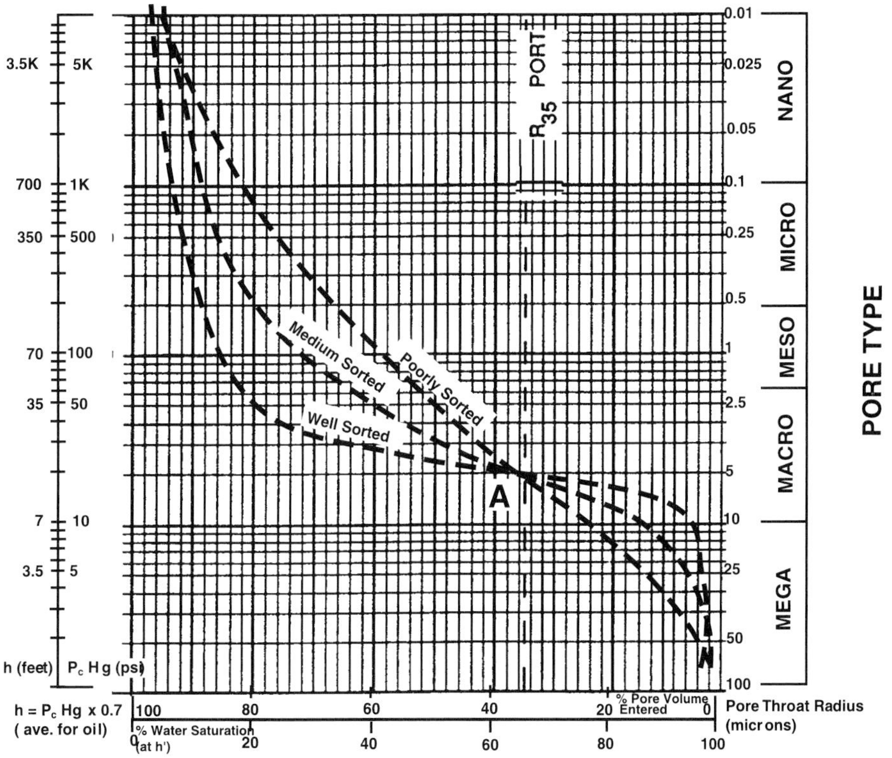

Figure 9–23.

Making S_w profiles from P_c curves

If a P_c curve is available, then a profile of S_w can be approximated using information from the curve. To make an S_w profile of a reservoir using a P_c curve, use the table below.

Step	Action
1	Convert pressure scale (Y-axis) to hydrocarbon column length (*h*), where h = $P_c \times$ conversion factor (if conversion is unknown, use 0.7 for oil and 0.4 for gas).
2	Using the same scales, plot the curve next to a structure section showing the trap. Place the base of the curve at the free water level (see Figure 9–23).
3	Estimate S_w for any point in the reservoir by reading the S_w that corresponds to the depth.

Converting P_c Curves to Buoyancy, Height, and Pore Throat Radius

Introduction

A capillary pressure (P_c) curve is generated in the lab using a mercury pressure cell, a porous plate, or a centrifuge. Fluid systems used in these techniques include air–water (brine), oil–water, air–mercury, or air–oil. Data generated by these techniques cannot be compared directly to each other or to reservoir conditions. Below, we demonstrate how to convert pressures measured in the lab to

- Standard pressure scale (mercury P_c)
- Reservoir pressure
- Height above free water
- Pore throat size

If true reservoir conditions are at least partially oil wet, then the water saturation–height plot shifts away from the pore volume–height plot (P_c curve).

Converting lab capillary pressure data

Follow the steps in the table below to convert P_c to buoyancy pressure, pore throat size (r), or hydrocarbon column height (h'). Assume water-wet conditions in the reservoir (γ = interfacial tension, Θ = contact angle).

Step	Action	Equation
1	Rescale P_c from one lab system to a common technique (i.e., air–brine to air–mercury).	$P_{c\ system1} = P_{c\ system2}(\gamma\cos\Theta$ of system1$/\gamma\cos\Theta$ of system2)
2	Convert lab P_c to reservoir P_c (i.e., air–mercury to water–oil).	$P_{c\ res} = P_{c\ lab}(\gamma\cos\Theta_{res}/\gamma\cos\Theta_{lab})$
3	Convert reservoir P_c to height (h').	$h' = P_{c\ res}/$(water gradient – hydrocarbon gradient) Typical gradients in psi/ft: Water = 0.433 – 0.45, Oil = 0.33, Gas = 0.07 (range = 0.001–0.22)
4	Convert lab P_c to pore throat radius (r) in microns.	$r = -2\gamma\cos\Theta/P_{c\ lab}$ or $C(\gamma\cos\Theta_{lab})/P_{c\ lab}$ where C is the constant 0.29

Example

The following is an example of applying the conversion of lab P_c data to reservoir conditions.

Use these assumptions:

- Maximum air–brine P_c value for a sample is 40 psi.
- Air–mercury is the base data set.
- The reservoir is oil filled.

Determine these parameters:

A. Equivalent air–mercury P_c ($P_{c\ Hg}$)
B. Equivalent oil P_c (buoyancy pressure in the reservoir)
C. Height above the free water (h')
D. Pore throat radius for $P_{c\ Hg}$ as determined at A

Converting P_c to Buoyancy, Height, and Pore Throat Radius, continued

Example (continued)

Answers (refer to the table below for values)

A. $P_{c\,Hg} = P_{c\,brine}\left(\frac{\gamma\cos\Theta \text{ for Hg}}{\gamma\cos\Theta \text{ for brine}}\right) = P_{c\,brine}\left(\frac{367}{72}\right) = 40(5.1) = 204 \text{ psi}$

B. Equivalent oil $P_c = P_{c\,lab}\left(\frac{\gamma\cos\Theta_{res}}{\gamma\cos\Theta_{lab}}\right) = P_{c\,lab}\left(\frac{26}{367}\right) = P_{c\,lab}\ (0.071) = 204(0.071) = 14.5 \text{ psi}$

C. $h = \frac{P_{c\,res}}{(\text{water gradient} - \text{hydrocarbon gradient})} = \frac{14.5}{(0.45 - 0.33)} = 120 \text{ ft}$

D. $r \text{ at } P_{c\,Hg} = \frac{-2\gamma\cos\Theta}{P_{c\,lab}} \text{ or } C\left(\frac{\gamma\cos\Theta_{lab}}{P_{c\,lab}}\right) = 0.29 \times \frac{367}{204} = 0.52\ \mu$

$P_{c\,Hg}$ is equivalent to $P_{c\,lab}$

Conversion variables

The conversion from one lab system to another requires values for the contact angle of the fluids to the grain surfaces (Θ) and interfacial tension (γ) between the two fluids. Theta is a reflection of wettability. This information is also required to determine an equivalent buoyancy pressure in the reservoir. Some typical lab and reservoir values are shown in the table below.

Laboratory Measurements				
System	Θ	**cos**Θ	γ	γ**cos**Θ
Air–water	0	1.0	72	72
Oil–water	30	0.866	48	42
Air–mercury	40	0.766	480	367
Air–oil	0	1.0	24	24
Reservoir Measurements				
System	Θ	**cos**Θ	γ	γ**cos**Θ
Water–oil	30	0.866	30	26
Water–gas	0	1.0	50	50

What is Permeability?

Introduction

Absolute permeability (K_a) is the property of a rock that characterizes the flow of fluid through its interconnected pores. It is a measure of the fluid conductivity of a rock. The permeability of a flow unit in a reservoir is not an absolute value but is a relative value that varies with water saturation (*see* "Relative Permeability and Pore Type" following). Understanding the methodology for permeability measurements is important for understanding how to assess reservoir rock quality or to compare the quality of one flow unit to another.

Horizontal and vertical K_a

Horizontal K_a (i.e., parallel to bedding) is generally greater than vertical K_a (i.e., normal to bedding) because of vertical changes in sorting and because of bedding laminations. High vertical K_a generally results from fracturing or even burrowing that cuts across bedding. Most K_a calculations are made from measurements of horizontal plugs.

Steady-state permeability equation

Permeability is not measured; it is calculated. The steady-state equation for calculating permeability (using an integrated form of Darcy's law) is

$$K_a = \frac{2000\, P_{atm} Q\, L\, \mu}{A\,(P_1 - P_2)}$$

where:

- K_a = permeability to air, md
- P_{atm} = atmospheric pressure, atm
- A = cross-sectional area of the plug face, cm^2
- Q = flow, cm^3/sec
- L = length, cm
- P_1 = pressure at input end, atm
- P_2 = pressure at output end, atm
- μ = air viscosity, cp

The following diagram of a plug illustrates some of these variables.

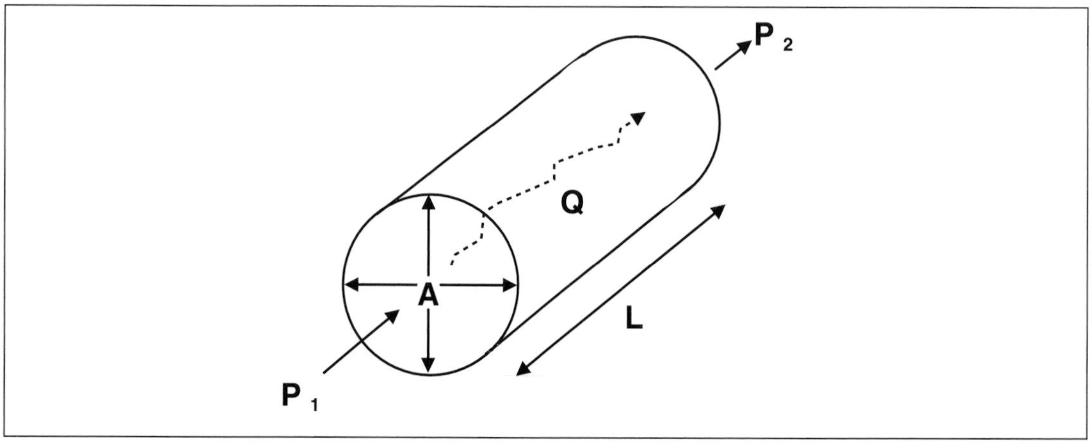

Figure 9–24.

Limitations of Darcy's equation

Why do two reservoirs with similar K_a but different porosities yield different performances? The standard conversion of air flow through a rock to K_a is accomplished using the Darcy relationship. Since the cross-sectional area (A) is of the plug face and not of the pores exposed on the surface of the plug, this equation cannot adjust for the ratio of number vs. size of pore throats exposed at the end of the plug.

Example

In the photos below, flow unit 1 is a sucrosic dolomite. On a face of a plug of flow unit 1, a very large number of very small pore throats (capillaries) occur, resulting in a measurable flow (Q). That Q, at a measured cross-sectional area A of the plug, yields a K_a of approximately 20 md.

The sample from flow unit 2 with the same A has fewer, larger pore throats (capillaries) exposed in the face of the plug. If the Q for flow unit 2 is slightly lower than flow unit 1, then the K_a will be lower (by using the same A).

Flow unit 1 has a porosity of 30%, and flow unit 2 has a porosity of 10%. The variance in porosity becomes the indicator of the contrast in pore throat size when converted to port size. For flow unit 1, the port size is approximately 1.1μ; for flow unit 2, port size is approximately 3μ.

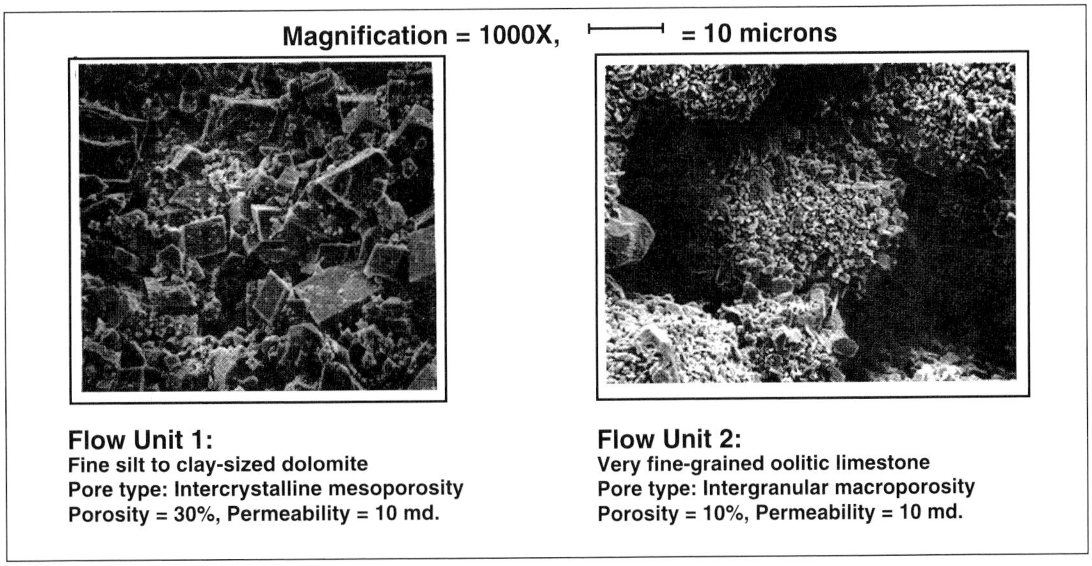

Magnification = 1000X, = 10 microns
Flow Unit 1:
Fine silt to clay-sized dolomite
Pore type: Intercrystalline mesoporosity
Porosity = 30%, Permeability = 10 md.
Flow Unit 2:
Very fine-grained oolitic limestone
Pore type: Intergranular macroporosity
Porosity = 10%, Permeability = 10 md.

Figure 9–25.

Relative Permeability and Pore Type

Absolute, effective, and relative permeability

Reservoirs contain water and oil or gas in varying amounts. Each interferes with and impedes the flow of the others. The aquifer portion of a reservoir system by definition contains water as a single phase (100% S_w). The permeability of that rock to water is absolute permeability (K_{ab}). The permeability of a reservoir rock to any one fluid in the presence of others is its effective permeability to that fluid. It depends on the values of fluid saturations. Relative permeability to oil (K_{ro}), gas (K_{rg}), or water (K_{rw}) is the ratio of effective permeability of oil, gas, or water to absolute permeability. Relative permeability can be expressed as a number between 0 and 1.0 or as a percent. Pore type and formation wettability affect relative permeability.

Why K_{ro} or K_{rg} is less than K_{ab}

A pore system saturated 100% with any fluid transmits that fluid at a rate relative to the pore throat size and the pressure differential. In the drawing below, the absolute pore throat size (A) is noted as the distance between grain surfaces. When a sample contains oil or gas and water (where water wets the grain surface), the pore throat size (B) for oil or gas flow is less than the absolute pore throat size (A). The thickness of the water layer coating the grains is proportional to the S_w of the rock. In other words, as buoyancy pressure increases, S_w decreases and the effective size of the pore throat for oil or gas flow (B) increases.

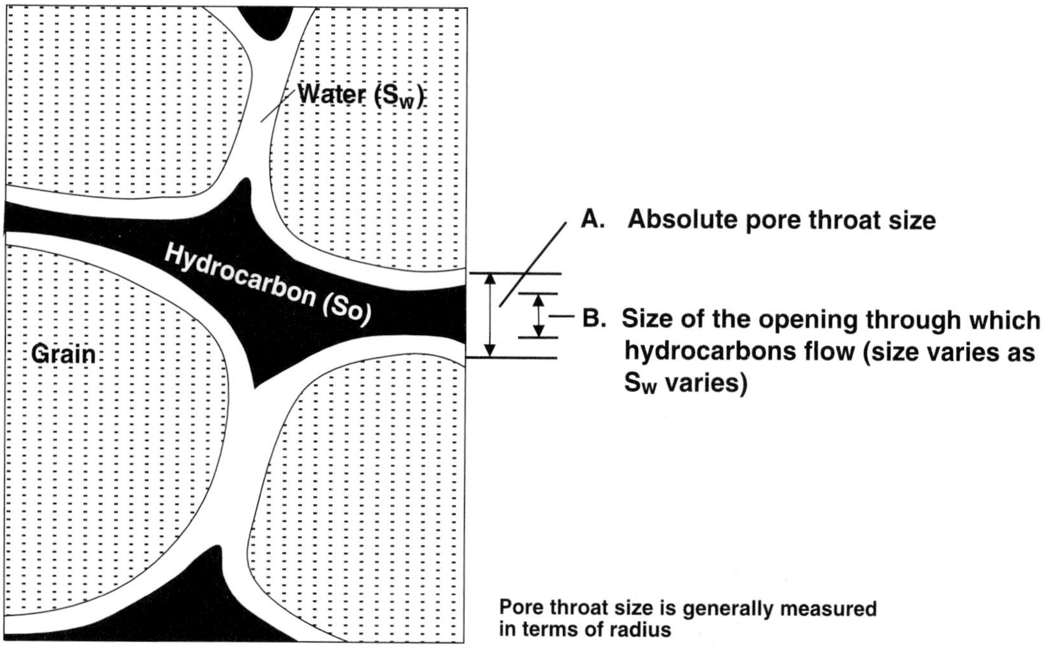

Figure 9–26.

Interpreting a relative permeability curve

The diagram below shows relationships between relative permeability curves (drainage and imbibition), capillary pressure, and fluid distribution in a homogeneous section of a reservoir system. The reservoir system rock has a porosity of 30% and a permeability of 10 md (r_{35} = 1.1μ). Laboratory single-phase air permeability is typically used to represent absolute permeability (K_a) when determining relative permeability to oil or water at a specific S_w.

The figure below depicts three relative permeability curves:

1. Water (K_{rw})—similar for both drainage and imbibition tests
2. Oil drainage ($K_{ro\text{-}D}$)—reflects migrating oil displacing water (decreasing S_w) with increasing buoyancy pressure (P_b)
3. Oil imbibition ($K_{ro\text{-}I}$)—reflects reduction in oil saturation (S_o) as a water front moves through a rock sample, resaturating it with water (S_{xo})

The curve labeled K_{ro} represents the relative permeability of a formation to oil in the presence of varying water saturation (S_w). The curve labeled K_{rw} represents the relative permeability of the formation to water.

Consider points A–D below. Point A, at S_w = 100%, is the original condition of the sample. Here $K_{rw} \approx K_a$ (10 md). At point B ($S_w \approx$ 90%, S_o = 10%), oil breaks through the sample, representing the migration saturation of the sample; K_{ro} = 1.0. At point C ($S_w \approx$ 50%, $S_o \approx$ 10%), K_{rw} is less than 1% of K_a and water, now confined to only the smallest ports, ceases to flow while oil flow approaches its maximum. At point D on the $K_{ro\text{-}D}$ curve ($S_w \approx$ 20%, $S_o \approx$ 80%), relative permeability is approaching 1.0 (~ 10 md).

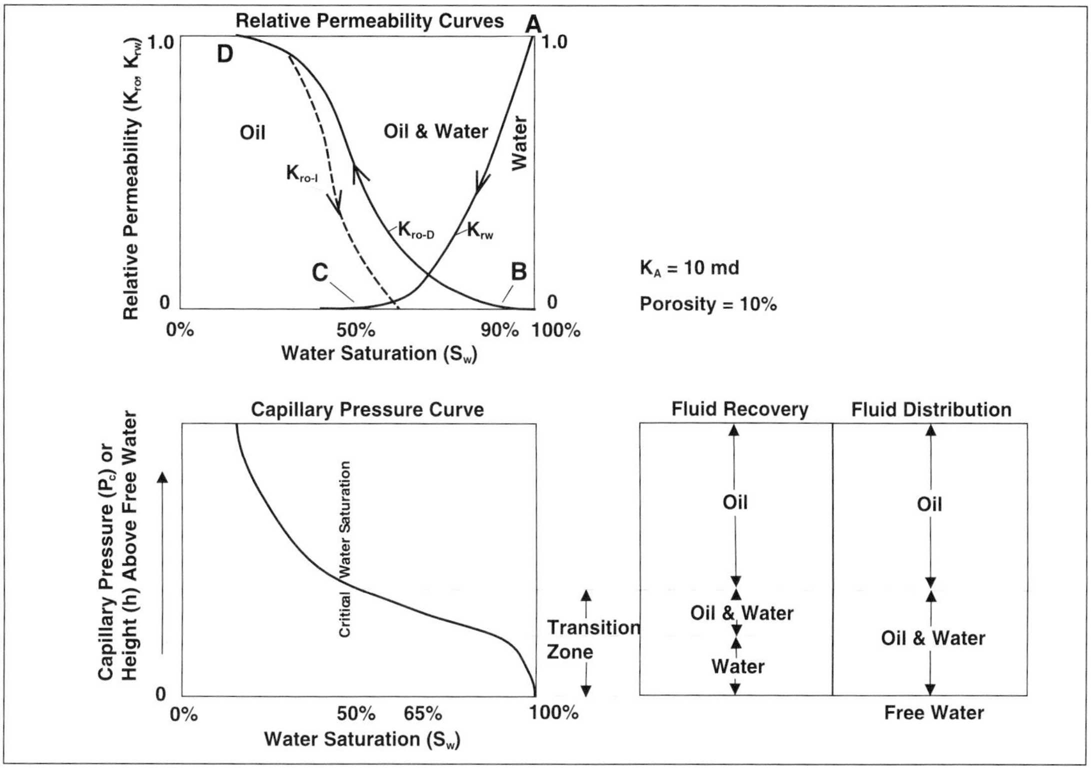

Figure 9–27. Modified from Arps, 1964; courtesy AAPG.

Interpreting a relative permeability curve (continued)

Figure 9–27 is an example of "drainage" relative permeability of a water-wet reservoir. It shows changes in K_{ro} and K_{rw} as S_w decreases, as in a water-drive reservoir during hydrocarbon fill-up. "Imbibition" K_{ro} and K_{rw} have a different aspect, being measured while S_w increases, as it does during production in a reservoir with a water drive.

Drainage vs. imbibition curves

The **drainage curve** determines from computed S_w whether a zone is representative of lower transitional ($K_{rw} > K_{ro} - D$), upper transitional ($K_{rw} < K_{ro} - D$), or free oil ($K_{rw} \approx 0$). The **imbibition curve** relates to performance due to filtrate invasion from water injection or flushing from natural water drive.

Pore throat size and K_r

Every pore type has a unique relative permeability signature. Consider the hypothetical drainage relative permeability type curves shown below. Curves A, B, and C represent the relative permeability relationships for rocks with different port types: macro, meso, and micro, respectively. Curve A represents a rock with greater performance capability than B or C. Note how critical water saturation decreases as pore throat size increases. Also note the changing position of K_{ro}–K_{rw} crossover with changes in pore throat size.

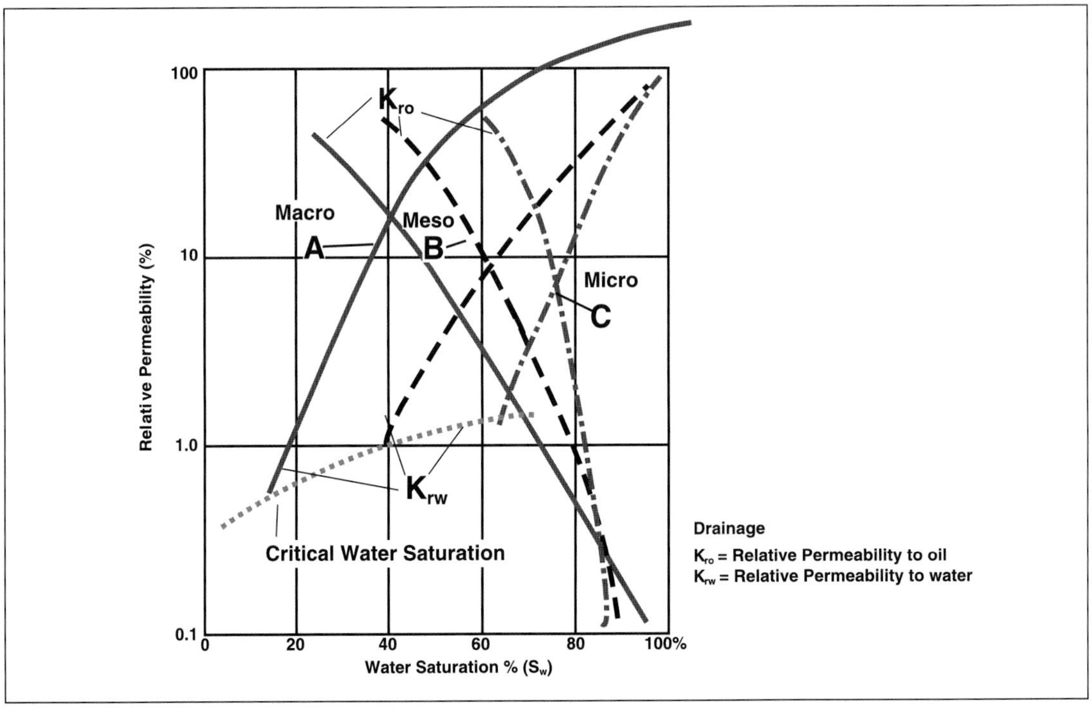

Figure 9–28.

Critical water saturation

Critical S_w is the point where water saturation is so low that no significant water cut can be measured; only hydrocarbon flows from the reservoir. At S_w higher than critical S_w, water flows with hydrocarbon. Where S_w becomes great enough, only water flows.

Critical water saturation (continued)

The critical S_w value is different for each port type. Curve A in Figure 9–28 represents rocks with macroporosity. It has a critical S_w less than 20%. Curve B represents a rock with mesoporosity. Mesoporous rocks have a critical S_w of 20–60%. Curve C represents rocks with microporosity. They have a critical S_w of 60–80%.

The table below summarizes representative critical S_w values for macro-, meso-, and micropore types that correspond to A, B, and C, respectively, in Figure 9–28.

Pore type	Micro	Meso	Macro
Critical S_w	60–80%	20–60%	<20%
Length of transition zone	>30 m	2–30 m	0–2 m

Section D
Water Saturation

Introduction

Water saturation of a reservoir is a function of height above free water (*h*) and pore type. S_w interpretations should be made accounting for h, r_{35}, and pore throat size distribution in the reservoir. The Archie equation is the most widely used method of determining S_w.

This section discusses how to calculate S_w from the Archie equation using various numerical and graphical techniques and how to interpret the results.

In this section

This section contains the following subsections.

Subsection D1
Determining Water Saturation

Introduction

Water saturation can be measured directly from a sealed core, which is an expensive method, or it can be calculated from the Archie equation, which is less expensive. S_w can also be estimated using a graphical representation of the Archie equation known as the Pickett crossplot. This subsection discusses how to calculate S_w using the Archie equation, how to determine values for variables of the Archie equation, and how to make a Pickett crossplot.

In this subsection

This subsection contains the following topics.

Calculating S_w from the Archie Equation

What is the Archie equation?

Archie (1942) developed his famous equation to calculate, from well log parameters, the water saturation (S_w) of the uninvaded zone in a formation next to a borehole. The Archie equation can be expressed as follows:

$$S_w{}^n = \frac{R_w}{(\Phi^m \cdot R_t)}$$

where:

- S_w = water saturation of the uninvaded zone
- n = saturation exponent, which varies from 1.8 to 4.0 but normally is 2.0
- R_w = formation water resistivity at formation temperature
- Φ = porosity
- m = cementation exponent, which varies from 1.7 to 3.0 but normally is 2.0
- R_t = true resistivity of the formation, corrected for invasion, borehole, thin bed, and other effects

Limitations of the Archie equation

Even though numerous other relationships have been developed over the years, the Archie equation remains the most flexible and generally useful approach. Yet its proper application requires knowledge of its limitations. The equation was empirical in origin and therefore needs modification in rock–fluid combinations different from Archie's experiments. Modifications need to be made in rocks with the following characteristics:

- Non-Archie pore geometries (i.e., not intergranular or intercrystalline)
- Conductive minerals such as clays and pyrite
- Very fresh formation waters

Caveat

This section discusses the Archie equation in general terms; suggested methods are most useful when dealing with modern log suites of good quality.

Deriving values for Archie variables

Values for the five Archie variables are relatively easy to derive when a formation is thick, has a clay-free matrix, and/or is dominated by intergranular or intercrystalline porosity (Archie porosity). Formations that are thin bedded (i.e., below limits of logging tool resolution), have clay in their matrix, or have moldic, vuggy, or fracture porosity require adjustments. The table below lists the five variables and methods for deriving or estimating them.

Step	Find	Use...	If...	Then...
1	n	• 2.0 for Archie porosity • 1.8 (or less) for rocks with clayey matrix or fractures • 4.0 for very strongly oil-wet rocks	Not sure of rock type	Use 2.0
2	R_w	• Value calculated from SP log • Estimated from R_w catalogs • Estimated from wet zone R_o value • Measured from water sample	Thin beds, hydrocarbons in zone, or fresh formation waters make SP calculations uncertain	Use thin-bed correction or another method
3	Φ	Value derived from cores, density, density–neutron, or sonic logs	Density–neutron log matrix setting does not match formation matrix	Use density–neutron crossplot
4	m	• 2.0 for Archie porosity • 1.7–2.0 for shaly sandstones • 2.0–2.5 for porosity with connected vugs • 2.5–3.0 for nonconnected moldic porosity • ~1.0 for fractured rocks	Not sure of rock type or pore geometry	Use 2.0
5	R_t	Value derived from deep resistivity log such as RILD or RLLD	Beds are thin, invasion occurred or borehole has washouts	Use chartbook corrections

Determining R_t

Introduction

The true resistivity (R_t) of a formation is its resistivity when not contaminated by drilling fluids. It may contain formation water only (S_w = 100%) or formation water and hydrocarbons (S_w < 100%). Using a valid R_t is fundamental when analyzing well logs for the presence of hydrocarbons. For a discussion of resistivity concepts see Asquith, 1982.

How invasion affects R_t measurement

During the drilling process, filtrate water from the drilling fluid invades the formation. Its resistivity (R_{mf}) is either greater than, less than, or equal to R_t and can distort deep resistivities. Distortions to resistivities due to invasion must be corrected to get a valid R_t value. The diagram below shows resistivity profiles of formations with fresh and saltwater mud filtrate invasion.

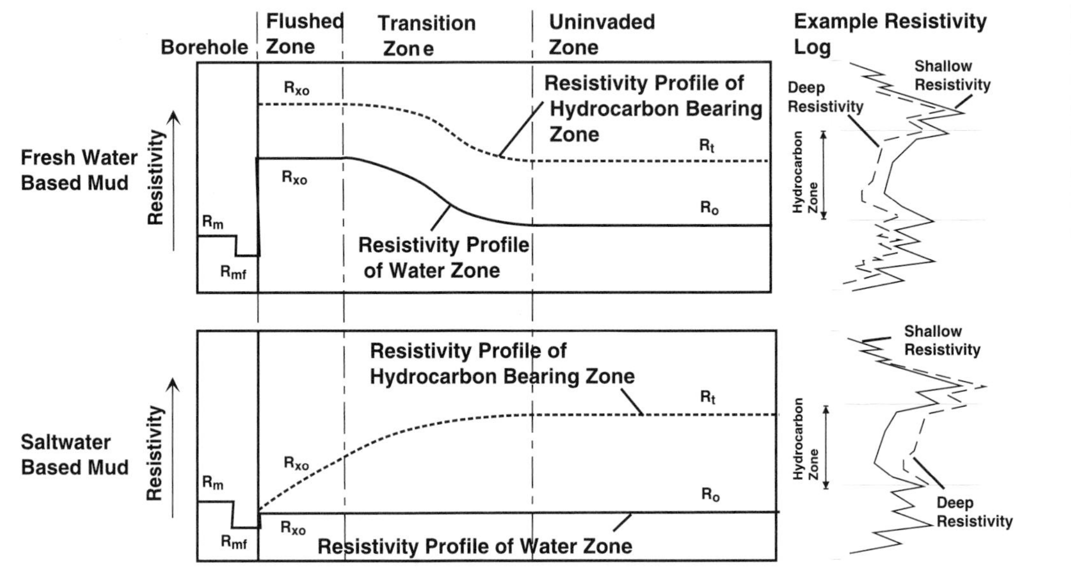

Where R_m = mud resistivity, R_{mf} = mud filtrate resistivity, R_{xo}= flushed zone resistivity, R_o = resistivity of formation 100% water saturated, R_t = uninvaded zone resistivity

Figure 9–29.

Obtaining a valid R_t value

Use the table below to obtain an uninvaded zone resistivity (R_t).

<table>
<tr><th>Step</th><th>Action</th></tr>
<tr><td>1</td><td>Read the resistivity of the log with deepest investigation (ILD, LLD, etc.).</td></tr>
<tr><td>2</td><td>Use the table below to determine how to make corrections.
<table>
<tr><th>If...</th><th>Then...</th></tr>
<tr><td>Bed is < 20 ft thick for an induction log or < 4 ft thick for a laterolog</td><td>Correct for this bed using appropriate service company chart</td></tr>
<tr><td>Shallow, medium, and deep investigating tools measure, different resistivities (i.e., log has step profile)</td><td>Correct for invasion using appropriate service company tornado chart</td></tr>
</table></td></tr>
</table>

Determining Porosity from Density–Neutron Logs

Introduction

The combination of the density and neutron logs provides a good source of porosity data, especially in formations of complex lithology. Better estimates of porosity are possible with the combination than using either tool or sonic separately because inferences about lithology and fluid content can be made.

Density log

The density log measures the electron density of a formation. The logging device is a contact tool that emits gamma rays from a source. Emitted gamma rays collide with formation electrons and scatter. A detector, located a fixed distance from the tool source, counts the number of returning gamma rays. The number of returning gamma rays is an indicator of formation bulk density. The litho-density tool (LDT) also provides a photoelectron (P_e) cross section curve, an independent indicator of lithology.

Obtaining porosities from a density log

Formation bulk density is a function of matrix density, porosity, and fluids contained in the pore space. Formation bulk density measured by the log must be corrected for borehole irregularities. Convert bulk density to porosity using charts in a log interpretation chartbook, or calculate porosity from bulk density using this equation:

$$\Phi = \frac{\rho_{ma} - \rho_b}{\rho_{ma} - \rho_f}$$

where:

Φ = porosity
ρ_{ma} = matrix density (see table below)
ρ_b = formation bulk density (log value)
ρ_f = density of the fluid saturating the rock immediately surrounding the borehole—usually mud filtrate (use 1.0 for freshwater and 1.1 for saltwater mud)

Use the lithology matrix densities to determine porosity and average P_e to determine lithology listed in the table below.

Lithology	Density, g/cc	Average P_e
Sandstone	2.65	1.8
Limestone	2.71	4.8
Dolomite	2.876	3.0
Anhydrite	2.977	5.05
Salt	2.032	4.6

Neutron log

The neutron log mainly measures hydrogen concentration in a formation. The logging device is a noncontact tool that emits neutrons from a source. Emitted neutrons collide with nuclei of the formation and lose some of their energy. Maximum energy loss occurs when emitted neutrons collide with hydrogen atoms because a neutron and a hydrogen atom have almost the same mass. Therefore, most neutron energy loss occurs in the part of the formation that has the highest hydrogen concentration.

Neutron energy loss can be related to porosity because in porous formations, hydrogen is concentrated in the fluid filling the pores. Reservoirs whose pores are gas filled may have a lower porosity than the same pores filled with oil or water because gas has a lower concentration of hydrogen atoms than either oil or water.

Obtaining porosities from a neutron log

Lithology, porosity, fluid type, and tool type affect neutron log response. When interpreting neutron logs, use the specific log for the specific tool, i.e., the charts in logging chart books that are specific to the sidewall neutron log (SNP) or the compensated neutron log (CNL).

To obtain porosity, read the value directly from the log. If the log is recorded in limestone units and the formation you wish to evaluate is sandstone or dolomite, then correct the log value by using the appropriate chart in a log interpretation chartbook.

Combination density–neutron logs

The density–neutron log is a combination log that simultaneously records neutron and density porosity. In some zones, porosities recorded on the logs differ for three reasons:

- The matrix density used by the logging program to calculate porosity is different from the actual formation matrix density.
- Gas is present in the formation pore space.
- Shale/clay is present in the formation.

Obtaining porosity from density–neutron logs

It is always best to read porosities directly from the logs where the lithologic units match the formation lithology. To obtain correct porosities from density–neutron logs when the two logs record different porosities for a zone, use one of the methods listed below.

Condition	Method
Log matrix lithology is known and the two log curves separate (density porosity is less than neutron porosity)	If density porosity is less than neutron porosity, such as in a sandstone with shale/clay content, the density log provides a reasonable approximation of formation porosity.
Log matrix lithology is known and there is crossover (density porosity is greater than neutron porosity)	Crossover (density porosity is greater than neutron porosity) is due to the presence of gas in the formation. Recompute density porosity using $\Phi = \frac{\rho_{ma} - \rho_b}{\rho_{ma} - \rho_f}$ Use gas density instead of water density.
Chartbook is available	Plot the porosities on a density–neutron crossplot from a log interpretation chartbook. Use the appropriate crossplot for the log type (i.e., SNP, CNL) and mud type (fresh or salt).
Chartbook is not available	Calculate porosity using the equation $\Phi = \left(\frac{\Phi_N^2 + \Phi_D^2}{2}\right)^{1/2}$ where Φ is percent porosity, Φ_N is neutron percent porosity, and Φ_D is density percent porosity.

Determining Porosity from Density–Neutron Logs, continued

Example density–neutron log

The example log below was recorded in sandstone units. Where the density and neutron logs nearly track together, the formation lithology normally is assumed to be sandstone (in the figure below). The slight separations may be due to changes in lithology as in more shale/clay. Where the density and neutron logs separate, either the lithology is different (neutron porosity > density porosity) from the recorded lithologic units (points 1 and 5) or gas is present (points 2, 3, and 4). A density–neutron crossplot resolves the separation problem (see Figure 9–31).

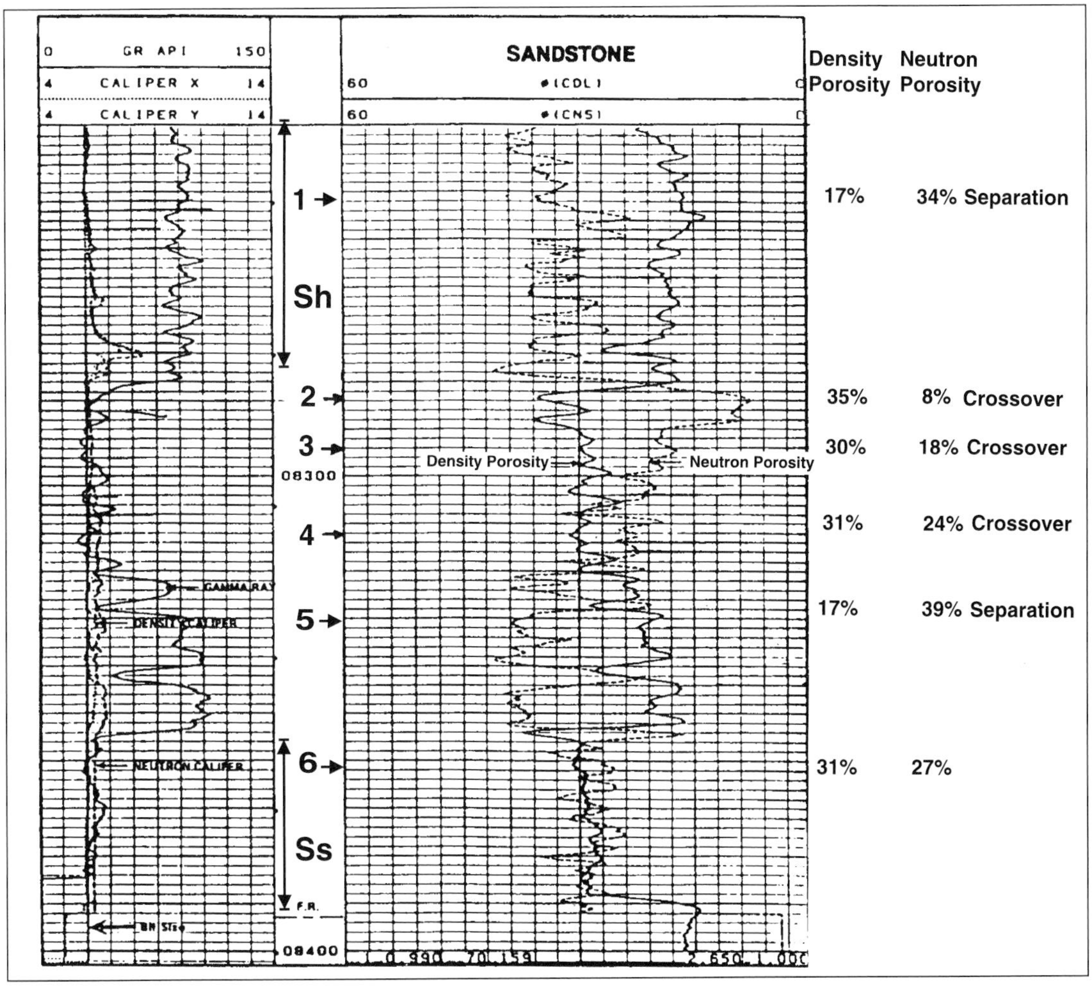

Figure 9–30. From Alberty, 1994; courtesy AAPG.

Using a density–neutron crossplot

To determine lithology or correct porosities for lithologic or gas effects from a density–neutron crossplot, follow the steps listed in the table below.

<table>
<tr><th>Step</th><th>Action</th></tr>
<tr><td>1</td><td>Use the table below to determine how to enter a neutron porosity value.
<table>
<tr><th>If...</th><th>Then...</th></tr>
<tr><td>Neutron porosity is in limestone units</td><td>Enter the chart along the x-axis with neutron porosity. Project up to density porosity.</td></tr>
<tr><td>Neutron porosity is in sandstone or dolomite units</td><td>Enter the chart on the sandstone or dolomite line. Project up or down to a density value.</td></tr>
</table></td></tr>
<tr><td>2</td><td>Use the table below to determine how to enter a density porosity value
<table>
<tr><th>If...</th><th>Then...</th></tr>
<tr><td>Density log porosity is in sandstone, limestone or dolomite units</td><td>Find the density log percent porosity value on the diagonal line that matches the lithologic units recorded on the log (i.e., use the sandstone line if the log was recorded in sandstone units). Move left or right to intercept the neutron projection.</td></tr>
<tr><td>Density log scale is bulk density</td><td>Enter the y-axis with the log bulk density value and intercept the neutron projection.</td></tr>
</table></td></tr>
<tr><td>3</td><td>Use the table below to determine formation lithology and porosity.
<table>
<tr><th>If...</th><th>Then...</th></tr>
<tr><td>Point falls on a diagonal line</td><td>The point defines the lithology of the formation by which line it falls on and the porosity is the value marked on the line at that point.</td></tr>
<tr><td>Point falls away from appropriate diagonal line</td><td>Move down and to the right parallel to the nearest dashed line until a diagonal line is intersected. Read the value for porosity at that point. The lithology is a combination of the lithologies of the lines on either side of the point of intersection. Gas is present if the original point is northwest of the appropriate diagonal lithology line.</td></tr>
</table></td></tr>
</table>

Example density–neutron crossplot

The figure below is an example density–neutron crossplot. Points 1–5 are from the log (Figure 9–30). Points 2, 3, and 4 are from a zone that shows crossover. Crossover occurs when the density log reads higher than the neutron log in a zone of the same lithology as the log matrix lithology, i.e., sandstone. Point 2 has the greatest crossover; Point 4, the least. Once completed, the well from which this log was taken showed Point 2 to be in a gas reservoir, Point 3 to be in light oil reservoir, and Point 4 to be in a zone with residual oil.

Porosities corrected for gas effect are 24%, 25%, and 28%. Points 1 and 5 are in shale zones, even though they plot as dolomite. They are shale reference points for this interval of the log.

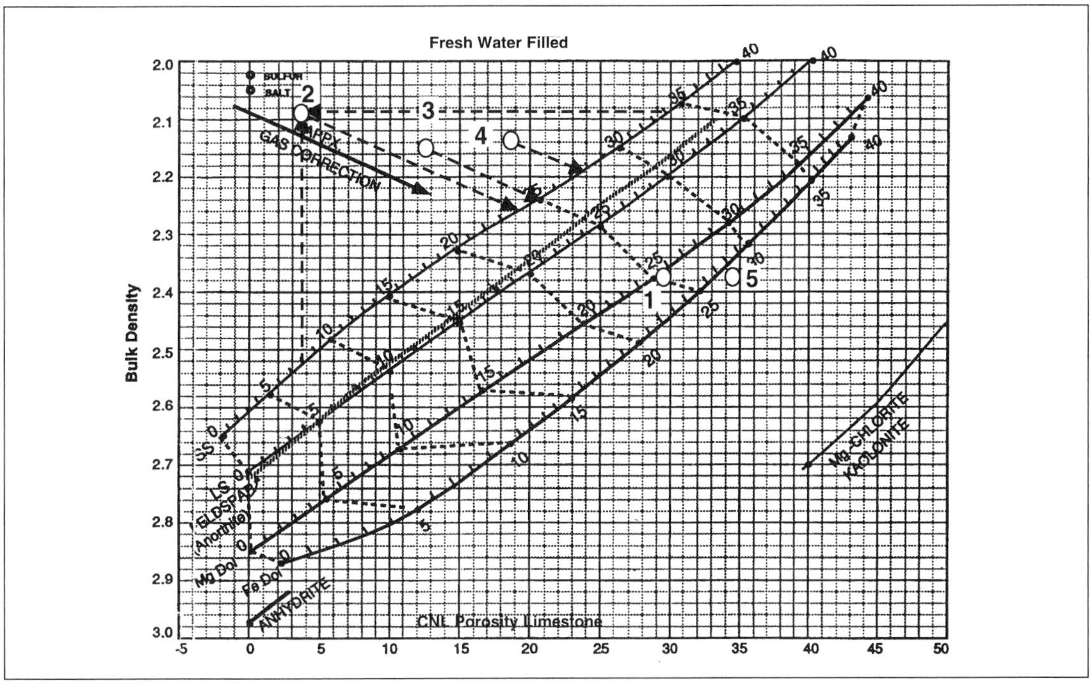

Figure 9–31. From Alberty (1992); courtesy AAPG.

Stratigraphic knowledge critical to interpretation

The density–neutron crossplot helps determine lithology of oil- or water-filled formations that are pure lithologies like sandstone, limestone, or dolomite. The density–neutron crossplot analysis can be ambiguous when the formation is of mixed mineralogies, like a dolomite-cemented sandstone.

When gas is present, the situation is much more complicated. Knowing the mineralogical compositions of formations to be drilled is critical when interpreting a density–neutron crossplot and predicting the presence of gas.

As an example, the presence of clay in a sandstone drives a crossplot point toward the shale reference point. Adding gas to the same sandstone makes it look like a clean sandstone. As another example, add gas to a dolomite and it looks like a limestone, not a dolomite with gas. In both cases, if we know the stratigraphic details, we can interpret the presence of gas from the crossplot.

Calculating R_w from SP Logs

Introduction

Water resistivity, or R_w, is a critical component of log analysis in calculating water saturation using the Archie equation. R_w can be measured from a sample of formation water taken from the zone of interest at the well site or a nearby well, or it can be calculated using spontaneous potential (SP) log data.

Data required

To calculate R_w from SP, we need the following data:

- Resistivity of the mud filtrate (R_{mf}) at measured temperature, found on the log header. If only mud resistivity (R_m) is given, convert it to R_{mf} as explained below.
- Bottom-hole temperature (BHT) and total depth, found on the log header.
- SP reading from a porous zone at least 20 ft thick. (A bed thickness correction is necessary if the zone SP is measured from is less than 20 ft thick.)

Converting R_m to R_{mf}

If the log header gives R_m only, then R_m must be converted to R_{mf} using this procedure:

Step	Action
1	Enter R_m and move across (Figure 9–32) to the appropriate mud weight.
2	Project to the bottom of the chart to estimate R_{mf}.

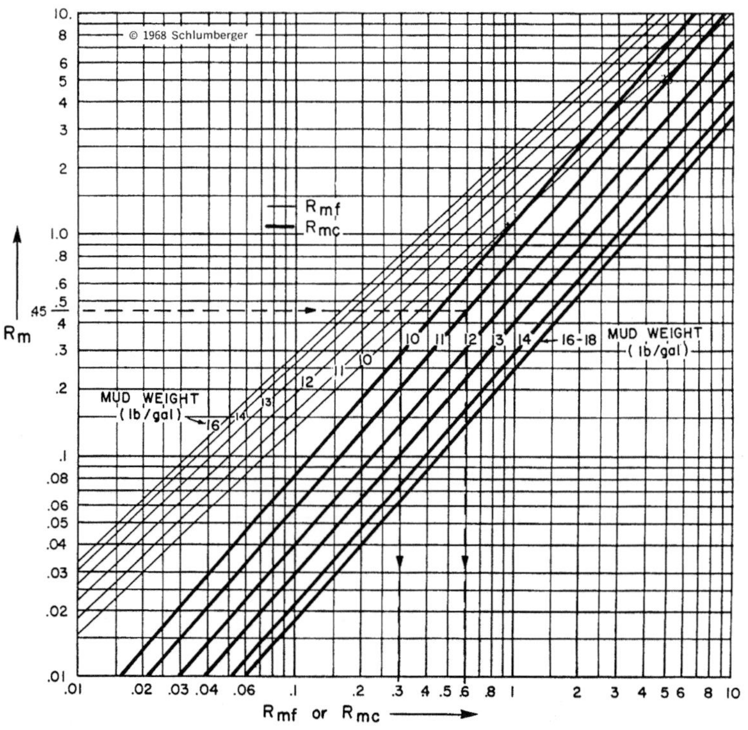

Figure 9–32. Courtesy Schlumberger.

Note: It is better to have a measured R_{mf}, but most service companies use a calculated R_{mf}.

Calculating R_w from SP Logs, continued

Steps for calculating R_w

There are five steps for calculating R_w from the SP log. The table below summarizes these steps, which are detailed in the rest of this section.

Step	Action
1	Estimate formation temperature.
2	Convert R_{mf} to formation temperature.
3	Convert R_{mf} to $R_{mf\ eq}$.
4	Read SP response and estimate R_{we}.
5	Convert R_{we} to R_w and NaCl at formation temperature.

Step 1: Estimate formation temperature

Formation temperature (T_f) can be estimated by using the following formula:

$$T_f = T_s + D_f \frac{BHT - T_s}{TD}$$

where:

T_s = average surface temperature
D_f = depth to the formation
BHT = bottom-hole temperature (found on log header)
TD = total depth (make sure BHT and TD are from same log run)

Step 2: Convert R_{mf} to R_{mf} at formation temperature

Follow this procedure to convert R_{mf} (measured at surface temperature) to R_{mf} at formation temperature.

Step	Action
1	Enter Figure 9–33 along the resistivity of solution axis and the temperature axis using the measured values for R_{mf} and surface temperature found on the log header.
2	Follow the appropriate salinity line intercepted at step 1 to the appropriate formation temperature and mark on the chart.
3	Project down the chart from this mark to the resistivity scale and read R_{mf} at formation temperature. Record the value of R_{mf} at a specific temperature.

Calculating R_w from SP Logs, continued

Step 2: Convert R_{mf} to formation temperature (continued)

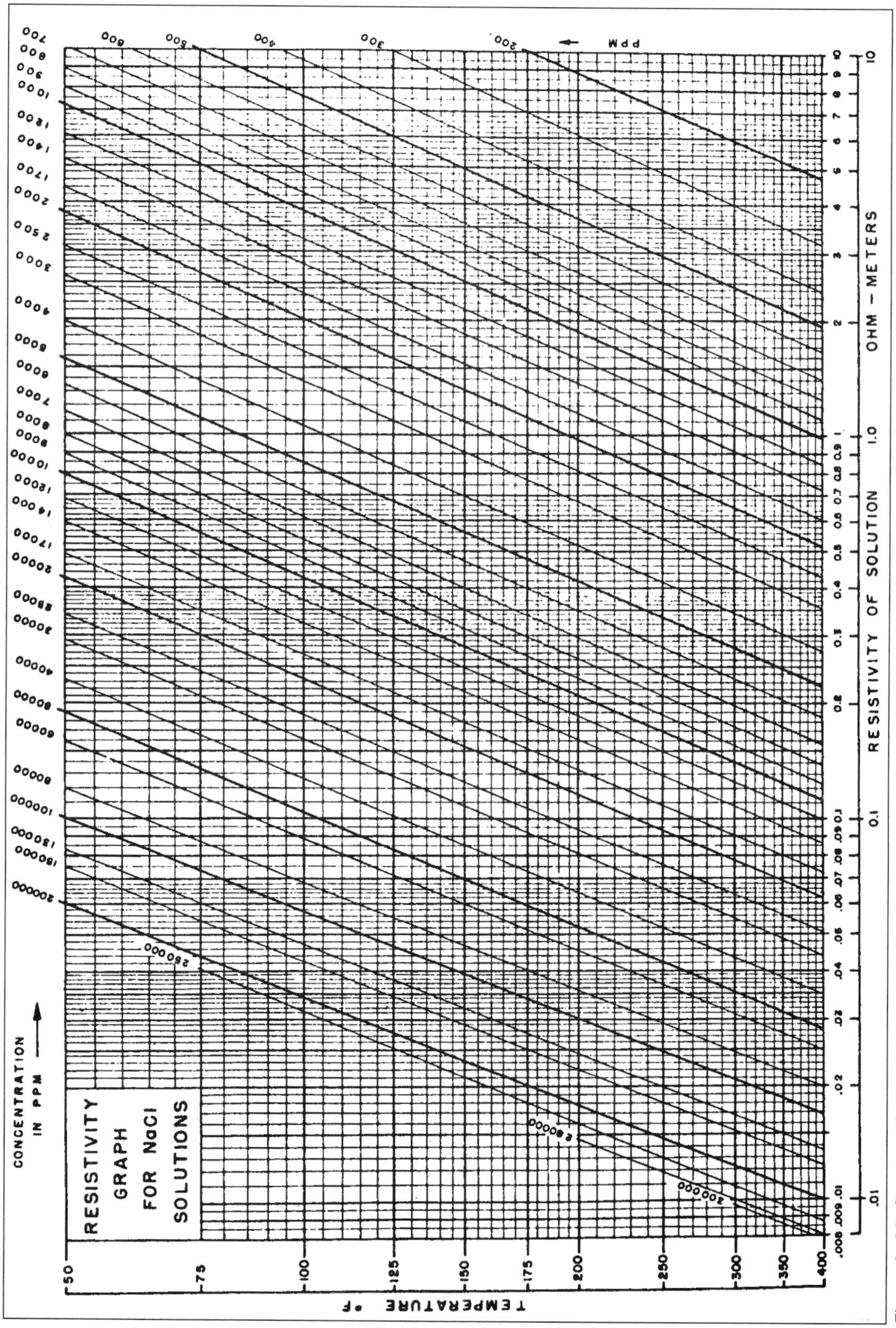

Figure 9–33. Courtesy Schlumberger.

Calculating R_w from SP Logs, continued

Step 3: Convert R_{mf} to $R_{mf\ eq}$

Use the R_{mf} at formation temperature obtained above and follow the procedure below to convert R_{mf} to equivalent mud filtrate resistivity ($R_{mf\ eq}$).

Step	Action
1	Enter Figure 9–34 with R_{mf} at formation temperature on the vertical axis.
2	Move across the chart to the appropriate formation temperature contour, and mark this point on the figure.
3	Read down to $R_{mf\ eq}$. This value is used in the equation $R_{we} = R_{mf\ eq}$ ($R_{mf\ eq}/R_{we}$ value).

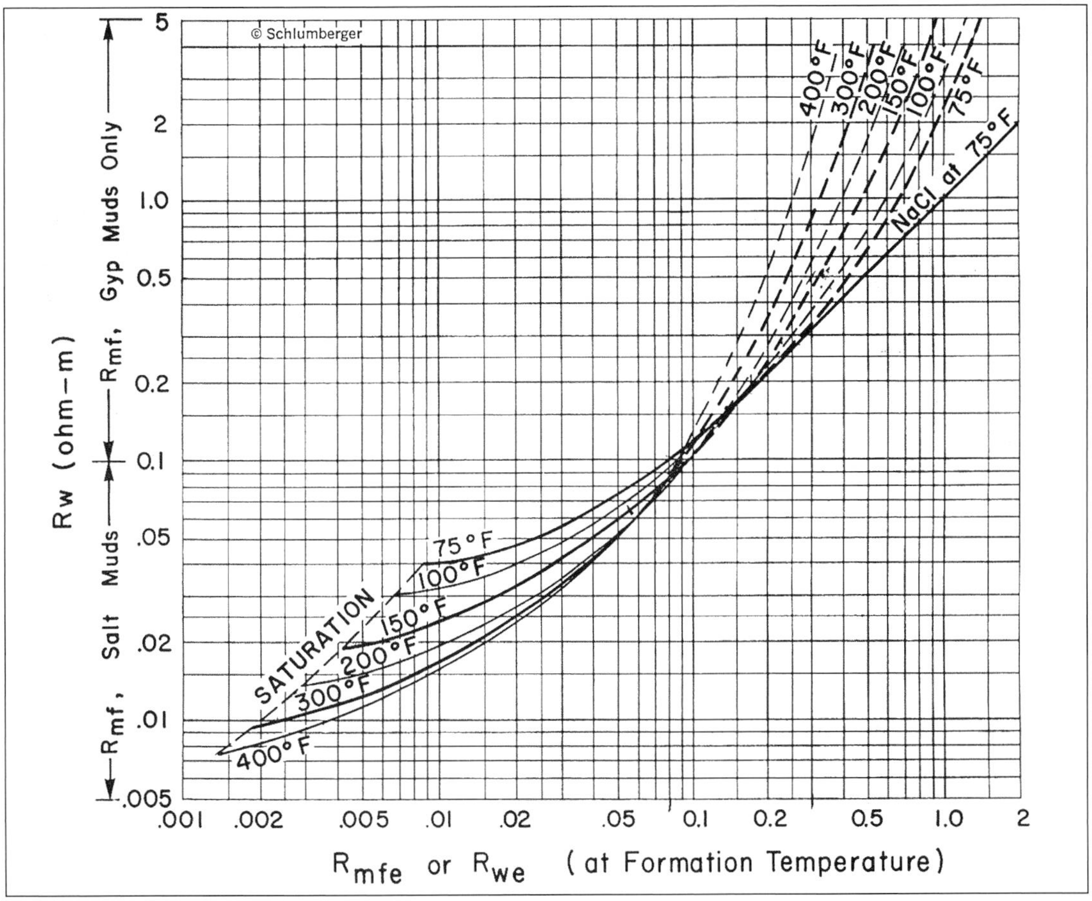

Figure 9–34. Courtesy Schlumberger.

Calculating R_w from SP Logs, continued

Step 4: Convert SP to R_{we}

Follow the procedure below to convert SP from the zone of interest to equivalent formation water resistivity (R_{we}).

Step	Action
1	On the log, establish the shale base line for the SP curve.
2	Read the maximum SP response in a zone at least 20 ft thick.
3	Enter the base of Figure 9–35 with SP (SP is negative if it deflects to the left of the shale base line). Follow the SP grid line up the chart to the appropriate formation temperature. At this point, move across the chart and read the $R_{mf\ eq}/R_{we}$ value.
4	Solve for R_{we} using the equation $R_{we} = R_{mf\ eq}/(R_{mf\ eq}/R_{we}$ value).

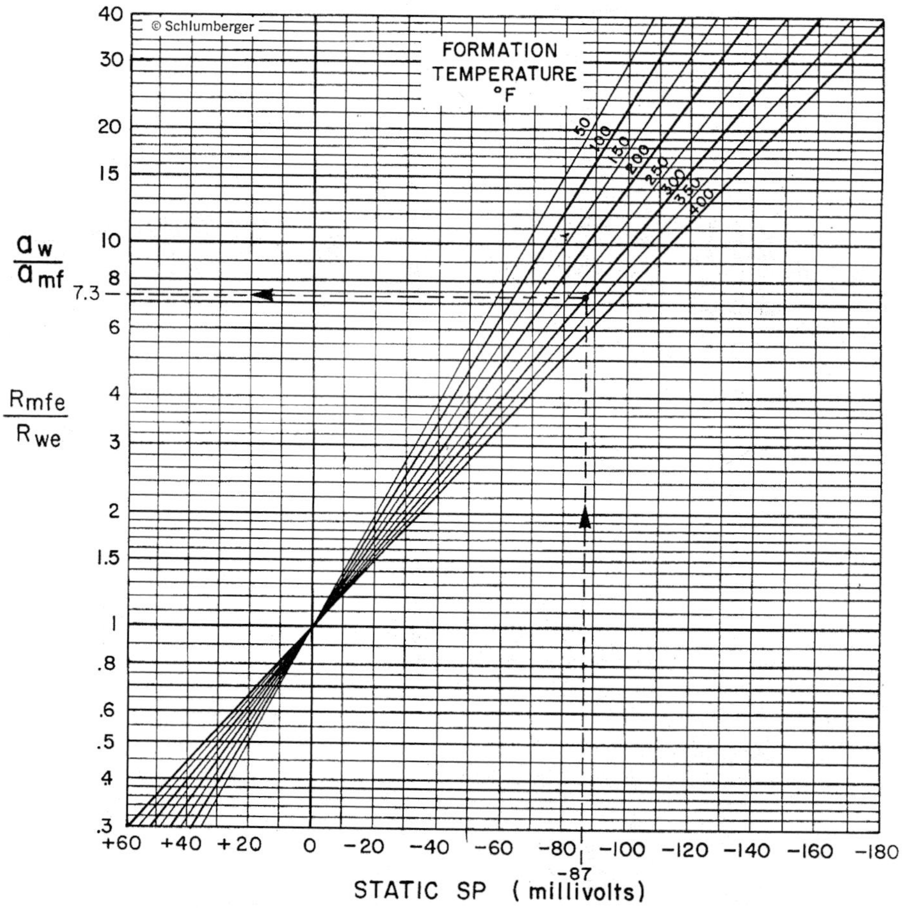

Figure 9–35. Courtesy Schlumberger.

Calculating R_w from SP Logs, continued

Step 5: Convert R_{we} to R_w

Follow the procedure below to convert R_{we} to R_w.

Step	Action
1	Enter Figure 9–34 again with R_{we} (along the base). Move up the chart until R_{we} intersects the temperature slope.
2	Directly across from the intersection point, read R_w from the vertical axis.

Constructing a Pickett Plot

Introduction

A Pickett plot lets us compare water saturations of different parts of a reservoir in one or many wells. The Pickett plot (Pickett, 1973) is a visual representation of the Archie equation and therefore is a powerful graphic technique for estimating S_w ranges within a reservoir. All that is needed to make a Pickett plot is a set of porosities and corresponding resistivities taken from well logs and 2×4 cycle log-log paper. The procedure for making a Pickett plot consists of five steps, detailed below.

Step	Action
1	Plot points of matching porosity and true resistivity (R_t) on log-log paper.
2	Plot R_w point on the R_t scale.
3	Determine *m* using the table of values.
4	Plot the 100% S_w line.
5	Plot the lines representing lower values of S_w.

Step 1: Plot points

Plot points of matching porosity and true resistivity (R_t) values obtained from well logs on 2×4 cycle log-log paper, as shown below. Use the x-axis for the resistivity (R_t) scale and the y-axis for the porosity (Φ) scale.

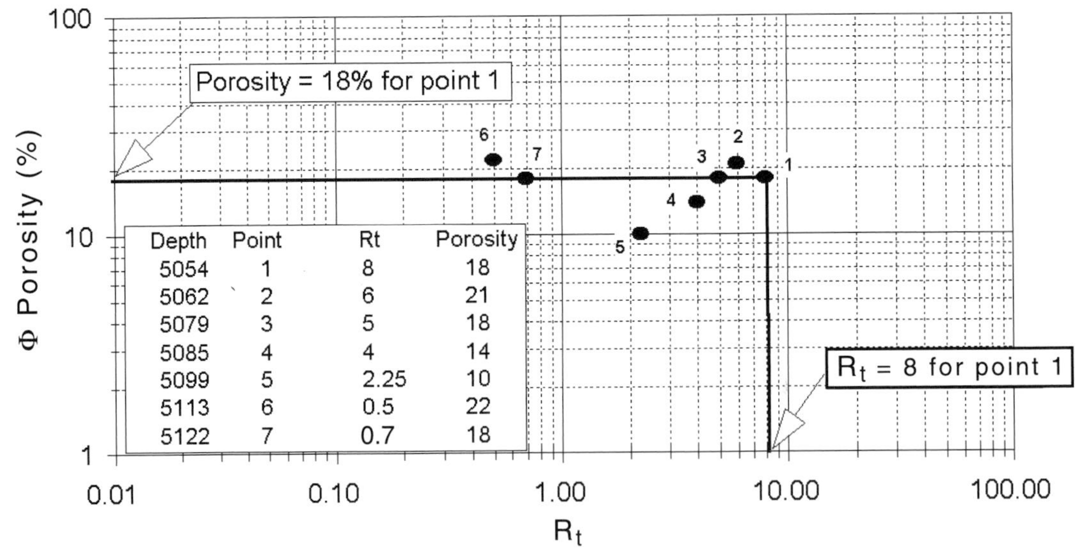

Depth	Point	Rt	Porosity
5054	1	8	18
5062	2	6	21
5079	3	5	18
5085	4	4	14
5099	5	2.25	10
5113	6	0.5	22
5122	7	0.7	18

Figure 9–36.

Step 2: Plot R_w point

Plot the R_w value (resistivity of formation water) by plotting the R_w point along the R_t scale on the x-axis at the top of the graph grid where porosity is 100%, as shown below. R_w values are published by logging companies, or we can calculate them from the SP log.

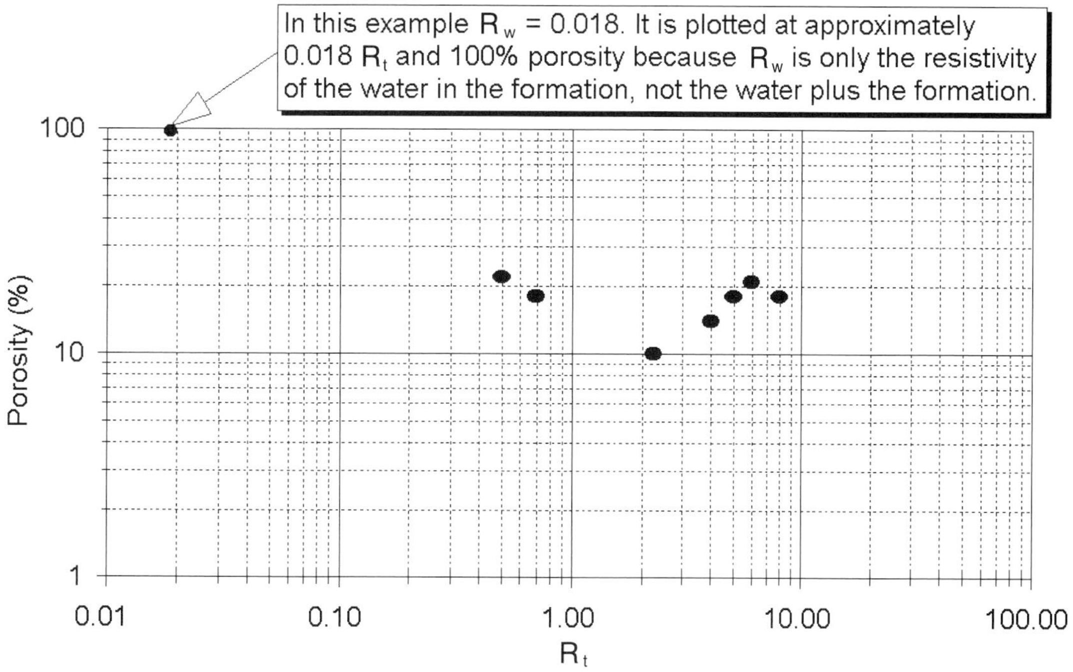
In this example R w = 0.018. It is plotted at approximately 0.018 R t and 100% porosity because R w is only the resistivity of the water in the formation, not the water plus the formation.
100
10
1
Porosity (%)
0.01
0.10
1.00
10.00
100.00
R t

Figure 9–37.

Step 3: Determine *m*

Estimate *m* (cementation factor) using the table below. Laboratory analysis is necessary for a precise determination of *m*. However, by knowing what the expected porosity type is, we can estimate the value. If you are unsure of the porosity type, use an *m* of 2.

Porosity Type	Value for *m*
Sandstones with diagenetic or detrital clay in pores	1.7–1.8
Formations with clean, macro- to micro-sized pore throats (Archie rocks)	2
Formations with vuggy porosity (touching to nontouching)	2.2–3.0

Step 4: Plot the 100% S_w line

On a Pickett plot, the value of *m* determines the slope of the S_w lines. The first S_w line plotted on a Pickett plot is the 100% S_w line. To plot this line, draw a line with a negative slope equal to *m* that begins at the R_w point. Use a linear scale to measure the slope; for example, go down 1 in. and over 2 in.

The example below shows how to plot an *m* of 2.

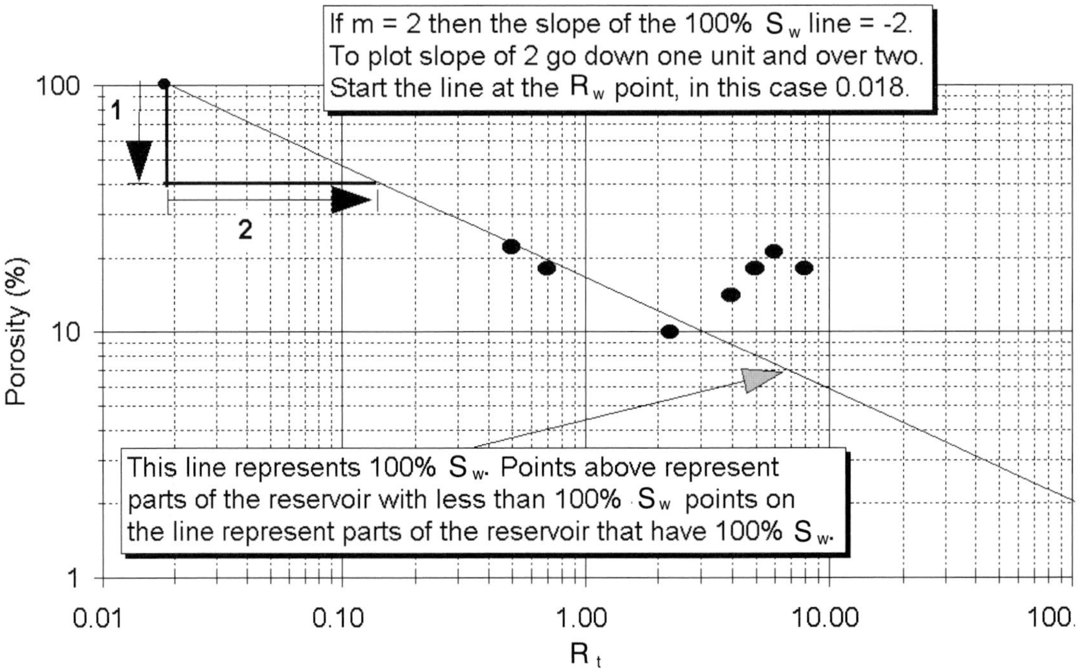

Figure 9–38.

Constructing a Pickett Plot, continued

Step 5: Plot S_w lines

After plotting the 100% S_w line, plot the lines representing lower percentages of S_w using this procedure.

Step	Action
1	Find the intercept of R_t = 1 and the 100% S_w line (made in the last procedure).
2	From this intercept, draw a line parallel to the x-axis across the plot. Any point on this line has the same porosity.
3	Where this line passes through R_t of 2, 4, 6, 8, 14, and 20, draw a series of lines parallel to the 100% S_w line.
4	Points on these lines correspond to S_w of 71, 50, 41, 35, 27, and 22%. These percentages are calculated from the Archie equation using m = 2 and n = 2 at R_t of 2, 4, 6, 8, 14, and 20.

The figure below is an example of following this procedure.

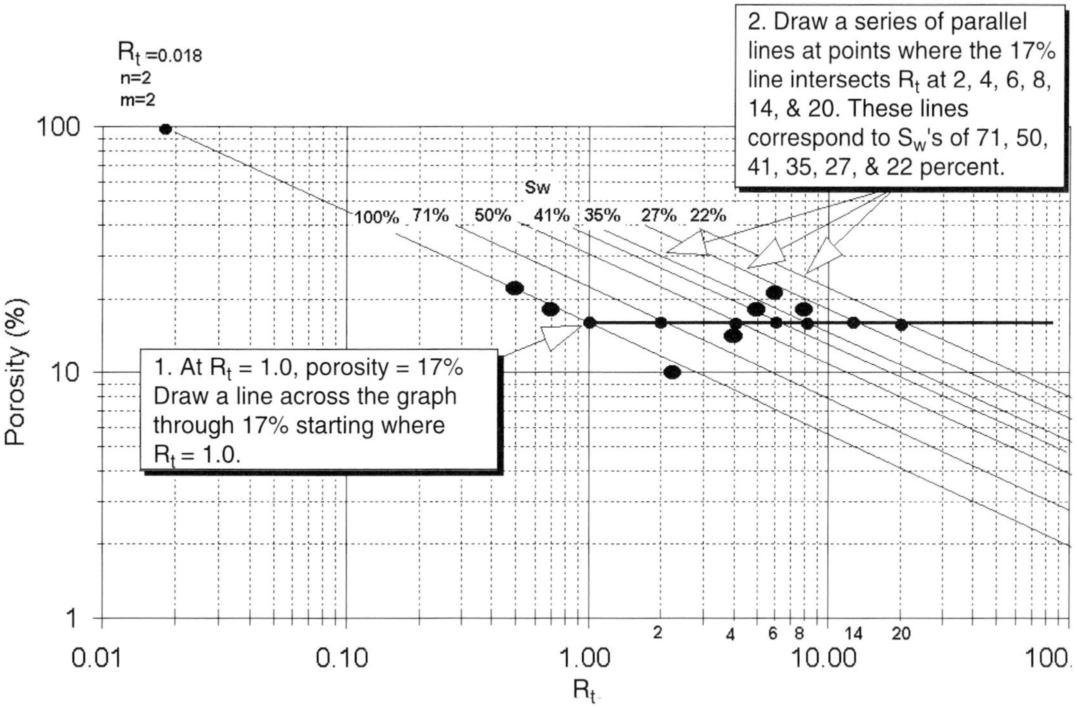

Figure 9–39.

Subsection D2

Interpreting Water Saturation

Introduction

Water saturation values contribute little when interpreted in isolation. Rather, S_w values should be interpreted in the context of pore type, pore geometry, and height above the free-water level. This subsection discusses how to interpret S_w using capillary pressure curves, Buckles plots, and S_w–depth plots. It discusses how to interpret hydrocarbon shows by interpreting S_w data and how to predict hydrocarbon recovery.

In this subsection

This subsection contains the following topics.

Interpreting S_w Distribution in a Reservoir

Introduction

The distribution of water saturation values within a reservoir depends on the height above free water, hydrocarbon type, pore throat-size distribution, and pore geometry. Mapping S_w distribution in a reservoir helps us predict trap boundaries.

BVW

Bulk volume water (BVW) equals $\Phi \times S_w$. In zones with the same pore type and geometry, BVW is a function of the height above the free water level. Above the transition zone, BVW is fairly constant. Below the transition zone, BVW is variable.

A Buckles plot is a plot of S_w vs. porosity. Contours of equal BVW are drawn on the plot.

- Points plot on a hyperbolic BVW line where the formation is near immobile water if the points come from a reservoir with consistent pore type and pore geometry.
- Points scatter on a Buckles plot where the formation falls below the top of the transition zone.

The figure below shows how a Buckles plot relates to capillary pressure, fluid distribution, and fluid recovery in a reservoir.

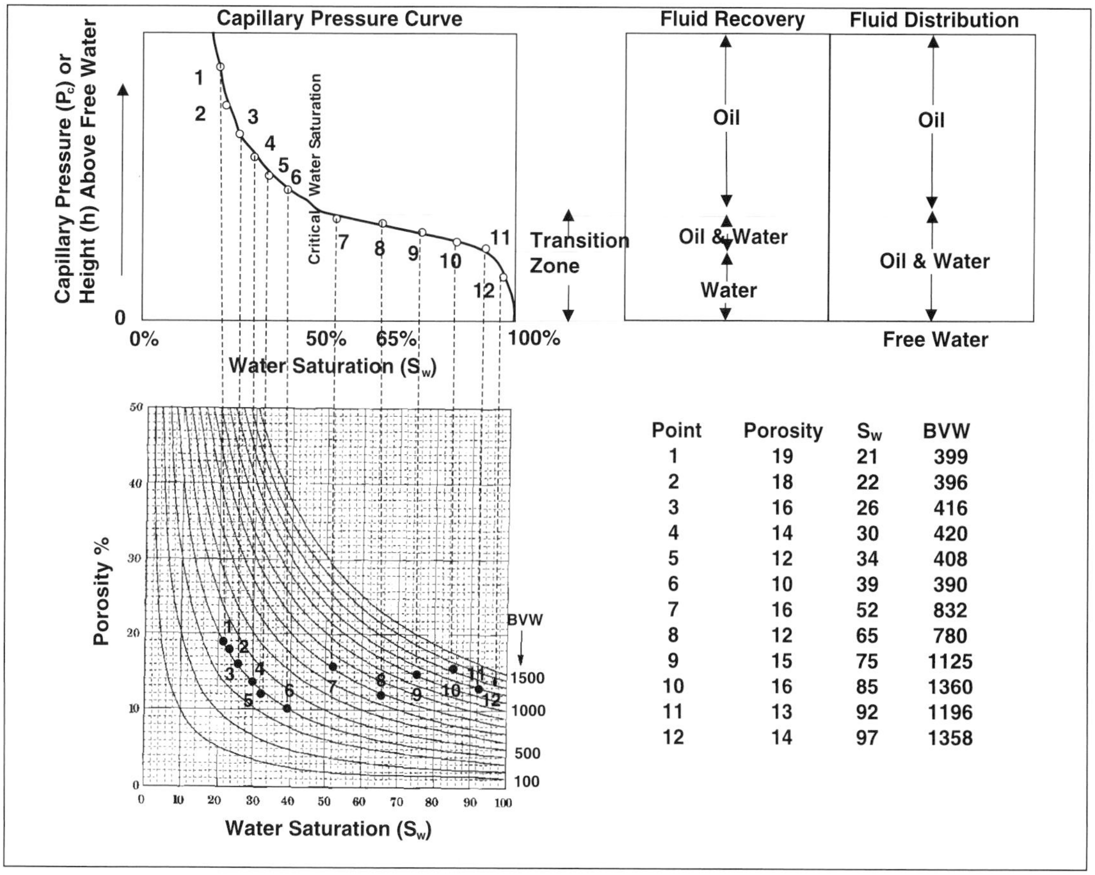

Point	Porosity	S_w	BVW
1	19	21	399
2	18	22	396
3	16	26	416
4	14	30	420
5	12	34	408
6	10	39	390
7	16	52	832
8	12	65	780
9	15	75	1125
10	16	85	1360
11	13	92	1196
12	14	97	1358

Figure 9–40.

Limitations of BVW

BVW and Buckles plots can be confusing in interbedded lithologies or in areas where facies changes occur because of changing pore types.

S_w–depth plots

S_w–depth plots are simple plots of S_w vs. depth. They illustrate how S_w varies within a hydrocarbon-bearing zone. Variations reflect different pore types and/or height above free water. An S_w–depth plot can be used to delineate three things:

1. Transition and waste zones
2. Flow units
3. Containers

Individual plots can be prepared for wells along dip and strike and correlated to show S_w changes across a reservoir or field. Below is a hypothetical example of an S_w–depth plot with estimated S_w distribution curves for several flow units for a hydrocarbon-bearing zone in a well.

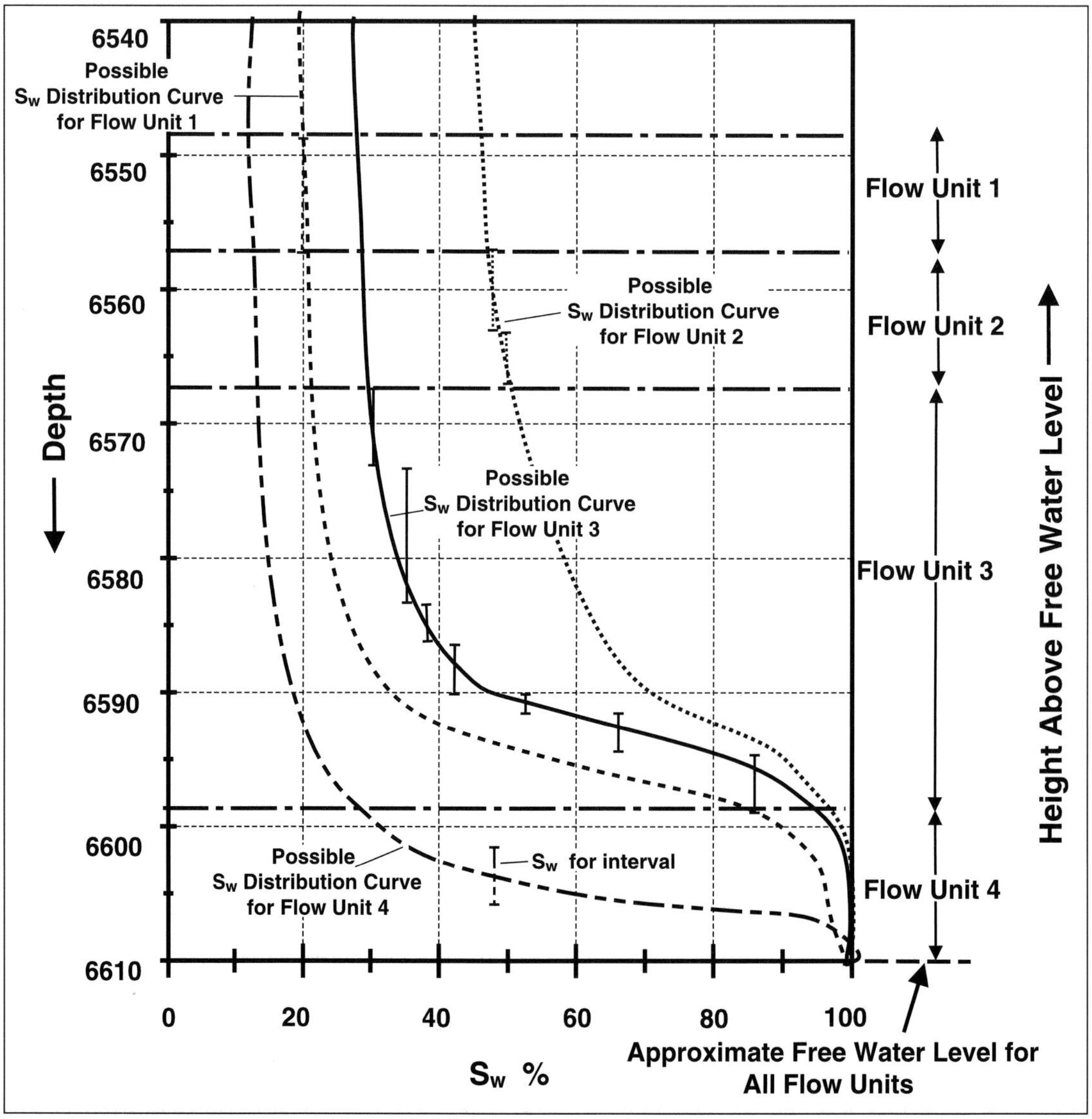

Figure 9–41.

Height–S_w–pore type diagram

The empirical ternary diagram below is handy for estimating either height above free water, port type (r_{35}), or S_w for a flow unit when the other two variables are known. For example, if S_w for a flow unit is 20% and the pore type is macro with a port size of approximately 3μ, then the height above free water for the flow unit is approximately 100 ft. Assumptions for the diagram include 30°API gravity oil, saltwater formation water, and water wet.

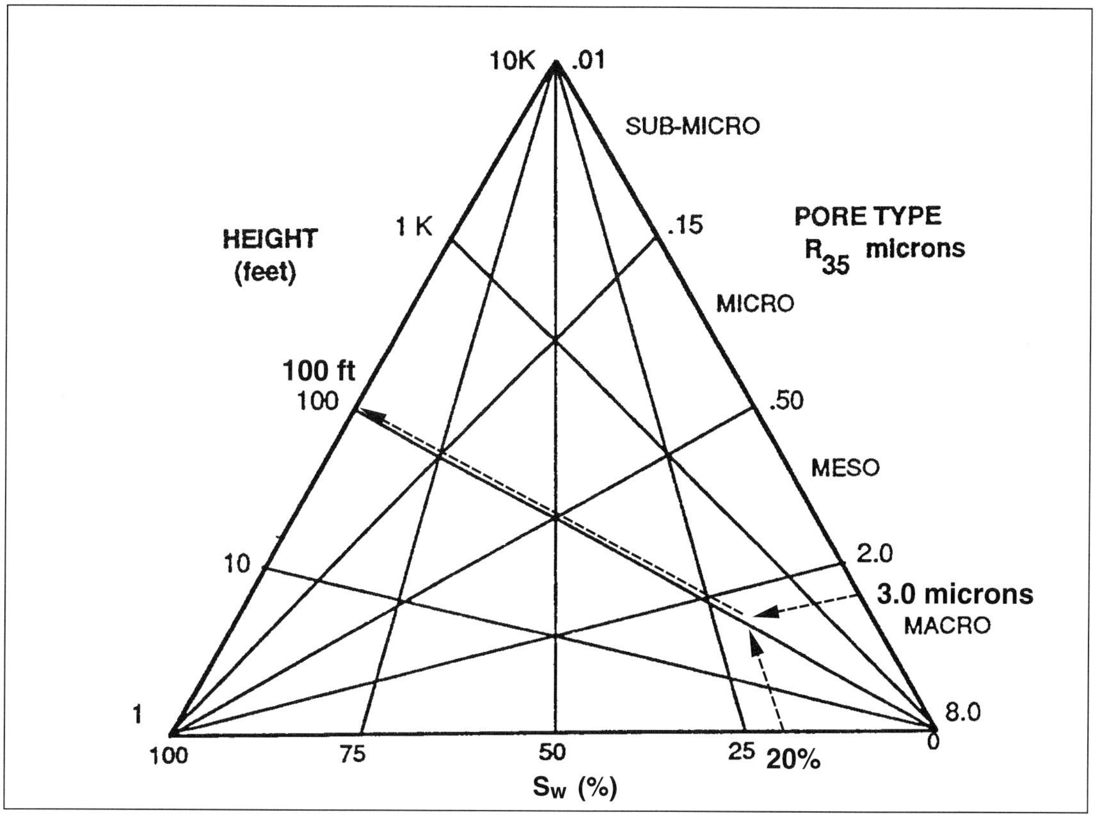

Figure 9–42.

Interpreting Hydrocarbon Shows

Introduction

One powerful use of petrophysical analysis is in interpreting shows. An understanding of the interrelationship of water saturation, relative permeability, pore throat-size distribution, and height above the free water level lets us interpret the significance of a hydrocarbon show.

Types of shows

Direct indications of hydrocarbons—seen in drilling fluids, cuttings, cores, or formation tests—may be of several types (Schowalter and Hess, 1982):

Show Type	Significance	Origin
Continuous phase	Trapped oil or gas	A slug or filament of oil or gas with a continuous connection through the pore network of a rock
Residual	Migrated hydrocarbons	A discontinuous phase of oil or gas which formed as a result of a breached or leaky trap
Dissolved gas	Gas present in the petroleum system	Gas exsolving from formation water from pressure release
In kerogen	Oil or gas present in source rock	Oil liberated from kerogen in the oil generation phase

Oil show type manifestations

The table below lists similarities and differences between different oil show types.

Show Type	Core or Cuttings	Mud Log	S_w%	Log Analysis	DST	RFT
Continuous-phase oil	Yes	Yes	<65 for Ss, <45 for Ls or dolomite	Moveable oil	Free oil or oil-cut fluids	Hydrocarbon gradient
Residual oil	Yes	Yes	>65 for Ss, >45 for Ls or dolomite	No moveable oil	No recovery	Hydrostatic gradient
In-kerogen oil	Yes	No	100 or less	No moveable oil	No recovery	Hydrostatic gradient

Interpreting Hydrocarbon Shows, continued

Gas show type manifestations

Gas show types are similar to oil show types but need to be considered separately. Use the table below to help with gas show interpretation.

Show Type	Core or Cuttings	Mud Log	S_w%	Log Analysis	DST	RFT
Continuous-phase gas	Yes	Yes	<65 for Ss, <45 for Ls or dolomite	Moveable gas	Gas to surface at measurable sustained rate	Hydrocarbon gradient
Residual gas	Yes	Yes	>65 for Ss, >45 for Ls or dolomite	No moveable gas	Short flow period caused by pressure drop near wellbore	Hydrostatic gradient
Dissolved gas	Yes	Yes	100	No moveable gas	Gas-cut water or mud	Hydrostatic gradient

Shows from transition and waste zones

Shows from waste and transition zones are continuous-phase shows. Waste zones occur at the top of traps; transition zones occur at the bottom. The table below lists ways to distinguish transition zone shows from waste zone shows (after Schowalter and Hess, 1982).

Characteristic	Transition	Waste
Fluid production	Oil or gas with water, or water only	Oil or gas with water, or water only
Flow rate	High in high-permeability rocks	Low
Water saturation	High, decreases upward	Low, increases upward
Calculated hydrocarbon column	Small	Large

Residual shows

Residual hydrocarbons occur as dead oil or as water displacement residual hydrocarbons. Dead oil forms as a result of water washing, thermal cracking, or biodegradation. Water displacement residual hydrocarbons form in reservoirs as a result of a leaky or breached trap or as a result of production.

Dissolved-gas shows

Dissolved-gas shows are reported as mud-log shows, trip gas, gas-cut fluids, and gas bubbles in samples. Dissolved-gas shows occur when gas is liberated from water as pressure drops in rock cuttings pores as they rise to the surface during drilling. The amount of gas contained in formation water depends on the salinity. Fresher formation water absorbs more gas. Quantities range up to 14 scf/bbl of water (Schowalter and Hess, 1979). Dissolved gas has no capacity to flow into a wellbore, and dissolved shows are significant only in that hydrocarbons are present.

In-kerogen shows

In-kerogen shows occur when solvents are used on cuttings containing kerogen. The solvents liberate some oil from the kerogen, and this oil can be mistaken for evidence of free oil. Kerogen is the precursor to oil or gas and, when heated, generates oil and/or gas. In-kerogen shows indicate the presence of source rocks that have generated oil or gas.

Residual and continuous-phase shows

During reservoir water drainage, hydrocarbons enter a trap. The trap starts at 0% hydrocarbon saturation (S_o), or 100% S_w, and ends up with a higher S_o. Water refills the reservoir as hydrocarbons exit a trap (fill-up). During fill-up some hydrocarbons are permanently left behind as a residual accumulation. There is no relative permeability to hydrocarbons in rocks containing residual hydrocarbons. At a point during fill-up, hydrocarbons no longer drain because they are no longer connected in a column but are isolated in pores. A DST of a zone with residual hydrocarbons produces no oil or gas, and an RFT would not show a hydrocarbon gradient.

The figure below shows drainage and fill-up relative permeability curves for an oil reservoir. In this example, the reservoir ends up with approximately 60% S_w, or 40% residual hydrocarbon saturation.

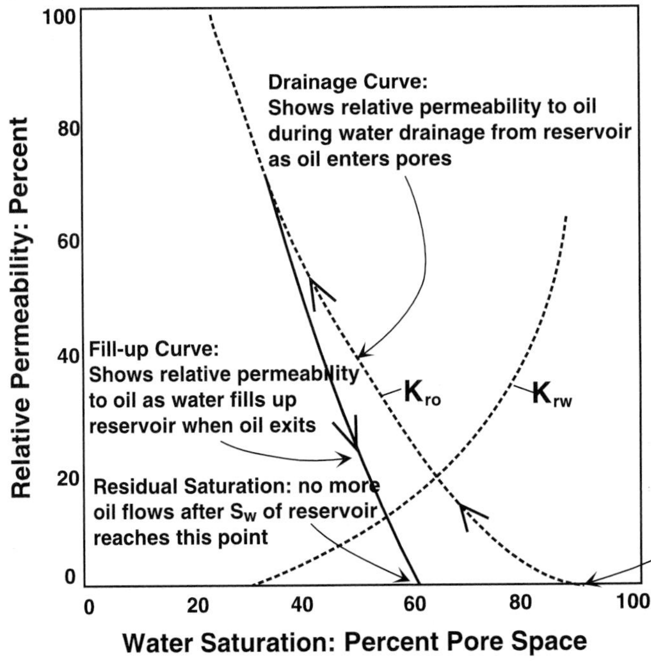

Figure 9–43.

Trap with transition zone

The figure below is a schematic cross section of a stratigraphic trap with transition, reservoir, and waste zones and their corresponding show characteristics.

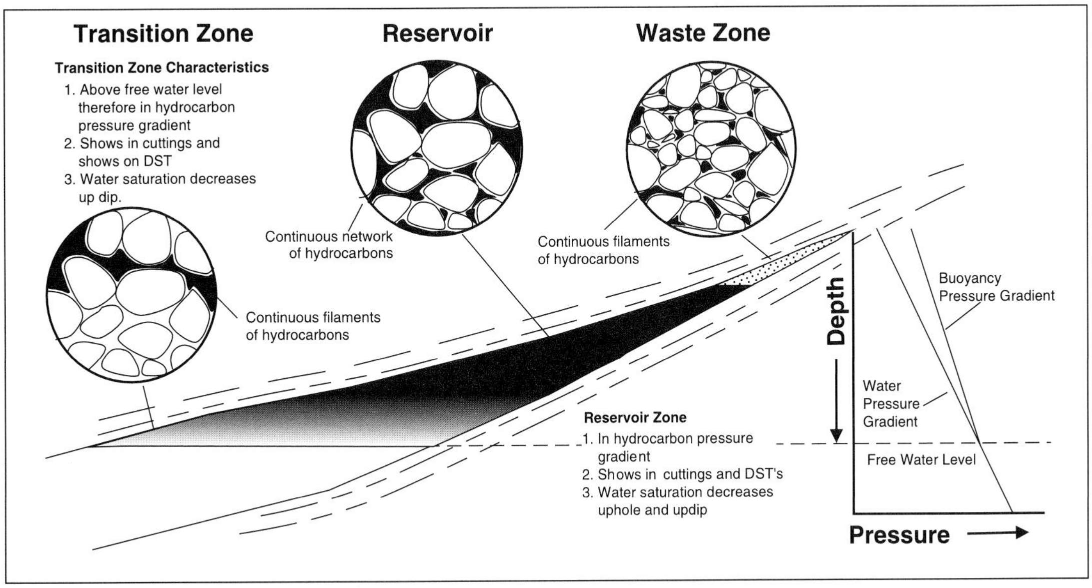

Figure 9–44.

Trap with residual hydrocarbon zone

The figure below is a schematic cross section of a stratigraphic trap with residual hydrocarbon saturation, reservoir, and waste zones and their corresponding show characteristics.

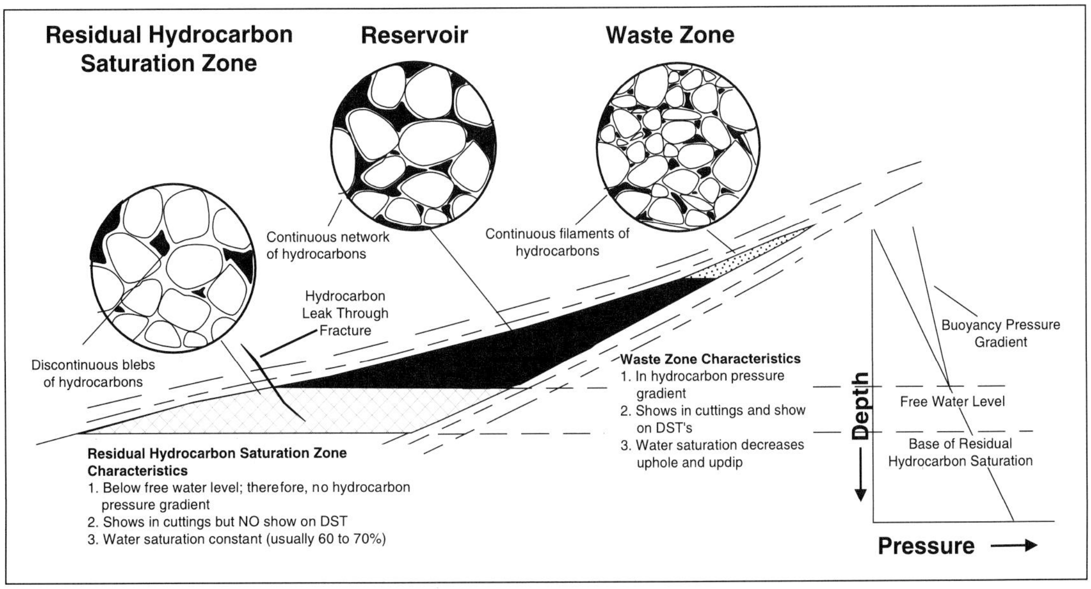

Figure 9–45.

Predicting Hydrocarbon Recovery

Introduction

The volume of hydrocarbon contained in a reservoir is a function of pore volume and water saturation (S_w). Reservoir size and porosity determine pore volume. Pore throat-size distribution, pore geometry, and hydrocarbon column height determine S_w. Estimating hydrocarbon volume in place before drilling a well is a matter of predicting pore volume and S_w. Recovery of hydrocarbons depends on the efficiency of the reservoir drive mechanism. Predicting recovery depends on predicting reservoir quality and reservoir drive.

Calculating oil volume in place

To calculate volume of original oil in place (OOIP), use the following formula:

$$OOIP = \frac{7758 \cdot A \cdot h \cdot \Phi \cdot (1 - S_w)}{B_{oi}}$$

where:

- 7758 = conversion factor from acre-ft to bbl
- A = area of reservoir, acres from map data
- h = thickness of reservoir pay, ft
- Φ = porosity (decimal, not percent)
- S_w = water saturation (decimal, not percent)
- B_{oi} = formation volume factor = 1.05 + (N × 0.05), where N = number of ft^3 of gas produced per bbl of oil (GOR). For example, if a well has a GOR of 1,000, then B_{oi} = 1.05 + (10 × 0.05) = 1.1.

Calculating gas volume in place

To calculate volume of original gas in place (OGIP), use the following formula:

$$OGIP = 43{,}560 \cdot A \cdot h \cdot \Phi \cdot (1 - S_w) \cdot \left(\text{depth} \cdot \frac{0.43}{15}\right)$$

where:

- 43,560 = conversion factor from acre-ft to ft^3

Estimating recoverable volume of oil or gas

Estimating recoverable oil or gas depends on predicting reservoir quality and reservoir drive. Reservoir analogs help narrow the range of values for variables that determine recovery factor (R.F.). Use the equation below to estimate the recoverable oil or gas in a reservoir:

$$\text{Recoverable oil or gas} = OHIP \cdot R.F.$$

where:

- OHIP = original hydrocarbons in place

Estimating recovery factor

Drive mechanism has the greatest geological impact on recovery factor. Narrowing the range in recovery factor is a matter of estimating how much difference pore type and reservoir heterogeneity impact the efficiency of the drive mechanism. To estimate the recovery factor, use the procedure below.

Step	Action
1	Decide which drive mechanism is most likely from the geology of the prospective reservoir system and by comparing it with reservoir systems of nearby analog fields or analog fields in other basins.
2	Multiply OOIP or OGIP by the recovery factor for the expected drive.
3	Narrow the recovery factor range by predicting the thickness of the reservoir by port type. Port type affects recovery rate. For example, in a reservoir with strong water drive and macroporosity, recovery will be up to 60%, mesoporosity recovery will be up to 20%, and microporosity recovery will be 0%.

Recovery factors for different drive types

The table below shows recovery factor percentages for different drive mechanisms for oil vs. gas reservoirs.

Reservoir Drive Mechanism	Percent Ultimate Recovery	
	Gas	Oil
Strong water	30–40	45–60
Partial water	40–50	30–45
Gas expansion	50–70	20–30
Solution gas	N/A	15–25
Rock	60–80	10–60
Gravity drainage	N/A	50–70

Section E

Predicting Reservoir System Quality

Introduction

The interrelationship of reservoir porosity, permeability, thickness, and lateral distribution determines reservoir system quality. Although quality prediction is most effective with large amounts of superior data, useful predictions can still be made from very limited data. This section discusses methods for predicting the quality of sandstone and carbonate reservoir systems.

Sandstones vs. carbonates

Sandstones and carbonates are the dominant reservoir rocks. Although quite similar, they are different. The table below (after Choquette and Pray, 1970) compares variables affecting reservoir system quality for sandstones vs. carbonates.

Variable	Sandstones	Carbonates
Sediment composition	High variability (depending on provenance and depositional environment)	Low variability [variations of $CaCO_3$ and $MgCa(CO_3)_2$]
Cement mineralogy	Quartz, calcite, dolomite, clay, and anhydrite, etc.	Aragonite, high- and low-Mg calcite, dolomite
Original pore geometry	Intergranular	Intergranular predominates, but intragranular is important
Ultimate pore geometry	Intergranular = intercrystalline > moldic	Intergranular = intercrystalline = moldic > microporosity
Uniformity of pore size, shape, and distribution	Fairly uniform within a facies	Ranges from fairly uniform to extremely heterogeneous, even within a facies
Influence of diagenesis	Minor to major	Usually major

In this section

This section contains the following subsections.

Subsection E1

Predicting Sandstone Porosity and Permeability

Introduction

An effective method of predicting sandstone reservoir system porosity and permeability is (1) to predict sandstone porosity and permeability at deposition and then (2) to predict the probable changes to porosity and permeability as the sandstone was buried. Since other texts (Barwis et al., 1989; Galloway and Hobday, 1983) cover the impact of depositional environment on porosity and permeability, this subsection concentrates on predicting porosity and permeability by considering the effects of diagenesis.

In this subsection

This subsection contains the following topics.

Sandstone Diagenetic Processes

Introduction

Diagenesis alters the original pore type and geometry of a sandstone and therefore controls its ultimate porosity and permeability. Early diagenetic patterns correlate with environment of deposition and sediment composition. Later diagenetic patterns cross facies boundaries and depend on regional fluid migration patterns (Stonecipher and May, 1992). Effectively predicting sandstone quality depends on predicting diagenetic history as a product of depositional environments, sediment composition, and fluid migration patterns.

Diagenetic processes

Sandstone diagenesis occurs by three processes:

- Cementation
- Dissolution (leaching)
- Compaction

Cementation destroys pore space; grain leaching creates it. Compaction decreases porosity through grain rearrangement, plastic deformation, pressure solution, and fracturing.

Diagenetic zones

Surdam et al. (1989) define diagenetic zones by subsurface temperatures. Depending on geothermal gradient, depths to these zones can vary. The table below summarizes major diagenetic processes and their impact on pore geometry.

Zone	Temp.	Major Diagenetic Processes	
		Preserves or Enhances Porosity	Destroys Porosity
Shallow	<80°C or 176°F (<5,000 to 10,000 ft)	• Grain coatings (inhibit later overgrowths) • Nonpervasive carbonate cements that can be dissolved later	• Clay infiltration • Carbonate or silica cement (in some cases irreversible) • Authigenic kaolinite • Compaction of ductile grains
Intermediate	80–140°C or 176–284°F	• Carbonate cement dissolved • Feldspar grains dissolved	• Kaolinite, chlorite, and illite precipitate as a result of feldspar dissolution • Ferroan carbonate and quartz cement
Deep	> 140°C or 284°F	• Feldspar, carbonate, and sulfate minerals dissolved	• Quartz cement (most destructive) • Kaolinite precipitation • Illite, chlorite form as products of feldspar dissolution • Pyrite precipitation

From Surdam et al., 1989; courtesy RMAG.

Effect of temperature

Depending on geothermal gradient, the effect of temperature on diagenesis can be significant. Many diagenetic reaction rates double with each 10°C increase (1000 times greater with each 100°C) (Wilson, 1994a). Increasing temperatures increase the solubility of many different minerals, so pore waters become saturated with more ionic species. Either (1) porosity–depth plots of sandstones of the target sandstone that are near the prospect area or (2) computer models that incorporate geothermal gradient are probably best for porosity predictions.

Below is a porosity–depth plot for sandstones from two wells with different geothermal gradients. The well with the greater geothermal gradient has correspondingly lower porosities than the well with lower geothermal gradient. At a depth of 7000 ft, there is a 10% porosity difference in the trend lines.

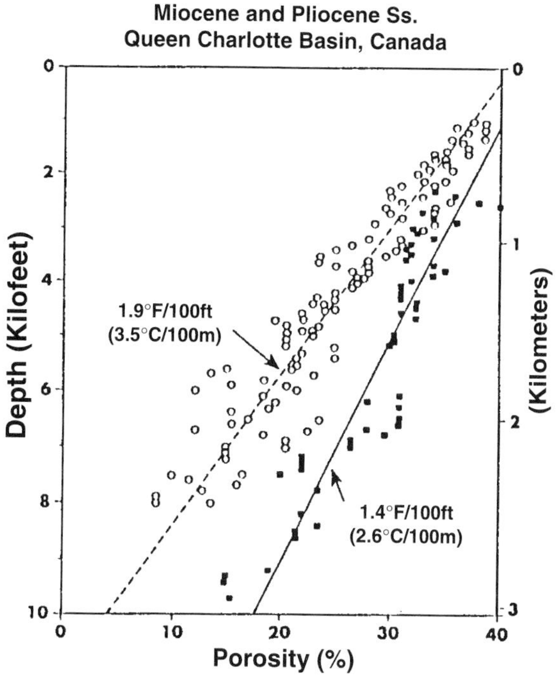

Figure 9–46. From Wilson, 1994a; courtesy SEPM.

Effect of pressure

The main effect of pressure is compaction. The process of porosity loss with depth of burial is slowed by overpressures. Basing his findings mainly on North Sea sandstones, Scherer (1987) notes sandstones retain approximately 2% porosity for every 1000 psi of overpressure during compaction. He cautions this figure must be used carefully because the influence of pressure on porosity depends on the stage of compaction at which the overpressure developed.

Effect of age

In general, sandstones lose porosity with age. In other words, porosity loss in sandstone is a function of time. According to Scherer (1987), a Tertiary sandstone with a Trask sorting coefficient of 1.5, a quartz content of 75%, and a burial depth of 3000 m probably has an average porosity of approximately 26%. A Paleozoic sandstone with the same sorting, quartz content, and burial depth probably has an average porosity of approximately 13%.

Effect of Composition and Texture on Sandstone Diagenesis

Composition and diagenesis

Composition affects sandstone diagenesis in two ways:

- The higher the quartz content, the greater the mechanical stability (less compaction occurs).
- The higher the variety of minerals, the lower the chemical stability (more cementation or dissolution occurs).

Sandstones with abundant lithics, feldspars, or chert have less occlusion of porosity by quartz overgrowths and more secondary porosity through dissolution of less stable grains. The ratio of quartz to ductile grains is key to compaction porosity loss.

Sediment composition and provenance

Provenance determines sand grain mineralogy and sediment maturity. Mechanical and chemical weathering affects sand grains during transportation. The final product reflects the origin, amount of reworking, and transport distance.

For example, sandstones derived from subduction trench margins are generally mineralogically immature. They often contain terrigenous detritus with abundant volcaniclastics and pelagic material. Sandstones derived from the margin of a cratonic basin tend to be mineralogically and texturally mature and contain reworked sedimentary detritus.

The figure below summarizes the effects of sediment composition on mechanical stability and chemical stability.

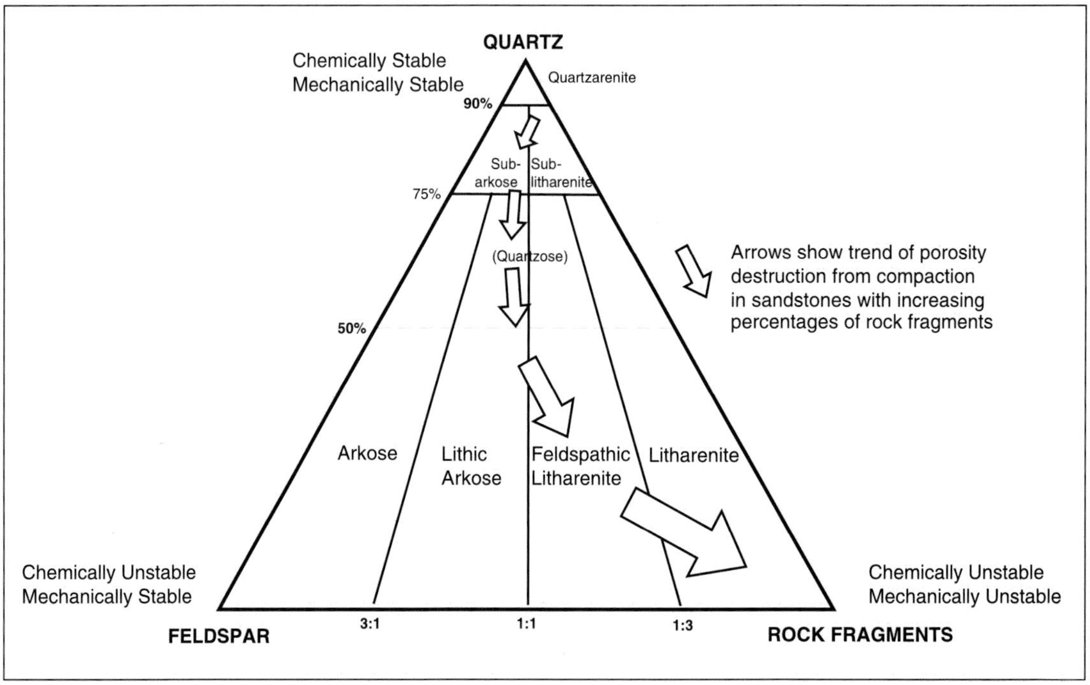

Figure 9–47. From Loucks et al., 1984; courtesy AAPG.

Effect of Composition and Texture on Sandstone Diagenesis, continued

Influence of grain size on porosity and diagenesis

Sorting and grain size are textural parameters that intuitively might seem to have the same effects on the porosity of a reservoir system sandstone. Studies show, however, that porosity is largely independent of grain size for unconsolidated sand of the same sorting (Beard and Weyl, 1973). Size does affect permeability; the finer the sand, the lower the permeability. Permeability indirectly affects porosity through diagenesis. Stonecipher et al. (1984) suggest that slow fluid fluxes, resulting from low permeability, promote cementation; rapid fluxes promote leaching. In rapid fluxes, solutes do not remain in pore spaces long enough to build local concentration that promotes precipitation of cement. In slow fluxes, they do. Also, size affects the surface area available for diagenetic reactions: the finer the grain size, the greater the grain surface area for a volume of sediment or rock.

Influence of sorting on porosity

Sorting and porosity strongly correlate in unconsolidated sandstones (Beard and Weyl, 1973). The better the sorting, the higher the porosity. The initial porosities of wet, unconsolidated sands show a range of 44–28% porosity for well-sorted vs. poorly sorted grains. Well-sorted sands tend to have a higher percentage of quartz than do poorly sorted sands, and they tend to maintain higher porosities during burial than poorly sorted sands. Poorly sorted sands have more clay matrix and nonquartz grains.

Hydrology and Sandstone Diagenesis

Type of water flushes

Much diagenesis occurs in open chemical systems whose initial chemistry is set at deposition. After that, the chemistry of the system changes as flowing water moves chemical components through pores and causes either leaching or cementation of grains. Diffusion also moves chemicals in and out of rocks, although at significantly lower rates. During deep burial, chemical systems close and diagenesis is primarily by pressure solution and quartz overgrowths (Wilson and Stanton, 1994).

Galloway (1984) lists three types of flow of water in a basin:

1. **Meteoric flow**—water infiltrates shallow portions of a basin from precipitation or surface waters. Deeper infiltration occurs from (a) eustatic sea level changes and/or (b) tectonic elevation of basin margins.
2. **Compactional flow**—compaction expels water upward and outward from the pores of sediments.
3. **Thermobaric flow**—water moves in response to pressure gradients caused by generation of hydrocarbons, release of mineral-bound water, and/or increased heat flow.

The figure below shows the water movement processes mentioned above.

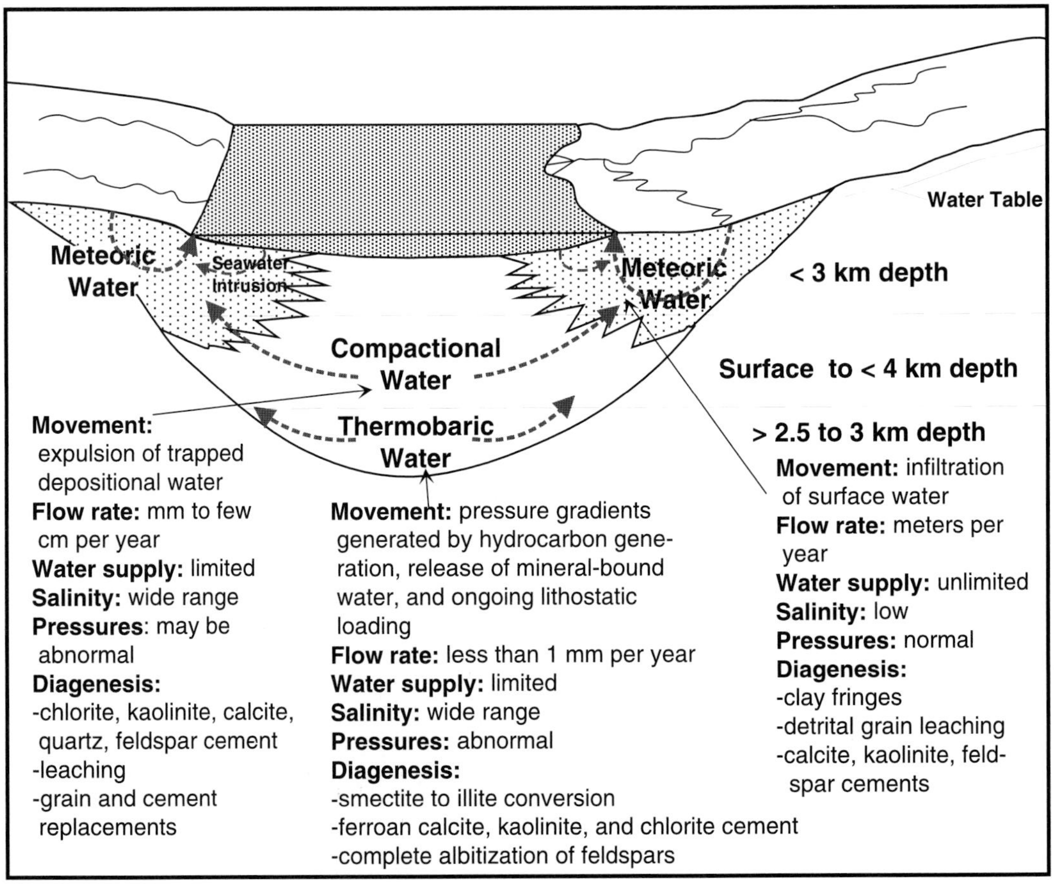

Figure 9–48. After Galloway, 1984, and Harrison and Temple, 1993; courtesy AAPG.

Pore-water chemistry

Depositional environment and climate control initial pore-water chemistry of a sandstone. When the rock is buried below the level of meteoric groundwater influence, pore-water chemistry changes as a result of two things:

- Increasing mineral solubility due to increasing temperatures.
- Acidic fluids released by maturing organic-rich shales or organic matter in sandstone. Acidic pore water leaches carbonate cement and grains.

Eh–pH graph

The figure below is an Eh–pH diagram, showing the approximate distribution of various types of subsurface fluids.

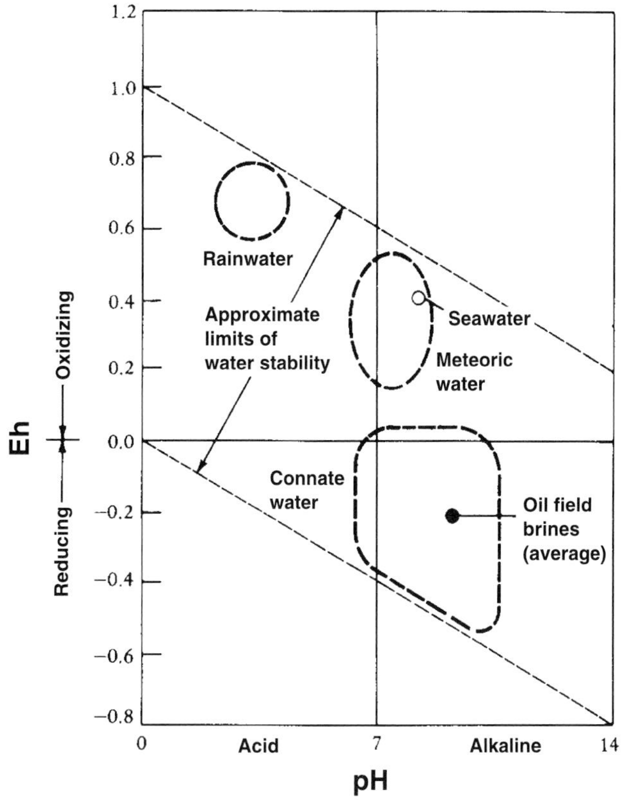

Figure 9–49. From Shelley, 1985; courtesy W.H. Freeman and Co.

Pore-water chemistry and cements

The table below lists common sandstone cements and the water chemistry associated with precipitation.

Cement	pH	Water Type	Typical Cement Derivation
Quartz	Acidic	Meteoric feldspars	Clay compaction, weathering of Ca-Na
Calcite	Alkaline	Marine	Dissolution of skeletal material and carbonate minerals; precipitation from bicarbonate and calcium in sea water
Kaolinite	Acid	Meteoric	Breakdown of K-feldspar or mica grains by fresh water
Illite	Alkaline	Marine	Conversion of smectite to illite, hydrolysis of micas, intense weathering of K-feldspar
Chlorite	Alkaline	Brackish	Weathering of basic volcanic detritus and Fe-Mg minerals
Smectite	Alkaline	Brackish to marine	Breakdown of plagioclase grains and mafic minerals rich in Ca and Na

Subsurface dissolved solids

The figure below shows the general trend of increasing dissolved solids in subsurface fluids with increasing depth.

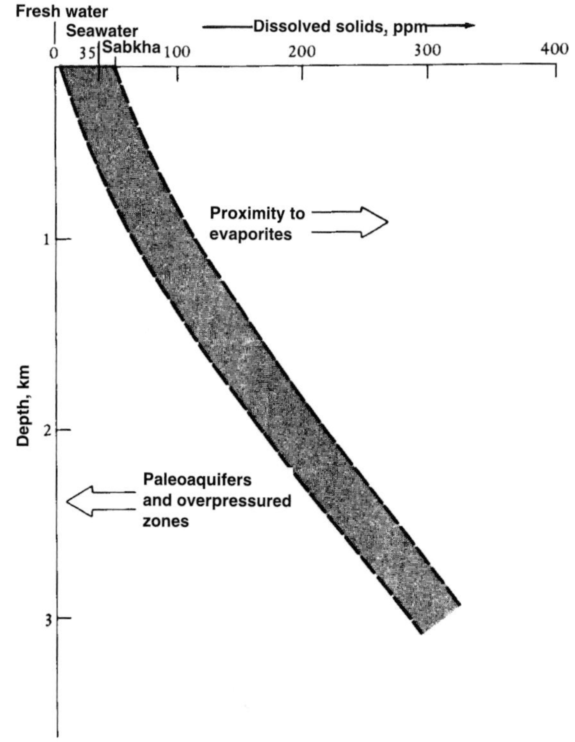

Figure 9–50. From Shelley 1985; courtesy W.H. Freeman and Co.

Influence of Depositional Environment on Sandstone Diagenesis

Introduction

Depositional environment influences many aspects of sandstone diagenesis. The flow chart below shows the interrelationship of depositional environment with the many factors controlling sandstone diagenesis.

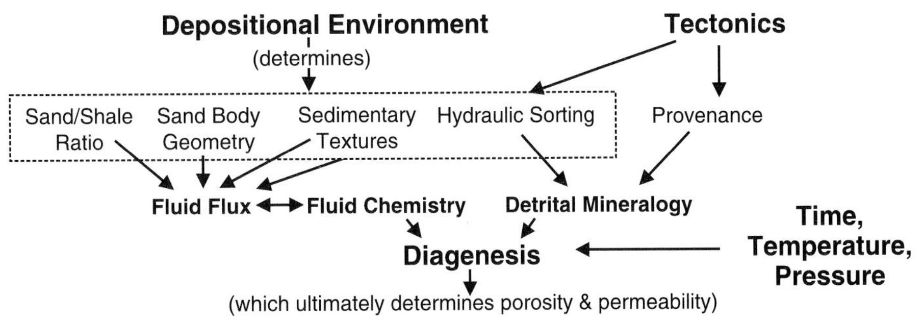

Figure 9–51. After Stonecipher et al., 1984; courtesy AAPG.

Sediment texture and composition

Depositional environment affects sediment composition by determining the amount of reworking and sorting by size or hydraulic equivalence. Sediments that have a higher degree of reworking are more mechanically and chemically stable. The energy level of depositional environments affects sorting by size or hydraulic equivalence and consequently produces different detrital mineral suites (Stonecipher and May, 1992).

For example, different facies of the Wilcox Group along the Gulf Coast of Texas have different compositions that are independent of their source area (Stonecipher and May, 1992). Wilcox basal fluvial point bar sands are the coarsest and contain the highest proportion of nondisaggregated lithic fragments. Prodelta sands, deposited in a more distal setting, contain fine quartz, micas, and detrital clays that are products of disaggregation. Reworked sands, such as shoreline or tidal sands, are more quartzose.

Depositional pore-water chemistry

Depositional pore-water chemistry of a sandstone is a function of depositional environment. Marine sediments typically have alkaline pore water. Nonmarine sediments have pore water with a variety of chemistries. In nonmarine sediments deposited in conditions that were warm and wet, the pore water is initially either acidic or anoxic and has a high concentration of dissolved mineral species (Burley et al., 1985).

Marine pore-water chemistry

Marine water is slightly alkaline. Little potential for chemical reaction exists between normal marine pore water and the common detrital minerals of sediments deposited in a marine environment. Therefore, diagenesis of marine sandstones results from a change in pore-water chemistry during burial or the reaction of less stable sediment with amorphous material (Burley et al., 1985).

Marine diagenesis

The precipitation of cements in quartzarenites and subarkoses deposited in a marine environment tends to follow a predictable pattern beginning with clay authigenesis associated with quartz and feldspar overgrowths, followed by carbonate precipitation. Clay minerals form first because they precipitate more easily than quartz and feldspar overgrowths, which require more ordered crystal growth. Carbonate cement stops the further diagenesis of aluminosilicate minerals.

The diagram below summarizes typical diagenetic pathways for marine sediments.

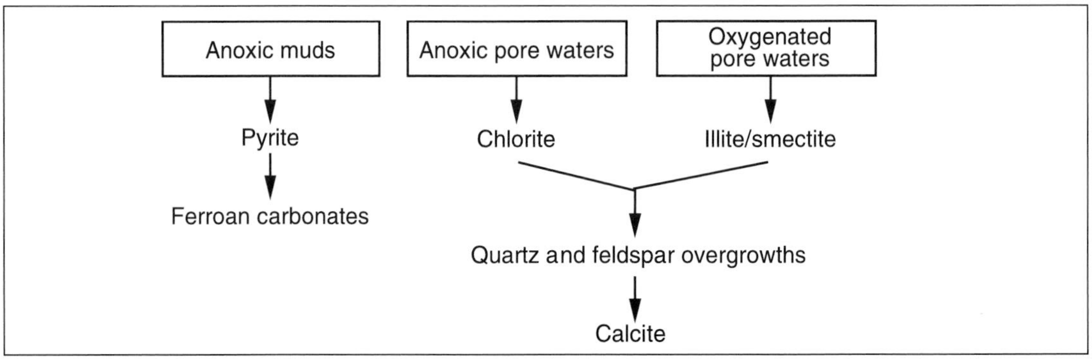

Figure 9–52. From Burley et al., 1985; courtesy Blackwell Scientific.

Nonmarine pore-water chemistry and cements

Nonmarine pore-water chemistry falls into two climatic categories: (1) warm and wet or (2) hot and dry. The chemistry of pore waters formed in warm and wet conditions is usually acidic or anoxic with large concentrations of dissolved mineral species. The interaction of organic material with pore water is a critical factor with these waters. The depositional pore water of sediments deposited in hot and dry conditions is typically slightly alkaline and dilute.

The diagram below shows typical diagenetic pathways for warm and wet nonmarine sediments.

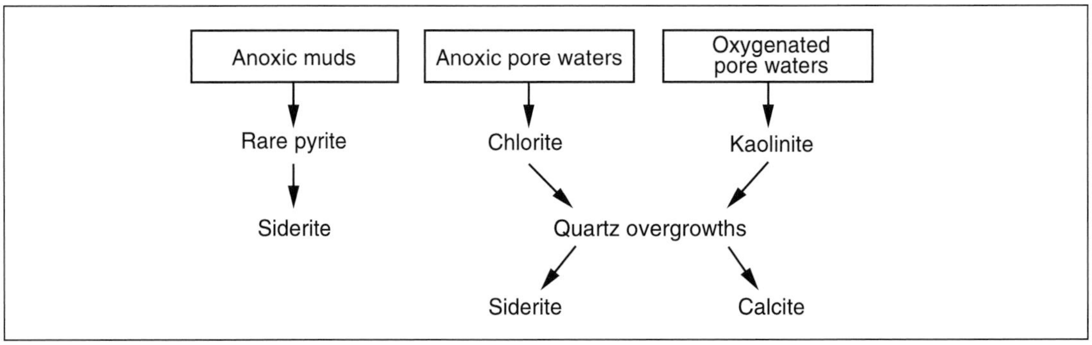

Figure 9–53. From Burley et al., 1985; courtesy Blackwell Scientific.

Cements

The table below, compiled from data by Thomas (1983), shows the cements that generally characterize specific depositional environments.

Environment	Facies	Cement
Eolian	Dune	Quartz overgrowths dominate; also clay coats
	Interdune	Grain-coating clays; in areas that were alternately moist and dry anhydrite, dolomite, or calcite common
Fluvial	Flood plain	Chlorite, illite, smectite, and mixed-layer clay
	Channel	Calcite at base, grading up into calcite plus quartz, quartz plus clay minerals, and clays plus minor carbonate
Nearshore marine	All	Carbonate minerals such as calcite or siderite; illite in sands deposited where fresh and marine water mix
Marine shelf	All	Calcite mainly; also dolomite, illite, chlorite rims, and quartz
Deep marine	All	Greater variety than other environments; cements include quartz, chlorite, calcite, illite, and occasional siderite or dolomite

Diagenesis and depositional pore waters

In the Wilcox of the Texas Gulf Coast, certain minerals precipitate as a result of the influence of depositional pore-water chemistry (Stonecipher and May, 1990):

- Mica-derived kaolinite characterizes fluvial/distributary-channel sands flushed by fresh water
- Abundant siderite characterizes splay sands and lake sediments deposited in fresh, anoxic water
- Chlorite rims characterize marine sands flushed by saline pore water
- Glauconite or pyrite characterizes marine sediments deposited in reducing or mildly reducing conditions
- Illite characterizes shoreline sands deposited in the mixing zone where brackish water forms
- Chamosite characterizes distributary-mouth-bar sands rapidly deposited in the fresh-water–marine water mixing zone

Predicting Sandstone Reservoir Porosity

Introduction

We might have the impression that abundant data and powerful computer models are necessary for porosity prediction. They help. But even with sparse data, by using a little imagination we can predict ranges of porosity. This section presents different methods of predicting sandstone porosity. Choose the method(s) most appropriate to your situation.

Porosity–depth plots

A pitfall of using porosity–depth plots for porosity prediction is that regression relationship averages out anomalies and complicates predictions of unusually porous sandstones. Use porosity–depth plots for porosity prediction with caution. If enough porosity data are available to make a meaningful plot, keep the "data cloud" on the plot in order to view the ranges of porosity at different depths. In a frontier exploration setting, the usefulness of porosity–depth plots may be limited if global data sets must be used.

Below is an example of regression porosity–depth plots for different formations along the U.S. Gulf Coast. Unfortunately it does not include the raw data, so we cannot see porosity variations within each formation. Formations on the left side of the plot, like the Vicksburg, tend to be quartz cemented. Formations on the right side, like the Frio (areas 4–6), tend to be clay cemented.

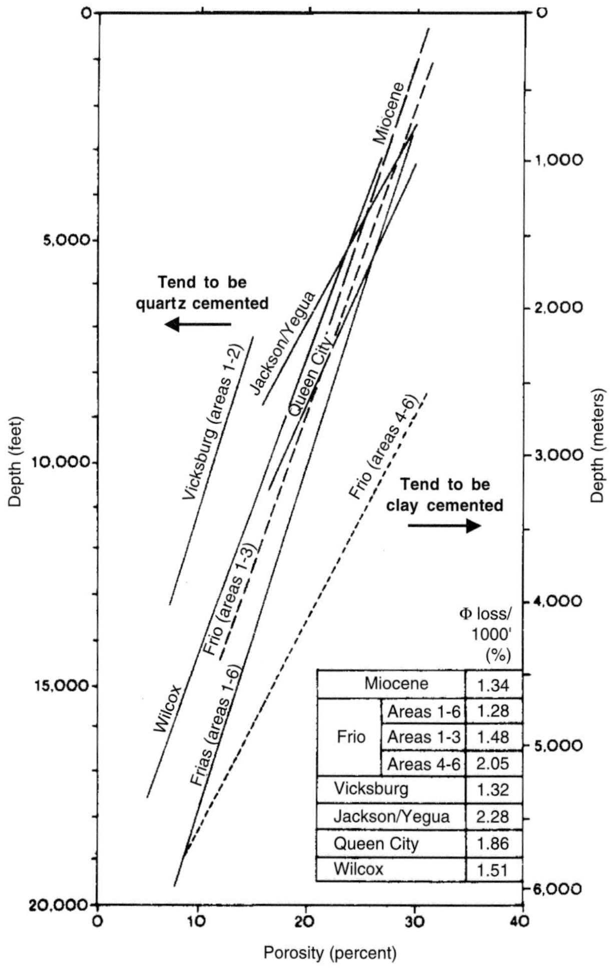

Figure 9–54. From Loucks et al., 1984; courtesy AAPG.

Equation for porosity prediction

Scherer (1987) studied the cores of 428 worldwide sandstones and listed the most important variables for predicting sandstone porosity:

- Percentage of quartz grains
- Sorting
- Depth of burial
- Age

Using regression analysis, he developed the following equation:

$$\text{Porosity} = 18.60 + (4.73 \times \text{in quartz}) + (17.37/\text{sorting}) - (3.8 \times \text{depth} \times 10^{-3}) - (4.65 \times \text{in age})$$

where:

Porosity = percent of bulk volume
In quartz = percent of solid-rock volume
Sorting = Trask sorting coefficient
Depth = meters
In age = millions of years

The equation can be used with a high degree of confidence in uncemented to partly cemented sandstones. But if the reduction of porosity by cement exceeds 2.1% bulk volume, then corrections need to be made based on local sandstone quality characteristics. Numbers for percent solid volume quartz and sorting may be difficult to obtain. Use 75% for percent solid volume quartz and 1.5 for sorting when these values are not known.

The table below shows numbers that Scherer (1987) developed by his analysis of reservoir sandstones.

Parameter	Unit	Range	Mean	Standard Deviation
Porosity	Percent bulk volume	3.9–36.6	20	7.9
Age	Millions of years	1–460	59	40.0
Depth	Meters	0–5,960	2,230	1,150.0
Quartz	Percent solid rock volume	12–97	75	23.0
Sorting	Trask coefficient	1.1–4.2	1.5	0.6

Predicting effects of diagenesis on porosity

Sandstone porosity prediction is a matter of estimating original composition and subsequent diagenesis. Use the table below to predict sandstone porosity.

Step	Action
1	Estimate the original composition of the sandstone from provenance (use Figure 9–55) and depositional environment.
2	Estimate the effects of near-surface diagenetic processes (see Figure 9–56).
3	Estimate the effects of mechanical diagenetic processes (see Figure 9–57).
4	Estimate the effects of intermediate and deep burial diagenesis, especially with respect to the creation of secondary porosity.
5	Using information collected in steps 1 through 4, predict the final porosity ranges using burial history (next procedure).

Predicting effect of provenance on diagenesis

Use the flow chart below to predict the effect of original sediment composition on subsequent diagenesis.

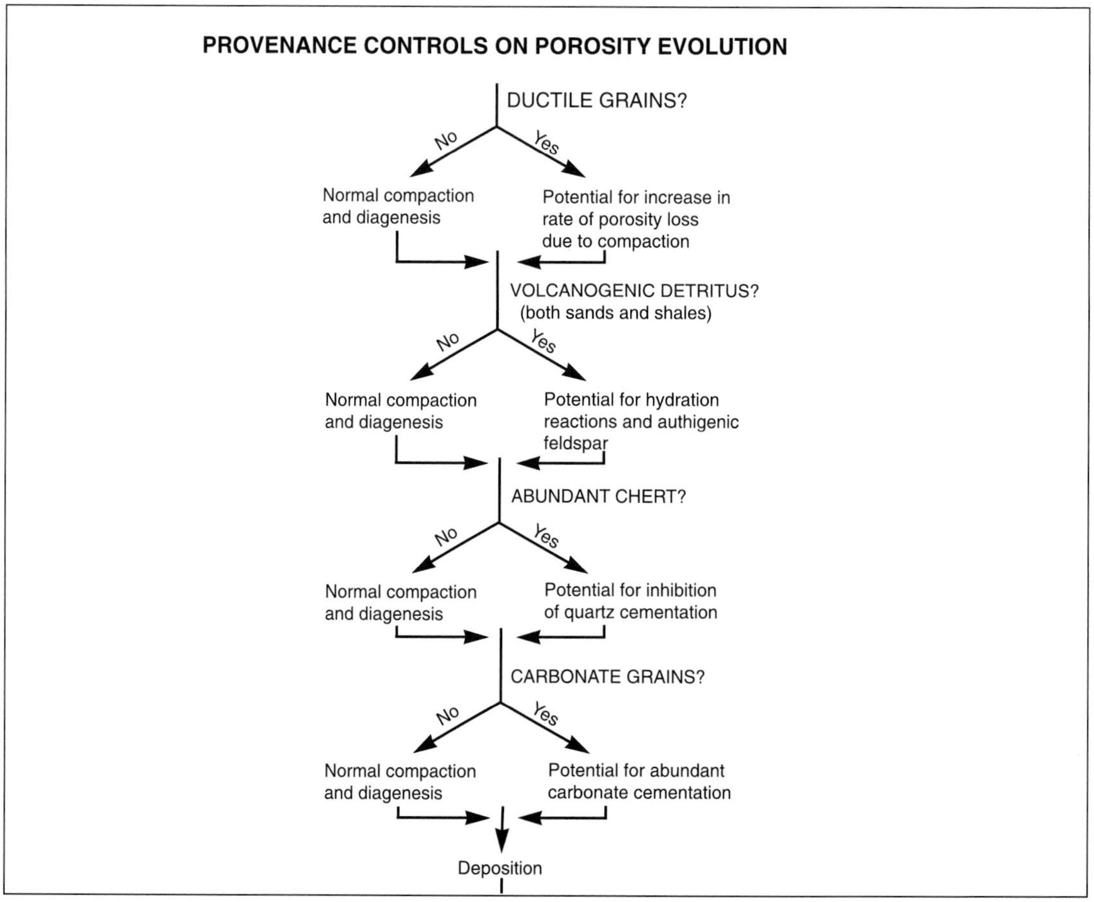

Figure 9–55. From Surdam et al., 1989; courtesy RMAG.

Estimating effect of near-surface diagenesis

Use the flow chart below to estimate the effects of near-surface diagenesis (depth to point where temperature reaches 80°C).

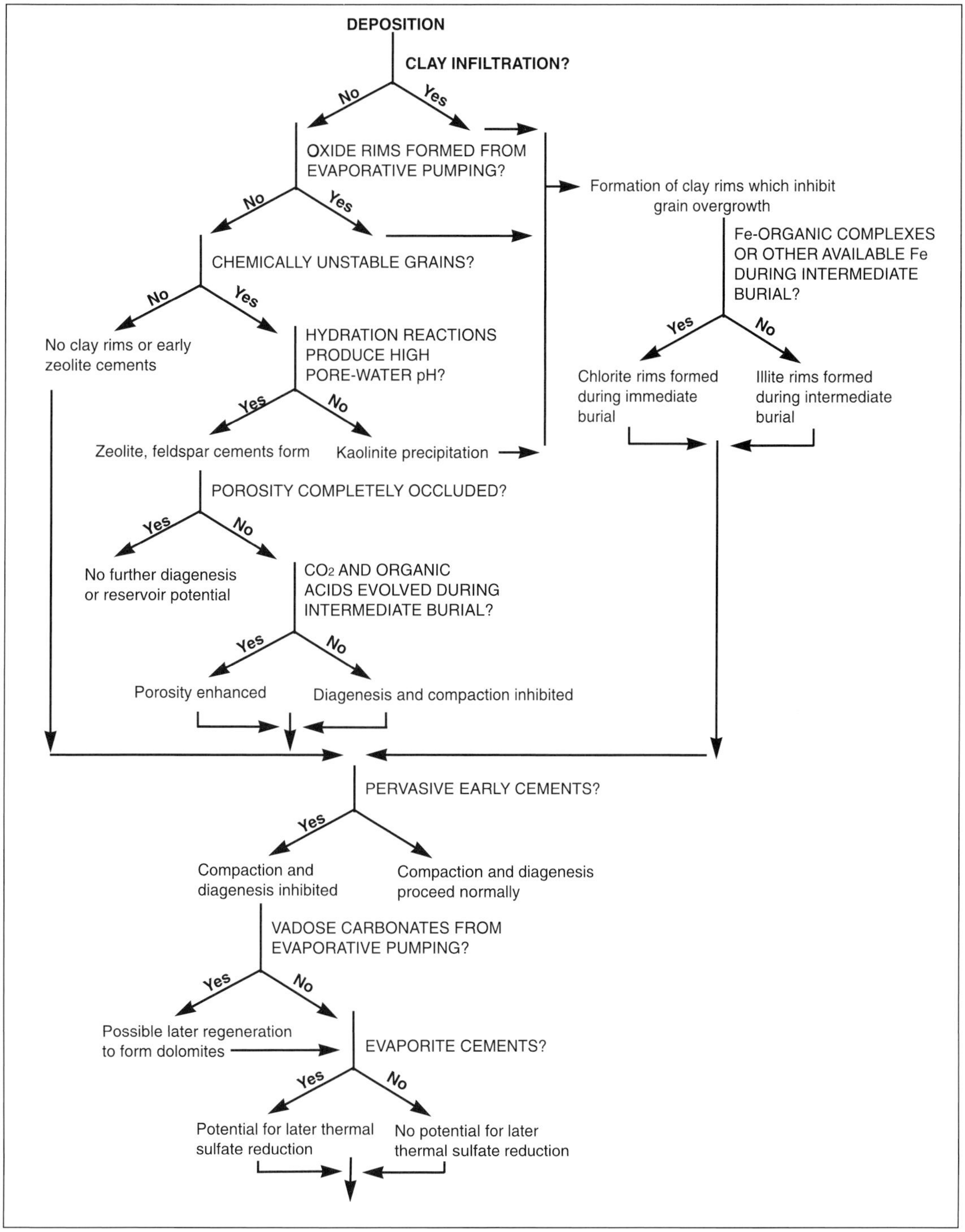

Figure 9–56. From Surdam et al., 1989; courtesy RMAG.

Predicting effect of mechanical diagenesis

Use the chart below to predict the effects of mechanical diagenesis on sandstone porosity.

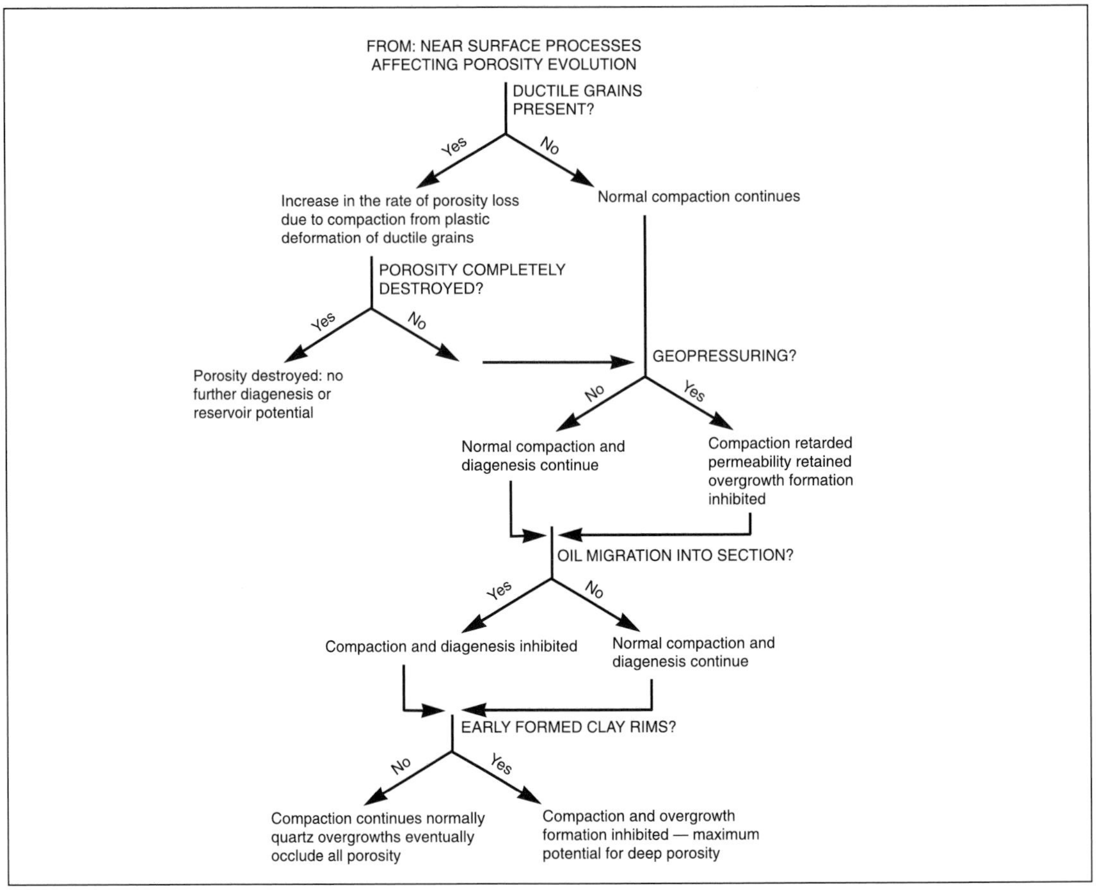

Figure 9–57. From Surdam et al., 1989; courtesy RMAG.

Using burial history to predict porosity

Reconstructing burial history aids sandstone porosity prediction. A burial history diagram integrates tectonic and hydrologic history with diagenetic evolution to predict sandstone porosity. The table below outlines steps for predicting porosity from burial history and is illustrated in Figure 9–58.

Step	Action
1	Construct a burial history diagram for the formation of interest in the prospect area.
2	Plot the tectonic history of the basin in the prospect area along the lower x-axis.
3	Plot the hydrologic history of the prospect area along the lower x-axis. Use the tectonic history to infer the hydrologic history of the prospect.
4	Plot the porosity curve by combining concepts of diagenetic processes with burial and hydrologic histories of the prospect.

Example of using burial history

Below is an example of a diagram showing diagenetic and burial history for the Brent Group Sandstones, North Sea. Line thicknesses indicate relative abundance of diagenetic components.

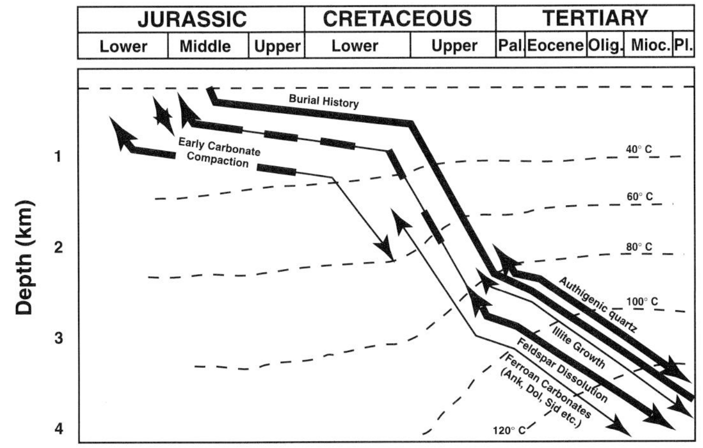

Figure 9–58. From Wilson, 1994b; courtesy SEPM.

The diagram below is an example of sandstone porosity prediction using burial history.

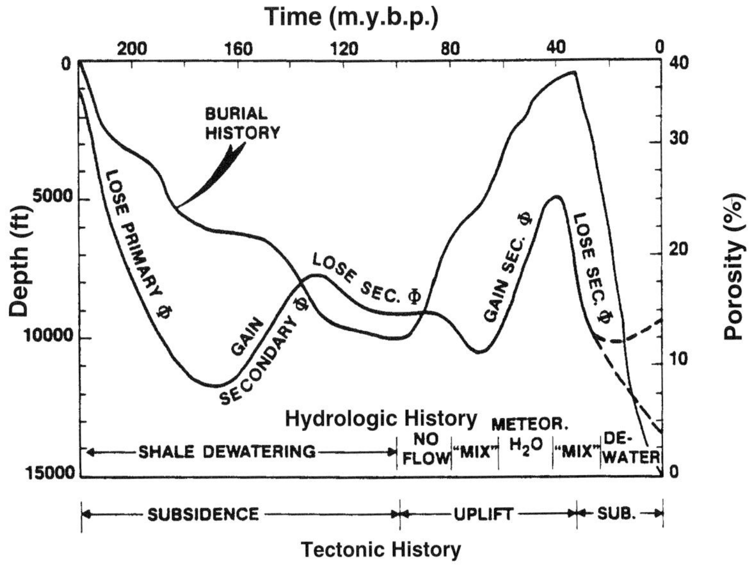

Figure 9–59. From Hayes, 1983; courtesy AAPG.

Analog porosity

Analog porosity values for different depositional environments can help us predict the porosity of reservoir system rocks when the target formation is unsampled within the basin. Analog values, however, may have wide ranges within facies and subfacies of depositional environments. Therefore, we should use care when applying analog data.

Predicting Sandstone Permeability from Texture

Introduction

Pore type, pore geometry, and fluid properties are critical factors affecting permeability. Sandstone texture directly affects pore type and geometry. Knowing what textures and fluids to expect, as well as what authigenic clays might be present, can help us predict permeability.

Effects of pore type and geometry

Pore type, defined by pore throat size (i.e., macroporosity), directly controls rock permeability. Pore throat size limits flow capacity. Pore geometry also affects permeability, but not as much. The rougher the surface of the pore, the more difficult for fluid to flow through the pore and the lower the permeability.

Effects of texture

Sandstone texture affects permeability as follows:

- Decreasing grain size decreases permeability.
- Increasing grain sorting increases permeability.
- Increasing grain rounding increases permeability.

The figure below shows how grain size affects permeability and porosity.

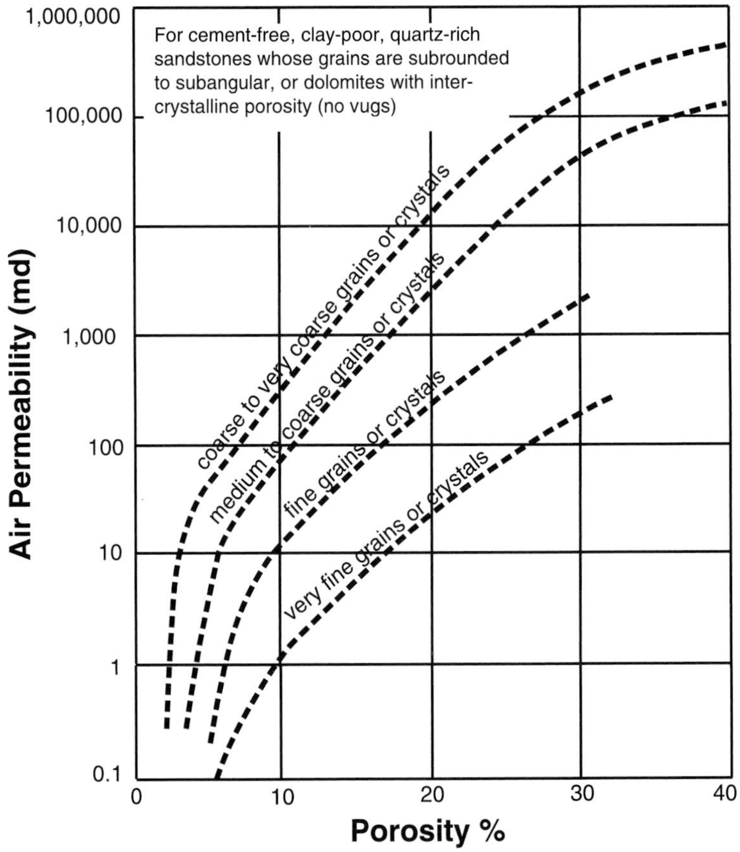

Figure 9–60. From Coalson et al., 1990.

Predicting Sandstone Permeability from Texture, continued

Rules of thumb for gas vs. oil

Use the following rules of thumb for permeability for oil vs. gas reservoirs:

- At >10 md, the reservoir can produce oil without stimulation.
- At >1 md, the reservoir can produce gas without stimulation.
- At 1–10 md, the reservoir probably requires stimulation for oil production.

Effect of authigenic clays

Pore-bridging clays, like illite, decrease porosity slightly but can destroy sandstone permeability. Discrete particle clay, like kaolinite, lowers porosity and permeability only slightly. The diagram below compares porosity–permeability relationships for kaolinite-, chlorite-, and illite-cemented sandstones. Note there is no significant change in porosities, but permeabilities range over four orders of magnitude.

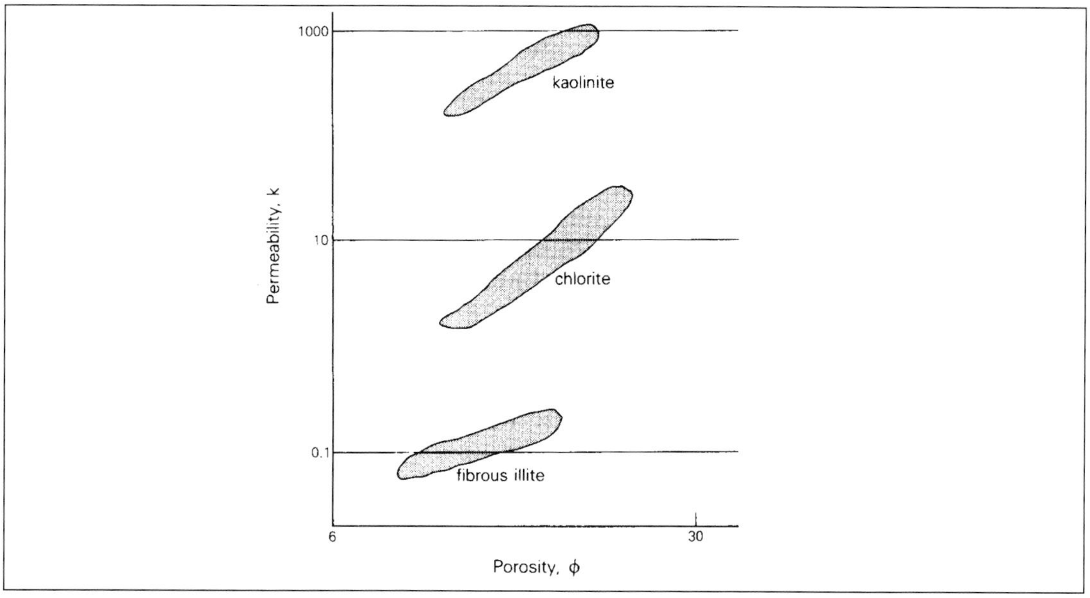

Figure 9–61. From North, 1985; courtesy Allen & Unwin.

Pore geometry and clay minerals

The diagram below shows pore lining and discrete particle clays that decrease porosity and permeability only slightly in contrast to pore-bridging clays, which decrease porosity slightly but substantially lower permeability.

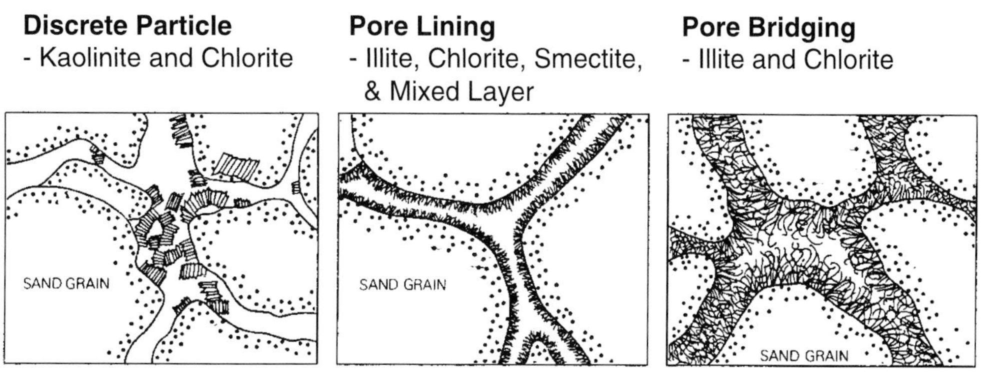

Figure 9–62. After Neasham, 1977; courtesy SPE.

Detrital clay and permeability

Detrital clays can be part of sandstone matrix or grains. As matrix, detrital clays can obliterate permeability. Detrital grains of clay are often ductile and can be compacted into pore spaces during burial. The percentage of detrital clay in a rock determines permeability. The figure below shows different types of detrital clays in a sandstone.

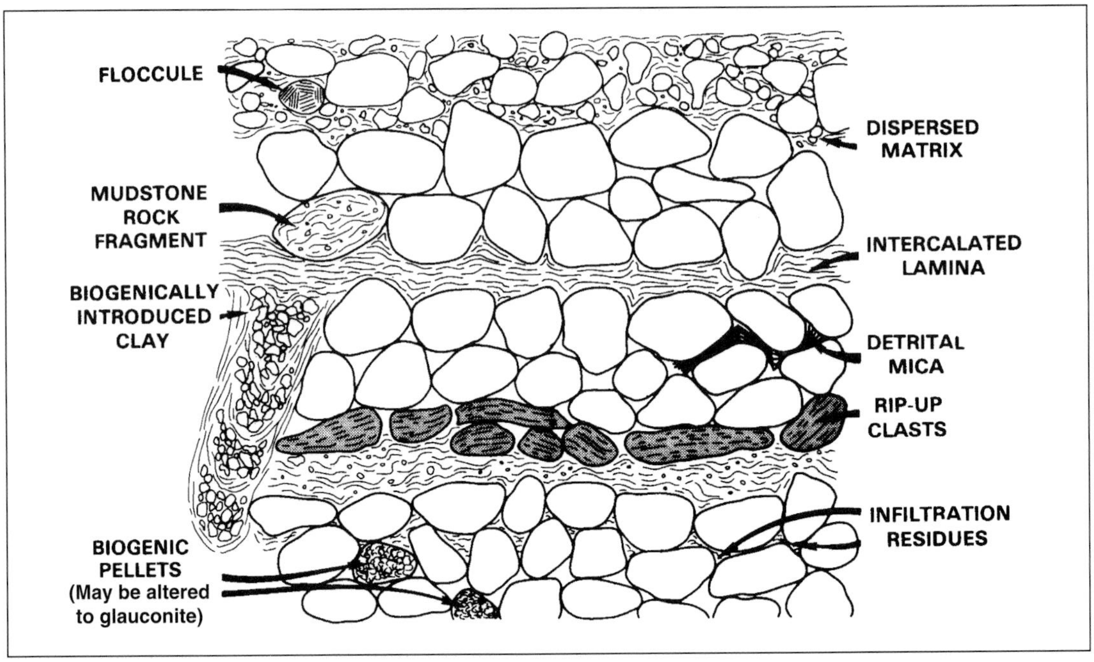

Figure 9–63. After Wilson and Pittman, 1977; courtesy Journal of Sedimentary Petrology.

Effect of quartz overgrowths

In general, as quartz cement precipitates, the pore–pore throat size ratio approaches 1 (Hartmann et al., 1985). Throats are reduced less than pore space; therefore, permeability is affected less than porosity. During cementation, the size of the pore spaces between the pore-filling crystals decreases until it approaches the size of the pore throats. Throats become more tabular or sheet-like. Sandstone porosity may be quite low (<5%) and still have some permeability (<10 md) where cemented with quartz.

Effect of fractures

Fractures enhance the permeability of any sandstone reservoir. Fractures are especially important for improving the permeability of sandstone reservoirs with abundant microporosity or disconnected dissolution porosity.

Predicting Sandstone Permeability from Texture, continued

Predicting from texture and clay content

Predicting sandstone reservoir permeability is possible as long as we realize that potential errors may be large. Any process that decreases pore throat size decreases permeability, so predict accordingly. Use the table below to help predict sandstone reservoir permeability.

Step	Action
1	Estimate grain size, sorting, and porosity using the depositional environment. For example, if a reservoir is a beach sand, it should be fine- to medium-grained and well sorted with well-rounded quartz grains
2	Apply information from Step 1 to the porosity–permeability–grain size plot (Figure 9–60). Use porosity and grain size from sandstone to estimate the permeability on the chart.
3	If the sandstone is poorly sorted or is cemented, then discount permeability downward.
4	Determine if authigenic clay is present. If so, what kind: pore lining, discrete particle, or pore throat bridging? Adjust permeability downward according to clay type present.
5	Determine if detrital clay is present using depositional environment (i.e., high energy = low clay content). If detrital clay is likely, then expect permeability to be low.

Estimating Sandstone Permeability from Cuttings

Introduction

Sneider and King (1984) developed a cuttings-based method of permeability estimation. Where cuttings are available, permeability estimates can be made by examining the surfaces of cuttings for petrophysical permeability indicators. Estimates of the permeability for a particular formation can be extended into areas without data in order to predict permeability.

Basis

Sneider and others at Shell Oil Company developed a methodology for estimating permeability from cuttings by calibrating permeability measured from cores with rock-pore parameters described in cuttings. Cores of known permeability were ground up until chips from the core were the size of cuttings. By using comparators made from core chips, they estimated formation permeability from cuttings with surprising accuracy. Although Sneider and King (1984) describe the method for estimating sandstone permeability from cuttings (presented below), procedures could just as easily be developed to predict permeability of carbonates from cuttings.

Petrophysical description

From examination of cuttings, sandstone permeability can be predicted using the following petrophysical descriptions:

- Grain size and sorting
- Degree of rock consolidation
- Volume percent of clays
- Pore sizes and pore interconnections
- Size and distribution of pore throats

Sneider's pore classification for clastics

Sneider and King (1984) developed a simple method of classifying pore types from cuttings. The classification of clastic rock pore types from cuttings is made by comparing pore types with production tests and log analysis. The pore types are as follows:

Type	Description
I	Rocks with pores capable of producing gas without natural or artificial fracturing.
II	Rocks with pores capable of producing gas with natural or artificial fracturing and/or interbedded with type I rocks.
III	Rocks too tight to produce at commercial rates even with natural or artificial fracturing.

Estimating Sandstone Permeability from Cuttings, continued

Sneider's pore classification for clastics (continued)

The table below lists the characteristics of pore types I, II, and III.

Pore Type	Characteristics of Dry, Freshly Broken Surfaces at 20× Magnification			Permeability
	Visible	Pinpoint	Consolidation	
I	Abundant to common; interconnection visible on many pores	Very abundant to common	Needle probe easily dislodges many grains from rock surface	Type I Subclasses IA: >100 md IB: 10–100 md IC: 1–10 md ID: ±0.5–1 md
II	Scattered	Abundant to common	Needle probe can only occasionally dislodge a grain from rock surface	± 0.5–1.0 md (depending on particle size, sorting, and clay mineral content)
III	None to very isolated	None to a few pores	Usually very well consolidated and/or pores filled with clays or other pore-filling material	Too tight to produce gas at commercial rates even when fractured or interbedded with type I rocks

Examples of pore type I

The SEM microphotographs below are examples of rocks with types IA, IB, IC, and ID. Note the amount and connectivity of pore space of each subclass.

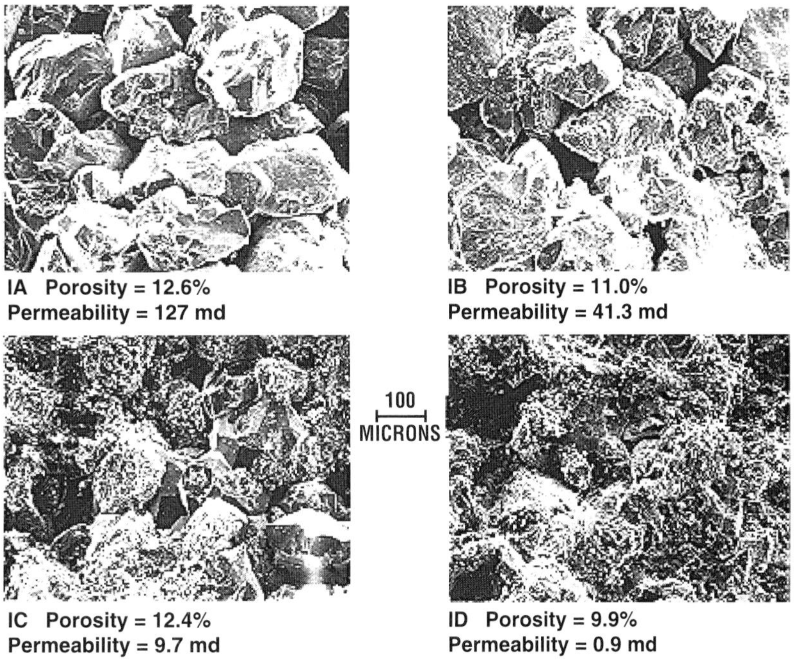

Figure 9–64. From Sneider and King, 1984; courtesy AAPG.

Pore types II and III

The SEM microphotographs below are examples of rocks with types II and III. Note the amount and connectivity of pore space of each subclass.

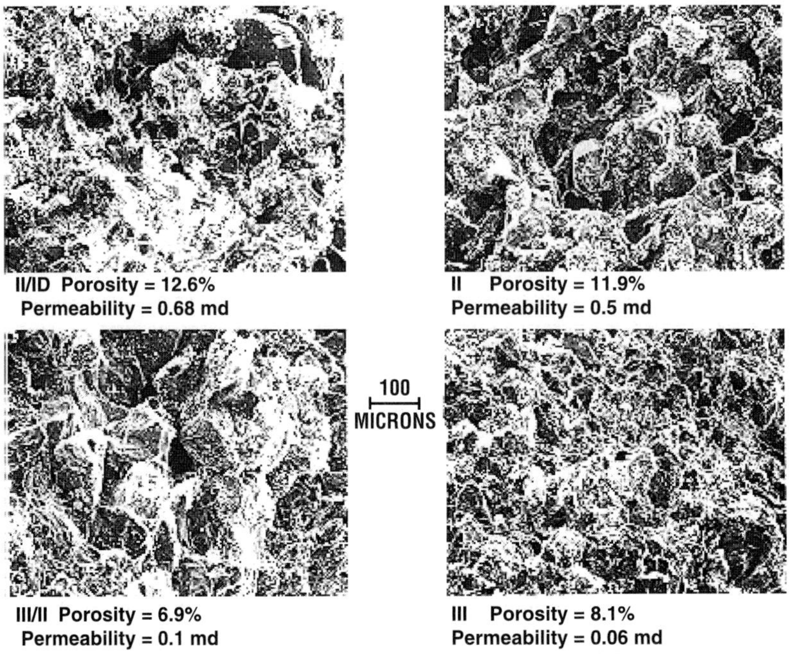

Figure 9–65. From Sneider and King, 1984; courtesy AAPG.

Procedure: Predicting sandstone permeability

The procedure below is for predicting the permeability of sandstones from cuttings using 20× magnification (from Sneider and King, 1984).

Step	Action
1	Estimate grain size and sorting using standard size-sorting comparators, thin section and SEM photomicrographs, and rock photographs.
2	Estimate volume percentages using Terry-Chillingar charts made for volume estimates.
3	Estimate consolidation using the scheme described in the preceding table.
4	Describe the visible and pinpoint porosity and interconnectedness.
5	Estimate permeability from rocks on comparators and/or using rock characteristics described in the preceding table. (Comparators can be made or purchased.)
6	Predict permeability for the formation in prospective areas where petrophysical characteristics are believed to be similar

Subsection E2

Predicting Carbonate Porosity and Permeability

Introduction

Predicting reservoir quality in carbonate rocks can be difficult because of the complexity of their pore systems. Applying a combination of concepts of depositional environment, diagenesis, and sequence stratigraphy increases the chances of predicting the quality of reservoir needed for a successful play. Sequence stratigraphic models are especially useful for modeling pore-space evolution and enhance prediction of the location and quality of potential carbonate reservoir rocks.

In this subsection

This subsection contains the following topics.

Carbonate Facies

Factors that control facies

An interplay of hydrologic and biologic factors produces carbonates in place. Deposition of carbonate sediments is limited to water that is warm, shallow, clear, sunlit, and free of suspended clay. When these conditions prevail, carbonates accumulate rapidly.

Basic carbonate facies zones

In general, carbonate facies develop on gently sloping shelves that can be divided into three main zones:

1. A seaward zone below normal wave base
2. A zone where wave energy interacts with sediment
3. A landward low-energy zone

Depositional slope, geologic age, water energy, and climate control the basic facies pattern. The diagram below shows typical carbonate facies that develop within the three zones.

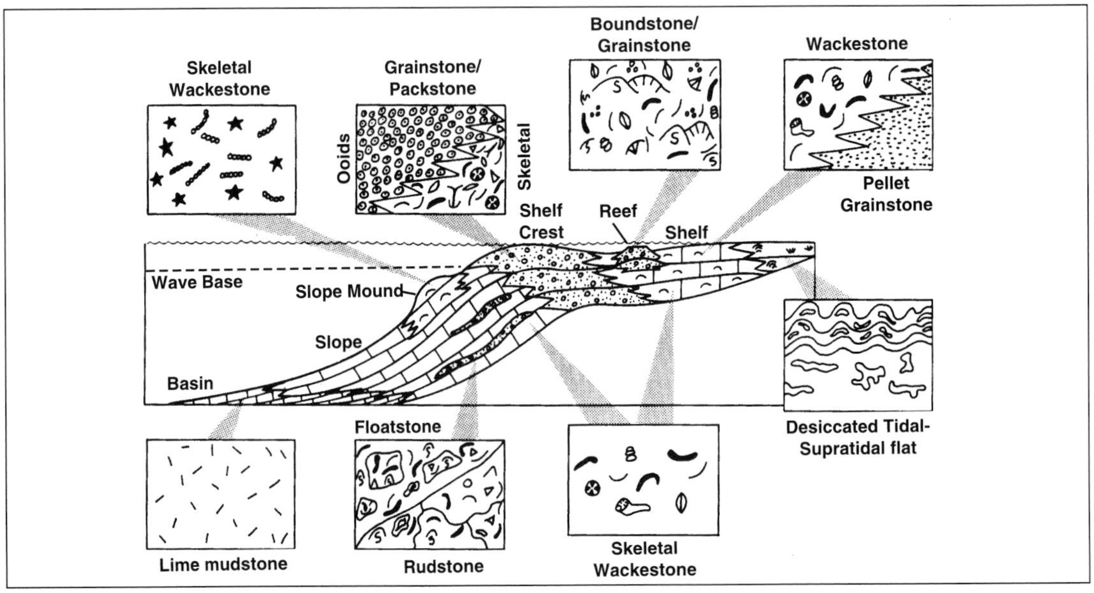

Figure 9–66. After Sarg, 1988; courtesy SEPM.

Platform or ramp development

The high accumulation rates of carbonate sediments relative to subsidence generate shelf-to-basin submarine topography with a seaward face of variable steepness. As shown in the diagram below, a platform's seaward edge steepens with time because subsidence cannot keep pace with carbonate sedimentation.

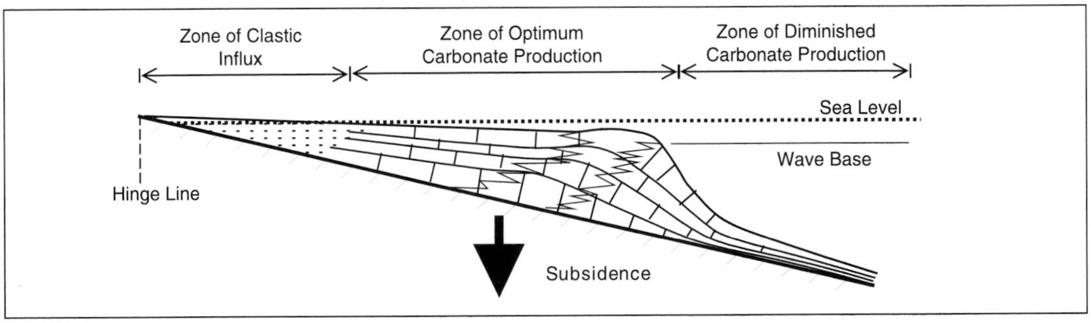

Figure 9–67.

Carbonate Diagenetic Stages

Stages affect porosity

Three major geologic stages determine the porosity of carbonate rocks (Choquette and Pray, 1970):

1. Predepositional
2. Depositional
3. Postdepositional

The **predepositional stage** is the time from when sedimentary material first forms to when it is finally deposited. Porosity created during the predepositional stage is mainly chambers or cell structures of skeletal grains or within nonskeletal grains such as pellets or ooids.

The **depositional stage** is the relatively short time involved in the final deposition at the site of ultimate burial of a carbonate sediment. Most porosity formed is intergranular, although some can also be framework.

The **postdepositional stage** is the time after final deposition. All the porosity that forms during this stage is diagenetic or secondary in origin. Diagenetic processes are related to changes in water chemistry, temperature, pressure, and water movement.

Time–porosity table

The following table and chart list time–porosity terminology and relationships.

Stage	Predepositional	Depositional	Postdepositional		
Substage			Eogenetic	Mesogenetic	Telogenetic
Porosity Terms	*Primary Porosity*		*Secondary Porosity*		
	Predepositional Porosity	Depositional Porosity	Eogenetic Porosity	Mesogenetic Porosity	Telogenetic Porosity
"Typical" Relative Time Span	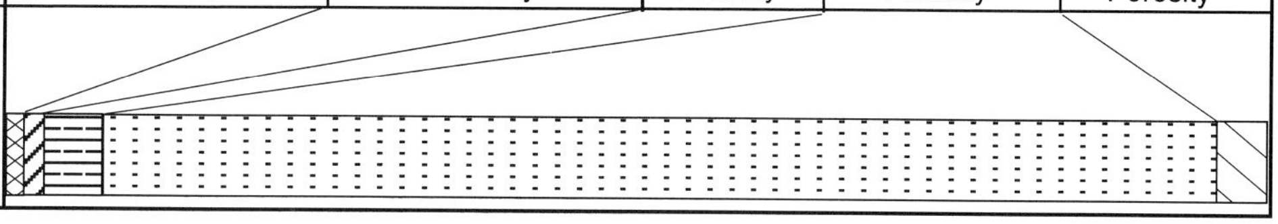				

Figure 9–68. After Choquette and Pray, 1970; courtesy AAPG.

Postdepositional substages

The postdepositional time period, which can be quite long (millions of years), can be divided into three substages:

1. Eogenetic (early)
2. Mesogenetic (middle)
3. Telogenetic (late)

The **eogenetic substage** (early diagenetic period) is the time from final deposition to the time when the sediment is buried below the zone of influence from surface processes. The eogenetic zone extends from the surface to the base of the zone of influence of surface processes. Even though the eogenetic substage may be geologically brief and the zone thin, the diagenesis that occurs is more varied and generally more significant than any other substage. Eogenetic processes are generally fabric selective. The major porosity

Carbonate Diagenetic Stages, continued

Postdepositional substages (continued)

change is reduction through carbonate or evaporite mineral precipitation. Internal sedimentation also reduces porosity. Although minor in comparison, the most important porosity creation process is selective solution of aragonite (Choquette and Pray, 1970).

The **mesogenetic substage** (middle diagenetic) encompasses the time when the sediment is out of the influence of surface diagenetic processes. Cementation is the major process. Porosity obliteration occurs when mosaics of coarsely crystalline calcite precipitate in large pores. Pressure solution occurs at higher pressures.

The **telogenetic substage** (late diagenetic) occurs when sedimentary carbonates are raised to the surface and erosion occurs along unconformities. The telogenetic zone extends from the surface to the point where surface processes no longer influence diagenesis. Solution by meteoric water creates porosity. Internal sedimentation and cementation by precipitation from solution destroy porosity.

Path of diagenesis

The parts of the path of diagenesis that a carbonate sediment follows determine the evolution of its porosity. The figure below summarizes the diagenesis that occurs along the path.

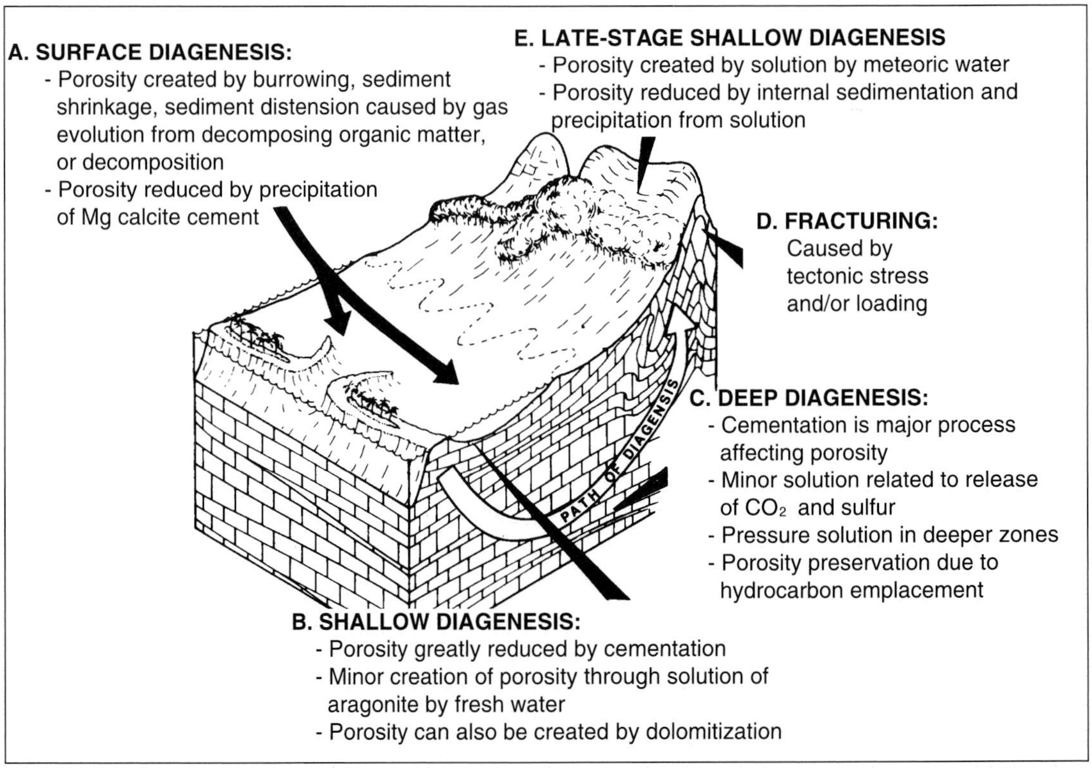

A. SURFACE DIAGENESIS:
- Porosity created by burrowing, sediment shrinkage, sediment distension caused by gas evolution from decomposing organic matter, or decomposition
- Porosity reduced by precipitation of Mg calcite cement
E. LATE-STAGE SHALLOW DIAGENESIS
- Porosity created by solution by meteoric water
- Porosity reduced by internal sedimentation and precipitation from solution
D. FRACTURING:
Caused by tectonic stress and/or loading
C. DEEP DIAGENESIS:
- Cementation is major process affecting porosity
- Minor solution related to release of CO_2 and sulfur
- Pressure solution in deeper zones
- Porosity preservation due to hydrocarbon emplacement
PATH OF DIAGENESIS
B. SHALLOW DIAGENESIS:
- Porosity greatly reduced by cementation
- Minor creation of porosity through solution of aragonite by fresh water
- Porosity can also be created by dolomitization

Figure 9–69. Modified from Harris et al., 1985; courtesy SEPM.

Early Carbonate Diagenesis

Diagenetic environments

Early diagenesis occurs at the surface or in the shallow subsurface. It is usually responsible for much of the cementation of carbonate sediments. Early diagenesis occurs in a consistent sequence of four diagenetic zones:

- Marine phreatic
- Vadose
- Freshwater phreatic
- Mixing

Each zone has characteristic cement textures and alteration features. The sequence of diagenesis usually follows the above order; however, a rock may be exposed to a variety of environments many different times, making diagenetic sequence interpretation difficult.

Summary diagram

The block diagram below summarizes early diagenetic processes and products that occur in carbonate environments.

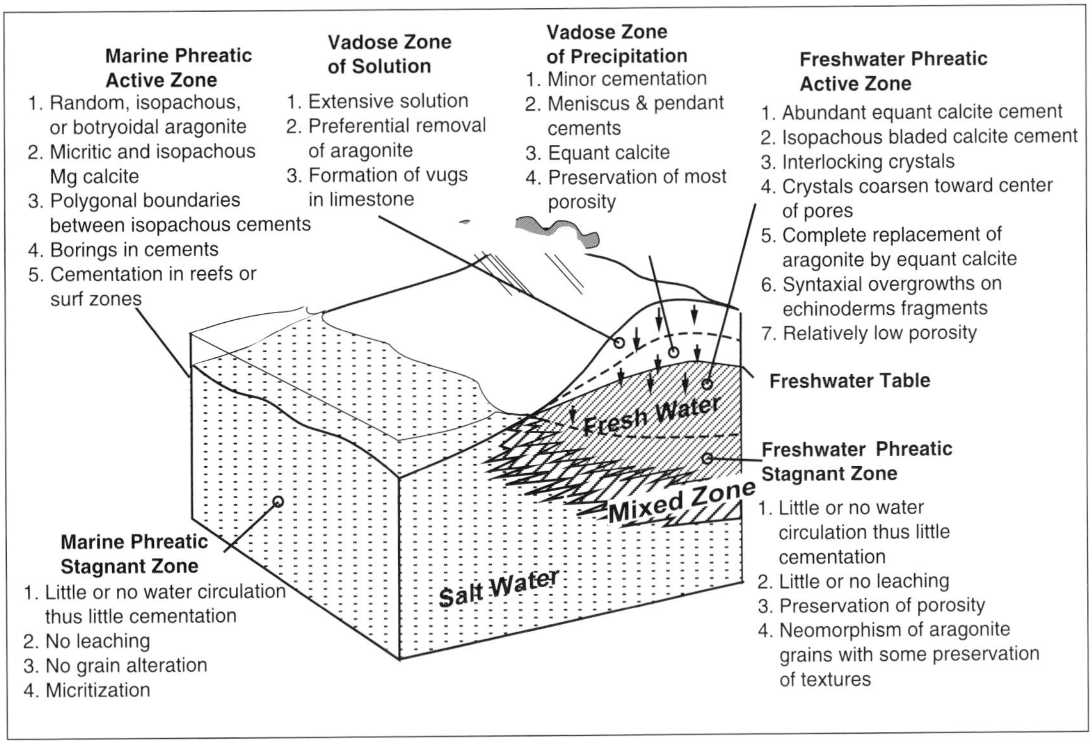

Figure 9–70. Data from Longman, 1980; courtesy AAPG.

Early Carbonate Diagenesis, continued

Marine phreatic environment

The marine phreatic environment, in most cases, is where carbonate sediments originate and begin their diagenetic history. It can be divided into two distinct zones that represent two ends of a spectrum (Longman, 1980):

1. Active marine zone where water flow combined with other factors result in precipitation of aragonite or magnesium (Mg) calcite.
2. Stagnant marine zone in which there is little or no water movement and consequently no cementation or sediment alteration.

Active marine phreatic zone

The cementation rate is greatest in the active marine phreatic environment where three conditions occur:

- pH increases above 9 due to photosynthesis and respiration of a reef biomass
- CO_2 degassing
- Waves, tides, or currents force water through pores (works best at shelf margins where buildup is present or along shoreface)

Magnesium calcite or aragonite are the only cements that precipitate in the active marine phreatic zone. Both are unstable in Mg-deficient water regardless of whether it is marine, brackish, or fresh and tend to alter to low-Mg calcite because most water is magnesium deficient. Their common form is isopachous coatings on grains. Micritization of grains occurs in the active marine phreatic zone.

The diagram below summarizes the diagenesis of this zone.

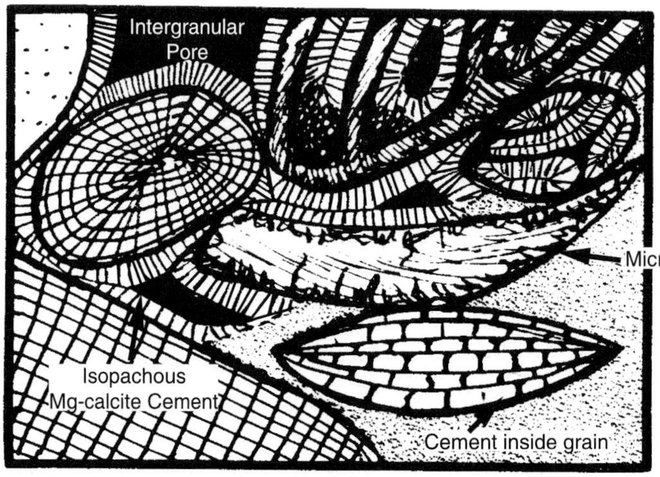

Figure 9–71. After Longman, 1980; courtesy AAPG.

Stagnant marine phreatic

Micritization and minor intragranular cementation are the only diagenetic processes occurring in the stagnant marine phreatic zone. Cementation is limited because of little or no water movement. Micritization by boring algae occurs at the sediment–water interface to 1 m below the interface (Longman, 1980). Sediments deposited in lagoons, below the wave base on carbonate ramps, or on a debris slope have diagenetic histories that begin in the stagnant marine phreatic zone.

Vadose zone

The vadose zone extends from the land surface to the water table. The pore space of sediments in the vadose zone contains both air and water. Solution of carbonate sediment or rock occurs in the vadose zone as a result of meteoric water movement. Initially, meteoric water is undersaturated with $CaCO_3$, but it quickly becomes saturated as it moves downward and dissolves carbonate grains or cements. Organic matter in the soil zone produces CO_2. It combines with the water to aid in the solution process. Saturated meteoric water precipitates calcite through evaporation or CO_2 degassing.

Climate greatly affects vadose diagenesis. In arid climates diagenetic alteration may be limited, whereas in humid climates it may be extensive. In humid climates, a thick soil zone develops and there is abundant meteoric water.

The vadose zone can be divided into three zones (Longman, 1980):

- Soil zone
- Solution zone
- Precipitation zone

Vadose solution zone

The vadose solution zone extends tens to hundreds of meters below the surface, depending on associated relief of nearby land. Any form of calcium carbonate may dissolve in the vadose solution zone. Aragonite grains are especially susceptible to dissolution. Caves may form with prolonged exposure. Distinguishing leaching in the vadose solution zone from solution in the freshwater phreatic zone is difficult (Longman, 1980).

Vadose precipitation zone

The vadose precipitation zone begins where water in the vadose zone becomes saturated with $CaCO_3$. Slight temperature increases or CO_2 degassing causes calcite to precipitate. Cementation is generally minor and reflects pore-water distribution. Meniscus cement precipitates where water clings between grains in a meniscus manner. Pendulous or microstalactitic cement precipitates where water droplets form underneath grains. Cement tends to be very fine equant calcite crystals. If magnesium is present in pore water, then calcite precipitation may be inhibited and aragonite or even dolomite may precipitate (Longman, 1980).

The sketches below illustrate recent limestones from the intertidal–supratidal zone. They show petrographic aspects of vadose precipitation zone cements.

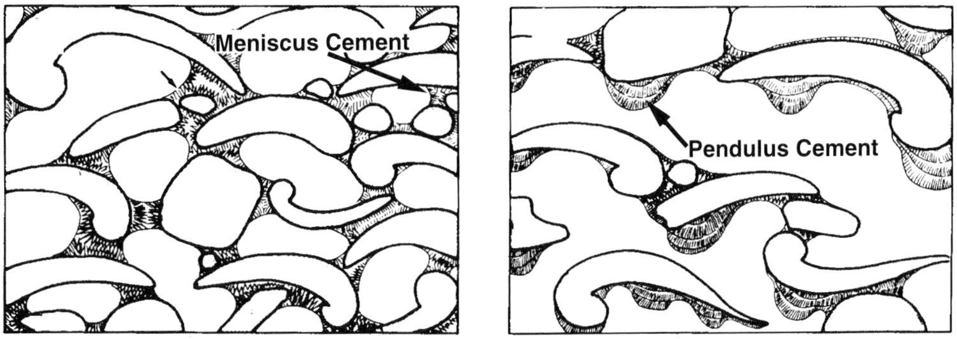

Figure 9–72. From Purser, 1978; courtesy Journal of Petroleum Geology.

Freshwater phreatic zone

The freshwater phreatic zone lies between the vadose and mixing zones. It is 100% saturated with fresh water. Water enters the zone through the vadose zone or directly enters the zone through streams and lakes. Rainfall amounts, pore type, and relief determine its size and geometry. It is generally lens shaped. Climatic and sea level changes cause the zone to be dynamic. It changes shape with changes in rainfall amounts or sea level. In arid climates the zone can be completely missing. As a rule of thumb, for every meter the zone lies above sea level, there are 32 m of fresh water below sea level.

Active and stagnant zones

Based on diagenesis, the freshwater phreatic zone can be divided into two major zones:

- Active freshwater phreatic zone
- Stagnant freshwater phreatic zone

The **active freshwater phreatic zone** is where freshwater movement occurs in the phreatic zone. Meteoric water that enters the phreatic zone without passing through the vadose is undersaturated with respect to $CaCO_3$ but becomes saturated as it dissolves grains. Based on $CaCO_3$ saturation, the active freshwater phreatic zone may be subdivided into undersaturated and saturated zones. In the undersaturated zone, solution occurs, creating moldic or vuggy porosity. In the active saturated freshwater phreatic zone extensive and rapid cementation occurs. Cement is equant calcite that coarsens toward pore centers. Syntaxial overgrowths on echinoderm fragments are common.

The **stagnant freshwater phreatic zone** occurs where there little to no movement. Pore water is near equilibrium with surrounding rock and lack of water movement means little cementation occurs. Consequently, primary porosity is generally preserved.

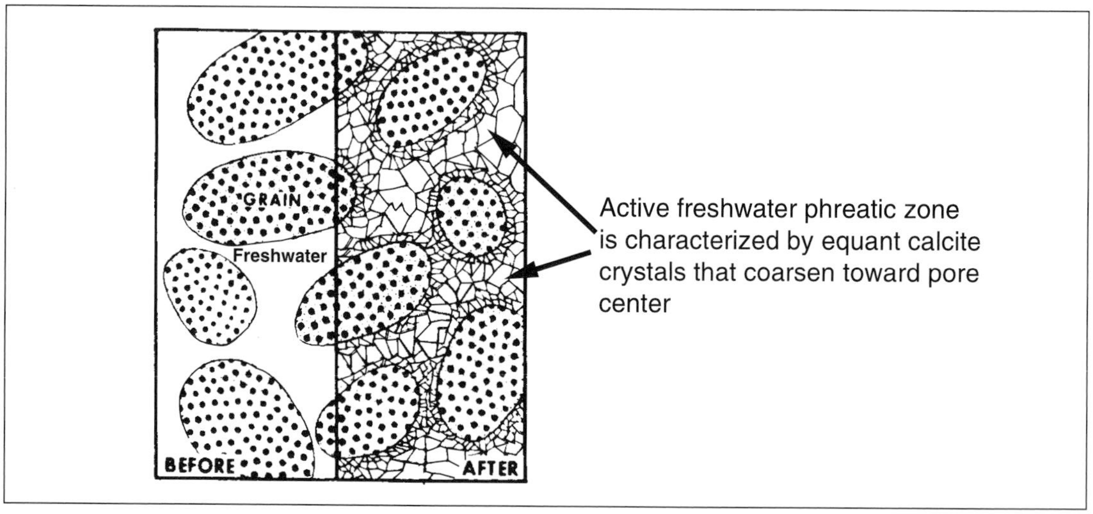
GRAIN
Freshwater
BEFORE
AFTER
Active freshwater phreatic zone is characterized by equant calcite crystals that coarsen toward pore center

Figure 9–73. From Longman, 1980; courtesy AAPG.

Basics of Carbonate Porosity Formation and Preservation

Early influences

How much influence does the original fabric of a carbonate rock (grains, mud, and pore space) have on with the pore space in the rock now? Which has more impact on reservoir quality of carbonates: early or late diagenesis? The interaction of early diagenesis with original fabric elements determines, in many cases, the ultimate reservoir quality of a carbonate. A rock that begins with good porosity and permeability, either from depositional or early diagenetic processes, has a better chance of retaining those qualities than an initially poor-quality rock becoming a good-quality rock. Porosity can be created late in a rock's life; however, concentrating on the early history of a carbonate rock is generally more rewarding when searching for reservoir-quality rocks.

Diagenesis and rock fabric

The initial solid constituents of a carbonate rock normally determine its initial pore type and geometry and strongly influence diagenesis. Early pore space in carbonate rocks generally has fabric-selective characteristics; creation of late pore space does not (Choquette and Pray, 1970). Surface and shallow diagenesis mainly occurs in fabric-selective pore geometries that allow the greatest fluid flow (mostly interparticle or intercrystalline). Late-stage shallow diagenesis mainly occurs in nonfabric-selective pore geometries that allow the greatest fluid flow (mostly fracture related). Deep diagenetic processes can be both fabric selective (fluid flow through interparticle or intercrystalline pores) or nonfabric selective (compaction).

Fabric and nonfabric selection porosity

The figure below shows fabric and nonfabric pore geometries and processes that create them.

Fabric Selective Porosity		Nonfabric Selective Porosity	
Geometry	Genesis	Geometry	Genesis
Interparticle	Diagenetic	Fracture	Deformation
Intraparticle	Depositional	Channel	Dissolution
Intercrystalline	Diagenetic	Vug	Dissolution
Moldic	Diagenetic	Cavern	Dissolution
Fenestral	Depostional		
Shelter	Depositional		
Growth or Framework	Depositional		

Figure 9–74. Modified from Choquette and Pray, 1970; courtesy AAPG.

Basics of Carbonate Porosity Formation and Preservation, continued

Early diagenesis and pore-system quality

The diagram below shows the general pathways that different carbonate rock types might take during early diagenesis as their pore systems evolve. The parallel lines are contours of equal pore throat size. In terms of quality, points plotting along the contours represent rocks with equal flow characteristics (*see* "Characterizing Rock Quality" earlier in this chapter). With the exception of the creation of connected vugs and dolomitized mudstone, carbonate rocks generally lose porosity and permeability as a result of diagenesis.

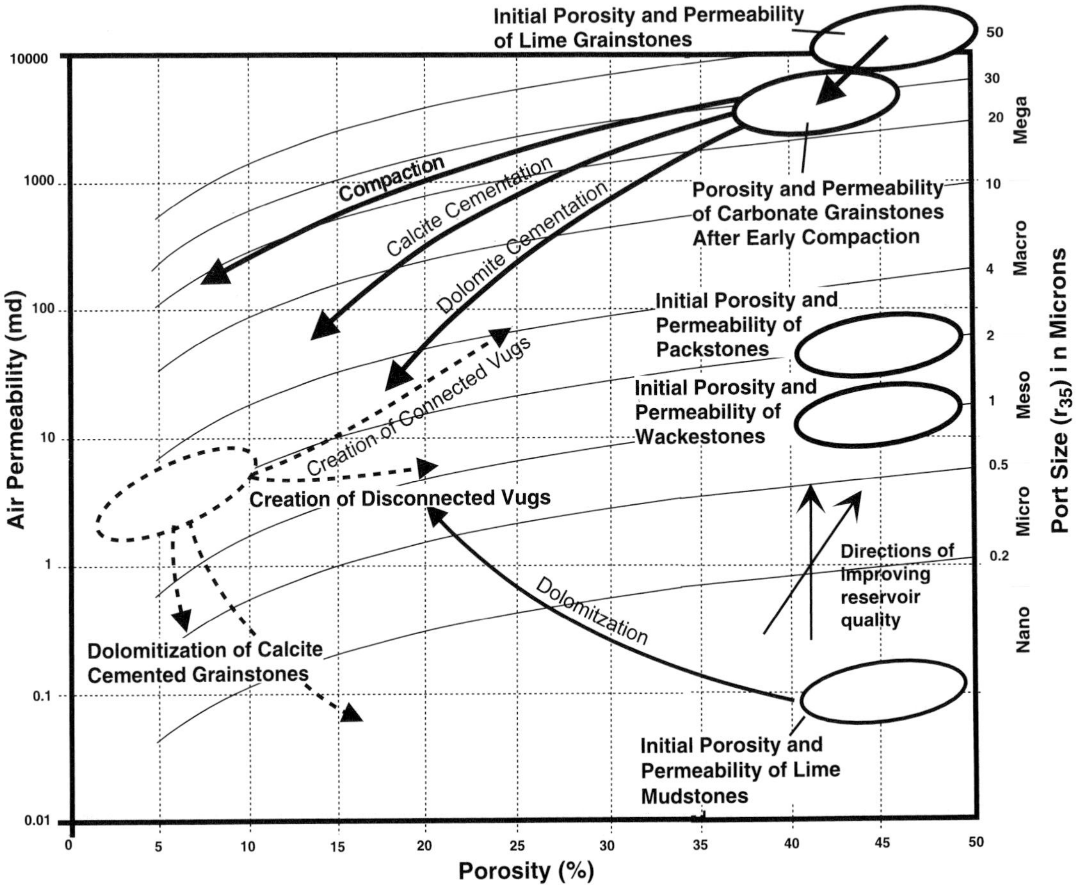

Figure 9–75.

Preserving pore systems

Some pore systems gain quality as a result of diagenesis. The general trend of pore system quality with time and burial, however, is toward destruction. Certain processes can temporarily interrupt this trend. These are "preserved" pore systems. Some of the processes that preserve pore systems are as follows (Feazel and Schatzinger, 1985):

- Reduced burial stress from overpressuring
- Increased rigidity of framework grains
- Oil entry into pore space
- Permeability barriers that isolate the reservoir from fluid flow

Sea Level Cycles and Carbonate Sequences

Cycles and sequences

Sea level cycles interact with subsidence, sedimentation rate, and climate to create the stratigraphy of carbonate sequences. The chart below lists five orders of sea level cycles and defines them by duration.

Order	Duration, m.y.	Stratigraphic Name	Typical Thickness, m
1st	50–350	Megasequence	
2nd	5–50	Supersequence	
3rd	0.5-5	Sequence	100–1000
4th	0.1–0.5	Parasequence	1–10
5th	0.5–0.01	Parasequence	1–10

Parasequence sets or systems tracts

Sets of parasequences generally stack in retrogradational, aggradational, or progradational patterns. A parasequence set approximately corresponds to a systems tract and is categorized by its position within third-order sequences (i.e., highstand, lowstand, and transgressive).

Superimposition of cycles

Fourth- and fifth-order cycles combine with third-order cycles to create complex composite curves. The diagram below shows third-, fourth-, and fifth-order sea level cycles and a composite curve of all three.

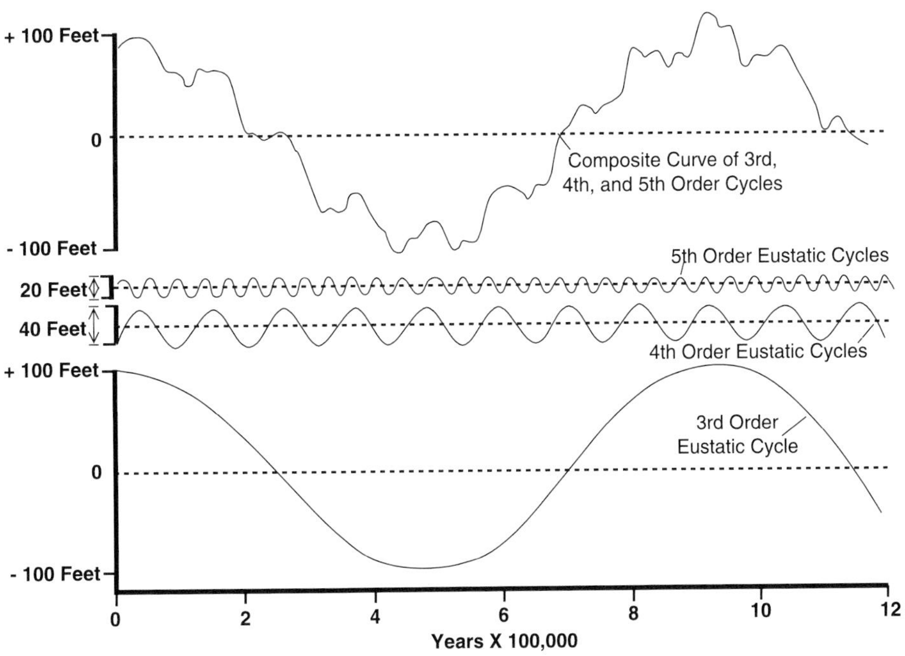

Figure 9–76. After Van Wagoner et al., 1990; courtesy AAPG.

Relative changes of sea level

Combining eustatic sea level change with tectonic subsidence produces relative changes of sea level. Relative changes of sea level create space for sediment accumulation (called accommodation space).

Tectonic subsidence primarily controls sediment thickness; as sea level cycles up and down, tectonic subsidence creates permanent space. Sea level cycles control lithofacies distribution and stratal patterns.

Interpreting parasequence facies deposition

A simple, effective approach to interpreting facies deposition in carbonate parasequences or sequences is to assume the following:

- Tectonic subsidence is constant.
- Carbonate sediment accumulation rates are greater than subsidence rates.
- The major causes of changes in carbonate facies patterns are cyclic eustatic sea level changes and climatic changes.

Example of interpreting parasequences

The diagram below shows the correlation of eustatic sea level change with parasequence deposition.

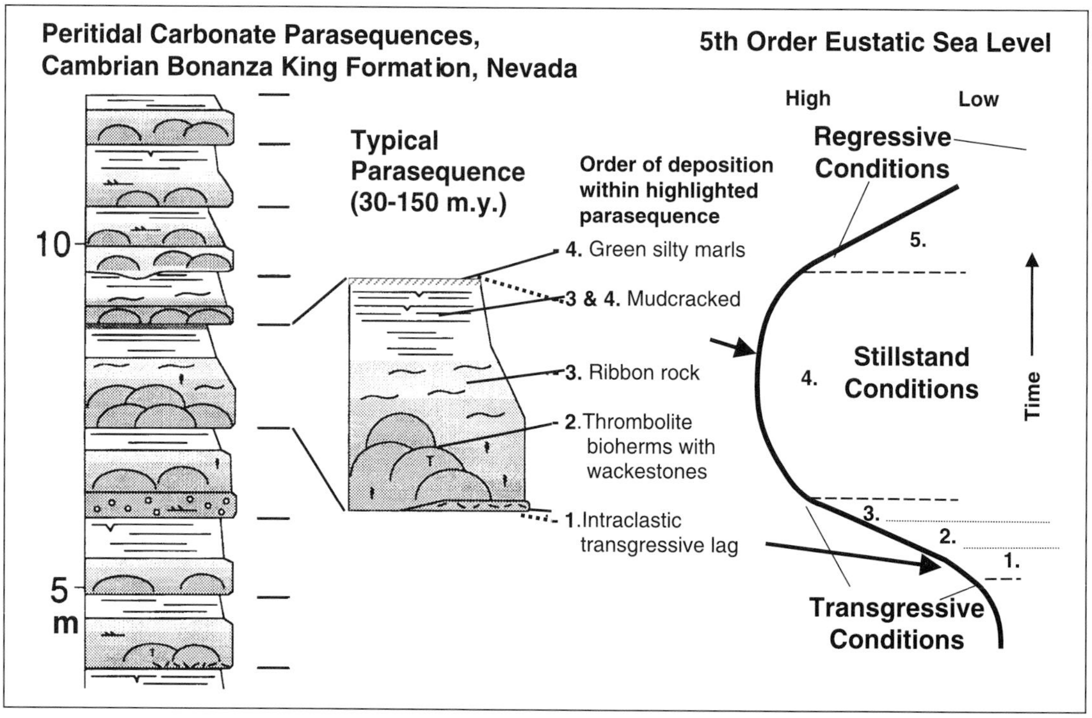

Figure 9–77. After Montañez and Osleger, 1993; courtesy AAPG.

Sea Level Cycles and Carbonate Sequences, continued

Depositional order of example

If subsidence and sediment production were constant and sea level cyclic, the lithofacies in the parasequence highlighted in the above diagram could have been deposited as follows.

Step	Action	Description
1	Intraclastic transgressive lag formed.	Transgressions occurred rapidly because the surface of the platform was wide, flat, and had a very gentle dip. A relative sea level rise of only a few meters inundated large areas of the platform. During this start-up phase (Sarg, 1988), the carbonate factory could not go into full production until sea level rose enough to allow efficient circulation on the platform.
2	Thrombolite bioherms with wackestone deposited.	Water depth may have been 2 or 3 m initially and sediment quickly built up to sea level as the carbonate factory went into full production. This was the "catch-up" phase.
3	Ribbon rock and cryptalgal laminite formed.	During the "keep-up" phase, the sediment accumulation rate closely matched sea level rise and subsidence rate.
4	Sheet floods deposited thin, green, mud-cracked, silty marl and some or most of the mud-cracked cryptalgal laminite.	This occurred across the tops of supratidal flats during highstand conditions. The thin marl and mud-cracked laminites indicate little available accommodation space was available because of slowing sea level rise.
5	Vadose diagenetic features formed.	Pendant and meniscus cements formed in the upper part of the sequence as a result of subaerial exposure during a sea level fall.

Correlation of cycles with sequences

Below are schematics of carbonate lithofacies portrayed both in depth and time. In the lower part, the composite third- and fourth-order sea level curve shows the correlation of third- and fourth-order sea level change with the sequences and parasequences of the diagram.

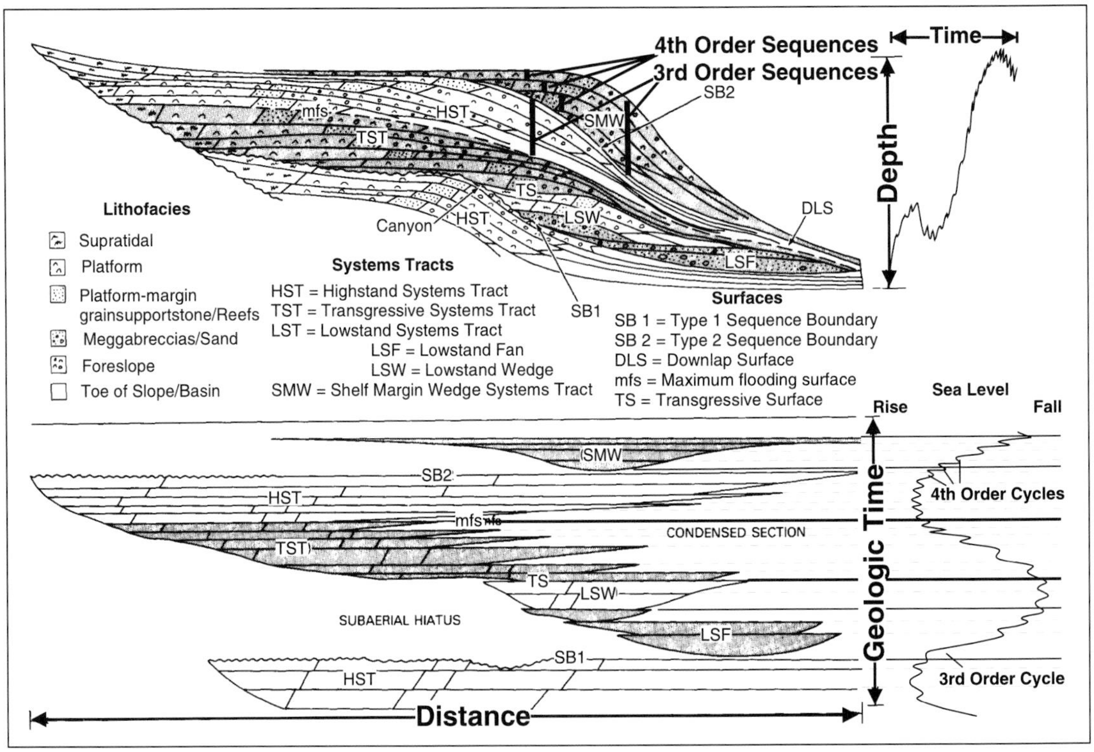

Figure 9–78. Modified from Sarg, 1988; courtesy SEPM.

Sea Level Cycles and Carbonate Diagenesis

Introduction

Most of the diagenesis seen in carbonate rocks can be attributed to processes that occurred during short-term fourth- or fifth-order cycles (10–500 k.y.) and, to a lesser extent, long-term third-order cycles (1–10 m.y.). Early diagenesis that takes place during fourth- or fifth-order cycles can have a great deal of influence on the amount of paleohydrology and diagenesis that occurs during the longer term third-order cycles. For example, if porosity is occluded early, then later diagenesis does not occur or is greatly reduced because there is little or no pore-water movement.

High-frequency cycles

High-frequency sea level cycles (fourth or fifth order) cause the cyclical migration of the vadose, freshwater phreatic, and marine phreatic zones and the diagenetic processes occurring within those zones. Cycle amplitude and frequency determine the thickness and number of times a sequence is subjected to the processes that characterize each diagenetic zone. Each cycle leaves a diagenetic sequence mainly seen in the form of different cement types (Read, 1995).

Example

The diagram below shows the sequence of diagenetic events occurring in a prograding tidal flat during a high-frequency sea level cycle. Also shown are two pre-existing topographic highs that were propagated upward through the section by differential compaction. The stippled pattern represents limestone; the brick pattern is dolomite.

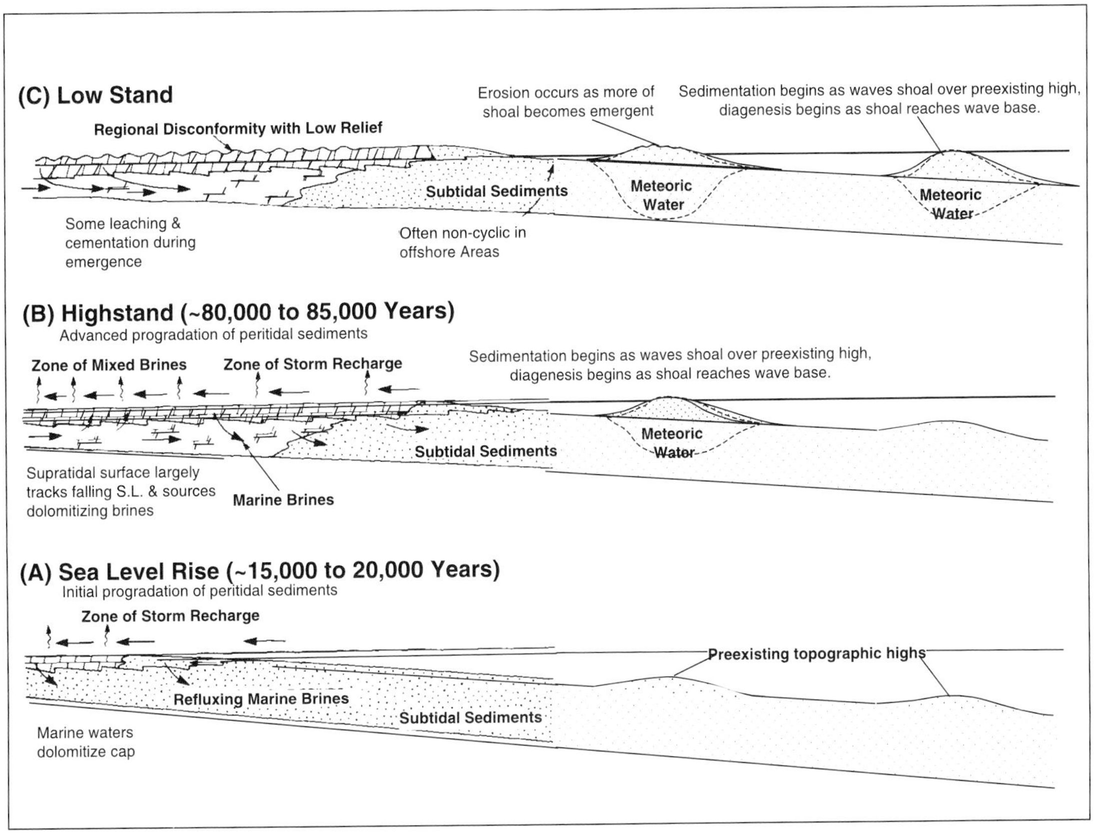

Figure 9–79. Modified from Read, 1995; courtesy SEPM.

Example (continued)

The following diagenetic processes occurred during this period.

- Time A occurs during rising sea level and is the beginning of the "keep-up" phase when the carbonate factory becomes established and progradation begins. Storm and tidal flooding of flats generate brines that dolomitize the laminite cap of the sequence.
- Time B is the highstand of sea level and represents advanced progradation. Updip, where there is no sedimentation, the supratidal surface becomes a disconformity. Refluxing brines dolomitize most of the inner platform section. Offshore, shoaling waves cause the deposition of ooid grainstones over the shallower pre-existing high. The shoal eventually emerges as it builds to sea level and a meteoric lens is established. Diagenesis of shoal sediments is mainly in marine and freshwater phreatic zones.
- Time C is the lowstand of sea level. A regional disconformity develops over the tidal-flat laminites as they are subaerially exposed. Minor leaching occurs in the subtidal sediments as the result of an influx of meteoric water. The pre-existing high in deeper water is shallow enough for shoaling, and the same sequence occurs that took place earlier on the shallower pre-existing high. The shallower pre-existing high is now an island where diagenesis occurs in the vadose and phreatic zones. Its longer exposure causes greater diagenesis than occurs in the shoal over the deep pre-existing high.

Diagenesis related to long-term cycles

Major unconformities that form as a result of uplift or third-order sea level lowstand can cause extensive diagenesis. In humid regions diagenesis can extend downdip for many miles and down section for hundreds to thousands of feet (Read and Horbury, 1993). Early down-section water flow is diffusive, mainly moving through intergranular pores. Later, down-section water movement becomes dominated by conduit flow. The change in flow character is a result of plugging intergranular pores and leaching that widens joints and turns vugs into caves.

Reservoirs associated with long-term karsting tend to be highly compartmentalized (Read and Horbury, 1993). Vadose karst reservoirs tend to be of poor quality contrasted with phreatic reservoirs, which tend to be of high quality (Richard Fritz, personal communication). The amount of karstification decreases with decreasing rainfall. In very arid regions there may be relatively little diagenesis during emergence.

Dolomitization can occur during a subsequent transgression across the unconformity. The unconformity may be recognized in well logs by a high gamma ray count due to glauconite or uranium if the unconformity is covered by marine clastics or basinal facies.

Sea Level Cycles and Climate

Global climatic effect of cycles

The earth's climate has ranged from times of cooler temperatures (icehouse) to times of warmer temperatures (greenhouse) (Read and Horbury, 1993). Continental glaciation characterizes icehouse conditions and causes large sea level changes because ice ties up large volumes of water. Sea level rises rapidly during glaciation and falls gradually during deglaciation. Sea level changes are small during greenhouse times because the ice volume was smaller.

The table below summarizes characteristics of fourth- and fifth-order sea level cycles during icehouse, greenhouse, and transitional periods.

Characteristic	Icehouse	Transition	Greenhouse
Amplitude (m)	High (50–100)	Moderate (20–50)	Low (1–20)
Dominant frequency (k.y.)	100	50	20

Greenhouse vs. icehouse times

The chart below shows periods of icehouse and greenhouse conditions. Also shown are age and paleolatitudes of ice-rafted deposits (bar chart), net climate forcing CO_2+ solar luminosity (upper curved line), and the Vail sea level curve (lower curved line).

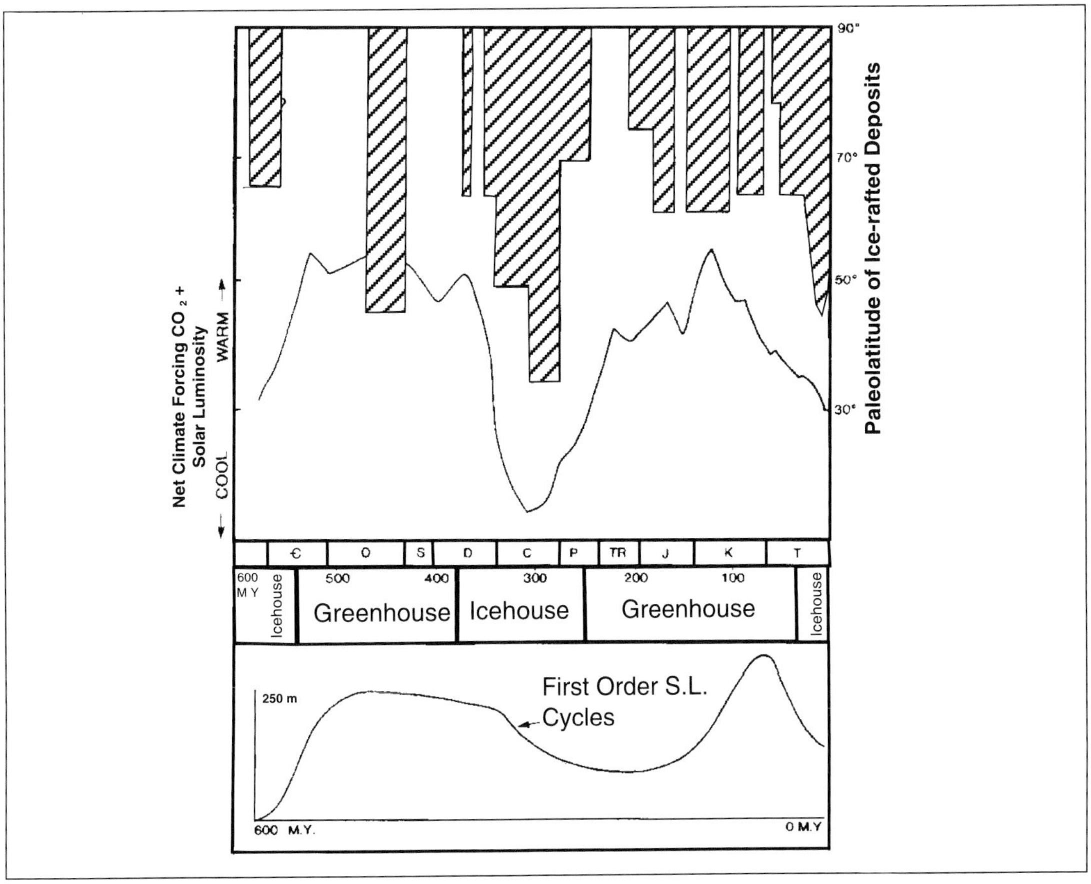

Figure 9–80. From Read, 1995; courtesy SEPM.

Sea Level Cycles and Climate, continued

Regional climates

Arid or humid conditions can occur simultaneously in different regions during icehouse or greenhouse periods. The aridity or humidity of a region strongly affects carbonate deposition and diagenesis. For example, carbonates deposited under arid conditions tend to be associated with evaporites, and carbonate sequences are partly to completely dolomitized. In humid regions where rainfall is greater, carbonates are subject to greater dissolution; therefore, vuggy porosity and karst features are common.

Sea level and climate

Long-term sea level cycles influence regional climates (Read, 1996). More humid conditions tend to prevail during deposition of transgressive system tracts, and more arid conditions tend to prevail during deposition of late highstand-lowstand system tracts. Climatic conditions of an area are likely to be arid when a platform interior is subaerially exposed during long-term, sea level late highstand and lowstand. From the Precambrian to the Silurian, the lack of land plants might have amplified this aridity. Humid conditions prevail when extensive shallow epicontinental seaways present during long-term transgressions cause increased rainfall.

Sedimentation rate and climate

Light is a critical element of carbonate sedimentation. The photic zone in tropical carbonate settings is only 20–30 m. This is contrasted to cooler water carbonate settings where the photic zone extends to 100 m or deeper. Tropical carbonate faunal assemblages strongly depend on light, which is why sedimentation rates below 10 m water depth drop rapidly. Carbonate-producing assemblages of temperate zones do not have a strong light dependence; hence, the sedimentation rate, although lower, is constant from the surface to more than 100 m water depth (Read, 1996).

The table below contrasts features of tropical carbonate settings with temperate carbonate settings.

Characteristic	Tropical Carbonate Settings	Temperate Carbonate Settings
Photic zone depth	20–30 m	100 m+
Sedimentation rate	High in 10 m or less of water, then rapid drop	Low but more constant in water 100 m or deeper
Dominant fauna	Reef-building assemblages (light-dependent biota)	Bryozoans, mollusks, forams, crinoids (biota not as light dependent)
Depositional topography	Reef-rimmed platforms	Gently sloping ramps on prograding seaward-thickening sediment wedges

Sequences During Low-Amplitude, High-Frequency Cycles

General characteristics

During greenhouse times, third- through fifth-order cycles of sea level change because of little or no polar ice, and they tend to have high frequency and low amplitude. Read (1996) lists the general characteristics of carbonate platforms deposited during these cycles:

- Cycles of 20 k.y. or less sometimes superimposed on 100- and 400-k.y. cycles
- Carbonate platforms aggraded and flat topped to gently sloping
- Peritidal parasequences with regionally extensive tidal flat caps
- High-relief buildups absent from the platform top
- Parasequences with layer cake stacking patterns
- Reef and/or grainstone facies of platform margins with limited lateral migration, thick and poorly partitioned or highly compartmentalized
- Relatively poorly developed cycle-capping disconformities
- Small sea level changes limiting groundwater table vertical migration and consequently diagenesis

Arid zone characteristics

Carbonates deposited in arid zones during greenhouse times generally have the following characteristics (Read, 1996):

- Oolitic and cryptalgal mound facies with intertidal laminite caps
- Completely to partly dolomitized parasequences
- Reservoirs less than 3 m thick
- Reservoir-quality facies that are
  — Dolomitized intertidal laminites (intercrystalline porosity)
  — Siliciclastic supratidal caps (intergranular porosity)
  — Variably dolomitized subtidal grainstone/packstone shoals (intergranular and intercrystalline porosity)
- Regional top and lateral seals composed of sabkha evaporites, making traps strongly stratified with potential for multiple pay zones
- Sulfate minerals plugging the pores in grainstones (calcite plugging rarely significant but hard to leach if present)

Examples are the Cambrian–Early Ordovician of the U.S., Early Silurian Interlake Formation of the Williston basin, and Upper Pennsylvanian San Andres–Grayburg Formations of the Permian basin.

Humid zone characteristics

Carbonates deposited in humid zones during greenhouse times generally have the following characteristics (Read, 1995):

- Parasequence facies of very fossiliferous subtidal wackestones to grainstones with fenestral or rare supratidal caps
- Planar to microkarsted cycle tops
- Leached aragonite fossils
- Fibrous marine and vadose–phreatic sparry calcite cements plugging fenestral porosity
- Best original porosity in subtidal facies; cycle tops more porous than arid counterparts
- Good reservoir facies in downdip, noncyclic, subtidal grainstone complexes
- Poor internal top and updip seals; traps form only as a result of later events such as being sealed by overlying transgressive systems tract organic muds or shales

Examples of low-amplitude cycles in humid zones include Middle Ordovician peritidal sequences, Middle to Late Devonian Swan Hills–Judy Creek Formations in Canada, and Mississippian sequences in Virginia (Read, 1995).

Contrasting arid and humid zone cycles

The diagram below contrasts low-amplitude carbonate arid zones sequences with humid zone sequences.

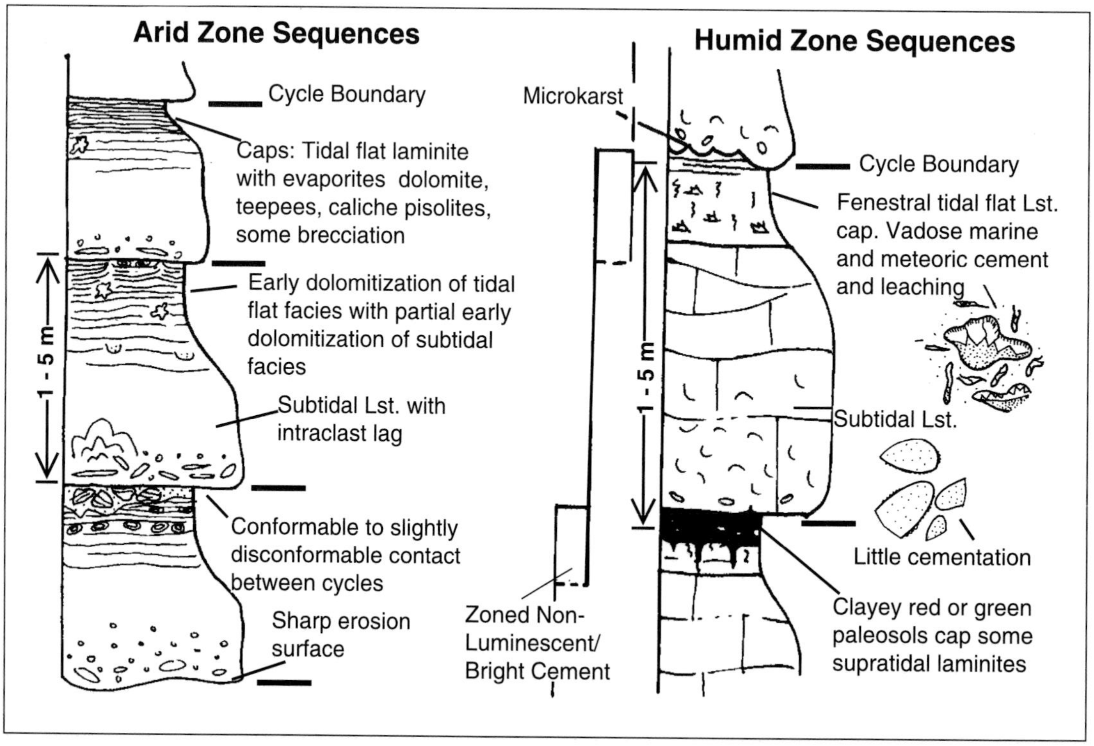

Figure 9–81. Modified from Read, 1995; courtesy SEPM.

Sequences During Moderate-Amplitude, High-Frequency Cycles

Introduction

Fourth- or fifth-order moderate sea level cycles (20–50 m) occurred when global climate was transitional between major continental glaciation (commonly but not necessarily ice-house times) and greenhouse times (Read, 1995). Arid and humid zones existed simultaneously at different parts of the globe during transitional periods.

General characteristics

The following are general characteristics of fourth- and fifth-order carbonate sequences deposited during transitional periods (Read, 1995):

- More shingled and less layer caked than low-amplitude sequences
- Platform tops and ramps of greater slope than greenhouse platforms
- Grainstones widespread due to lateral migration, particularly on ramps
- Rare tidal-flat facies
- Regionally mappable disconformities on sequence tops
- Abundant siliciclastics in bases and/or tops of sequences of land-attached platforms
- Primary porosity greatest in grainy upper parts of sequences and thicker (10 m or more) than greenhouse sequences
- Muddy lower parts of sequences as internal flow barriers

Arid zone characteristics

Characteristics of carbonates deposited in arid zones are as follows (Read, 1995):

- Porosity in the sequence tops plugged by caliche and vadose fibrous cements
- Porosity in subtidal grainy parts of sequences generally lacks early sparry cements; primary porosity preserved where marine fringing cement present
- Top and lateral seals may form where peritidal dolomite and evaporite progrades over third-order sequences

An example is the Late Mississippian ramp reservoirs of the eastern and central United States.

Humid zone characteristics

Following are characteristics of carbonates deposited in humid zones (Read, 1995):

- Tops may show karsting and soil development
- Grains in the upper part of sequences may undergo dissolution, and moldic or vuggy pores develop
- Vadose and upper phreatic sparry calcite cement often plugs primary and secondary porosity in the upper parts of sequences
- Primary porosity may be greatest in the middle or lower parts of sequences
- Meteoric diagenesis extends down into underlying older sequences because of deep groundwater zones; internal barriers may mitigate the effect

Examples are the British Dinantian (Mississippian) platforms.

Arid vs. humid zone sequences

The diagram below compares moderate-amplitude carbonate sequences from arid zones with carbonate sequences from humid zones. Arid zone grainstones tend to be oolitic, while humid zone grainstones tend to be skeletal. Humid zone sequences show the effects of repeated sea level changes by their distinctive cement zones precipitated in thick meteoric water lenses.

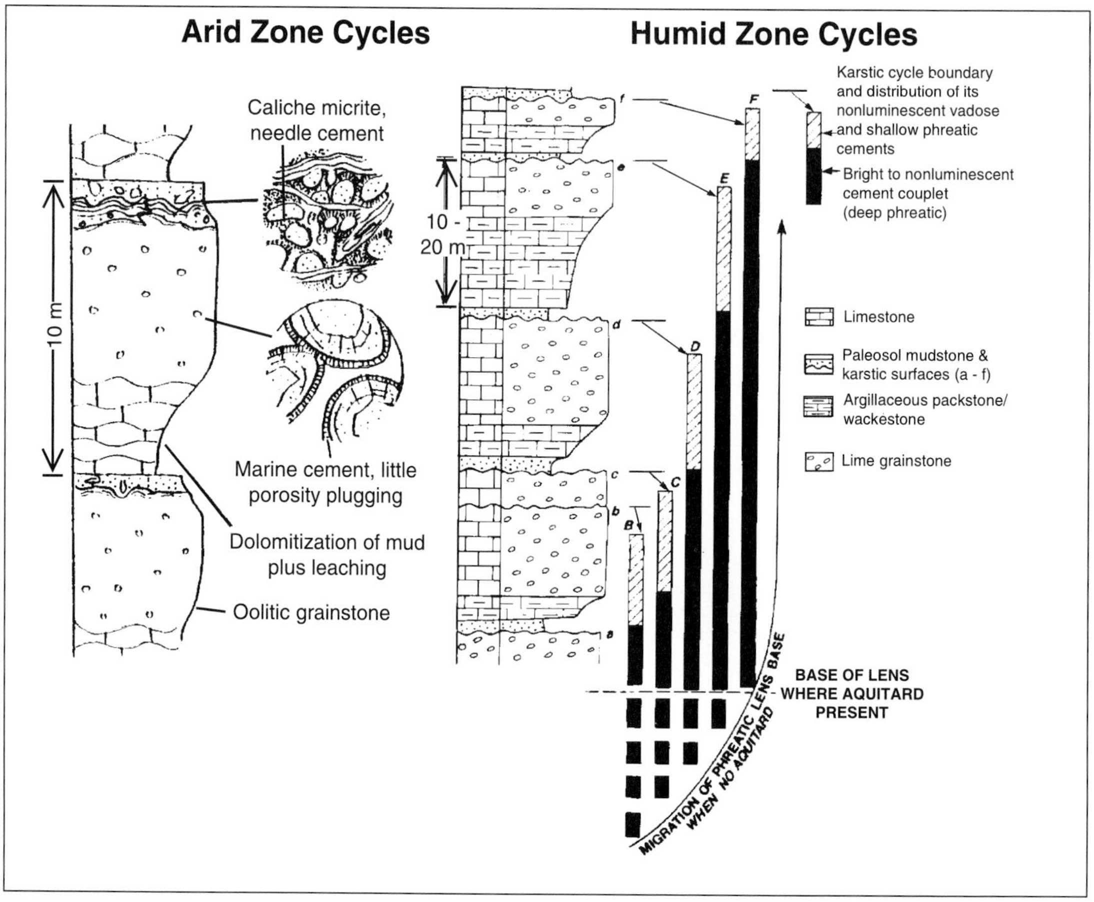

Figure 9–82. Modified from Read, 1995; courtesy SEPM.

Sequences During High-Amplitude, High-Frequency Cycles

Introduction

High-amplitude (60 to over 100 m), high-frequency (fourth- and fifth-order) sea level fluctuations occurred during periods of global continental glaciation (Read, 1996). These icehouse periods were late Precambrian, Pennsylvanian to Early Permian, and Pleistocene.

General characteristics

The following are general characteristics of carbonate sequences deposited during icehouse conditions (Read, 1995):

- Flat-topped platforms with layer cake, 1–10-m-thick fourth-order sequences bounded by regional disconformities; sequences on platform margins shingled
- Ramp sequences highly shingled and erosionally bounded
- Pinnacle reefs and high-relief banks common on tropical platforms
- Tidal flat facies absent except adjacent to shorelines
- Deeper water facies juxtaposed with shallow-water facies and emergence features (except on the shallowest parts of platforms) because of large sea level changes
- Karstic sinkholes and cave systems extend down through several sequences
- Intense leaching/cementation (and sometimes dolomitization) possible because stillstands repeatedly localize paleowater tables
- Diagenesis usually complex because large sea level changes repeatedly cause large vertical and lateral migration of diagenetic zones

Arid zone characteristics

Carbonate sequences deposited in arid zones tend to have the following characteristics (Read, 1995):

- Porosity plugged by caliche at sequence caps
- Below caliche cap porosity is intergranular in shoals and in nondolomitized build-ups
- Porosity is intercrystalline and remnant intergranular in dolomitized sequences that consist of inner platform highstand sabkha facies or late highstand to lowstand evaporite basin facies

Humid zone characteristics

Carbonate sequences deposited in humid zones tend to have the following characteristics (Read, 1995):

- Single to multiple caliche zones at sequence tops if wet–dry seasons
- In a sequence package that lacks internal seals, the uppermost sequences generally have preserved intergranular porosity in contrast to lower sequences, which generally have moldic, vuggy, and cavernous porosity
- In a sequence package that contains internal seals, the upper part of each sequence can have preserved primary porosity because the seals protect the sediments from diagenesis

High-amplitude sequences schematic

The figure below shows (1) a typical succession of carbonate lithofacies sequences that formed during high-amplitude, high-frequency sea level fluctuations and (2) a corresponding sea level curve related to diagenesis. In this example, sequences lack internal barriers or seals to inhibit the vertical and lateral migration of the paleowater table; therefore, sequence sediments are subjected to a complex sequence of diagenetic events due to large-scale sea level fluctuations. If internal barriers were present, diagenesis would be lessened.

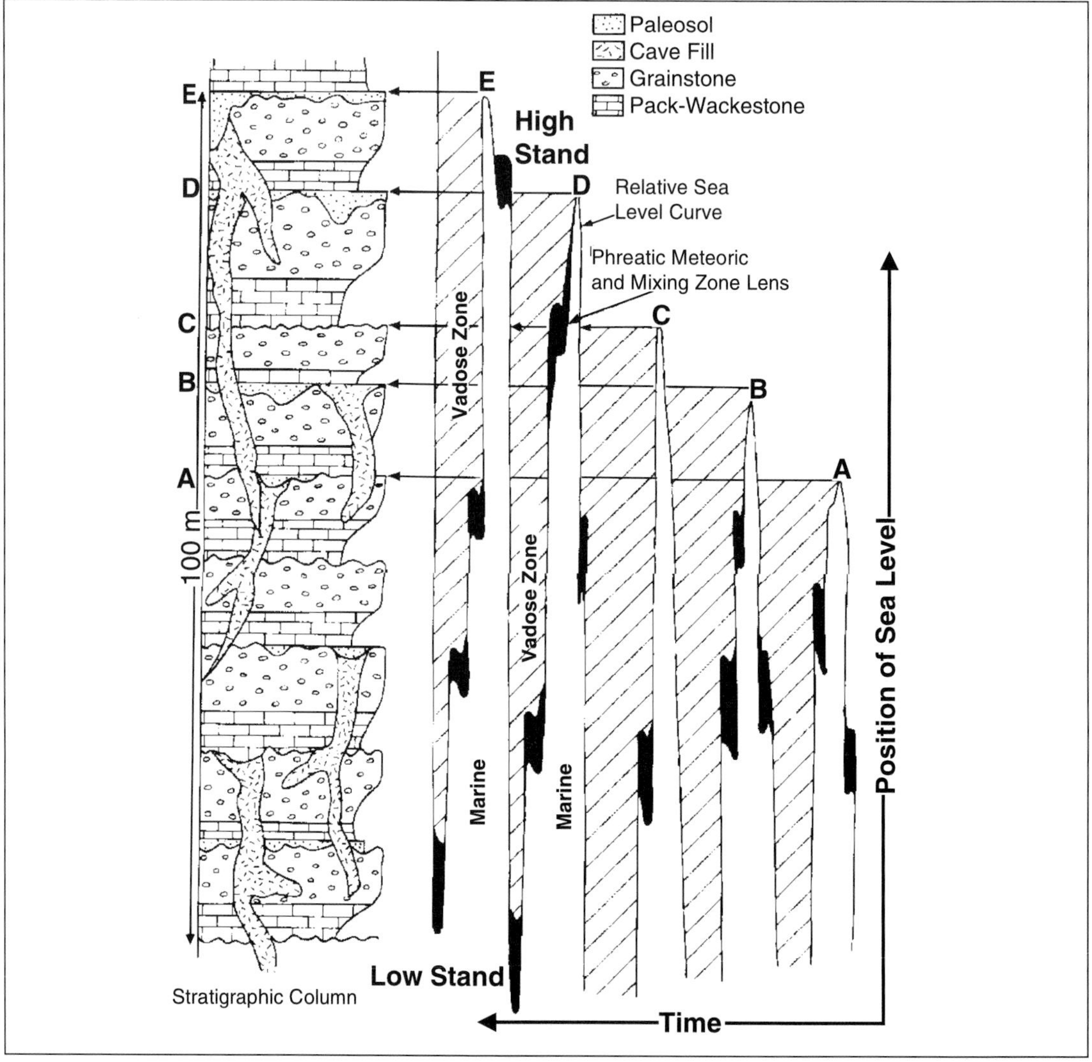

Figure 9–83. From Read and Horbury, 1993; courtesy AAPG.

Predicting Carbonate Reservoir Location and Quality

Introduction

Earlier in this chapter, reservoir quality was defined as the "ability of a reservoir to store and transmit oil or gas." We also can include the thickness and lateral extent as aspects of reservoir quality.

Procedure: Predicting location and quality

How do we predict the quality of a carbonate reservoir? The procedure outlined below is one way to approach this problem. Use the parts of the suggested procedure that fit your situation. For detailed information and examples, see Read et al., 1995; Loucks and Sarg, 1993; or Sarg, 1988.

Step	Action
1	Make regional strike and dip stratigraphic cross sections.
2	Break down cross-section stratigraphy into sequences and parasequences.
3	Group parasequences into sets by identifying progradational, aggradational, or retrogradational patterns within sets. Make isopachs of systems tracts using parasequence sets and their correlation surfaces.
4	Map paleogeography and facies tracts through time using systems tract maps; use core and log data to infer shorelines and platform edge locations.
5	Study known accumulations that occur within the target formation. • What are the trap types? • What are the pore types, pore geometry, thickness, and lateral extent of porous facies? • What are the facies sequences within parasequences? • How does facies distribution relate to trapping?
6	Put known accumulations into the paleogeographic framework. Are they near the platform edge or near the shoreline? Nearshore sea level cycles cause more frequent changes in pore-water chemistry than offshore where subsidence is greater. Therefore, the diagenetic evolution of carbonate sediment is less complex offshore.
7	Put known accumulations into a sequence stratigraphic framework. Were reservoir rocks deposited in transgressive, highstand, or lowstand systems tracts?
8	Put target formation in a global and regional climatic framework. At the time of deposition, was the global climate in greenhouse, icehouse, or transitional conditions? Was the local climate arid or humid? Do expected geologic features due to climate correlate with observed features?
9	Predict reservoir location and quality using knowledge of known accumulations and regional geologic framework developed above. • Can you find undrilled areas that share similar qualities to areas that produce from the target formation? • If prospects exist, will reservoir quality be similar? • If not, why not? • Does the geology suggest other plays?

Making regional cross sections

Regional cross sections are critical for all interpretations in an exploration play. Regional cross sections establish the correlations that structural, facies tract, and paleogeographic mapping is based on. They show stratigraphic patterns like progradation.

The scale should generally be 100 mi or more, and a grid of strike and dip sections should be made. Use all data that would aid in correlations, and show stratigraphic patterns including well data (logs, cuttings, and cores), seismic sections, and outcrop data.

Use the diagram below to help identify large-scale carbonate platform stratal patterns in log cross sections or seismic sections.

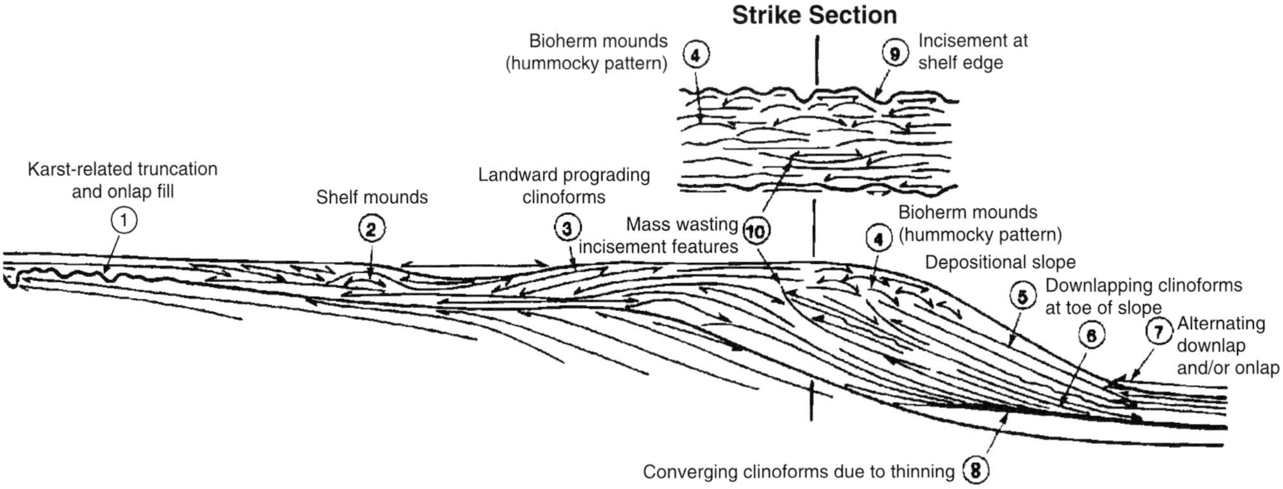

Figure 9–84. From Handford and Loucks, 1994; courtesy AAPG.

Section F

Examples of Petrophysical Evaluation

Introduction

This section, written by Edward Coalson, contains two examples of applying the concepts and methods presented in the previous sections of this chapter. The first shows how saturation profiles can be used to understand the distribution of water saturations within a field or prospect. The second example shows how to determine trap type by evaluating seal capacity.

In this section

This section contains the following subsections.

Subsection F1
Evaluation of Saturation Profiles

Introduction

The case study presented in this subsection is a summary of a larger study of the Sorrento field, southeast Colorado, by Hartmann and Coalson (1990). This study of cores and logs from four field wells shows how multiple oil–water contacts and apparent anomalies in saturation profiles in the Sorrento field were due to multiple flow units from two separate reservoirs. The study helps us understand shows and water saturations in wells outside Sorrento and therefore is useful for finding other traps in the same formation.

In this subsection

This subsection contains the following topics.

Setting and Structure of the Sorrento Field

Index map

The Sorrento field is in southeastern Colorado on the north flank of the Las Animas Arch. The map below shows the location of the Sorrento field. Structure is contoured on the base of the Pennsylvanian.

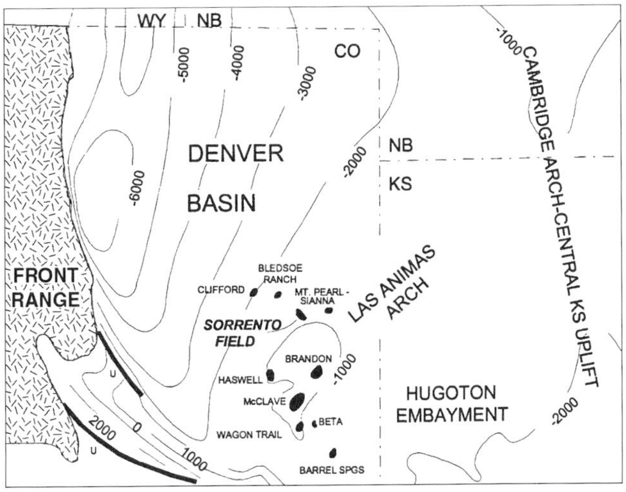

Figure 9–85. From Sonnenberg, 1985; courtesy RMAG.

Morrow structure map

The Sorrento field reservoir is Pennsylvanian Morrow valley-fill sandstones. As shown in the figure below, structure contours on a marker bed above the Morrow Sandstone reflect the irregular thickness of the sandstone body and a small structural nose and closure. The oil column is 70 ft (20 m) and exceeds structural closure. This is a combination structural–stratigraphic trap. Fluvial sandstones lap onto marine shale at the margins of the valley, forming lateral seals.

In the figure below, circled wells represent Marmaton wells; triangles, Mississippian wells; and large X's, study wells. The rest of the oil wells produce from the Morrow. Each unit in the grid is 1 sq mi.

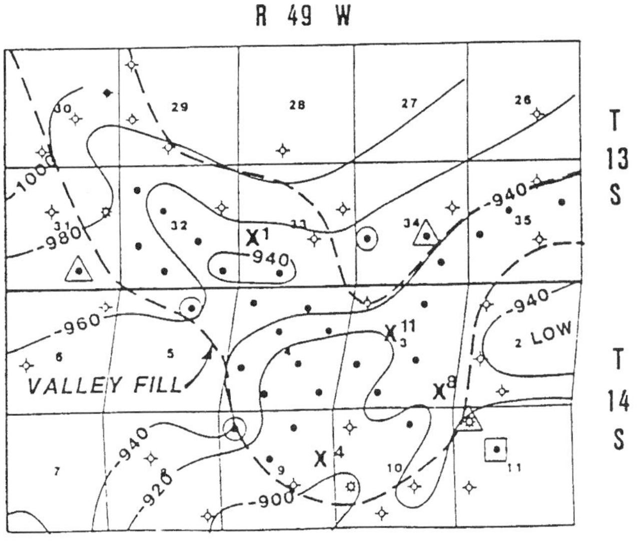

Figure 9–86. Modified from Sonnenberg, 1985; courtesy RMAG.

Morrow Lithofacies and Pore Types

Introduction

By studying core and log data from one well (well 11, see Figure 9–86), we see a picture of a clastic reservoir with wide heterogeneity in total porosities, pore-throat sizes, and capillary pressures. In addition, the depositional environment of these sandstones (fluvial valley fill and sandstone) indicates they probably have limited lateral continuity within the valley-fill complex.

Reservoir lithologic description

Morrow sandstones in the Sorrento field are slightly shaly, range in grain size from very coarse to fine, and are poorly sorted. As a consequence, pores and pore throats also have wide ranges in size. Hand-sample petrography indicates the dominant porosity is intergranular micro- to megaporosity. Clay crystals create minor intercrystalline microporosity in larger pores. Moldic (cement solution?) porosity also may be present but is minor.

Reservoir porosity and permeability

Morrow sandstones in Sorrento field have a wide range in porosity and permeability. Maximum observed porosity (Φ) is 20–22%, but more typical values are 10–15%. Air permeabilities (K_a) are as great as 1–2 darcies but more commonly are 200–500 md.

Below is a K_a/Φ crossplot for well 11 (see Figure 9–87). Dots and polygons represent measured K_a/Φ values. Curves are the graphical solution of Winland's r_{35} equation (Pittman, 1992) and represent equal r_{35} values (port size).

The crossplot shows a large variation in port size for the samples from well 11. Areas between dashed lines group points into beds with similar port size, or flow units.

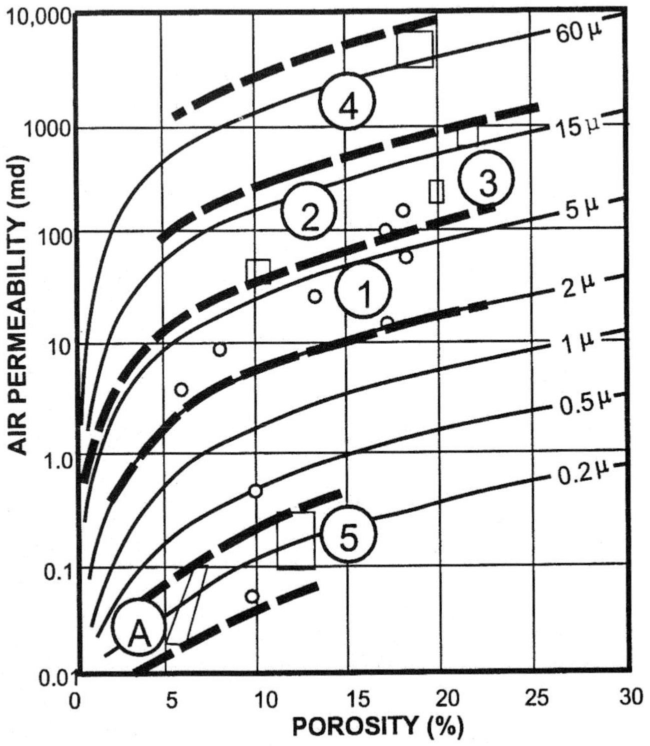

Figure 9–87. From Hartmann and Coalson, 1990; courtesy RMAG.

Extrapolated capillary pressure curves and pore types

No capillary pressure measurements were available for this study. They were estimated-by plotting r_{35} values on a semilog crossplot of fluid saturation vs. capillary pressure. A capillary pressure curve for each sample passes through its correlative r_{35} value. Calculations of r_{35} for well 11 indicate a large variety of capillary pressures and pore types. Pore types for the Morrow samples from this well are mega, macro, and micro.

The numbers on the curves in the figure below correspond to the numbers on the K_a/Φ crossplot on Figure 9–86. Minimum water saturatuions ("immobile" water) estimated from log calculations let us extrapolate the P_c curves into low S_w ranges.

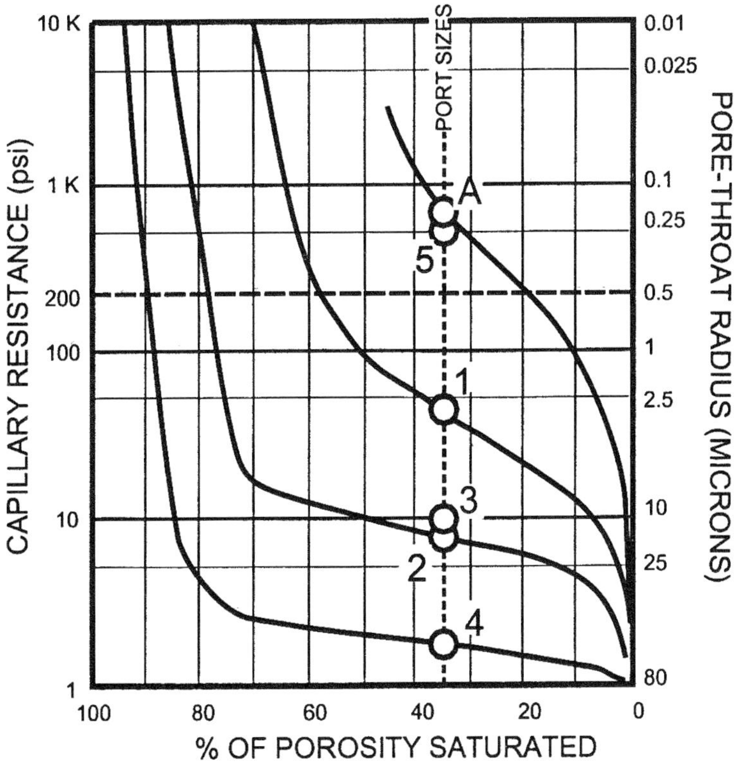

Figure 9–88. From Hartmann and Coalson, 1990; courtesy RMAG.

Sorrento Water Saturation Calculations

Method

Density logs were the primary source of porosity values. Matrix density appears to be about 2.68 g/cc, based on core-measured grain densities (consistent with the presumed mineralogy of the sandstones). Crossplot porosities were not used to avoid introducing a systematic error in these variably shaly sandstones (Patchett and Coalson, 1982).

Pickett plot

Formation-water resistivities and water saturations were estimated from Pickett plots. The inferred cementation exponent (*m*) is 1.8 because of the presence of clays, well-connected solution pores (e.g., James, 1989; Muller and Coalson, 1989), or pyrite (Kristinick, personal communication). Formation factors measured on core samples from well 1 support this interpretation.

The Pickett below shows data from well 11. The number labels represent the flow units from Figure 9–88.

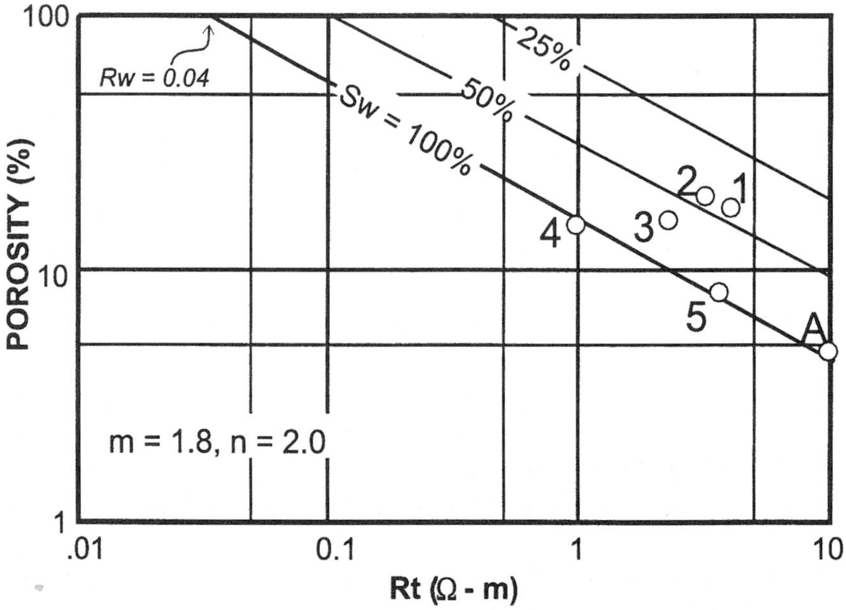

Figure 9–89. From Hartmann and Coalson, 1990; courtesy RMAG.

Saturation exponents, *n*

Saturation exponents (*n*) measured on samples from well 1 showed variations that relate to pore geometry. Microporous siltstones displayed *n* greater than 2, indicating either very tortuous pore systems or incomplete saturation by brine during testing. Saturation exponents were less than 2 in the best porosity type. This implies the reservoir is somewhat shaly. However, *n* was assumed equal to 2 for log calculations because the lab data were not far from that value and because lab measurements of saturation exponents are notoriously difficult.

Petrophysical Analysis of Sorrento Field Wells

Well 11 flow units

Flow units were determined in well 11 by plotting and grouping routine core data. The top and bottom of the Morrow (flow units A and 5) are microporous, low-permeability sandstones that are wet but too tight to produce. Between these are 30 ft (8.5 m) of meso- to macroporous sandstone (flow units 1–4).

All pertinent petrophysical data for well 11 are summarized on Figure 9–90. Sandstone descriptors found on porosity logs are as follows:

VF	=	very fine grained	C	=	coarse grained	SLTY	=	silty
F	=	fine grained	VC	=	very coarse grained	SLT	=	siltstone
M	=	medium grained	SHY	=	shaly	SH	=	shale

Subsea elevation of –1,030 ft (–314 m) is marked in the depth track.

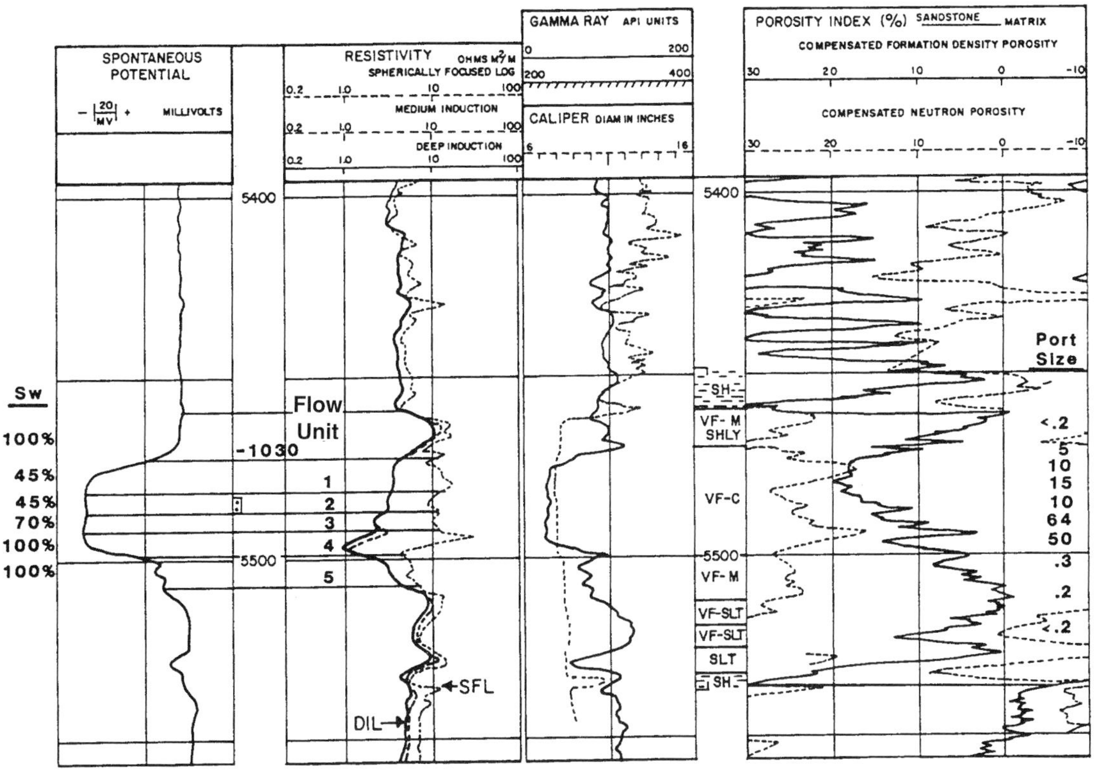

Figure 9–90. From Hartmann and Coalson, 1990; courtesy RMAG.

Well 11 water saturations

Flow unit 4 is macroporous but wet (S_w = 100%); this indicates an oil–water contact. Flow unit 3 is macroporous and has intermediate water saturation (S_w = 70%). This looks like a transition zone. Flow units 2 and 1 are mesoporous and are at immobile water saturation (S_w = 45%). This is verified by the well testing about 100 bo/d and 300 Mcfg/d (16 m^3 oil and 8,500 m^3 gas per day) with no water from perforations in these flow units and by a bulk-volume-water plot following. This lack of water production is remarkable, considering that the well lies only about 25 ft (7 m) above the free water level.

Well 11 water saturations (continued)

Below is the bulk-volume-water (Buckles) plot for well 11.

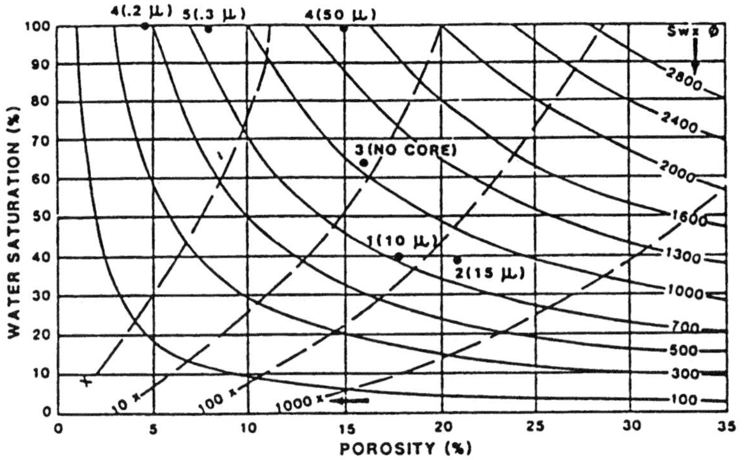

Figure 9–91. From Hartmann and Coalson, 1990; courtesy RMAG.

Well 4

Well 4 hit the Morrow near the top of the oil column. It had the lowest saturations and best flow rates of all the wells studied, even though it had the thinnest reservoir. This is because it contained rock with large pore throats (r_{35} up to 50μ) that was fully saturated with oil (S_w = 25–30%). The well tested 230 bo/d and 387 Mcfg/d (37 m^3 oil and 11,000 m^3 gas per day). Initial production was 51 bo/d and 411 Mcfg/d (8 m^3 oil and 12,000 m^3 gas per day). The difference could be due to a loss of reservoir thickness near the well bore, judging from the thinness of the reservoir.

The figure below summarizes the petrophysical characteristics of well 4.

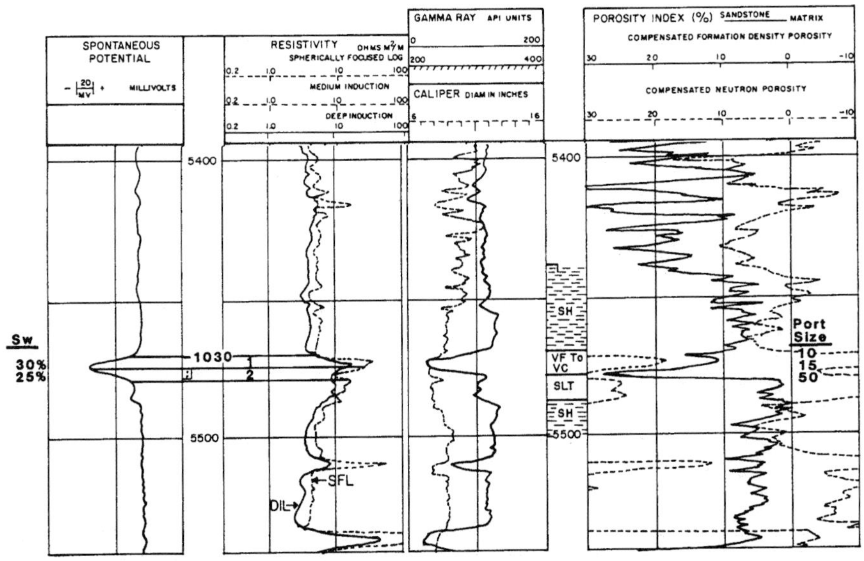

Figure 9–92. From Hartmann and Coalson, 1990; courtesy RMAG.

Well 8

Wells 8 and 1 both are interpreted as encountering transition zones, based on porosity types and log-calculated saturations. Well 8 encountered the Morrow just above the water level. Pore throats are meso- to macroporous. The two upper flow units probably are close to immobile water saturation. However, the two basal zones (3 and 4) have high saturations of mobile water. This explains why the well cut water on initial potential testing. This water production should increase with time as the water leg rises.

The figure below summarizes the petrophysical characteristics of well 8.

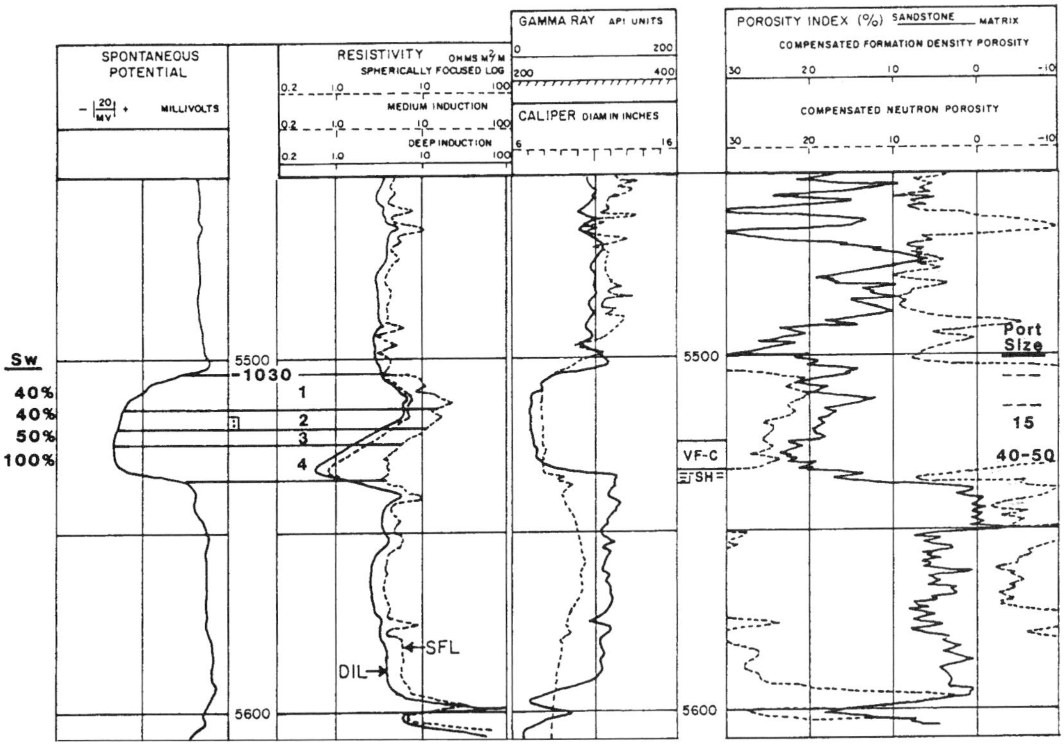

Figure 9–93. From Hartmann and Coalson, 1990; courtesy RMAG.

Well 1

Well 1 is similar to well 8, except that flow unit 2 of well 1 shows an anomalous low resistivity. The interval tested 32 bo/d and 15 Mcfg/d (5 m^3 oil and 425 m^3 gas per day) with no water. Therefore, the zone by definition is at immobile water saturation (S_{wi} = 40%). The discrepancy suggests that the log resistivity was too low due to bed resolution problems. If true resistivity is 9 ohm-m^2/m (used for the calculation), then the true water saturation is less than 40%.

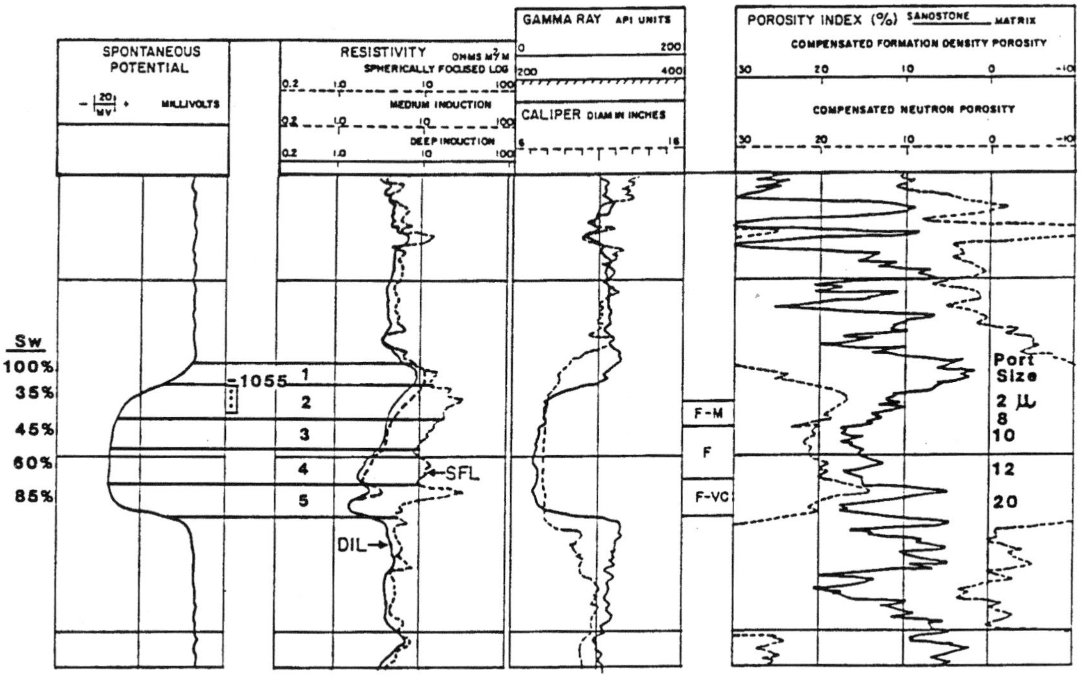

Figure 9–94. From Hartmann and Coalson, 1990; courtesy RMAG.

Caveat

While these petrophysical methods of analyzing wells are reliable and widely applicable in water-wet reservoirs, there is at least one source of potential error: the assumption that there are no lithologic changes that affect log-calculation parameters without affecting permeability–porosity relationships. Examples include vuggy or fracture porosity and variable shale effects. If such changes occur, then we must modify the relationships between calculated saturations and producibility.

Water Saturation Profile for Sorrento Field

Introduction

Morrow sandstone reservoirs reportedly display multiple oil–water contacts in several fields in the area (Sonnenberg, personal communication). Reliably recognizing separate reservoirs in a field requires considering capillary pressures, heights above free water, and observed water saturations. One convenient way to do this is to plot water saturation against structural elevation while differentiating pore throat sizes.

S_w–elevation plot

An S_w–elevation plot (shown below) for study wells 4, 8, and 11 defines a trend of decreasing water saturation with increasing height. Well 1 is not on the same trend. Differences in water saturation attributable to differences in capillary pressures are apparent but are not great enough to explain the discrepancy. Ignoring possible hydrodynamic effects, the difference in trends probably represents two separate oil columns and therefore two reservoirs.

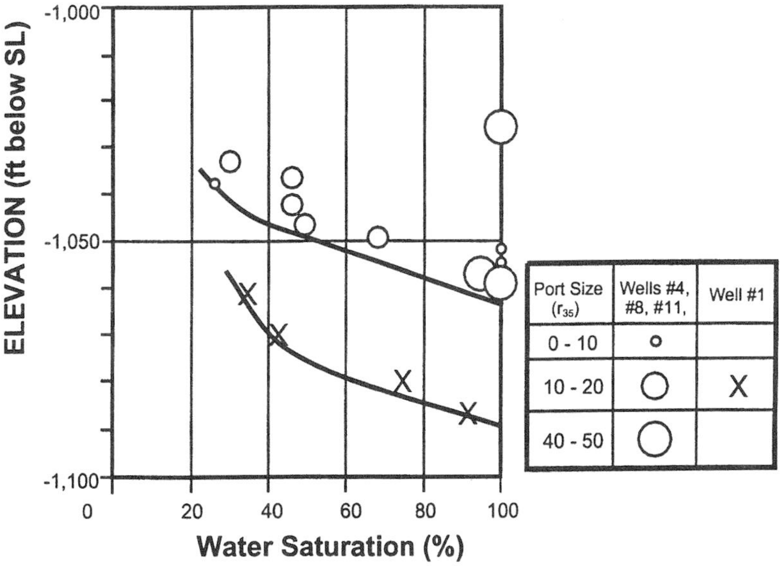

Figure 9–95. From Hartmann and Coalson, 1990; courtesy RMAG.

Subsection F2

Evaluation of Trap Type

Introduction

Some workers question whether Weyburn field of Saskatchewan is a stratigraphic trap or a combination hydrodynamic–stratigraphic trap. Weyburn field provides an excellent case history of trap type evaluation.

The case history presented in this subsection documents the procedure used to determine if the capillary properties of an updip poor-quality rock have the capacity to retain the 600-ft column of oil shared by Weyburn and a nearby field. If not, then Weyburn is partly hydrodynamic. Estimating the breakthrough pore throat size is critical to determine seal capacity. As is shown by this case history, this is not an easy task. The available evidence favors a stratigraphic seal. Uncertainty remains that could be eliminated with further core work.

This case history summarizes work reported by Coalson et al. (1990), Goolsby et al. (1991), and Coalson et al. (1994).

In this subsection

This subsection contains the following topics.

Weyburn Field Location and Trap Problem

Petroleum geology

Weyburn field, in the Williston basin of Saskatchewan, produces oil from the Midale member of the Mississippian Mission Canyon Formation (Chetin and Fitkin, 1959). Weyburn has ultimate recoverable reserves of about 300 million bbl of oil (48×10^6 m^3). The main pay interval is the lower part of the Midale, called the Midale "Vuggy" beds. The Midale Vuggy underlies the Midale "Marly" beds, which produce only minor amounts of oil.

Below is a map showing the location of Weyburn field.

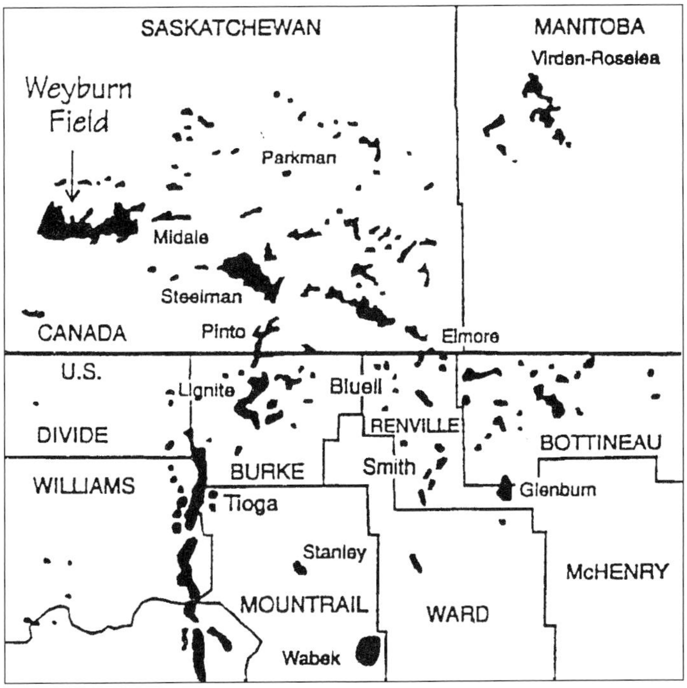

Figure 9–96. From Coalson et al., 1994; courtesy RMAG.

Weyburn trap problem

To determine the trap type of Weyburn field, we have to know what forms the lateral closure. It is not structural because dip is homoclinal to the southwest. The field lies southeast of the truncation edge of the Midale member, where it wedges out beneath Triassic rocks and above older Mississippian rocks. Early workers understood this truncation to be the cause of the trap. Yet there is an area lying downdip from the truncation edge of the Midale and updip from the oil pool in which porous Midale Vuggy rocks were present but tested wet with shows of oil.

This raises the possibility that either a stratigraphic change (Winland, 1972, 1976; Wegelin, 1986; Kent et al., 1988) or hydrodynamics (Petroleum Research Corporation, 1961; Dahlberg, 1982; Hannon, 1987), or perhaps both provide the updip, transverse ("lateral") seal. From producing wells at Weyburn and nearby Steelman, the oil column height appears to be 600 ft (183 m). This raises the next question: Could the Midale Marly beds provide a seal for a 600-ft oil column, or must hydrodynamics be present to augment the seal quality of the Midale Marly beds?

Weyburn structure map and cross section

The figure below is a structure map of the Weyburn field area, contoured on top of the Mississippian Midale Member. The map also shows the northern erosional limit of the Midale evaporite and the location of the field. Circles indicate cores studied.

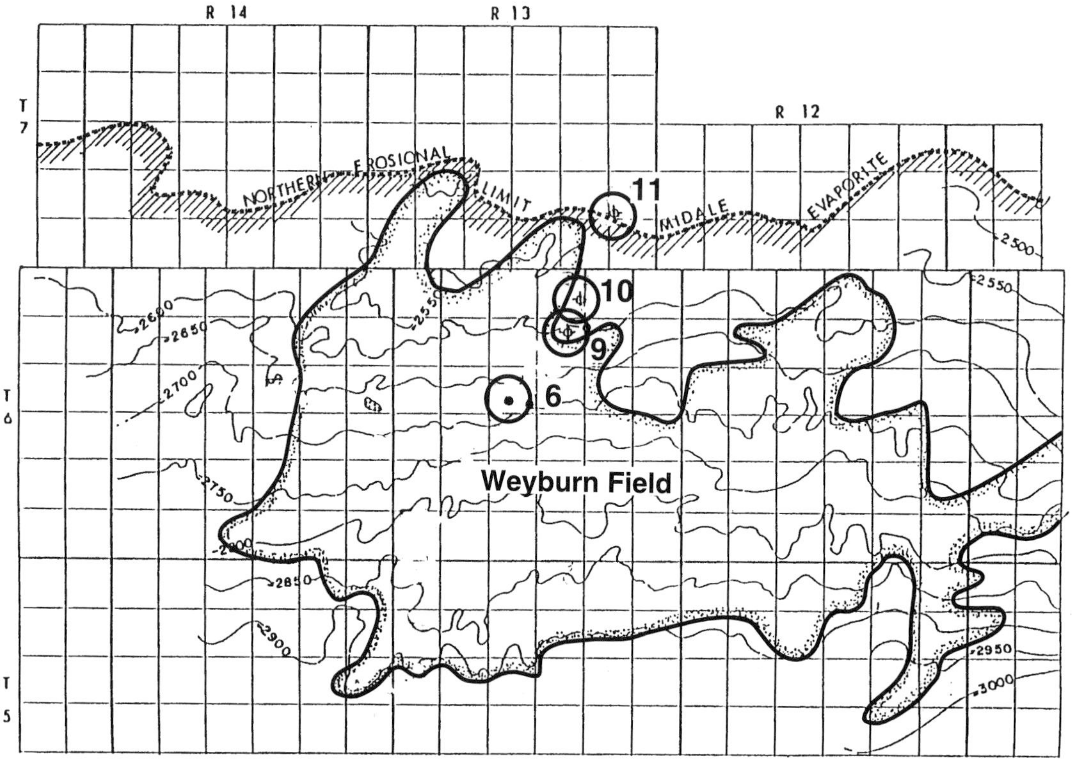

Figure 9–97. From Winland, 1972; courtesy Amoco Production Co.

Weyburn diagrammatic cross section

The figure below is a diagrammatic dip-oriented cross section of Weyburn field. It shows the truncation of the Midale Marly and Vuggy beds and the updip facies change in the Midale Vuggy from a vuggy grainstone to a vuggy mudstone to an anhydrite.

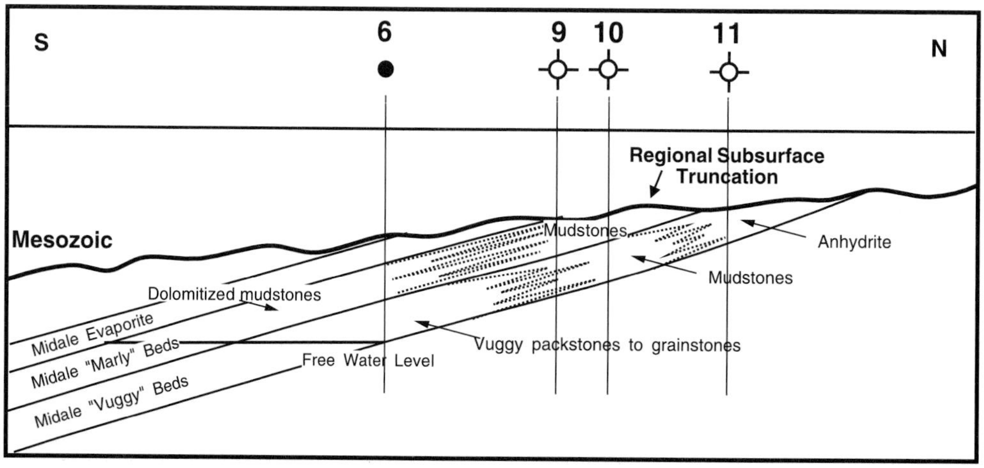

Figure 9–98.

Midale Lithofacies and Distribution

Productive facies

The Midale in the Weyburn area is carbonates and evaporites deposited near a low-energy shoreline on a marine ramp. The main producing carbonate facies ("vuggy packstone" facies) is shoal deposits of fossiliferous, peloidal, *Ortonella*-bearing nodular wackestones to grainstones. The principal occluding cements are sparry calcite and anhydrite.

Reservoir SEM and capillary pressure curve

The figure below shows the petrophysical characteristics of the main Weyburn reservoir facies: *Ortonella*-bearing vuggy wackestones to packstones. The sample is macroporous, its pore system dominated by large pores and pore throats. The capillary pressure curve shows relatively low entry (and presumably breakthrough) pressure. The port size (r_{35}) of the sample is approximately 3μ.

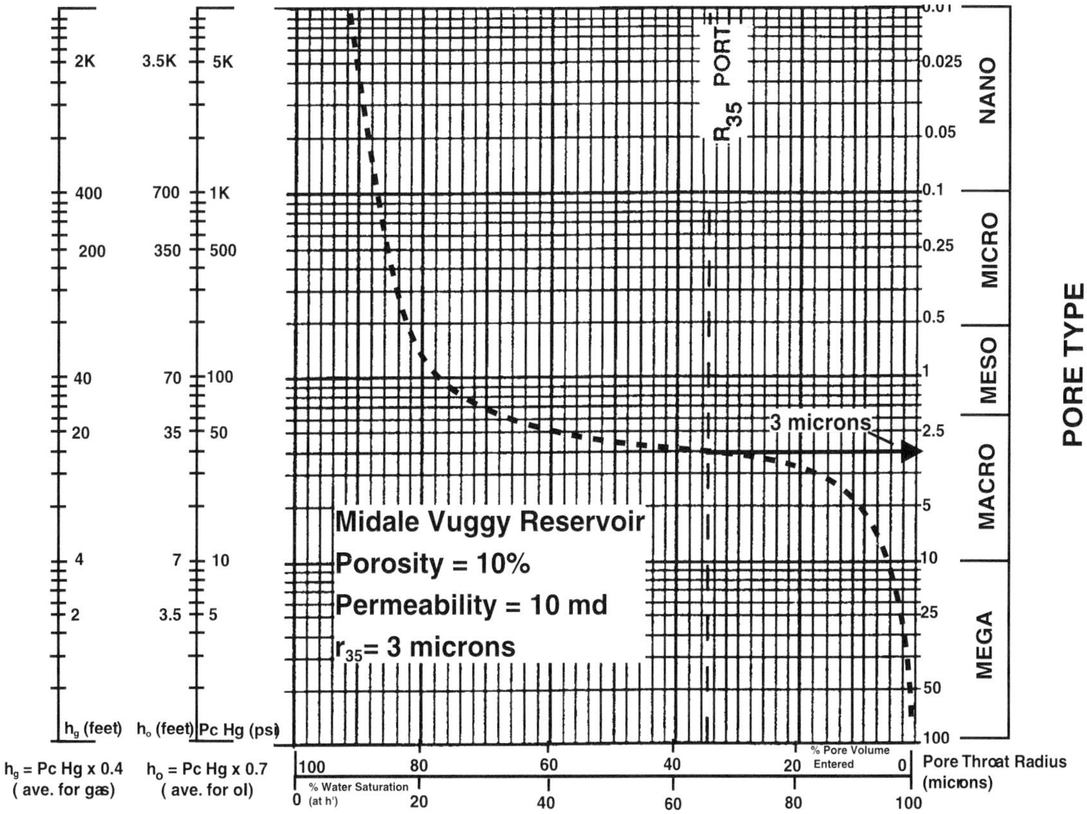

Figure 9–99.

Nonproductive facies

The main nonproductive updip carbonate facies ("porous mudstone") is locally laminated and burrowed peloidal lime and dolomite mudstones to wackestones. These tighter rocks originated on a low-energy to restricted shelf and in lagoons.

Nonreservoir SEM and capillary curve

The figure below illustrates the petrophysical characteristics of the main nonreservoir facies in the field: lime and dolomite mudstones to wackestones. The sample pore system consists of fine intergranular and unconnected vuggy pores and pore throats. The capillary pressure curve shows the higher entry pressure of the nonreservoir facies compared to the reservoir facies. The r_{35} and r_{10} values for the sample are 0.2 and 0.25μ, respectively.

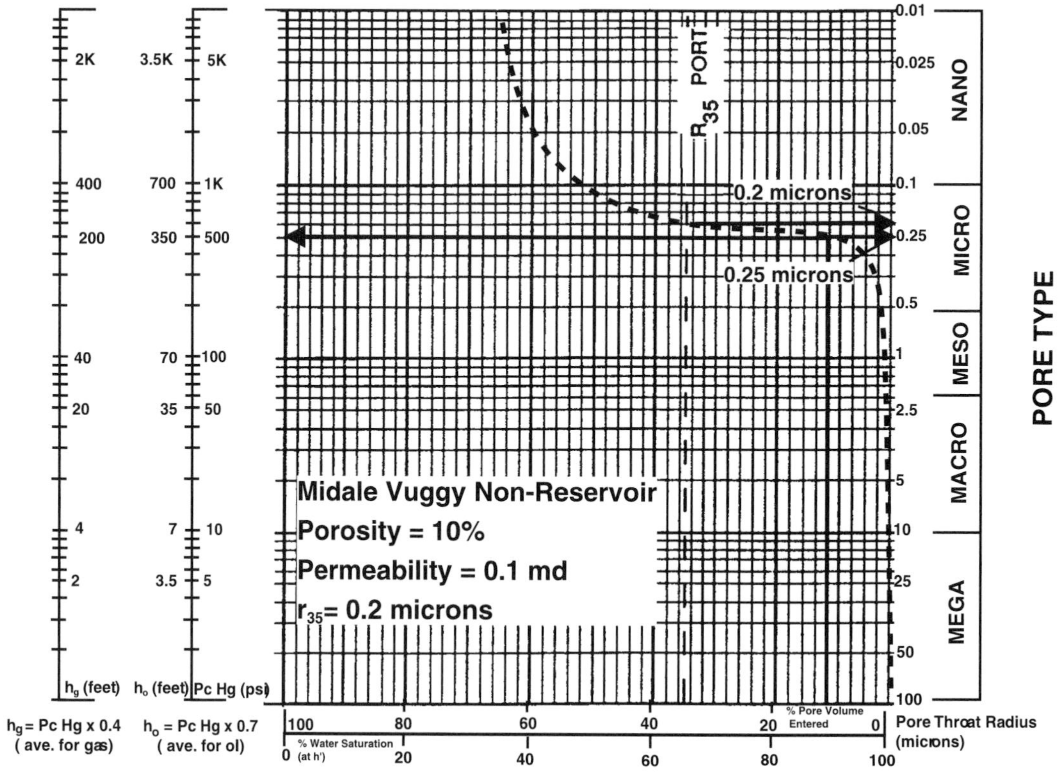

Figure 9–100.

Facies tracts of Midale Vuggy beds

The Midale Vuggy beds contain three facies tracts that parallel the paleo-shoreline (northwest).

- In and downdip from Weyburn field, the rocks consist primarily of the vuggy packstone facies, although there are numerous thin interbeds of porous mudstone facies.
- Landward (now updip) from this facies tract, the reservoir grades into porous mudstone facies with scattered lenses of poorly developed, vuggy packstone facies.
- Still farther northeast but downdip from the truncation edge of the Midale, the rocks change facies into anhydrite.

Overlying and underlying beds

The beds overlying the Midale Vuggy, i.e., the Midale Marly beds, consist almost entirely of the porous mudstone facies. The beds underlying the Midale Vuggy are tight carbonates and evaporites.

Midale Lithofacies and Distribution, continued

Weyburn well log

The figure below is an example of log characteristics of Midale beds in a Weyburn field well. The well was continuously cored through the Midale interval. The brick pattern denotes packstone facies with vuggy and intergranular porosity; hachures indicate porous dolomitic mudstone facies. Log and core data for representative (if extreme) data points, numbered 1–8, also appear in Figures 9–102 through 9–104.

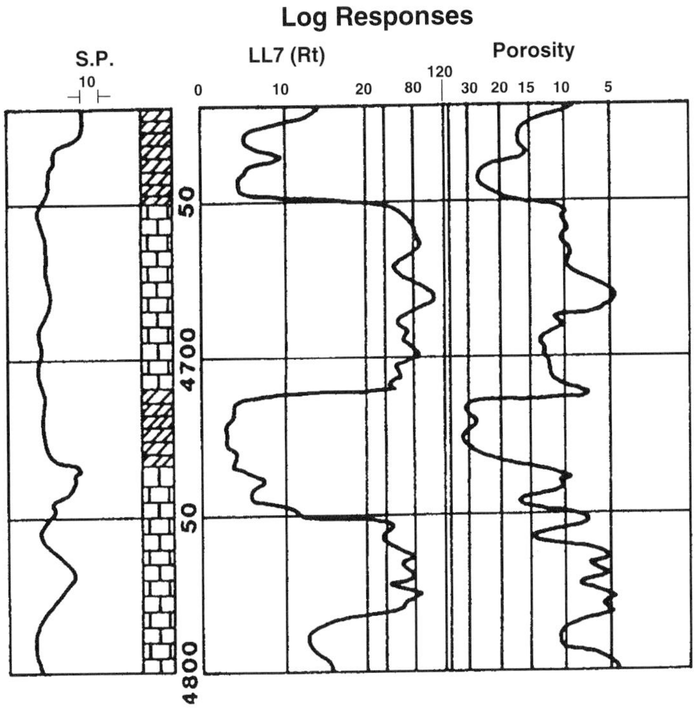

Zone	Core Analysis Porosity (%)	Core Analysis Perm (md)	Porosity Type
1	18	0.8	B
2	28	4	B
3	12	15	A
5	<0.1		
4	13	10	A
5	30	3	A
6	15	100	A
7			
8	12	250	A

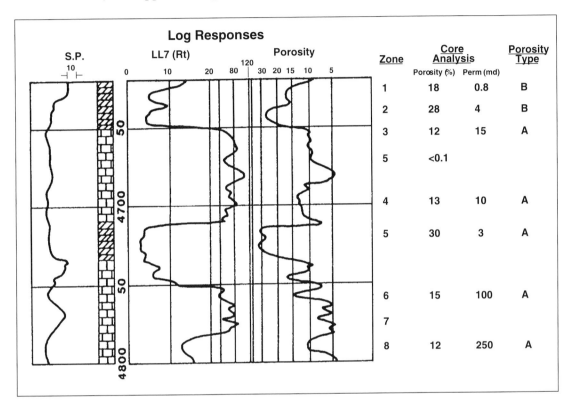

Figure 9–101. From Coalson et al., 1990.

Midale Porosity, Pore Geometries, and Petrophysics

Reservoir pore geometry and pore type

Most of the porosity in the vuggy packstone facies is molds and vugs developed by solution of micrite, algal clasts, and skeletal fragments. There is a range in sizes of the vugs. Most of the larger vugs are connected and effective. Smaller pinpoint vugs and molds lack interconnection and are ineffective. The vuggy packstone facies also contains intergranular (partly modified to intercrystalline) meso- to macroporosity. On the basis of SEM analyses, the particles are larger than 50μ (equivalent to very fine-grained sand). Capillary pressure data and petrographic analyses indicate the vugs and intergranular pore throats are large, 4–10μ, and well sorted. The r_{35} analyses (port size) puts the reservoir facies in the macropore type.

Reservoir character

Good reservoir properties are seen in the vuggy packstone facies, congruent with the observed pore geometries. Permeabilities in rock with only 10% porosity are as high as 10 md.

Below is a crossplot of routine core porosity and permeability from Midale in an example well at Weyburn field. The diagonal lines are contours of equal r_{35} values. On the plot, vuggy packstone facies (group A; data points 3, 4, 6, and 8) are characterized by lower porosity but higher permeability.

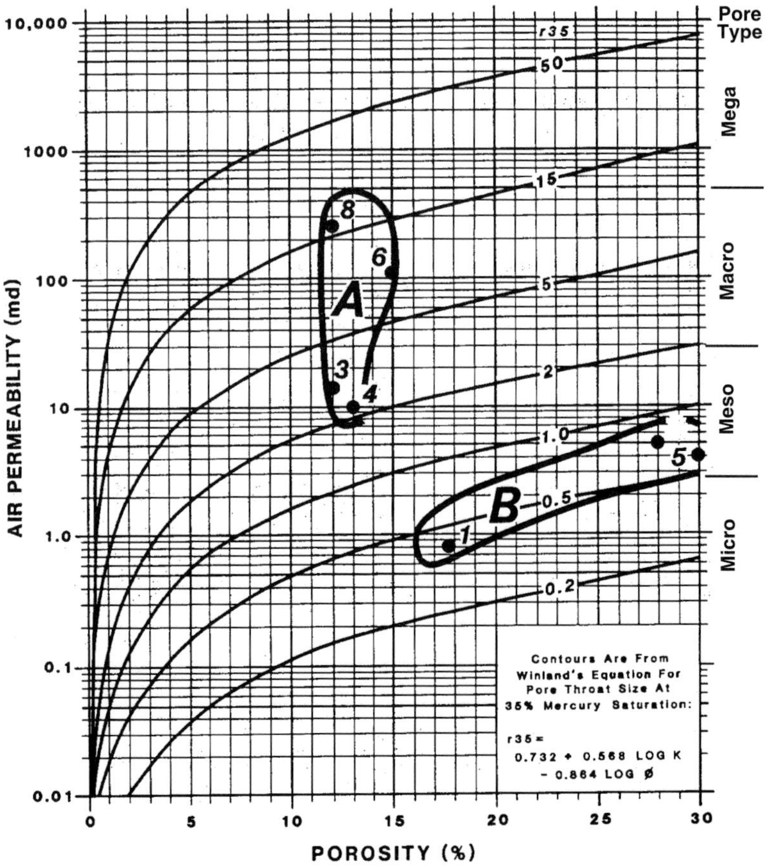

Figure 9–102. From Coalson et al., 1994; courtesy RMAG.

Nonreservoir pore geometry and pore type

In contrast to the vuggy packstone facies, the porous mudstone facies displays poor permeability (5 md or less), even though porosity can be as high as 30% (points 1 and 5, group B in Figure 9–102). This is because the porosity is pinpoint vugs isolated within fine intercrystalline meso- to microporosity formed by silt-sized (10μ or less) dolomite rhombs. Capillary pressure and SEM data indicate the pore throats are less than 1μ in radius, with an abundance of pore throats about 0.5μ in radius or smaller (see Figure 9–100). Port size puts much of this rock in micropore type. While localized lenses of porous mudstone have as much as 30% porosity and 20 md permeability, these probably are laterally isolated from each other.

Effect of Pore Geometry on S_w in Midale Rocks

Log response and S_w

Variations in pore geometry have the expected effect on log responses and water saturations (S_w). The Midale Vuggy in a cored field well consists of interbeds of packstone and mudstone. Below is a Pickett plot for the Midale Vuggy from an example well in Weyburn field. Data points cluster around higher resistivities for packstones (group A) and lower resistivities for mudstones (group B), reflecting the higher water saturations of the mudstones.

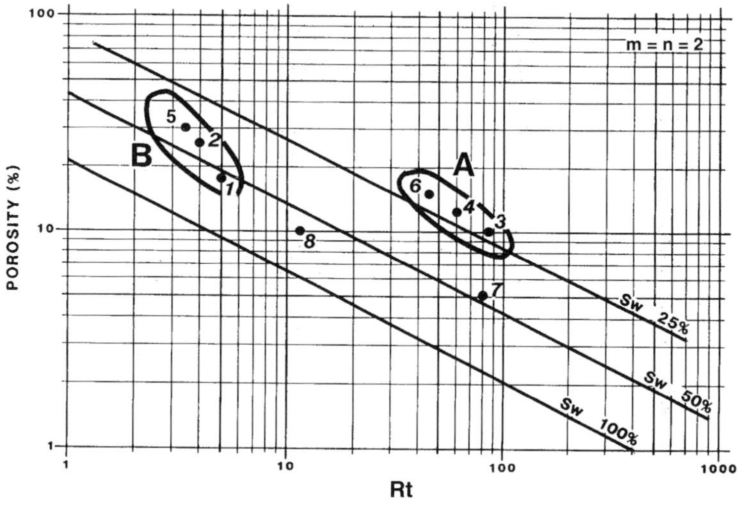

Figure 9–103. From Coalson et al., 1994; courtesy RMAG.

Buckles plot

As shown on Figure 9–102, mudstones (B) are micro- to mesoporous; packstones (A) are meso- to macroporous. The mudstones have more pores with smaller pore throats than the packstones. This means mudstones have greater pore surface area and higher immobile S_w. As a consequence, S_w values for mudstones are higher at any given elevation in the oil column.

Following is a Buckles plot for the Weyburn well. The hyperbolic curves represent equal values of $S_w \times \Phi$. Points from the same pore type that fall along a hyperbolic curve are at immobile S_w. Curves with higher values represent higher immobile S_w.

On the plot, data for packstones (A), except for point 8, fall on a hyperbolic curve with a value between 100 and 300. This indicates these beds are at immobile water saturations. Point 8 is from a transition zone. Mudstones (B) also are at immobile water saturations but fall on a hyperbolic curve with higher numbers, between 1000 and 1300.

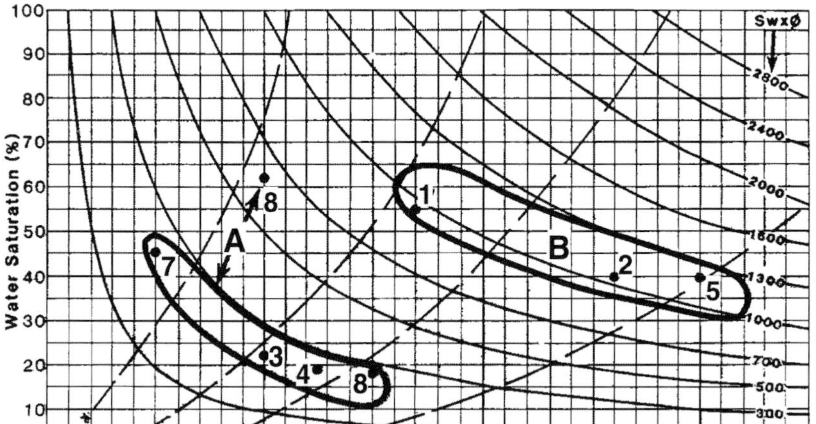

Figure 9–104. From Coalson et al., 1994; courtesy RMAG.

Weyburn Seal Capacity

Weyburn trap model

A working trap model for Weyburn field is that of a macroporous vuggy packstone reservoir lying downdip from a microporous intercrystalline mudstone seal. How much hydrocarbon column could a trap like this retain, especially since superficially the seal doesn't appear to be a seal at all. Instead, it consists of rocks with appreciable porosity, local oil staining, local log-calculated water saturations less than 100%, and the capability of producing significant amounts of water on DST.

Total oil column height

Weyburn and nearby Steelman fields appear to produce from a single, pressure-communicated oil column (Hannon, 1987). If so, then the total height of this combined column is about 600 ft (180 m). Could rocks of the porous mudstone facies act as a lateral seal for this much oil column? To calculate oil column height, we use the following equation:

$$h = \frac{0.670 \times \gamma \cos\theta}{R_{bt}(\rho_w - \rho_h)}$$

where:

γ = interfacial tension (dynes/cm)
θ = contact angle
R_{bt} = breakthrough pore throat size (μ)
ρ_w = formation water density (g/cc)
ρ_h = hydrocarbon density (g/cc)

Calculating oil column height at Weyburn

We can calculate the potential oil column height that could be sealed by the porous mudstone facies using maximum reasonable estimates for the above parameters. Weyburn field oil densities grade from 35°API in the updip portion of the field to 27°API near the base. A representative gravity of 30°API is used for the column as a whole. The formation water is brackish NaCl brine (35,000 ppm).

Other parameters:

Reservoir temp. = 150°F (66°C) (possibly a low estimate)
GOR = 100 CFG/BO (18 m^3 gas/m^3 oil) (probably low estimate)
Reservoir press. = 3,000 psi (20.7 × 10^3 kPa)
γ = 35 dynes/cm at STP
θ = 0° (seal is assumed to be very strongly water wet)

Estimates of in situ values:

ρ_w = 1.01 g/cc (from Schowalter, 1979, his Figure 2)
ρ_h = 0.85 g/cc (from Schowalter, 1979, his Figure 3)

Therefore:

$(\rho_w - \rho_h)$ = 0.16 (0.12 from approximations in preceding section)
γ = 27 dynes/cm (from Schowalter, 1979, his Figure 11)
$\cos\theta$ = 1 (very strongly water wet)

Therefore:

$\gamma \cos\theta$ = 27 dynes/cm (26 dynes/cm from approximations in preceding section)

Substituting these values into the above equation results in h (ft) = $176/R_{bt}$ (μ). All that is left is to estimate R_{bt}.

Estimating R_{bt}

A generally accepted concept is that oil migrates after filling only the minimum possible percentage of the largest pore throats that is required to establish a continuous, thread- or rope-shaped channel through the rock (e.g., Dembicki and Anderson, 1989; Catalan et al., 1992; Hirsch and Thompson, 1995). This is the breakthrough or critical nonwetting phase saturation. Clearly, estimating R_{bt} or the size of the largest connected pore throats that control hydrocarbon breakthrough is critical to this analysis.

There are at least three ways to estimate R_{bt}.

1. Measure R_{bt} directly on core samples, then correct it to reservoir conditions using methods of the preceding section (e.g., Thomas et al., 1968; Schowalter, 1979).
2. Estimate the breakthrough pressure from the shape of a capillary pressure curve (Katz and Thompson, 1987).
3. Use the Winland method (Pittman, 1992) to derive a measure of pore throat size in the seal.

Winland approach to estimate R_{bt}

The Winland approach is perhaps the simplest method for obtaining R_{bt} because it uses readily available core analyses. The method relates a core sample's porosity and permeability to the pore throat size indicated at a given nonwetting-phase saturation. Once breakthrough saturation is estimated, the Winland method yields pore throat sizes representative of that mode of pore throats, or R_{bt}.

Choosing a breakthrough saturation

The difficulty is knowing the breakthrough saturation for a formation without lab data from samples from that formation. There are conflicting opinions about how to estimate breakthrough saturation:

- Thomas et al. (1968), Schowalter (1979), and general industry opinions suggest oil or gas migration through plug-size samples occurs at nonwetting phase saturations of about 10% (4–17%), i.e., that the largest 10th percentile of pore throats controls breakthrough.
- Catalan et al. (1992) observed breakthrough saturations of 4–20% in pack experiments. Relative permeability analysis of core plugs shows the first nonwetting phase flow occurs at approximately the same saturations for most rocks.
- Other workers (Alan Byrnes, personal communication, 1995) have observed breakthrough in plug samples at highly variable saturations—sometimes more than 50%.

It would seem best to calculate R_{bt} for different reasonable breakthrough saturations to test the sensitivity of the solution.

Winland's r_{10}

Breakthrough saturation of 10% is reasonable to use for most rocks. Using a statistical analysis similar to that of Winland, Franklin (Coalson et al., 1994) developed the following formula for R_{bt} at 10% nonwetting phase saturation (also called r_{10}):

$$\log R_{bt} = 0.353 + 0.427 \log K_a - 0.184 \log \phi$$

where:

K_a = air permeability, md
ϕ = porosity, % (not decimals)

Most of the cores in the porous mudstone facies found updip from the productive area have porosities of about 10% and permeabilities of about 0.1 md (or less), based on routine core analyses from the 1960s. Unfortunately, the core permeabilities are too high, given (1) the tendency to "high-grade" core plugs in better rock and (2) the fact that the parameters used on these samples could not measure values < 0.1 md. We can assume 0.5 md a representative value for the seal rocks. This implies $R_{bt} = 0.4\mu$ for these rocks, consistent with petrographic data. If r_{35} is a better approximation of R_{bt}, then Winland's equation yields $R_{bt} = 0.1\mu$.

Weyburn oil column height

If $R_{bt} = r_{10} = 0.4\mu$ and h = 113 ft/R_{bt}, then the estimated oil column is 283 ft (86 m). If $R_{bt} = r_{35} = 0.1\mu$, then h = 892 ft (272 m).

Using estimated oil or gas column heights

Hannon (1987) calculated only 100 ft (30 m) of seal capacity for this field. His calculations assumed a breakthrough pressure of 10–15 psi (69–103 kPa), based on "a multitude of capillary pressure curves" that he did not document. Yet we can estimate several reasonable breakthrough pressures from any given capillary pressure curve, depending on the assumed nonwetting phase saturation.

Seal Capacity and Trap Type

Significance of R_{bt} for seal capacity

Midale Marly beds are universally accepted as being the top seal for this accumulation. They are essentially the same facies as the Midale Vuggy beds, analyzed here as a possible updip seal. This study shows the updip change in pore throat sizes could account for 280–890 ft (95–298 m) of oil column. The column height shown from producing wells at Weyburn and nearby Steelman fields is 600 ft. We are left with two possible conclusions:

- If the estimate of oil column height using R_{bt} from the Winland r_{10} equation is correct, the Midale Marly beds do not have the capacity from their capillary properties to seal the column of oil shared by Weyburn and Steelman. Weyburn is a hydrodynamic trap or a combination hydrodynamic–stratigraphic trap.
- If the calculation of R_{bt} from the Winland r_{35} equation is correct, then the capillary properties of the Midale Marly beds could seal Weyburn field without hydronamics.

Representative sampling

This way of calculating seal capacity assumes that the core samples used are representative of the seal. Ideally, the rock samples should represent the seal at several geographic points. For instance, a stratigraphic trap may have variable seal capacity along the lateral seal. The best seal rocks might be located at the structurally highest point above a hydrocarbon column and might be capable of holding a 600-ft (180-m) oil column. Yet if the seal lying 100 ft (30 m) structurally downdip and laterally along the seal had seal capacity of 200 ft (60 m), then the total column could not exceed 300 ft (90 m).

Summary

As often happens in oil-field studies, this one did not yield a unique solution. This analysis is not sufficiently precise to answer the question of a capillary vs. hydrodynamic seal, but it does show the probability that more thorough quantitative work of the type illustrated would be definitive. Particularly helpful would be detailed analysis of r_{10} or r_{35} values of the updip Midale Vuggy beds.

Therefore, any estimate of oil or gas column heights should be tested against all other information available. Column height and the buoyancy pressure it generates should make sense in context with shows of oil or gas, water saturations, trap closure, and pressure data.

Section G
Annotated References

Alberty, M.W., 1994, Standard interpretation; part 4—wireline methods, *in* D. Morton-Thompson and A.M. Woods, eds., Development Geology Reference Manual: AAPG Methods in Exploration Series 10, p. 180–185.

Archie, G.E., 1942, Classification of carbonate reservoir rocks and petrophysical considerations: AAPG Bulletin, vol. 36, no. 2, p. 218–298. *A classic paper written way before its time.*

Arps, J.J., 1964, Engineering concepts useful in oil finding: AAPG Bulletin, vol. 48, no. 2, p. 943–961. *Explains concepts of rock/fluid interaction in easy-to-understand terms.*

Barwis, J.H., J.G. McPherson, and J.R.J. Studlick, 1989, Sandstone Petroleum Reservoirs: New York, Springer-Verlag, 583 p. *Contains case histories of fields with reservoirs that represent each of the major depositional environments.*

Beard, D.C., and P.K. Weyl, 1973, Influence of texture on porosity and permeability of unconsolidated sand: AAPG Bulletin, vol. 57, no. 2, p. 349–369.

Berg, R., 1975, Capillary pressures in stratigraphic traps: AAPG Bulletin, vol. 59, no. 6, p. 939–956.

Burley, S.D., J.D. Kantorowicz, and B. Waugh, 1985, Clastic diagenesis, *in* P.J. Brenchley and B.P.J. Williams, eds., Sedimentology: Recent Developments and Applied Aspects: London, Blackwell Scientific Publications, p. 189–228.

Catalan, L., F. Xiaowen, I. Chatzis, and F.A.L. Dullien, 1992, An experimental study of secondary oil migration: AAPG Bulletin, vol. 76, no. 5, p. 638–650.

Chetin, A.K., and W.W. Fitkin, 1959, Geology of the Weyburn field, Saskatchewan: Canadian Mining and Metallurgical Bulletin, December, p. 751–761.

Choquette, P.W., and L.C. Pray, 1970, Geologic nomenclature and classification of porosity in sedimentary carbonates: AAPG Bulletin, vol. 54, no. 2, p. 207–250. *Classic reference for basic concepts regarding carbonate porosity.*

Coalson, E.B., D.J. Hartmann, and J.B. Thomas, 1990, Applied Petrophysics in Exploration and Exploitation: Notes from short course sponsored by Univ. of Colo.–Denver, var. pages.

Coalson, E.B., S.M. Goolsby, and M.H. Franklin, 1994, Subtle seals and fluid-flow barriers in carbonate rocks, *in* J.C. Dolson, M.L. Hendricks, and W.A. Wescott, eds., Unconformity Related Hydrocarbons in Sedimentary Sequences: RMAG Guidebook for Petroleum Exploration and Exploitation in Clastic and Carbonate Sediments, p. 45–58.

Dahlberg, E.C., 1982, Applied Hydrodynamics in Petroleum Exploration: New York, Springer Verlag, 161 p.

Dembicki, H., Jr., and M.L. Anderson, 1989, Secondary migration of oil: experiments supporting efficient movement of separate, buoyant oil phase along limited conduits: AAPG Bulletin, vol. 73, no. 9, p. 1018–1021.

Doveton, J.H., 1995, Wireline Petrofacies Analysis: Notes from short course presented in Calgary, Alberta, April 24–28, 176 p.

Ebanks, J., N.H. Scheihing, and C.D. Atkinson, 1993, Flow units for reservoir characterization, *in* D. Morton-Thompson and A.M. Woods, eds., Development Geology Reference Manual: AAPG Methods in Exploration Series 10, p. 282–285.

Erlich, R., S.J. Crabtree, K.O. Horkowitz, and J.P. Horkowitz, 1991, Petrography and reservoir physics, 1: objective classification of reservoir porosity: AAPG Bulletin, vol. 75, no. 10, p. 1547–1563.

Feazel, C.T., and R.A. Schatzinger, 1985, Prevention of carbonate cementation in petroleum reservoirs, *in* N. Schneidermann and P.M. Harris, eds., Carbonate Cements: SEPM Special Publication 36, p. 97–106.

Galloway, W.E., 1984, Hydrogeologic regimes of sandstone diagenesis, *in* D.A. McDonald and R.C. Surdam, eds., Clastic Diagenesis: AAPG Memoir 37, p. 3–14.

Galloway, W.E., and D.K. Hobday, 1983, Terrigenous Clastic Depositional Systems: Applications to Petroleum, Coal, and Uranium Exploration: New York, Springer-Verlag, 438 p. *Summarizes reservoir characteristics of major sandstone depositional environments, especially with respect to sand body geometries.*

Garb, F.A., and G.L. Smith, 1987, Estimation of oil and gas reserves, *in* H.B. Bradley, ed., Petroleum Engineering Handbook: SPE, p. 40-1–40-32.

Goolsby, S.M., M.H. Franklin, M.L. Hendricks, and E.B. Coalson, 1991, Hydrodynamics and pore-throat modifications beneath an unconformity at Weyburn field, Saskatchewan, *in* J. Dolson, ed., Unconformity Related Hydrocarbon Exploitation and Accumulation in Clastic and Carbonate Settings: Continuing education course notes, var. pages.

Handford, C.R., and R.G. Loucks, 1995, Carbonate depositional sequences and systems tracts—responses of carbonate platforms to relative sea-level changes, *in* R.G. Loucks and J.F. Sarg, eds., Carbonate Sequence Stratigraphy: Recent Developments and Applications: AAPG Memoir 57, p. 3–42.

Hannon, N., 1987, Subsurface water flow patterns in the Canadian sector of the Williston Basin: RMAG 1987 Symposium Guidebook, p. 313–321.

Harris, P.M., 1985, Carbonate cementation—a review, *in* N. Schneidermann and P.M. Harris, eds., Carbonate Cements: SEPM Special Publication 36, p. 79–95.

_____, C.G. St.-C. Kendall, and I. Lerche, 1985, Carbonate cementation—a brief review, *in* N. Schneidermann and P.M. Harris, eds., Carbonate Cements: SEPM Special Publication 36, p. 79–95.

Harrison, W.J., and R.N. Tempel, 1993, Diagenetic pathways in sedimentary basins, *in* A.D. Horbury and A.G. Robinson, eds., Diagenesis and Basin Development: AAPG Studies in Geology 36, p. 69–86.

References, continued

Hartmann, D.J., and E.B. Coalson, 1990, Evaluation of the Morrow sandstone in Sorrento field, Cheyenne County, Colorado, *in* S.A. Sonnenberg, L.T. Shannon, K. Rader, W.F. von Drehle, and G.W. Martin, eds., Morrow Sandstones of Southeast Colorado and Adjacent Areas: RMAG Symposium, p. 91–100.

Hayes, J.B., 1983, Sandstone diagenesis as an exploration tool: AAPG Clastic Diagenesis School, June 27–July 1, Monterey, California.

Hirsch, L.M., and A.H. Thompson, 1995, Minimum saturations and buoyancy in secondary migration: AAPG Bulletin. vol. 79, no. 5, p. 696–710.

James, S.W., 1989, Diagenetic history and reservoir characteristics of a deep Minnelusa reservoir, Hawk Point field, Powder River basin, Wyoming, *in* E.B. Coalson, S.S. Kaplan, C.W. Keighin, C.A. Oglesby, and J.W. Robinson, eds., Petrogenesis and Petrophysics of Selected Sandstone Reservoirs of the Rocky Mountain Region: RMAG Symposium, p. 81–96.

Katz, A., and A.H. Thompson, 1987, Prediction of rock electrical conductivity from mercury injection measurements: Journal of Geophysical Research, vol. 92, p. 599–607.

Kent, D.M., F.M. Haidl, and J.A. MacEachern, 1988, Mississippian oil fields in the northern Williston Basin, *in* S.M. Goolsby and M.W. Longman, eds., Occurrence and Petrophysical Properties of Carbonate Reservoirs in the Rocky Mountain Region: RMAG Symposium, p. 193–210.

Levorsen, A.I., 1954, Geology of Petroleum: San Francisco, W.H. Freeman, 703 p.

Longman, M.W., 1980, Carbonate diagenetic textures from nearsurface diagenetic environments: AAPG Bulletin, vol. 64, no. 4, p. 461–487.

Loucks, R.G., and J.F. Sarg, eds., 1993, Carbonate Sequence Stratigraphy, Recent Development and Applications: AAPG Memoir 57, 545 p.

_____, M.M. Dodge, and W.E. Galloway, 1984, Regional controls on diagenesis and reservoir quality in Lower Tertiary sandstones along the Texas Gulf Coast, *in* D.A. McDonald and R.C. Surdam, eds., Clastic Diagenesis: AAPG Memoir 37, p. 15–45.

Montañez, I.P., and D.A. Osleger, 1993, Parasequence stacking patterns, third-order accommodation events, and sequence stratigraphy of Middle to Upper Cambrian platform carbonates, Bonanza King Formation, southern Great Basin, *in* R.G. Loucks and J.F. Sarg, eds., Carbonate Sequence Stratigraphy—Recent Developments and Applications: AAPG Memoir 38, p. 305–326.

Muller, M.M., and E.B. Coalson, 1989, Diagenetic and petrophysical variations of the Dakota sandstone, Henry field, Green River basin, Wyoming, *in* E.B. Coalson, S.S. Kaplan, C.W. Keighin, C.A. Oglesby, and J.W. Robinson, eds., Petrogenesis and Petrophysics of Selected Sandstone Reservoirs of the Rocky Mountain Region: RMAG Symposium, p. 149–158.

Neasham, J.W., 1977, The morphology of dispersed clay in sandstone reservoirs and its effect on sandstone shaliness, pore space, and fluid flow properties: Proceedings of the SPE Annual Meeting, October 9–12, paper SPE-6858.

North, F.K., 1985, Petroleum Geology: London, Allen & Unwin, 607 p.

Patchett, J.G., and E.B. Coalson, 1982, The determination of porosity in sandstone and shaly sandstone, part 2: effects of complex mineralogy and hydrocarbons: 23rd Annual SPWLA Logging Symposium, July 6–9, paper T, 50 p.

Petroleum Research Corporation, 1961, Hydrodynamic exploration for unconformity traps: Research Report A-11, 47 p. (unpublished report, available at Colorado School of Mines Library, Golden, CO).

Pickett, G.R., 1966, A review of current techniques for determination of water saturation from logs: Journal of Petroleum Technology, November, p. 1425–1433.

_____, 1973, Pattern recognition as a means of formation evaluation: The Log Analyst, vol. 14, no. 4, p. 3–11.

Pittman, E.D., 1992, Relationship of porosity to permeability to various parameters derived from mercury injection–capillary pressure curves for sandstone: AAPG Bulletin, vol. 76, no. 2, p. 191–198.

_____ and J.B. Thomas, 1979, Some applications of scanning electron microscopy to the study of reservoir rock: Journal of Petroleum Technology, November, p. 1375–1380.

Purser, B.H., 1978, Early diagenesis and the preservation of porosity in Jurassic limestones: Journal of Petroleum Geology, vol. 1, no. 2, p. 83–94.

Read, J.F., 1995, Overview of carbonate platform sequences, cycle stratigraphy and reservoirs in greenhouse and ice-house worlds, *in* J.F. Read, C. Kerans, L.J. Webber, J.F. Sarg, and F.M. Wright, eds., Milankovitch Sea-level Changes, Cycles, and Reservoirs on Carbonate Platforms in Greenhouse and Ice-house Worlds: SEPM Short Course 35, 183 p. *Good summary of concepts of climatic effect on sea level cycles, carbonate deposition, and reservoir development.*

_____ and A.D. Horbury, 1993, Eustatic and tectonic controls on porosity evolution beneath sequence-bounding unconformities and parasequence disconformities on carbonate platforms, *in* A.D. Horbury and A.G. Robinson, eds., Diagenesis and Basin Development: AAPG Studies in Geology 36, p. 155–197.

_____, C. Kerans, L.J. Webber, J.F. Sarg, and F.M. Wright, 1995, Milankovitch Sea-level Changes, Cycles, and Reservoirs on Carbonate Platforms in Greenhouse and Ice-house Worlds: SEPM Short Course 35, 183 p. *Discusses concepts of carbonate sequence stratigraphy and methods for predicting carbonate reservoir quality.*

Sarg, J.F., 1988, Carbonate sequence stratigraphy, *in* C.K. Wilgus, B.S. Hastings, C.G. St. C. Kendall, H.W. Posamentier, C.A. Ross, and J.C. Van Wagoner, eds., Sea Level Changes: An Integrated Approach: SEPM Special Publication 42, p. 155–182.

Scherer, M., 1987, Parameters influencing porosity in sandstones: a model for sandstone porosity prediction: AAPG Bulletin, vol. 71, no. 5, p. 485–491.

Schowalter, T.T., 1979, Mechanics of secondary hydrocarbon migration and entrapment: AAPG Bulletin, vol. 63, no. 5, p. 723–760.

_____ and P.D. Hess, 1982, Interpretation of subsurface hydrocarbon shows: AAPG Bulletin, vol. 66, p. 723–760.

Shelley, R.C., 1985, Elements of Petroleum Geology: San Francisco, W.H. Freeman, 449 p.

Sneider, R.M., and H.R. King, 1984, Integrated rock-log calibration in the Elmworth field—Alberta, Canada: part I: reservoir rock detection and characterization, *in* J.A. Masters, ed., Elmworth—Case Study of a Deep Basin Gas Field: AAPG Memoir 38, p. 205–214.

Sonnenberg, S.A., 1985, Tectonic and sedimentation model for Morrow sandstone deposition, Sorrento field area, Denver basin, Colorado: The Mountain Geologist, October, p. 180–191.

Stonecipher, S.A., and J.A. May, 1990, Facies controls on early diagenesis: Wilcox Group, Texas Gulf Coast, *in* D. Meshri and P.J. Ortoleva, eds., Prediction of Reservoir Quality Through Chemical Modeling, I: AAPG Memoir 49, p. 25–44.

Stonecipher, S.A., R.D. Winn, Jr., and M.G. Bishop, 1984, Diagenesis of the Frontier Formation, Moxa Arch: a function of sandstone geometry, texture and composition, and fluid flux, *in* D.A. McDonald and R.C. Surdam, eds., Clastic Diagenesis: AAPG Memoir 37, p. 289–316.

Surdam, R.C., T.L. Dunn, D.B. MacGowan, and H.P. Heasler, 1989, Conceptual models for the prediction of porosity evolution with an example from the Frontier Sandstone, Bighorn basin, Wyoming, *in* E.B. Coalson, S.S. Kaplan, C.W. Keighin, L.A. Oglesby, and J.W. Robinson, eds., Sandstone Reservoirs: Rocky Mountain Association of Geologists, p. 7–21.

Thomas, L.K., P.L. Katz, and M.R. Tek, 1968, Threshold pressure phenomena in porous media: SPE Journal, June, p. 174–184.

Van Wagoner, J.C., R.M. Mitchum, K.M. Campion, and V.D. Rahmanian, 1990, Siliciclastic Sequence Stratigraphy in Well Logs, Cores, and Outcrops: AAPG Methods in Exploration Series 7, 55 p. *This book describes the basics concepts of sequence stratigraphy in useful, clear terms.*

Wardlaw, N.C., and J.P. Cassan, 1978, Estimation of recovery efficiency by visual observation of pore systems in reservoir rocks: Bulletin of Canadian Petroleum Geology, vol. 26, no. 4, p. 572–585.

Wegelin, A., 1984, Geology and reservoir properties of the Weyburn field, southeastern Saskatchewan, *in* J.A. Lorsong and M.A. Wilson, eds., Oil and Gas in Saskatchewan: Saskatchewan Geological Society Special Publication 7, p.71–82.

References, continued

Wilson, M.D., 1994a, Non-compositional controls on diagenetic processes, *in* M.D. Wilson, ed., Reservoir Quality Assessment and Prediction in Clastic Rocks: SEPM Short Course 30, p. 183–208. *Discusses the effect that variables such as temperature and pressure have on diagenesis of sandstones. A good reference for predicting sandstone reservoir system quality.*

_____, 1994b, Assessing the relative importance of diagenetic processes and controls, *in* M.D. Wilson, ed., Reservoir Quality Assessment and Prediction in Clastic Rocks: SEPM Short Course 30, p. 259–276.

_____ and E.D. Pittman, 1977, Authigenic clays in sandstones: recognition and influence on reservoir properties and paleoenvironmental analysis: Journal of Sedimentary Petrology, vol. 47, no. 1, p. 3–31.

_____ and P.T. Stanton, 1994, Diagenetic mechanisms of porosity and permeability reduction and enhancement, *in* M.D. Wilson, ed., Reservoir Quality Assessment and Prediction in Clastic Rocks: SEPM Short Course 30, p. 59–118.

Winland, H.D., 1972, Oil accumulation in response to pore size changes, Weyburn field, Saskatchewan: Amoco Production Company Report F72-G-25, 20 p. (unpublished).

_____, 1976, Evaluation of gas slippage and pore aperture size in carbonate and sandstone reservoirs: Amoco Production Company Report F76-G-5, 25 p. (unpublished).

Chapter 10

Evaluating Top and Fault Seal

by

Grant M. Skerlec

Grant M. Skerlec

Grant M. Skerlec is head of SEALS International, specializing in the application of fault seal analysis to prospect assessment and field development. He received a BA degree from Franklin & Marshall College in 1968 and a Ph.D. from Princeton University in 1979. He joined Exxon Production Research Company where he began working on fault seal analysis in 1978. In 1982 he joined Esso Norway, and later Esso Exploration & Production UK, as an exploration geologist applying quantitative seal analysis to prospect and play assessments in the North Sea, Norwegian Sea, and Barents Sea. In 1987 Skerlec formed SEALS International, a company that provides services, software, and training for routine fault seal analysis as well as global databases of fault seal behavior in hydrocarbon basins. Current work involves the compilation of the joint-industry *Fault Seal Behavior in the Gulf Coast Atlas* and the recent completion of a similar atlas for North Sea–Norwegian Sea oil and gas fields.

Overview

Introduction

This chapter discusses seal analysis techniques. Both top seal and fault seal are fundamental to prospect and play assessment as well as to production and field development. Despite our understanding of the variables that control seals (Downey, 1984), practical techniques are few and seal is commonly risked in an intuitive, qualitative manner. However, quantitative seal analysis, using those few techniques available, improves success ratios and reduces costly errors in field development.

Importance of seal

Top seal and fault seal are important because they control the following:

- Presence or absence of hydrocarbons
- Percent fill
- Vertical and lateral distribution of hydrocarbons
- Migration pathways and charge volumes
- Distribution and movement of hydrocarbons during field development

Seals are fundamental; no seal, no trap. Seals, or their absence, also define leak points that control the percent fill for hydrocarbon accumulations. Assessment of percent fill without the ability to risk seal (top or fault) is reduced to a statistical guessing game. They control the vertical and lateral distribution of hydrocarbons, both within individual fields and within basins.

Seals control migration pathways into traps. A trap may be empty not because a fault *leaked* once-trapped hydrocarbons but because a fault *sealed* and prevented hydrocarbons from migrating into a trap and filling it in the first place. Similarly, top seals can restrict vertical migration into shallow traps and control the vertical and lateral distribution of hydrocarbons within a basin.

Hydrocarbons migrate until they encounter the first intact seal. Because of variations in seal integrity and capacity, drainage areas are four-dimensional. Prospect analysis using drainage areas defined by simple structure-depth maps on the top reservoir can be very misleading. Plays appear and disappear in response to seal behavior.

Seals also control the movement of hydrocarbons during production. Efficient field development, well placement, ultimate recovery, and economic success or failure depend on risking seal.

In this chapter

This chapter contains the following sections.

Section A
Evaluating Fault Seal

Introduction

Routine fault seal analysis of prospects and fields is a necessary part of all exploration and production. The sealing behavior of faults is important because it controls the following:

- **Trapped hydrocarbon volumes**—faults control the presence or absence of hydrocarbons, the percent fill of individual fault compartments, and the vertical and lateral distribution of hydrocarbons within a field.
- **Migration pathways into traps**—faults control both the volume and migration direction of hydrocarbons available to charge a trap.
- **Hydrocarbon movement during field development**—faults can retard hydrocarbon flow, limit sweep efficiency, and create isolated compartments bounded by sealing faults. If the faults leak, they provide field-wide communication among numerous fault compartments.

The risking process

Evaluating, or risking, fault seal is a four-step process, as outlined in the table below and discussed in detail within this section.

Step	Task
1	Establish empirical threshold for seal/leak in existing fields.
2	Construct a fault plane profile to show juxtaposition relationships.
3	Analyze fault seal quantitatively to predict seal behavior and identify fault-dependent leak points.
4	Construct migration pathway maps.

In this section

This section contains the following subsections.

Subsection A1
Fault Seal Behavior

Introduction

Understanding fault seal behavior in existing fields is a prerequisite for predicting seal behavior in untested prospects. Empirical studies have established patterns of seal behavior, identified seal/leak thresholds for quantitative analysis of a fault seal, provided real analogs for prospect assessment, and demonstrated how important fault seal behavior is in controlling hydrocarbon accumulations (Smith, 1980; Skerlec, 1990, 1997a,b; Yielding et al., 1997).

In this subsection

This subsection contains the following topics.

Fault Seal Behavior Basics

Introduction

Fault seal behavior is analyzed on the basis of the following:

- Hydrocarbon contacts
- Fault-dependent leak points
- Pressure data

Types of behavior

The two basic types of fault seal behavior are (1) cross sealing or cross leaking and (2) dip sealing or dip leaking. **Cross seal and leak** refers to the *lateral* communication across the fault between juxtaposed sands. **Dip seal and leak** refers to the *vertical* communication along the fault between stacked sands.

The type of seal behavior is important in controlling the type of fault-dependent leak points. Fault-dependent leak points limit the volume of trapped hydrocarbons. The ability to identify these fault-dependent leak points is a fundamental tool for prospect assessment.

Finite seal capacity

Faults may have some finite seal capacity. A fault might support the pressure exerted by a 50-m hydrocarbon column yet leak if the column increases to 51 m (Smith, 1980).

Caveat

A fault does not simply seal or leak; many variations exist:

- A fault can seal at one point and leak at another.
- A fault can juxtapose many individual reservoirs, and each fault/reservoir intersection can seal or leak independently.
- A fault can seal on one side and leak on the other.
- A fault can seal oil but leak gas.
- A fault can be sealing to some finite column of hydrocarbon but leaking to a larger column.
- A fault can change seal behavior during migration and fill as well as during production. Seal behavior is time dependent.

Cross-leaking Faults

Introduction

A cross-leaking fault allows lateral communication of hydrocarbons between juxtaposed reservoirs. Cross-leaking faults can be identified using any of the following criteria:

- Common hydrocarbon contacts
- Common free water levels (FWL)
- Juxtaposed lithology leak points (JLLP)
- Common pressures

Common hydrocarbon contacts

Common hydrocarbon contacts imply communication across the fault and cross leakage. The cross-leaking fault in the following figure shows two sands, R_u and R_d, juxtaposed by a fault. The two sands have common oil–water (OWC) and gas–water (GWC) contacts. The fault is cross leaking to both oil and gas.

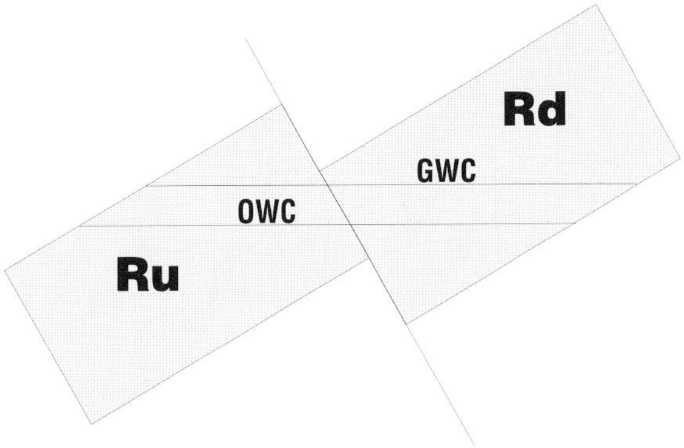

Figure 10–1.

Common free-water levels

A cross-leaking fault can have different hydrocarbon contacts across the fault. The difference in hydrocarbon contacts can be caused not by the fault zone material but by differences in the displacement pressure (P_d) of the juxtaposed reservoirs. There is, however, a common free-water level (FWL).

An example of a cross-leaking fault with different OWCs and a common FWL is shown in the following figure. The P_d of the R_d sand is greater than that of the R_u sand. The fault is cross leaking despite different OWCs.

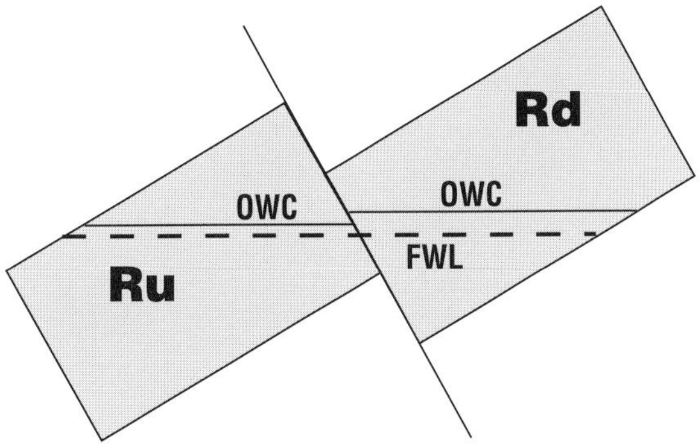

Figure 10–2.

Cross-leaking Faults, continued

Capillarity and OWCs

The following figure illustrates the effect of capillary properties on oil–water contacts. Decreasing pore throat radius, represented by three capillary tubes of decreasing diameter (left), creates a higher OWC within the reservoir. If the pore throat is large (low P_d), the OWC coincides with the free water level. If the pore throat is small (high P_d), the OWC is higher than the free water level. In a reservoir with a lateral facies change, a fault can be cross leaking but still separate sands with different hydrocarbon contacts (right).

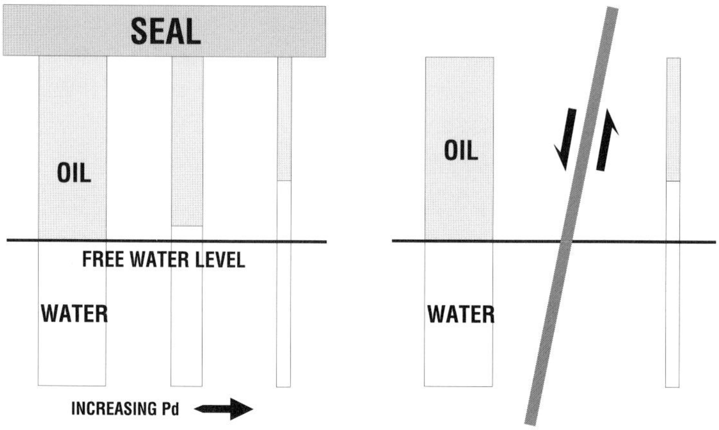

Figure 10–3.

Juxtaposed lithology leak points

Cross leakage commonly creates fault-dependent leak points limiting the percent (Smith, 1966, 1980; Allan, 1989; Harding and Tuminas, 1989). One type of fault-dependent leak point is illustrated in the following figure. The coincidence of the hydrocarbon contact with the top of the sand juxtaposed across the fault is a juxtaposed lithology leak point (JLLP). Hydrocarbons are trapped only where there is sand/sand juxtaposition along the fault. Hydrocarbons leak across the sand/sand juxtapositions.

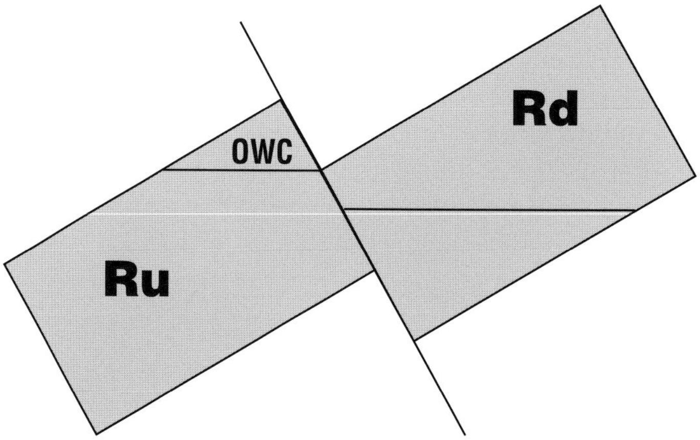

Figure 10–4.

Identifying JLLPs is an important method of assessing percent fill in prospects and determining seal behavior in existing fields. JLLPs exist only if the fault is cross leaking.

Cross-leaking Faults, continued

Common pressures

Common pressures across a fault imply communication and cross leakage. If a new well in a separate fault compartment encounters pressures equal to the current field depleted pressures, the fault is cross leaking.

In the figure below, wells 1 and 2 are separated by a cross-leaking fault. The initial pressures of both wells lie on a common, field-wide pressure depletion curve.

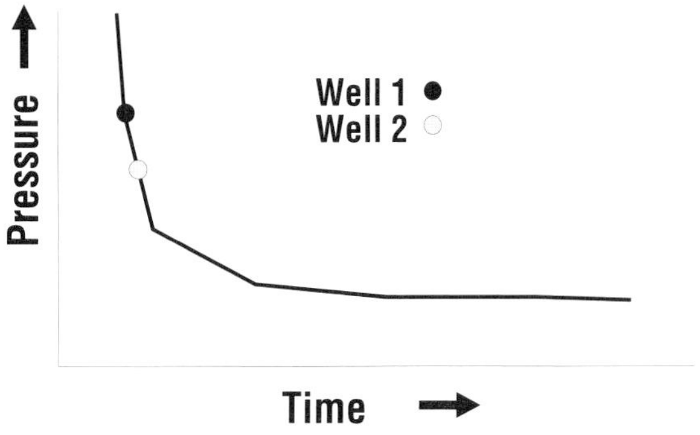

Figure 10–5.

Caveat

In fields with a long, complex production history, pressures and hydrocarbon contacts can be misleading as indicators of long-term fault seal behavior. Different pressures can exist across a fault despite cross leakage. Pressures in these fields may reflect short-term, production-induced disequilibrium. Pressure differences may exist across a fault that was cross leaking during migration and fill; the implied cross seal may not have existed during migration and fill when the fault was at equilibrium. The longer time spans of migration and fill allow equilibrium; the short spans of production favor disequilibrium.

In addition, the pressure distribution within a closure is affected by all of the adjacent faults, the rates of production and depletion of individual fault compartments, reservoir permeability and continuity, and the relative permeability of both reservoirs and fault zones. Apparent "permeability barriers" within a fault compartment may also be artificial creations of more distant bounding faults (van Poollen, 1965; Prasad, 1975; Earlougher and Kazemi, 1980; Stewart et al., 1984; Yaxley, 1987).

Cross-sealing Faults

Introduction

A cross-sealing fault prevents communication of hydrocarbons between juxtaposed sands (reservoirs). Cross-sealing faults can be identified using the following criteria:

- Hydrocarbon-bearing sands against water-wet sands
- Different hydrocarbon contacts
- Different pressures

Hydrocarbon against water

A fault is cross sealing if it juxtaposes hydrocarbon-bearing sands with water-wet sands, as illustrated in the following figure. Both oil and gas are prevented from flowing into the sand in the hanging wall (R_d) by the cross-sealing fault.

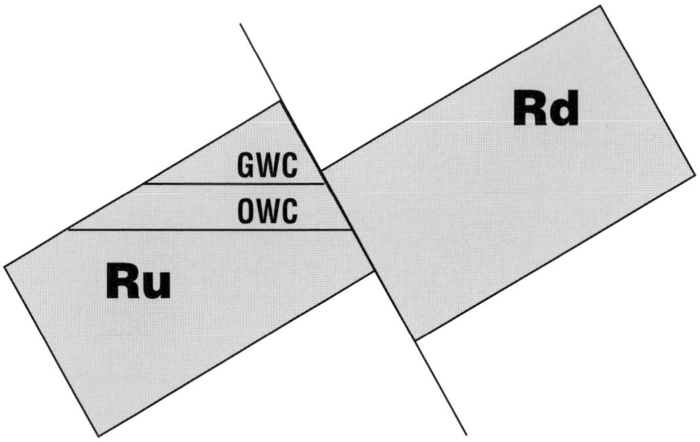

Figure 10–6.

Different hydrocarbon contacts

A fault is also cross sealing if it juxtaposes sands with different hydrocarbon contacts and/or different free water levels, as illustrated in the following figure. Small differences in hydrocarbon contacts do not necessarily imply a cross-sealing fault because the capillary properties of the juxtaposed sands can create different hydrocarbon contacts even across a cross-leaking fault. Different free water levels do imply a cross-sealing fault.

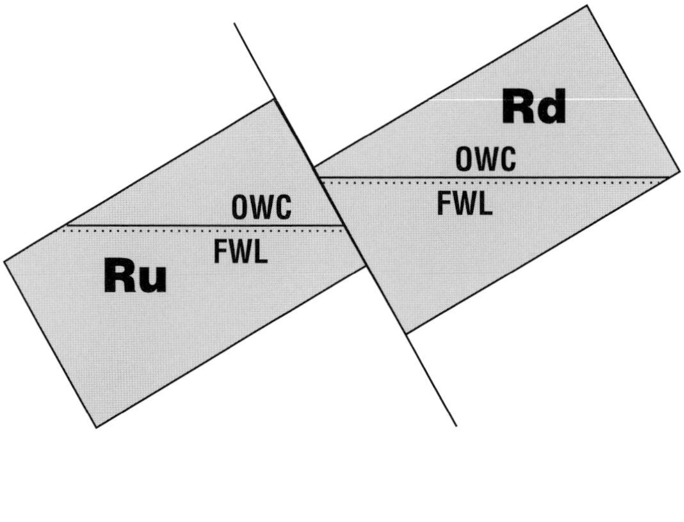

Figure 10–7.

Cross-sealing Faults, continued

Different pressures

Different pressures across a fault imply cross seal. In the figure below, wells 1 and 2 are separated by a cross-sealing fault. Well 2 encountered virgin pressures in contrast to the lower pressures in the main field.

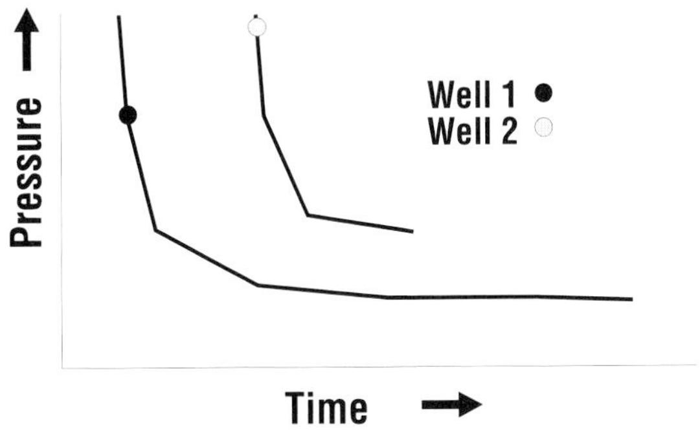

Figure 10–8.

Dip-sealing Faults

Introduction

A dip-sealing fault traps hydrocarbons against the fault plane.

Importance of dip-sealing faults

Dip-sealing faults are important because they can create purely fault-dependent traps. No independent structural closure is required for entrapment. Where independent structural closure does exist, as in the figure below, a dip-sealing fault can trap additional volumes of oil against the fault. Dip-sealing faults can trap hundreds of meters of oil without independent closure. In the following figure, both oil and gas are trapped against the fault and have not leaked up the fault zone.

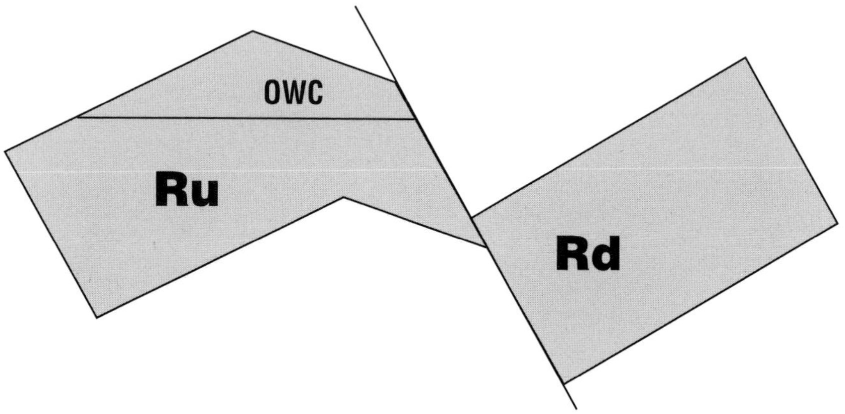

Figure 10–9.

Dip-leaking Faults

Introduction

A fault is dip leaking if hydrocarbons have migrated along the fault plane. Dip-leaking faults can be identified by the presence of a fault plane leak point (FPLP).

Fault plane leak point (FPLP)

An FPLP is a type of fault-dependent leak point in which the hydrocarbon contact coincides with the intersection of the fault plane and the top of the reservoir. As shown in the following figure, an FPLP limits the hydrocarbon to the structurally independent closure. The lack of hydrocarbons in contact with the fault plane implies leakage has occurred vertically along the fault (Smith, 1966; Allard, 1993; Harding and Tuminas, 1988).

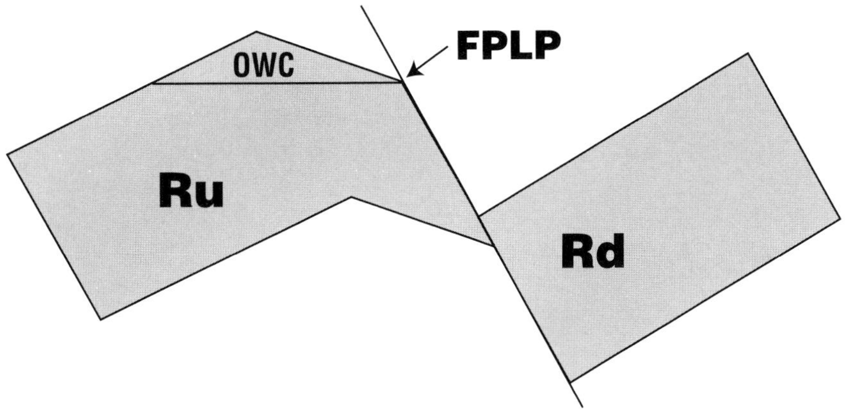

Figure 10–10.

The ability to predict leakage is important in prospect assessment. An FPLP limits the hydrocarbon volume. Where no independent closure exists, prospects may be completely emptied by dip leakage.

Asymmetric dip leakage

A fault may dip seal on one side of a fault and dip leak on the other. This asymmetric dip leakage is caused primarily by variations in the sand–shale ratio of the fault gouge. Other possible controls in some basins include asymmetric fracture density and/or preferential hydraulic fracturing in the hanging wall (Weber et al., 1978; Skerlec, 1990).

Example of asymmetric dip leakage

An example of asymmetric dip leakage is the Chocolate Bayou field, U.S. Gulf Coast, shown in the following figure. All of the hanging wall gas accumulations are limited by FPLPs and dip leak. The three gas accumulations in the footwall, however, are all dip sealing; all have gas columns in contact with the fault plane. This pattern of behavior is common in both the U.S. Gulf Coast and the Niger Delta (Weber et al., 1978).

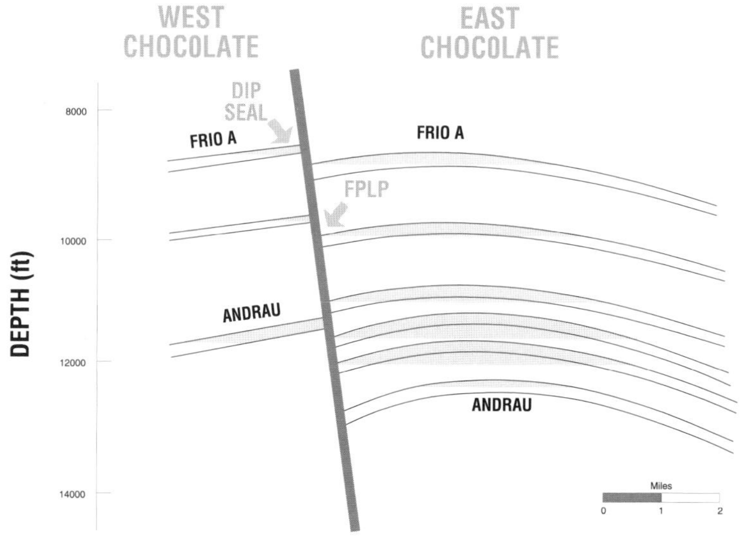

Figure 10–11. After Myers, 1968; courtesy Gulf Coast Assoc. of Geologists.

Low-side traps

Low-side traps may have very different fault seal risk compared with high-side traps. In the following figure, a map shows that dip leakage in the hanging wall limits fill (shaded) to the structurally independent closure. Dip seal in the footwall allows fill in excess of the independent closure. The footwall contains purely fault-dependent traps. The hanging wall relies upon independent closure for entrapment.

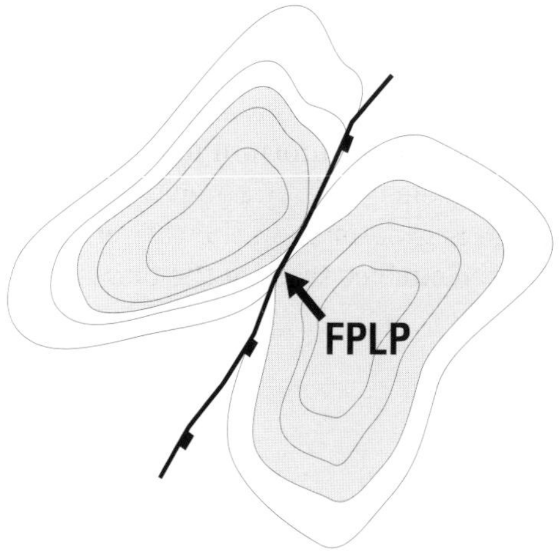

Figure 10–12.

Dip-leaking Faults, continued

Dip leakage of gas vs. oil

A fault may dip seal oil and dip leak gas or vice versa. The following illustration shows a fault that is dip leaking to gas in both the hanging wall and footwall. Both gas accumulations are limited by an FPLP. The oil accumulation in the footwall, however, is filled beyond the structurally independent closure. The fault is dip sealing to oil but dip leaking to gas.

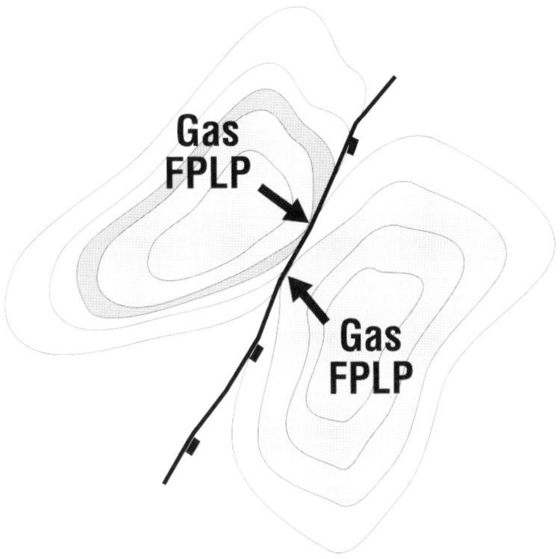

Figure 10–13.

Direction of dip leakage

Although dip leakage is generally understood as the migration *up* the fault zone due to buoyant forces, leakage *down* the fault zone can also occur. Refraction of flow lines can occur when fluids cross a fault zone of differing permeability from the wall rock. Fluid flow across a fault of lower permeability than the adjacent wall rock could dip leak down the fault zone (Hubbert, 1953). Similarly, a fault zone with higher permeability than the wall rock will refract flow lines up the fault zone. Pressure differences along and across faults can also cause down-dip flow in the area of lowest pressure (Knutson and Erga, 1991; Niemann and Krowlow, 1992).

Caveat

Faults in most basins are at equilibrium. Those faults that were going to leak have leaked. The present structure and juxtapositions control fault seal behavior and spill points. However, disequilibrium may exist in basins now undergoing rapid migration and fill. The Los Angeles basin (California) is one example. Faults may be dip leaking, but the rate of charge is greater than the rate of leakage. These faults appear to dip seal—despite seeps along the surface trace of the faults, which indicate dip leakage.

Controls on Percent Fill

Introduction

The percent fill of a trap is the percentage of the trap volume filled with hydrocarbons compared with its total volume. Percent fill can be controlled by a number of factors, including the following:

- Top seal capacity/integrity
- Synclinal spill points
- Charge
- Fault seal capacity
- Fault-dependent leak points

Control summary

The following figure summarizes the various controls on percent fill and hydrocarbon column height. The maximum fill case is the synclinal spill point (SSP). A cross-leaking fault limits the percent fill to the juxtaposed lithology leak point (JLLP). A dip-leaking fault limits the percent fill to the fault plane leak point (FPLP).

A cross-sealing fault allows fill below the JLLP and possibly as deep as the SSP. A trap also may be partially filled (PF) due to either charge or top seal capacity. A partially filled trap can have a hydrocarbon contact at any depth.

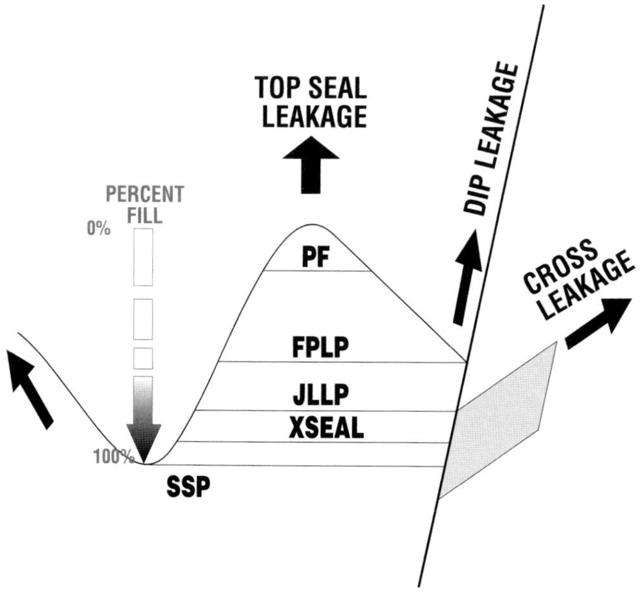

Figure 10–14.

Finite seal capacity of faults

Sealing faults may have some finite seal capacity. A fault may be able to support the pressure exerted by a 50-m hydrocarbon column but leak if the column increases to 51 m (Smith, 1980). Recent work suggests there may be a maximum seal capacity related to the percentage of shale in the fault gouge (Yielding et al., 1997; Skerlec, 1997b). In most cases, however, the percent fill is significantly less and is limited by fault-dependent leak points rather than the seal capacity of the gouge.

Subsection A2
Fault Plane Profile Analysis

Introduction

A fault plane profile is a cross section in the plane of the fault that shows both the hanging wall and footwall cutoffs (Van Wijhe et al., 1980; Allan, 1989; Harding and Tuminas, 1989). Fault plane profiles are a fundamental tool for prospect assessment as well as a first step in understanding seal behavior in existing fields. Fault plane profiles are important because they show what is being juxtaposed across the fault. By doing so, they show areas of sand/sand and sand/shale juxtaposition, establish seal relationships, define potential fault-dependent leak points, and help assess hydrocarbon volumes.

In this subsection

This subsection contains the following topics.

Constructing a Fault Plane Profile

Introduction

A fault plane profile (FPP) is a cross section in the plane of the fault that shows both the hanging wall and footwall cutoffs.

An FPP is distinctive in two ways:

1. It is a cross section in the plane of the fault rather than normal to the fault.
2. Both the hanging wall and footwall stratigraphic cutoffs are shown on the same cross section.

Procedure

We construct an FPP as we do any geologic cross section. Using structure–depth maps, we project the top of each mapped stratigraphic unit at its intersections with the fault plane to its correct depth on the fault plane profile (Allan, 1989).

Because only a fraction of the stratigraphy is mapped routinely, well logs are used to project the remainder of the detailed stratigraphy onto the FPP.

Example: FPP of cross-leaking fault

The following figure is a simple example of a fault plane profile. The sand reservoirs in the hanging wall (dark gray) and footwall (light gray) are shown on the same cross section drawn in the plane of the fault. In this example, all hydrocarbon accumulations (black) are limited by JLLPs (juxtaposed lithology leak points). Hydrocarbons cross-leak from the footwall sands into the hanging wall sands.

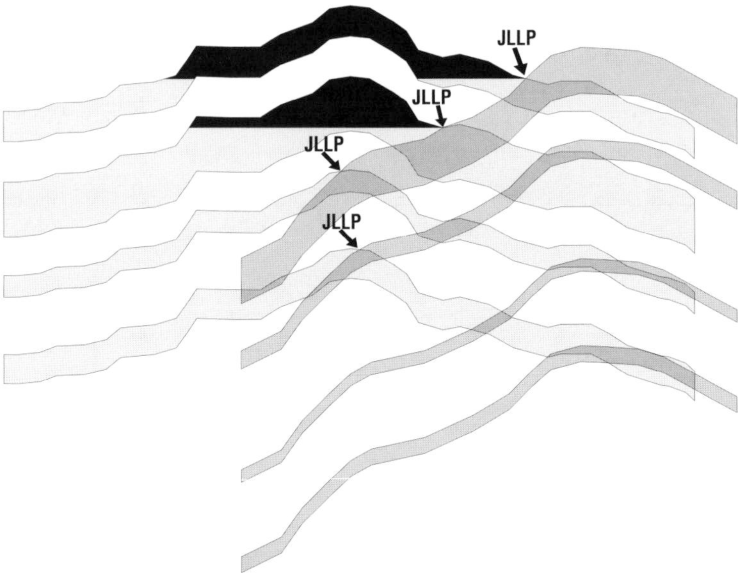

Figure 10–15.

The fault cross-leaks along its entire surface at sand/sand juxtapositions. At each sand/sand juxtaposition, a JLLP spills the hydrocarbons across the fault. There is sufficient charge to fill all closures to a fault-dependent leak point. Potential reservoirs with JLLPs at the crest are dry. The percent fill for other sands is constrained by the JLLPs (Allan, 1989). If bed dips in the hanging wall allow entrapment against the fault, hydrocarbons could be trapped in both the hanging wall and footwall reservoirs. With sufficient charge, common hydrocarbon contacts could exist.

Example: FFP that cross seals, cross leaks

The fault plane profile in the following figure is similar to the profile in Figure 10–15 except that the fault is cross sealing at the fault/reservoir intersection in the lowest footwall sand. Despite a sand/sand juxtaposition at the crest of this reservoir, the fault traps hydrocarbons at a cross sealing segment. Higher sands continue to cross-leak. The percent fill of the lowest sand is limited by either the P_d of the fault zone, the charge volume, or the top seal—not a JLLP.

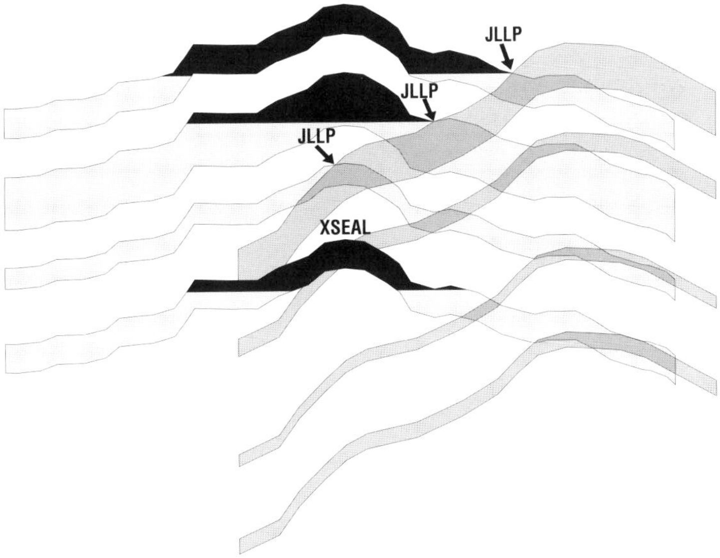

Figure 10–16.

For an example of a fault plane profile of a fault in a Gulf Coast field, refer to Figure 10–26.

Avoiding Pitfalls of Fault Plane Profile Analysis

Pitfalls

There are three pitfalls to avoid in using fault plane profiles:

- Assuming cross leakage
- Incorrectly projecting bed thickness and bed tops
- Erroneous structural interpretations

Assuming cross leakage

We must not assume that a fault always cross-leaks at sand/sand juxtapositions. Cross seal is common. If the fault is cross sealing, it is impossible to identify JLLPs from fault plane profiles. Seal behavior can be predicted using quantitative fault seal analysis (refer to Subsection A3).

Plotting bed thickness incorrectly

If all bed boundaries are taken from mapped surfaces, there are no problems. Because this is almost never the case, problems arise when unmapped bed boundaries, including bed bases, are plotted on fault plane profiles by "isopaching down" from mapped surfaces. Errors arise due to confusion regarding apparent thickness. Errors in bed thickness lead to mistaken identity of what is juxtaposed along the fault as well as mistaken leak points and percent fill.

Construction methods

Fault plane profiles can be constructed in two different ways:

- Constructed in the plane of the fault
- Projected onto a vertical plane parallel to the fault trace

The illustration to the right shows bed cutoffs on the fault plane as well as those projected onto a vertical fault plane profile. The top of the bed is correctly plotted at a depth of 1000 ft along both the fault plane and the vertical profile.

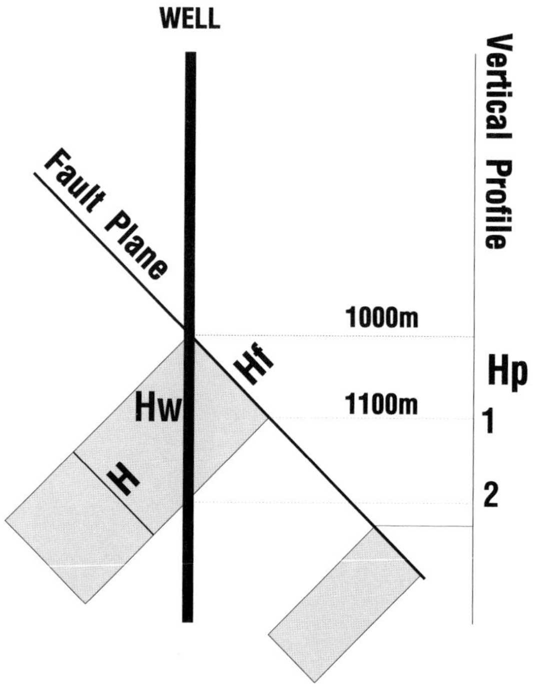

Figure 10–17.

Apparent thickness

Projecting the base of the bed requires determining the correct **apparent thickness.** The true stratigraphic thickness is H. Several apparent thicknesses are involved:

- H_w—apparent thickness measured in a well log
- H_f—apparent thickness along the plane of the fault
- H_p—apparent thickness along the fault plane profile

Well-log thickness

Use of the well-log thickness (H_w) to project the base on either fault plane profile clearly gives an incorrect bed thickness at H_{p2} in Figure 10–17. Note that $H = H_f$ only because the bed is normal to the fault plane in this specific case. The correct apparent thickness to be plotted on the fault plane profile is H_{p1} at 1100 ft.

Determining correct thickness

The correct thickness can be determined from trigonometry (Skerlec, 1990) or from a simple proportion, as illustrated in the following figure. The base of the sand is plotted by using a simple proportion between the thickness in the well (H_w) and the distance to the next mapped horizon in the well (D_w), and between the thickness (H_p) on the FPP and the distance to the next mapped horizon on the FPP (D_p):

$$H_w/D_w = H_p/D_p$$

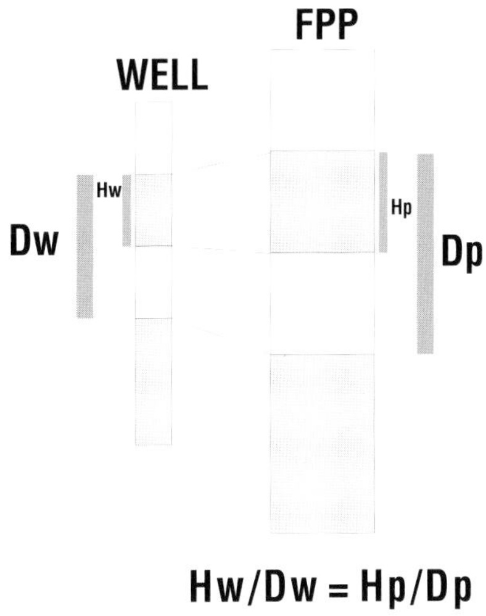

Figure 10–18.

Erroneous structural interpretation

The interpretation of the juxtaposition relationships along the fault plane profile is only as good as the original maps. Older 2-D seismic surveys are inadequate unless there is abundant well control. One of the indirect benefits of routine fault seal analysis is that it focuses the explorationist on the details of fault geometry and fault-bed cutoffs that are critical to trap definition as well as to seal analysis. Modern 3-D seismic surveys are essential for reliable risk of fault seal. It is also true that using expensive 3-D seismic surveys only to make top of reservoir structure maps without fault seal analysis wastes a significant part of the information available for prospect assessment.

Subsection A3
Quantitative Fault Seal Analysis

Introduction

Modern quantitative methods of risking fault seal properties have established an empirical relationship between the observed sealing behavior of faults and the inferred sand–shale content of the fault zone (Bouvier et al., 1989; Allard, 1993; Jev et al., 1993; Skerlec, 1997a,b; Yielding et al., 1997).

Importance of quantitative analysis

Quantitative fault seal analysis lets us predict fault seal behavior. Fault seal behavior is rarely random. Once we understand the pattern of seal behavior in existing fields, we can risk seal behavior in untested prospects.

In this subsection

This subsection contains the following topics.

How Fault Zones Affect Seal

Introduction

Fault zones in siliciclastic sequences consist of various proportions of sand and shale. There is a relationship between seal behavior and the inferred sand–shale ratio of the fault zone. Sand-rich portions of the fault zone leak; shale-rich portions of the fault zone seal. Given the complex structure and composition of fault zones and the many factors that could affect a seal, it has been surprising to find such a simple relationship, basin after basin.

Example: Smear gouge

The following figure is an example of smear gouge along a normal fault found in a sequence of Permian–Carboniferous sand and shales near Lynemouth, U.K. Ductile, light gray shales have been incorporated in the fault zone as a continuous layer sourced from a bed in the footwall (upper left). Similarly, a bed of coal (black) in the footwall and sandstone in the hanging wall have been incorporated as discontinuous fragments in the fault zone. The coal, however, is intensely fractured, reflecting brittle rather than ductile deformation.

Both brittle sands and coals as well as ductile shales are incorporated in the fault zone. The mechanism of gouge formation is much more complex than a simple "smearing" of ductile shales into the fault zone. Although faults exhibit a complete spectrum of behavior from brittle to ductile, interbedded sand–shale sequences with strong ductility contrast commonly exhibit this transitional behavior.

Figure 10–19.

Example: Smear gouge (continued)

Shale-rich gouge zones can create impermeable barriers. The following figure, a normal fault in Jurassic and Triassic sediments near Lilstock, U.K., shows a gouge zone approximately 5 m thick. The gouge consists predominantly of ductile shales and marls as well as small amounts of brittle limestones. Faults with similar shale-rich gouge in producing fields create seals.

Figure 10–20.

How Fault Zones Affect Seal, continued

Example: Spectrum of gouge compositions

Fault gouge can range from sand rich to shale rich. The following figure shows three fault zones exhibiting a spectrum of sand–shale ratios. The table below describes the position of the three faults, their sequences and characteristics, and their location.

Position	Sequence	Characteristics	Location
Left	Sand–siltstone	Gouge with high sand–shale ratio	Tertiary, Isle of Wight, U.K.
Center	Limestone–shale	Gouge with intermediate "sand"–shale ratio	Jurassic, Kilve, U.K.
Right	Limestone–shale	Gouge with low "sand"–shale ratio	Jurassic, Kilve, U.K.

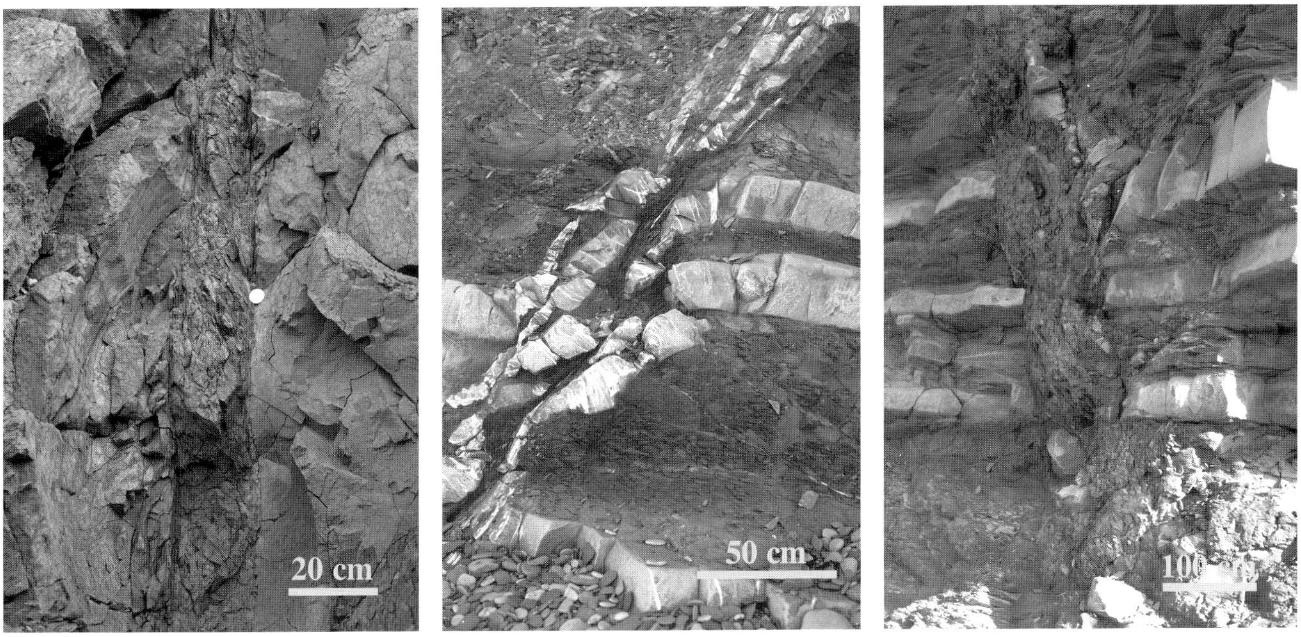

Figure 10–21.

Quantitative Fault Seal Analysis

Introduction

The capacity of a fault to leak or seal hydrocarbons is largely controlled by the smear–gouge ratio (SGR). The SGR is an estimate of the composition of that portion of the fault zone through which leakage or seal must occur. We calculate the SGR by measuring the cumulative shale and sand that has moved past that zone. A fault cross-leaks or dip-leaks if the sand–shale ratio is high in the zone (high SGR). A fault cross-seals or dip-seals if the sand–shale ratio is low in the zone (low SGR).

Several other algorithms for estimating gouge composition exist (Bouvier et al., 1989; Allard, 1993; Jev et al., 1993; Gibson, 1994; Yielding et al., 1997). All have established a relationship between the actual seal behavior and inferred gouge composition.

Procedure

The following table outlines the procedure for quantitative fault seal analysis.

Step	Task
1	Analyze logs to block out sands and shales.
2	Calculate the SGR.
3	Determine the SGR threshold for seal/leak.

Step 1: Analyze logs

The first step in quantitative fault seal analysis is determining the detailed sand–shale content of the stratigraphy. A standardized method of sand–shale discrimination is an absolute necessity. Digital logs and log analysis software simplify the process. Routine methods of sand–shale discrimination are a basic part of analysis and most log analysis software (Doveton, 1986).

Step 2: Calculate the SGR

The following figure is an example of an SGR calculation for a portion of a fault at progressive throws of 50, 100, and 200 ft. Sands are patterned; shales are black. The black trace is an SP log.

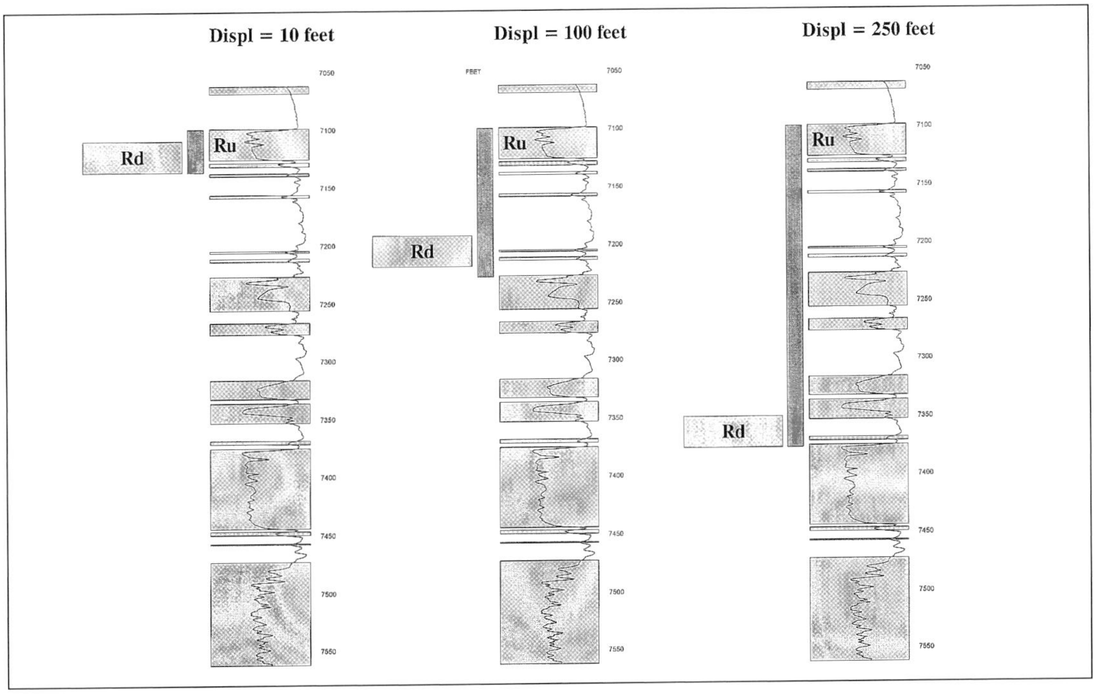

Figure 10–22.

The portion of the fault analyzed is adjacent to the R_d sand in the hanging wall. The SGR is the ratio of the total sand divided by the total shale that has moved past the fault. The stratigraphy that has moved past this portion of the fault is marked in red. As the throw increases, more of the stratigraphy below the R_u and R_d sands moves past the fault and the SGR changes.

A plot of SGR vs. throw, taken from the preceding example, is shown in the following figure. At small throws, very little shale has moved past the fault, the R sand is not completely offset, and the SGR is high. As the throw increases, progressively more shale is moved past the fault and the SGR decreases. At larger throws, a thick sand package begins to move past the fault and the SGR increases.

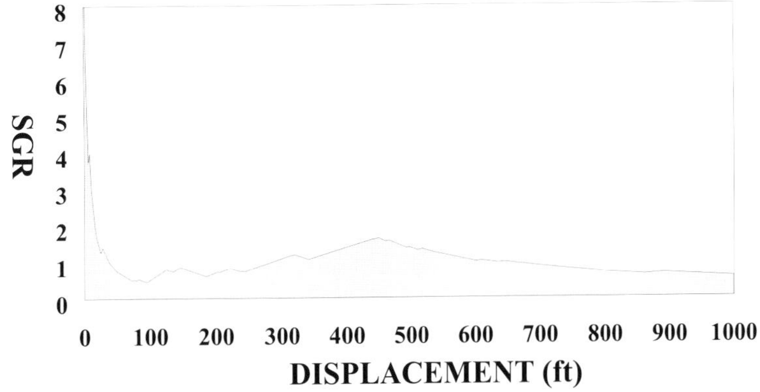

Figure 10–23.

Step 2: Calculate the SGR (continued)

An SGR–throw plot shows the variation in SGR with increasing displacement for only one small area along the fault plane. In practice, SGR is calculated and mapped over the surface of the entire fault plane. The following figure shows the variation in SGR for each point along the fault.

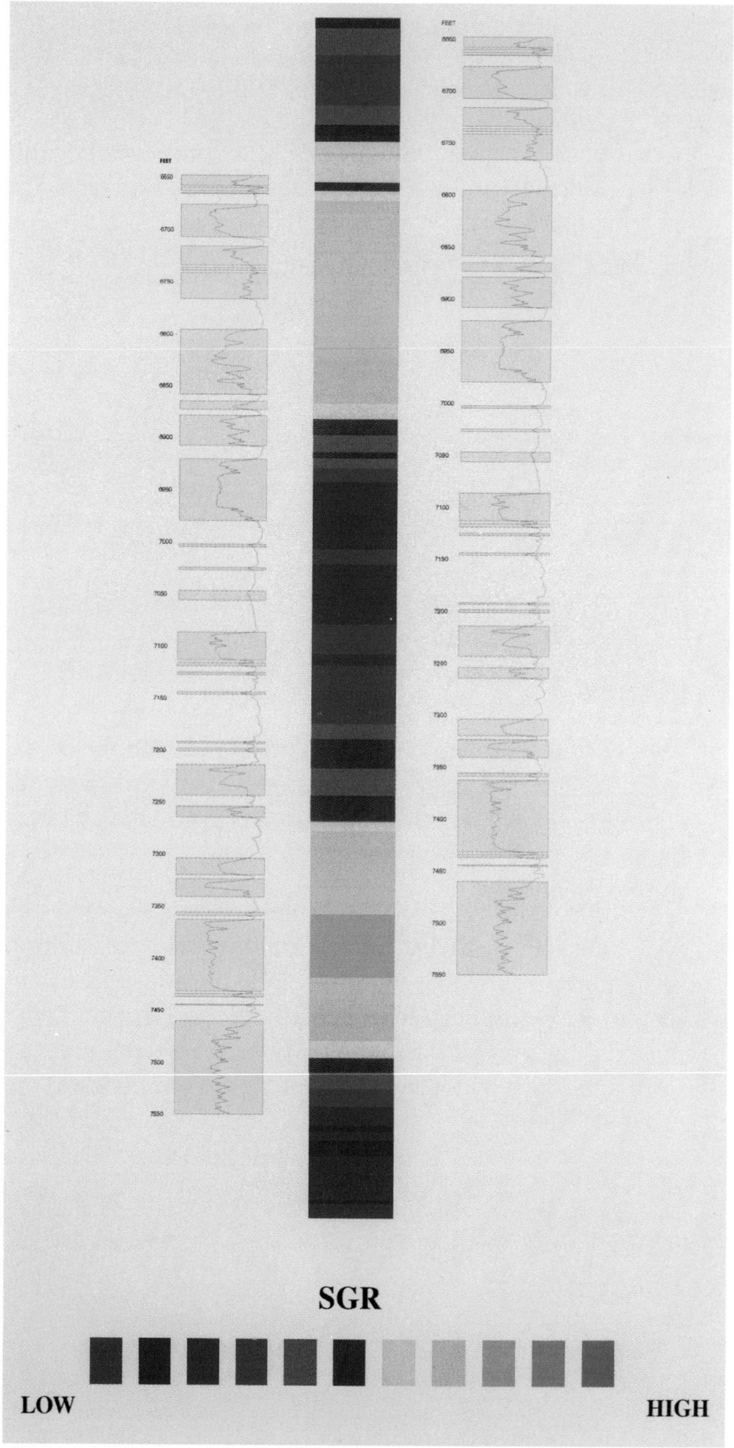

Figure 10–24.

Determine SGR threshold

The SGR threshold for a basin is defined by determining the SGR for known sealing and leaking faults in producing fields. The empirical threshold can then be used to assess prospects and plays and well as develop fields. SGR thresholds vary among basins.

The following example of an SGR threshold plot for the U.S. Gulf Coast directly assigns fault seal risk based upon the variation in SGR and seal behavior observed in a data set of approximately 160 faults. The plot shows the percent of faults cross sealing for oil as a function of changing SGR. The actual SGR values have been deleted intentionally.

Above a specific SGR value, 100% of all faults in the Gulf Coast cross-leak oil. Below a specific SGR value, 100% of the faults cross-seal oil. A narrow transition zone defines the threshold for seal/leak. Separate thresholds exist for cross-seal/-leak, dip-seal/-leak, oil, and gas.

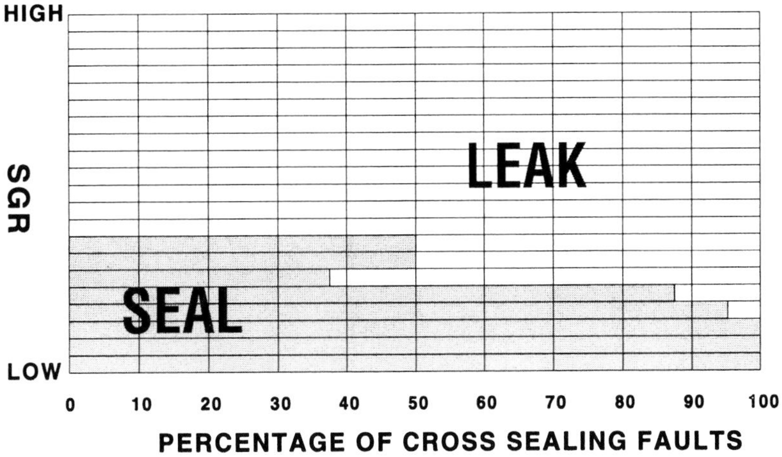

Figure 10–25.

Limitations of Quantitative Fault Seal Analysis

Introduction

Quantitative fault seal analysis is a proven tool in numerous basins. There are, however, limitations.

Limitations

The limitations of quantitative fault seal analysis follow:

- It applies only to faulted sand/shale sequences. It is not applicable to massive carbonate, chert, or sand reservoirs. It has yet to be tested in interbedded shale–carbonate sequences.
- The seal/leak threshold SGR must be empirically calibrated for each basin, using known sealing and leaking faults. An SGR threshold for the Gulf Coast cannot be used for assessing prospects in the Gippsland basin. The confidence with which a seal can be risked is thus much greater in a production setting or mature basin than it is in a frontier setting.
- It does not apply to all structural styles, and specifically it does not necessarily apply to faults in foreland fold and thrust belts or strike-slip basins. All basins in which quantitative fault seal analysis has been proven to date are dominated by detached or basement-involved normal faults.
- Cataclasis, diagenetic effects, localized fracturing, sharp changes in the permeability or displacement pressure of sands, reactivation of earlier normal faults in compression, "shale-outs," and the lack of lateral sand continuity in fluvial sequences can affect seal behavior.
- The ability to predict fault seal behavior is only as good as the ability to predict the stratigraphy and structure. As with most variables in prospect assessment, uncertainties in structure and stratigraphy lead to a minimum, maximum, and most likely fault seal risk.

Example of Routine Fault Seal Analysis: Gulf Coast

Introduction

Routine fault seal analysis integrates both fault plane profiles and quantitative fault seal analysis. This discussion contains an example from a field in the Gulf Coast and demonstrates the application of routine fault seal analysis.

Procedure

The table below outlines a procedure for analyzing fault seal behavior.

Step	Action
1	Construct a fault plane profile (FPP).
2	Determine seal behavior of the fault.
3	Calculate the smear–gouge ratio.
4	Construct a smear–gouge ratio map.
5	Determine the smear–gouge ratio threshold.

Construct an FPP

The following figure is an FPP of a portion of a fault in a Gulf Coast field. It shows the juxtaposition of sands along the fault and the observed distribution of hydrocarbons. Sands are shown in gray (hanging wall) and orange (footwall).

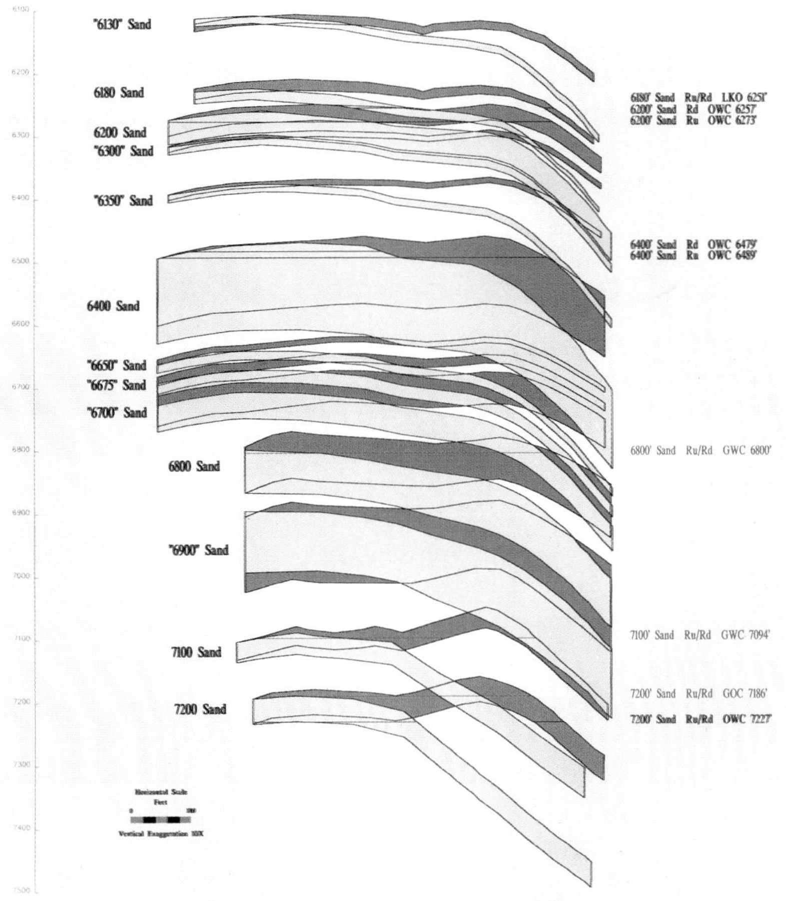

Figure 10–26.

Determine seal behavior

Examples of cross-leaking and cross-sealing portions of the fault are shown in the following figure, which is a detail of Figure 10–26. Juxtapositions of the 7100/7100 sands and the 7200/7200 sands are cross leaking (left). These sand/sand juxtapositions have common hydrocarbon contacts across the fault. The portion of the fault juxtaposing the 7100/7200 sands, however, is cross sealing (right). Hydrocarbons in the 7200 sand in the hanging wall (R_u) are juxtaposed with water-wet sands of the 7100 sand in the footwall (R_d).

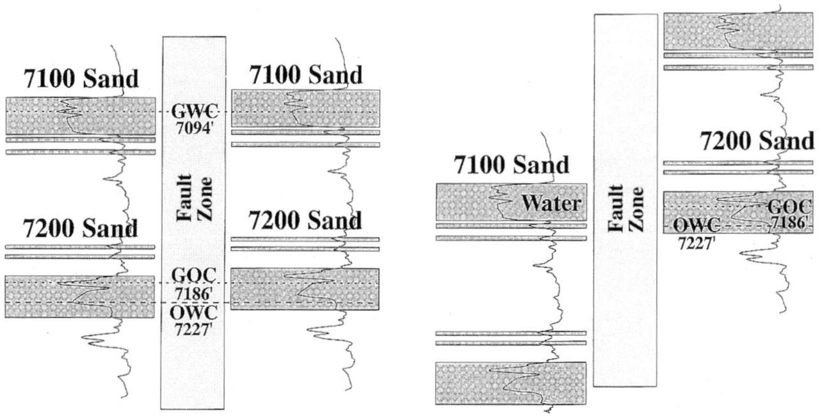

Figure 10–27.

Example of Routine Fault Seal Analysis: Gulf Coast, continued

Calculate SGR and construct SGR map

SGR is calculated over the surface of the entire fault. The following figure is a map of the SGR contoured on the FPP of the fault in Figure 10–26. SGR—and seal potential—vary over the surface of the fault as the throw and stratigraphy change. Areas of high SGR are shown in red and orange. Areas of low SGR are shown in purple and blue.

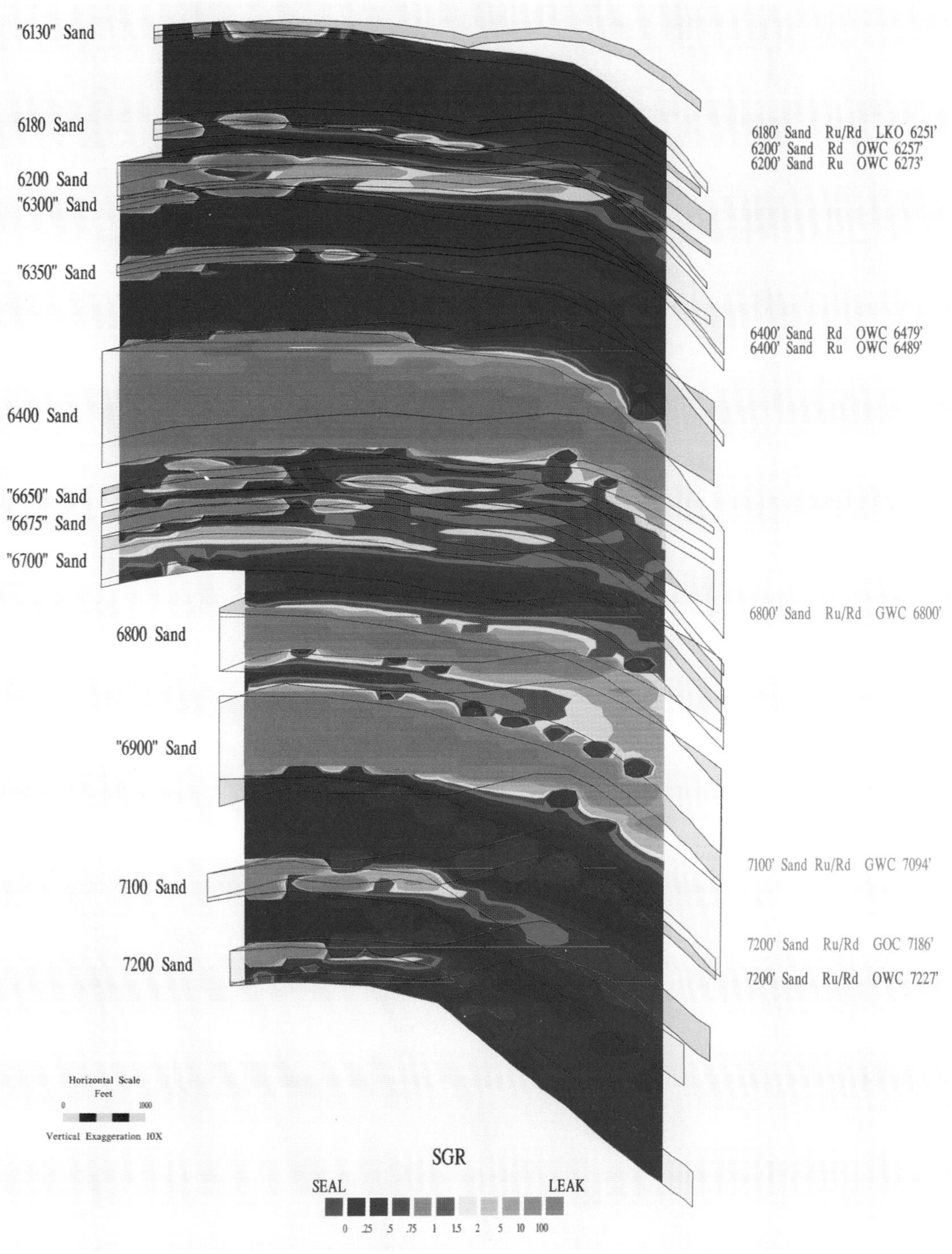

Figure 10–28.

Calculate SGR and construct SGR map (continued)

The SGR is calculated by "rubber-banding" the stratigraphy in adjacent well logs to fit the stratigraphic cutoffs on the FPP. The detailed log stratigraphy is necessary for reliably calculating SGR. The rubber-banding corrects for apparent thicknesses in both the well and fault plane profile.

Example: correlating SGRs, seal behavior

The SGR is calculated for each known sealing and leaking segment of the fault. The SGRs of two cross-leaking and cross-sealing segments of the fault are shown in the following figure (location is on Figure 10–33). SGR values along the cross-leaking sand/sand juxtapositions are high (red). Cross-leakage (right) occurs at both the 7100/7100 and 7200/7200 juxtapositions. Cross-seal (left) occurs where the 7100 sand is juxtaposed with the 7200 sand. This cross-sealing segment is characterized by low SGRs (blue). Cross-leakage occurs where the SGR is high; cross-seal occurs where it is low.

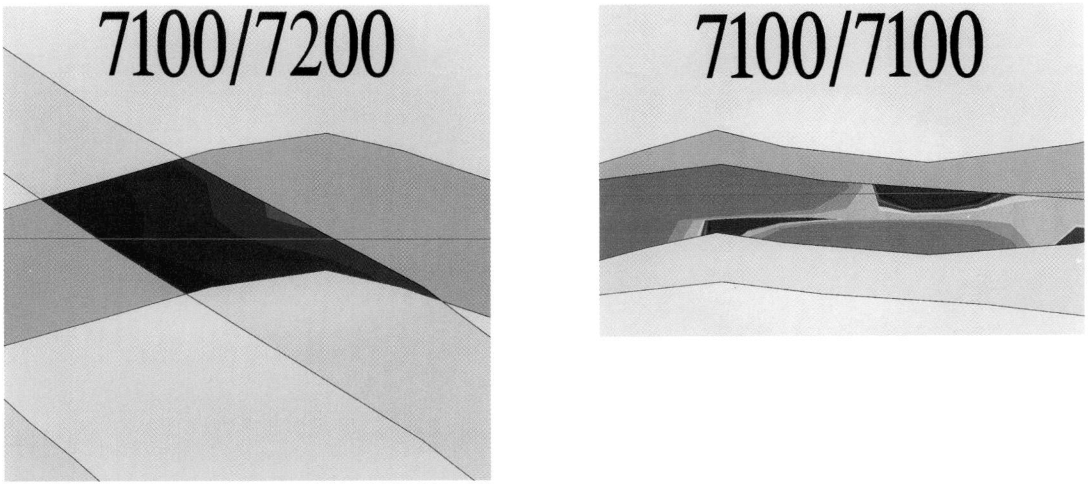

Figure 10-29.

Calibrating SGR threshold

This same iterative process is used to construct SGR threshold plots and to calibrate the critical SGR necessary for seal and leak. The SGR threshold plot of the Gulf Coast noted earlier in this subsection was constructed from a similar analysis of 160 known sealing and leaking fault segments. The constantly expanding database now includes 246 faults in the Gulf Coast. The result is the ability to risk fault seal behavior with a high degree of confidence. Fewer than 10% of the faults analyzed in the Gulf Coast are exceptions to this pattern.

Subsection A4
Fault Seal and Migration Pathways

Introduction

The sealing behavior of faults controls not only the entrapment of hydrocarbons but also the migration pathways into a trap. Fault seals control not only whether a trap retains hydrocarbons but also the volume of hydrocarbons available to migrate into a trap.

Migration pathway maps trace hydrocarbon movement between source and trap within a complexly faulted field and between fields. Migration maps that consist solely of dip arrows drawn on maps of the top reservoir can be very misleading. A migration pathway map must use the detailed information available from routine fault seal analysis.

In this subsection

This subsection contains the following topics.

How Faults Control Trap Fill and Migration Pathways

Introduction

A sealing fault can trap hydrocarbons but also will act as a barrier for hydrocarbon migration into traps beyond that fault. In addition, faults can act as baffles by deflecting hydrocarbons along migration pathways that may not be perpendicular to structural contours.

Controlling trap fill

Dry traps, or traps with limited fill, may exist because hydrocarbons have been trapped downdip along sealing faults. A fault can act as a barrier to (1) all hydrocarbons or (2) some of the hydrocarbons, allowing a limited volume to migrate. It can also act as a barrier along part of the fault plane and as a conduit along other parts of the fault plane.

Controlling migration

Where complex fault systems exist between a trap and a source kitchen or between two traps, migration pathways are correspondingly complex. Traps in this setting can have widely different migration/fill or charge risks, depending upon fault seal behavior.

Migration parallel to faults

Where the dip of carrier beds is not perpendicular to faults, even cross-leaking faults can act as barriers as long as the permeability of the carrier bed is higher than that of the fault. Hydrocarbons can then migrate parallel to a fault rather than across the fault, even though the fault cross-leaks. This baffle effect can direct hydrocarbons away from potential traps as well as toward others. Migration pathway maps are critical to prospect assessment.

Example: Hudson field

The Hudson field, North Sea, is an excellent example of how faults control migration pathways and charge (Hardman and Booth, 1991). The map and cross section in the following figure show that the first well, 210/24a-1, was located on the crest of an obvious structural high. This well encountered water-wet Brent Group sands. A second well on the flank, 210/24a-2, encountered oil shows suggestive of a local stratigraphic trap. Thirteen years after the initial well, the 210/24a-3 well discovered the Hudson field: a fault-dependent trap.

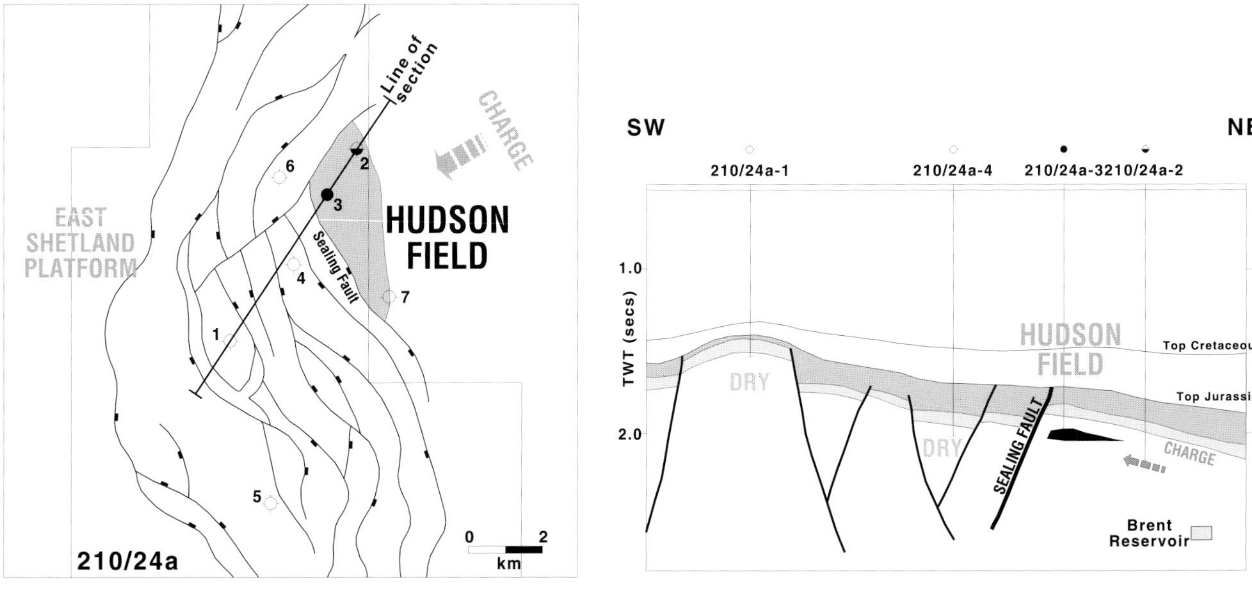

Figure 10–30. After Hardman and Booth, 1991; courtesy Geological Society of London.

How Faults Control Trap Fill and Migration Pathways, continued

Example: Hudson field (continued)

The sealing fault trapped hydrocarbons in a flank fault compartment and prevented hydrocarbons from migrating into the more obvious structural high to the west. Predrill fault seal analysis and a migration pathway map would have correctly identified the sealing fault and would have placed a much greater risk on the success of the first well. In this case, new seismic data identified the sealing fault; however, numerous examples exist where the same error is made with high-quality seismic data. Hydrocarbons do not simply migrate into the crest of structural highs.

Example: Don field

In the Don field, North Sea, sealing faults prevent hydrocarbons from migrating into fault compartments on the crest of a large structural high (Hardman and Booth, 1991). Instead, hydrocarbons are trapped in several fault compartments on the flank of the structure against cross-sealing faults that have sand/sand juxtapositions. Wells in three fault compartments (211/18-5, 10, and 16) in the crest of the structure are dry. Hydrocarbons have either been trapped downflank or have been deflected to the southwest by sealing faults.

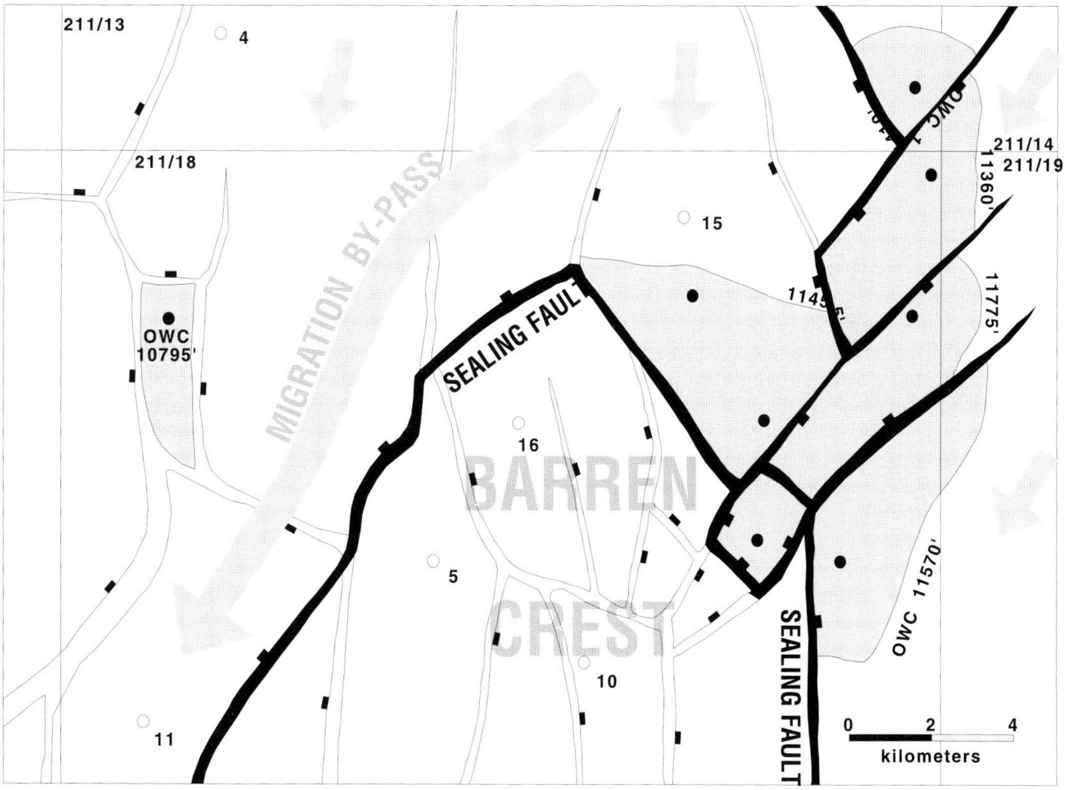

Figure 10–31. After Hardman and Booth, 1991; courtesy Geological Society of London.

How to Construct Migration Pathway Maps

Introduction

A migration pathway map is a fundamental tool for prospect assessment and field development. In simple migration pathway maps, arrows are drawn perpendicular to structural contours. However, migration pathway maps must also define those faults and those parts of faults that juxtapose sand/sand as well as those faults that cross-seal/cross-leak and dip-seal/dip-leak.

Requirements for map construction

The following table lists the requirements for constructing a migration pathway map.

Requirement	Explanation
Structure–depth maps	Defines buoyant vectors for hydrocarbon migration
Fault plane profile	Defines sand/sand and sand/shale juxtaposition and potential juxtaposed lithology leak points (JLLPs)
Quantitative fault plane analysis	Defines real JLLPs, areas of cross-seal or cross-leak, and areas of dip seal or dip leak

Example: Fault controlling migration

The figure on the right illustrates how completely a fault can control migration pathways across a fault. In this fault plane profile of a fault in a Gulf Coast field, SGR was calculated and contoured only on areas of sand/sand juxtaposition. Areas of sand/shale juxtaposition are uncolored. No hydrocarbon migration will occur across these uncolored regions or across the sand/shale juxtapositions with low SGRs (blue-purple). These high SGR areas are essentially holes for fluid migration in the fault plane. It will only occur across the areas of sand/sand juxtaposition with high SGRs (red-orange).

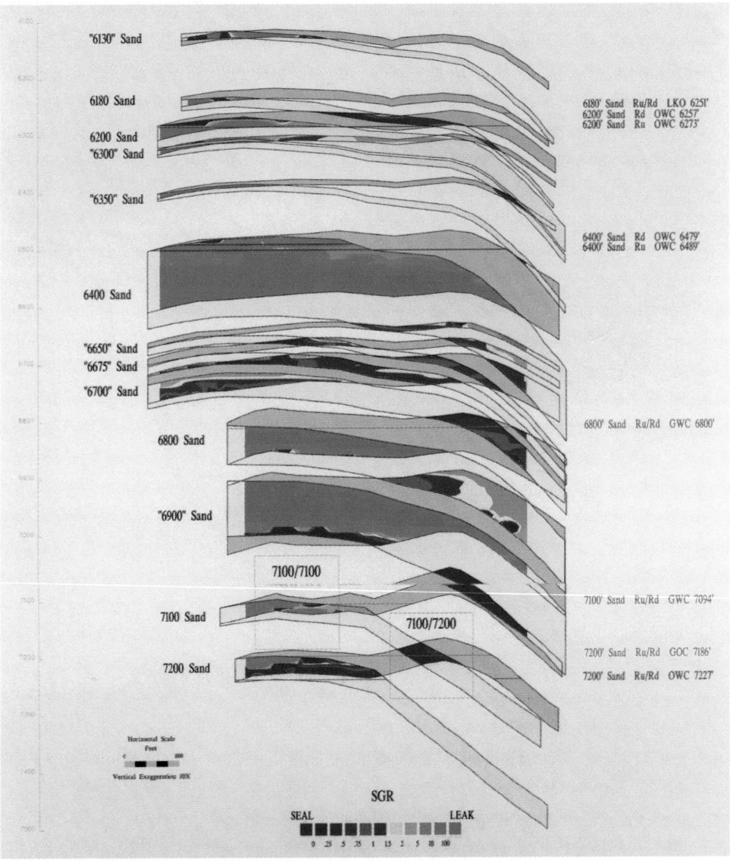

Figure 10–32.

Effect of Seal on Hydrocarbon Yield Estimates

Calibration factor

Hydrocarbon yield models estimate the volume of hydrocarbons that can be generated from a given volume of source rock and thermal history. These calculations are commonly calibrated by comparing the volume of hydrocarbons that should have been generated in a drainage area with the volume actually trapped. This "calibration factor" then is used routinely in yield estimates.

Potential errors

The logical error in many of these yield calibration studies is assuming that the hydrocarbon volume trapped is the total volume that migrated into the trap. If the trap contains a fault-dependent leak point, however, the volume that migrated in may have been much greater than the volume now trapped. The additional hydrocarbons spilled across a fault-dependent leak point and migrated updip. If these fault-dependent leak points are not identified and we assume the trap contains all the hydrocarbons generated in the source kitchen, then calibration factors and yield estimates can be extremely misleading. In addition, hydrocarbons may spill from adjacent traps rather than being directly derived from source kitchens.

Subsection A5

How Faults Affect Field Development

Introduction

Routine fault seal analysis is an important part of field development and field unitization, yet it is routinely ignored at considerable cost (Knutson and Erga, 1991; Jev et al., 1993). Faults control the following:

- Vertical and lateral distribution of hydrocarbons within fault compartments
- Communication between fault compartments
- Movement of hydrocarbons during production

In this subsection

This subsection contains the following topics:

Hydrocarbon Distribution

Introduction

Faults control both the vertical and lateral distribution of hydrocarbons within fields. Some compartments and sands are dry; others contain subeconomic accumulations. Risking percent fill using fault seal analysis helps avoid needless wells.

Distribution example

The following figure is an example of faults controlling the distribution of hydrocarbons within a Gulf Coast field. The field contains 33 separate reservoir sands. At each mapped reservoir level, the field is divided into three major compartments (A, B, D) by faults. Compartment D is almost always empty, while the other compartments commonly contain hydrocarbons. In only 5 of the 33 reservoirs does Compartment D contain hydrocarbons.

Compartment D is commonly empty because a series of JLLPs along the western portion of Fault A allows hydrocarbons to leak into Compartment B and then across the eastern portion of Fault A into the next highest reservoir. Only when Fault A is cross sealing does Compartment D contain hydrocarbons. Cross seal is created by shale-prone gouge with low SGRs or sand/shale juxtaposition.

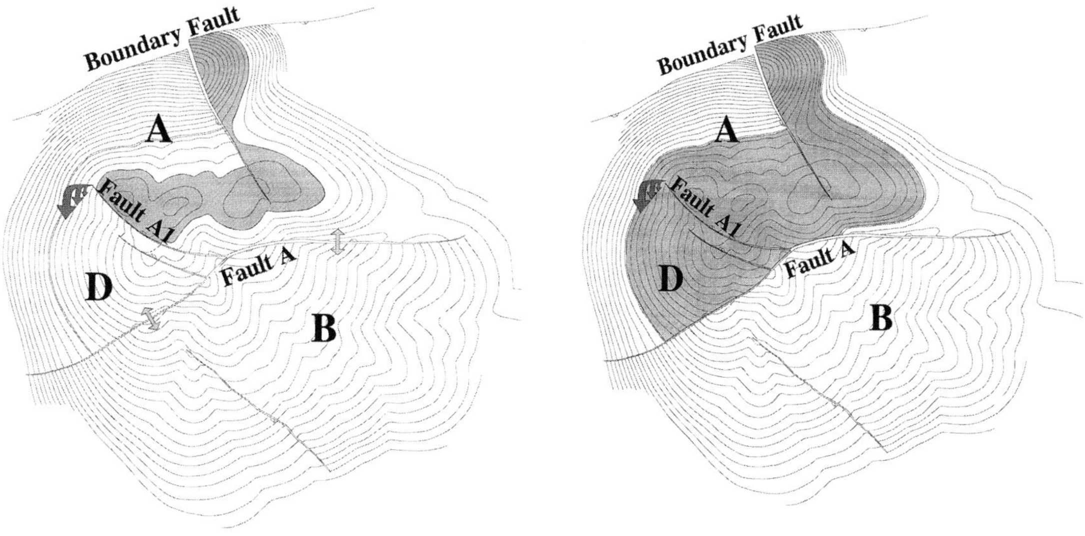

Figure 10–33.

Assessing percent fill

Despite numerous examples of this type, we often erroneously assign an equal chance of some specific percent fill when assessing a prospect's reservoirs and fault compartments. We must understand the following:

- All reservoirs in a series of stacked sands do not have the same chance of being filled with hydrocarbons.
- Each fault compartment of a single reservoir does not have the same chance of being filled with hydrocarbons.
- We can predict (predrill) which sands and fault compartments contain hydrocarbons and which are dry.

Communication of fluids across faults

Understanding communication of fluids across faults lets us develop fields more efficiently. Routine fault seal analysis during production avoids needless wells and helps us position necessary infill wells for producing residual accumulations. Cross-sealing faults compartmentalize a reservoir. Isolated compartments created by cross-sealing faults require individual production wells. In contrast, cross-leaking faults allow some fault-bounded compartments to be produced from adjacent compartments and additional wells may be unnecessary.

Reservoir Simulations and Field Unitization

Introduction

Fault plane profiles and quantitative fault seal analysis are required for realistic reservoir simulations. Neither the seal behavior, transmissibility, permeability, nor areas of sand/sand juxtaposition are constant over the entire fault surface.

Movement of hydrocarbons

Faults can "pond" hydrocarbons and affect sweep and waterflood efficiency. Routine fault seal analysis may be required for producing residual oil accumulations missed by assuming a laterally continuous reservoir.

Fault control of pressure gradients

Faults control changing pressure gradients within a field. Hydrocarbons move in response to these pressure gradients and not necessarily in response to structural dip. Gas in the Beryl field, for example, migrated downdip during production in response to changing pressure gradients, pressure compartments, and migration pathways controlled by sealing and leaking faults (Knutson and Erga, 1991; Skerlec, 1997b).

Fault seal behavior alteration

Faults can also leak over geologic time spans but seal during production time spans. Even a low fault-zone permeability may allow hydrocarbons to leak given a time span of 10^6 m.y. High production rates, however, creating pressure changes over a span of 1–10 years, will cause low-permeability fault zones to act as barriers to hydrocarbon movement. A cross-leaking fault may develop different hydrocarbon contacts and different pressures during production. SGR thresholds for seal behavior may have to be calibrated separately for exploration and for reservoir simulations.

Fault seal and field unitization

Fault seal is important in field unitization. Ignoring fault seal and depending solely on reservoir parameters and estimated hydrocarbon contacts can lead to extremely unequal division of reserves. The sealing behavior of faults controls both the original distribution of hydrocarbons in a field as well as the volumes of hydrocarbons produced from individual fault compartments.

Fault Seal Breakdown During Production

Introduction

Changes in pressure differentials across faults can change seal behavior. A cross-sealing fault is cross sealing to a finite column of hydrocarbons. As the buoyant pressure increases at the crest of the hydrocarbon column, the buoyant pressure will ultimately exceed the displacement pressure of the fault zone and the fault will cross-leak (Smith, 1966; Buck and Robertson, 1996).

Pressure differentials and leakage

Pressure depletion during production can create large pressure differentials across a fault and consequent leakage. This process occurs when the pressure depletion is sufficiently rapid, or the fault has sufficiently low permeability, to cause a large pressure differential across the fault. The change from sealing to leaking is not caused by any mechanical rupturing but simply by the relative change in buoyant pressure vs. displacement pressure.

Example

The following figure shows the pressure depletion curves for two wells separated by an initially cross-sealing fault. The pressure depletion curve for well A is shown in light gray (top); that for well B, in black (bottom). The buoyant pressure at the crest of the oil column against the fault seal in well A remains constant as the pressure in well B decreases. The pressure differential (ΔP) increases until the displacement pressure of the fault zone is exceeded and the fault begins to cross-leak. A fault in the Beryl field has broken down during production (Buck and Robertson, 1996). A fault in the Akaso field, Nigeria, may have undergone this type of breakdown with a differential pressure of 4137 kPa (600 psi) (Jev et al., 1993).

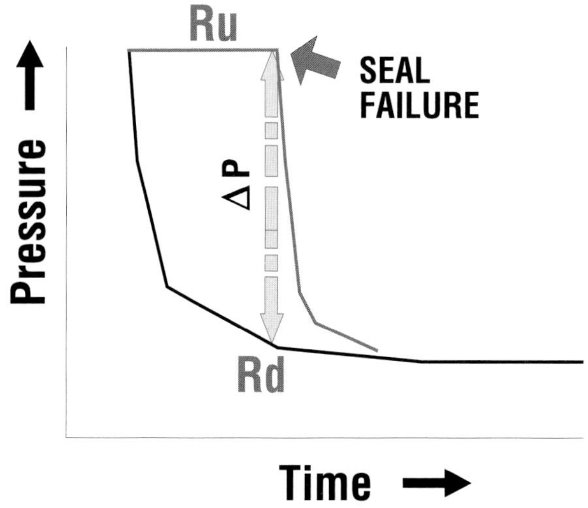

Figure 10–34.

Section B
Evaluating Top Seal Integrity

Introduction

Fracturing can destroy top seal integrity. This section discusses two practical techniques for evaluating loss of top seal integrity resulting from strain or hydraulic fracturing. Sufficiently intense deformation in excess of top seal ductility can fracture a top seal. In addition, sufficiently high pore pressures in excess of the fracture pressure can induce natural hydraulic fracturing.

In this section

This section contains the following subsections.

Subsection B1
Strain Analysis of Top Seals

Introduction

Loss of top seal integrity by high strain and fracturing is an important cause of dry holes and partially filled traps (Skerlec, 1982, 1992). Although fracturing is commonly predicted from stress, the advantage of strain analysis is that it provides a practical, predrill tool for evaluating prospects using seismic data.

Rates of leakage

Even a small amount of fracturing can result in staggering leakage rates. The volume of hydrocarbon that could be lost from a typical North Sea field, assuming a fractured top seal with a relatively low fracture permeability of only 0.05 md, is more than 100 billion bbl/m.y. (Skerlec, 1990). Fracture permeability can be as high as tens of darcys (Stearns and Friedman, 1972) and leakage rates consequently can be much higher.

Natural seeps confirm these high rates of hydrocarbon loss. The Palos Verde fault in Santa Monica Bay, California, seeps oil at the rate of 10–15 bbl/d or more than 5 billion bbl/m.y. The Coal Point seep in the Santa Barbara Channel, California, is leaking 50–70 bbl/d or more than 25 billion bbl/m.y. (Wilkinson, 1971).

In this subsection

This subsection discusses techniques for evaluating the loss of seal integrity resulting from deformation and contains the following topics.

Seal Ductility

Introduction

The most important mechanical property for evaluating seal integrity is ductility. Ductile rocks make good top seals; brittle rocks make poor top seals. Shales and salt are two of the most ductile rock types and, not surprisingly, two of the most common top seals (Grunau, 1987).

What is ductility?

Ductility is the amount of strain a seal can withstand before brittle failure and the loss of top seal integrity. Rocks with an extremely high ductility can deform without brittle failure. On the other hand, rocks with low ductility can accommodate only a small amount of strain before fracturing. A seal can be brittle but unfractured; a seal can be ductile but fractured. Fracture depends upon whether the strain exceeds the seal ductility.

Variables that control ductility

Seal ductility is controlled by at least nine different variables. The table below lists these variables and briefly notes how they control ductility.

Variable	Control on Ductility
Lithology	Grain mineralogy and cement type control ductility. Brittle seals include dolostone, quartzite, anhydrite, and some shales. Ductile seals include halite, some shales, and some limestones.
Composition	Not all limestones or shales have the same ductility. Compositional variations such as total organic carbon (Chong et al., 1980) and clay mineralogy (Corbett et al., 1987) change ductility.
Confining pressure	Increasing confining pressure increases ductility.
Pore pressure	Increasing pore pressure decreases ductility.
Fluid composition	The presence or absence of fluids and their composition affects ductility.
Temperature	Increasing temperature increases ductility.
Strain rate	High strain rates decrease ductility.
Time	Ductility changes with time as seals undergo burial and diagenesis.
Compaction state	Ductility decreases with progressive compaction and diagenesis.

Estimating Ductility of Top Seals

Introduction

The ductility of a top seal can be estimated (1) by using laboratory data and log-derived density values that reflect the compaction state or (2) by comparing the strains in tested traps associated with successes and failures.

Shale ductility and density

The ductility of a shale top seal is a function of compaction state. Uncompacted, low-density shales are extremely ductile and can thus accommodate large amounts of strain without undergoing brittle failure and loss of top seal integrity. Highly compacted, dense shales are extremely brittle and undergo brittle failure and loss of top seal integrity with very small amounts of strain.

The following figure shows the relationship between ductility and density for 68 shales. The ductility of the shales was measured in the laboratory at confining pressures of 1, 200, and 500 kg/cm^2. All samples were deformed in compression.

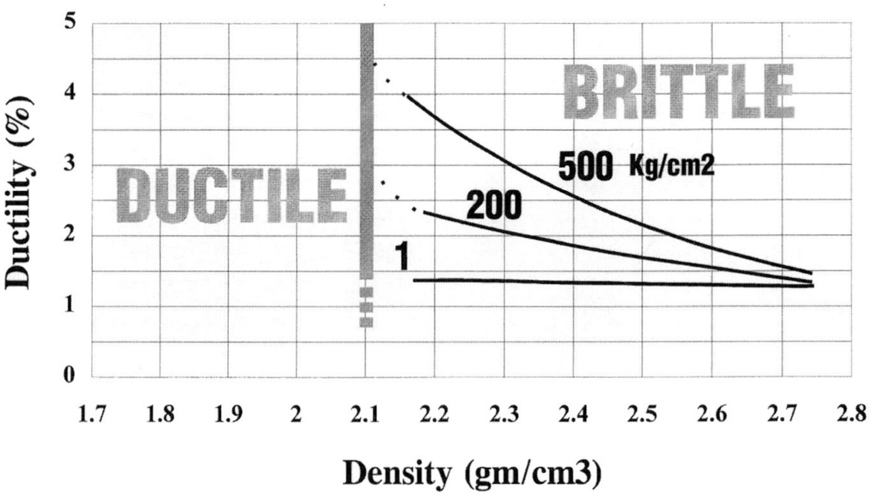

Figure 10–35. Data from Hoshino et al., 1972.

Figure 10–35 illustrates the following:

- Shales with a density less than approximately 2.1 g/cm^3 deform ductilely and not by brittle failure at the range of confining pressures found in most sedimentary basins.
- Shales with a density greater than 2.1 g/cm^3 will undergo brittle failure given sufficient strain.
- The ductility can be inferred from the density. Denser shales are more brittle and can withstand less strain before fracturing. Less-dense shales are more ductile and can withstand larger strains before fracturing.
- Ductility increases with increasing confining pressure.

Estimating Ductility of Top Seals, continued

Use in other lithologies

This technique has been used on other seal lithologies besides shales, including siltstones, marls, and chalks (Skerlec, 1990). There is no relationship between the density and the ductility of sandstones where high permeability and diagenetic effects alter the more simple relationship observed in less permeable rocks.

Shale ductility vs. depth

The ductility of a shale top seal *decreases* with progressive burial, compaction, and diagenesis within a sedimentary basin. The mechanical properties are not constant but change with progressive burial as the top seal is converted from a mud to a rock.

The ductility of a shale top seal also *increases* in response to increasing confining pressure. Thus, a shale with constant mechanical properties will have a lower ductility at shallow depths than at greater depth. Since a shale top seal does not have constant mechanical properties with progressive burial, compaction decreases ductility at the same time as confining pressure increases ductility.

Shale density–ductility vs. depth

The following figure shows the change in density and ductility of shales with increasing depth. Laboratory data are plotted on a normal shale compaction curve showing density vs. depth. The figure shows the ductility of each shale at that depth or confining pressure, with ductile samples shown by gray circles and brittle samples shown by black circles. Ductile shales did not fracture; brittle shales fractured. A low-density shale at a depth of 500 m is more ductile than a highly compacted shale at a depth of 5000 m in the center of the basin. Identical traps, one in the graben deep and one on an adjacent marginal platform, have different seal risk.

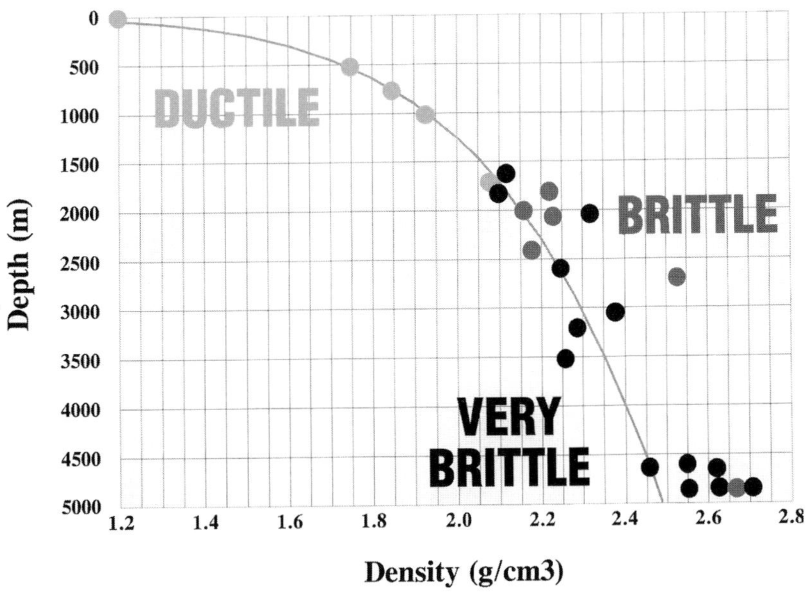

Figure 10–36. Data from Hoshino et al., 1972.

Ductility vs. time Ductility changes not only with depth of burial but also with time and progressive subsidence. A shale top seal now buried at 4000 m and having a density of 2.6 g/cm^3 was once buried at a more shallow depth and had a lower density. This now-brittle seal was once ductile.

Predicting paleoductility To predict paleoductility, we must know both the density and the confining pressure at the time of deformation. A database of top seal mechanical properties over a range of pertinent confining pressures is a basic tool for seal analysis.

Ductility–time plots Ductility–time plots can be constructed from shale compaction curves and burial history curves. Burial history curves give the depth of burial of a top seal at a specific time. Shale compaction curves let us infer the shale density at a specific depth of burial and time.

The following figure is a ductility–time plot for an Upper Jurassic top seal in the Central Graben, North Sea. The plot shows the paleodensity and inferred paleoductility during progressive burial of shales at the 141- and 151-m.y. sequence boundaries. Prior to approximately 100 m.y., the Late Jurassic shale top seal had a density of < 2.1 g/cm^3 and was ductile. Strain prior to 100 m.y. would not contribute to seal risk. Any deformation occurring after 100 m.y. could have caused fracturing, given sufficiently high strains.

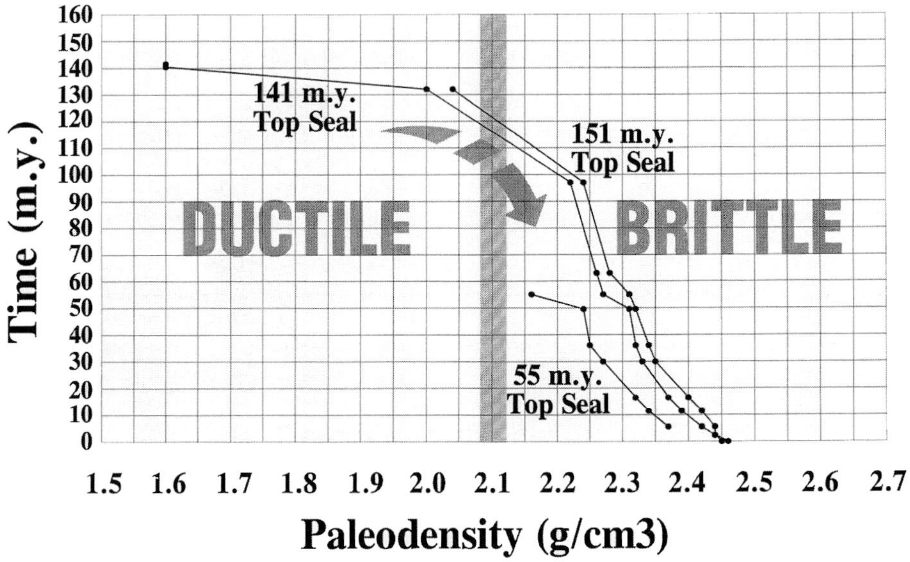

Figure 10–37.

Estimating Strain in Top Seals

Introduction

Once the ductility or paleoductility of a seal is known, the amount of strain that has affected the seal must be determined. One of the most useful techniques is **incremental strain analysis.** Originally applied to fractured reservoirs (Watts, 1983), the technique is equally applicable to top seal analysis (Skerlec, 1982, 1992; Koch et al., 1992).

Incremental strain analysis

Incremental strain analysis measures the change in line length of sequence boundaries on depth-converted seismic lines to calculate strain magnitude as well as the strain occurring at different time intervals. The advantages of this technique are that it can be applied to prospects before drilling and it yields a quantitative estimate of strain that can be compared directly with strain measurements of top seals in the laboratory. Incremental strain analysis yields not only a quantitative strain value but also shows how strain has varied with time.

Calculating incremental strain

The following figure is a simple cross section of a low-relief salt structure showing three seismic sequences. The figure shows how strain is calculated: by comparing the original undeformed line length with the deformed line length between two arbitrary points, A and B. In this figure, l_0 is the initial, undeformed line length; l_1 is the deformed line length of the 60-m.y. sequence boundary; and l_2 is the deformed line length of the 131-m.y. sequence boundary. The strain (ε) on the 131-m.y. sequence boundary is $\varepsilon = (l_2 - l_0)/l_0 = 2.5\%$. The strain on the 60-m.y. sequence boundary is $\varepsilon = (l_1 - l_0)/l_0 = 0.5\%$. All strains are extensional.

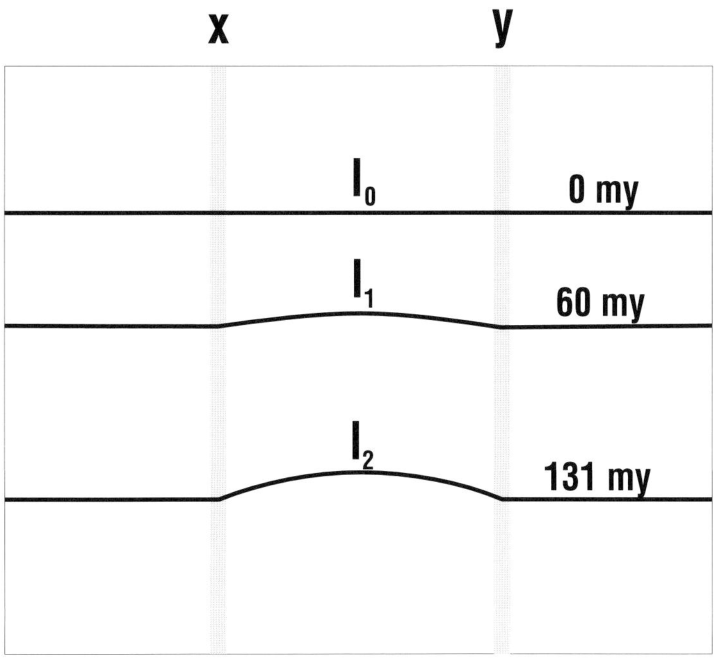

Figure 10–38.

Estimating Strain in Top Seals, continued

Calculating incremental strain (continued)

This method provides both an estimate of quantitative strain and the timing of strain. The incremental strain is the strain occurring during the time interval between two sequence boundaries. In the preceding figure, 0.5% strain occurred between 60 Ma and the present, while 2.5% strain occurred between 131 Ma and the present. Consequently, 2.0% strain occurred between 60 and 131 Ma. Strain–time plots display the strain affecting the top seal from the onset of deformation to the present.

Correction for compaction

Analysis requires decompaction of the sediments to correct for the apparent strain caused by compaction. In the Central Graben, the effect is generally minimal.

Empirical threshold for top seal failure

How much strain can a top seal withstand? In a mature basin, risk assessment of the strain threshold at which failure occurs is determined empirically by analyzing successes and failures. The empirical threshold varies from basin to basin. In a frontier setting, estimates of the strain required for failure must be based on (1) laboratory data on seal properties and (2) estimates of the confining pressure and seal ductility at the time of trap formation.

Limitations of incremental strain analysis

Incremental strain analysis provides only an estimate of strain. More detailed calculations of stain may be warranted. Incremental strain analysis is an average of strain over the entire structure. Local areas of high strain can have important control on spill points. Recent analyses have taken shorter line-length increments over the structure to calculate small-scale variations in strain (Koch et al., 1992). In addition, the method assumes fixed end points, whereas a limited amount of flexural slip occurs.

Example: Evaluating Top Seal Integrity

Introduction

Following is an example of evaluating, or risking, top seal integrity using two traps in the Central Graben, North Sea. One trap was dry; one trap is now a producing field. Both are low-relief salt structures, a common trap style in the Central Graben, with Upper Jurassic reservoirs sealed by Upper Jurassic–Lower Cretaceous shales. A seismic line across both traps is shown in the following figure. Trap A is at the left; trap B is at the center.

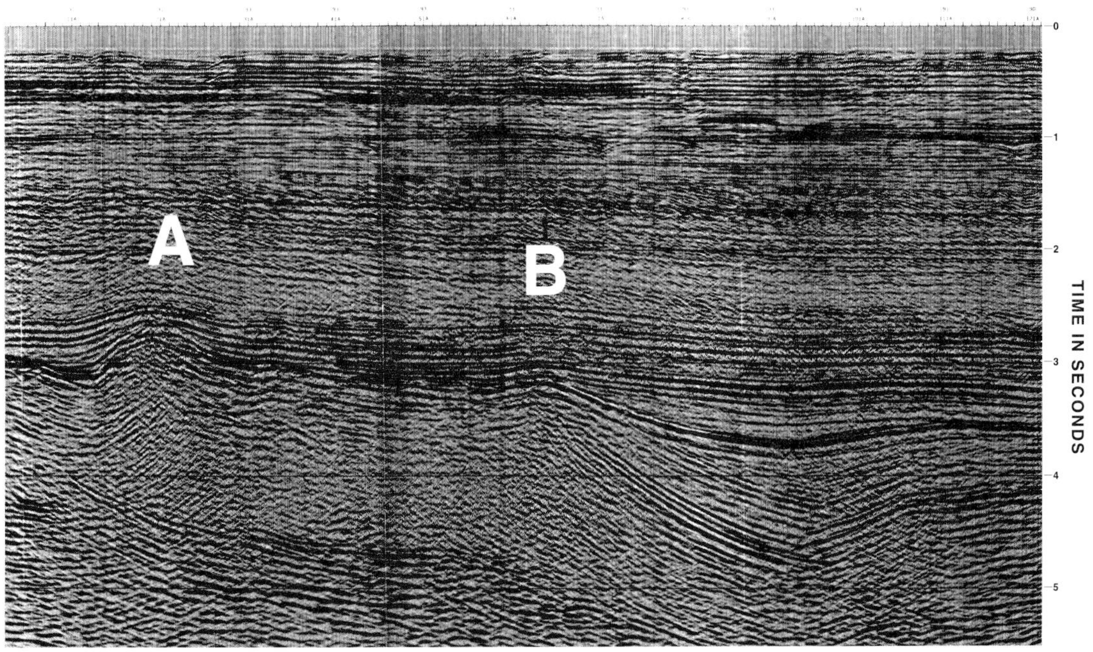

Figure 10–39. Courtesy Esso Exploration and Production U.K.

Method

Incremental strain was calculated from depth-converted seismic profiles over the most highly strained portion of each structure using a series of seismic sequence boundaries that could be mapped throughout the basin. The sea floor (0 Ma sequence boundary) represents the original, undeformed line length across each structure.

Example: Evaluating Top Seal Integrity, continued

Strain–time plots

The following strain–time plots show the incremental strains affecting the top seal above each trap and the wide variation in strain magnitude as well as strain history in these traps. Trap A has a maximum strain of 4.5%, which contributes to the risk of top seal fracturing. The time of maximum strain occurred 97–60 Ma. Today, trap A is a dry hole because of fracturing and loss of top seal integrity. Trap B has a maximum strain of only 1%, which occurred before 100 Ma, and only a 0.2% strain that occurred 97–60 Ma. Today, trap B is a producing structure with an intact top seal capable of trapping hydrocarbons in the underlying Upper Jurassic sands.

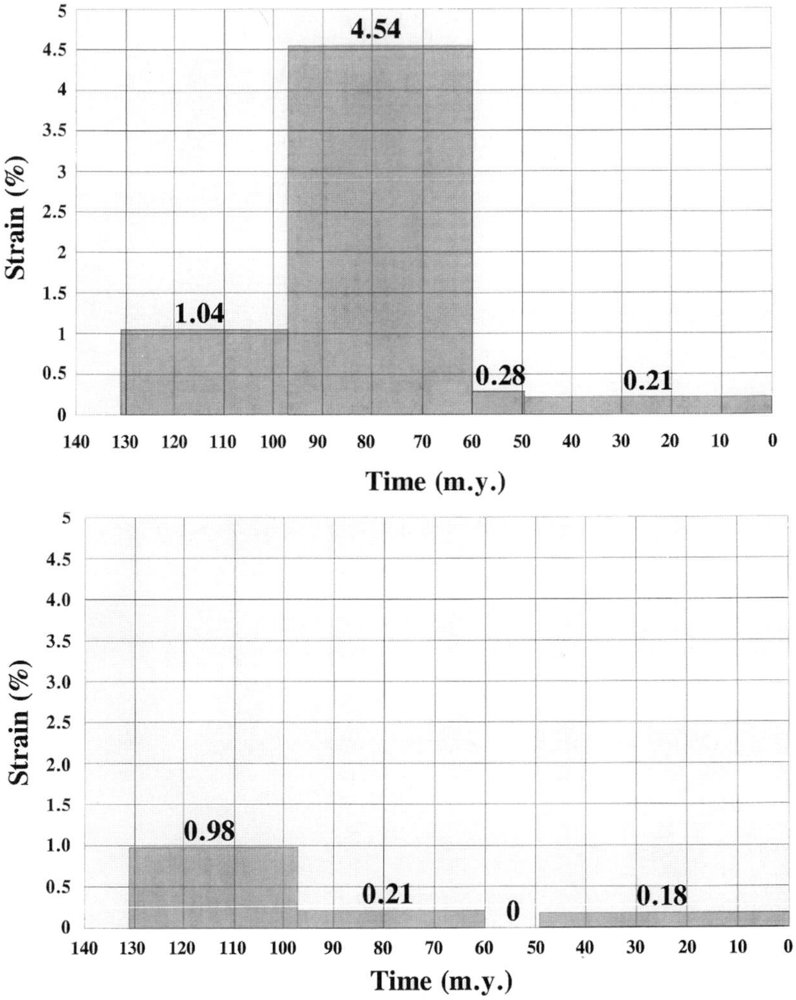

Figure 10–40.

Paleoductility analysis

Paleoductility analysis demonstrates that the top seals in these structures were extremely ductile prior to 100 Ma and would not have fractured within the range of strains developed. Since 100 Ma, these same seals were sufficiently compacted so that fracturing could have occurred if the strain exceeded the ductility of the top seal. The only strain that contributes to seal risk is the strain that occurred after 100 Ma.

Example: Evaluating Top Seal Integrity, continued

Strain threshold for failure

Incremental strain analysis of a group of successes and failures in the Central Graben defines a strain threshold at approximately 1.6%. In the following figure, traps with a maximum post-100 Ma incremental strain > 1.6% are dry (traps H, I, J). Traps with a strain < 1.6% are still intact and contain hydrocarbons (traps B–G). Trap A, a structure with very low strain, is dry because of natural hydraulic fracturing. Traps that were dry due to other causes such as lack of reservoir or source are not included in this plot.

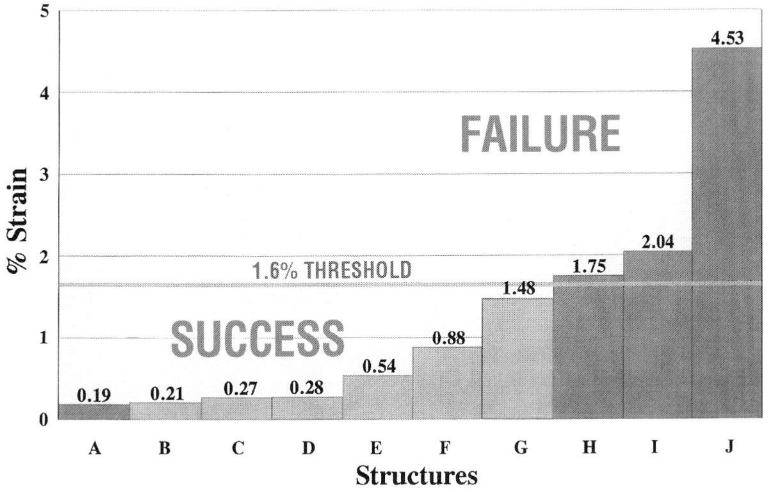

Figure 10–41.

This empirical threshold provides an important tool for evaluating top seals. Prospects can be evaluated before drilling using incremental strain analysis. In this case, high-risk prospects are those with strains exceeding the threshold of 1.6%. Low-risk prospects are those with strains below the threshold.

Importance to exploration

Routine top seal analysis changes the ranking of prospects as well as the exploration strategy in the Central Graben. Large prospects, normally at the top of the ranking, unfortunately may also be large-strain, high-risk structures. The chances of success can be increased by drilling low-strain, low-risk structures. Note that prospect size and strain magnitude are not necessarily related. Large prospects could be low-relief, low-strain structures. Continued drilling in the Central Graben has confirmed this strain threshold with a larger sample of tested traps (Koch et al., 1992).

Applying strain analysis to structural styles

Incremental strain analysis is not limited to analyzing low-relief salt structures like those used in the above example. It can be applied to any structural style involving deformation of the top seal, including traps in foreland fold-and-thrust belts, Gulf Coast growth faults, and North Sea normal faults. Deformation may involve shortening or extension.

Subsection B2

Overpressure and Natural Hydraulic Fracturing

Introduction

Top seals can be hydraulically fractured by high pore fluid pressure. This section discusses evaluating natural hydraulic fracturing and presents pertinent examples.

In this subsection

This subsection contains the following topics.

Natural Hydraulic Fracturing of Top Seals

Introduction

Fracturing and consequent loss of top seal integrity can occur by increasing pore pressure. High pore pressure can overcome the normal stresses that keep fractures closed. Similar fracturing is artificially induced during leak-off tests, well stimulations, and subsurface waste disposal (Evans, 1996).

Importance of hydraulic fracturing

High pore pressure has fractured the top seal and lost hydrocarbons in several basins, including the North Sea (Skerlec, 1982, 1992; Caillet, 1993; Leith et al., 1993), the Norwegian Sea (Ungerer et al., 1990), and the Malay basin (Scharr, 1976). The process is undoubtedly more widespread. Loss of top seal integrity due to natural hydraulic fracturing also appears to control the risk economics and vertical distribution of hydrocarbons in the Gulf Coast (Fertl and Leach, 1988; Leach, 1993a,b).

Theoretical fracture pressure, P_f

The overpressure required to cause fracturing is traditionally calculated by determining the theoretical fracture pressure, P_f (Hubbert and Willis, 1957):

$$P_f = \alpha\, \sigma_3 + p$$

where:

- P_f = theoretical fracture pressure
- σ_3 = effective least principal stress or confining pressure
- p = pore pressure
- α = poroelastic constant, assumed to be 1 in most analyses (see Engelder and Lacazette, 1990)

Fracture pressure is the fluid pressure necessary to overcome the normal stress that keeps the fractures closed.

Natural Hydraulic Fracturing of Top Seals, continued

Calculating P_f

Use the steps outlined in the following table to calculate P_f.

Step	Action	Method
1	Calculate σ1, overburden stress.	Use density logs to calculate overburden stress. For example, a 1-cm cube with a density of 2.4 g/cm^3 exerts an overburden stress of 2.4 g/cm^2 at the base of the cube.
2	Determine ν, Poisson's ratio.	Calculate the ratio from leak-off tests. Take care since leak-off tests may report the pressure value either prior to or after the fracture pressure point (Eaton, 1969). Leak-off tests are also commonly taken where casing has been set and may reflect the mechanical properties of the cement casing rather than the wall rock. Alternatively, Poisson's ratio can be estimated from available laboratory data (Lama and Vutukuri, 1978). Poisson's ratio increases with depth to approach a maximum of 0.5.
3	Determine p, pore pressure.	Pore pressure can be determined from measurements or regional pressure maps or estimated from burial history (Mann and Mackenzie, 1990). It may be necessary to predict paleopore pressure.
4	Calculate σ_3, effective confining pressure.	Solve the equation $\sigma_3 = (\sigma_1 - p)\left(\frac{\nu}{1-\nu}\right)$
5	Calculate P_f, theoretical fracture pressure.	Solve the equation $P_f = \alpha\,\sigma_3 + p$. The fracture pressure is commonly expressed as a gradient, and the equation becomes $P_f/Z = \alpha\,\sigma_3/Z + p/Z$, where Z is depth.

Other ways to calculate P_f

Variations on this equation as well as empirical relationships are common (Hubbert and Willis, 1957; Matthews and Kelly, 1967; Eaton, 1969; Breckles and Van Eekelen, 1982; Brennan and Annis, 1984). An alternative method of determining the principal stresses and fracture gradient is through the use of borehole deformation (Bell, 1990; Evans and Brereton, 1990).

Fracture Threshold in the Real World

Introduction

We don't really know how high the pore pressure must be to induce fracturing. In field examples, failure seems to occur below the fracture pressure (Skerlec, 1982, 1992; Dutta, 1987; Lerche, 1990; Ungerer et al, 1990). Risk increases as overpressure increases relative to P_f, but failure may occur below the theoretical fracture pressure. Other factors, not yet understood, control the point at which failure occurs.

Theoretically, fracturing occurs when the pore pressure reaches P_f. However, P_f increases as pore pressure increases. Although the theory generally is described in terms of the pore pressure needed to overcome the horizontal stress keeping the fractures closed, in practice the pore pressure must approach the lithostatic pressure for brittle failure to occur (Lorenz et al., 1991).

The following figure charts P_f vs. pore pressure for a range of overburden stress gradients (0.5–1.0). The pore pressure equals or exceeds P_f only when the pore pressure is equal to or greater than the lithostatic stress. Fracture occurs when P_f equals the pore pressure.

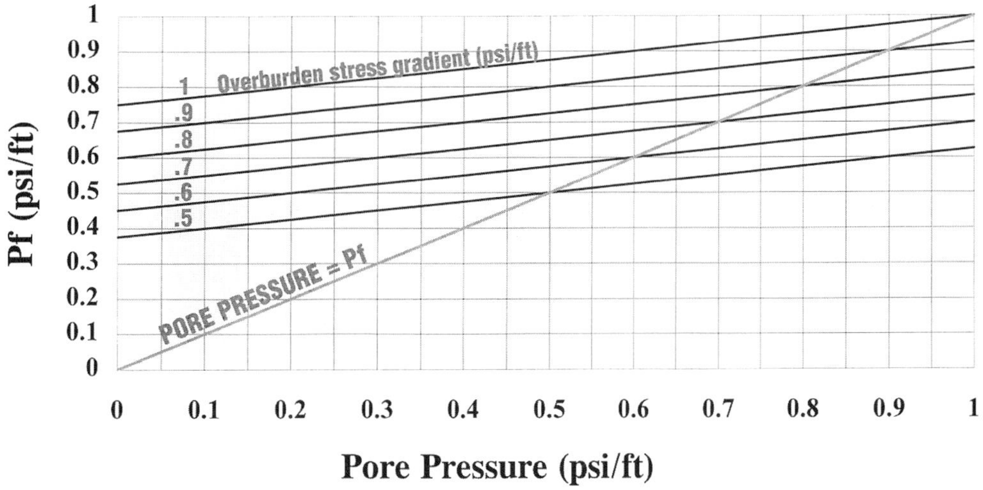

Figure 10–42.

Stress and Poisson's ratio variation

Although the variables used to calculate the fracture pressure commonly are generalized as a smooth curve, there are local variations and departures from this generalized curve. The principal horizontal stress, σ_3* and Poisson's ratio depend on lithology and bed geometry as well as depth and compaction (Lorenz et al., 1991).

Pore pressure variations

Pore pressure (p) is not always a smooth curve (Engelder and Leftwich, 1993). Decompaction is controlled in part by the permeability of sediment layers. Shales adjacent to high-permeability layers may undergo rapid decompaction while thick shale sequences with no immediate access to high-permeability layers will decompact more slowly and have high pore pressures. Local variations in pore pressure may be important in evolving seal integrity during basin subsidence.

Effect of water depth, stratigraphy, and facies changes

Pore pressure alone does not control hydraulic fracturing. Changes in the overburden stress change the theoretical fracture pressure and seal risk. For example, water depth alters the overburden stress and therefore P_f. The figure below compares the fracture gradient pressure for the case of a well on land and the same well with an additional 298 ft (100 m) of water column. The water column substitutes low-density water for high-density rock. The result is a shift of P_f to lower values. If the water depth were sufficiently great, there would be an increased likelihood of hydraulic fracturing with no change in pore pressure.

Similarly, facies changes within a basin can alter the density distribution in the sediment column and seal risk. A facies change from dense carbonates to less dense siliciclastics changes the overburden stress gradient. A higher pore pressure is required to fracture a top seal in the denser sediment column. Seal risk is greater in the less dense sediment column. The overburden stress gradient and seal risk similarly change with progressive subsidence and compaction.

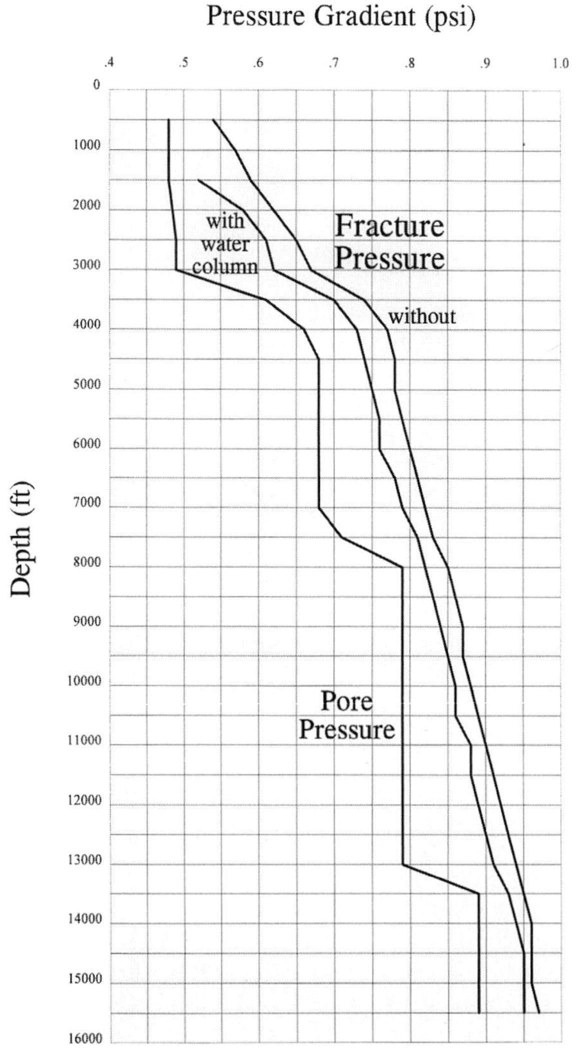

Figure 10–43.

Natural Hydraulic Fracturing Example, North Sea

Trap description

A trap in the Central Graben, North Sea, appears to have been bled dry by natural hydraulic fracturing. This trap is a low-relief salt structure with a dry hole and has less-than-sufficient strain to fracture the top seal.

Evidence

Evidence for hydraulic fracturing and seal rupture include the following:

- A fossil oil--water contact exists at the synclinal spill point of the trap. The trap was once filled with hydrocarbon, but something happened after trap fill to bleed off hydrocarbons.
- Hydrocarbon shows exist throughout the sediment column above the reservoir. These hydrocarbons are direct evidence of a breached top seal.
- The pore pressure is close to the theoretical fracture pressure. In adjacent fields, the pore pressure is significantly less than P_f.
- Cores show vertical, open extension fractures rather than the more common shear fractures found in adjacent fields. These fractures are identical to fractures produced by hydraulic fracturing.

Figure 10–44 shows that the pore pressure is close to the fracture pressure at the base of the top seal (approximately 1300 ft). The pore pressure is inferred from mud weight and RFT measurements (solid dots). Leak-off tests (LOT) help constrain the fracture pressure. The fracture pressure is close to the lithostatic pressure or overburden pressure.

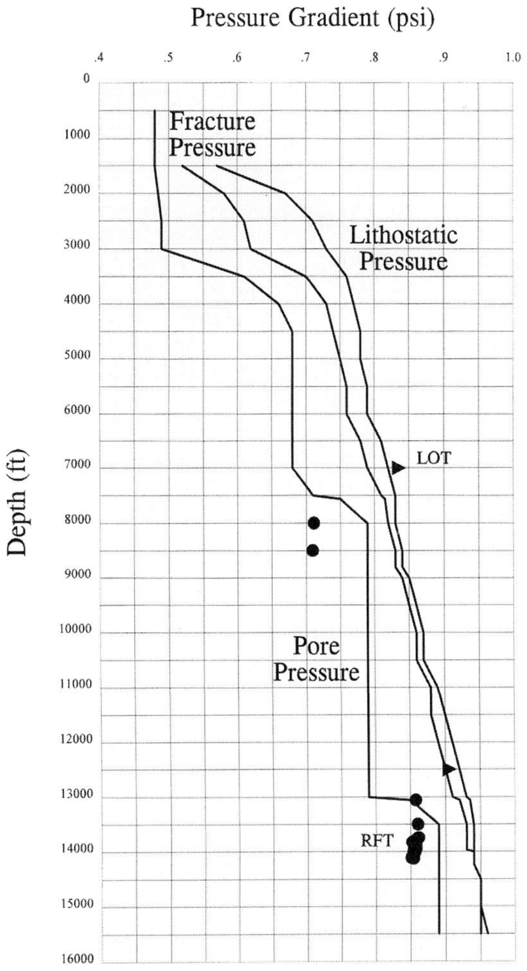

Figure 10–44. Courtesy Esso Exploration and Production, U.K.

Overpressure and Hydrocarbon Distribution, Gulf Coast

Introduction

Studies of the hydrocarbon distribution in the Gulf Coast relative to the top of overpressure suggest hydraulic fracturing and seal integrity influence the vertical distribution of hydrocarbons, success ratios, and seal risk (Fertl and Leach, 1988; Leach, 1993a,b).

Success rate vs. depth

The chance of finding an economically successful accumulation in the Gulf Coast decreases with depth. This decrease is a result of several changes, including reservoir quality and migration pathways. Most importantly, however, the distribution of hydrocarbons is closely related to the top of the overpressure zone. The figure shows the distribution of oil and gas production from more than 20,000 wells. Most hydrocarbons are found near or slightly above the top of the overpressured zone. The chance of success is reduced by 90–95% at depths of 2,000–5,000 ft below the top of overpressure (Leach, 1993b).

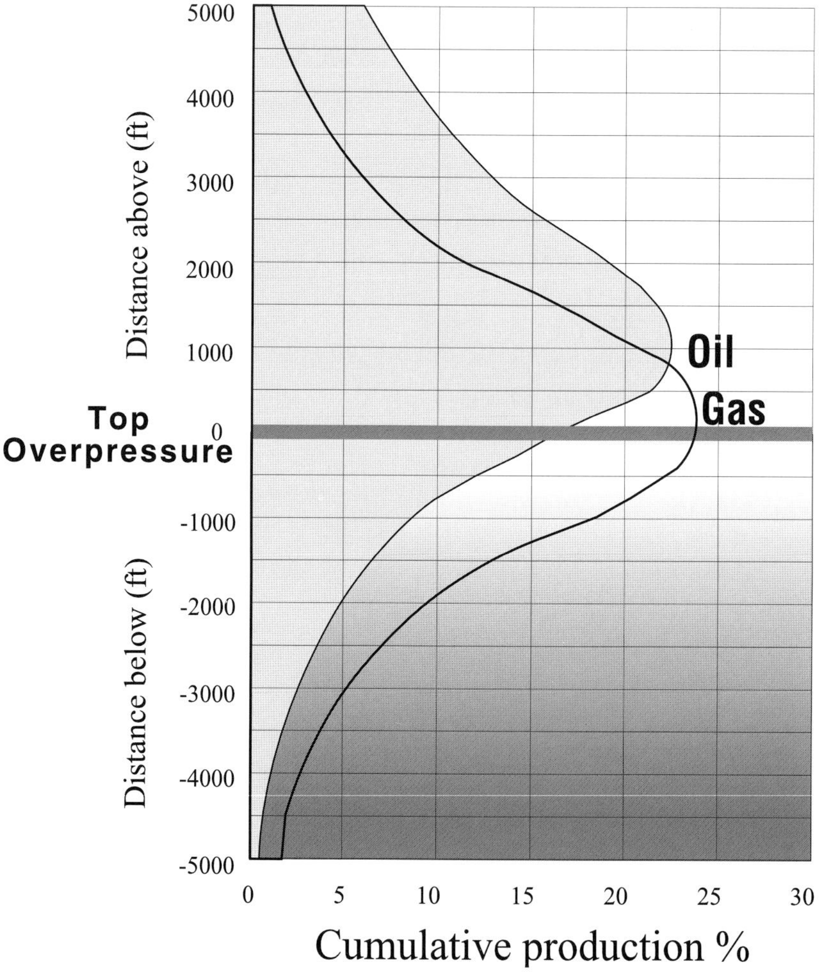

Figure 10–45. After Leach, 1993b; courtesy Oil & Gas Journal.

Overpressure and Hydrocarbon Distribution, Gulf Coast, continued

Hydrocarbon distribution vs. overpressure

The distribution of hydrocarbons relative to the top of overpressure changes as reservoir depth changes is shown in the figure below. This pattern is consistent with loss of top seal integrity because of hydrofracturing rather than a simple loss of reservoir quality or other variable. Deeper reservoirs have the peak gas occurrence below the top of overpressure. This is consistent with the changing P_f with depth. As depth increases, confining pressure increases and thus the amount of pressure required to fracture the top seal (P_f) increases. As fracture pressure increases, the depth of the first intact top seal increases.

The relationship between depth of reservoir and depth of maximum cumulative production below the top of overpressure is fundamental to seal risk. Further work is required to relate the distribution of hydrocarbons to actual fracture pressure rather than simply depth below top of overpressure.

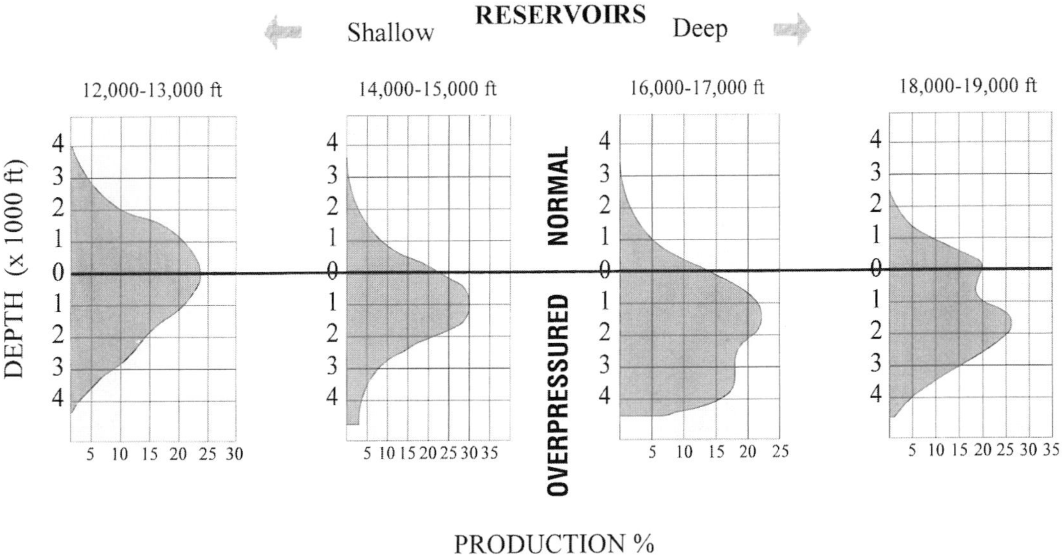

Figure 10–46. After Leach, 1993b; courtesy Oil & Gas Journal.

Section C

Evaluating Intact Top Seal

Introduction

An intact top seal is a seal that has not undergone fracturing. An intact top seal can trap only a finite column of hydrocarbon. In theory, the height of hydrocarbon column that can be trapped can be calculated from the capillary properties of the seal pores system and the physical character of the hydrocarbons and pore fluids. This venerable approach to analyzing top seals has been covered in depth by Berg, 1975; Schowalter, 1979; Watts, 1987; and Vavra et al., 1992.

Here, we will discuss briefly the three steps involved in evaluating seal capacity of intact top seals:

Step	Action
1	Determine fluid properties, including density, interfacial tension, and contact angle, at reservoir conditions.
2	Determine displacement pressure of the seal and reservoir.
3	Calculate seal capacity.

In this section

The steps in the procedure above as well as problems that can occur are discussed in the following subsections.

Subsection C1

How Capillary Properties Control Seal

Introduction

Hydrocarbons invading the pore space of a seal must displace the pore fluids. The pressure necessary to force the hydrocarbons into the seal and form a continuous filament is the **displacement pressure.** The pressure which forces the hydrocarbons into the seal is the **buoyant pressure** of the hydrocarbon phase. The trapping capacity of a top seal is the balance between the displacement pressure and the buoyant pressure. When the buoyant pressure exerted by the hydrocarbon column exceeds the displacement pressure of the seal, the seal leaks. For example, a shale top seal that could seal a 100-m column of oil might leak if the column increased to 101 m.

In this subsection

This subsection contains the following topics.

Buoyant Pressure

Calculation

The buoyant pressure (P_b) exerted by a column of hydrocarbons against the overlying seal is as follows:

$$P_b = (\rho_w - \rho_h)\, g\, h$$

Or, in the mixed units of the oil field:

$$P_b = (\rho_w - \rho_h)\, 0.433\, h$$

where:

ρ_w = density of water, g/cm^3
ρ_h = density of hydrocarbon, g/cm^3
g = acceleration due to gravity, cm/sec^2
h = thickness of the hydrocarbon column, ft

Pressure–depth plot

The following figure is a pressure–depth plot through an oil column trapped beneath a top seal. The buoyant pressure of the oil column at any depth is the difference in pressure between the oil gradient and the water gradient. The maximum buoyant pressure (P_{max}) is at the crest of the oil column. The buoyant pressure is zero at the free water level (FWL).

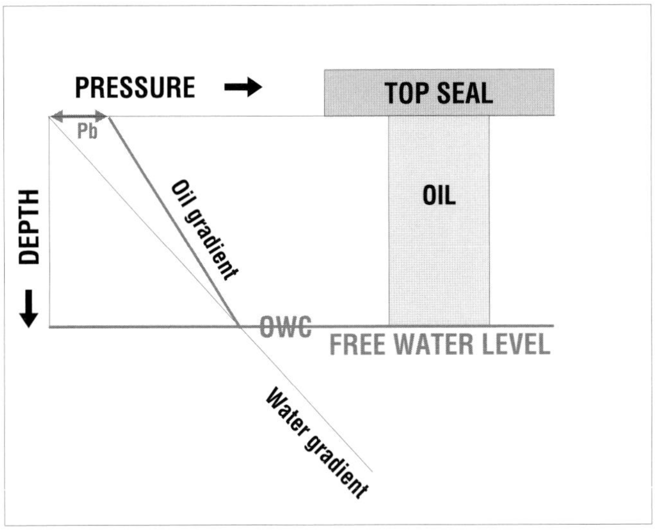

Figure 10–47.

Top Seal Displacement Pressure

Calculation

Displacement pressure (P_d) is the pressure necessary to force hydrocarbons into the pore space of a rock and form a continuous hydrocarbon filament (Schowalter, 1979). Displacement pressure, which is measured in dynes/cm^2, can be calculated by the following formula:

$$P_d = \frac{(2\gamma \cos \theta)}{R}$$

where:

γ = interfacial tension, dynes/cm
θ = contact angle or wettability, degrees
R = pore throat radius, cm

Variables

The displacement pressure of a seal depends on both the physical character of the seal (pore throat radius and pore throat size distribution) and the physical character of the hydrocarbons (interfacial tension and wettability).

Wettability

The wettability, or contact angle θ, is 0° for hydrocarbon/water (Berg, 1975). If the wetting phase is oil or gas rather than water, the contact angle can range from 0 to 180°. Not all rocks are water wet, and oil-wet seals may not be as rare as commonly thought (Cuiec, 1987). Organic-rich sediments may be source, seal, and oil wet.

Interfacial tension

Hydrocarbon/brine interfacial tension values typically range from 15–72 dynes/cm (Vavra et al., 1992; Schowalter, 1979; Watts, 1987). Laboratory studies provide interfacial tension values for a range of gas and oil compositions (Firoozabadi and Ramey, 1988).

Calculating Maximum Hydrocarbon Column

Calculation

The maximum column of hydrocarbons that can accumulate under a seal occurs when P_b equals P_d. If P_b exceeds P_d, the hydrocarbons will leak through the seal. If P_b is less than P_d, it would be possible to seal a greater column of hydrocarbons.

Therefore, for the maximum hydrocarbon column

$$P_b = P_d$$

$$(\rho_w - \rho_h)\, g\, h = \frac{2\gamma \cos \theta}{R}$$

$$h = \frac{\left(\frac{2\gamma \cos \theta}{R}\right)}{(\rho_w - \rho_h)\, g}$$

or, in mixed units,

$$h = \left(\frac{P_d}{\rho_w - \rho_h}\right) 0.433$$

where:

h = height of the hydrocarbon (ft)

Effect on seal capacity

The height of the hydrocarbon column (h) in the above equations is a theoretical maximum. The actual height is less because of the effect of the reservoir. If the reservoir itself had zero displacement pressure, the height of the hydrocarbon column would attain the theoretical maximum and the OWC would coincide with the free water level. If the reservoir has some displacement pressure greater than zero, then the height of the hydrocarbon column is less than the theoretical maximum, or

$$h = \left(\frac{P_{ds} - P_{dr}}{\rho_w - \rho_h}\right) 0.433$$

where:

P_{ds} = displacement pressure of the seal
P_{dr} = displacement pressure of the reservoir

Subsection C2

Estimating Displacement Pressure

Introduction

In practice, the displacement pressure is estimated from laboratory measurements. In real rocks, the single pore-throat radius of the equations on page 10–68 is replaced by a complex pore-throat size distribution.

Estimating techniques

The following table lists techniques commonly used to estimate the displacement pressure of a top seal.

Technique	Needed for the technique
Mercury injection measurements	Cores or cuttings
Log analysis	Logs and database of laboratory measurements
Sedimentary facies	Facies maps and database of laboratory measurements
Pore-size distribution	Thin sections, cores, or cuttings

In this subsection

This subsection contains the following topics which correlate with the techniques listed in the table above.

Measuring P_d Using Mercury Injection

Introduction

The displacement pressure is routinely inferred by forcing mercury into the pore space of a sample (cores or cuttings) and measuring the percent of mercury saturation vs. increasing pressure.

Procedure

This figure shows a typical mercury capillary curve for a sandstone. Mercury is first forced into the largest connected pore throats. Saturation increases with increasing pressure as mercury continues to be forced into progressively smaller pore throats.

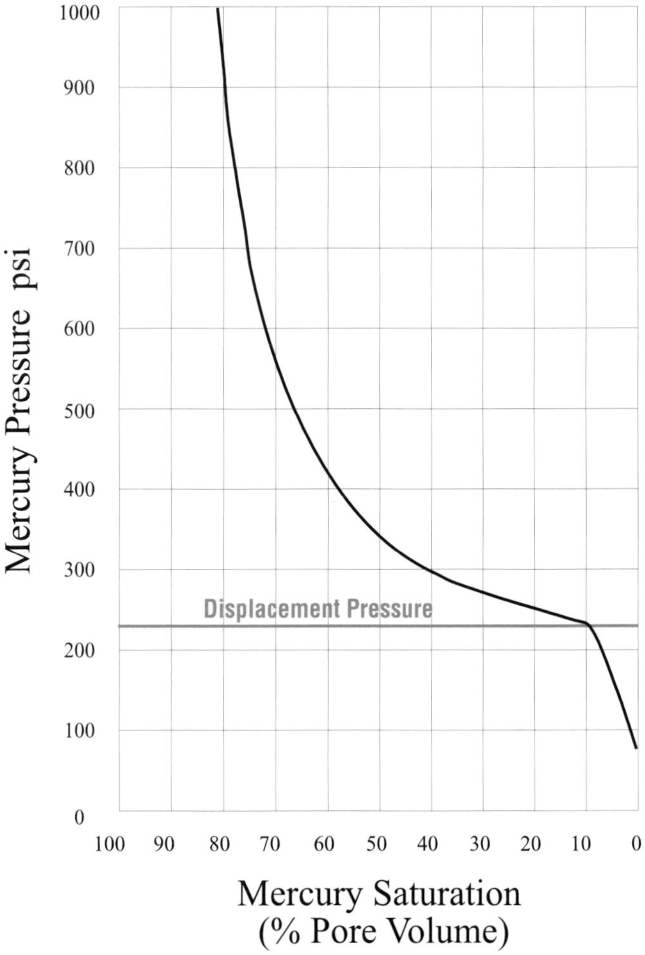

Figure 10–48. After Schowalter, 1979; courtesy AAPG.

Values of P_d

Displacement pressure (P_d) is defined as the pressure necessary to form a continuous hydrocarbon filament in the pore space of the seal. It is commonly inferred from the injection pressure at 10% saturation (Schowalter, 1979) for two reasons:

1. Most reservoirs have a pronounced plateau along which saturation rapidly increases. The pressure at 10% or 40% saturation gives a similar P_d.
2. Measured saturations required to create a continuous hydrocarbon filament range from 5–17% with an average of 10% (Schowalter, 1979).

Alternatively, some workers define P_d as the pressure at the first inflection point of capillary curve (Katz and Thompson, 1986). Figure 10–49 above shows the inferred P_d at both 10% saturation and at the inflection point.

Measuring P_d Using Mercury Injection, continued

Cores, cuttings, and low-permeability rocks

Samples for mercury injection laboratory analysis can include cores as well as cuttings. Measurements made from cuttings do not yield the same value as those from cores, so they require an empirical correction factor that ranges from 15–250 psi (Sneider and Neasham, 1993).

Seals with low permeability and small pore throats may require longer equilibration times during mercury injection (Vavra et al., 1992).

Converting laboratory measurements

Since laboratory measurements of P_d are given in the air–mercury system rather than the oil–water or gas–water systems, we must convert from P_{dm}, using mercury, to P_{dh}, or hydrocarbons:

$$P_{dh} = \frac{\gamma_h \cos \theta_h P_{dm}}{\gamma_m \cos \theta_m}$$

Displacement pressures measured in the air–mercury system are then converted to the hydrocarbon–water system at subsurface conditions. To convert, we must know the temperature, pressure, wettability, and coefficient of interfacial tension for the hydrocarbon phase. These parameters are commonly inferred from the composition, gas–oil ratio, and API gravity (Schowalter, 1979; Vavra et al., 1992). For the air–mercury system, the wettability of mercury is 140° (cos 140 = 0.766). The coefficient of interfacial tension for mercury is 485 dynes/cm (Vavra et al., 1992).

Estimating P_d from Sedimentary Facies and Well Logs

Introduction

Displacement pressure has been inferred from the relationship between capillary properties and sedimentary facies (Vavra et al., 1992; Shea et al., 1993). Two examples demonstrate the ability to construct regional facies maps and then assign maximum limits to the amount of hydrocarbon that could be trapped beneath these seals.

Example: Ardjuna basin, Indonesia

The top seal and capillary properties of rocks from the Ardjuna basin (offshore Java, Indonesia) are related to mappable facies (Vavra et al., 1992). The Talang Akar Formation consists of deltaic facies ranging from channel sandstones, delta plain shales, and channel abandonment siltstones to prodelta and delta-front shales as well as shelfal carbonates.

Each of these facies has a distinct range of displacement pressures. The following figure shows the range of seal capacities for the different facies. Shelfal carbonates and delta-front shales are excellent seals, with displacement pressures > 1000 psia (air–mercury) and capable of trapping approximately 1000–10,000 ft of oil. Delta-plain shales are relatively poor seals, with displacement pressures of 80–90 psia (air–mercury° and capable of trapping only 90–100 ft of oil.

These values place an upper limit on the amount of hydrocarbon that can be trapped. Other factors, however, limit the sealing potential of these seals. Seal risk was defined by combining P_d with qualitative assessments of ductility, fracturing, thickness, and lateral continuity (Vavra et al., 1992).

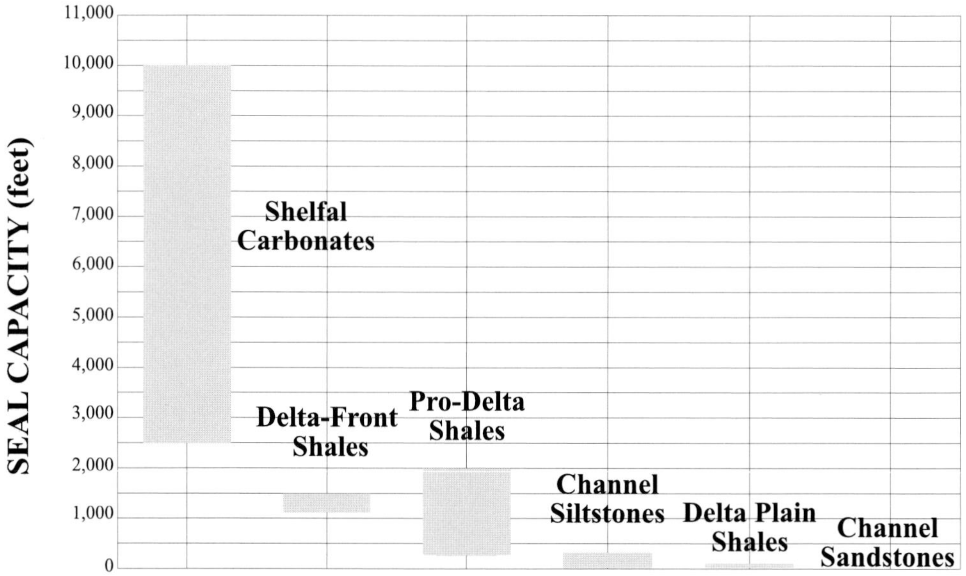

Figure 10–49. Data from Vavra et al. (1992).

Estimating P_d from Sedimentary Facies and Well Logs, continued

Example: Onshore African basin

A study of an African basin found differences in displacement pressure among flood plain, lacustrine, and overbank facies (Shea et al., 1993). Flood plain mudstones have displacement pressures of 1,500 psi (air–mercury) and can trap more than 300 m (1,000 ft) of oil. Lacustrine and overbank facies contain some siltstones that have displacement pressures of 500 psi (air–mercury) or less. These seal–rock facies can be correlated among wells and used to predict lateral facies variations and seal distribution in uncored wells.

Recent developments

An encouraging development is the attempt to establish a relationship between log response and displacement pressure (Alger et al., 1989; Shea et al., 1993; Sneider and Bolger, 1993; Sneider and Neasham, 1993). Resistivity logs directly reflect the relative proportions of clay minerals and organics to quartz and other minerals. Clay-rich seals with high displacement pressures have low resistivities. Clay-poor rocks with lower displacement pressures have high resistivities (Sneider and Bolger, 1993).

Estimating P_d from Pore Size

Method

Displacement pressure can be estimated from pore size using Washburn's (1921) equation,

$$P_d = \frac{-2\gamma\cos\theta}{r}$$

Techniques for estimating *r*

Pore throat radius, *r*, can be estimated in three ways:

- Thin-section analysis of pore throats (Dullien and Dhawan, 1974; Etris et al., 1988; Macdonald et al., 1986; see also Wardlaw, 1990)
- Thin-section analysis of grain size and assumptions of spherical grains and rhombohedral packing (Berg, 1975)
- Empirical correlation of permeability, porosity, and pore throat radius (Wardlaw and Taylor, 1976; Wells and Amaefule, 1985; Wardlaw, 1990; Pittman, 1992)

Although these methods can estimate the P_d of sands, they do not apply easily to shales and finer grained rocks that comprise top seals. The assumptions of spherical grains and rhombohedral packing used to infer pore throat radius to not apply to shales that contain plate-like clay minerals (Berg, 1975). Nor is the pore-size distribution easily determined from thin sections of fine-grained shales (Krushin, 1993). Use of permeability and porosity is thwarted by the lack of a distinct apex in the mercury injection data of low-permeability rocks (Pittman, 1992), as well as the difficulty of measuring the permeability of shales.

Theory and experiment

Predicting top seal capacity is difficult—even in idealized experiments in which all variables are known to a degree unobtainable in practical prospect assessment. The predicted height of hydrocarbon columns calculated from pore throat diameters in uniform glass bead packs is 160–500T larger than heights actually observed in experiments (Catalan et al., 1992). If we cannot predict the height of hydrocarbon columns trapped in a controlled experiment with uniform glass beads and known variables, then we must be cautious in prospect analysis.

Subsection C3
Seal Capacity

Introduction

A range of seal capacities have been reported for various rock types. In addition, a number of other factors—depth, hydrocarbon phase, seal thickness, fault-dependent leak points—affect the height of trapped hydrocarbon columns.

In this subsection

This subsection contains the following topics.

Seal Capacity of Different Rock Types

Range of capacities

The figure to the right shows the range of seal capacities of different rock types. This figure was compiled from published displacement pressures based upon mercury capillary curves. Column heights were calculated using a 35°API oil at near-surface conditions with a density of 0.85 g/cm^3, an interfacial tension of 21 dynes/cm, and a brine density of 1.05 g/cm^3. Data were compiled from Smith (1966), Thomas et al. (1968), Schowalter (1979), Wells and Amaefule (1985), Melas and Friedman (1992), Vavra et al. (1992), Boult (1993), Khrushin (1993), and Shea et al. (1993).

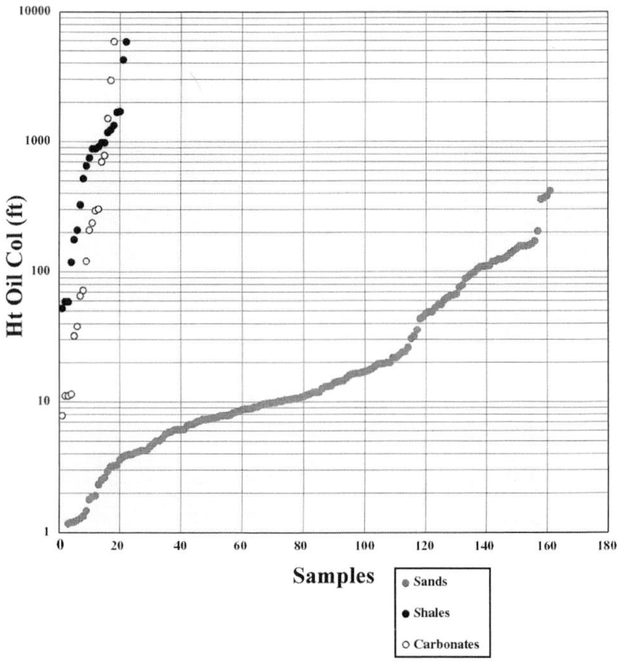

Figure 10–50.

Generalizations

These data show the following:

- Good shales can trap thousands of feet of hydrocarbon column.
- Most good sands can trap only 50 ft or less of oil column.
- Poor sands and siltstones can trap 50–400 ft of oil column.

Shale seals

Shales have high displacement pressures and can trap large columns of oil as large as 1830 m (6000 ft). Nonsmectite shales have pore throat radii of less than 12 nm and can trap gas columns of more than 1000 m (3,000 ft) (Krushin, 1993). Shales in the Cretaceous section of the Powder River basin have displacement pressures of 1000–4000 psi and can trap gas columns of 460–1830 m (1500–6,000 ft) (Jiao et al., 1993). The shortest oil columns among the shale data include some true shales as well as siltstones, silty mudstones, and interbedded sand/shale cores.

Sand seals

Sands commonly have low displacement pressures and can trap only small oil columns. Three-quarters of the sands, most of which are Gulf Coast reservoirs, are capable of trapping less than 50 ft of oil. Sands can have sufficiently high displacement pressures to trap hundreds of feet of oil. Oil column heights between 50–400 ft are from sands with diagenetic pore fillings, tight gas sands, and very fine-grained sands that probably include siltstones.

Carbonate seals

Carbonates have a wide range of displacement pressures. Some carbonates can seal as much as 1500–6000 ft of oil. These better seals are argillaceous limestones and shelf carbonates. In the Gulf Coast basin, shorter oil columns are sealed by grainstones, mudstones, and wackestones of the Smackover Formation and chalk.

Variation in Seal Capacity with Depth and Hydrocarbon Phase

Introduction

Seal capacity is controlled by the physical properties of both the seal and the hydrocarbon. Because the seal alone does not control seal capacity . . .

- It is possible to trap more gas than oil despite the higher buoyant pressure of gas,
- At depths below 9,000–10,000 ft a seal is always capable of trapping more gas than oil, and
- The dominance of gas in the deeper parts of basins may reflect seal capacity as well as maturation.

Changes with depth

Compaction and diagenesis during burial cause a progressive reduction in pore throats in most seal lithologies. In addition, the interfacial tension of the hydrocarbons changes with depth and affects seal capacity. Most importantly, the interfacial tension of oil and gas changes at different rates (Watts, 1987; Schowalter, 1979).

Seal capacity for oil and gas

Because the interfacial tension of gas increases at a different rate from that of oil with depth, it is possible to trap more gas than oil. The following figure shows the seal capacity (in feet) of a top seal for different hydrocarbon compositions with depth (after Watts, 1987). Curves show the seal capacity for three different oils, ranging from 30–40° API and a GOR of 400–800. Methane has two different pressure gradients (0.7 and 0.45 psi/ft. The pore throat of the seal decreases with depth and compaction.

Below 9000 ft, the seal capacity is greater for gas than it is for any of the oil compositions. Even above 9000 ft, the seal capacity for gas is greater for some oil compositions. The seal capacity for gas is greatest at a normal pressure gradient and less for an overpressured gradient.

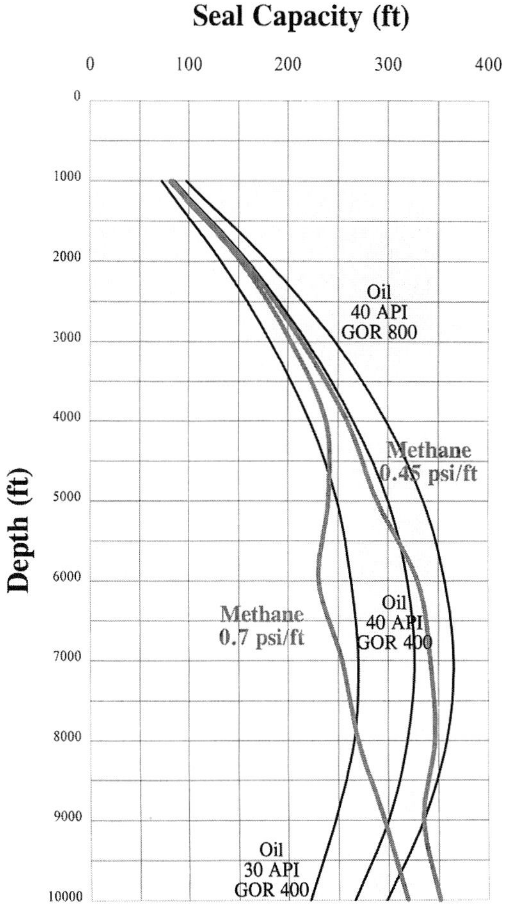

Figure 10–51. After Watts, 1987; courtesy Marine and Petroleum Geology.

Variation in Seal Capacity with Depth and Hydrocarbon Phase, continued

Gas and oil distribution in basins

Seal capacity rather than maturation may cause the deeper portions of some basins to be gas prone. Traditionally the deep, gas-prone parts of many basins have been interpreted to be a result of increasing maturation. An alternative explanation is that seals at greater depth are more effective at trapping gas than oil.

Gas loss by diffusion

Diffusive loss of gas through a top seal can also limit seal capacity (Leythaeuser et al., 1982; Nelson and Simmons, 1995). Seal capacity is not simply related to the displacement pressure. Although diffusion can be important in entrapment of gas, diffusion coefficients for oil are so small that diffusion does not affect seal capacity relative to oil.

Estimates of the diffusive loss of gas in the McClave field, Colorado, demonstrate that 57 bcf of gas can diffuse from a trap in only 0.5–5.0 m.y. (Nelson and Simmons, 1995).

Seal Capacity and Two-Phase Hydrocarbon Columns

Two phases are better than one

Seal capacity depends on both the hydrocarbon phase and the physical character of the top seal. Since displacement pressure is a function of the seal and the coefficient of interfacial tension of the hydrocarbon phase beneath the seal, it is possible to trap a thicker two-phase hydrocarbon column than oil alone or gas alone (Watts, 1987). The gas in contact with the base of the seal determines the displacement pressure (P_d) of the seal. The buoyant effect of the oil column, however, is less than that of a pure gas column, and a greater total hydrocarbon column can be trapped.

Single phase vs. two phase

The following figure compares the seal capacity of a top seal with a single-phase oil accumulation, a single-phase gas accumulation, and a two-phase accumulation with both an oil leg and a gas cap. The largest hydrocarbon column is sealed by the two-phase accumulation. This best applies to traps with a geometry such that only the gas column is in contact with the seal. It also applies to fault traps.

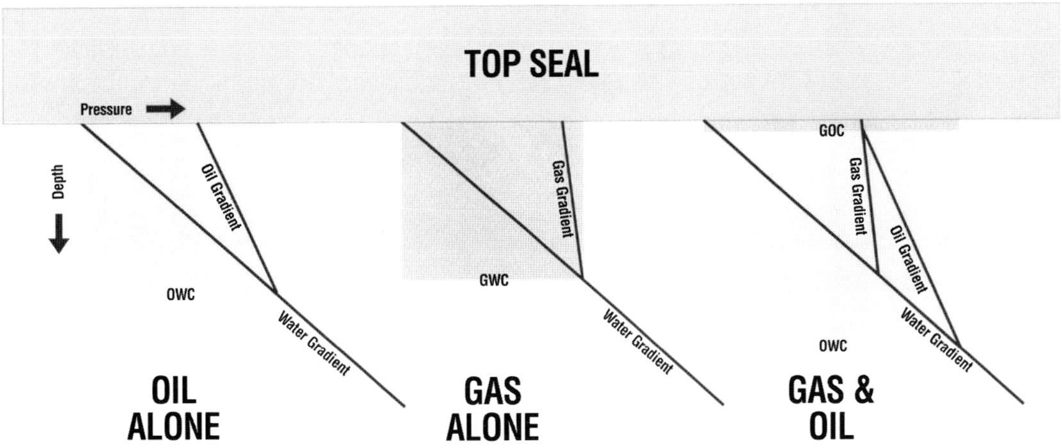

Figure 10–52. After Watts, 1987; courtesy Marine and Petroleum Geology.

Seal Thickness

How thick is necessary?

There is no simple relationship between seal thickness and the height of the hydrocarbon column. Seals can be extremely thin—less than 1 m thick that seal individual hydrocarbon accumulations. There are also examples of traps with thick shale seals that are dry. This difficulty in establishing a relationship between seal thickness and column is especially true since many hydrocarbon columns are controlled by fault-related spill points that are independent of top seal thickness.

Seal thickness studies

Data compiled from fields in California and the Rocky Mountains show no relationship between seal thickness and hydrocarbon column height (Zieglar, 1992). Nonetheless, some workers have suggested a correlation between seal thickness and seal capacity (Nederlof and Mohler, 1981; Sluijk and Nederlof, 1984).

Seal continuity and fracturing

Seal thickness is not an independent variable. Thin seals have a higher probability of being laterally discontinuous, of being fractured completely, or of having local variations in fracture intensity or pore throat diameter that provide a leakage pathway. Similarly, thick seals have a higher probability of being laterally continuous, having fractures terminate within the seal, and having at least one shale lamina with a high displacement pressure.

Fault-dependent Leak Points, Continuity, and Charge

Introduction

In many basins the major control on hydrocarbon column heights is not the displacement pressure of top seals but fault-dependent leak points, the lateral continuity of seals, and charge.

Fault-dependent leak points

A comparison of top seal capacity determined from displacement pressures and actual hydrocarbon column heights in one African basin demonstrates that while top seals are capable of trapping more than 1000 ft of oil, most traps contain only a few hundred feet of oil (Shea et al., 1993). Oil column heights in this basin are controlled instead by fault-dependent leak points (Allard, 1993; Shea et al., 1993).

Similarly, only 5–10% of the fields in the Rocky Mountains and California are thought to have hydrocarbon column heights controlled by top seal capillary properties (Zieglar, 1992). The remaining 90–95% are controlled by some other factor, including charge, faults, and synclinal spill points.

Seal continuity

The lateral extent and continuity of top seals can create and destroy plays within basins. In many basins, thick, continuous, areally extensive sequences of shale or salt act as regional top seals. The Gippsland basin and North Sea are only two of numerous examples. In some basins, this regional seal is lacking or limited. In the Gulf Coast, the North Frisco City field exists because the Buckner Anhydrite, a regional seal, is missing above a local basement high. Only where the regional seal is breached are hydrocarbons able to escape from the Smackover reservoir into the overlying Lower Haynesville sands (Stephenson et al., 1992). Where the Buckner Anhydrite is continuous, there is no Haynesville play.

Subsection C4

Pitfalls and Limitations of Estimating Seal Capacity

Introduction

Although it is tantalizing to be able to measure the capillary properties of a seal and then assess hydrocarbon volumes, some practical problems exist:

- It is not easy to characterize the displacement pressure of a top seal from a few, or many, measurements.
- Few empirical field studies compare the predicted and observed hydrocarbon column heights. This is worrisome because idealized laboratory experiments have significant errors in the predicted hydrocarbon column heights.
- Hydrocarbon saturations required for flow through top seals—and, consequently, displacement pressures—may be much higher than commonly assumed.
- Hydrocarbon columns beneath breached seals and hydrocarbon-wet seals may not be related to the capillary properties of the seal in any easily understood way.
- Diffusion can cause loss of large volumes of gas but not oil through a top seal.
- Hydrodynamic flow can alter top seal capacity.

In this subsection

This subsection contains the following topics.

Difficulty of Characterizing P_d of a Seal

Reasons

It is difficult to determine the displacement pressure of a top seal.

- First, seal capacity is based on the presence of a single, continuous, high-P_d layer, not upon an arithmetic average of all P_d values. The trapping capacity is determined by the highest displacement pressure within a seal, theoretically even if that interval is a layer only one grain thick. A 500-m-thick siltstone may appear incapable of trapping more than 1 m of hydrocarbon. The presence of a 1-cm-thick claystone layer, however, may create a seal for thousands of meters of hydrocarbon. Predicting these local seals is difficult and adds a measure of risk to any evaluation of intact top seals using capillary theory.
- Second, experiments demonstrate that hydrocarbon migration through a seal does not occur along a broad, uniform front but along narrow fingers reflecting local, tortuous pathways of low displacement pressure (Dembecki and Anderson, 1989; Catalan et al., 1992).

Pathways in experiments

These tortuous pathways develop even in bead packs of uniform, closely packed glass spheres. Natural seals are even more heterogeneous.

The difficulty of defining these narrow zones during sampling complicates our ability to predict the critical displacement pressure of a seal. Although 99% of the samples from a trap may indicate a top seal capable of trapping a 500-m oil column, the seal may well leak through a narrow pathway only centimeters in diameter.

Does the Theory Predict Reality?

Introduction

Rarely is the actual column of trapped hydrocarbon compared with the prediction from measured displacement pressures. Empirical studies are needed because simple, idealized laboratory experiments show significant errors between the predicted and observed hydrocarbon column heights (Catalan et al., 1992). These experiments at best have column heights 19–23% larger than predicted. At worst, they are 125–217% larger than predicted. (The larger differences are probably the result of short equilibration times.)

Benton field

Benton field, Illinois, in one example in which the trapped column heights match the measured displacement pressure of the top seal (Sneider and Neasham, 1993). Measured displacement pressures predict the top seal is capable of trapping 29–34 m (94–110 ft) of hydrocarbon. The actual column of hydrocarbon in the field in the Tar Springs reservoir is 29 m (95 ft).

Bodalla South field

The Bodalla South field, Eromanga basin, Australia, has short oil columns—less than 12 m high—that appear to be limited by the displacement pressure of the top seal (Boult, 1993). The following cross section shows the top seal and oil accumulations. The top seal, the Birkhead Formation, consists of fluvial channel and point bar deposits as well as more shale-prone levee bank, crevasse splay, floodplain, and coal swamp facies. Measured displacement pressures of the top seal have an average range of 150–200 psi (air-mercury) and can seal 10.86–12.64 m of oil. The maximum height of the actual trapped oil column is 11.25 m.

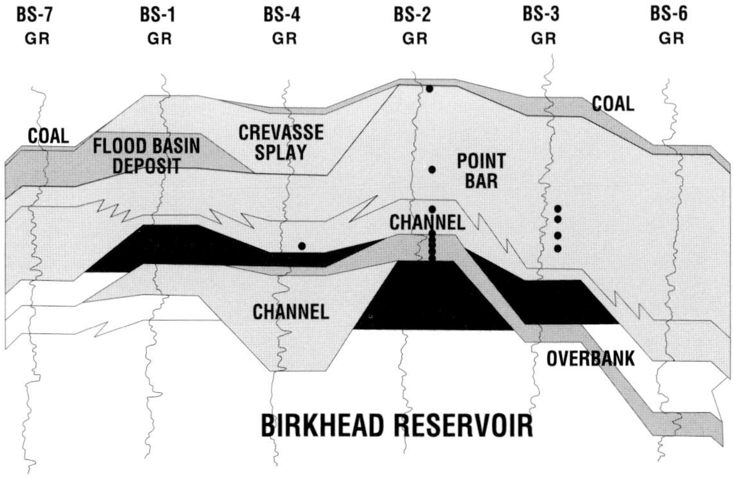

Figure 10–53. After Boult, 1993; courtesy Marine and Petroleum Geology.

Top seal quality variation

Although predicted and observed data apparently agree, units within the top seal may be able to trap much greater oil columns. Measured displacement pressures of the shaly overbank facies are greater than 3000 psi (air–mercury). These facies are not thought to be effective seals because they are either thin or lack lateral continuity (Boult, 1993). More empirical studies are needed.

Saturations Required for Hydrocarbon Flow

Traditional definitions

Hydrocarbons flow through a water-wet seal when there is a continuous, interconnected pathway of hydrocarbon-filled pore space. Flow through a seal occurs with saturations of 4.5–17% of the rock pore volume, averaging 10% (Schowalter, 1979). This is one reason displacement pressure is defined at 10% saturation.

Possible modifications

Other experiments, including lower porosity rocks, indicate much higher oil saturations of 25–91% may be required (England et al., 1987). The current assumption that seal capacity is based upon the displacement pressure at only 10% saturation could be very misleading. The value could be two or more orders of magnitude greater than that predicted at 10% saturation.

Seal Capacity of Breached and Hydrocarbon-wet Seals

Introduction

Hydrocarbon column heights may not be related only to the displacement pressure of the top seal. Once a seal has been breached and hydrocarbons forced through the seal, theoretically the hydrocarbon column will shrink until the buoyant pressure equals the displacement pressure and the system again seals. In practice, however, hydrocarbons continue to flow through the seal until there is no longer a continuous hydrocarbon filament. Although the process is not completely understood, laboratory studies suggest that flow continues until the hydrocarbon column shrinks to half its original height (Roof, 1970; Schowalter, 1979).

Most traps half full

The preceding discussion suggests that in basins where there is charge sufficient to fill all traps to maximum seal capacity, traps limited by the capillary properties of intact top seals should be half full (Watts, 1987). Rather than the hydrocarbon columns matching the displacement pressures of the seal, all filled traps would have leaked hydrocarbons until the buoyant pressure (P_b) is half the displacement pressure (P_d). Continued charging of traps after initial fill could result in larger hydrocarbon columns. Only in basins with insufficient hydrocarbons to fill all traps to the maximum seal capacity, or with charge after leakage, would there be a large number of traps greater than half full.

The following figure illustrates the fill history of a trap with some finite seal capacity that has been filled to seal capacity and then leaked. The final hydrocarbon column is half of that predicted by the displacement pressure of the top seal.

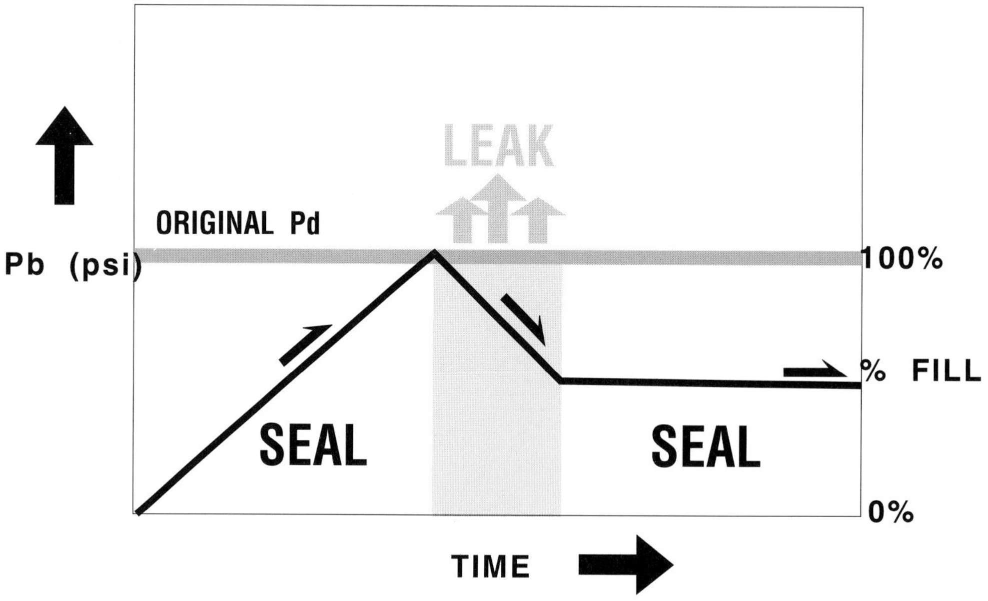

Figure 10–54. After Boult, 1993; courtesy Marine and Petroleum Geology.

Water wet vs. oil wet

Estimates of seal capacity from measured displacement pressures commonly assume the seal is water wet. Oil-wet seals may be more common than we think. Organic-rich shales, a common top seal, are probably oil wet (Cuiec, 1987). Similarly, episodic leakage of hydrocarbons through a seal may alter the seal capacity.

Hydrodynamic Flow and Pressure Transients

Introduction

Pressure gradients and the resulting buoyant pressures are not always static. Both hydrodynamic flow and pressure transients change seal capacity.

Hydrodynamic flow

A hydrodynamic gradient will either increase or decrease the height of a trapped hydrocarbon column (Schowalter, 1979; Dahlberg, 1982; Lerche and Thomsen, 1994). Flow in the direction of the buoyant vector decreases the seal capacity. Flow opposite the direction of the buoyant vector increases the seal capacity.

The hydrodynamic effect has been demonstrated to be important in trapping hydrocarbons in the western Canada basin (Dahlberg, 1982; Lerche and Thomsen, 1994).

Pressure transients

Fluid pressure gradients may fluctuate dramatically during faulting and basin evolution (Sibson et al., 1975). Estimates of trapping capacity based upon the capillary model assume a static pressure gradient or a uniform regional hydrodynamic gradient. Measurements of fluid inclusions, however, suggest pressure transients along faults of as much as 126 MPa (1,825 psi) (Parry and Bruhn, 1990). Similar episodic fluid flow events are inferred from sandstone cements in the North Sea (Robinson and Gluyas, 1992). Leakage through seals and seal capacity may be as episodic as hydrocarbon generation, migration, and pressure transients.

Section D
References

Alger, R.P., D.L. Luffel, and R.B. Truman, 1989, New unified method of integrating core capillary pressure data with well logs: Society of Petroleum Formation Evaluation, vol. 4, no. 2, p. 145–152.

Allan, U.S., 1989, Model for hydrocarbon migration and entrapment within faulted structures: AAPG Bulletin, vol. 72, no. 7, p. 803-811.

Allard, D.M., 1993, Fault leak controlled trap fill, rift basin examples (abs.), *in* J. Ebanks, J. Kaldi, and C. Vavra, eds., Seals and Traps: A Multidisciplinary Approach: AAPG Hedberg Conference, Crested Butte, Colorado, June 21–23.

Bell, J.S., 1990, Investigating stress regimes in sedimentary basins using information from oil industry wireline logs and drilling records, *in* A. Hurst, M.A. Lovell, and A.C. Morton, eds., Geological Applications of Wireline Logs: Geological Society London Special Publication 48, p. 305–325.

Berg, R.R., 1975, Capillary pressure in stratigraphic traps: AAPG Bulletin, vol. 59, no. 6, p. 939–956.

Boult, P.J., 1993, Membrane seal and tertiary migration pathways in the Bodalla South oilfield, Eronmanga Basin, Australia: Marine and Petroleum Geology, vol. 10, no. 1, p. 3–13.

Bouvier, J.D., C.H. Kaars-Sijpesteigen, D.F. Kluesner, C.C. Onyejekwe, and R.C. Vander Pal, 1989, Three-dimensional seismic interpretation and fault sealing investigations, Nun River field, Nigeria: AAPG Bulletin, vol. 73, no. 11, p. 1397–1414.

Breckles, I.M., and H.A.M. Van Eekelen, 1982, Relationship between horizontal stress and depth in sedimentary basins: Journal of Petroleum Technology, vol. 34, no. 9, p. 2191–2199.

Brennan, R.M., and M.R. Annis, 1984, A new fracture gradient prediction technique that shows good results in Gulf of Mexico abnormal pressure: SPE paper 13210, 6 p.

Buck, S., and G. Robertson, 1996, Fault seal behavior at Beryl field, UK North Sea: observations from 20 years of production, drilling and injection data: AAPG Annual Meeting Abstracts, San Diego, May 19–22, p. A20.

Caillet, G., 1993, The caprock of the Snorre field (Norway): a possible leakage by hydraulic fracturing: Marine and Petroleum Geology, vol. 10, no. 1, p. 42–50.

Catalan, L. F. Xiaown, I. Chatzis, and F.A.L. Dullien, 1992, An experimental study of secondary oil migration: AAPG Bulletin, vol. 76, no. 5, p. 638–650.

Chong, K.P., P.M. Hoyt, J.W. Smith, and B.Y. Paulsen, 1980, Effects of strain rate on oil shale fracturing: International Journal of Rock Mechanics, vol. 17, no. 1, p. 35–43.

Corbett, K., M. Friedman, and J. Spang, 1987, Fracture development and mechanical stratigraphy of Austin Chalk, Texas: AAPG Bulletin, vol. 71, no. 1, p. 17–28.

Cuiec, L., 1987, Wettability and oil reservoirs, *in* J. Kleppe, E.W. Berg, A.T. Buller, O. Hjemeland, and O. Torsaeter, eds., North Sea Oil and Gas Reservoirs: London, Graham and Trotman, p. 193–207.

Dahlberg, E.C., 1982, Applied Hydrodynamics in Petroleum Exploration: New York, Springer-Verlag, 161 p.

Dembecki, H., Jr., and M.J. Anderson, 1989, Secondary migration of oil: experiments supporting efficient movement of separate, buoyant oil phase along limited conduits: AAPG Bulletin, vol. 73, no. 8, p. 1018–1021.

Doveton, J.H., 1986, Log analysis of subsurface geology: New York, John Wiley & Sons, 273 p.

Downey, M.W., 1984, Evaluating seals for hydrocarbon accumulations: AAPG Bulletin, vol. 68, no. 11, p. 1752–1763.

Dullien, F.A.L., and G.K. Dhawan, 1974, Characterization of pore structure by a combination of quantitative photomicrography and mercury porosimetry: Journal of Colloid and Interface Science, vol. 47, no. 2, p. 337–349.

Dutta, N.C., 1987, Fluid flow in low permeability porous media, *in* B. Doligez, ed., Migration of Hydrocarbons in Sedimentary Basins: Paris, Editions Technip, p. 567–596.

Earlougher, R.C., Jr., and H. Kazemi, 1980, Practicalities of detecting faults from buildup testing: JPT, January 1980, p. 18–20.

Eaton, B.A., 1969, Fracture gradient prediction and its application in oilfield operations: Trans. AIME, October, p. 1353–1360.

Eisenberg, R.A., R.J. Brenneman, and A.A. Adeogba, 1996, Integrated fault seal analysis and risk assessment: Okan and Meren fields, Nigeria: AAPG Annual Meeting Abstracts, vol. 5, San Diego, May 19–22, p. 41.

Engelder, T., and A. Lacazette, 1990, Natural hydraulic fracturing, *in* N. Barton and O. Stephansson, eds., Rock Joints: Rotterdam, A.A. Balkema, p. 35–43.

______ and J. Leftwich, 1993, An analysis of geopressure profiles from south Texas: the search for higher quality reservoirs in the Tertiary sections of the Gulf Coast: AAPG Hedberg Research Conference, unpublished abstract.

England, W.A., A.S. Mackenzie, D.M. Mann, and T.M. Quickley, 1987, The movement and entrapment of petroleum fluids in the subsurface: Journal of the Geological Society, London, vol. 144, no. 2, p. 327–347.

Evans, C.J., and N.R. Brereton, 1990, In situ crustal stress in the United Kingdom from borehole breakouts, *in* A. Hurst, ed., Geological Applications of Wireline Logs: Geological society Special Publication 48, p. 327–338.

Evans, D.M., 1966, The Denver area earthquakes and the Rocky Mountain Arsenal disposal well: The Mountain Geologist, vol. 3, no. 1, p. 23–36.

Fertl, W.H., and W.G. Leach, 1988, Economics of hydrocarbon reserves in overpressured reservoirs below 18,000 feet in south Louisiana: SPE paper 18146, 16 p.

Firoozabadi, A., and H.J. Ramey, Jr., 1988, Surface tension of water-hydrocarbon systems at reservoir conditions: Journal of Canadian Petroleum Technology, vol. 27, no. 3, p. 41–48.

Gibson, R.G., 1994, Fault-zone seals in siliciclastic strata of the Columbus basin, offshore Trinidad: AAPG Bulletin, vol. 78, no. 9, p. 1372–1385.

Grunau, H.R., 1987, A world-wide look at the cap-rock problem: Journal of Petroleum Geology, vol. 10, no. 3, p. 245–266.

Harding, T.P., and A.C. Tuminas, 1988, Interpretation of footwall (lowside) fault traps sealed by reverse faults and convergent wrench faults: AAPG Bulletin, vol. 72, no. 7, p. 738–757.

Hardman, R.F.P., and J.E. Booth, 1989, Structural interpretation of hydrocarbon traps sealed by basement normal fault block faults at stable flank of foredeep basins and at rift basins: AAPG Bulletin, vol. 73, no. 7, p. 813–840.

——— and ———, 1991, The significance of normal faults in the exploration and production of North Sea hydrocarbons, *in* A.M. Roberts, G. Yielding, and B. Freeman, eds., The Geometry of Normal Faults: London, Geological Society of London, p. 1–16.

Hoshino, K., H. Koide, K. Inami, S. Iwamura, and S. Mitsui, 1972, Mechanical properties of Japanese Tertiary sedimentary rocks under high confining pressures: Geological Survey of Japan Report 244, 200 p.

Hubbert, M.K., 1953, Entrapment of petroleum under hydrodynamic conditions: AAPG Bulletin, vol. 37, no. 8, p. 1954–2026.

——— and D.G. Willis, 1957, Mechanics of hydraulic fracturing: JPT, vol. 9, no. 6, p. 153–168.

Jev, B.I., C.H. Kaars-Sijpesteign, M.P.A.M. Peters, N.W. Watts, and J.T. Wilkie, 1993, Akaso field, Nigeria: use of integrated 3-D seismic, fault-slicing, clay smearing and RFT pressure data on fault trapping and dynamic leakage: AAPG Bulletin, vol. 77, no. 8, p. 1389–1404.

Jiao, Z.D., R.C. Surdam, R.S. Martinsen, and W.P. Iverson, 1993, Capillary seals and pressure compartment boundaries in the Cretaceous section in the Power River basin, *in* J. Ebanks, J. Kaldi, and C. Vavra, eds., Seals and Traps: A Multidisciplinary Approach: AAPG Hedberg Research Conference, unpublished abstract.

Katz, A.J., and A.H. Thompson, 1986, Quantitative prediction of permeability in porous rock: Physical Review Bulletin, vol. 34, p. 8179–8181.

Knutson, C.A., and R. Erga, 1991, Effect of horizontal and vertical permeability restrictions in the Beryl reservoir: Journal of Petroleum Technology, vol. 43, p. 1502–1509.

Krushin, J., 1993, Entry pore throat size of nonsmectite shales, *in* J. Ebanks, J. Kaldi, and C. Vavra, eds., Seals and Traps: A Multidisciplinary Approach: AAPG Hedberg Research Conference, unpublished abstract.

Lama, R.D., and V.S. Vutukuri, 1978, Handbook of Mechanical Properties of Rocks: Rockport, MA, Trans. Technical Publications.

Leach, W.G., 1993a, Fluid migration, HC concentration in south Louisiana Tertiary sands: Oil & Gas Journal, vol. 91, no. 11, p. 71–74.

______, 1993b, Maximum hydrocarbon window determination in south Louisiana: Oil & Gas Journal, vol. 91, no. 13, p. 81–84.

Leith, T.L., I. Kaarshad, J. Connan, J. Pierron, and G. Caillet, 1993, Recognition of caprock leakage in the Snorre field, Norwegian North Sea: Marine and Petroleum Geology, vol. 10, no. 1, p. 29–41.

Lerche, I., 1990, Basin Analysis I: San Diego, Academic Press, 562 p.

______ and R.O. Thomsen, 1994, Hydrodynamics of Oil and Gas: New York, Plenum Press, 308 p.

Leythauser, D., R.G. Schaeffer, and A. Yukler, 1982, Role of diffusion in primary migration of hydrocarbons: AAPG Bulletin, vol. 66, no. 4, p. 408-–429.

Lorenz, J.C., L.W. Teufel, and N.R. Warpinski, 1991, Regional fractures: a mechanism for the formation of regional fractures at depth in flat-lying reservoirs: AAPG Bulletin, vol. 75, no. 11, p. 1714–1737.

Macdonald, I.F., P. Kaufmann, and F.A.L. Dullien, 1986, Quantitative image analysis of finite porous media 2: Specific genus of cubic lattice models and Berea sandstone: J. Microscopy, vol. 144, p. 297–316.

Mann, D.M., and A.S. Mackenzie, 1990, Prediction of pore fluid pressures in sedimentary basins: Marine and Petroleum Geology, vol. 7, no. 1, p. 55–65.

Matthews, W.R., and J. Kelly, 1967, How to predict formation pressure and fracture gradient from electric and sonic logs: Oil & Gas Journal, vol. 65, no. 8, p. 92–106.

Melas, F.F., and G.M. Friedman, 1992, Petrophysical characteristics of the Jurassic Smackover Formation, Jay field, Conecuh Embayment, Alabama and Florida: AAPG Bulletin, vol. 76, no. 1, p. 81–100.

Myers, J.D., 1968, Differential pressures: a trapping mechanism in Gulf Coast oil and gas fields: Gulf Coast Assoc. of Geologists Transactions, vol. 18, p. 56–80.

Nederlof, M.N., and H.P. Mohler, 1981, Quantitative investigation of trapping effect of unfaulted caprock: AAPG Bulletin, vol. 65, no. 6, p. 964.

Nelson, J.S., and E.C. Simmons, 1995, Diffusion of methane and ethane through the reservoir cap rock: Implications for the timing and duration of catagenesis: AAPG Bulletin, vol. 79, no. 7, p. 1064–1074.

Niemann, J., and M. Krowlow, 1992, Delineation of a pressure fault seal from shale resistivities, *in* J. Ebanks, J. Kaldi, and C. Vavra, eds., Seals and Traps: A Multidisciplinary Approach: AAPG Hedberg Research Conference, unpublished abstract.

Parry, W.T., and R.L. Bruhn, 1990, Fluid pressure transients on seismogenic normal faults: Tectonophysics, vol. 179, no. 3–4, p. 335–344.

Prasad, R.K., 1975, Pressure transient analysis in the presence of two intersecting boundaries: Society of Petroleum Engineers paper 4560.

Pittman, E.D., 1992, Relationship of porosity and permeability to various parameters derived from mercury injection-capillary pressure curves for sandstone: AAPG Bulletin, vol. 76, no. 2, p. 191–198.

Robinson, A., and J. Gluyas, 1992, Duration of quartz cementation in sandstones, North Sea and Haltenbanken basins: Marine and Petroleum Geology, vol. 9, no. 3, p. 324–327.

Roof, J.G., 1970, Snap-off of oil droplets in water-wet pores: SPE Journal, vol. 10, no. 1, p. 85–90.

Scharr, G., 1976, The occurrence of hydrocarbons in overpressured reservoirs of the Baram delta, offshore Sarawak, Malaysia: Fifth Annual Convention, Indonesian Petroleum Association, Proceedings, p. 163–169.

Schowalter, T.T., 1979, Mechanics of secondary hydrocarbon migration and entrapment: AAPG Bulletin, vol. 63, no. 5, p. 723–760.

Shea, W.T., J.R., Schwalbach, and D.M. Allard, 1993, Integrated rock-log evaluation of fluvio-lacustrine seals, *in* J. Ebanks, J. Kaldi, and C. Vavra, eds., Seals and Traps: A Multidisciplinary Approach: AAPG Hedberg Research Conference, unpublished abstract.

Sibson, R.H., J. Moore, and A.H. Rankin, 1975, Seismic pumping—a hydrothermal fluid transport mechanism: Journal of the Geological Society of London, vol. 131, p. 653–659.

Skerlec, G.M., 1982, Risking top seals in the Central Graben: Exxon Production Research Company internal report.

______, 1990, SEALS: A short course for risking top seal and fault seal: Franklin, Pennsylvania, SEALS International, 600 p.

______, 1992, Snap, crackle & pot: risking top seal integrity: AAPG Annual Convention program abstracts, p. 21.

______, 1997a, Atlas of fault seal behavior in the North Sea/Norwegian Sea: Franklin, Pennsylvania, SEALS International, 3948 p.

______, 1997b, Atlas of fault seal behavior in the Gulf Coast: Franklin, Pennsylvania, SEALS International, 4356 p.

Slujik, D., and M.H. Nederlof, 1984, Worldwide geological experience as a systematic basis for prospect appraisal, *in* G. Demaison and R.J. Murris, eds., Petroleum Geochemistry and Basin Evaluation: AAPG Memoir 35, p. 15–26.

Smith, D.A., 1966, Theoretical considerations of sealing and non-sealing faults: AAPG Bulletin, vol. 50, no. 2, p. 363–374.

______, 1980, Sealing and non-sealing faults in the Gulf Coast Salt basin: AAPG Bulletin, vol. 64, no. 2, p. 145–172.

Sneider, R.M., and G. Bolger, 1993, Estimating seals from wireline logs of clastic seals and reservoir intervals, *in* J. Ebanks, J. Kaldi, and C. Vavra, eds., Seals and Traps: A Multidisciplinary Approach: AAPG Hedberg Research Conference, unpublished abstract.

______, and J. Neasham, 1993, Comparison of seal capacity determination (SCD) from cores with SCD's from cuttings of the same interval, *in* J. Ebanks, J. Kaldi, and C. Vavra, eds., Seals and Traps: A Multidisciplinary Approach: AAPG Hedberg Research Conference, unpublished abstract.

Stearns, D.W., and M. Friedman, 1972, Reservoirs in fractured rock: AAPG Memoir 16, p. 82–106.

Stephenson, M., J. Cox, and P. Jones-Fuentes, 1992, How 3D seismic-CAEX combination affected development of N. Frisco City field in Alabama: Oil & Gas Journal, vol. 90, no. 43, p. 127–130.

Stewart, G., A. Gupta, and P. Westaway, 1984, The interpretation of interference tests in a reservoir with sealing and partially communicating faults: Society of Petroleum Engineers, paper 12967.

Thomas, L.K., D.L. Katz, and M.R. Ted, 1968, Threshold pressure phenomena in porous media: Transactions of SPE, vol. 243, p. 174–184.

Ungerer, P. J. Burrus, B. Doligez, P.Y. Chenet, and F. Bessis, 1990, Basin evaluation by integrated two-dimensional modeling of heat transfer, fluid flow, hydrocarbon generation, and migration: AAPG Bulletin, vol., 74, no. 3, p. 309–335.

van Poollen, H.K., 1965, Drawdown curves give angle between intersecting faults: Oil & Gas Journal, vol. 63, no. 52, p. 71–75.

Van Wijhe, D.H., M. Lutz, and J.P.H. Kaasschieter, 1980, The Rotliegend in the Netherlands and its gas accumulations: Geologie en Minjbouw, vol. 59, no. 1, p. 3–24.

Vavra, C.L., J.G., Kaldi, and R.M. Sneider, 1992, Geological applications of capillary pressure: a review: AAPG Bulletin, vol. 76, no. 6, p. 840–850.

Wardlaw, N.C., 1990, Quantitative determination of pore structure and application to fluid displacement in reservoir rocks, *in* J. Kleppe, E.W. Berg, A.T. Buller, O. Hjemeland, and O. Torsaeter, eds., North Sea Oil and Gas Reservoirs: London, Graham & Trotman, p. 229–243.

______ and R.P. Taylor, 1976, Mercury capillary pressure curves and the interpretation of pore structure and capillary behavior in reservoir rocks: Canadian Petroleum Geology Bulletin, vol. 24, no. 2, p. 225–262.

References, continued

Washburn, E.W., 1921, Note on a method of determining the distribution of pore sizes in a porous material: Proceedings of the National Academy of Science, vol. 7, p. 115–116.

Watts, N.L., 1983, Microfractures in chalks of the Albuskjell field, Norwegian sector, North Sea: possible origin and distribution: AAPG Bulletin, vol. 67, no. 2, p. 201–234.

______, 1987, Theoretical aspects of cap-rock and fault seals for single and two-phase hydrocarbon columns: Marine and Petroleum Geology, vol. 4, no. 4, p. 274–307.

Weber, K.J., G. Mandl, W.F. Pilaar, F. Lehner, and R.G. Precious, 1978, The role of faults in hydrocarbon migration and trapping Nigerian growth fault structures: Proceedings, Offshore Technology Conference, Houston, p. 2643–2652.

Wells, J.D., and J.O. Amafuele, 1985, Capillary pressure and permeability relationships in tight gas sands: SPE/DOE paper 13879.

Wilkinson, E.R., 1971, California offshore oil and gas seeps: California Oil Fields–Summary Operations, vol. 57, no. 1, p. 5–28.

Yaxley, L.M., 1987, Effect of a partially communicating fault on transient pressure behavior: Society of Petroleum Engineers, paper 14311.

Yielding, G., B. Freeman, and D.T. Needham, 1997, Quantitative fault seal prediction: AAPG Bulletin, vol. 81, no. 6, p. 897–917.

Zieglar, D.M., 1992, Hydrocarbon columns, buoyancy pressures, and seal efficiency: comparisons of oil and gas accumulations in California and the Rocky Mountain area: AAPG Bulletin, vol. 76, no. 4, p. 501–508.

Acknowledgments Many of these ideas and techniques have evolved over the past 20 years in courses and workshops on seal analysis as well as prospect and play assessments for numerous companies. I am grateful to them for contributing to our understanding of seals. I especially wish to thank my former colleagues at Exxon Production Research Company who have been leaders in developing many of these techniques for fault seal analysis. R. Vierbuchen first pointed out the relationship between shale density and ductility. Esso Exploration and Production kindly authorized permission to publish the examples of seal analysis in the North Sea. Chevron USA provided data for the Gulf Coast field example of routine fault seal analysis.

Chapter 11

Predicting Preservation and Destruction of Accumulations

by

Alton A. Brown

Alton A. Brown

Alton Brown (Ph.D.) is an exploration advisor at ARCO Exploration and Technology Co. in Plano, where he has worked on exploration research problems for the last 17 years. His research has concentrated on interdisciplinary problems concerning petroleum charge, migration, trapping, gas geochemistry, and carbonate deposition and diagenesis.

Overview

Introduction

Several processes deplete or destroy hydrocarbon accumulations. In many prospects it is not enough just to know that a trap is present in a basin where hydrocarbons were generated and migrated. We also must know that the trap was preserved over time.

This chapter discusses the mechanisms by which petroleum accumulations are destroyed. It also discusses the causes of destruction of accumulations and ways to predict accumulation preservation and destruction.

In this chapter

This chapter contains the following sections.

Section A

Basics: Destructive Processes and Age

Introduction

Some petroleum accumulations are likely to persist for hundreds of millions of years with relatively little alteration or dilution. Other accumulations, however, may be destroyed. It is imperative that explorationists know destructive processes and how to determine the age of an accumulation.

The problem

Petroleum may have accumulated at a prospect sometime in the past but may not be preserved in economic quantities, even where trapping geometry is still intact. Or a trap may still contain petroleum, but the oil and/or gas has been diluted or altered so that accumulations are no longer economic.

From an explorationist's point of view, these accumulations are destroyed. The problem is to determine where destruction of accumulations is likely and what mechanisms are likely to lead to destruction of accumulations in different geological settings.

Destructive processes

Petroleum can be destroyed as a result of the following processes, each of which is discussed in this chapter.

Process	Description
Spillage	Trapping geometry changes so petroleum spills below the sealing lithology.
Leakage	Lack of integrity of sealing lithology allows petroleum to leak through the seal.
Destruction	Petroleum is destroyed, altered, or diluted with nonhydrocarbon gases.
Cementation	Reservoir quality drops below economic limits.

Determining age of accumulations

Accumulations should be dated to evaluate the potential importance of accumulation destruction in an area of interest. Leakage, spillage, petroleum destruction, and cementation are more likely to alter the size and quality of old accumulations than young accumulations. Young accumulations with active petroleum charge are more likely to be affected by displacement of oil by later gas charge. Accumulation preservation is a function of tectonic setting, trap type, depth of burial, and seal type (Mcgregor, 1996).

Three methods help us determine the age of accumulations.

1. Dating the generation of the trapped hydrocarbons
2. Dating the formation of the reservoir, seal, and trap
3. Directly measuring entrapment by radiometric means

In **dating the generation of the trapped hydrocarbons**, we use geohistory models to determine when the oil or gas charged an accumulation. If the migration distance is short, this date is an estimate of the age of the accumulation. Oil and gas may remigrate later due to structural growth, so these dates may overestimate the true age of the accumulation. For example, by this approach Sho-Vel-Tum trend oil fields in southern Okla-

Determining age of accumulations (continued)

homa accumulated from the Atokan (early Pennsylvanian), when generation began in the Ardmore basin, to Permian, when oil generation ended in the Ardmore and Anadarko basins. Because no significant tectonic events have changed the structure of these fields since trapping, these accumulations are at least 250 m.y. old—maybe as old as 300 m.y.

In **dating the formation of the reservoir, seal, and trap**, the age of an accumulation can be no older than the age of the reservoir, seal, or trapping geometry. For example, offshore Gulf of Mexico accumulations in Pleistocene reservoirs can be no older than the Pleistocene.

Direct radiometric measurements are difficult to perform because most reservoirs do not have datable material that formed during charging. The Groningen gas field (Permian, the Netherlands) has been dated as pre-Late Jurassic by the retardation effect of gas on radiometrically datable illite cements in the reservoir (Lee et al., 1985).

Section B
Spillage

Introduction

Spillage occurs in one of three ways:

- Changes in the trapping geometry
- Changes in the fluid contact due to hydrodynamics
- Reduction in reservoir volume due to postaccumulation cementation

Petroleum loss across faults is considered spillage, not leakage, because faults are part of the trapping geometry. Petroleum shows in spilled accumulations are usually immobile at relatively constant residual saturation over a thick section of the reservoir, with a paleo-fluid contact located near the base of the residual saturation. Petroleum in structurally spilled accumulations is relatively unaltered; oil in hydrodynamically spilled accumulations, on the other hand, is usually altered.

In this section

This section contains the following topics.

Changes in Trapping Geometry

Introduction

We often assume that a structure remains static when charged by petroleum. Traps may be charged during structural growth, and accumulations can be partially or completely spilled by later structural deformation.

Traps charged during structural growth are not destroyed by spillage as long as the trapping geometry is maintained during deformation because petroleum migrates with the structural closure much faster than the rate of structural growth (Hubbert, 1953). Conversely, if structural closure is destroyed during deformation, spillage occurs rapidly.

Paleofluid contacts may be tilted where spillage results from structural tilting. For example, Prudhoe Bay field, charged during the Late Cretaceous and tilted during the late Eocene (Atkinson et al., 1990), resulted in a tilted paleo oil–water contact.

Change in a fold trap

The figure below shows how continued growth of a foreland-sloping duplex preserves an accumulation in an early duplex but displaces the accumulation relative to the reservoir rock. The stippled area outlining the initial accumulation is fixed relative to the rock. The solid area on the lower figure marks the accumulation at the top of the structure after movement.

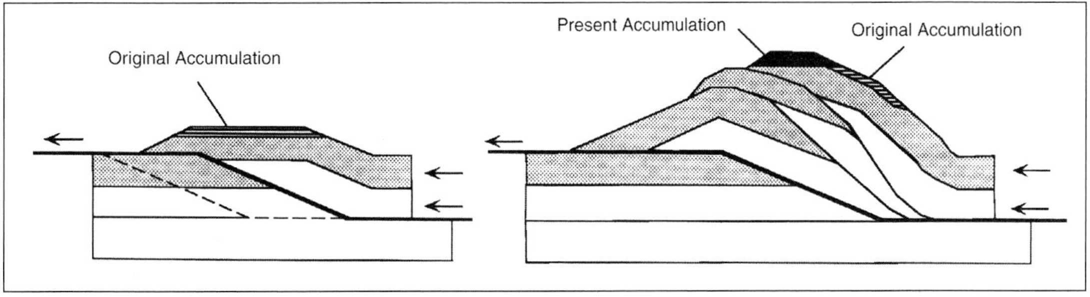

Figure 11–1. Modified from Mitra, 1986; courtesy AAPG.

Similarly, where the axis of a fault-bend fold on a hanging wall is fixed relative to the bend of the fault on the foot wall, the actual rock occupying the fold changes during movement along the fault. However, the position of the trap remains approximately fixed relative to the footwall and the fault bend.

Changes in Trapping Geometry, continued

Change in a fault trap

Traps in which faults form part of the closure are especially susceptible to spillage during structural growth because movement on the fault may result in leakage. Movement on the fault is also likely to juxtapose permeable lithologies across the fault at some point in the movement. The figure below shows spillage resulting from movement on a sealing fault.

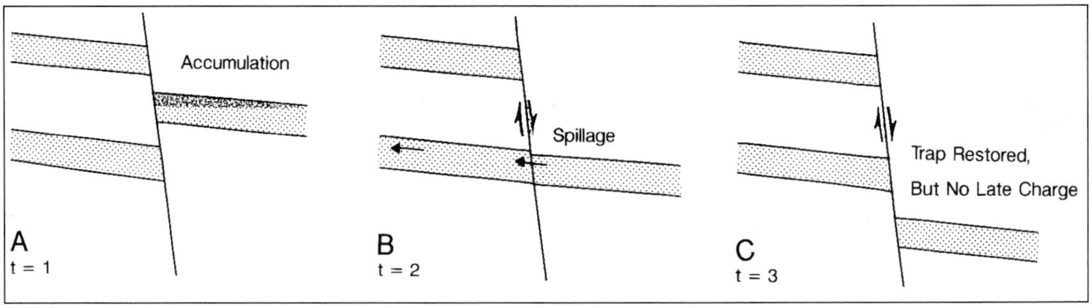

Figure 11–2.

As the fault displaces the units, an early charged trap (A, at t = 1) is juxtaposed against a sandstone at some later time (B, at t = 2). This probably will result in rapid spillage. If further fault movement restores favorable seal juxtaposition (C, at t = 3), additional petroleum charge will be needed to fill the new trap.

Evaluating spillage

Structural spillage is avoided if trapping geometry is maintained during deformation after charging. Structural closure must be maintained at all times during subsequent deformation. Throws on faults likely to cut the seal at the accumulation should be less than the seal thickness to avoid spillage by juxtaposition across the fault plane.

Spillage potential can be evaluated by combining geohistory analysis and structural analysis. **Geohistory analysis** (combined analysis of burial, thermal, and generation history) of gathering areas for prospects gives the range of charging times for the prospect [essentially the time of generation in nearby gathering areas (England et al., 1991)]. **Structural analysis**, using balanced structural cross sections as well as cross-cutting and superposition relationships, gives the range of times for trapping geometry formation and failure.

Changes in Hydrodynamic Configuration

Introduction

Fluid contacts can tilt in response to fluid potential gradients in underlying water. If the tilt of the fluid contact exceeds the dip of the reservoir–seal interface on the down-potential (flow downdip) side of the trap, the accumulation will spill downdip. If petroleum is trapped under hydrodynamic conditions on an unclosed structure, decrease in the potential gradient may result in spillage of the petroleum updip.

The figure below shows the effects of hydrodynamics on trapping. During water movement (Hydrodynamic, top figure), oil accumulations are displaced from the structural crest; gas may remain near the crest of the structure (A). Even unclosed structures can be traps, as long as the downdip tilt is steeper than the tilt to the oil–water contact (B).

If water movement stops (Hydrostatic, lower figure), the accumulations quickly return to trapping at the crest of structural closures (C). Some structural closures may have accumulations; nearby closures may not (D).

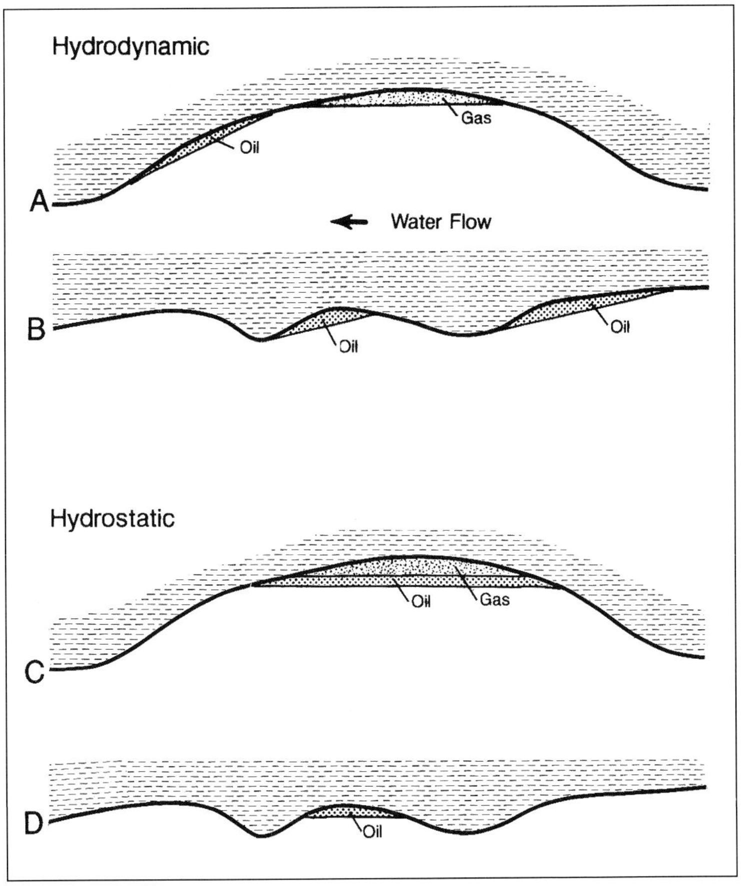

Figure 11–3.

Duration of hydrodynamic regimes

Petroleum distribution adjusts to trapping hydrodynamics much faster than changes in natural hydrodynamic regimes (Hubbert, 1953). In general, hydrodynamic regimes, especially those established by elevation–head differences in recharge, are time-transient events that are much shorter than the theoretical lifetime of accumulations under hydrostatic conditions. If present hydrodynamic flow affects fluid contacts of reservoirs charged in the past, then spillage and tertiary migration probably have occurred.

Hydrodynamic mapping

To evaluate the potential for spillage from hydrodynamic effects, we can construct maps (potentiometric; U,V,Z; hydrodynamic) for the reservoir horizons of interest. U,V,Z mapping determines present oil and gas potential minima (traps) [described by Hubbert (1953) and Dahlberg (1982)]. Where data quality is good, hydrodynamic mapping can identify (1) structural closures that have spilled as a result of hydrodynamics and (2) hydrodynamic traps.

Evaluating ancient spillage

Ancient hydrodynamic events that have occurred since charging can be identified by evaluating topographic evolution in the area around the basin of interest (evaluate patterns of subsurface salt dissolution, tectonic history, and map unconformities around the basin). Direction and magnitude of flow can be inferred but not quantified. Although petroleum resumes its hydrostatic configuration once hydrodynamic conditions cease, some traps may have essentially all movable petroleum flushed from their structural fetch area if potentiometric gradients were steep (as shown in Figure 11–3, A and B).

Postaccumulation Cementation

Introduction

Although the presence of a petroleum phase may retard diagenesis in an accumulation, sooner or later reservoir quality decreases with increasing age and burial (Bloch, 1991).

The process

As the pore volume within a trap decreases due to burial cementation, several phenomena combine to destroy the economic accumulation.

Step	Phenomenon
1	Petroleum is displaced from the trap at the spill point as the pore volume within the structural closure decreases. If porosity is lowered sufficiently, the accumulation may be subeconomic in size.
2	Reduced porosity may result in lower permeability so that production rates are subeconomic, even where economic quantities of petroleum are still trapped.
3	As pore size decreases in a petroleum-filled reservoir, the capillary pressure of the petroleum phase must increase to occupy the pore spaces (assuming no change in wettability). In low-permeability tight sands or carbonates, the capillary displacement pressure in the reservoir rock may approach that of moderate-quality seals. As a result, a lithology that could seal an accumulation at shallow depth may no longer be effective at deeper depths because it differs little from the reservoir rock.

Predicting spillage by cementation

Reduced porosity can be predicted from empirical–statistical evaluation of porosity data for reservoir intervals with similar composition and burial history as the prospect (Schmoker and Gautier, 1988; Bloch, 1991). In general, porosity decreases with increasing age, depth, and temperature. Numerical modeling techniques are not yet refined enough to quantitatively predict prospect reservoir quality loss.

Consequences of Spillage

Introduction

Spillage can occur in three different ways, as discussed in this section. We also need to note the consequences that result from spillage.

Consequences of spillage

The following changes can occur due to spillage:

- Where charging occurred with large-scale deformation, large volumes of rock not in present-day traps may have acquired residual petroleum saturation as porous intervals occupied former traps.
- Structural growth might have allowed migrating petroleum to escape to the surface. Once lost, the petroleum is no longer available to fill accumulations to economic size, so overall migration efficiency may decline.
- Areas of structural growth after charging can leak if the seal is fractured during deformation (see section C, "Leakage").
- Areas with hydrodynamic trapping may have problems with variable oil quality due to biodegradation (see section D, "Petroleum Destruction").

Section C
Leakage

Introduction

Leakage occurs when petroleum escapes a trap through the sealing lithology. Escape of petroleum up a fault which cuts the sealing lithology is also leakage. Leakage along faults can occur by the same mechanisms which control leakage through top seals.

In this section

This section covers the following topics.

Leakage Mechanisms

Introduction

Five major seal failure mechanisms form the basis for this section's discussion on seal leakage.

Seal failure mechanisms

A given seal can leak by one of several mechanisms, as defined by Watts (1987).

Seal Type	Seal Failure Mechanism
Intact membrane	Capillary pressure (created by the height of the underlying petroleum column) exceeds seal capillary displacement pressure. This seal type does not fracture during deformation.
Fractured membrane	Capillary pressure (created by the height of the underlying petroleum column) exceeds displacement pressure of fracture porosity in the seal.
Hydrofractured	Total fluid pressure (capillary pressure plus water pressure) exceeds minimum compressive stress of the seal; seal fails by natural hydraulic fracturing.
Micropermeability	Leakage is caused by low displacement pressures of oil-wet seals or by capillary pressure of the reservoir exceeding displacement pressure of the seal in a water-wet seal. Accumulations are preserved for geologically significant time if leakage rate is low. Rate of leakage is controlled by seal effective permeability.
Diffusive	Gas is lost by dissolving in water and diffusing through interstitial water of the seal.

Comparison of mechanisms

The first three mechanisms listed in the table above have minimum pressure criteria to be exceeded before leakage occurs. Even after leakage, an economic column of petroleum may remain. The last two mechanisms can destroy an accumulation, given enough time.

Intact Membrane Seal Leakage

Introduction

An intact membrane seal fails when the capillary pressure (created by the height of an underlying petroleum column) exceeds the seal capillary displacement pressure. This type of seal does not fracture during deformation.

Ductility and capillary displacement pressure

Fine-grained, water-wet ductile rocks will seal as long as the capillary pressure exerted on the seal (the difference between the water and the petroleum fluid pressure) is less than the capillary displacement pressure of the matrix porosity of the seal. Under these conditions, the relative permeability of the seal to petroleum is zero. The accumulation remains preserved until one of three things happens:

1. The seal is ruptured or altered.
2. The structure is spilled.
3. The petroleum is altered.

Most old accumulations have seals of this type.

Claystones, salt, and sulfates (gypsum and anhydrite) make seals of this sort because they are ductile under most geological strain rates and confining pressures. Ductility is important; if fracturing occurs, oil can leak through the fractures without invading the matrix porosity.

Deeply buried claystones, salts, and anhydrite have capillary displacement pressures great enough to exceed the buoyancy pressure from any reasonable oil column height (hundreds to thousands of feet). Conversely, silty mudrocks, shallow-buried claystones, and argillaceous siltstones have displacement pressures low enough to allow leakage even where the petroleum column has not filled to the structural spill point.

Predicting leakage

The failure of intact membrane seals after charging is rare because the capillary displacement pressure of mudrock seals increases with compaction and burial. Intact seal failure usually results in failure to trap in the first place. Limitations on the height of the petroleum column due to intact membrane seal failure can be evaluated by laboratory capillary pressure tests (Berg, 1975) in conjunction with estimates of in situ petroleum density.

Fractured Membrane Seal Leakage

Introduction

Fractured membrane seals fail when the capillary pressure created by the height of an underlying petroleum column exceeds the displacement pressure of the fracture porosity in the seal.

Characteristics

Many rock types with high capillary displacement pressures rarely seal petroleum accumulations. These rocks are often characterized by brittle behavior, i.e., they fracture easily at geological strain rates and confining pressures.

Fracture apertures may be much larger than matrix pore apertures in fine-grained rocks, so it is easier for petroleum to invade the fractures than the matrix porosity. In fact, many fractured rocks with open fractures have apertures so wide that they generally cannot seal economically thick petroleum columns.

The seal capacity of brittle, fine-grained rocks is not confirmed by capillary-pressure tests because seal failure is through the fractures, not the matrix pore network.

Lithologies

Brittle, fine-grained rocks—cherts, clay-free limestones and dolomites, and well-sorted siltstones—almost never seal. Intermediate lithologies such as calcareous or siliceous shales, argillaceous siltstones, and argillaceous or anhydritic limestones can seal where the rocks have not been excessively strained, such as in stratigraphic traps or broad, gentle folds. Even relatively intact, thick seals may be fractured at the high strain rates and total strains in some disturbed belts.

Predicting leakage

Leakage due to fractured membrane seal failure is most likely to destroy an accumulation when the seal is deformed after charging. In general, the tighter the folding and the faster the deformation rate, the more likely a given seal lithology will fail by fracture. The more brittle the lithology, the more likely seal failure will occur with deformation. Thick seals are less likely to fail by fracturing than thin seals of similar lithology at the same level of deformation because deformation is less likely to form an open fracture pathway as the pathway lengthens.

Seal response to deformation can be evaluated empirically by examining nearby accumulations or outcrops in similar tectonic settings.

Hydrofractured Seal Leakage

Introduction

In settings with extreme overpressure, pore-water pressure approaches the pressure required for natural hydraulic fracturing. If the petroleum column is thick enough, the sum of the capillary pressure and fluid pressure can equal or exceed the pressure needed to fracture the rock. The result is natural hydraulic fracturing: the seal becomes hydrofractured and the petroleum leaks.

Characteristics

Unlike other fractured seals, hydrofractures remain open only as long as pore pressure exceeds fracture pressure. Once the total pressure drops, the fracture closes. The petroleum column height remains approximately in equilibrium with the difference between the water pressure and the fracture pressure.

Hydraulic fracture seal failure affects all rock types, but the fracture gradient is a function of rock type and basin. Usually hydraulic fracturing limits the petroleum column height during charging instead of destroying accumulations after charging. This occurs where accumulations are charged during times of peak geopressure so the trap capacity is minimal. Charging occurs during times of peak geopressure because both charging and geopressure are a response to high sedimentation and heating rates.

Predicting leakage in deep accumulations

Hydrofractured seal leakage limits the thickness of a petroleum column whether the seal fails during or after charging. Leakage in deeply buried accumulations occurs only where geopressure is close to the fracture gradient (hard geopressures). Hard geopressures are characteristic of shale-dominated basins that have undergone recent rapid subsidence.

We can use downhole fluid pressure analysis techniques (e.g., Caillet, 1993) to evaluate hydrofractured seal failure for an area. Leak-off tests estimate the fracture gradient, and mud weight, well logs, or seismic data approximate the fluid pressure gradients. Because gas and condensate have much lower densities than oil, gas columns are more likely to have hydraulic failure than oil columns of the same height in similar settings.

Predicting leakage in shallow accumulations

Hydrofractured seals also leak in shallow accumulations of normal water pressure. At depths < 1000 ft, the absolute magnitude of the difference between water pressure and geostatic pressure is relatively small—on the order of several hundred pounds per square inch. Exceptionally thick (1000–2000 ft) columns of gas or oil have a capillary pressure equal to or greater than this difference, so hydrofracturing may occur.

The potential for shallow hydrofractured leakage is best evaluated from a pressure–depth diagram, where

- Water pressure gradient is estimated from water salinity.
- Geostatic pressure gradient is estimated from density logs or porosity trend.
- Petroleum density is estimated from the gas–oil ratio (GOR), API gravity, temperature, and pressure.

Micropermeable Seal Leakage

Introduction

Micropermeable leakage is caused by a variety of seal failure mechanisms, as discussed in the following sections.

Characteristics

Some fine-grained rocks, such as mature source rocks, are oil wet (McAuliffe, 1980). Leakage through these seals does not require that capillary pressure exceed displacement pressure because oil spontaneously imbibes into oil-wet rocks. Likewise, some water-wet seals have petroleum column heights that may exceed the capillary displacement pressure of matrix porosity. The effective permeability to petroleum is no longer zero, but it may be small. Finally, where fractures are few or where fracture apertures are very small, fracture porosity may be invaded, but the leakage rate may be small.

In these cases, accumulations can last for a geologically significant amount of time if the permeability of the seal to petroleum is low enough. These seals most likely occur in young basins where traps are still actively charged. Because the seals leak, the height of the petroleum column decreases with time since charging. Permeability and relative permeability of fine-grained rocks are difficult to analyze; however, accumulations apparently sealed by oil-wet source rocks have existed for tens to hundreds of millions of years, so at least in some settings the leakage rate is low enough to ignore.

Example: Ekofisk field

Like many North Sea chalk reservoirs, Ekofisk field has distinctive geochemical and geophysical evidence of gas escape into overlying Cenozoic mudrocks (Van den Bark and Thomas, 1981). The mechanism of seal failure leading to a micropermeable seal is undocumented, but overlying Paleocene shales are immature and therefore are not oil wet. Pore pressures decrease downward into the field from the seal. In both the seal and the reservoir, fluid pressures are less than 75% of overburden stress. This indicates natural hydraulic fracturing of the seal is unlikely unless tectonically assisted (Watts, 1983). Because capillary pressures at the top of the reservoir exceed 180 psi, the intact membrane seal is probably leaking.

Predicting leakage

Micropermeable leakage is difficult to predict from rock properties because wettability and permeability of seals are poorly known in exploration settings. Micropermeable leakage can be geophysically and geochemically detected where it occurs at a moderately rapid rate in a dynamic basinal environment, as in the preceding example.

Leakage by any mechanism obviously goes through a drainage stage when the seal leaks like a micropermeable seal. Because micropermeable leakage can be slow, it is more likely to destroy old rather than young accumulations. Many fields not filled to the spill point in oil basins with former prolific generation (such as those along the Aylesworth anticline in the Anadarko basin) were probably once filled to the spill point and have since leaked to their present contacts. Marginal seal lithologies such as argillaceous carbonates or siltstone are more likely to suffer micropermeable leakage than accumulations under salt or claystone seals (Grunau, 1987).

Diffusive Seal Leakage

Introduction

Natural gas can dissolve in water to a significant enough degree that diffusion through water in the seal rock can result in substantial loss of gas, given geological time. Because of their very low solubility in water, black oils and high molecular-weight components of oil cannot leak by this mechanism, even at high temperatures (McAuliffe, 1980). Leakage rates determined in various published studies demonstrate the likelihood of gas accumulations lasting for tens to hundreds of million years (e.g., Montel et al., 1993).

Predicting leakage

Only gas accumulations can be destroyed by diffusive leakage. For most seal lithologies, loss by diffusion is very slow; so most gas accumulations are preserved for tens to hundreds of millions of years. Rates of loss have been modeled (e.g., Montel et al., 1993), but data necessary to quantitatively predict accumulation preservation at a particular prospect are difficult to acquire.

Diffusive leakage is favored by high temperature, high pressure, and a thin, porous seal. Older accumulations are more likely to be destroyed by this process, and late Cenozoic accumulations are not likely to be destroyed by this process.

Predicting Overall Seal Failure

Introduction

A seal can fail when capillary pressure exceeds seal entry pressure, open fractures bypass matrix pore systems, hydrofracturing occurs, leakage takes place through micropermeable lithologies, or gas is diffused. The most likely mechanism is controlled by the seal lithology and the geological history.

Seal failure timing

Seals are most likely to fail during trapping, so an accumulation does not form in the first place. Top-seal failure after charging is most likely caused by fracturing during deformation or by cumulative micropermeability or diffusive seal loss.

Leakage associated with faults

Leakage is commonly associated with faults. Fault leakage is a function of fault-fill lithology, lithology of surrounding rocks, and timing. Note these characteristics to evaluate fault-associated leakage:

- Calculate smear-gouge ratio or shale smear factor to estimate fault-fill lithology. Petroleum leakage up faults is a type of membrane seal failure. The higher the shale content of the fault fill, the less the chance of fault-plane leakage.
- Faults may localize fracturing through the top seal, so evaluate the potential for fractured membrane seal leakage in the top-seal lithology (p. 11–16).
- Faults must connect to permeable beds higher in the section or to the surface to leak significant amounts of petroleum. If growth faults die upsection into a shale interval, leakage may be minimal except where natural hydrofracture ruptures seals (p. 11–17).
- Fractures and fault fill may heal by cementation once fault movement stops. Leakage is less likely if trap charge significantly postdates fault movement.
- Conversely, fault movement during or after charge of the trap will always result in some leakage, probably by a form of natural hydraulic fracturing along the fault plane. If charge is sufficient, leakage may be slower than charge, so petroleum may accumulate and be preserved as long as charging continues.

Recognizing leaky traps

Traps with leaky seals or reduced seal capacity may still maintain an economic column of petroleum. Partially leaked traps are characterized by a zone of residual petroleum saturation thicker than the transition zone predicted by capillary pressure tests. Shows in traps that have leaked are similar to those in spilled traps. Paleofluid contacts are usually flat, not tilted like spilled traps.

Section D
Petroleum Destruction

Introduction

Petroleum can be destroyed either in the burial environment or in the near-surface environment.

In this section

This section covers the following topics.

Burial Destruction

Introduction

Given the strong economic control of petroleum type on development of an accumulation, the conversion of oil to gas or dilution of gas by nonhydrocarbon components in the deep burial environment may make an accumulation uneconomic and, from an exploration point of view, "destroyed." The following burial processes destroy accumulations by altering the properties of the petroleum:

- Gasification
- Gas destruction
- Gas dilution

Gasification

Gasification is the conversion of oil to gas resulting from thermal cracking. It primarily takes place during burial. If oil is spilled from a trap by gas displacement during gasification, the oil may occur in economic accumulations updip along the migration pathway (Gussow, 1954).

Predicting and recognizing gasification

The following characteristics can help us predict and recognize gasification.

- Geohistory analysis with proper gasification kinetics can usually predict at what depth accumulations have been gasified.
- As a rule of thumb, oil should not be expected at subsurface temperatures > 150°C or a maturation level much above 1.3% R_o. Dry gas accumulations can occur at shallower depths, but oil is not likely at greater depths.
- Gasification of oil in reservoirs is associated with the formation of pyrobitumen (Tissot and Welte, 1984, p. 460–461).
- Displacement of oil from a trap by gas is associated with asphaltene precipitates and/or relatively unaltered oil stain.
- Absence of an oil leg in the trap prior to charging by gas is indicated by the absence of oil stain with heavy molecular components.
- In accumulations that have been gasified, the presence of pyrobitumen can significantly reduce reservoir permeability due to gas or condensate.

Gas destruction

Methane is the most thermodynamically stable hydrocarbon in sedimentary basins (Hunt, 1979). Methane apparently can be destroyed only by oxidation. The most common form of oxidation in the burial environment is thermogenic sulfate reduction (Krouse, 1979). The presence of oxidized iron can also remove methane at high temperatures.

Studies by Barker and Takach (1992) indicate water can oxidize methane to carbon dioxide and hydrogen gas at temperatures as low as 200°C, assuming systems are at thermodynamic equilibrium. Where oxygen fugacity is buffered at modestly reducing conditions, methane is calculated to remain stable to temperatures > 400°C (Green et al., 1987).

Predicting gas destruction

It is not the destruction of methane as much as the lack of economic accumulations which occurs at higher maturation levels. Methane occurs in fluid inclusions from lower crustal depths, and shows of methane are not unusual where drilling through low-grade metamorphic rocks—even those at a grade high enough to contain graphite instead of kerogen ($R_o > 8\%$). For example the Shell Barret #1 well in Hill County, Texas, had a 30-minute methane flare at over 13,000 ft depth in rock described as dolomite and calcite marble with graphitic inclusions (Rozendal and Erskine, 1971).

The following characteristics can help us predict and recognize gas destruction:

- Economic gas accumulations become more unusual with maturation levels > 2.8% R_o (Bartenstein, 1980). This is the traditional base of the gas preservation zone.
- The major gas accumulation with the highest well-documented maturity level where charging occurred before or during exposure to the high temperatures occurs at a maturation level 3.5–3.8% R_o equivalent (Wilburton field, Oklahoma, Hendrick, 1992).

Gas dilution

Carbon dioxide, hydrogen sulfide, and nitrogen can constitute a significant percentage of natural gas from some accumulations. In some cases, natural gas is uneconomic due to the high nonhydrocarbon gas content.

Although low concentrations of carbon dioxide can be derived from organic sources or byproducts of silicate reactions at moderate temperatures (Smith and Ehrenberg, 1989), high concentrations of carbon dioxide are usually associated with igneous intrusion or regional heating of impure limestones (Farmer, 1965).

Hydrogen sulfide concentration increases with depth in gas reservoirs with anhydrite, indicating that it, too, is a product of higher maturity (Krouse, 1979). The methane is reacting with the sulfate to form hydrogen sulfide and carbon dioxide gas. The reaction is probably kinetically controlled.

The origin of nitrogen gas is not well characterized. In nonpetroleum basins, nitrogen may have high concentration because no other gas is present to dilute it. High-nitrogen gas in thermally mature basins is possibly from coal sources (Stahl et al., 1978) or from the mantle or deep crust (Jenden and Kaplan, 1989).

Predicting burial destruction

The following characteristics can help us predict and recognize burial destruction.

- Analyzing geohistory or mapping maturation indicators can identify reservoir maturation levels where methane accumulations may be uneconomic. Most sizable gas accumulations occurring at maturation levels > 2.8% R_o have thick claystone seals that help preserve the accumulation.
- Presence of intrusives in the fetch area can indicate a potential for carbon dioxide dilution (e.g., Parker, 1974).
- If reservoir rocks are associated with evaporite cements or beds, expect hydrogen sulfide if the reservoir is exposed to temperatures > 150°C and iron is not present to remove the hydrogen sulfide.
- Nitrogen is released during the late stages of coal maturation (Jüntgen and Karweil, 1966). Therefore, if a prospect is charged by a type III source rock only during its late maturation stage (R_o > 2.5%), nitrogen dilution is possible. High nitrogen gas content is also characteristic of evaporative settings and hydrocarbon-poor basins.
- Nonhydrocarbon gas concentrations in mature basins can be estimated from evaluating regional gas concentration trends.

The table below summarizes techniques that help us predict hydrocarbon destruction during burial.

Process	Prediction Techniques	
Gasification	• Geohistory analysis • Mapping maturation indicators (no oil, where reservoir R_o > 1.3%)	
Gas destruction	• Geohistory analysis • Mapping maturation indicators (gas unlikely where reservoir Ro> 2.8%)	
Gas dilution	Identified by	Indicates potential for
	• Intrusives in fetch area	• Carbon dioxide
	• Evaporite cements or beds at depths where temperature > 150°C	• Hydrogen sulfide
	• Gas sourced from coal, high thermal maturity	• Nitrogen
	• Low methane charge	• Carbon dioxide, nitrogen

Near-Surface Destruction

Introduction

Oil and gas in near-surface accumulations and in seeps can be destroyed by three processes that may act concurrently:

1. Biodegradation
2. Water washing
3. Devolatilization

The solid fraction of oil unaffected by these processes ultimately is recycled in the erosional regime. Because all three processes result in oil with higher viscosity, sulfur, and nitrogen, the processes may reduce the economic value of the accumulation before the accumulation is actually destroyed.

Biodegradation

Saturated fractions of oil and gas are readily biodegraded in the near-surface environment by a host of microbial communities; as biodegradation proceeds, other components of the oil can also be destroyed (Palmer, 1991). These factors aid biodegradation:

- Availability of oxidant and nutrient
- Inoculation of the reservoir by a microbial community that can degrade the oil
- Temperature below approximately 170°F (Tissot and Welte, 1984)

Geochemical signatures of biodegradation

The geochemical signatures of biodegradation are very distinctive. Shown below are whole-oil gas chromatographs of a heavily biodegraded oil (A) and its undegraded precursor (B) on an example from offshore Louisiana. Normal paraffins (sharp peaks in B) have been removed by bacterial action.

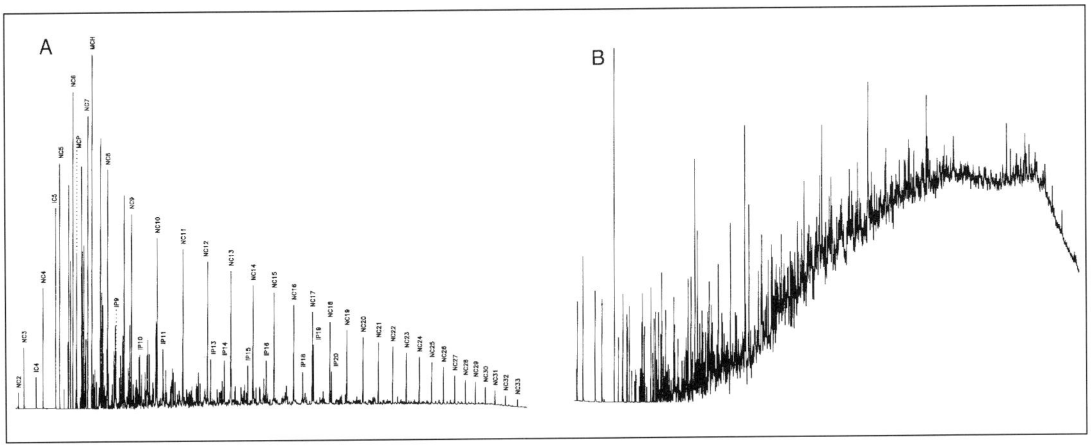

Figure 11–4.

Near-Surface Destruction, continued

Predicting and recognizing biodegradation

The following characteristics can help us predict and recognize biodegradation.

- Biodegradation occurs most rapidly in oil accumulations exposed to active meteoric water circulation because the water supplies the oxidants or nutrients.
- Because biodegradation apparently does not significantly affect asphaltenes and many high-molecular-weight aromatics, severe biodegradation does not destroy the oil entirely.
- For aromatic oils, biodegradation results in loss of only 10–20% of the mass of the oil (Horstad et al., 1992).
- Because many oils have a high fraction of saturate molecules (Tissot and Welte, 1984), it is possible that over 50% of the mass of the oil and gas may be removed.
- Condensates and dry gases are also affected by biodegradation (Walters, 1990).
- Most biodegraded oils are characterized by higher viscosity and lower API gravity than unaltered petroleum, but biodegraded high-wax oils may have lower viscosity.
- Sulfur and nitrogen concentration increases in most biodegraded oils.

Water washing

Water washing is the dissolution of light molecular species from oil and gas into water (Lafargue and Barker, 1988). Significant water washing requires rapid water flow under the accumulation. Light aromatic molecules are affected most severely. Severe water washing may remove at most 5–10% of the oil mass, so it does not lead to destruction of accumulations by itself. Water washing at shallow depths is usually accompanied by biodegradation and devolatilization.

Devolatilization

Where the reservoir is exhumed or where the seal is breached near the surface, light molecular species will evaporate into the atmosphere due to their high vapor pressure. The volatile hydrocarbons are presumably oxidized in the atmosphere. This is devolatilization. The process selectively strips the oil of components up to a carbon number of about 15 or so. This process can account for destruction of up to 50% of the mass of the oil and essentially all gas and condensate. Most devolatilized oils have viscosity so high that conventional recovery may be uneconomic.

Example: Near-surface loss

Kern River field (San Joaquin basin, California) is an accumulation of 4 billion bbl of original oil in place of 13°API, biodegraded, water washed, and devolatized oil at a subsurface depth of tens to hundreds of feet. The trap is a combination hydrodynamic/structural trap on the south and west sides (Kodl et al., 1990), with stratigraphic trapping due to tar-sealing and sand pinch-outs on the homoclinally dipping east side of the field (Nicholson, 1980). Oil source is the same for undegraded, 34° oils farther downdip on the Bakersfield nose.

By assuming that asphaltene and resin volumes were just concentrated and not altered by near-surface processes, the amount of oil components lost in the near-surface environment can be calculated. An estimated 77% of the oil reaching the Kern River field was lost by near-surface processes, 92% of the saturates were lost, and 60% of the aromatics were lost. This means approximately 16 billion bbl of oil reached the vicinity of Kern River field, of which about 12 billion bbl were lost by near-surface processes as the field was charged.

Near-Surface Destruction, continued

Predicting near-surface destruction

Analyze low-gravity oils and bitumens to determine if the poor oil quality is due to biodegradation, maturation level, or source type. Water washing and biodegradation are usually associated with active aquifers, which can be determined from potentiometric maps. Temperature or geothermal gradient maps can outline parts of reservoir formations where biodegradation is likely to be active (T < 76°C). Basin-peripheral tar sands may result from degrading of oil as the migration pathway intersects the surface. These indicate where and in which formation migration occurs. Look downdip from tar sands for possible productive accumulations on the migration pathway.

Section E
References

Atkinson, C., J. McGowen, S. Block, L. Lundell, and P. Trumbly, 1990, Braidplain and deltaic reservoirs, Prudhoe Bay field, Alaska, *in* J. Barwis, J. McPherson, and J. Studlick, eds., Sandstone Petroleum Reservoirs: New York, Springer-Verlag, p. 7–30.

Barker, C., and N.E. Takach, 1992, Prediction of natural gas composition in ultradeep sandstone reservoirs: AAPG Bulletin, vol. 76, p. 1859–1873.

Bartenstein, H., 1980, Coalification in NW Germany: Erdöl und Kohle-Erdgas-Petrochemie: vol. 33, p. 121–125.

Berg, R.R., 1975, Capillary pressures in stratigraphic traps: AAPG Bulletin, vol. 59, p. 939–956.

Bloch, S., 1991, Empirical prediction of porosity and permeability in sandstones: AAPG Bulletin, vol. 75, p. 1145–1160.

Caillet, G., 1993, The caprock of the Snorre field, Norway: a possible leakage by hydraulic fracturing: Marine and Petroleum Geology, vol. 10, p. 42–50.

Dahlberg, E.C., 1982, Applied Hydrodynamics in Petroleum Exploration: New York, Springer-Verlag, 161 p.

England, W.A., A.L. Mann, and D.M. Mann, 1991, Migration from source to trap, *in* R.K. Merrill, ed., Source and Migration Processes and Evaluation Techniques: AAPG Treatise of Petroleum Geology Handbook of Petroleum Geology, p. 23–46.

Farmer, R.E., 1965, Genesis of subsurface carbon dioxide, *in* A. Young and J. Galley, eds., Fluids in Subsurface Environments: AAPG Memoir No. 4, p. 378–385.

Green, D.H., T.J. Falloon, and W.R. Taylor, 1987, Mantle-derived magmas—roles of variable source peridotite and variable C-H-O fluid compositions, *in* B. O. Mysen, ed., Magmatic Processes: Physiochemical Principles: The Geochemical Society Special Publication No. 1, p. 139–153.

Grunau, H., 1987, A worldwide look at the cap rock problem: Journal of Petroleum Geology, vol. 10, p. 245–266.

Gussow, W.C., 1954, Differential entrapment of oil and gas: a fundamental principle: AAPG Bulletin, vol. 38, p. 816–853.

Hendrick, S.J., 1992, Vitrinite reflectance and deep Arbuckle maturation at Wilburton field, Latimer County, OK: Oklahoma Geological Survey Circular 93, p. 176–184.

Horstad, I., S. Larter, and N. Mills, 1992, A quantitative model of biological petroleum degradation within the Brent Group reservoir in the Gullfaks field, Norwegian North Sea: Organic Geochemistry, vol. 19, nos. 1–3, p. 107–117.

Hubbert, M.K., 1953, Entrapment of petroleum under hydrodynamic conditions: AAPG Bulletin, vol. 37, p. 1954–2026.

Hunt, J.M., 1979, Petroleum Geochemistry and Geology: San Francisco, W.H. Freeman, 617 p.

Jenden, P.D., and I.R. Kaplan, 1989, Origin of natural gas in Sacramento basin, California: AAPG Bulletin, vol. 73, p. 431–453.

Jüntgen, V.H., and J. Karweil, 1966, Gasbildung and gasspeicherung in steinkohlenfluzen, I. gasbildung: Erdöl und Kohle-Erdgas-Petrochemie, vol. 19, p. 339–344.

Kodl, E.J., J.C. Eacmen, and M.G. Coburn, 1990, A geologic update of the emplacement mechanism within the Kern River Formation at the Kern River field, *in* J. Kuespert and S. Reid, eds., Structure, Stratigraphy, and Hydrocarbon Occurrences of the San Joaquin Basin California: Pacific Section SEPM Guidebook 64, p. 59–71.

Krouse, H.R., 1979, Stable isotope geochemistry of non-hydrocarbon constituents of natural gas: Proceedings of the Tenth World Petroleum Congress, vol. 4, p. 85–91.

Lafargue, E., and C. Barker, 1988, Effect of water washing on crude oil composition: AAPG Bulletin, vol. 72, p. 263–276.

Lee, M., J.L. Aronson, and S.M. Savin, 1985, K/Ar dating of time of gas emplacement in Rotliegendes sandstone, Netherlands: AAPG Bulletin, vol. 69, p. 1381–1385.

McAuliffe, C.D., 1980, Oil and gas migration: chemical and physical constraints, *in* W. Roberts and R. Cordell, eds., Problems of Petroleum Migration: AAPG Studies in Geology 10, p. 89–108.

Mcgregor, D.S., 1996, Factors controlling the destruction or preservation of giant light oilfields: Petroleum Geoscience, vol. 2, p. 197–217.

Mitra, S., 1986, Duplex structures and imbricate thrust systems: geometry, structural position, and hydrocarbon potential: AAPG Bulletin, vol. 70, p. 1087–1112.

Montel, F., G. Caillet, A. Pucheu, and J. Caltagirone, 1993, Diffusion model for predicting reservoir gas losses: Marine and Petroleum Geology, vol. 10, p. 51–57.

Nicholson, G., 1980, Geology of the Kern River field, *in* Kern River Oilfield Field Trip: AAPG Pacific Section Guidebook, p. 7–17.

Palmer, S., 1991, Effect of biodegradation and water washing on crude oil composition, *in* R.K. Merrill, ed., Source and Migration Processes and Evaluation Techniques: AAPG Treatise of Petroleum Geology—Handbook of Petroleum Geology, p. 47–54.

Parker, C., 1974, Geopressures and secondary porosity in the deep Jurassic of Mississippi: Transactions of the Gulf Coast Association of Geological Societies, vol. 24, p. 69–80.

Rozendal, R.A., and W.S. Erskine, 1971, Deep test in Ouachita structural belt of Central Texas: AAPG Bulletin, vol. 56, p. 2008–2017.

Schmoker, J.W., and D.L. Gautier, 1988, Sandstone porosity as a function of thermal maturity: Geology, vol. 16, p. 1007–1010.

Smith, J.T., and S.N. Ehrenberg, 1989, Correlation of carbon dioxide abundance with temperature in clastic hydrocarbon reservoirs: relationship to inorganic chemical equilibrium: Marine and Petroleum Geology, vol. 6, p. 129–135.

Stahl, W., H. Boigk, and G. Wollanke, 1978, Carbon and nitrogen isotope data of upper Carboniferous and Rotliegend natural gases from north Germany and their relationship to the maturity of the organic source material: Advances in Organic Geochemistry 1976, p. 539–559.

Tissot, B.P., and D.H. Welte, 1984, Petroleum Formation and Occurrence, 2 ed.: New York, Springer-Verlag, 699 p.

Van den Bark, E., and O.D. Thomas, 1981, Ekofisk: first of the giant oil fields in western Europe: AAPG Bulletin, vol. 65, p. 2341–2363.

Walters, C.C., 1990, Organic geochemistry of gases and condensates from Block 551A High Island South Addition offshore Texas, Gulf of Mexico, *in* D. Schumacher and B.F. Perkins, eds., Gulf Coast Oils and Gases—Their Characteristics, Origin, Distribution, and Exploration and Production Significance: Proceedings of the Ninth Annual Research Conference, GCS-SEPM, October 1990, p. 185–198.

Watts, N.L., 1983, Microfractures in chalks of Albuskjell field, Norwegian sector, North Sea: possible origin and distribution: AAPG Bulletin, vol. 67, p. 201–234.

_____ 1987, Theoretical aspects of cap-rock and fault seals for single- and two-phase hydrocarbon columns: Marine and Petroleum Geology, vol. 4, p. 274–307.

Acknowledgment The author thanks ARCO Exploration and Technology Company for permission to publish. A. Holba, B. Hughes, L. Lundell, S. Mitra, and T. O'Brien contributed ideas and reviewed early versions of this chapter.

Part IV

Predicting the Occurrence of Oil and Gas Traps

Introduction

Petroleum exploration methods are largely determined by the target trap type. Some methods are universally applicable. Part IV contains chapters that discuss general exploration methods and methods for locating structural and stratigraphic traps.

In this part

Part IV contains the following chapters.

Chapter 12

Interpreting Seismic Data

by

Christopher L. Liner

Christopher L. Liner

Chris Liner received a B.S. (1978) in geology from the University of Arkansas and an M.S. (1980) in geophysics from The University of Tulsa. In 1980, Liner joined Western Geophysical as a research geophysicist located in London and in 1981 joined Conoco as an exploration geophysicist working midcontinent areas of the United States. After completing his Ph.D. from the Colorado School of Mines (1989), he worked as a research geophysicist with Golden Geophysical in Denver.

Since 1990, he has been on the faculty of the Geosciences Department at The University of Tulsa. He is currently associate professor and is serving as editor of *Geophysics*. Liner is the author of several papers in the areas of seismic processing, wave propagation, and seismic survey design. He is also the author of two books: *Greek Seismology* (1997) and *Elements of 3-D Seismology* (1999). Liner received the Best Poster Paper award at the 1998 SEG Annual Meeting.

Overview

Introduction

A useful analogy can be made between seismic and medical imaging. Not so long ago a mysterious ailment might have meant high-risk exploratory surgery (equivalent to pattern drilling). Wherever possible, surgery today is orthoscopic and highly targeted (equivalent to directional drilling). This is possible because we now have high-quality medical images (equivalent to seismic data) available to guide the surgeon. In this day and age, who would undergo surgery without an X-ray, ultrasound, cat scan, or some kind of medical imaging?

The purpose of both medical imaging and seismic imaging is to reduce risk. In the search for petroleum, seismic imaging reduces risk of many kinds—drilling dry holes, drilling marginal wells, under- or overestimating reserves. Seismic information is a good interpolator between wells. It transfers the detailed information obtained at well locations to the area between wells.

Clearly, a single chapter (or book) cannot cover seismology in detail. This chapter discusses major aspects of the subject from a conceptual standpoint. It focuses on the fundamentals of seismic data, emphasizing interpretion of 3-D seismic data.

In this chapter

This chapter contains the following sections.

Section A

Seismic Primer

Introduction

This section discusses basic concepts of the seismic method. Although the use of 3-D seismic data is the focus of this chapter, many of the concepts discussed apply to 2-D seismic data analysis as well.

In this section

This section contains the following topics.

Phases of a Seismic Project

Introduction

Generally speaking, there are three phases of a seismic project:

- Acquisition
- Processing
- Interpretation

In this chapter we concentrate on interpretation, but it is hard to ignore the importance of the other phases.

Acquisition

A good interpreter knows the basics of seismic survey design and can recognize problems when they arise. Even a well-designed survey can be ruined by sloppy acquisition methods. Common culprits are poor positioning or cabling information (i.e., which receivers are live for which shots).

A 3-D seismic survey is designed to give optimum results for a particular depth interval containing the target(s). If there are design, acquisition, or processing problems, then the data may contain artifacts. These are most commonly seen as map-view amplitude patterns and are called an acquisition footprint. One should avoid footprints because they can mask or confuse geologic patterns in the data.

Processing

Raw seismic data look as much like an image of the earth as a hamburger looks like a cow. An enormous amount of computer and human effort is required to transform raw seismic data into a usable image. Each step involves many user-supplied parameters that can change the result—maybe a little, maybe a lot. In short, processing should rightly be coupled with the interpretation process since the processor makes decisions affecting data quality. However, this is rarely the case because few individuals possess sufficient expertise in both areas.

Getting the most from seismic data

In a perfect world, one person or a small team would design, oversee acquisition, process, and interpret a seismic survey. All too often, an off-the-shelf design is shot by a low-bid contractor, processed with standard flow and parameters, then delivered for interpretation. The company that breaks out of this cycle of mediocrity can expect to pay more but can also achieve a competitive advantage.

Recurring Themes

Introduction

From the broad field of seismology, a few things seem to pop up with regularity. Some of these have been collected here. Keep them in mind when working with seismic data—in particular, 3-D seismic data.

The onion

The knowledge required for working with seismic data is built of several layers like an onion. The figure below illustrates the idea. At the heart of the onion are 1-D seismic concepts like wavelet, convolution, traveltime, and reflection coefficient. All this shows up in the next layer, 2-D seismic, plus arrays, offset, dip, and lateral velocity variation. The next layer, 3-D seismic, includes all of 2-D plus azimuth, bins, and the data volume. Finally, 4-D seismic is time-lapse 3-D, which introduces repeatability, fluid flow, and difference volume.

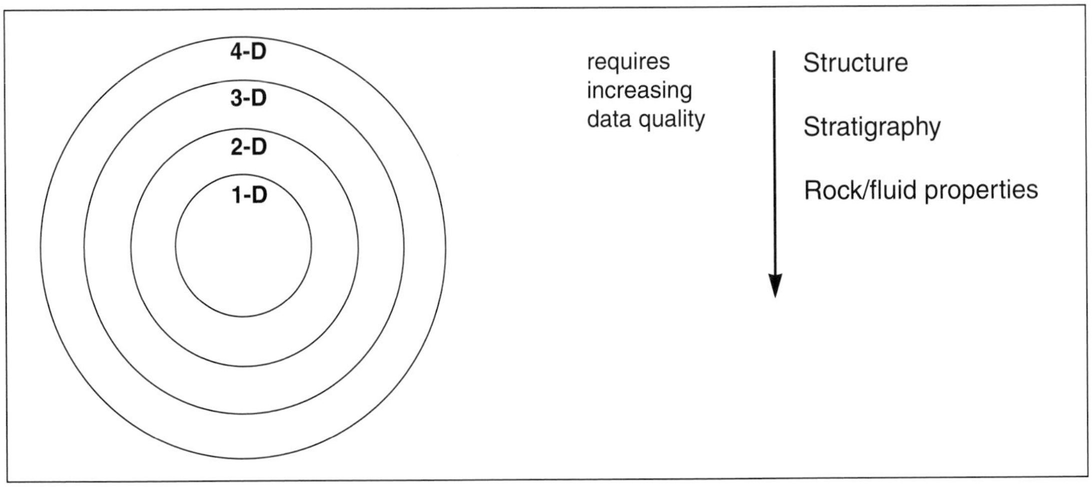

Figure 12–1. From Liner, 1999; courtesy PennWell.

Data quality

The main job for seismic interpretation is to map three things:

1) Structure
2) Stratigraphy
3) Rock/fluid properties

In this order, each task requires increasing data quality. Quality is a nebulous term largely determined at acquisition time by correct survey design and execution. Processing generally has less impact on quality but is still very important.

Echo location

The seismic technique is an echo-location method similar to sonar, radar, and medical ultrasound. A wave is emitted, and it rattles around in the material. Part of it is reflected back. From the part that returns, we attempt to determine what is out there.

Traveltimes and amplitudes

In one sense, seismic data consist of traveltime, amplitude, and waveform information. Structure mapping involves only the traveltimes, stratigraphy involves both traveltime and amplitude, and rock/fluid property information lives in the amplitude and waveform.

Recurring Themes, continued

Edges

If you look at a rock outcrop, you see sandstone, shale, limestone, etc. If you look at seismic data, you see the edges of rock units. The figure below shows the edge effect on a Gulf of Mexico salt dome example. Seismic is, in effect, an edge detection technique. The bigger the velocity and/or density contrast between the rocks, the stronger the edge.

To be fair, seismic impulses respond to much more than just lithology. Any vertical variation in rock property that modifies the velocity or density can potentially generate seismic reflections, including a fluid contact, porosity variation, or shale density change.

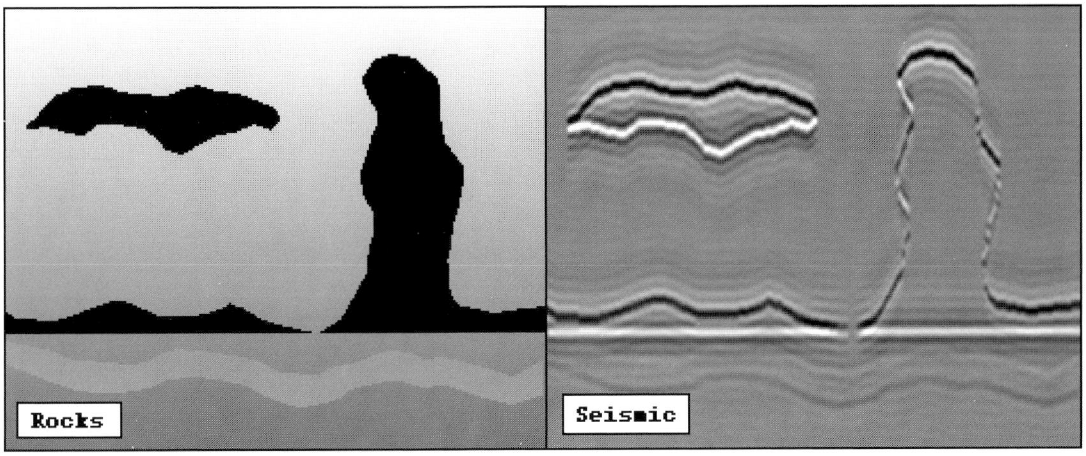

Figure 12–2. From Liner, 1999; courtesy PennWell.

Event tracking

A key part of the interpretation process for 3-D seismic data is event tracking. To picture this, think of the 3-D seismic data volume as a block of vanilla ice cream with chocolate streaks. Tracking means we follow a streak into the cube and find out where it goes—this is structure mapping. We also keep track of how dark the chocolate is as we follow it—this is amplitude mapping.

Computer limitations

Available computer speed and memory impose severe limitations on the use of advanced 3-D seismic processing. Current hardware is sufficient for the interpretation process, but the software can be complicated and expensive ($5,000–$180,000).

3-D Seismic: The Data Cube

Introduction

Seismic prospecting has been around since the 1920s and was almost exclusively two-dimensional until the mid-1980s. Three-dimensional techniques were experimented with as early as the 1940s but did not progress far until digital processing became common in the 1970s. Current worldwide seismic effort is estimated to be over 50% 3-D, and the percentage is growing rapidly. This would apply to dollar volume and/or acquisition effort. International (non-U.S.) seismic prospecting could be as high as 75% 3-D. We live in a 3-D world and now understand that 2-D seismic data is prone to many pitfalls and problems. A great advance of the last 25 years has been the development of the 3-D seismic technique, which has much more risk-reducing information content than an equivalent amount of 2-D seismic.

3-D advantages

What is the attraction of 3-D? Why do you want a 3-D survey rather than a (less expensive) grid of 2-D seismic lines? A 3-D seismic survey has many advantages over a 2-D line or a grid of 2-D lines—even a dense one. [A 2-D grid is considered dense if the line spacing is less than about 1/4 mile (1,320 ft; 400 m).] The advantages of 3-D include the following:

- True structural dip (2-D may give apparent dip)
- More and better stratigraphic information
- Map view of reservoir properties
- Much better areal mapping of fault patterns and connections and delineation of reservoir blocks
- Better lateral resolution (2-D suffers from a cross-line smearing, or Fresnel zone, problem)

Data sets

A 3-D seismic data set is a "cube" or volume of data; a 2-D seismic data set, on the other hand, is a panel of data. To interpret the 3-D data we need to investigate the interior of the cube. This is done almost universally on a computer due to the massive amounts of data involved. A 3-D data set can range in size from a few tens of megabytes to several gigabytes—the equivalent of a library of information.

Data volume concept

To understand the concept of a volume of data, think of a room. Imagine the room divided up into points, each, say, one foot apart. Any particular point will have an (x,y,z) coordinate and a data value. The coordinate is the distance from a particular corner of the ceiling. We choose the ceiling so that z points down into the room. At any given point the data value is, say, the temperature, so we have temperature as a function of (x,y,z). As we move around the room to other points, the temperature changes—high near incandescent lights and low near a glass of ice water.

A 3-D seismic data volume is like the room-temperature example except for two changes:

- The vertical axis is vertical reflection time, not depth.
- The data values are seismic amplitudes rather than temperature.

3-D Seismic: The Data Cube, continued

3-D data set example

Let's take our example a step further. Think of a 3-D seismic data set as a box full of numbers, each number representing a measurement (amplitude, for example). Each number has an *(x,y,z)* position in the box. For any point in the middle of the box, three planes pass through it parallel to the top, front, and side of the box.

The figure below illustrates 3-D data from north Texas. It measures about 1.5 mi^2 across the top. Figure 12–3A shows three views for a point in the middle of the box. The dark and light bands in the sections are related to rock boundaries. Keep in mind that seismic techniques detect edges. Figure 12–3B is a different view. It is a cube display with vertical and horizontal slices to show what is inside the data.

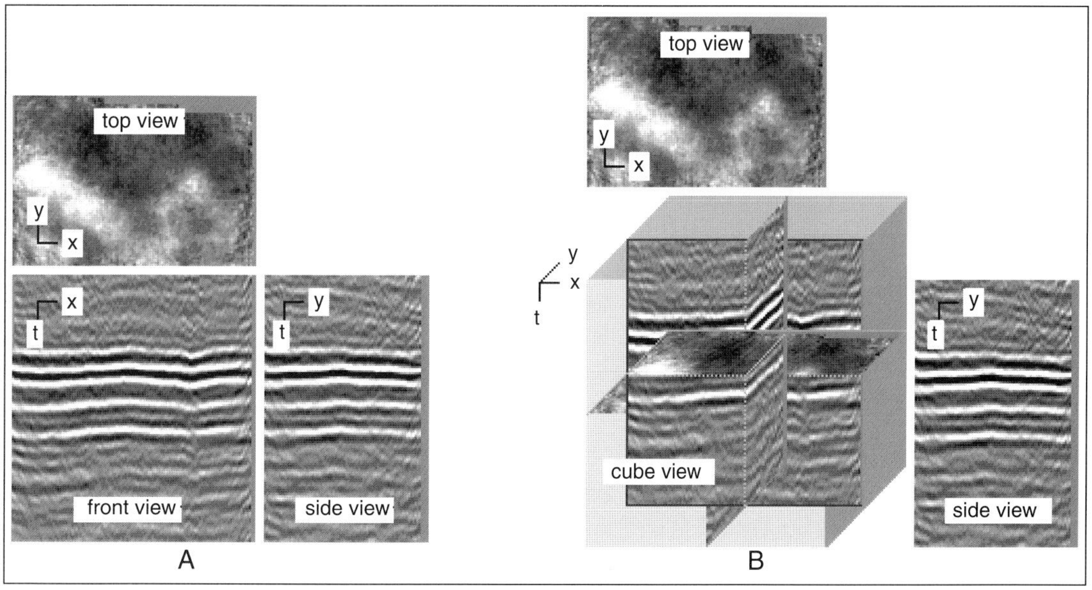

Figure 12–3. From Liner, 1999; courtesy PennWell.

Components of a 3-D Seismic Survey

Midpoints

To transmit energy into the subsurface, a shot is fired on the earth's surface. Many seismic receivers record the resulting echoes from underlying strata. Each receiver records the echoes in a trace called a **prestack trace.** Each prestack trace has a source and receiver coordinate, but the trace is plotted at the point halfway between the source and receiver pair, called the midpoint. The seismic method is designed so several prestack traces have the same midpoint.

Bins

For 2-D seismic, the prestack traces are sorted into groups associated with one midpoint on the earth's surface. The 3-D seismic data are sorted into discrete areas called bins. All actual midpoints that fall into the bin area belong to that bin. In effect, a grid is laid over the actual midpoints. Each bin has an in-line and cross-line dimension. The fold of each bin is the number of traces captured by that bin. Through the stacking process, all traces within a bin are summed to create a single stack trace, greatly improving signal quality.

The figure below illustrates the bin concept. The actual midpoints for a well-designed and executed survey will show natural clustering (A). On this cloud of midpoints we impose a grid of bins, each bin capturing all traces whose midpoints lie in it (B). After processing (stacking, migration, etc.), there is one trace at the center of each bin (C). These are the poststack data traces we interpret.

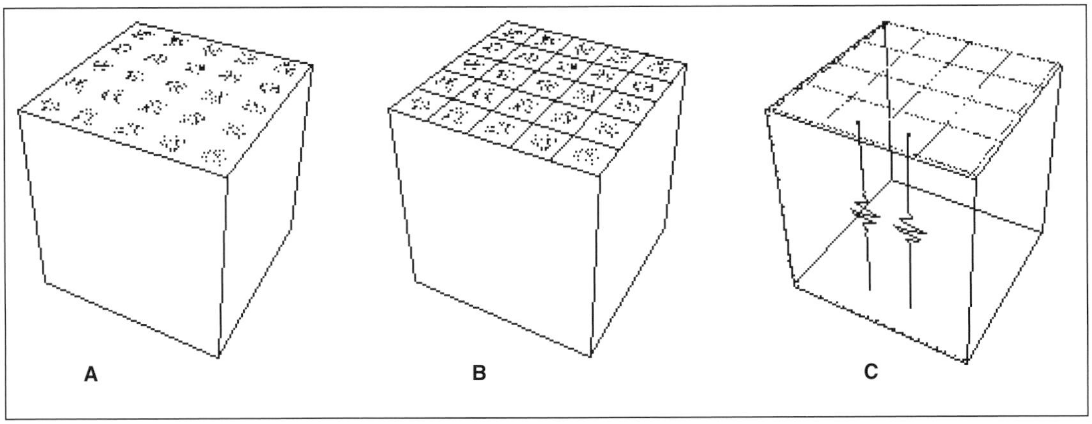

Figure 12–4. From Liner, 1999; courtesy PennWell.

3-D Seismic Data Views

Vertical slices

As it arrives on tape from the processor, 3-D seismic data are organized into lines composed of traces. In the computer these are all merged into a dense cube of data. The data cube can be sectioned, or sliced, in several ways. Vertical cuts through the data cube are called **lines** or **sections.** For marine surveys, in-line is the direction of boat movement (parallel to receivers) and cross-line is perpendicular to boat movement. For land surveys, there is no uniform definition of in-line and cross-line. A vertical section that is neither in-line nor cross-line is an arbitrary line and may be very irregular in map view as needed to pass through locations of interest.

The figure below shows how the vertical slices are labeled, depending on their orientation.

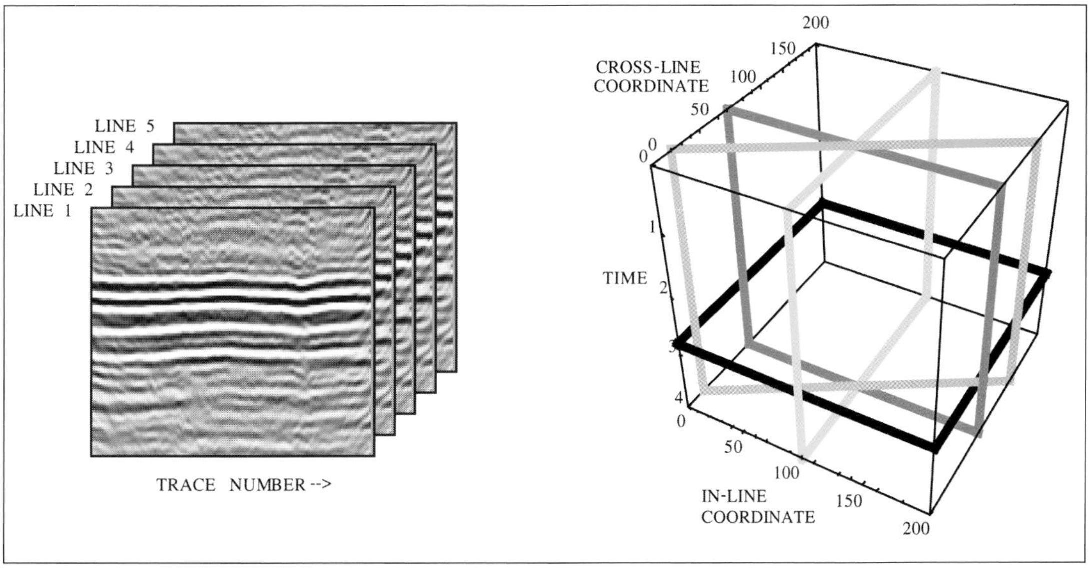

Figure 12–5. From Liner, 1999; courtesy PennWell.

Horizontal slices

Horizontal or subhorizontal cuts through a seismic data cube are called slices. As illustrated in Figure 12–5 above, horizontal slices can be

- Time slices (horizontal cuts of a time cube)
- Depth slices (horizontal cuts of a depth cube)
- Horizon slices (from tracking)
- Fault slices

Depth slices are only available if the data delivered from the processor are converted to depth. Fault slices require very high-quality data with clear, mappable fault surfaces. Both are rarely encountered.

Section B
Identifying Seismic Events

Introduction

Models of seismic data help us identify seismic events or reflections stratigraphically. The model is a hypothetical seismic trace called a synthetic seismogram and is generated from sonic and density logs. In this section we review the method of modeling and identifying seismic events.

In this section

This section contains the following topics.

Building a Stratigraphic Model

Introduction

The problem addressed in seismic modeling, or simulation, is calculating the seismic response (traveltime and amplitude) for a given stratigraphic model. The stratigraphic model consists of those physical properties that influence seismic wave propagation—typically compressional wave speed, shear wave speed, and mass density. This set of parameters can describe the simplest possible solid, called an isotropic elastic solid. For some purposes, it is sufficient to consider the earth as an acoustic (fluid) medium characterized by only two parameters: sound speed (v) and mass density (ρ). Seismic reflections are generated where there is a contrast in impedance (which is the product of velocity and density).

Velocity data sources

Depth-dependent velocity and density models are needed to identify events or to create a synthetic seismogram. Velocity information can come from a variety of sources. Here is a list, in order of preference:

- Vertical seismic profile (VSP)
- Sonic without checkshots
- Sonic with checkshots
- Checkshots only

VSPs

A vertical seismic profile (VSP) yields the best connection between geologic horizons and seismic events. It is recorded by using a source at the surface and many receiver locations down a wellbore, or vice versa. The receivers record full traces for interpretation. The receiver spacing is usually 10 ft. This gives actual traveltimes from the surface to points in the earth, and it is the best and most direct method of associating seismic events with geological horizons. The kind of VSP shown in Figure 12–6 (produced by commercial software) is often called a zero-offset VSP, meaning that only a single source position is used as close to the wellhead as possible. It is relatively inexpensive. There are also multioffset and multiazimuth VSPs, which use many source locations. These are much more expensive and sometimes are useful for local, high-resolution imaging. However, a zero-offset VSP is sufficient for event identification and 3-D seismic calibration.

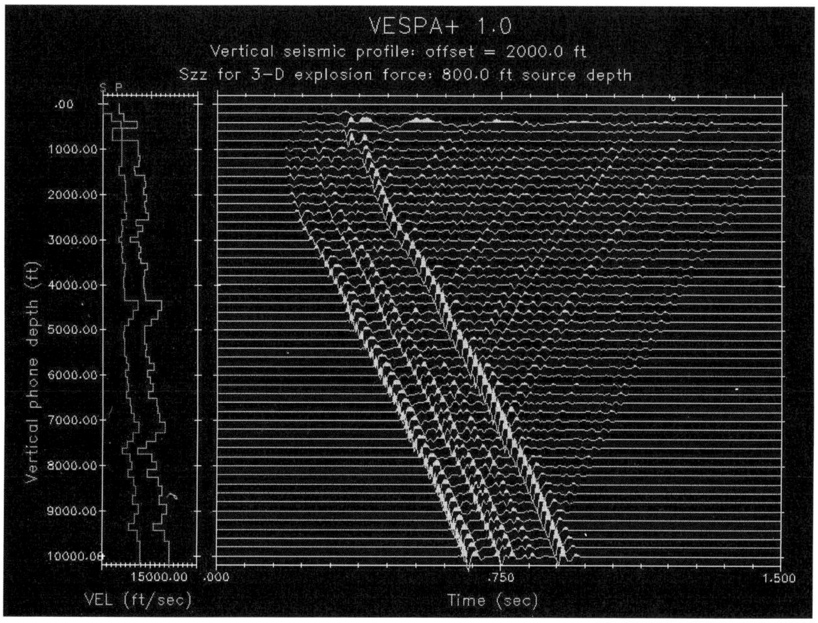

Figure 12–6. Courtesy Landmark Graphics.

Building a Stratigraphic Model, continued

Velocities from sonic logs

Velocities can be acquired from sonic logs with or without a checkshot survey. A checkshot survey is like a baby VSP. The receivers are sparsely located down the well, usually on key geologic boundaries. Also, the information recovered is limited to arrival time (a number), unlike the full trace a VSP gives. The checkshots help correct for any drift in a sonic log due to missing log intervals or hole problems. This makes the calculated traveltimes more reliable. One can obtain good velocity data from sonic logs without checkshots. However, if there are any hole integrity problems, significant errors can exist in the sonic data. If a sonic log is not available, very coarse velocity data can be obtained from a checkshot survey with only 5 or 6 traveltimes per well.

Velocity from density

Density information also contributes to creation of a synthetic seismogram. Density can be estimated from sonic data, but independent density information from a neutron density log is preferred.

Synthetic Seismograms

Introduction

Once a stratigraphic model has been built using velocities and densities, a synthetic seismogram (or synthetic) can be constructed to identify seismic reflections. A synthetic seismogram is the fundamental link between well data and seismic data, and it is the main tool (along with a VSP, if available) that allows geological picks to be associated with reflections in the seismic data. As discussed, if a VSP is available for a particular well, a synthetic is not needed. The VSP directly measures both time and depth to a formation of interest.

Creating a synthetic seismogram

Usually synthetic seismograms are created using specialized software. The user may be unaware of the process that creates them. The table below lists the steps necessary to create a synthetic seismogram manually.

Step	Action
1	Edit the sonic and density logs for bad intervals.
2	Calculate vertical reflection times.
3	Calculate reflection coefficients, R_0.
4	Combine the last two items to create a reflection coefficient time series.
5	Convolve the reflection coefficient series with the wavelet.

Reflection coefficient

The normal-incidence reflection coefficient for a rock contact is an important quantity. Sheriff (1984) defines it as "the ratio of the amplitude of the displacement of a reflected wave to that of the incident wave." Mathematically, reflection coefficient can be expressed as

$$R_0 = \frac{(\rho_2 v_2 - \rho_1 v_1)}{(\rho_2 v_2 + \rho_1 v_1)}$$

where:

ρ = rock density
v = rock velocity
1 = parameters above the interface
2 = parameters below the interface

Convolutional model

The final simulated seismic trace can be summarized by the convolutional model:

$$T(t) = R_0(t) * w(t) + n(t)$$

where:

$T(t)$ = seismic trace
$R_0(t)$ = reflection coefficient series (spikes)
$*$ = convolution
$w(t)$ = wavelet
$n(t)$ = noise

Convolutional model (continued)

This model of the seismic trace assumes many things, including removal of all amplitude effects except R_0. The job of seismic data processors is to deliver data to the interpreter in a form consistent with the convolutional model, but it is hard to get it right.

Example synthetic seismogram

The figure below shows a simple synthetic seismogram. We can see most of the components that go into the creation of a synthetic seismogram—the velocity model, reflection coefficient series, individual wavelets, synthetic trace, and simulated stack section (lower plot). The velocity model is from north-central Oklahoma. The density model is not shown.

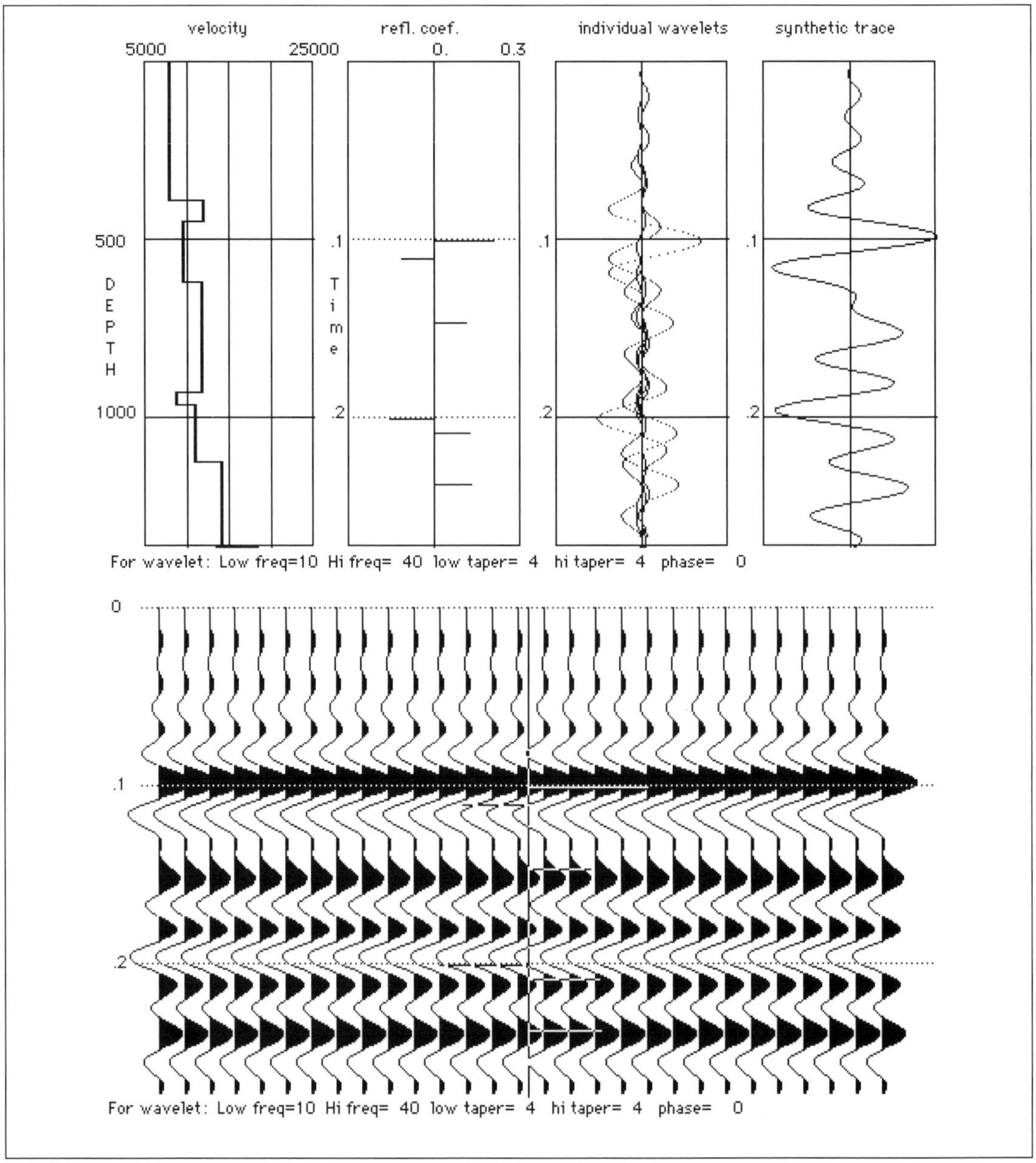

Figure 12–7. From software by S. Hill, Conoco.

Matching Synthetics to Data

Introduction

The goal of using a synthetic seismogram is to match stratigraphy as seen in well logs or outcrops to seismic field data. The field data need to have been migrated, since only then does the time axis represent vertical traveltime, which is calculated from sonic log measurements.

The matching process

The matching process involves simulating a seismic trace from well logs and user parameters (waveform, frequency, phase), then manually aligning the simulated trace with the field trace(s) in the vicinity of the well. This is normally done over some limited interval in the well, probably centered on the reservoir target. If the fit is not good enough, then the parameters are changed (updated) and another comparison is made. This continues until a match is achieved. It can be a tedious and time-consuming job, particularly for large projects involving many wells. But if not done properly, it is possible to incorrectly associate seismic events and geological horizons.

Problems with matching

In practice, synthetic seismograms are rarely a perfect match to field data. There are many reasons for this.

- **Frequency**—Sonic logging operates in the kilohertz frequency range (high frequency, short wavelength), while seismic data are typically 10–90 Hz (low frequency, long wavelength). This means the sonic log is influenced by a tiny volume of rock compared to a seismic wave passing the borehole.
- **Anisotropy**—Sonic logs measure velocity in the vertical direction, while seismic waves travel at significant angles away from the vertical. If anisotropy is present (and it usually is), then velocity depends on the direction the wave is traveling. It is not uncommon to see a 10–15% difference between horizontal and vertical velocities.
- **Hole**—Sonic logging is sensitive to washouts and other hole problems, while long-wavelength seismic waves are not.
- **Wavelet**—The user is required to specify the wavelet, and it is very easy to get it wrong. Some advanced software products can scan the data and attempt to extract the wavelet. But these scanners involve many user parameters.

Identifying Reflectors

Introduction

Whether using VSP, synthetic seismogram, or log overlay, the final step is to compare the object to seismic traces in the vicinity of the well and find a fit.

Example

In the figure below, a sonic log has been converted to time and velocity. Note that the time axis on the seismic section and the converted sonic log are linear, while the depth tick marks on the sonic are nonlinear. The geological horizons annotated on the sonic log are located via the depth tics from picks on other logs (electric, gamma ray, etc.). It is important to realize that a sonic log never goes to the surface; there is always a gap for the surface casing. So we do not expect time zero on the converted log to fit at time zero on the seismic section. In practice, the log is placed over the seismic section and shifted vertically until we are satisfied with the fit.

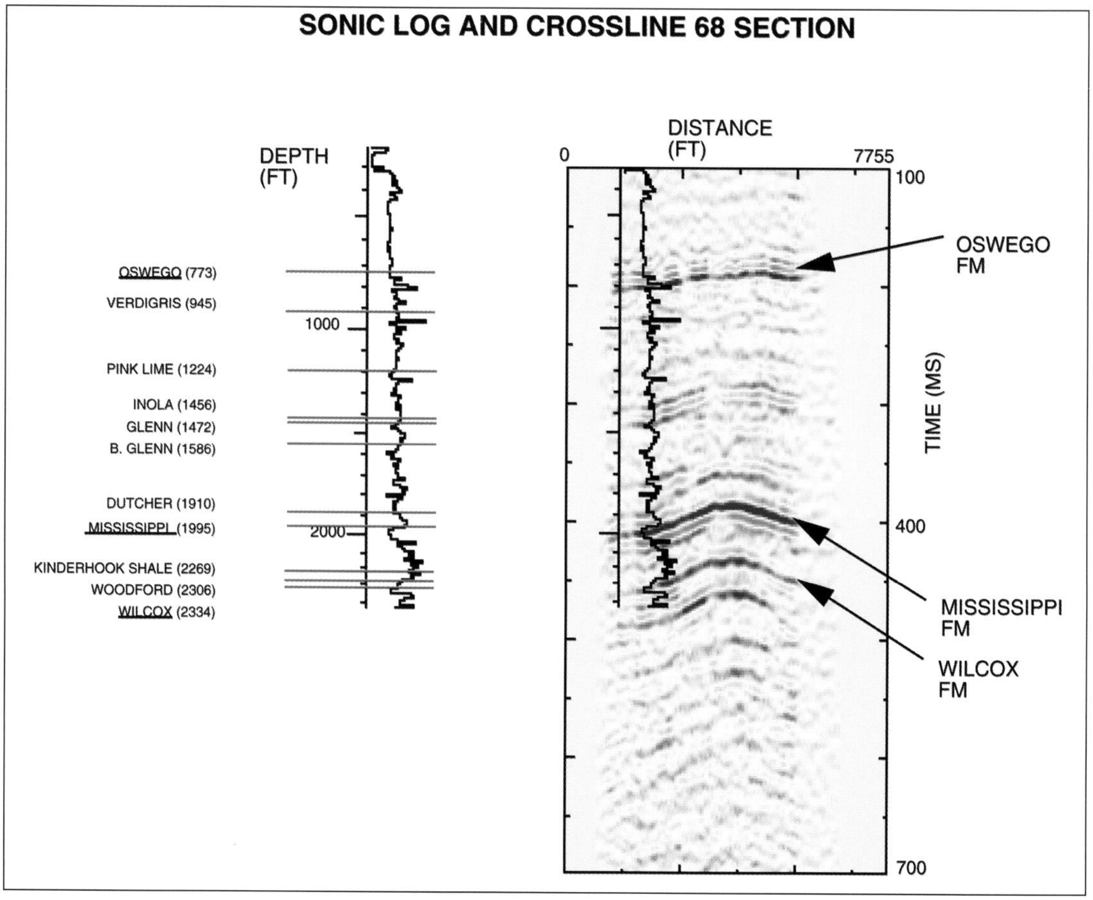

Figure 12–8. From Liner, 1999; courtesy PennWell.

Section C
Interpreting Structure

Introduction

Seismic interpretation has evolved significantly over the last 20 years or so (Wilson, 1984; Matteini and Salvador, 1986; Brown, 1992, 1999). Some changes are related to computer technology, while others are geophysical or geological advances. However, the basic goal of seismic interpretation has not altered: to identify likely hydrocarbon accumulations and reduce risk associated with drilling. This begins with structural mapping based on seismic plus well control. The product is $z(x,y)$, a depth value at each point inside the survey area.

This section reviews the classic techniques of mapping structure using seismic data.

In this section

This section contains the following topics.

Mapping Structure with Seismic Data

Introduction

Whether doing 2-D or 3-D seismic interpretation, the tasks are fundamentally the same. The work can sometimes be done by hand for 2-D data (paper sections and manual contouring of maps) but virtually requires computer assistance for 3-D data. The recipes described on the pages that follow apply to hand or computer work.

Four basic techniques

There are four basic techniques for getting structure from seismic data (the names are not standard).

Technique	Description
Classic	Mapping a surface of interest (from data) using average velocities
Modified Classic	Mapping a surface of interest using a densely drilled shallow horizon, avoiding the weathering layer at the earth's surface
Migrated Depth	Mapping an area using a 3-D seismic data cube with the vertical axis converted to depth (commonly used in complex areas but needs manual tweaking to match well control to seismic data)
Volumetric Depth Conversion	Mapping an area using migrated seismic data (with time axis) converted to a depth cube using a $v(x,y,z)$ velocity model

Preparing Seismic Data for Mapping

Introduction

Before seismic data can be used in maps, they must be checked for quality; they must have reflectors identified for key geologic horizons, which should be tracked throughout the data grid; and key sections must be interpreted structurally.

Example data set

The example given in this section is a small 3-D data set from the Glenn Pool field in northeastern Oklahoma. The target is the Ordovician Wilcox Formation. The interpretation was done using a system called Cubic.

Procedure

Follow the steps listed below to make a classic structural seismic interpretation.

Step	Action
1	Preview data for quality and consistency with acquisition and processing reports.
2	Make structure contour maps for key horizons using well control only.
3	Identify online wells with velocity control.
4	Compute a synthetic seismogram for each online well with a sonic or density log.
5	Associate reflectors at each online well with stratigraphic horizons using VSP, synthetic seismogram, or time-stretched logs.
6	Interpret seismic data using color identifiers (tracking) by extending reflection events across the entire survey area.
7	Mark faults and key structural details.

Step 1: Preview data

Preview seismic data for quality and consistency using acquisition and processing reports that come with the data. Note any geological conditions that might cause the interpretation method listed in the procedure to fail. As shown in Figure 12–9A, each 3-D seismic survey has a unique outline of live traces or image area. Use the outline of the image area with the processing report and well spots (Figure 12–9B) to confirm correct orientation of the survey. This might sound silly, but it is very easy to get the orientation wrong since there are many ways to orient a cube.

Step 1: Preview data (continued)

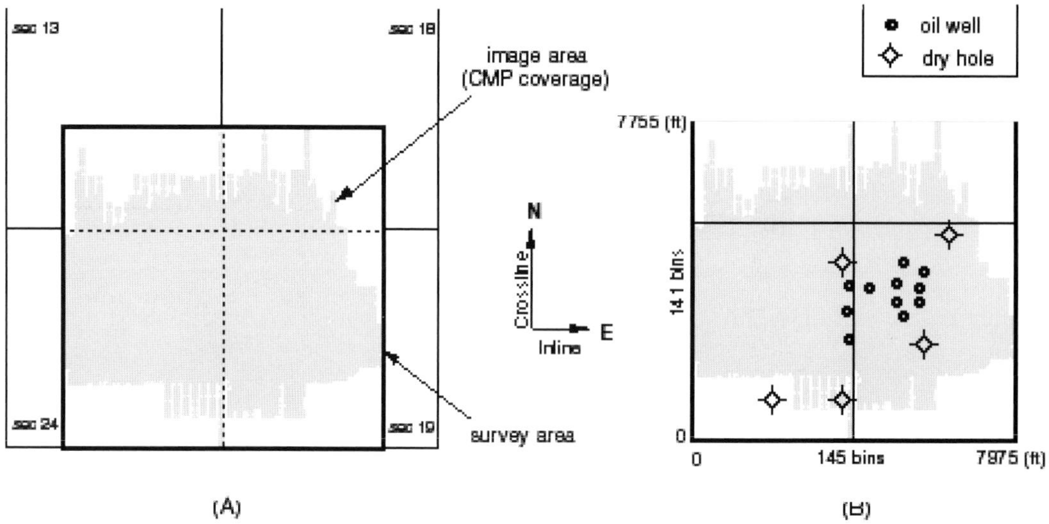

Figure 12–9. From Liner; courtesy PennWell.

Step 2: Create well control maps

A depth structure map should be constructed using all available well control to the horizon of interest. There are many ways of gridding or contouring depth points. Whatever the method, it should also be used in the depth conversion velocity map (next section). The wells-only depth structure map is a useful baseline.

Step 3: Identify wells with velocity control

Identifying online wells with velocity control is a vital point in the seismic mapping process. For a 2-D survey, online wells are located on a seismic line. For a 3-D survey every well in the image area is online. The velocity control can be (in order of preference)

1) Vertical seismic profile (VSP)
2) Sonic log
3) Checkshot survey

Step 4: Compute simulated seismic traces

For each online well with a sonic or density log, we can compute a simulated seismic trace (synthetic seismogram). Another option is to convert sonic log (or velocity, density, velocity * density) to time and directly overlay onto the seismic section being interpreted. Figure 12–8 (from the Glenn Pool survey) shows this approach. For wells with a VSP, a trace is available directly and need not be simulated.

Step 5: Identify stratigraphy of reflectors

Correlate seismic reflectors at each online well with key geological horizons using a VSP or a synthetic seismogram. A checkshot survey can be used as a last resort. Ideally, events should be correlated for every online well.

Preparing Seismic Data for Mapping, continued

Step 6: Track events

Interpret seismic data using color identifiers by extending reflection events across the entire survey area. This process is called tracking—following an event throughout the data volume.

Step 7: Mark faults

Mark faults and other structural details on the seismic sections. If necessary, jump-correlate picked events across faults. When a conflict exists, a well-tie correlation is preferred to seismic jump correlation across faults. The seismic section in the figure below shows a jump correlation. A small panel of data, labeled A, is outlined on the right side of the fault. Two key horizons are marked. The data panel was copied, then moved across the fault and adjusted until a satisfactory fit was made at B. Note the apparently continuous event connecting the yellow dot at A with the blue dot at B. This is a false correlation.

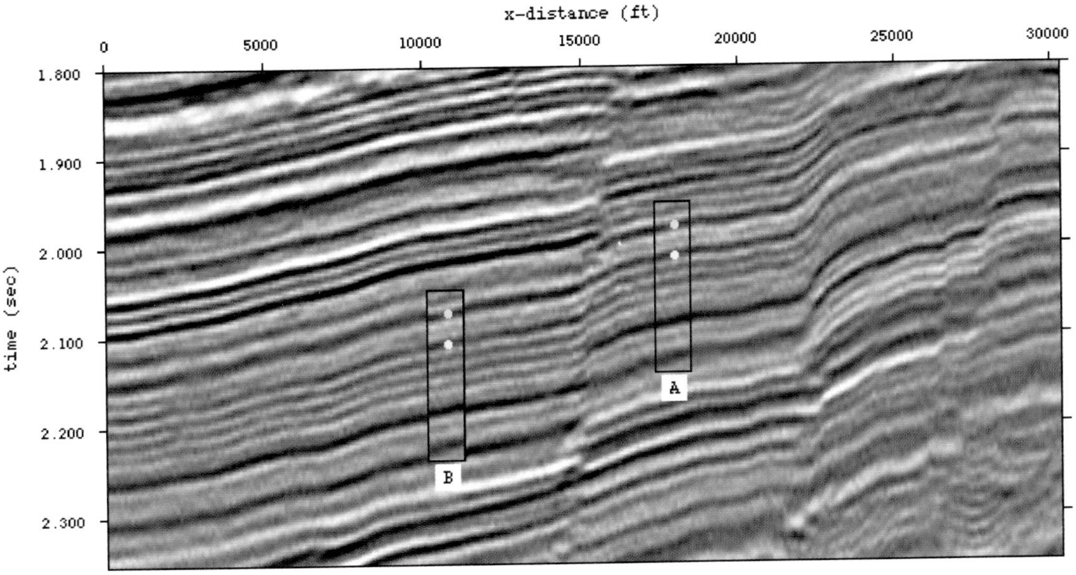

Figure 12–10. From Liner, 1999; courtesy PennWell.

Marking up key sections

Beyond jump correlation, an important part of structural interpretation is to mark up a few key lines in detail. Figure 12–11 shows part of such a marked-up section. Faults are marked in green, with line width denoting relative importance. Sense of throw is indicated as up (U) or down (D). Yellow dots indicate events used to calculate depth and fault throw, while yellow lines are events used for dip calculations. Fault numbers indicate relative age (1 = most recently active, etc.). Red arrows show stratigraphic bed terminations. The arrowhead indicates whether termination is from above or below. For depth, throw, and dip estimates, a simple linear velocity model was used: $v(z) = 5{,}000 + 0.4{*}z$, where v is in ft/sec and z is depth in feet. This velocity model is often useful in basins that contain unconsolidated sediments, such as the Gulf of Mexico. The data for Figures 12–10 and 12–11 come from Southeast Asia.

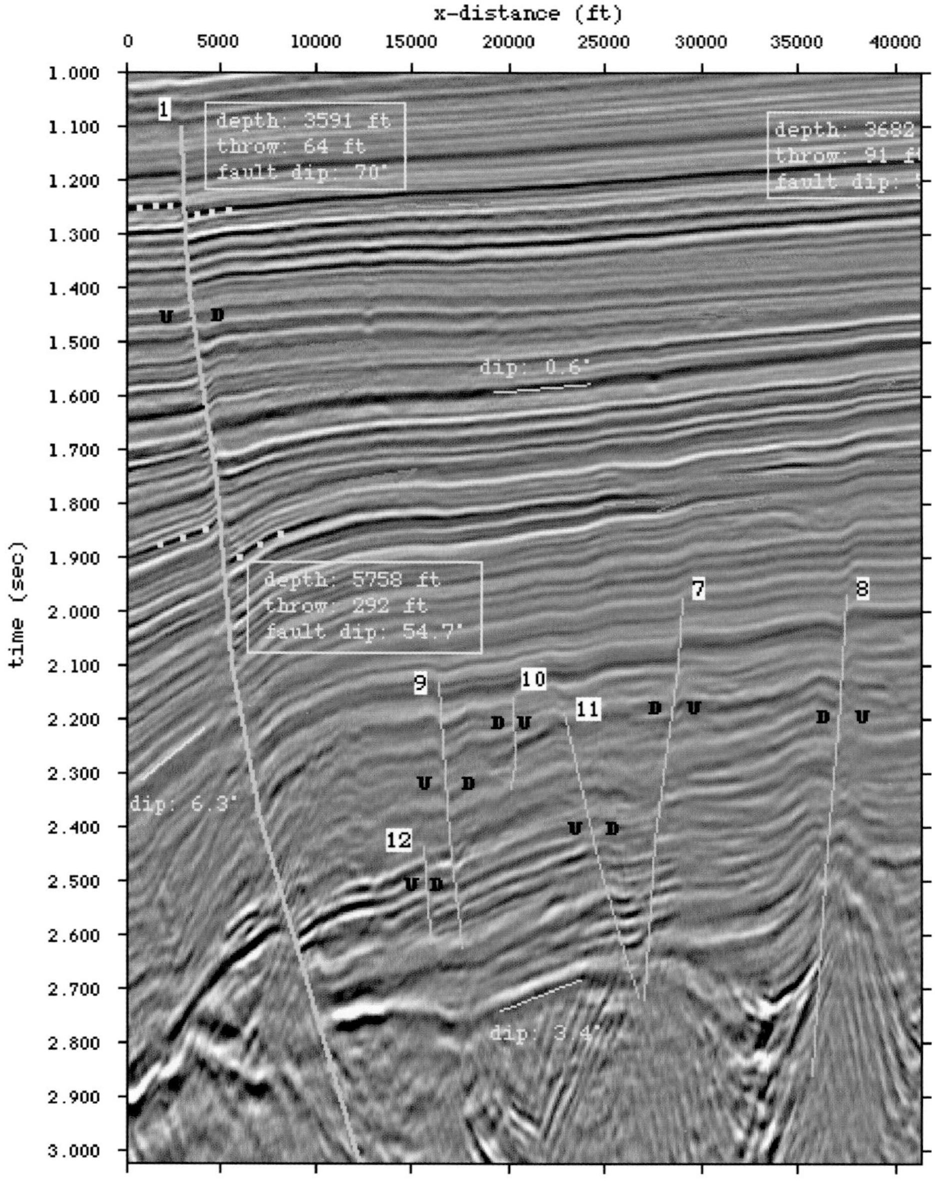

Figure 12–11. From Liner, 1999; courtesy PennWell.

Creating an Integrated Structure Map

Introduction

Below is a recipe for making a classic integrated structure map from seismic data and well control. It is based on mapping one horizon at a time and must be repeated for each horizon of interest. It may not work in areas with severe static problems (i.e., lots of topography or a rapidly changing weathered layer such as glacial till). It also fails when there are extreme lateral velocity variations in the subsurface (subsalt, subthrust, etc.). When it works, this method gives a map which, by definition, matches every well exactly. It uses seismic time structure to interpolate between wells and extrapolate beyond them.

Procedure

Follow the steps listed below for each seismic event to be mapped.

Step	Action
1	Make structure contour maps for key horizons using well control only.
2	Pick seismic horizons.
3	Calculate depth conversion velocity at locations where both well and seismic time picks exist.
4	Convert time to depth by multiplying the time structure map and the depth conversion velocity map.
5	Contour the integrated structure map, keeping in mind the structure map made earlier from well data only.

Step 1: Map structure from well data

Post well depths to key horizons and contour structure maps for key horizons using well control only. These well maps of structure should guide you when making structure maps that integrate both well and seismic data. Comparing this map with the final time structure map gives a good feel for the additional information supplied by the 3-D seismic section.

Creating an Integrated Structure Map, continued

Step 2: Pick seismic horizons

For 2-D data, only the traveltime to each event of interest is recorded with its coordinate along the line *t(x)*. For 3-D data, both traveltime and amplitude at each *(x,y)* are available from the seismic data cube, *t(x,y)* and *a(x,y)*. The traveltimes form a time structure map, and the amplitudes are a horizon slice. Figure 12–12A shows a representative line from the Glenn Pool data volume with sonic overlay and tracked events. Horizon amplitude and time structure maps for the Wilcox are shown in Figures 12–12B,C.

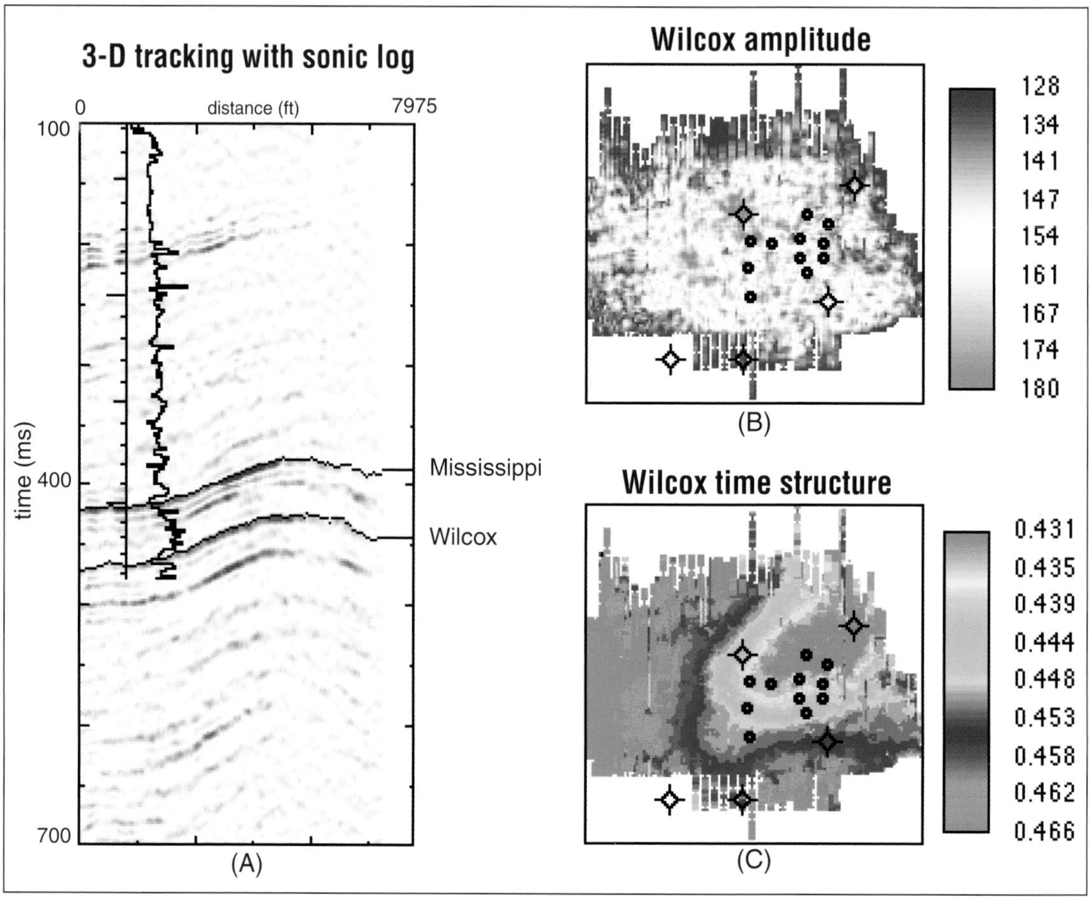

Figure 12–12. From Liner, 1999; courtesy PennWell.

Step 3: Calculate depth conversion velocity

Calculate depth conversion velocity at locations where both well and seismic time picks exist. The wells used as control do not need velocity or density logs but must penetrate the event of interest. The event depth z (measured from seismic datum) is known from well control, and the vertical reflection time t is known from the previous item. The depth conversion velocity is given by

$$v = \frac{2z}{t}$$

Depth conversion velocities are posted to a map and contoured or gridded to create $v(x,y)$.

Step 3: Calculate depth conversion velocity (continued)

The figure below shows a hypothetical well with important reference points as well the average velocity map for the Wilcox Formation in the Glenn Pool survey. This map has a fairly strong lateral velocity gradient, i.e., the velocity changes from about 11,400 ft/s for velocity (NE) to 10,200 ft/s (SW) in the space of just over a mile. When this occurs, time structure and depth structure can be significantly different.

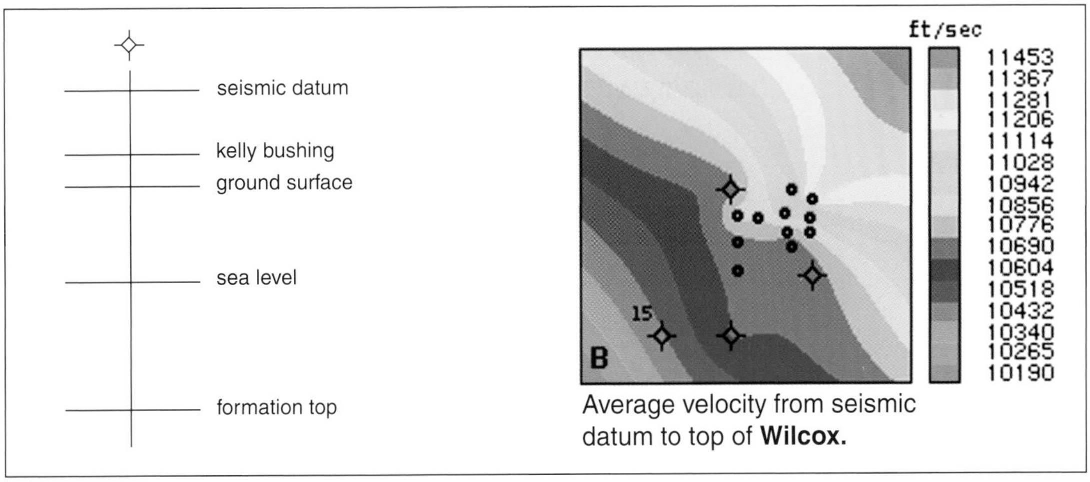

Figure 12–13. From Liner, 1999; courtesy PennWell.

Step 4: Convert time to depth

Convert time to depth by multiplying the time structure map and the depth conversion velocity map, i.e.,

$$z(x,y) = \frac{v(x,y)*t(x,y)}{2}$$

The factor of one-half is necessary because the times are two-way vertical times and we only want the one-way depth. The figure below shows the process and result for the Glenn Pool Wilcox horizon.

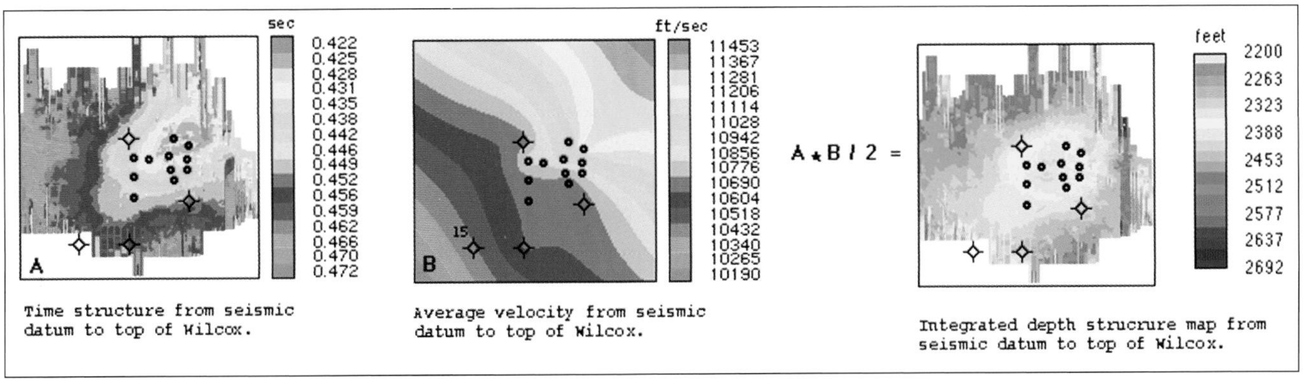

Figure 12–14. From Liner, 1999; courtesy PennWell.

Creating an Integrated Structure Map, continued

Step 5: Contour map

Contour or grid the integrated structure map with the same technique used for the wells-only depth map. This allows head-to-head comparison (Figure 12–16).

Integrated map

The final product *z(x,y)* is called an integrated structure map. It honors all well-control depth points (by definition) and uses the seismic events to interpolate between these points. The figure below is a comparison of the first depth map from well control only and the seismic plus well integrated depth map.

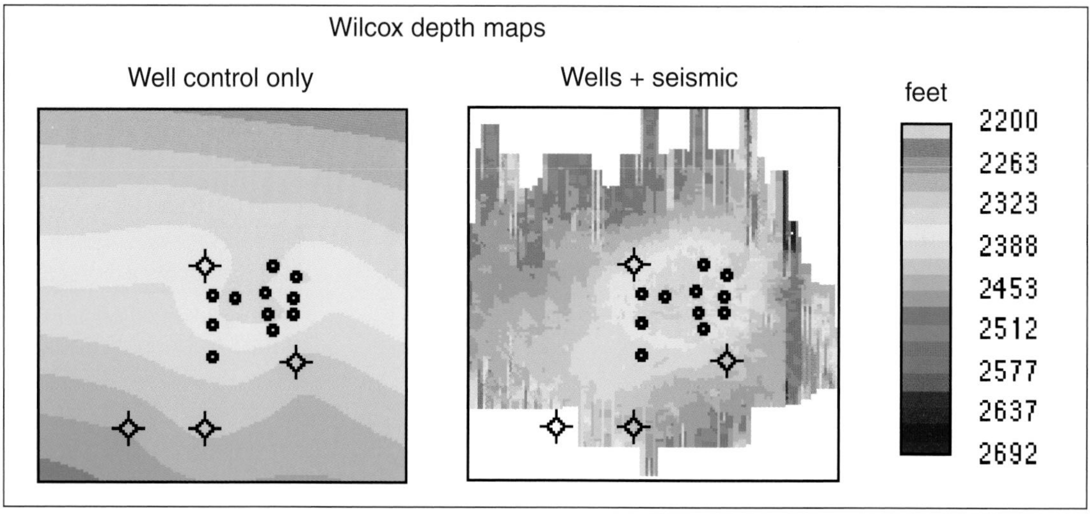

Figure 12–15. From Liner, 1999; courtesy PennWell.

Figure 12–16 is a zoom of the central area in the maps in Figure 12–15. Map A uses well control only, and map B uses well control plus seismic interpretation.

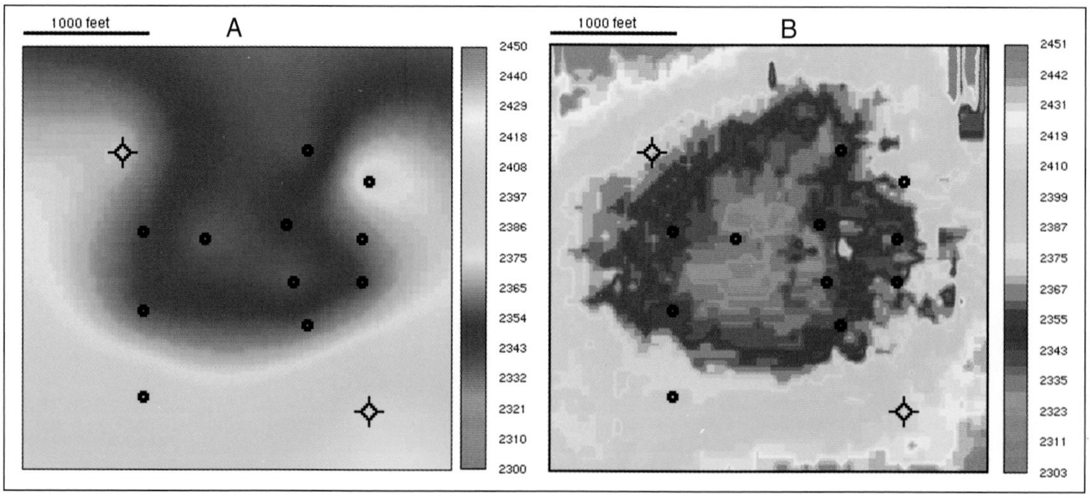

Figure 12–16. From Liner, 1999; courtesy PennWell.

Creating an Integrated Structure Map, continued

Conclusion

The mapping process described here can give useful results in many situations. However, the following cares should be considered:

- Strong lateral velocity variations may require depth migration and direct output to a depth cube.
- Existence of dense, shallow well control might allow depth mapping from a shallow seismic event. This minimizes the effect of topography and near-surface velocity problems.

Many depth conversion techniques should be available to the interpreter, since each is appropriate for commonly encountered problems. Each has strengths and weaknesses. Ultimately, however, structure maps should be delivered in depth, not time. Only then can the information be a useful guide to drilling decisions.

Section D
References

Brown, A.R., 1992, Seismic interpretation today and tomorrow: The Leading Edge, vol. 11, no. 11, 10–15.

_____, 1999, Interpretation of Three-Dimensional Seismic Data, 5th Ed.: AAPG Memoir 42, p. 514.

Liner, Chris, Elements of 3-D Seismology: Tulsa, PennWell, 1999.

Matteini, L., and L. Salvador, 1986, Computer-aided picking: a new approach to seismic interpretation: 56th Annual Internat. Mtg., Soc. Expl. Geophys., Expanded Abstracts, Session POS2.20.

Sheriff, R.E., 1991, Encyclopedic Dictionary of Exploration Geologists, 3rd Ed.: Tulsa, Society of Exploration Geophysicists.

Wilson, W.R., 1984, Seismic interpretation of 3-D structural features in time slice: a modeling study: 54th Annual Internat. Mtg., Soc. Expl. Geophys., Expanded Abstracts, Session S11.2.

Chapter 13

Interpreting 3-D Seismic Data

by

Geoffrey A. Dorn

Geoffrey A. Dorn

Geoff Dorn received his bachelor's degree in astrophysics (1973) from the University of New Mexico and a Ph.D. in geophysics (engineering geoscience, 1980) from the University of California, Berkeley. He joined ARCO's Exploration and Production Technology group in 1980, spending his first two years in seismic acquisition research. From 1982–1987 he directed ARCO's interactive interpretation research group but left management to pursue technical research interests in horizon and volume attribute analysis and 3-D visualization. In 1993 Dorn was named an ARCO Research Advisor for his contributions in 3-D seismic interpretation research and technical service. He returned to management in 1997 to direct ARCO's 3-D visualization research efforts. A member of the SEG Research Committee since 1990, he has helped organize several postconvention research committee workshops and was chairman of the 1993 SEG Summer Research Workshop on 3-D seismology. His interests include 3-D visualization, 3-D seismic interpretation, attribute analysis, and geophysical reservoir characterization. He is an active member of SEG, EAGE, and AAPG.

Overview

Introduction

Modern 3-D seismic interpretation involves interactive workstations and information technologies to interpret large volumes of data accurately and efficiently. The 3-D interpreter must understand the concepts of geology and seismology as well as the algorithms implemented in computer-aided interpretation tools to use these systems effectively. A good source place for a broad overview of the topic is *Interpretation of Three-Dimensional Seismic Data* by Alistair Brown. This chapter focuses on applications and techniques essential to the efficient and effective interpretation of 3-D seismic data.

In this chapter

This chapter contains the following sections.

Section A

Basics of Interpreting 3-D Seismic Data

Introduction

Three-dimensional (3-D) seismic data interpretation may be approached many different ways, depending on one's purpose. Data quality determines the level of the interpretation. For example, structural interpretation requires the least quality. Stratigraphic interpretation requires better quality data. Attribute analysis of 3-D data requires the highest quality data. The following procedure is suggested for interpreting 3-D seismic data.

Step	Action
1	Determine the goals for interpreting the 3-D data. Do you want to interpret straucture only or structure and stratigraphy, etc.?
2	Preview the 3-D data volume.
3	Pick critical horizons within the data using the appropriate autopicker.
4	Make strategic vertical, horizontal, and horizon slices.
5	If attribute analysis is possible and necessary to the interpretation goals, decide which attributes will best show the required geological features.

In this section

This section contains the following topics.

Data Preview

Why preview?

Why preview the 3-D volume? You have just received the final migrated volume from processing (late), and your manager is hounding you to produce maps at the reservoir or prospect level because he is looking at a deadline for a drilling commitment in the near future. Why not just dive in, do some quick picking at the reservoir level, grid and contour the picks, do a rough time-to-depth conversion, and move on? In most cases, this approach causes problems ranging from a loss in efficiency, to minor errors and omissions, to major inaccuracies in the interpretation.

Data preview provides an overview of the gross structural and stratigraphic environment. Variations in data quality can be identified, giving the interpreter an idea of the relative difficulty of interpretation in different areas. It is possible to identify the initial set of seismic horizons to interpret and the manner in which those horizons should be interpreted. Preview of a discontinuity volume could prove to be extremely valuable by obtaining an overall picture of the major faulting in the survey and by providing a better initial picture of any depositional stratigraphy imaged in the data. This information allows the interpreter to very effectively plan the interpretation of the volume and proceed in the quickest, most efficient manner possible.

Volume visualization

Volume visualization provides an effective tool for data preview. We can view animations of opaque slices through the data volume along any orientation, and we can control the slicing interactively. We can also control the opacity of the volume. By making the data volume partially transparent, we can see the structure of strong reflections prior to doing any interpretation. It may also be possible to isolate elements of depositional systems by controlling the color and opacity mappings.

Data preview example

The figure on the following page is an opaque volume from a 3-D seismic survey in the southern North Sea Gas Basin. Four horizons are indicated: Top Chalk, Top Keuper, Top Zechstein, and Top Rotliegend. By visualizing the volume with the opacity set so that only the strongest peaks and troughs are opaque, we can see the overall 3-D structure of these horizons prior to interpretation (Figure 1b).

Examining Figure 13–1b, we can note that the anticline at the Top Chalk has a different trend than the anticline at the Top Keuper. Some faulting is evident along the north end of the Top Keuper horizon extending roughly parallel to the trend of the anticline. The Top Zechstein and Top Keuper are approximately conformable in this volume, and the strong amplitude reflections from the west are dipping. Top Rotliegend fault blocks are also evident. By using motion (e.g., rotation around the time axis) and stereo displays, the structures, their relationships, and the positions of specific reflections become much more obvious than they are in the still images in Figure 13–1.

Data preview example (continued)

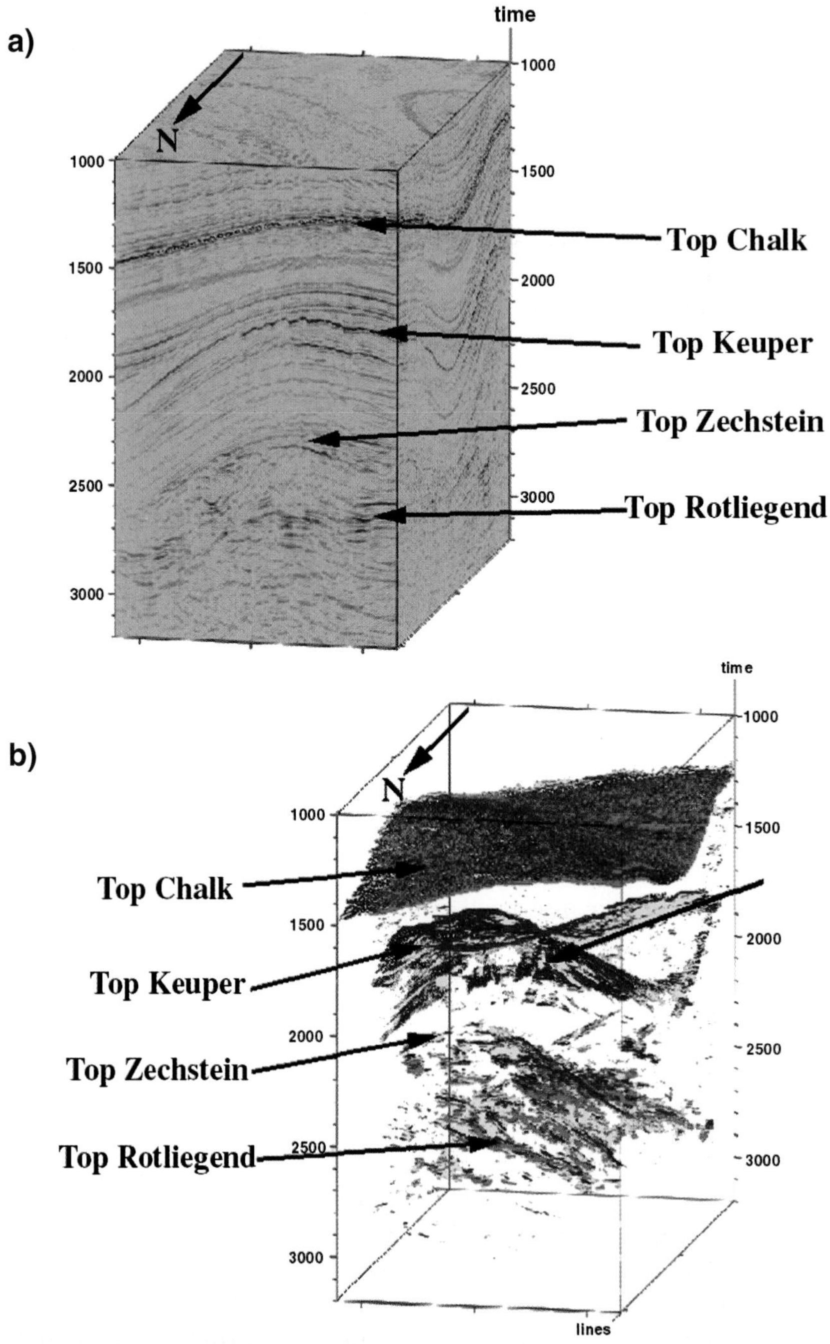

Figure 13–1. From Dorn, 1998; courtesy SEG.

Two- or Three-Dimensional Interpretation

Introduction

Three-dimensional seismic interpretation is not just dense 2-D seismic interpretation. Although it is certainly possible to interpret the 3-D seismic volume as a dense 2-D grid (in fact, some early interactive interpretation systems actually encouraged this), this is neither an effective nor an efficient approach to the interpretation. The results are generally of poorer quality and require significantly more effort than interpreting the data in a 3-D fashion.

The 2-D approach

Two-dimensional interpretation of a 3-D seismic volume involves limiting your views of the data, and your interpretation, to lines and cross-lines. Typically, this approach to interpretation has its roots in two things. First, the interpreter is comfortable with seismic sections. Second, the interpreter new to 3-D interpretation may simply decide that "there is too much data to possibly look at all of it." Two-dimensional interpretation of the 3-D volume results in loss of information and is the least efficient approach to interpreting the data. Modern interactive systems provide a variety of tools that allow interpreters to perform the interpretation in a more 3-D fashion.

Never enough data

The first rule of 3-D seismic interpretation is that *there is never enough data*. The problem we are trying to solve with seismic interpretation is always underdetermined. There is never enough information to uniquely define the geology of the subsurface in the area of the 3-D survey. In some instances, you may decide to disregard some of the data collected. If you do not use it all, then you are reducing resolution and control.

Weaknesses of vertical sections

A second rule for 3-D seismic interpretation is that the survey is always oriented at 45° to the trend of faults, channels, and other features of interest. There will always be faults or channels oriented at angles between 0° and 45° relative to the orientation of the vertical section you are interpreting. If you only look at vertical sections, you will always miss important features of the geology.

Example of seeing faults

The figure on the following page shows several images from a 3-D survey in the Gulf of Mexico. Figure 2a is a dip magnitude map at an interpreted horizon in the data, showing several steep dip (pink) lineaments associated with normal faults that cut the horizon. Arrows *b*, *c*, and *d* show the orientation and direction of three traverses cut through the volume at angles of approximately 90°, 45°, and 10° to the trace of the fault in the center of the horizon. Figures 2b, c, and d are traverses *b, c,* and *d,* respectively. The fault is clearly interpretable in the centers of the traverses that cut the fault at angles of 90° and 45°. However, it would be very difficult to interpret the fault on Figure 2d, the oblique traverse. This geometric effect produces a blind zone on vertical sections that are oriented between +/-20° of the trend of a fault. As a result, if you are only interpreting vertical seismic sections, you will fail to see faults that have trends in this zone. The same phenomenon occurs with depositional stratigraphy.

The best section to image a channel is a section oriented at 90° to the trend of the channel.

Example of seeing faults (continued)

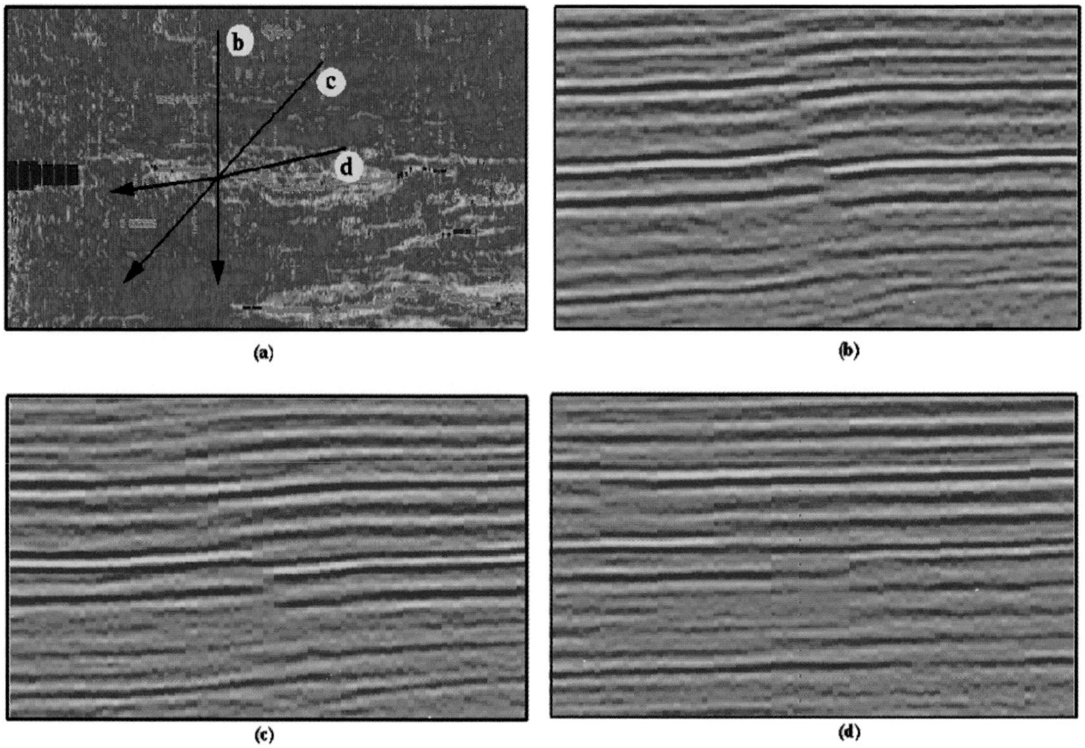

Figure 13–2. From Dorn, 1998; courtesy SEG.

Start with time slices

The first step toward 3-D interpretation of a 3-D volume is to use time slices. The value of time-slice interpretation for faults is fairly obvious. Regardless of the strike of the fault, most fault surfaces intersect the time slice at an angle between 45° and 90° to the plane of the time slice

Computer limitations

Depositional systems are typically more interpretable on time slices than they are on vertical sections. The figure below is a time slice from a 3-D survey in the North Sea. A portion of a braided stream system is clearly evident.

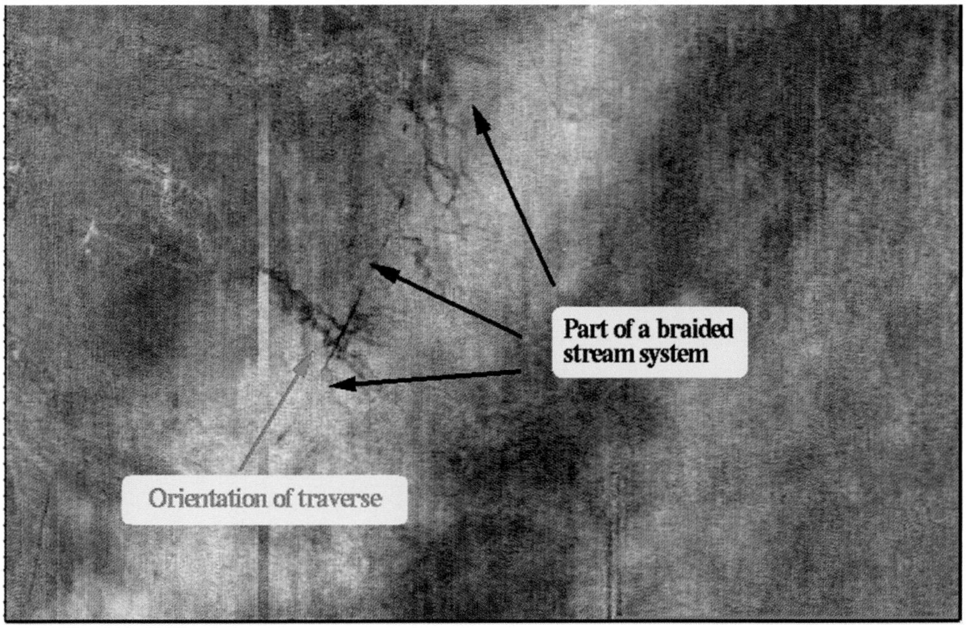

Figure 13–3. From Dorn, 1998; courtesy SEG.

The following figure is a traverse cut through the data in a direction perpendicular to the channel system. Horizontal arrows indicate when the channel system occurs, and vertical arrows show the location of each of a number of individual channels cut by the traverse. It is safe to say that most if not all of these channels would have been missed if the interpretation had been limited to vertical sections.

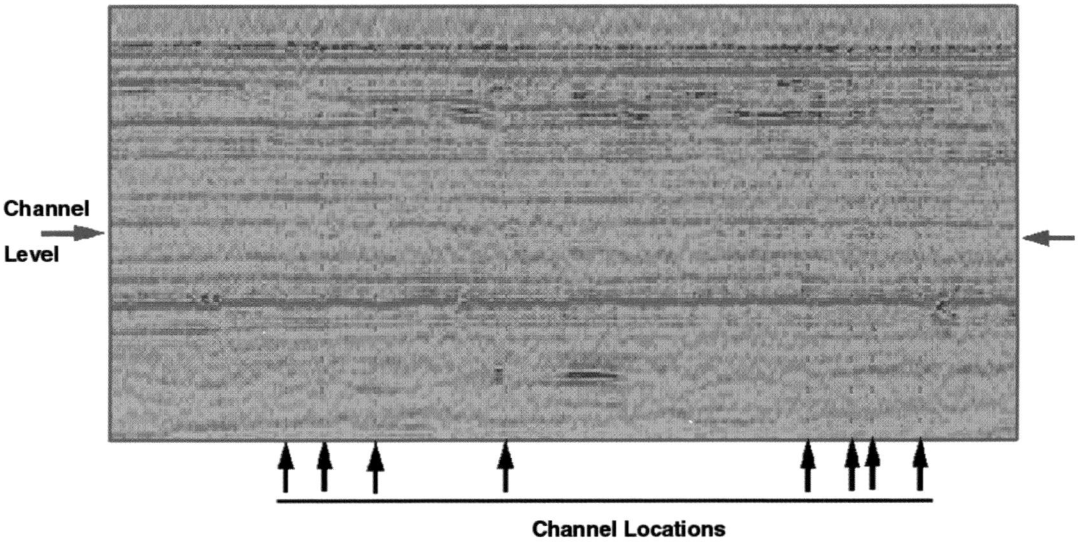

Figure 13–4. From Dorn, 1998; courtesy SEG.

Picking Horizons in 3-D Data

Introduction

Computer-assisted interpretation of seismic data is one of the areas where the tools of modern interactive interpretation systems have made the most significant impact. The interpreter needs to choose the technique that will allow the best interpretation to be achieved in the most efficient manner possible. In terms of interpretive efficiency, techniques would typically be ordered in the following way, from least efficient to most efficient:

- Manual picking
- Interpolating
- Autopicking
- Surface-slicing
- Voxel tracking

Manual picking

Manual picking is interpreting horizons on lines, cross-lines, time slices, and traverses by hand. This is the most familiar technique. It is also, by far, the least efficient horizon interpretation technique in terms of interpreter time and effort. While interpreting manually, the interpreter is looking for some degree of local continuity in the data and local similarity of character to identify the event to be picked.

Picking by interpolation

Interpolation is somewhat more efficient than manual interpretation. The use of interpolation, however, assumes that a horizon is locally very smooth and perhaps linear (or planar in two dimensions) between control points. If this assumption is violated between control points (e.g., there is a fault between the interpreted lines), then the results will be poor.

Autopicking

Autopicking (or autotracking) has been around in interactive interpretation systems since the early 1980s. The concept behind autopicking is quite simple. The interpreter places seed picks on lines and/or cross-lines in the 3-D survey. These seed points are then used as initial control for the autopicking operation. The algorithm looks for a similar feature on a neighboring trace. If it finds such a feature within specified constraints, it picks that trace and moves on to the next trace. Simple autopickers allow the user to specify a feature to be tracked, an allowable amplitude range, and a dip window in which to search.

The figure to the right is a sketch of how such an autopicker works. If any of the search criteria are not met (amplitude out of range, no similar feature in the dip window, etc.), the autotracker stops tracking at that trace. More sophisticated autopickers let the user specify additional criteria to control the picking.

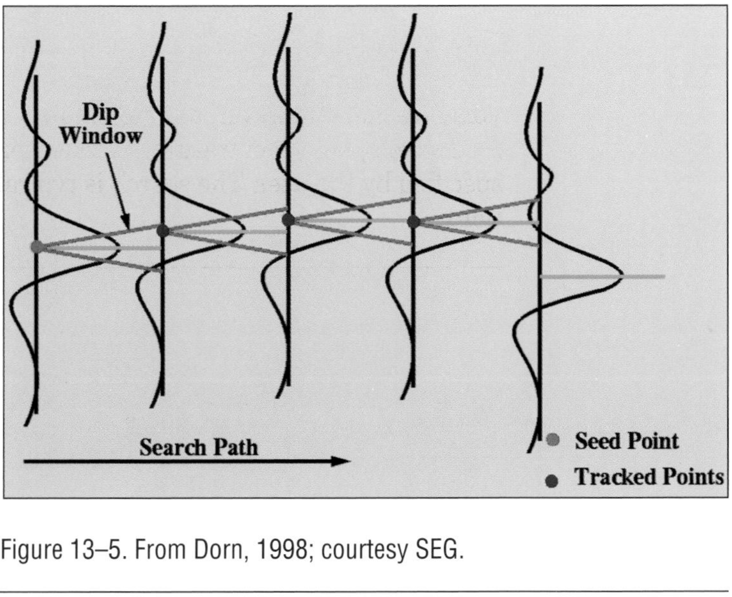

Figure 13–5. From Dorn, 1998; courtesy SEG.

Picking Horizons in 3-D Data, continued

Feature and correlation trackers

There are two classes of autopicker:

1) Feature trackers
2) Correlation trackers

The feature tracker searches for a similar configuration of samples within the dip window but does not perform any correlations between traces. It tries to track a configuration of samples on the seismic trace that defines a peak, trough, zero crossing, etc., from trace to trace.

A correlation tracker takes a portion of the seismic trace around the seed pick and correlates it with a neighboring trace through a set of lag times constrained by the specified dip search window. If a lag time is found with an acceptable correlation quality factor, then the pick on the new trace is accepted and the picker moves on to the next trace. Clearly, the correlation autopicker is much more computationally intensive than the feature tracker. It is also typically more robust in its picking.

Autopicker pathways

Another aspect of autopickers that must be considered is the path that the autopicker follows through the data. Many are not true volume autopickers because they track through the data only in the line or cross-line direction. In other words, the path they follow through the data is not truly three dimensional or even two dimensional. Some autopickers make consecutive passes through the data—one pass in the line direction, the next in the cross-line direction. A few autopickers actually move through the data in a true 2-D sense, expanding around control in both the line and cross-line directions in a single pass. The more sophisticated the path the autopicker follows, the more useful it will be in infilling the horizon from the interpreted seed points. The type of control the interpreter picks in the volume prior to autopicking should in part be dependent on the type of algorithm being used and the path it follows through the data.

Voxel tracking

A technique called voxel tracking has become available with the advent of volume rendering and visualization. A voxel is a volume element. In a 3-D seismic volume, it is a sample.

Voxel tracking is conceptually related to autopicking in the sense that an event or feature is tracked through the volume starting from seed control points picked by the interpreter. Voxel trackers, however, tend to follow a true 3-D path through the data. Starting at the seed voxels, the voxel tracker searches for connected voxels that satisfy the search criteria specified by the user. The search is typically conducted in line, cross-line, and time directions.

Picking Horizons in 3-D Data, continued

Voxel tracking assumptions

The figure below is a sketch of a simple voxel tracking algorithm and its behavior under two different continuity constraints. Six-way connectivity restricts the search from one voxel to only the neighboring voxels that are connected face to face. Twenty-six-way connectivity allows the search to proceed between neighboring voxels that are connected face to face, edge to edge, or corner to corner. The connectivity constraint that is used affects the outcome of the voxel tracking.

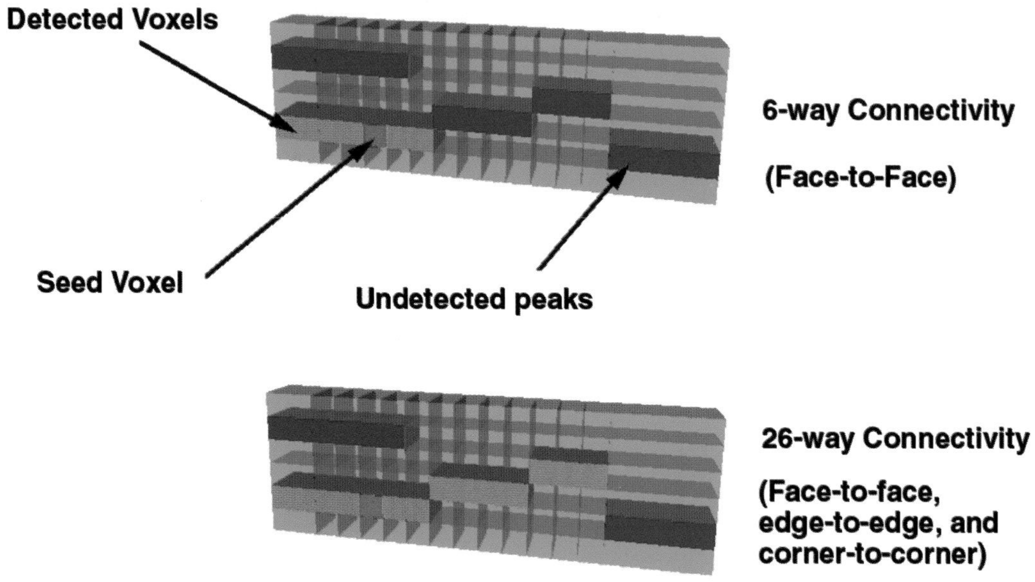

Figure 13–6. From Dorn, 1998; courtesy SEG.

Like autopicking, voxel tracking assumes that the data are locally continuous, consistent, and connected or smooth. Both techniques assume a consistent phase is being interpreted from the data.

Voxel tracking pros and cons

Because volume-rendering techniques typically place the entire volume being visualized into RAM memory on the workstation, and since the tracking algorithm is computationally simpler than most autopickers, voxel tracking can be many orders of magnitude faster than autopicking—when it works. Most voxel tracking algorithms are more sensitive to poor signal-to-noise ratio than correlation autopickers. However, on reflections with a good signal-to-noise ratio, voxel tracking is usually the most efficient approach to picking the horizon.

Surface Slicing

Introduction

Surface slicing is a novel approach to interpreting seismic horizons. This technique involves visualizing and interpreting areally finite portions of horizons on time slice slabs of the data. The slab thickness is a weak function of the bandwidth of the data and a stronger function of the dip of the reflections. For a detailed description of the technique see Stark (1996).

The figures below show the general concept of the technique. Figure 13–7 is a perspective view of a horizon structure (a) and the same structure split into 12-ms slabs and dissected (b). Suppose Figure 13–7 represented a reflection (say a peak) in a 3-D survey. This structure could be cut into time slabs and dissected. Figure 13–8 shows what these time-slice slabs might look like, where within each slab only the peaks are displayed. The dissected portions of the 3-D structure appear as annuli that fit perfectly within each other. Interpreting the horizon consists of selecting those elements that fit together, somewhat like assembling a jigsaw puzzle.

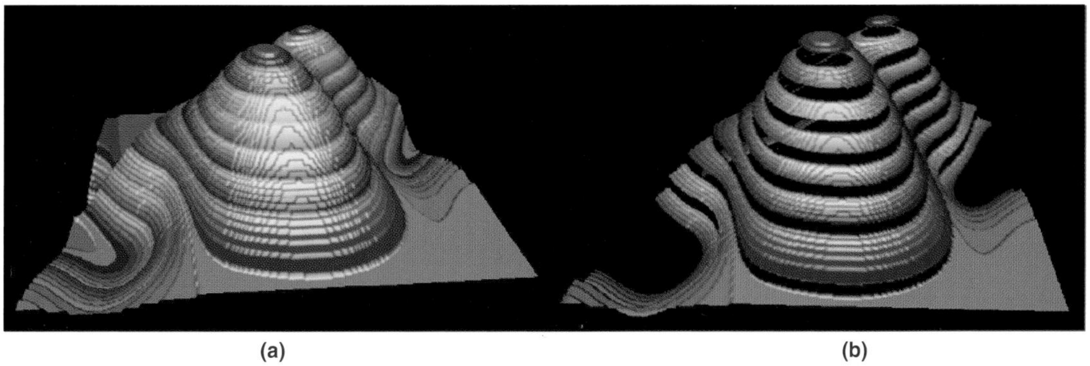

Figure 13–7. From Stark, 1996; courtesy SEG.

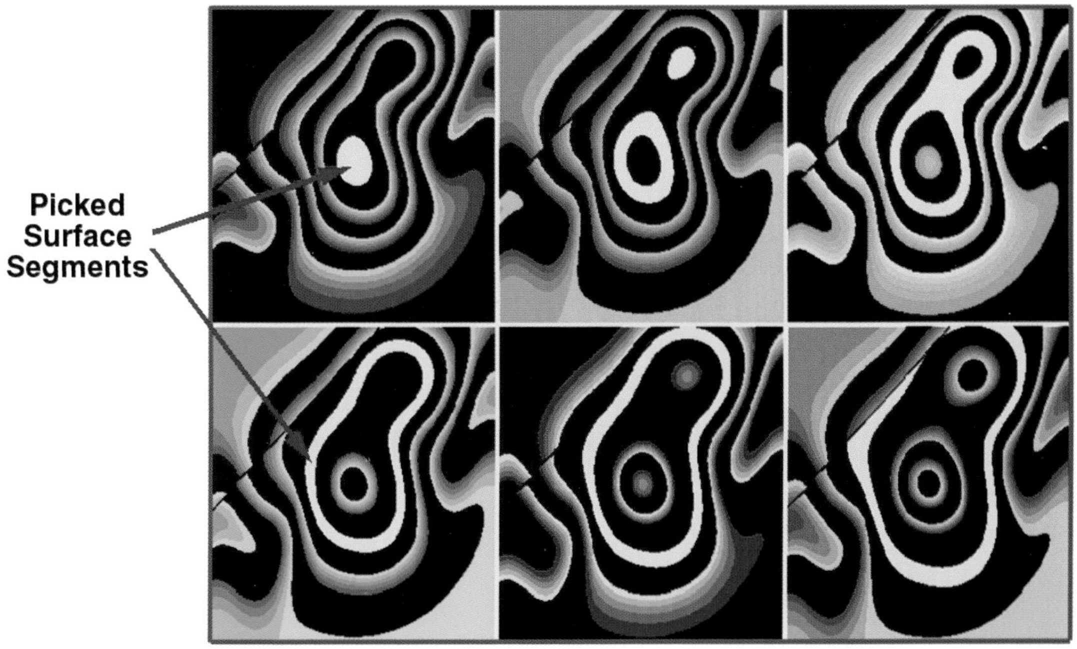

Figure 13–8. From Stark, 1996; courtesy SEG.

Surface Slicing, continued

Surface slicing assumptions

For an interpreter who is practiced in surface slice picking and in the appropriate settings of the various parameters that control the algorithm, surface slicing can be an extremely efficient way to interpret horizons. Since entire areas on the horizon are picked with each click of the mouse button, this technique is not very sensitive to the number of traces in the 3-D survey. It assumes local continuity and connectivity in the data, and it assumes a consistent phase is being interpreted. It is less sensitive to discontinuities and poor signal-to-noise ratio than voxel tracking or autotracking because it is not entirely an automatic technique; the interpreter controls the technique and frequently can achieve better results because interpretive judgment can be applied.

Choosing the appropriate technique

Clearly, any interpretation involves some combination of the techniques listed above. The strongest events might be voxel tracked. Many of the remaining events might be surface sliced. In some areas an autopicker might be necessary. All three of these techniques typically leave some holes or unpicked traces in the horizon that might be infilled by interpolation. And all of these techniques require some interpretation by hand on seismic sections to provide initial control to the picking process. The techniques should be viewed as a set of tools that the good interpreter knows how to apply to achieve the best interpretation in the shortest period of time.

Reviewing picks

While these techniques are all extremely valuable, we must understand that computer-assisted horizon picking is only as good as the algorithm, combined with its application by the interpreter. All of these techniques produce some cycle skips in the data (e.g., in areas of poor signal-to-noise ratio or in areas where the event being interpreted splits into a doublet). The interpreter must realize this and review the picks in the volume, on sections, and on attribute maps of the horizon that might accentuate cycle skips in the interpretation (e.g., dip magnitude maps). Cycle skips are also very obvious when 3-D visualization is used to view the horizon.

Picking faults

Computer-aided interpretation of fault surfaces is significantly less advanced than horizon interpretation. With horizons, a feature of the data—a reflection event—can be tracked in a controlled fashion through the volume. Fault surfaces, however, typically do not give rise to reflection events in the data. Faults are characterized by discontinuities in the horizons and by no-data zones, which are (at least conceptually) more difficult to track.

Fault autopicking

Fault surface autopicking algorithms have begun to appear in 3-D interpretation systems. In one fashion or another, these algorithms attempt to track discontinuities in the volume. Some require initial interpretive input—seed picks on fault surfaces that are to be tracked. Others require a preprocessing step that creates a volume to highlight discontinuities; then the discontinuities are tracked to form fault surfaces. Although these techniques are relatively new, they are developing rapidly and promise to significantly improve the efficiency of one of the most tedious aspects of 3-D structural interpretation.

Nonvertical slices

Seismic sections are vertical cuts through a seismic volume. Nonvertical cuts through a seismic data volume are also called slices. As illustrated in Figure 13–5, horizonal slices can be of several types:

- Time slices (horizontal cuts of a time volume)
- Depth slices (horizontal cuts of a depth volume)
- Horizon slices (cuts in the shape of interpreted horizons)
- Fault slices (cuts in the shape of interpreted fault surfaces)

Depth slices are only available if the data delivered from the processor are converted to depth. Fault slices require data with mappable fault surfaces.

Section B
Stratigraphic Interpretation Techniques of 3-D Data

Introduction

Besides the interpretation of vertical slices for stratigraphic features, 3-D seismic data also may be interpreted in nonvertical slices. These views include time, horizon, and proportional slices.

In this section

This section contains the following topics.

Time and Horizon Slices

Introduction

The time slice was described earlier as the first step toward 3-D interpretation of a 3-D seismic volume. A time-slice view of the data is an improvement over vertical sections for the interpretation of depositional systems because it provides the opportunity to see a portion of depositional systems in map view. This view is key to interpreting these systems because it allows a view of the morphology of the system, which facilitates its recognition.

Structural effects

A time slice provides at best an image of a small portion of a depositional system. Subsequent structural deformation of the depositional surface typically means that only a small portion of a depositional system is imaged on a time slice. In fact, as the structural relief increases, the anomalies on the time slice associated with the structure quickly dominate the image.

Horizon slices

One way to improve the imaging of the paleodepositional system is to create horizon slices through the 3-D volume. The interpreted reflection (horizon) is an approximation of a paleodepositional surface. Within the time interval where reflections are approximately conformable to the interpreted horizon in three dimensions, the shape of the horizon surface is a reasonable description of the shape of the paleodepositional surfaces.

Example vertical slice

Figures 13–9, 13–10, and 13–11 illustrate the value of the horizontal slice view of the data. The figure below is a portion of a vertical seismic section from a 3-D seismic survey in the North Sea. The interpreted horizon, at approximately 2 seconds, is the Top Paleocene. Approximately 120 ms below this, at about the level indicated by the arrows, the section crosses a 1-km-wide Paleocene deepwater turbidite channel.

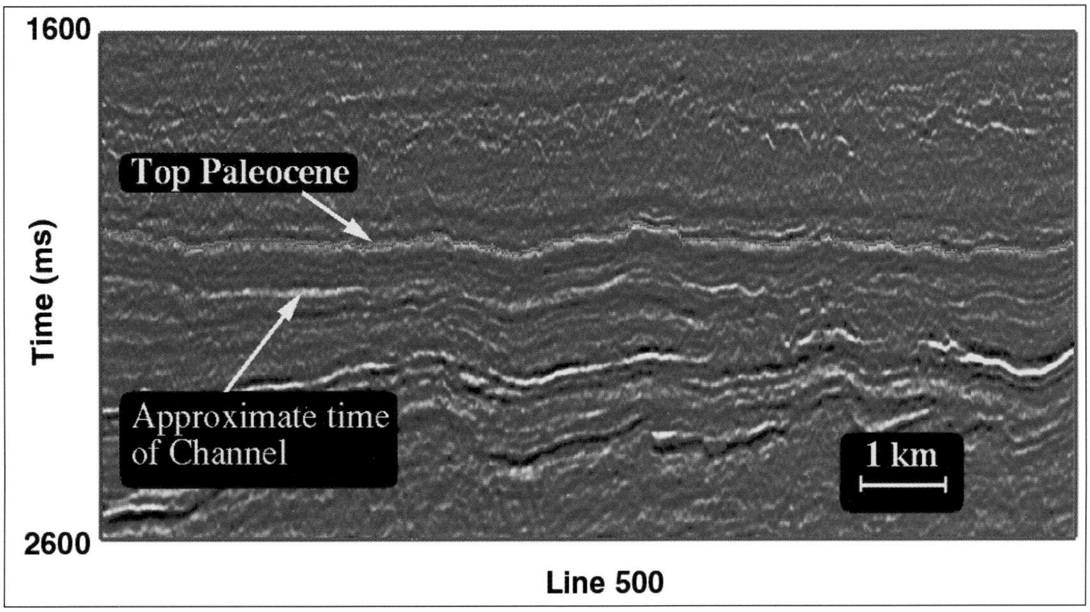

Figure 13–9. From Dorn, 1998; courtesy SEG.

Example time slice

The figure to the right is a time slice that intersects a portion of the channel. On both the vertical section (Figure 13–9) and the time slice, the channel is difficult to interpret, even though the feature is quite large. Most of the amplitude patterns on the time slice are associated with structure, not stratigraphy.

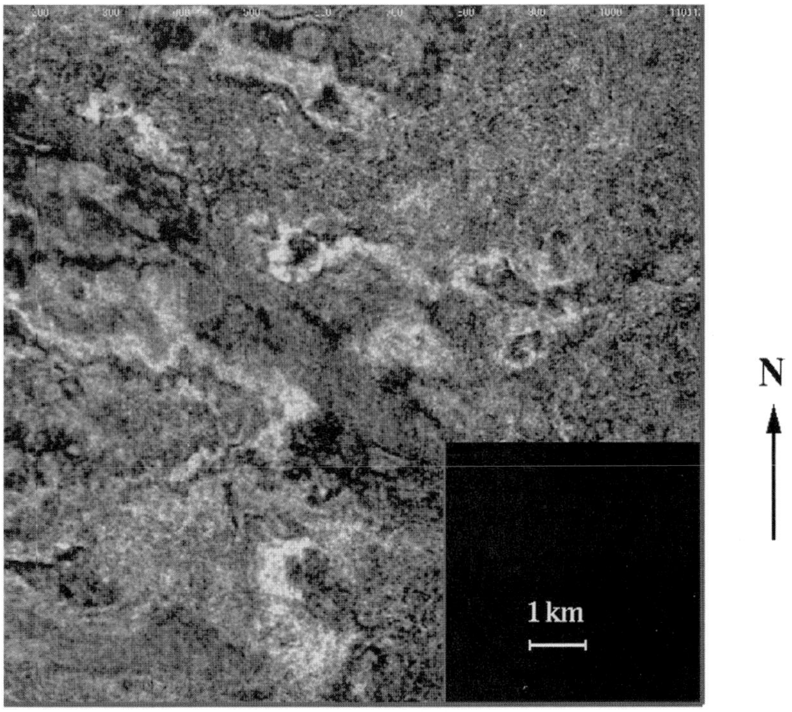

Figure 13–10. From Dorn, 1998, courtesy SEG.

Example horizon slice

This figure is a horizon slice 120 ms below the Top Paleocene horizon. The shape of the horizon slice is defined by the shape of the Top Paleocene horizon. This surface is shifted 120 ms down, and the seismic amplitudes are extracted where the shifted surface intersects the 3-D volume of data. The 1-km-wide channel is unmistakable on this view of the data, and both edges of the channel are readily interpretable.

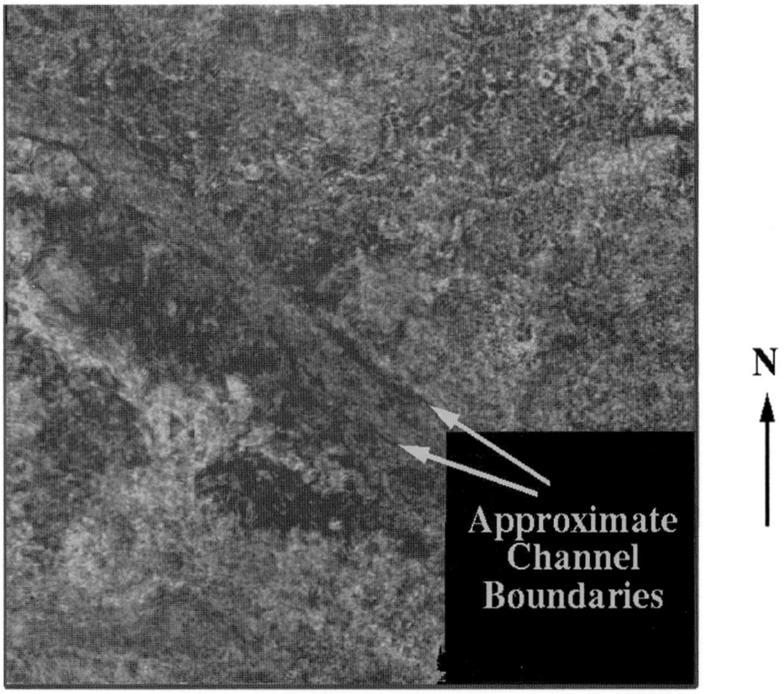

Figure 13–11. From Dorn, 1998, courtesy SEG.

Proportional Slices and 3-D Volume Visualization

Introduction

Additional refinement to the horizon-slice approach can be made to accommodate situations where there is growth, or differential deposition, in an interval between two interpreted horizons. For such an interval, the reflections between the two interval-bounding horizons are not parallel to either bounding horizon. To some extent, the shape of the reflections in this interval is intermediate between the shapes of the interval bounding horizons. A set of slices between the two bounding horizons, which more closely mimics the shape of the reflections in that interval, is given by

$$S = H_1 + R * (H_2 - H_1)$$

where:

S = the intermediate surface
H_1 = the shallower horizon
H_2 = the deeper horizon
R = a fraction that varies between 0 and 1

Definition

The new surface, S, is the shallower horizon time structure plus a fraction of the isochron between the two bounding horizons. Such a slice is called a **proportional slice** because it is proportionally between the two bounding horizons. In certain environments that exhibit significant growth in the interval, the proportional slice can provide a significantly improved image of the depositional stratigraphy compared to horizon slices in the shape of either bounding horizon.

Creating proportional slices

Horizon slices and proportional slices have been available for a number of years in interactive interpretation systems. Some of the implementations are awkward; creating the proportional slice, in particular, may be a multistep process. Ideally, creating these slices should be a fully interactive process, allowing the interpreter to explore intervals of interest in the 3-D seismic volume for indications of paleodepositional systems.

3-D volume visualization of depositional systems

Advances in pattern recognition and volume seeding have provided tools that allow the interpreter to seed and pick the depositional system as a 3-D body. This allows the interpreter to see the depositional system as a 3-D object within the seismic volume. Visualizing this object in three dimensions provides visual integration of the stratigraphy of the depositional system with the overprint of current structural relief.

Section C
Attributes

Introduction

Attributes are measurements based on seismic data such as polarity, phase, frequency, or velocity. Horizon attributes were first used in the mid-1980s for interpreting fault traces on reservoir horizons. Since then there has been an explosion in the number of attributes that can be generated and displayed in 3-D interpretation systems. New attributes are added to the list regularly. Because software providers frequently use different names for the same attribute, and since some of the names are rather obscure, it can be very difficult be sure what each attribute represents.

In this section

This section contains the following topics.

Basics of Attributes

Grouping attributes

At this time, no general reference includes a complete list of the attributes that can be created. One approach (Brown, 1999) to organizing the attributes is based on whether they are related to the following:

- Time
- Amplitude
- Phase
- Frequency in the seismic data

An alternative approach might be to group them into these categories:

- Horizon attributes (measures of the data that occur along a 3-D surface through the seismic volume)
- Volume attributes (measures of the data that occur over an interval of time through the seismic volume)

Attribute meanings

The meaning and use of some attributes can be quite straightforward. The reflection amplitude at a horizon can, under the correct circumstances, be related to porosity or net pay in a reservoir interval. With other attributes the physical interpretation of a variation in attribute value is somewhat more obscure. For example, arc length (also call reflection heterogeneity) is a measure of the length of the wiggle trace over a specified interval (technically, it is an approximation of the line integral of the trace over the interval). This measure is affected by amplitude, frequency, and the length of the interval. Associating a variation in arc length with a physical change in the geology is possible, but it can be more challenging.

Attribute interpretation

Attributes are used for both qualitative and quantitative interpretation. An example of qualitative interpretation would be to use maps of dip magnitude, dip azimuth, or residual structure to interpret detailed fault trace patterns on a horizon. An example of quantitative interpretation would be an attempt to correlate attributes with reservoir properties measured in the borehole. A large number of papers illustrating both applications of horizon and volume attributes are published each year in various professional journals. Examples of applications to structural interpretation include Brede and Thomas (1986), Denham and Nelson (1986), Dalley et al. (1989), Rijks and Jauffred (1991), and Dorn et al. (1996). Stratigraphic interpretation from attribute maps is discussed in Enachescu (1993a,b), Reymond and Stampfli (1994), and Dorn (1998). Examples of reservoir characterization from attributes include Dorn et al. (1996) and Brown (1999).

Using Attributes for Geological Interpretation

Rules of thumb

Here are a few rules of thumb that the interpreter should apply when approaching the use of attributes in a 3-D seismic survey:

- Consider the geology.
- Use different attributes.
- Use normalized attributes
- Avoid using an interval attribute that involves the summation of a data measure that varies in a cyclic fashion over an interval

Consider the geology

Consider the geological feature you are hoping to interpret and how varying that aspect of the geology might affect the seismic data. This can help guide the initial selection of attributes and will certainly help with interpreting the resulting data.

Using different attributes

Don't forget about using other attributes. It is not uncommon for there to be surprises in the data—unforeseen relationships that make physical sense once they have been discovered.

Normalized attributes

Be wary of using volume or interval attributes that are not normalized by the isochron of the interval over which they are calculated. This normalization can take the form of dividing the attribute by either the actual isochron or by the number of time samples in the interval. Although this normalization is not appropriate for some interval attributes (e.g., the maximum absolute amplitude in the interval), it is essential for any attribute that involves a summation over the interval. Without the normalization, the lateral attribute variation may simply be showing the variation in the isochron.

Cyclic variation of an attribute

Avoid using an interval attribute that involves the summation of a data measure that varies in a cyclic fashion over an interval. For example, in several systems it is possible to calculate the sum of trace amplitude over a user-specified interval. Since the trace amplitude has both positive and negative values over most intervals (unless the interval is so small as to include only a half-cycle of the data), the positive and negative values tend to cancel each other out. A second example would be the sum of instantaneous phase over an interval in the volume

Know the attribute

To apply these rules to attribute interpretation, it is essential for the interpreter to understand what the attribute is measuring in the data—the equation for the attribute. The only way the interpreter can know this is for the software vendor to provide well-written documentation, either on paper or online, that explains the mathematical calculation involved in generating the attribute. This combination—an interest on the part of the interpreter to understand the attributes and a willingness on the part of the vendor to provide that information—is essential to the intelligent and effective use of attributes in 3-D interpretation.

Section D

Visualization Techniques for 3-D Data

Introduction

Visualization is the graphical presentation of data in an intuitive fashion to develop an understanding of data and reveal new insight. The key word in this definition is "intuitive." Three-dimensional visualization applied to 3-D seismic data is an attempt to present this data, and its interpretations, in an intuitive fashion—the same fashion in which we perceive the world around us every day.

In this section

This section contains the following topics.

Visualization Fundamentals

Perceiving 3-D

More than half the neurons in the human brain are associated with vision. This significant resource can be applied to the interpretation of 3-D seismic data if the data are presented in 3-D fashion. Humans perceive the 3-D world through a variety of visual cues:

- Perspective
- Lighting/shading
- Depth of focus
- Depth cueing
- Transparency/obscuration
- Stereopsis
- Motion parallax
- Peripheral vision

3-D visualization in seismic data

Three-dimensional visualization has been used as a part of 3-D interpretation for the last 10 years. As each additional visual cue has been added to the 3-D displays of seismic data and seismic interpretations, there have been significant improvements in the 3-D interpretation process.

For a discussion of the applications of visualization to horizon attribute analysis, see chapter 8 in Brown (1999). For a more general discussion of the role of 3-D visualization in 3-D seismic interpretation, see Dorn et al. (1995).

Improvements using 3-D visualization

Three-dimensional visualization improves the efficiency, accuracy, and completeness of the interpretation, integrates large amounts of data in easily understood displays, and significantly improves the communication between different specialists on an asset team and between the asset team and management. If 3-D visualization is not used in the interpretive process, the interpreter will lose productivity and the interpretation will be incomplete or inaccurate.

Volume rendering

Volume rendering of seismic data, and its use in data preview, is one example of an area where visualization has a major impact on the efficiency of interpretation. In surface-slice interpretation, if a 3-D visualization of the horizon being interpreted is used along with the 2-D surface-slice map displays, the interpreter can be significantly more productive and avoid errors in the interpretation. For a number of years, 3-D visualization of attributes on a lighted 3-D horizon surface has provided a means of interpreting detailed fault patterns in a reservoir interval—faults that would have been missed if 3-D visualization had not been used (Dorn and Tubman, 1996).

Immersive Visualization

Introduction

In 3-D desktop visualization, perspective, lighting/shading, transparency, stereopsis, and in some cases head-tracking (changing the data appropriately for changes in the interpreter's head location with respect to the screen) has been applied to both surface and volume displays. With each additional visual cue used in presenting the data in 3-D, there have been improvements in efficiency. New insights have been gained about the data, and communication has improved. The next step in visualization is to engage peripheral vision—to become immersed in the data.

Facilities for immersive visualization

In 1997 ARCO, Texaco, and Norsk Hydro each installed large immersive visualization environments. The Texaco facilities are visionariums, large screens (8–10 ft tall) that curve horizontally through approximately 160° and can curve vertically. Data are projected on the screens using three projectors, each covering one-third of the screen. The sense of immersion is achieved primarily by engaging peripheral vision, filling most of the field of view with data.

Engaging peripheral vision

ARCO and Norsk Hydro have installed immersive visualization rooms, based on the CAVE™ invented at the University of Illinois, which consist of four projection surfaces—three orthogonal flat vertical walls and the floor. The images on the walls are rear projected, while the image on the floor is projected from the top down. The sense of immersion is achieved by engaging peripheral vision and by stereo projection of the data. In these environments, the data surround the interpreter, actually appearing to fill the room.

The figure shows interpretive work performed in the Immersive Visualization Environment at ARCO. The interpreter can walk through the data, along interpreted horizons, and between faults to locations where the wells penetrate the target horizons. Since head tracking is used to properly alter the data projections for changes in head position, the view of the data changes very intuitively as the interpreter moves through the data.

Figure 13–12. From Dorn, 1998; courtesy SEG.

Immersive Visualization, continued

Immersive rooms vs. visionariums

Both the immersive rooms and the visionariums have their application. The immersive room may be a better environment in which to actually interpret the data and plan the development, with a group of up to five people working together at one time. The visionarium may be a better arrangement for reviewing the prospect, drilling plan, or development plan for a larger management group.

Calculating depth conversion velocity

The application of these facilities and other immersive visualization devices is just beginning to be explored in the oil industry. In the not-too-distant future, these environments may fundamentally change the manner in which we do our business. One thing is certain: 3-D seismic interpretation 5–10 years from now will be very different from 3-D seismic interpretation today.

Section E
References

Brede, E.C., and S.W. Thomas, 1986, Interactive fault mapping: a case study: The Leading Edge, vol. 5, no. 9, p. 1262–1272.

Brown, A.R., 1999, Interpretation of Three-Dimensional Seismic Data, 5th ed.: AAPG Memoir 42, 525 p.

Dalley, R.M., E.C.A. Gevers, G.M. Stampfli, D.J. Davies, C.N. Gastaldi, P.A. Ruijtenberg, and G.J.O. Vermeer, 1989, Dip and azimuth displays for 3D seismic interpretation: First Break, vol. 7, no. 3, p. 86–95.

Denham, J.I., and H.R. Nelson, Jr., 1986, Map displays from an interactive interpretation: Geophysics, vol. 51, p. 1999–2006.

Dorn, G.A., 1998 Modern 3-D seismic interpretation: The Leading Edge, vol. 17, no. 9, p. 1262–1272.

_____, M.J. Cole, and K.M. Tubman, 1995, Visualization in 3-D seismic interpretation: The Leading Edge, vol. 14, no. 10, p. 1045–1049.

_____, K.M. Tubman, D. Cooke, and R. O'Connor, 1996, Geophysical reservoir characterization of Pickerill Field, North Sea, using 3-D seismic and well data, *in* P. Weimer and T. Davis, eds., Applications of 3-D Seismic Data to Exploration and Production: AAPG Studies in Geology 42, p. 107–121.

Enachescu, M.E., 1993a, Amplitude interpretation of 3-D reflection data: The Leading Edge, vol. 12, no. 6, p. 678–685.

_____, 1993b, Three-dimensional seismic imaging of a Jurassic paleodrainage system: 1993 SEG Summer Research Workshop on 3-D Seismology, Abstracts, p. 292–298.

Reymond, B.A., and G.M. Stampfli, 1994, Sequence stratigraphic interpretation of 3D seismic data offshore Louisiana—a case study: First Break, vol. 12, no. 9, p. 453–462.

Rijks, E.J.H., and J.C.E.M. Jauffred, 1991, Attribute extraction: an important application in any detailed 3-D interpretation study: The Leading Edge, vol. 10, no. 9, p. 11–19.

Stark, T.J., 1996, Surface slice generation and interpretation—a review: The Leading Edge, vol. 15, p. 818–819.

Acknowledgment The author and AAPG acknowledge and thank the Society of Exploration Geophysicists for permission to publish this chapter. The chapter was first published in *The Leading Edge,* September 1998, p. 1261–1272.

Chapter 14

Using Magnetics in Petroleum Exploration

by

Edward A. Beaumont

and

S. Parker Gay, Jr.

Edward A. Beaumont

Edward A. (Ted) Beaumont is an independent petroleum geologist from Tulsa, Oklahoma. He holds a BS in geology from the University of New Mexico and an MS in geology from the University of Kansas. Currently, he is generating drilling prospects in Texas, Oklahoma, and the Rocky Mountains. His previous professional experience was as a sedimentologist in basin analysis with Cities Service Oil Company and as Science Director for AAPG. Ted is coeditor of the Treatise of Petroleum Geology. He has lectured on creative exploration techniques in the U.S., China, and Australia and has received the Distinguished Service Award and Award of Special Recognition from AAPG.

S. Parker Gay, Jr.

Parker Gay is president and chief geophysicist of Applied Geophysics, Inc., Salt Lake City, Utah, a company he co-founded in 1971. He received his B.S. degree at MIT (1952) and his M.S. degree at Stanford University (1961). Gay served as a photointerpreter in the U.S. Air Force; worked as a geophysicist and geologist for Utah Construction Co. and Mining and its subsidiary, Marcona Mining Co.; was a geophysicist for Asarco, Inc.; organized and managed the U.S. subsidiary of Scintrex Ltd. in Salt Lake City; and founded American Stereo Map Co. in 1970 and Applied Geophysics in 1971, which he now heads. Applied Geophysics is a geophysical contracting organization. In 1974, Gay cofounded the International Basement Tectonics Assoc. He has written numerous papers and given many talks on basement control of geological structure and stratigraphy. He has published 16 papers on the interpretation of magnetic anomalies and their geological causes.

Overview

Introduction

Basement fault blocks often correlate with structural and stratigraphic features in the sedimentary section that control trap location. Magnetic technology senses the earth's magnetic field. This technology—and aeromagnetics, in particular—effectively delineates basement fault blocks through the use and interpretation of magnetic residual maps and profiles. Basement lithologic changes and the resulting magnetic susceptibility changes from block to block allow us to map the basement fault block pattern and to use this information in important new ways for finding oil and gas. This chapter discusses concepts of magnetics and how to apply them to petroleum exploration.

In this chapter

This chapter contains the following sections.

Section A
Magnetic Basics

Introduction

The lithology of basement rocks controls regional and local magnetic variations in the earth's field. Seeing local variations is critical to applying magnetic technology to petroleum exploration. This section discusses the basics of magnetic theory and mapping.

In this section

This section contains the following topics.

Basics of Magnetics

Theory

Magnetic disturbances caused by rocks are localized effects superimposed on the normal magnetic field of the earth. The distribution of magnetite in rocks is the primary cause of the local variations in the magnetic field observed in magnetic surveys. Magnetite is not the only magnetic mineral, but it is the dominant cause of magnetic anomalies (Nettleton, 1962). The magnetite content of basement rocks can be two orders of magnitude greater than the magnetite content of sedimentary rocks. Consequently, variations in the magnetic field result mainly from basement rocks underlying the sedimentary section.

The earth's magnetic field is measured in nanoTeslas (nT; formerly known as "gammas").

Effect of magnetic latitude

Magnetic anomalies for an object of the same size, composition, and depth have different signatures at different magnetic latitudes because the magnetic inclination—the angle at which the magnetic force field is oriented with the earth's surface—changes with latitude. The figure below shows profiles of magnetic total intensity anomalies for the same object at different latitudes in the northern hemisphere. In the southern hemisphere the profiles would be the opposite [north and south would reverse south of the equator and the inclination angles (*i*) would be negative].

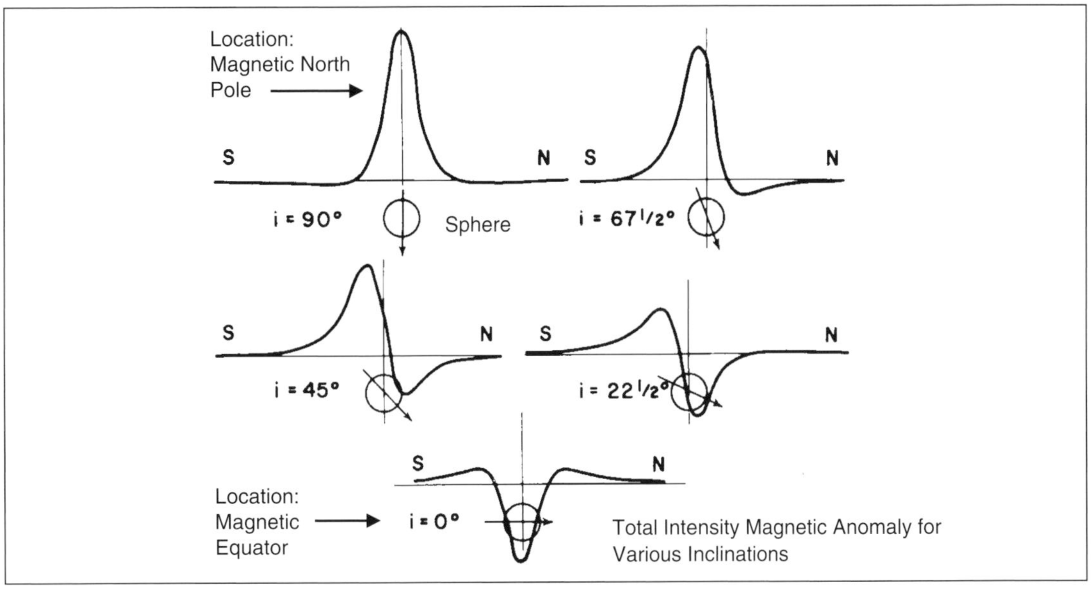

Figure 14–1. After Nettleton, 1962; courtesy Society of Exploration Geophysicists.

Gravity vs. magnetic anomalies

The table below summarizes the differences between gravity and magnetics.

Characteristic	Gravity	Magnetics
Anomaly cause	Horizontal density variations	Magnetite content variations
Best use	Defining large-scale geologic features and shape of structures, and determining offset of basement faults	Defining basement blocks, locating intrusive bodies; generalized depth to basement

Total Intensity and Residual Magnetic Maps

Introduction

Magnetic variation or susceptibility may be analyzed using either total intensity or residual maps. Magnetic residual maps reveal much more detailed geologic features—in particular, the geometry and configuration of individual basement blocks. They bring out the subtle magnetic anomalies that result from the changes in rock type across basement block boundaries. Total intensity maps show larger scale geologic features, such as basin shape or anomalous rock types deep within the basement.

What is total intensity?

Total intensity is the measurement from the magnetometer after a model of the earth's normal magnetic field is removed. It is generally a reflection of the average magnetic susceptibility of broad, large-scale geologic features.

What is residual?

Residual is what remains after regional magnetic trends are removed from the total intensity. Residual maps show local magnetic variations, which may have exploration significance. The regional trend of the total intensity can be calculated using a number of techniques, including running averages, polynomials, low-pass filters, or upward continuation techniques. The figure below shows magnetic profiles of total intensity, regional trend, and residual.

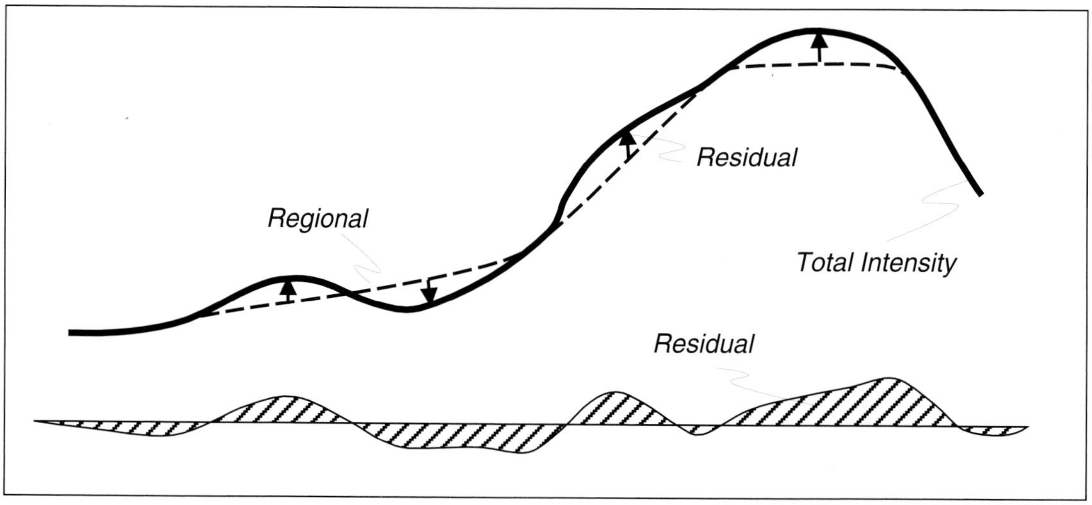

Figure 14–2. After Nettleton, 1962; courtesy Society of Exploration Geophysicists.

Total Intensity and Residual Magnetic Maps, continued

Total intensity and residual map example

The maps below are examples of a residual map (A) that was calculated from the total intensity magnetic map (B). The grid and small circles on the total intensity map are the flight path lines [approximately 2 km (1.2 mi) apart] and location points for the flight lines. The total intensity map strikingly does not resemble the residual map and would be of limited value for delineating basement fault blocks.

Total intensity magnetics responds to rock types over broad areas as well as those deep within the crust. We can see by a careful examination of map B, however, that many of the features shown by the residual map are vaguely apparent in the total intensity data. Fortunately, we no longer have to interpret such total intensity maps in petroleum basins because many enhancement techniques employing residuals, derivatives, polynomials, or downward continuation exist to reveal the subtle magnetic anomalies that result from the changes in rock type across basement block boundaries.

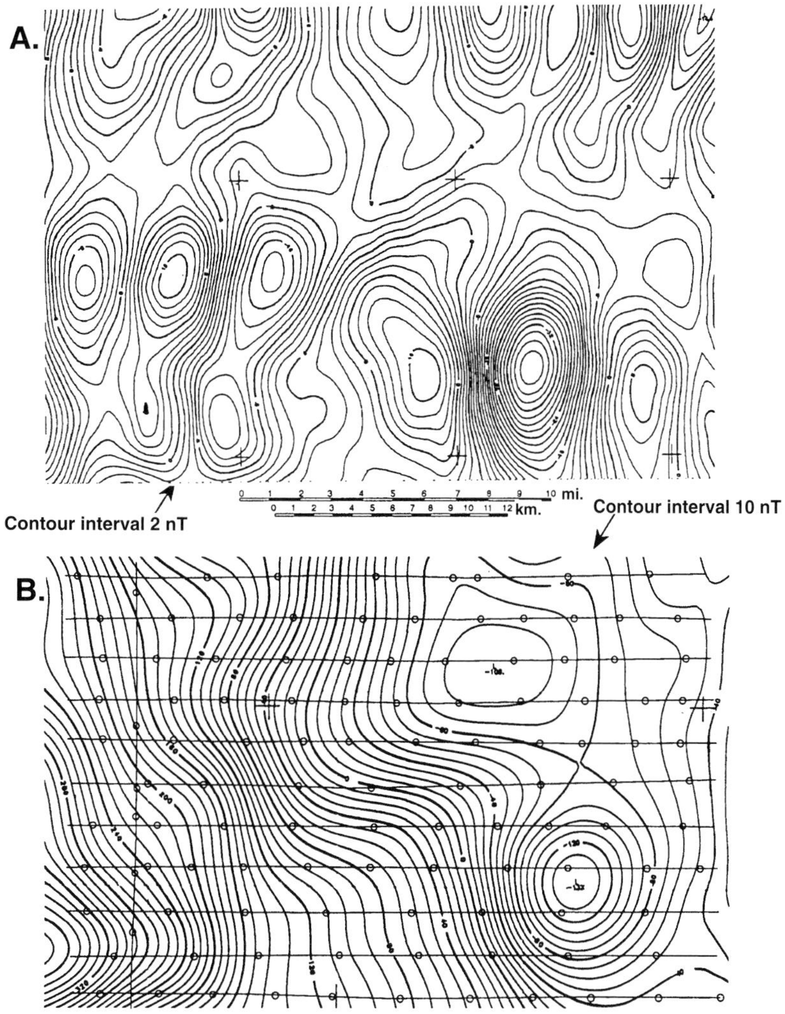

Figure 14–3. From Gay, 1995; courtesy International Basement Tectonics Assoc.

Section B

Interpreting Magnetic Data

Introduction

This section documents a number of one-on-one correlations of the basement fault block pattern, as mapped by modern aeromagnetic techniques. Structural and stratigraphic features in the sedimentary section that are important to petroleum exploration are displayed. Several pitfalls in aeromagnetic interpretation are due to the failure to recognize the existence of the basement fault block pattern and its control on the lithology of basement. These basement lithologic changes, and the resulting magnetic susceptibility changes from block to block, allow us to map the basement fault block pattern and to use this information in important new ways for exploring for oil and gas.

In this section

This section contains the following topics.

Basement Fault Blocks and Fault Block Patterns

Introduction

The basement fault block pattern in sedimentary basins was formed in multiple tectonic and metamorphic episodes during the Archean and Proterozoic eras. Basement tends to control most of the local structure and much of the stratigraphy within the overlying, younger sedimentary section. It is along the shear zones, or block boundaries of the basement, that we generally find the faults or other structures in the overlying sedimentary section. These zones of weakness are periodically reactivated by tectonic stresses or gravitational loading. Consequently, they have influenced depositional patterns and locations of structures throughout geologic time.

Study of shield areas

The following Landsat and SLAR images of exposed Precambrian crystalline crust show highly lineated terrains and demonstrate that the linears fall into multiple parallel or subparallel sets of varying strike directions. These overlapping fracture sets cut the basement into blocks of varying shapes and sizes. This collection of basement blocks is the **basement fault block pattern**.

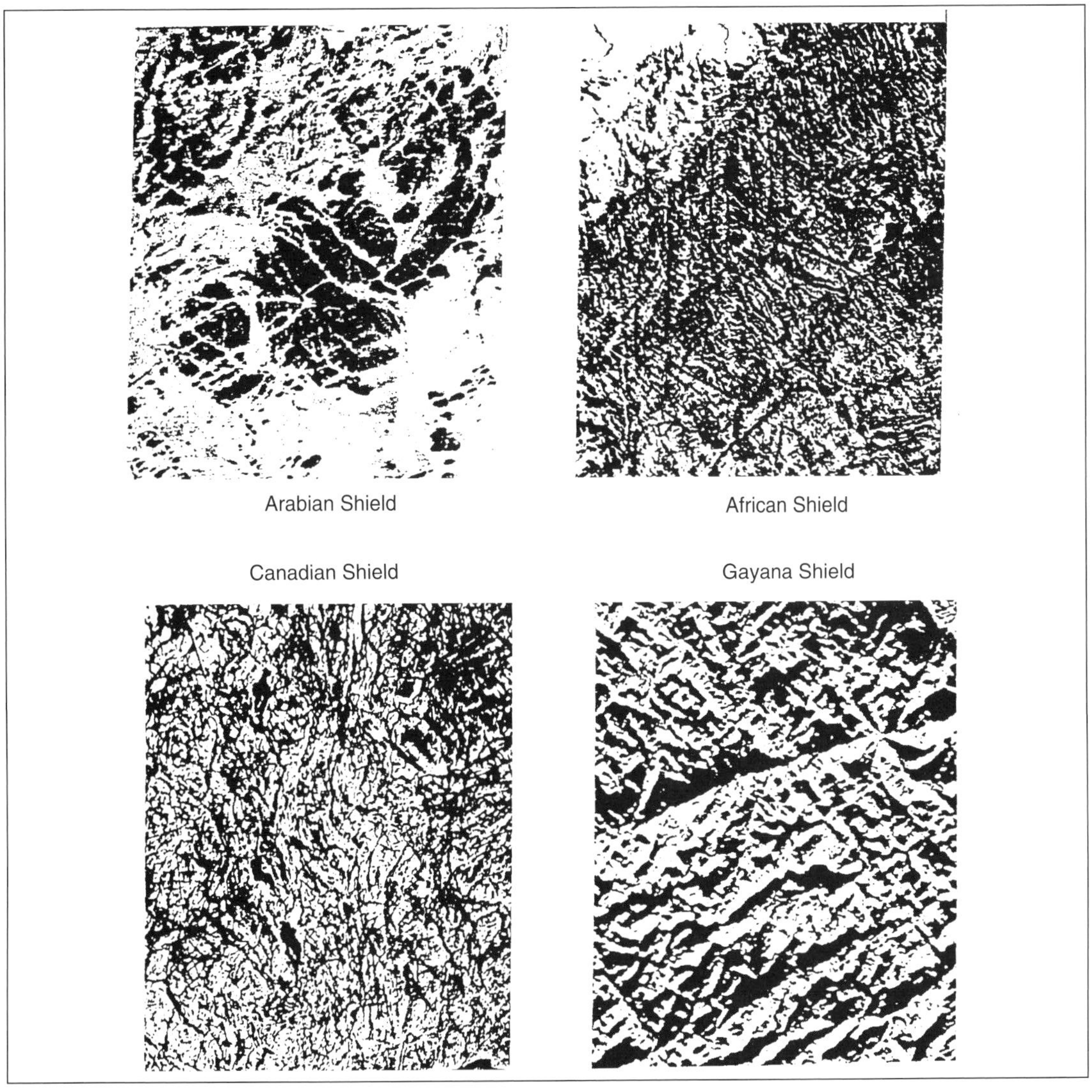

Figure 14–4. From Gay, 1995; courtesy International Basement Tectonics Assoc.

Precambrian surface topography

The intensity of fracturing and mylonitization of the rocks in shear zones explains why these zones generally erode low and why they tend to control the topography of the Precambrian surface. This surface, in turn, controls much of the structure in the lower part of the sedimentary section through gravitational compaction of the sedimentary rocks.

Canadian Shield example

The figure below is a geologic map of an area of crystalline basement in central Wisconsin on the southern edge of the Canadian Shield. Here, outcrops and rock exposures in shallow excavations, roadcuts, etc., abound. It is possible to map the basement geology in considerable detail. Five things stand out:

1. A series of parallel to subparallel shear zones has been mapped.
2. There is obvious periodicity to the shear zones, the spacing between them varying from about 4–8 km (2.5–5 mi).
3. There are rock type changes across these zones.
4. The width of the shear zones varies from about 1 km (LaBerge, personal communication) up to 2.5 km or more.
5. The shear zones and geology truncate abruptly and change style across line A–A′.

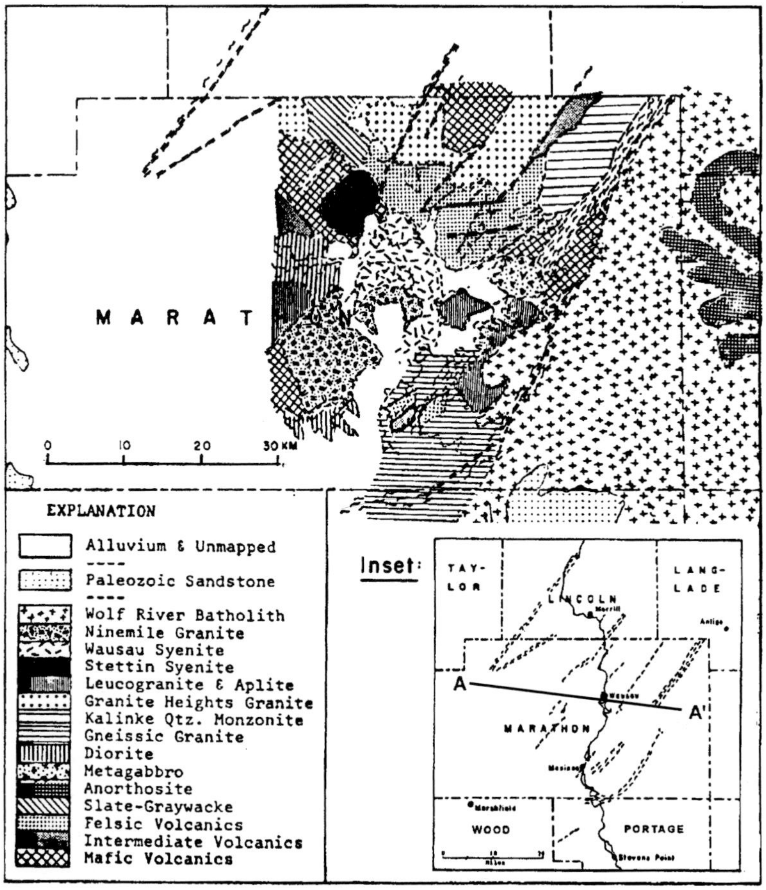

Figure 14–5. From LaBerge, 1976; courtesy International Basement Tectonics Assoc.

Local Magnetic Field Variations

Introduction

Variations in the local magnetic field are due mainly to the following:

- Lithologic changes of basement rocks with corresponding differences in magnetite content
- Elevation changes on the top of basement where basement is of uniform magnetic susceptibility (k)

However, lithologic changes tend to overwhelm the magnetic response of elevation changes in basement caused by fault throws or basement highs unless basement is deep (> 5 km, approximately). In this case the slightly magnetic sedimentary rocks begin to show in the magnetic pattern. Most of this is due to detrital magnetite in sandstones.

Elevation change due to a fault

The presence of a fault is a common interpretation of a magnetic increase or decrease. This interpretation assumes the fault throw, which changes the elevation to the top of basement, is the cause of the anomaly. It also assumes uniform lithology and uniform magnetic susceptibility of basement across a fault. Given this (usually incorrect) assumption, we can calculate the depth of the fault and its throw from the shape and amplitude of an observed magnetic curve. If we do not know the exact susceptibility, we can calculate a series of curves to establish a range of probable values of the throw. In all cases, the magnetic high necessarily appears on the upthrown side of the fault.

In the hypothetical cross section below, basement rock has the same susceptibility across the fault.

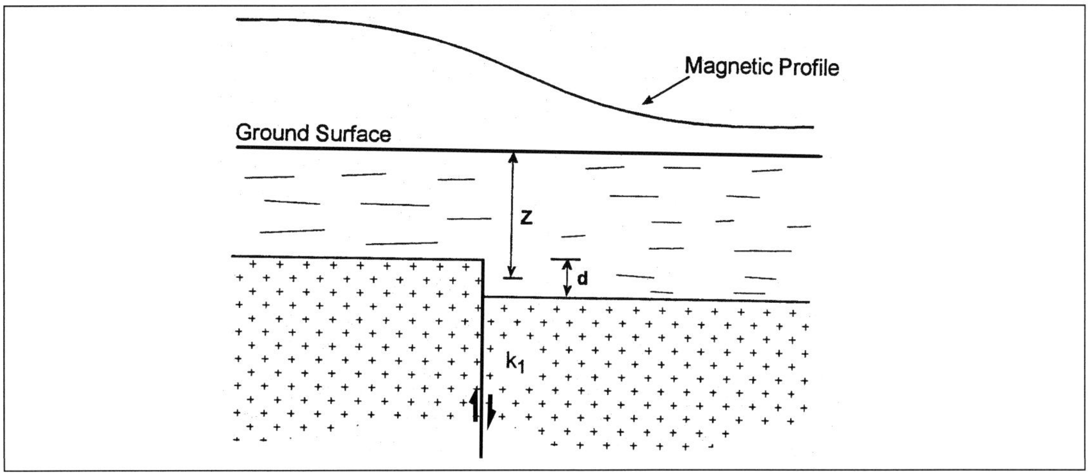

Figure 14–6

Lithologic changes due to a fault

Figure 14–7 shows a fault separating basement blocks of different lithologies and magnetic susceptibilities. If the average magnetic susceptibilities (k_1 and k_2) of the basement blocks are unknown, then we cannot determine the amount of throw of the fault—we cannot even determine the direction of throw if the signal resulting from susceptibility overrides that due to throw. Since susceptibilities of basement rocks commonly vary by hundreds, even thousands, of percent (Heiland, 1946; Jakosky, 1950; Dobrin, 1960) and the ratio of throw to depth of a fault can be, at most, 100%, then it follows that in most cases the magnetic response due to susceptibility overrides that due to throw. The result is that many faults (perhaps as high as 40–50%) show a magnetic low on the upthrown side.

Lithologic changes due to a fault (continued)

The hypothetical cross section shows a fault juxtaposing basement blocks of different lithologies and susceptibilities. The curves above the cross section are the magnetic profiles where the magnetic field is vertical for $k_1 > k_2$ and $k_1 < k_2$. It assumes no throw on the fault ($d = 0$). The dashed curves show the magnetic response if the fault has a finite throw *(d)*. Note how little impact the fault throw has on either profile.

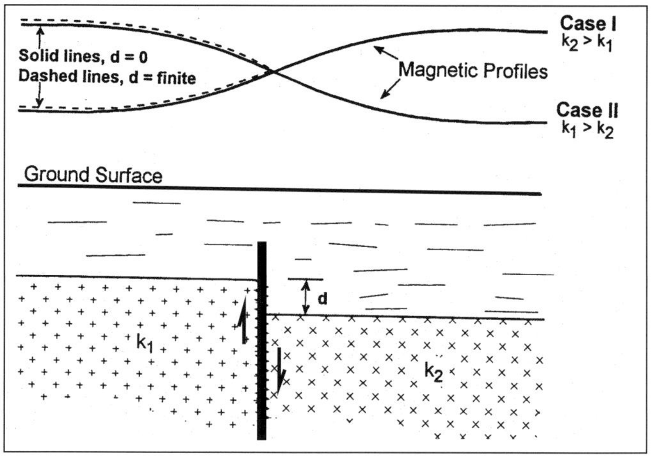

Figure 14–7. From Gay, 1995; courtesy International Basement Tectonics Assoc.

Detecting basement hills

The basement hill and obvious magnetic anomaly shown on the left side of the figure below assumes a uniform magnetic susceptibility for basement. However, given that basement is usually block faulted, is this type of feature detectable? If we are looking at a topographic prominence centered on a basement block, the detection problem becomes that shown on the right side of the figure. A series of adjacent basement blocks having different magnetic susceptibilities results in a residual magnetic pattern of alternating highs and lows (solid lines).

When the basement block on which the hill is carved is more magnetic than surrounding blocks, the hill contributes slightly to the magnetic high over the block as shown. The slight increase in anomaly amplitude due to the hill (top dashed line) generally is not distinguishable from a similar increase due to a slightly higher magnetic susceptibility for the whole block; hence, the hill is not generally detectable. If the block on which the hill is carved is less magnetic than the adjacent blocks, then the hill results in a lesser amplitude of the magnetic low over that block, but the low is still present (bottom dashed line). The hill generally is not detected.

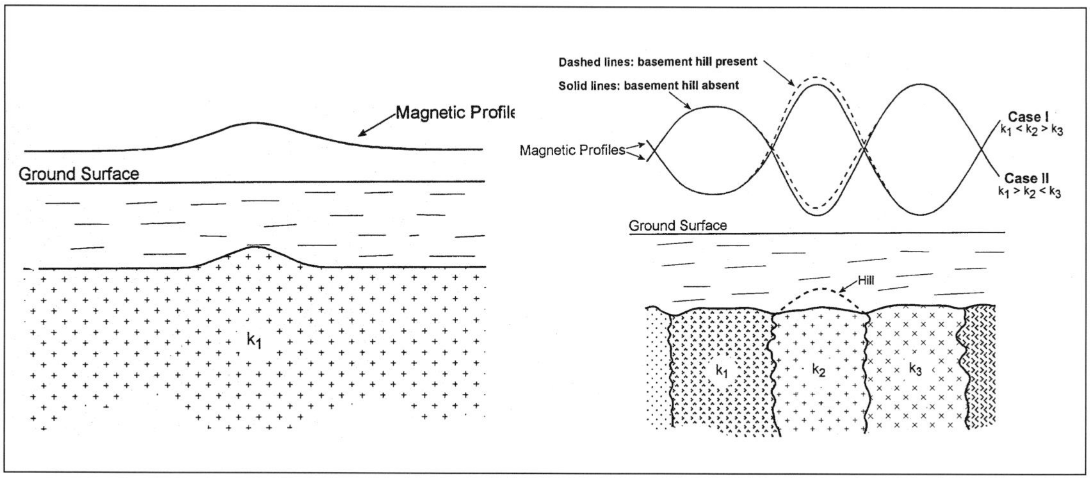

Figure 14–8.

Interpreting Residual Maps

Introduction

A major pitfall in interpreting magnetic residual maps is assuming that magnetic highs and lows are caused by elevation changes on basement rocks in a sedimentary basin. To the contrary, most magnetic anomalies are caused by lithologic changes and the corresponding changes in susceptibility. As shown in Figure 14–5, the basement is of complex lithology and is highly fractured. The fractures divide the basement into blocks and are zones of weakness along which faults occur. The most important and most reliable information obtainable from aeromagnetic maps is the configuration (in plan view) of the underlying basement fault block pattern.

Interpreting depth to basement

It is futile to attempt to define accurately the vertical dimension, Z, of adjacent source bodies with magnetics because of the inherent ambiguity of potential field methods in determining Z (see, e.g. Skeels, 1947). Furthermore, seismic and subsurface methods measure depth so much more accurately than magnetics that it is unwise to try to compete with these excellent techniques. This is not to say, however, that we should not use magnetics to estimate the approximate thickness of the sedimentary section in a new basin, i.e., in determining whether it is 2, 5, or 10 km thick, for example, to a usual accuracy of about ±15% under favorable conditions.

Interpreting fault throw

There is a fairly reliable way to determine the direction of throw of certain basement faults from magnetic maps. Faults that vertically offset basement or other magnetic sources generally show abrupt amplitude changes of magnetic anomalies, both the highs and lows. In the figure below, a series of four northeast-trending magnetic anomalies on the west (two highs, two lows) abruptly loses amplitude along a northwest-trending line (A–A′) that crosscuts them. The high and low magnetic trends can be identified easily on both sides of this obvious down-to-the-east fault. The four anomalies disappear altogether along another northwest-trending line farther east (B–B′). This may be a strike-slip fault, which is not common in this area, or another down-to-the-east fault that has down-dropped the four anomalies beneath the level of detection—the preferred interpretation.

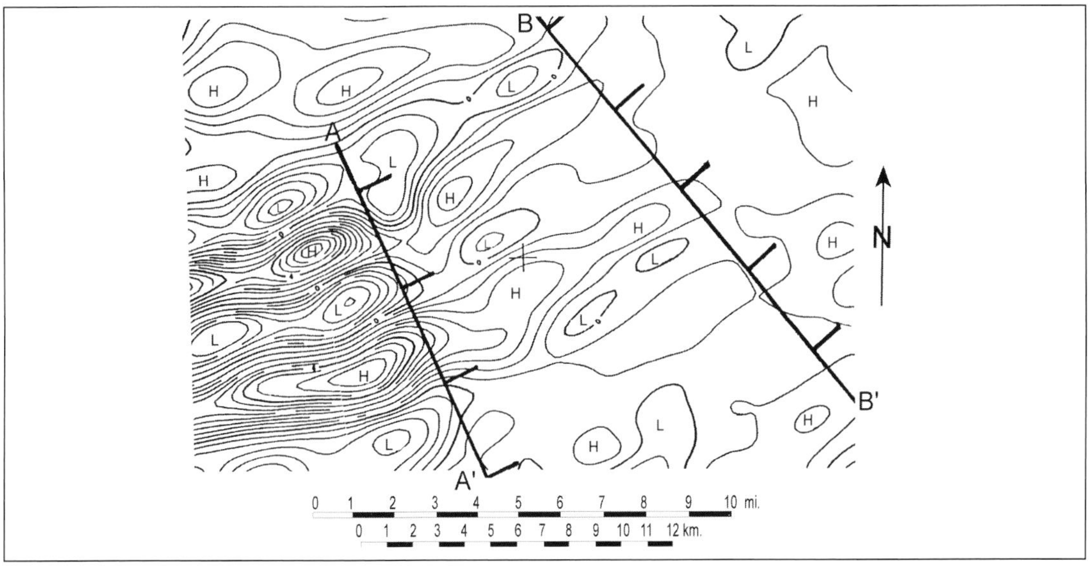

Figure 14–9.

Interpreting Residual Maps, continued

Interpreting shear zones

The figure below shows a residual aeromagnetic map of an area on the north shelf of the Anadarko basin in Oklahoma where the sedimentary section is approximately 3.6 km (12,000 ft) thick and basement lies about 3.8 km (12,500 ft) beneath flight level. The residual magnetic contours (a) are shown at a 2-nT interval. The interpreted shear zones are traced along the linear gradients separating the residual magnetic highs and lows and along truncation lines of anomalies. On the right figure (b), two faults located from subsurface mapping are shown, labeled U/D. The evidence for their existence is seen in subsurface mapping. Both are located exactly along the interpreted basement shear zones, or block boundaries, as represented by gradients on the magnetic map. Note, however, that most of the interpreted basement shear zones in this area have no corresponding overlying faults. These zones were never reactivated—at least not sufficiently enough to be detected by the existing subsurface data.

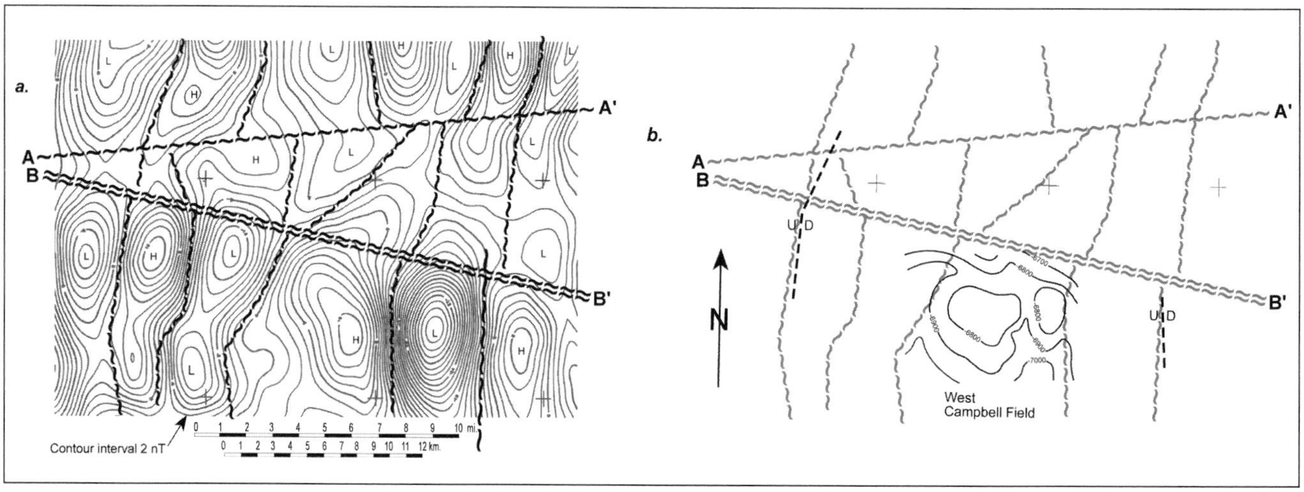

Figure 14–10.

Oil field example

In Figure 14–10, also note the structural high apparent in Devonian strata about 800 m (2500 ft) above basement in the West Campbell field, conveniently nestled between block boundaries. Block boundaries, i.e., shear zones, generally erode low, so it follows that the interiors of blocks must, in many cases, correspond to basement topographic highs. West Campbell field appears to be a case in point and is most likely underlain by such a basement topographic prominence, although there are no wells to basement here to document it. The culmination of structural closure nearer the north end of the block rather than at its center is probably due to the south dip of basement in this area.

Interpreting fault location

The figure below is a residual magnetic map of another area in northern Oklahoma with faults superimposed. Here the sedimentary section is approximately 2 km (6500 ft) thick, and the flight level was about 2.3 km (7500 ft) above basement. The faults shown were interpreted from a detailed subsurface study by Geomap Inc. The faults were mapped about 500 m (1600 ft) above basement and show 30–90 m (100–300 ft) of displacement. Note the high degree of correlation between these faults and the residual magnetic gradients corresponding to the interpreted basement shear zones. Some 64% of the total length of faults, in fact, lies on the predicted shear zones following magnetic gradients. Note also that many magnetic gradients in Figure 14–11 show no faults cutting the section. These may not have been reactivated.

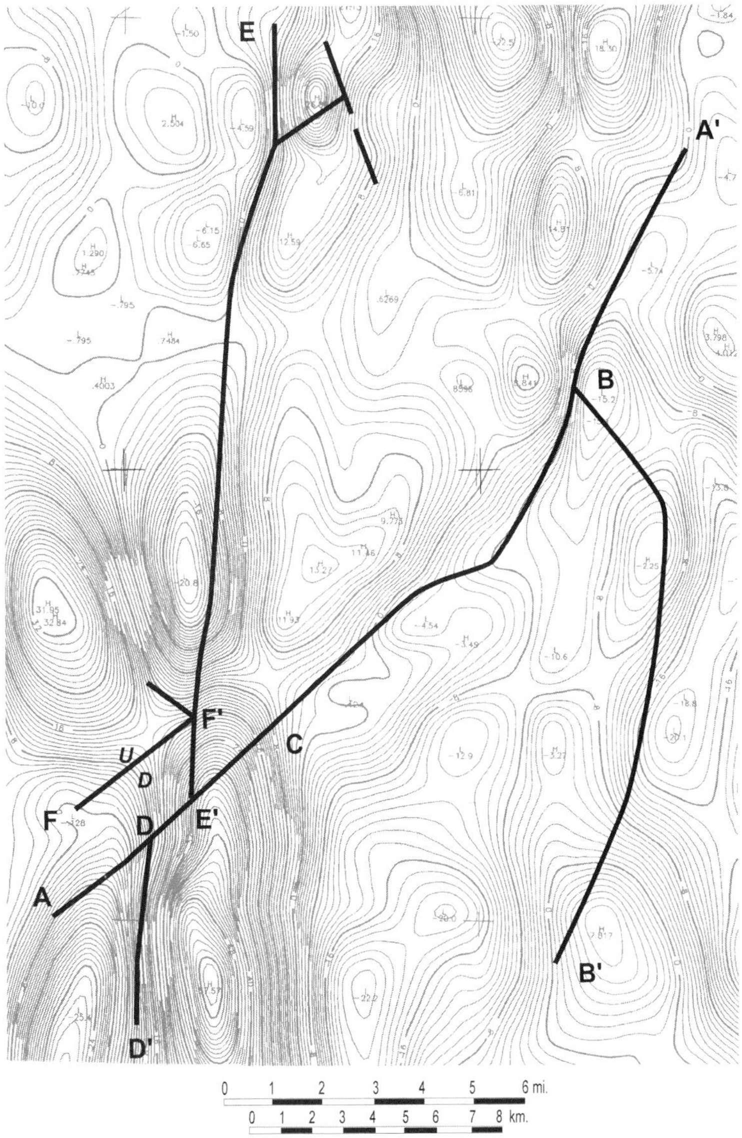

Figure 14–11. Details from Gatewood (1983).

Applying Magnetics to Petroleum Exploration

Introduction

Magnetics can be an extremely effective and economical exploration tool when properly employed. Its proper use, however, depends on the following:

- Avoiding several pitfalls described herein
- Integrating the magnetics with seismic, subsurface, and other data
- Developing the basement fault block pattern from the magnetic data
- Using concepts of basement control in working with all data sets

Applications

Magnetics can be applied to petroleum exploration for many reasons:

- Aiding 2-D and 3-D seismic interpretations
- Laying out new 2-D and 3-D seismic programs
- Aiding in exploration programs based primarily on subsurface (well) data
- Estimating depth to basement over broad areas

Interpreting fault location in seismic sections

Magnetics can be very valuable in interpreting seismic data by plotting residual magnetic profiles along seismic sections. This technique is valuable in looking for (1) subtle stratigraphic changes that can occur along basement block boundaries and (2) subtle fault offsets or other structural and stratigraphic features. The locations of the basement weakness zones provide focal points for examining the seismic data more closely.

The figure below shows an example of a magnetic profile on an interpreted seismic section from Logan County, Arkansas. The dark band corresponds to Cambrian through Mississippian sedimentary rocks. Note correlation between the location of the four normal faults interpreted in the seismic section and the location of faults in the magnetic profile (marked by diamonds).

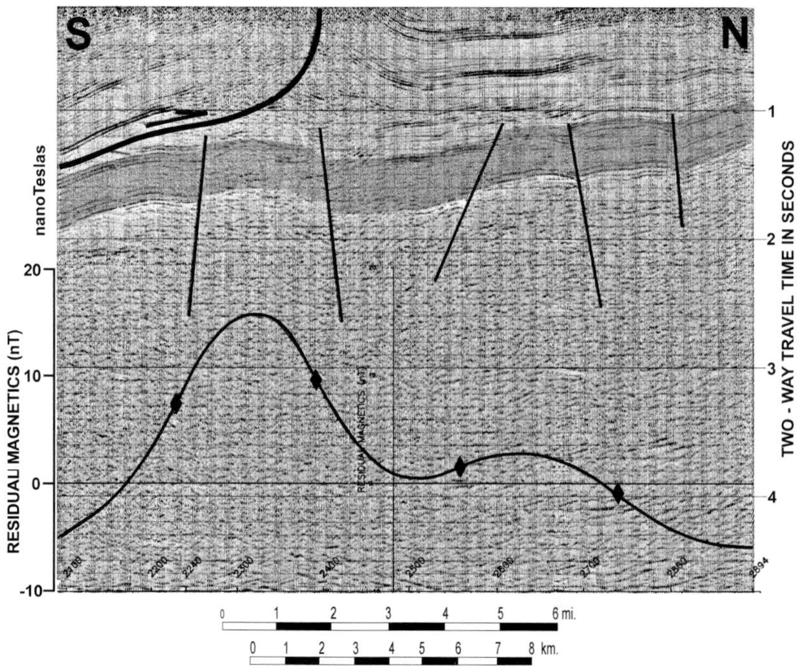

Figure 14–12.

Applying Magnetics to Petroleum Exploration, continued

Developing leads from analogs

Magnetic basement mapping in petroleum exploration can be applied to the search for leads or prospects that can be quickly and economically developed by comparing known traps or structure (and/or stratigraphy) with the basement fault block pattern. Some areas have never been tested by the drill where the structure at basement level is analogous to that over nearby producing properties. Some of these leads become viable prospects when subjected to follow-up seismic profiling or other appropriate exploration techniques. A common type of structural or stratigraphic data used to correlate to the magnetic data is subsurface mapping, developed from well data. However, on overseas projects or in frontier areas, the best (or only) data available may be 2-D seismic surveying. In either case, the procedure is to search for "look-alikes" on the magnetic data that correspond to features over known producing fields. Since the magnetic data can be acquired in continuous fashion over large areas at a very economical price, many good leads can be developed in a short time.

Laying out seismic programs

Suppose we have developed a basement fault block pattern as shown in the figure below. Also suppose this area has been tectonically active and is characterized by a fair degree of faulting. This being the case, we can expect that many of the basement shear zones have been reactivated and are now the locus of faults and fractures in the sedimentary section. Thus, A, D, and F in the figure are the wrong places to run 2-D seismic lines because of the probable poor seismic definition due to fracturing along these zones and the possibility of sideswipe. Lines B, C, and E, on the other hand, are good places to run seismic surveys because of the probable lack of fracturing and faulting at these localities. In addition, gravitational compaction structures are generally found within blocks; thus, line B or C would have found West Campbell field (WCF) but line A would not.

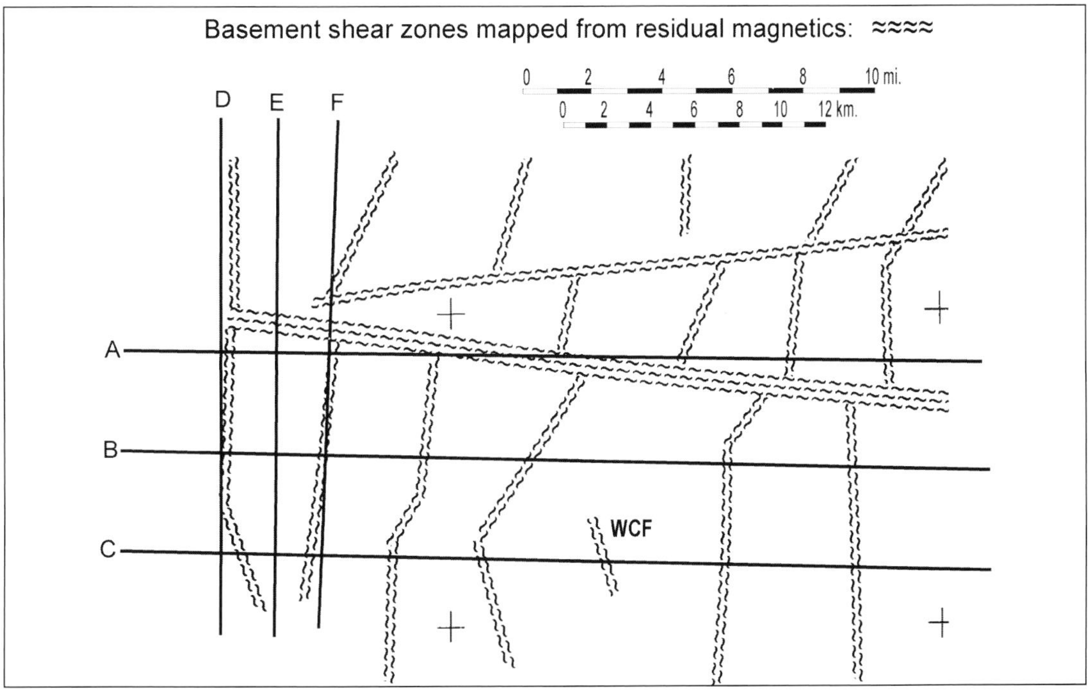

Figure 14–13.

Interpreting fault location in map view

Magnetics can be quite useful in interpreting existing seismic programs after they have been shot. In the example below, two 2-D seismic lines have been placed purposely in the worst possible positions relative to the basement fault block pattern.

Assuming all the basement shear zones represent faults in the sedimentary section, then "hooking-up" the faults in this area is a problem. Fault pick C on line 1, for example, does not connect straight across to fault pick G on line 2, nor even to H or I, which are some distance away. Instead, it hooks up to J, making this fault very oblique to the seismic lines. This is not a very common way of connecting faults on most seismic interpretations. The connection of B to H is straightforward but, again, is diagonal to the seismic lines, whereas F–K runs diagonally in the opposite direction. Fault picks D, G, E, and I do not connect to the other seismic line at all; they terminate somewhere in between.

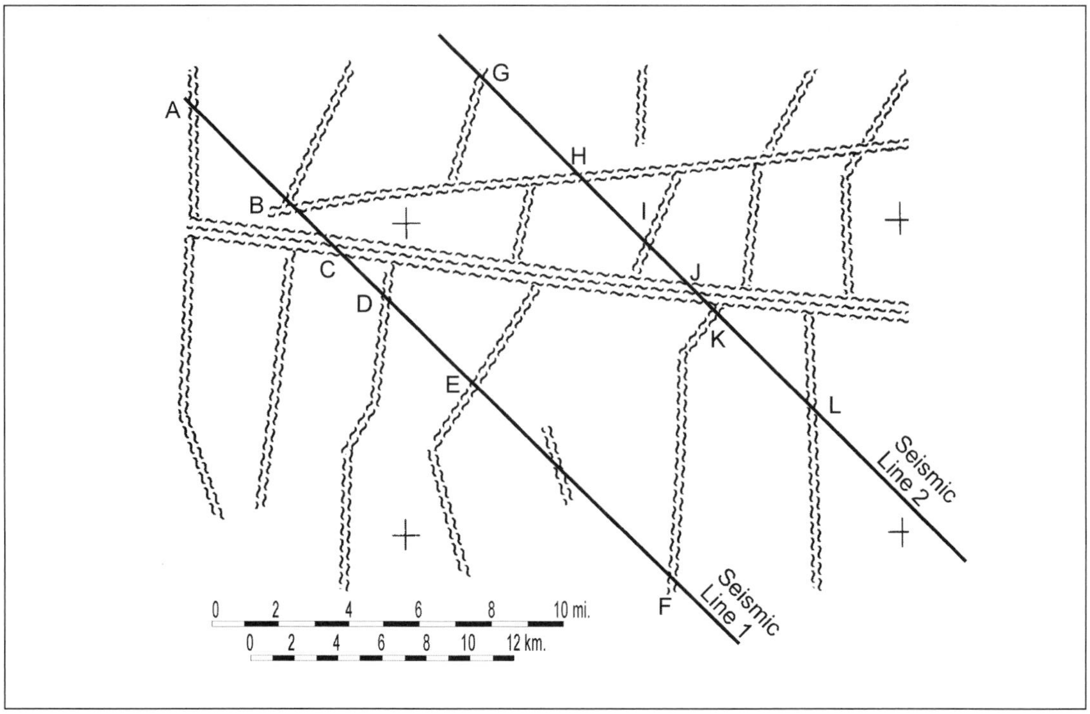

Figure 14–14.

Depth estimates

Depth estimates from aeromagnetic data can determine values for broad areas, such as the approximate thickness of the sedimentary section in a basin or at a limited number of points within the basin. Using depth estimates to distinguish between the depths of adjacent magnetic anomalies invites trouble.

Applying Magnetics to Petroleum Exploration, continued

Magnetics vs. other techniques

We might question the strong emphasis on magnetics for mapping the basement fault block pattern. However, is there any other way to reliably map this pattern beneath the sedimentary section? Methods that depend on surface information—Landsat, SLAR, conventional photo geology, and surface geology—are of limited value. That leaves only gravity and seismic techniques.

However, gravity techniques generally do not separate adjacent basement blocks because of the lack of density contrast between adjacent blocks and because of interference from density differences within the sedimentary section. On seismic data, the basement reflector is often difficult to recognize beneath complex structure and because of a lack of velocity contrast with the dense dolomites that overlie the basement in many areas. Furthermore, both seismic and gravity methods are expensive to apply over broad areas and cannot provide even a tiny percentage of the area coverage that can be obtained with magnetics for the same price.

The conclusion is that both seismic and gravity are excellent follow-up tools for profiling, or "cross-sectioning," specific leads developed from the basement fault block pattern by magnetics and are best used for this purpose.

Section C
References

Dobrin, M.B., 1960, Introduction to Geophysical Prospecting, 2d ed.: New York, McGraw-Hill, 446 p.

Gatewood, L., 1983, Viola–Bromide and Oil Creek Structure (map): Oklahoma City, privately sold and distributed.

Gay, S.P., Jr., 1995, The basement fault block pattern: its importance in petroleum exploration, and its delineation with residual aeromagnetic techniques, *in* R.W. Ojakangas, ed., Proceedings of the 10th International Basement Tectonics Conference, p. 159–207.

Heiland, C.A., 1946, Geophysical Exploration: Englewood Cliffs, New Jersey, Prentice-Hall, 1013 p.

Jakosky, J.J., 1950, Exploration Geophysics: Los Angeles, Trija Publishing Co., 1195 p.

LaBerge, G.L., 1976, Major structural lineaments in the Precambrian of central Wisconsin: Proceedings of the First International Conference on the New Basement Tectonics, Utah Geological Assoc., p. 508–518.

Nettleton, 1962, Elementary Gravity and Magnetics for Geologists and Seismologists: Society of Exploration Geophysicists Monograph Series 1, 121 p.

Skeels, D.C., 1947, Ambiguity in gravity interpretation: Geophysics, vol. 12, p. 43–56.

Chapter 15

Applying Gravity in Petroleum Exploration

by

David A. Chapin

and

Mark E. Ander

David A. Chapin

David A. Chapin received his B.S. degree (1979) from George Washington University and his M.S. degree (1981) from Lehigh University, both in geology. He was employed by Gulf Research from 1981 to 1984. In 1984 he joined Arco, specializing in the interpretation of gravity and magnetics data. He rose to senior principal geophysicist, responsible for research in new exploration technologies utilizing potential fields' data. In May 1998, he left Arco and became executive vice-president of LaCoste & Romberg. As an active member of SEG, he was a founding member of the SEG Gravity and Magnetics Committee and served as a member of the Technical Program Committees for 1989, 1993, and 1997. He is also a member of the Houston Potential Fields Group, AAPG, SPWLA, and Sigma Xi. He holds three patents in gravity methods and has authored numerous scientific papers.

Mark E. Ander

Mark E. Ander specializes in potential field and electromagnetic exploration methods. He is presently CEO of LaCoste & Romberg. He was vice president of EDCON from 1994 to 1996. Prior to that he spent fifteen years as a research geophysicist at Los Alamos National Laboratory. He received international attention for his geophysical scale measurements of the Universal Gravitational Constant and investigations into possible violations of Newton's inverse square law of gravity. In 1970 he received a B.S. in mathematics and physics from Jacksonville University. He received an MS in physics in 1974 and a Ph.D. in geology and geophysics in 1980 from the University of New Mexico. His professional affiliations include AGU, SEG, GSA, and SPE. He is an author of many scientific articles and abstracts.

Overview

Introduction

Gravity offers significant applications to petroleum exploration. Gravity measurements are affected by changes in rock density. Surface gravity surveys and subsurface surveys made with a borehole gravity meter are effective in locating faults and geologic structures with density contrasts to their surroundings. The borehole gravity meter has broad application, from locating porosity in wildcats or through casing in old wells to monitoring fluid changes in productive reservoirs. This chapter discusses the traditional application of gravity, from surface surveys to the application of borehole gravity measurements.

In this chapter

This chapter contains the following sections.

Section A
Applying General Gravity Methods

Introduction

Surface gravity methods help constrain subsurface structural interpretations and are particularly good at inexpensive reconnaissance studies in areas where either seismic is too expensive or where seismic imaging is poor. Gravity data provide another independently measured geophysical constraint for interpretation problems: lateral density distributions. Location and configuration of subbasins, identification and extensions of structures, and location of major subsurface faulting are the major uses of this technology. This section discusses concepts related to gravity acquisition, processing, and interpretation and applies these techniques to petroleum exploration.

In this section

This section contains the following topics.

Gravity Basics

Introduction

Gravity methods help us identify the size, shape, and depth of anomalous masses. Gravity effectively images lateral density contrasts within the subsurface. It is particularly good at locating geologic structures horizontally. However, it is not as good as magnetics in determining depth to source because density distributions tend to be diffuse in the subsurface.

Uses of gravity

Gravity has the following uses:

- Determining the shape of salt masses
- Locating structures under thrust plates or volcanics
- Locating major faults and determining sense of motion on faults
- Finding reefs
- Locating intrusives
- Defining overall basin configuration
- Determining structural trend continuation between wells and seismic data
- Mapping large tectonic features

Advantages of gravity

Gravity has advantages over other methods:

- Fast, inexpensive tool for evaluating large areas
- Can distinguish sources at exploration depths
- Nondestructive; measures an existing field through a passive measurement
- Can use old data today and easily integrate with new data
- Lends itself to simple enhancements
- Scalar measurement can yield a pseudostructure map

Disadvantages of gravity

Following are the disadvantages of using gravity vs. other methods:

- Needs geological and geophysical constraints to interpret
- Does not directly provide a structural cross section without additional geologic input
- Overlapping anomalies may confuse the interpretation
- Data quality may deteriorate in rougher terrain
- Tends to image gross structures; finer structures are more difficult to image
- Resolution deteriorates with depth

Theory

Gravity effects caused by subsurface geology are superimposed upon the earth's overall gravity field. These effects, called anomalies, are typically less than 100 ppm of the total field. Several corrections are made to remove the earth's field from the total measurement to image these anomalies. For petroleum exploration, gravity is measured in milligals (mGal). Typical exploration anomalies are generally < 25 mGal. Typical gravity sensors are capable of measurements < 0.5 mGal.

Gravity vs. magnetics

The figure below is a schematic of the earth, showing its gravity field (left) and magnetic field (right). The gravity field always points downward; thus, the measurements can be scalar. In contrast, the magnetic field can point in any direction; therefore, vector information is more important in interpreting magnetics.

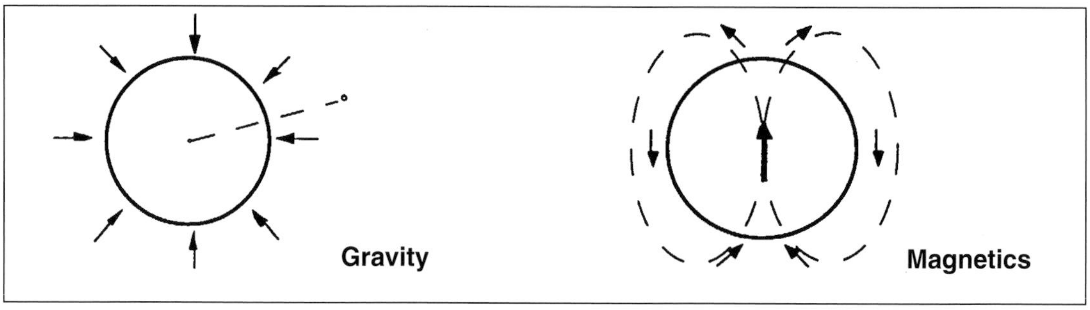

Figure 15–1.

Acquisition and instrumentation

Gravity can be collected on land, at sea, in the air, and by satellite. On land, sea, and air, most sensors consist of a mass at the end of a spring (see figure below). On land, the instrument is leveled and the mass is set to a null position for reading the spring tension.

In dynamic gravity measurements at sea or in the air, the position of the mass and the spring tension is recorded continuously. The instrument is on a stabilized platform during the measurement to maintain a vertical position. In a dynamic gravity measurement, extra care must be taken to keep track of the platform's position. The resulting gravity is usually not as accurate as land data.

Satellite gravity is derived from satellite radar altimetry of the sea surface. The sea conforms to the gravity field of the earth; the first derivative of the sea surface height is gravity at the sea surface level. Since the satellite can only measure gravity over water, only the marine areas and large lakes have such data. The data quality is somewhat comparable to surface-acquired data, although the wavelength resolution is usually worse for the satellite data.

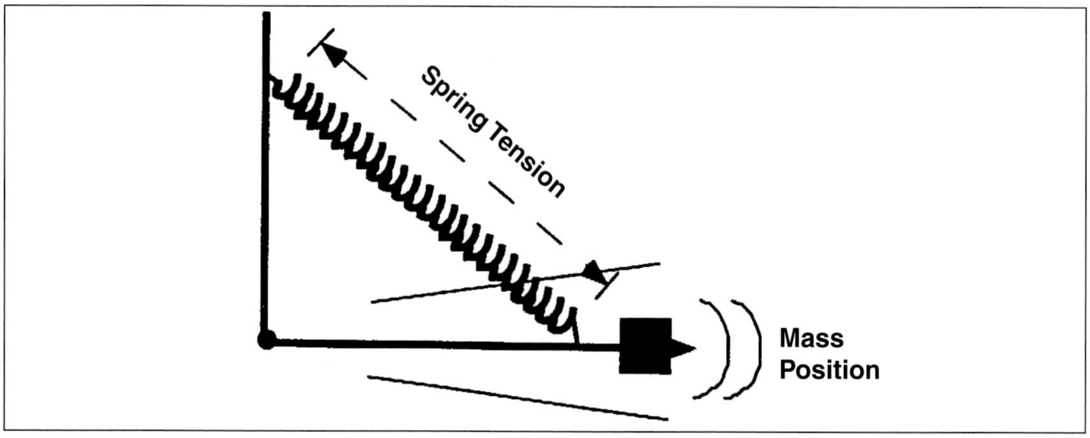

Figure 15–2.

Processing Gravity Data

Routine processing techniques

Gravity data as measured must be corrected for the earth's field (Chapin, 1996a). There are five categories of corrections.

Correction	Definition	Key Input Parameter(s)
Latitude	Whole-earth effect at sea level related to the shape and the spin of the earth	Latitude
Free air	Correction because the observation is not at sea level	Elevation
Bouguer	Free air correction to add back the rock between the observation and sea level	Elevation & surface density
Terrain	Simplified assumptions of Bouguer correction in high-relief areas	Detailed topography & surface density
Eötvös	Gravity collected on moving platforms has different angular velocities than the earth's for dynamic gravity	Platform's velocity & heading

One of the most critical parameters in typical surveys is the high accuracy needed in elevation control. Submeter accuracies are usually necessary, except for marine surveys which are, by definition, collected at sea level.

Interpretive processing techniques

After obtaining either free air gravity or Bouguer gravity, subsequent processing may be needed to enhance or suppress various geologic effects. For example, Bouguer gravity naturally has lower values over higher elevations and higher values over deep ocean basins because of variations in the crustal thickness, or *isostasy.* An isostatic correction to suppress this deep effect can be made if the data set is large enough (Chapin, 1996b). In smaller data sets, typically a long-wavelength surface can be removed from the data to suppress this effect. Other interpretive processing to enhance certain anomalies includes the following:

- Band-pass filtering—selecting a range of wavelengths to display
- Derivatives—edge-enhancing processes that tend to emphasize the shorter wavelength anomalies
- Upward/downward continuation—a process that attenuates or deattenuates data to simulate what might be observed at different vertical datums

Collectively, these are all termed *regional / residual operators.* Many different types are useful for different purposes.

Interpreting Gravity Measurements

Procedure

The table below outlines a suggested procedure for interpreting gravity.

Step	Action
1	Use well logs and outcrop data to make structural cross sections through critical areas containing gravity data to be interpreted.
2	Plot gravity profiles above structural cross sections and seismic sections. Add magnetic profiles if available.
3	From geology interpreted from data, build gravity model sections. Divide the section into intervals of approximately the same density.
4	Calculate a predicted gravity profile. Check the observed profile against the calculated profile. Where differences exist, adjust the gravity model and recalculate the gravity profile until a suitable match between observed and calculated is made.
5	Check the interpretation of the gravity map, i.e., location of faults, against the model profiles and all other available data.

Interpreting structure

In many places in the world, structural highs have higher density and are expressed in the data as gravity highs because dense basement rocks are closer to the surface. Therefore, a gravity map often is used directly as a pseudostructure map. However, there is not a one-to-one relationship between milligals and depth; therefore, the map must be viewed in a qualitative sense as a formline map. There are exceptions, as well, where structural highs are gravity lows because dense basement rocks are not closer to the surface. These structures may be of lower density than the surrounding rocks.

Rock densities

The range of densities for all rock types (igneous, metamorphic, and sedimentary) is typically 1.60–3.20 g/cm^3. The density values of sedimentary rocks typically range from 1.80 to 2.80 g/cm^3. Thus, small variations of density in sedimentary rocks may be invisible to the method. A 5–10% error in estimating subsurface densities from gravity is quite common. This is in contrast to magnetics, where typically there are orders of magnitude variations in susceptibilities.

Horizontal layers

Horizontal layers have no anomalous gravity response. Thus, it is impossible to determine the subsurface density distribution if there are no lateral changes. Layer-cake geology yields no anomalous gravity signal. A bed is considered infinite and horizontal if it is about five times wider in all directions than it is thick, with no dip.

Interpreting Gravity Measurements, continued

Interpretation ranges

Gravity interpretation can produce a range of answers. The better the geologic and geophysical constraints, the better the interpretation. A completely unconstrained interpretation produces several acceptable answers that can all produce the identical anomaly. While it is often easy to rule out certain classes of interpretations as geologically unreasonable, it is best to start with good constraints or to test reasonable geologic questions.

Depth-to-basement determination

Gravity is not as good at depth-to-basement or depth-to-density anomaly estimations as other geophysical methods. Though possible to do, it is often difficult to determine the appropriate depth to geologic source unless other constraints exist.

Positions of geologic bodies

Gravity is particularly good at locating horizontal positions of geologic bodies that have a different density than the surrounding rock—ore bodies or salt-cored bodies, for example.

Interpreting fault location

Faults usually can be identified through either steep gradients or truncation of trends.

The figure below contains two Bouguer gravity maps of Southern California, showing the expression of faults. In the left map, locations *a* and *b* show strong gradients, which indicate faults. A series of truncated trends (dashed) near location *c* also indicate faults. The right map shows the actual location of the major faults over the same gravity map.

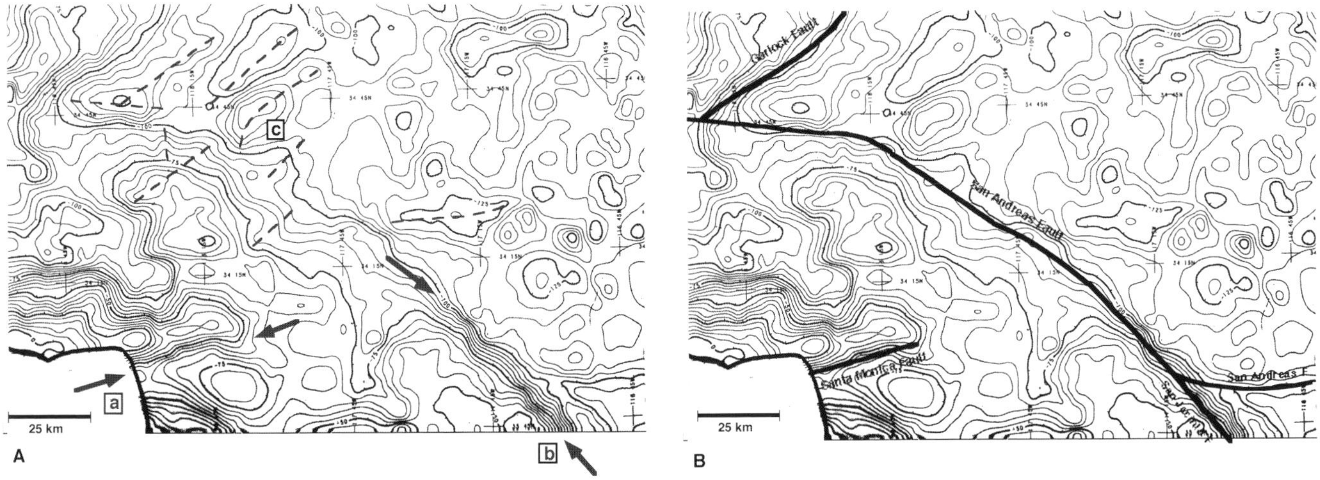

Figure 15–3.

Models of Gravity Anomalies

Introduction

Three key parameters of the source body affect the size and shape of the gravity response:

- Density
- Depth
- Size

In the following discussion, 2-D cross sections demonstrate each of these parameters on theoretical gravity profiles. While the models may not be geologically reasonable, the concepts they demonstrate provide important building blocks for more complex geometric modeling, which is often performed to solve real exploration problems. When modeling gravity effects, it is much more important to constrain the size (shape) and depth of the geologic body than it is to constrain the density.

Effect of density

The amplitude of a gravity anomaly has a linear relationship to density. Positive density contrasts produce gravity highs; negative density contrasts produce gravity lows. The wavelength of the anomaly is unaffected by differences in the density. The figure below shows the different gravity responses to a body with different positive density contrasts. In the upper half of the diagram are the gravity responses. The lower half of the diagram is a cross section. Values for the different densities are written next to the gravity response in the upper part of the figure.

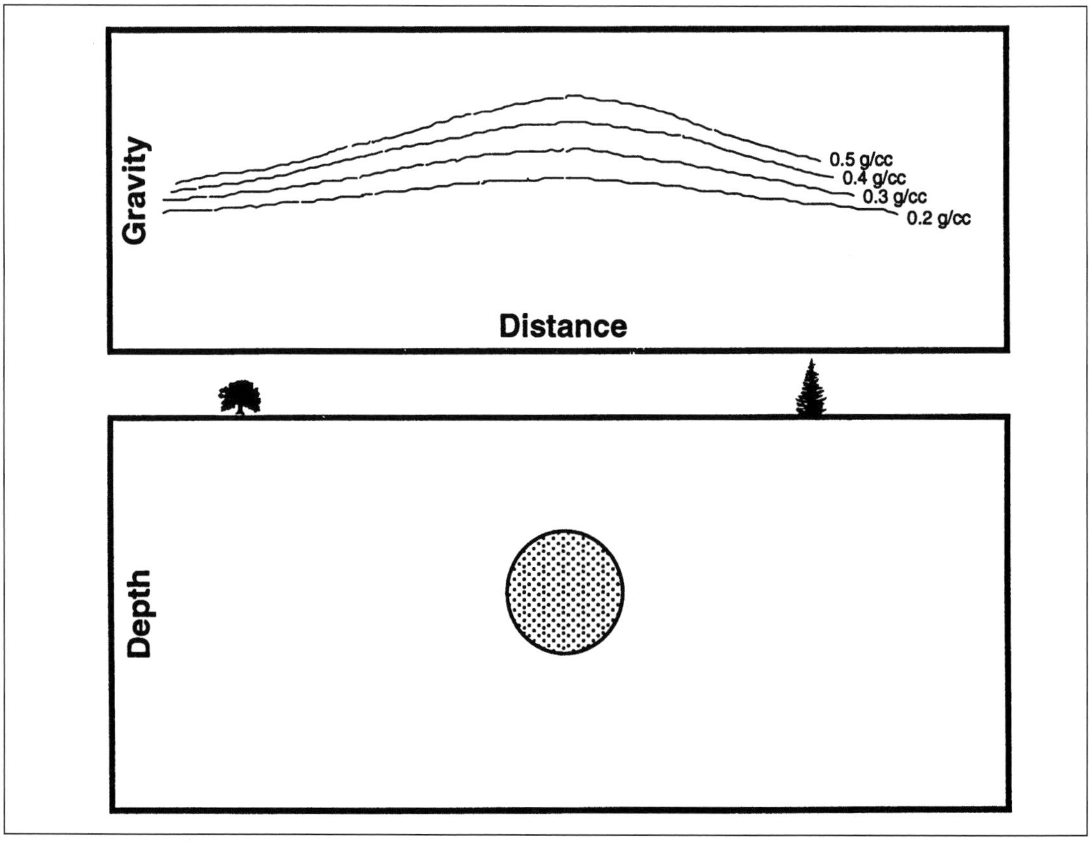

Figure 15–4.

Effect of depth

The amplitude of the gravity signal varies as a function of 1/depth^2 to the source. The figure below shows the gravity responses to a body of positive density contrast buried at different depths. The upper half of the diagram shows the gravity responses (labeled A, B, and C) to a body buried to depths A, B, and C, shown in the cross section in the lower half.

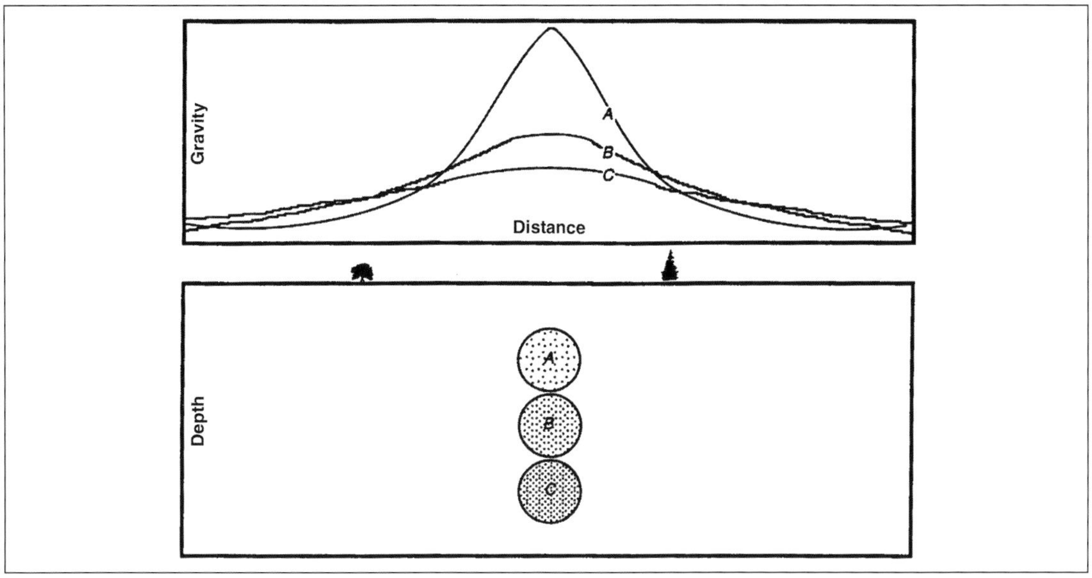

Figure 15–5.

Effect of size

The gravity response is related directly to the amount of anomalous mass. Size differences in three dimensions are X^3 functions. The figure below shows the gravity responses to bodies of the same density, at approximately the same depth, that are of different sizes.

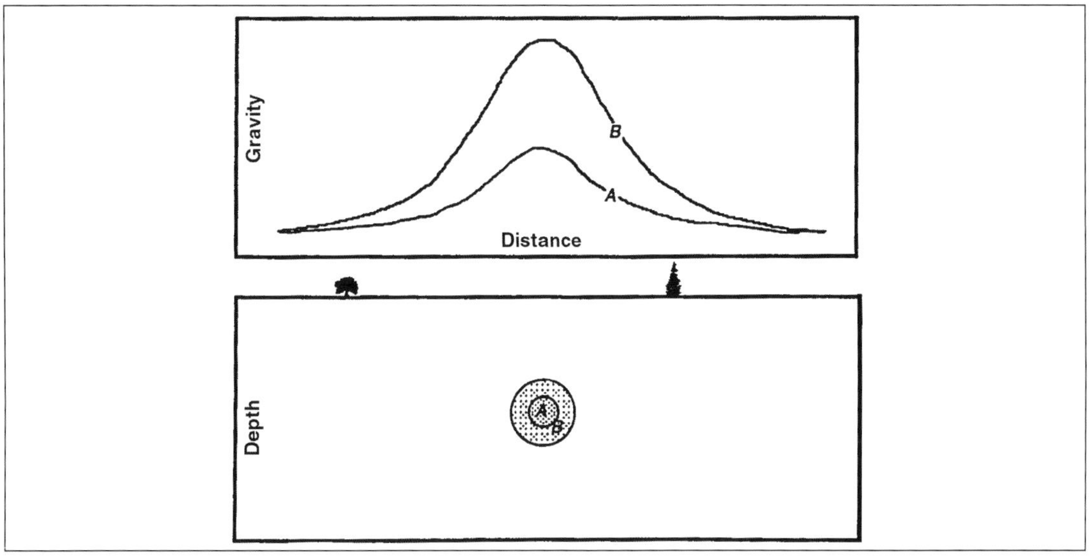

Figure 15–6.

Examples of Gravity Applications

Satellite gravity, Andaman Sea

The figure below shows a satellite-derived free air gravity color image of the Andaman Sea area of Southeast Asia. Cooler colors are gravity lows; warmer colors are gravity highs. A number of important tectonic elements can be interpreted easily from the image. The trenches are seen as deep blue, and the ridges are seen as bright red. The offshore extension of the Sumatra wrench fault system can be seen, as well as the active spreading center within the Andaman Sea (between the Alcock and Sewell seamounts). This type of data is useful for broad tectonic interpretations and to extend known geologic elements from onshore to offshore areas.

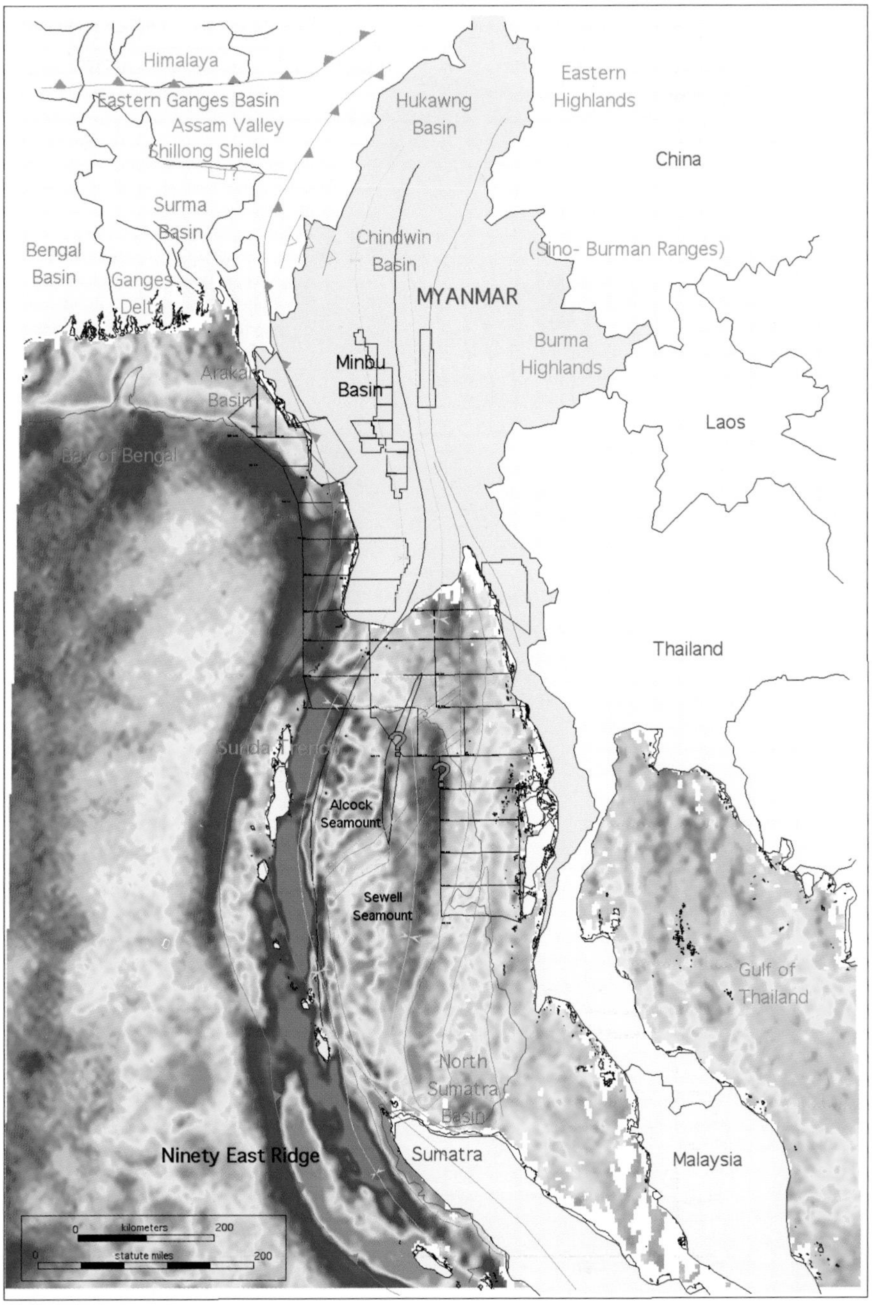

Figure 15–7. Courtesy ARCO Exploration and Production Technology.

Examples of Gravity Applications, continued

Land gravity from Sudan

In the figure below, the upper panel shows a map of a land gravity survey taken near Khartoum, Sudan. The stippled contours are gravity values of –50 mGal and lower. The exploration objective was to identify new Mesozoic subbasins along the Central African Rift system. These subbasins cannot be seen at the surface because they are covered by a thin veneer of alluvium, sand, and river deposits. However, the subbasins, because they are lower density than cratonic basement, can be identified in the gravity data as large gravity minima, shown in the stipled pattern.

Nearby in a similar geologic setting, Chevron made a series of discoveries in the Muglad area using gravity as a primary exploration tool (Giedt, 1990). The gravity lows in this map indicate hitherto undiscovered subbasins, identified along gravity profile A–A' in the bottom panel.

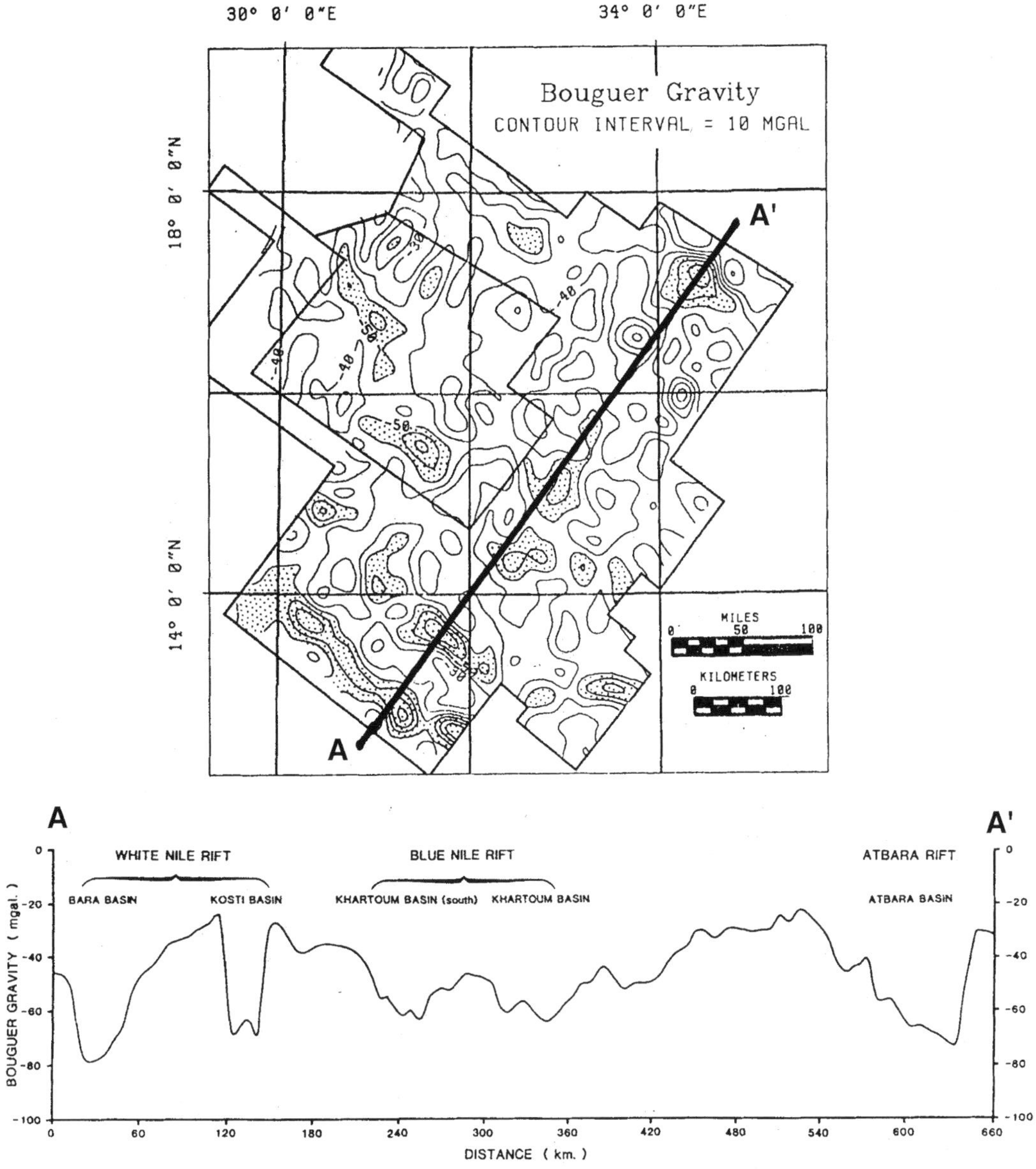

Figure 15–8. Modified from Jorgensen and Bosworth (1989) and Millegan (1990).

Marine gravity from U.S. East Coast

The figure below shows an integrated constrained interpretation of gravity and seismic data along USGS survey line 25. Line 25 is a dip line from offshore southern New Jersey across the continental margin (over the Baltimore Canyon Trough). The free air gravity was modeled using a Talwani-type 2-D algorithm (Talwani et al., 1959) and was constrained by a reflection seismic interpretation, wells, and seismic refraction data. A complex and detailed geologic cross section is the result of this study. The relationship between the synrift and postrift sediments was resolved in part by gravity modeling. In combination with the magnetic data, the type and configuration of the basement can also be resolved. Gravity interpretation had significant exploration impact in determining depth of sediment burial, migration direction, and trap development for hydrocarbon exploration within the Baltimore Canyon Trough.

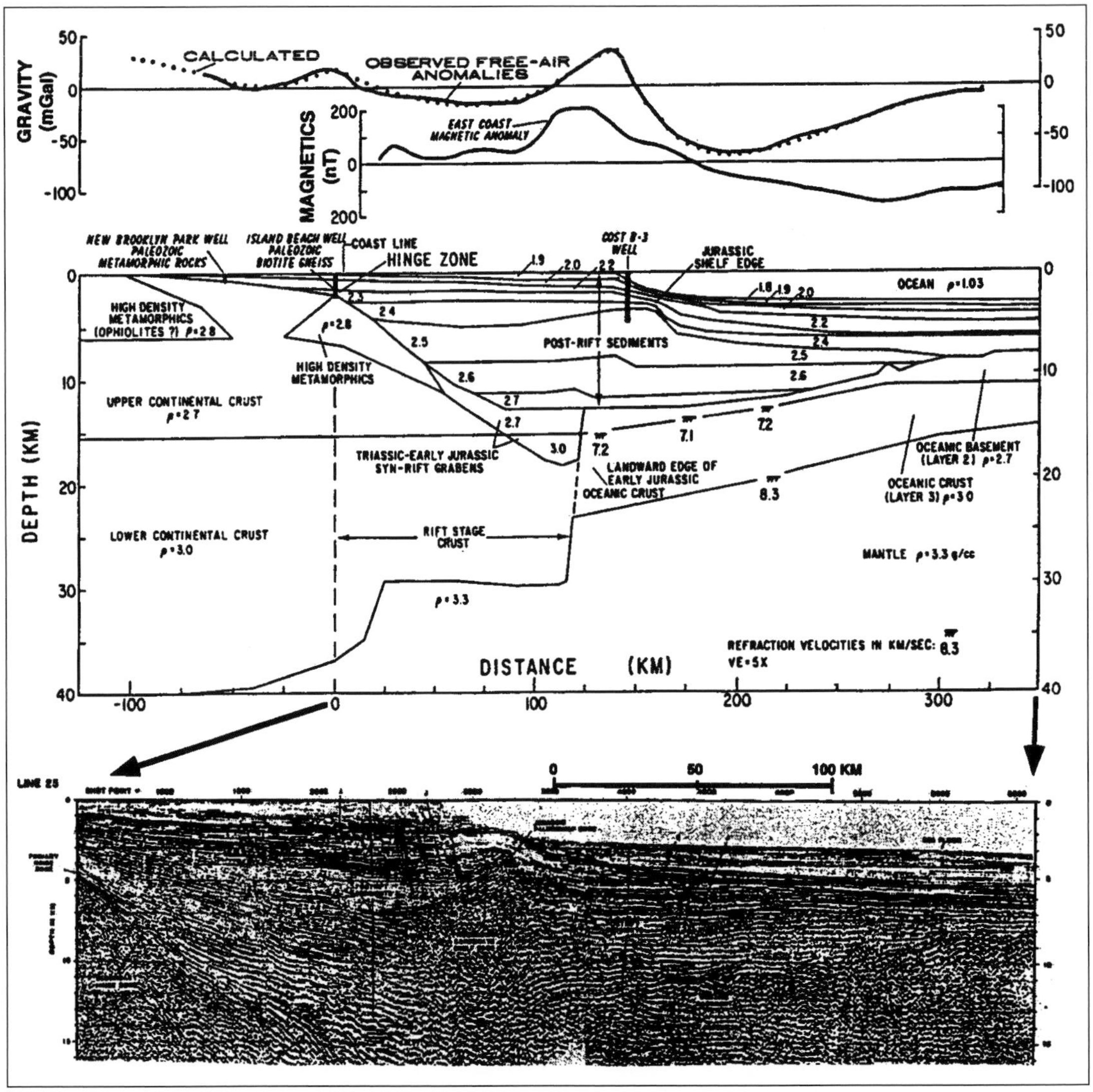

Figure 15–9. Modified from Grow et al. (1988) and Sheridan et al. (1988). Gravity model by D.R. Hutchinson and J.A. Grow (1980), courtesy USGS.

Section B
Applying Borehole Gravity Methods

Introduction

Borehole gravity is a density logging technology. It is the only logging method that can directly measure density at a significant distance away from a well. It is also the only logging method that can reliably obtain density through well casing. This information is often vital for accurate porosity measurements and in determining the presence and amounts of oil, gas, and water in a hydrocarbon reservoir. This section discusses concepts of borehole gravity theory, acquisition, and applications to petroleum exploration.

In this section

This section contains the following topics.

Basics of Borehole Gravity

Borehole gravity uses

Borehole gravity is especially effective for the following exploration and production purposes:

Exploration purposes

- Locating nearby salt structures
- Locating distance to nearby structures (e.g., reefs) for step-outs and sidetracks
- Better synthetic seismograms

Production purposes

- Measuring bulk density when radioactive tools are too risky
- Logging cased holes for lithologic changes
- Calculating overburden for hydrofracture jobs
- Monitoring injection fluids
- Monitoring reservoirs during fluid withdrawal
- Exploring for bypassed, behind-casing gas zones
- Evaluating reservoir porosity, especially in carbonate reservoirs where other tools are not as reliable

Borehole gravity advantages

The following characteristics give borehole gravity surveys advantages in certain situations:

- Directly measures bulk density
- Is a deep imaging tool
- Is effective in both cased and uncased wells
- Is unaffected by washouts, hole rugosity, or mud invasion effects
- Can help determine seismic wavelet scale density
- Is a passive measurement, e.g., does not have active radioactive sources

Borehole gravity disadvantages

The following characteristics give borehole gravity surveys disadvantages in certain situations:

- Direction away from the well to distant source cannot be determined without other information
- Engineering limitations of the tool restricts use to certain candidate wells (hole size, low deviation, slow reading)
- Only a few tools presently available for use
- Expensive to operate

Theory

Density effects caused by downhole geology can be detected by very sensitive instrumentation and by knowing precisely where the sensor is located in the borehole. For petroleum exploration, gravity typically is measured in microgals (µGal). Typical exploration anomalies are on the order of < 50 µGal. The present borehole gravity tool is capable of a 3-µGal repeatability.

The Borehole Gravity Tool

How the tool measures gravity

The figure below illustrates the fundamentals of measuring density using a borehole gravity sensor. Two gravity measurements, g_1 and g_2, are made downhole, separated in depth by Δz. The value G is the universal gravity constant. Thus, the gravity gradient, $\Delta g/\Delta z$, is related directly to the density of the intervening layer. The result is a direct computation of the bulk density of that layer.

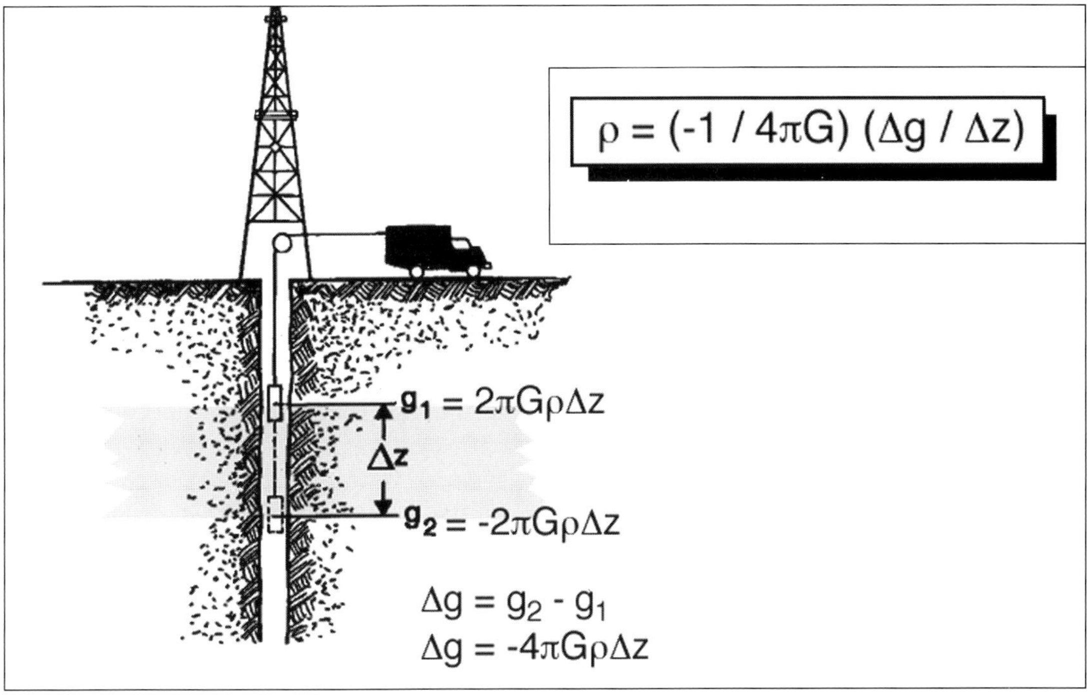

Figure 15–10.

Depth of investigation

The figure below shows how the depth of investigation is tunable by means of varying the separation between two gravity measurements, Δz. The rule of thumb is that 90% of the gravity effect can be imaged at a distance away from the borehole within five times Δz.

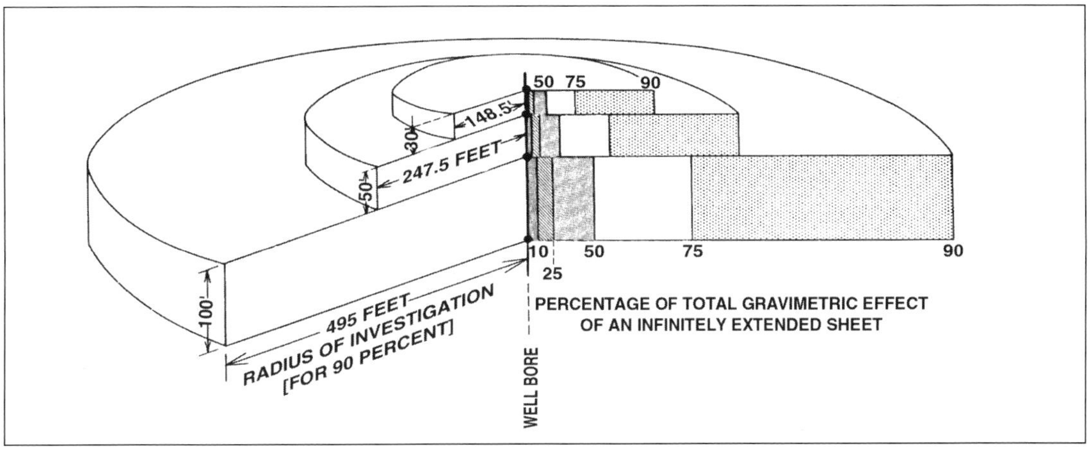

Figure 15–11. After McCulloh et al., 1968; courtesy SPWLA.

Depth of investigation of various logging methods

The following table, based on data from Beyer (1991), shows conservative estimates of the depth of investigation using various density logging tools. Borehole gravity can sample the farthest distance and investigate the most formation.

Logging Method	Radial Distance for 90% Effect		Formation Volume Investigated	
	in.	cm	ft^3	m^3
Conventional 5.25-in. (13-cm) core	2.6	6.6	1.5	0.04
Gamma-gamma log	8	20	17	0.5
Neutron log	14	36	40	1.1
Sonic log	18	46	59	1.7
Borehole gravity log	600	1,500	78,532	2,224

Logging procedure

In a typical logging operation, several downhole station locations are planned ahead of time. The tool is fitted to a conventional wireline and lowered to each station. Once the tool is stopped (in some wells it must be clamped to the side of the well), the measurement begins. The gravity values are telemetered to an operator at the surface. Because of vibrations, seismic activity, or residual tool movement, the measurements may take some time to settle to an acceptable noise level.

Tool limitations

There are three major problems with the present tool.

1. It is large. The smallest typical configuration is 4⅛" OD, but more widely used configurations are up to 5¼".
2. Because the sensor must be set to vertical to make a reading, it can only measure in wells of 14° deviation or less.
3. It takes a long time to make measurements, and it is not a continuous logging tool. The wireline must stop at each individual station, and the tool takes an average of 5–15 min per station for a reading. This means a typical borehole gravity logging operation can run from 24 to 48 hrs.

For the most part, these problems are engineering limitations of the present tool that could be overcome with new and modern sensor development. There is an active project underway to redesign the present tool to make it more useful in modern wells.

Examples of Borehole Gravity Applications

Distant reef exploration

The broad departure between the BHGM and gamma-gamma density logs in this Michigan reef example reveals the edge of the reef complex is within a few hundred feet of the well. The overlying low-density zone near the top of the log is salt. The sharp difference in density at the arrow is caused by a remote higher porosity zone not detected by the gamma-gamma density log. The broader difference anomaly observed over the length of the interval is explained by the influence of the entire reef complex.

The figure below shows three logs. The log under the scale on the left is the difference between the BHGM density measurements and the gamma-gamma log density measurements. The logs under the scale on the right are the density values measured by the BHGM (left line) and the gamma-gamma tools (right line).

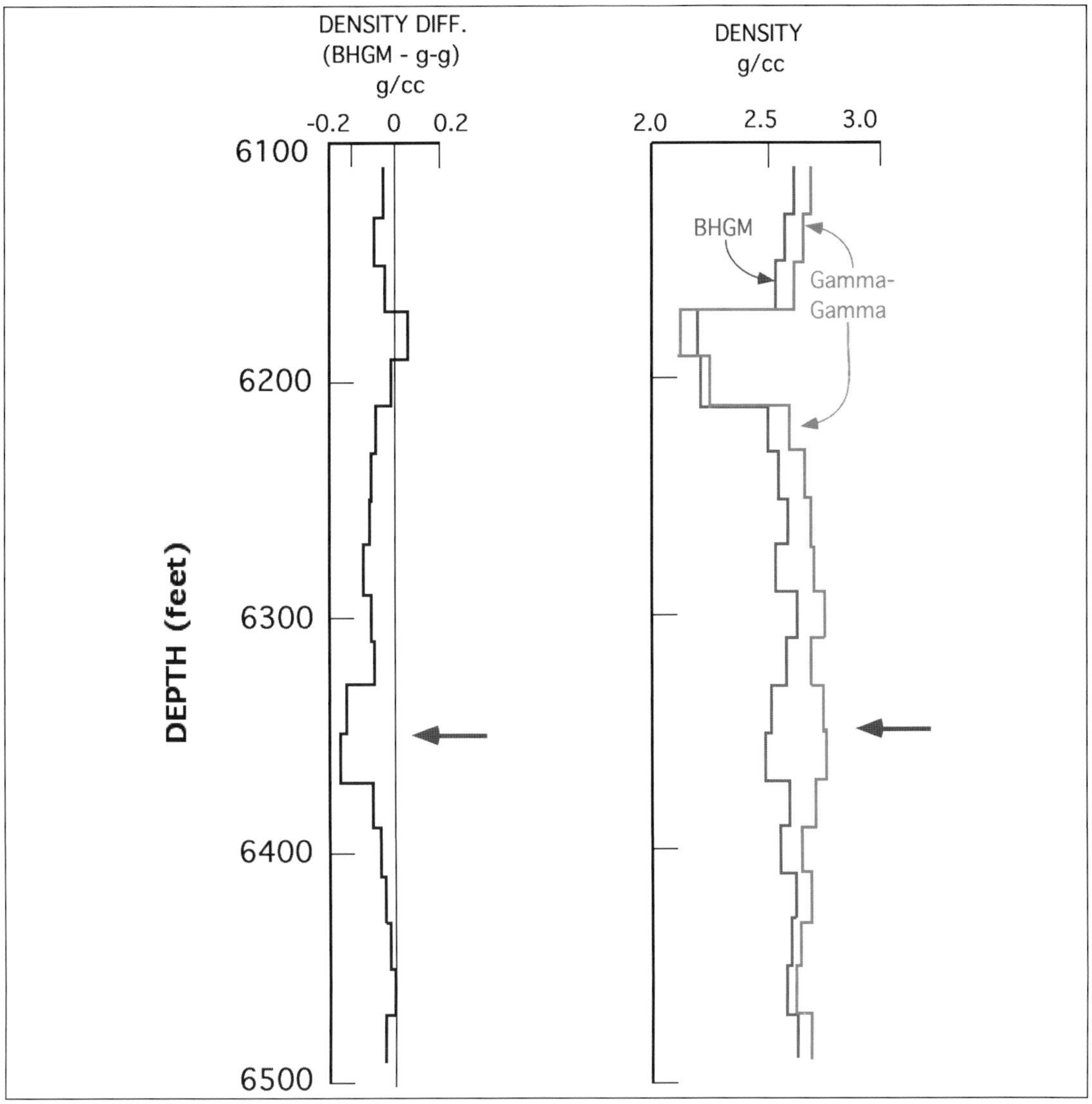

Figure 15–12. From Rasmussen, 1975; courtesy *The Log Analyst.*

Salt body geometry

In many Gulf of Mexico prospects, salt plays a key role in acting as a structural trap. Overhanging salt often forms seals, and sediments on salt flanks can have structural and stratigraphic pinch-outs against the salt. The exact shape of the salt is critical in understanding these traps. Unfortunately, seismic imaging often tends to be poor in these prospects. In this synthetic model (taken from a real structure), if a borehole gravity log were run, it would be able to tell conclusively which of the two seismic interpretations shown below in the figure was valid. Either interpretation would have a significant impact on the completion and economics of the exploration play. Figure (A) is predicted BHGM logs through a salt body in the Gulf of Mexico, (B) is a model of the salt body, and (C) is a seismic section through the salt body shown in the model (B).

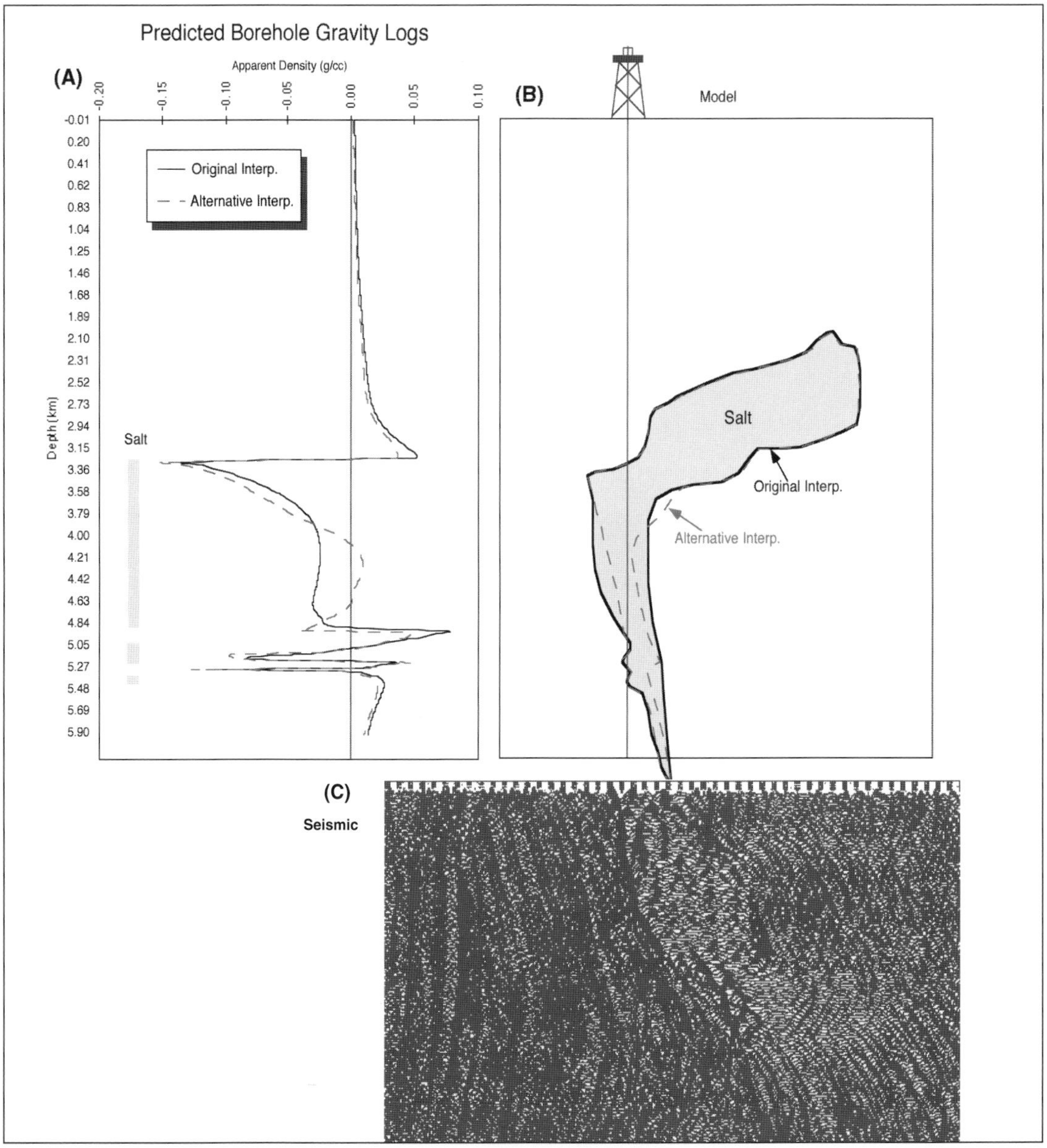

Figure 15–13. Courtesy ARCO Exploration and Production Technology, 1997.

Examples of Borehole Gravity Applications, continued

Monitoring well drawdown

One of the most attractive aspects of borehole gravity applications is its ability to detect gas, oil, and water contacts at large distances from the borehole. It can do this through multiple casing strings and formation damage—conditions where the neutron density tool performs poorly. In many hydrocarbon reservoirs, the oil has a gas cap. Frequently, these reservoirs have an underlying water zone. The shape of these interfaces over time is critical to production strategy. Methods can determine where those contacts exist in the wellbore, but only borehole gravity can determine their shape away from the well. Because the interfaces are mobile with time, their movement can be monitored with borehole gravity.

The figure below shows a synthetic model of the configuration of a theoretical drawdown gas cone around a producing well, modeled after the Prudhoe Bay field, Alaska. Since so little is known about the shape of gas coning, present logging methods can severely underestimate the true gas–oil contact in the reservoir away from wells. Borehole gravity can determine the shape of the gas cone as well as locate the true gas–oil contact at a distance from the producing wells. Logs A, B, and C correspond to different gas cones shown in the model.

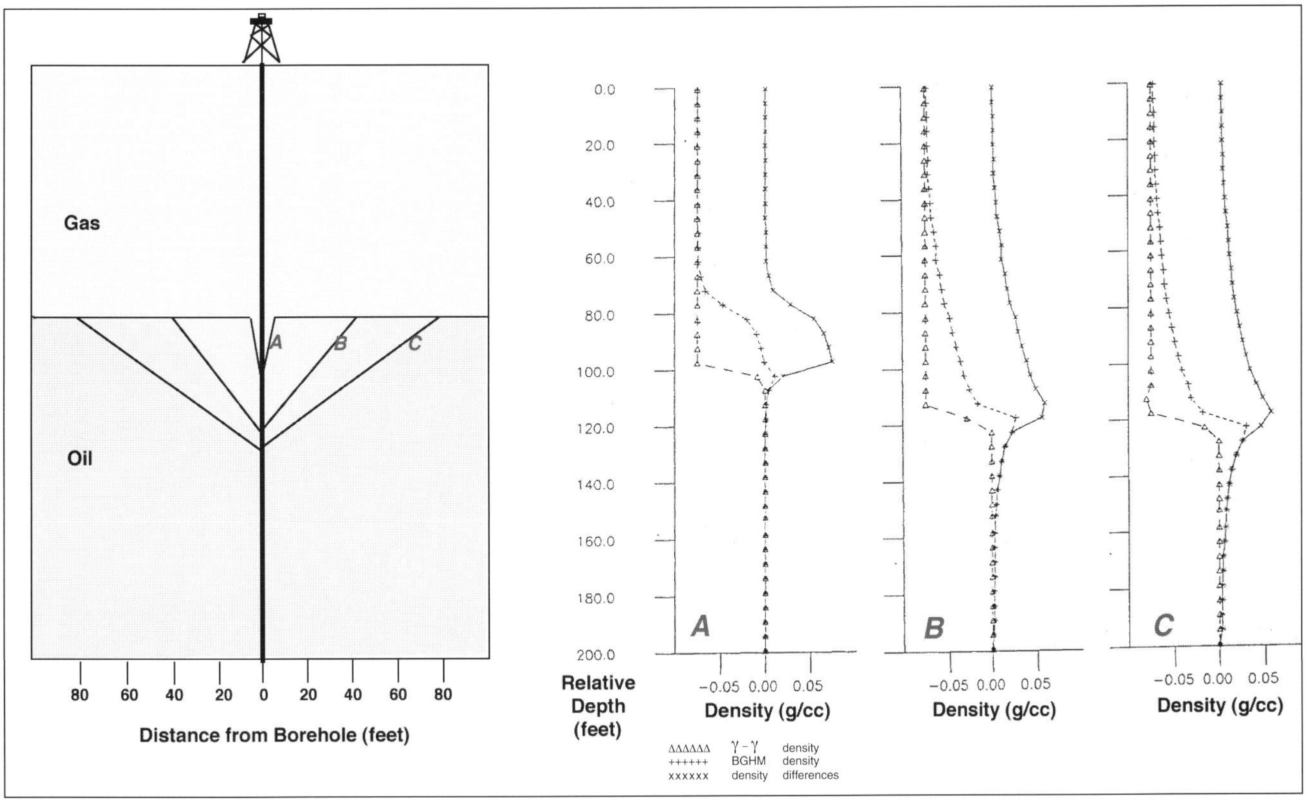

Figure 15–14. Courtesy ARCO Exploration and Production Technology, 1997.

Examples of Borehole Gravity Applications, continued

Bypassed pays

Because the borehole gravity meter is the only tool that can measure bulk density away from the borehole, it is ideal to use for finding bypassed pay zones. In the figure below, Case #1 shows a model of laterally homogenous geology and no density anomalies. Case #2 shows a region of lower density, possibly signifying the presence of missed hydrocarbons 60 m from the well. The density difference detects the distant density contrast as a broad, anomalous low with its minimum centered at the correct depth. Such a zone may be within range of a borehole sidetrack. In Case #3 the low-density missed pay zone is within 15 m of the well, and a strong density difference exists. Such pay zones may be in the range of a possible well completion after hydrofracturing the reservoir. In Case #4 the missed pay is about 1 m from the well, and the density difference is very pronounced. Such pay zones are within the range of normal well completions but would still be undetected by any other logging method.

These examples show that borehole gravity can indicate the presence of bypassed pay zones 1–60 m from the well. Once the well is cased, no other logging tool can do this. This is why the borehole gravity tool is currently the best technology available to search for bypassed hydrocarbons in existing wells.

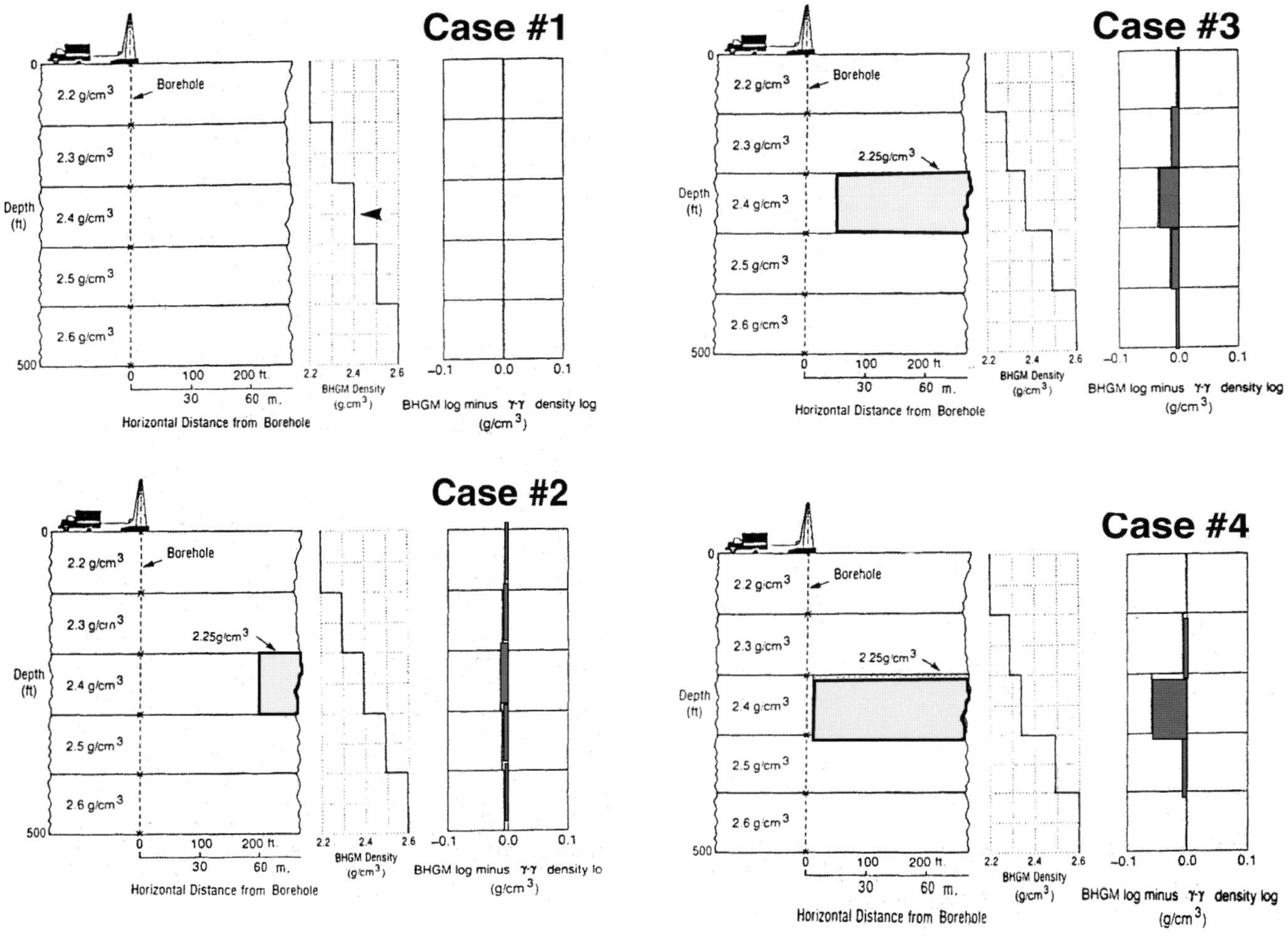

Figure 15–15. After Beyer, 1991; courtesy SEG.

Examples of Borehole Gravity Applications, continued

Combining BHGM with tomography

Between-well imaging jointly uses borehole gravity with seismic tomography. Because of the unique distant resolution capabilities of borehole gravity, these data provide a useful integrating tool at the seismic wavelet scale. In the Gulf of Mexico example shown in the figure below, Amoco used its borehole gravity log to help interpret a detailed cross-borehole seismic tomography image. The two wells were located less than 250 ft apart. Two faults, F1 and F2, are seen in both data sets, and excellent correlations are made of various sands labeled M5, M6, M8, M9, M10, and M10A. Note that the well on the left encountered more pay sands than the well on right. Also note that the M6 sand is missing in the well on the left. The between-well structural and stratigraphic changes in only 250 ft can be understood by combining the interpretations of the two comparable distant imaging tools: borehole gravity and seismic tomography.

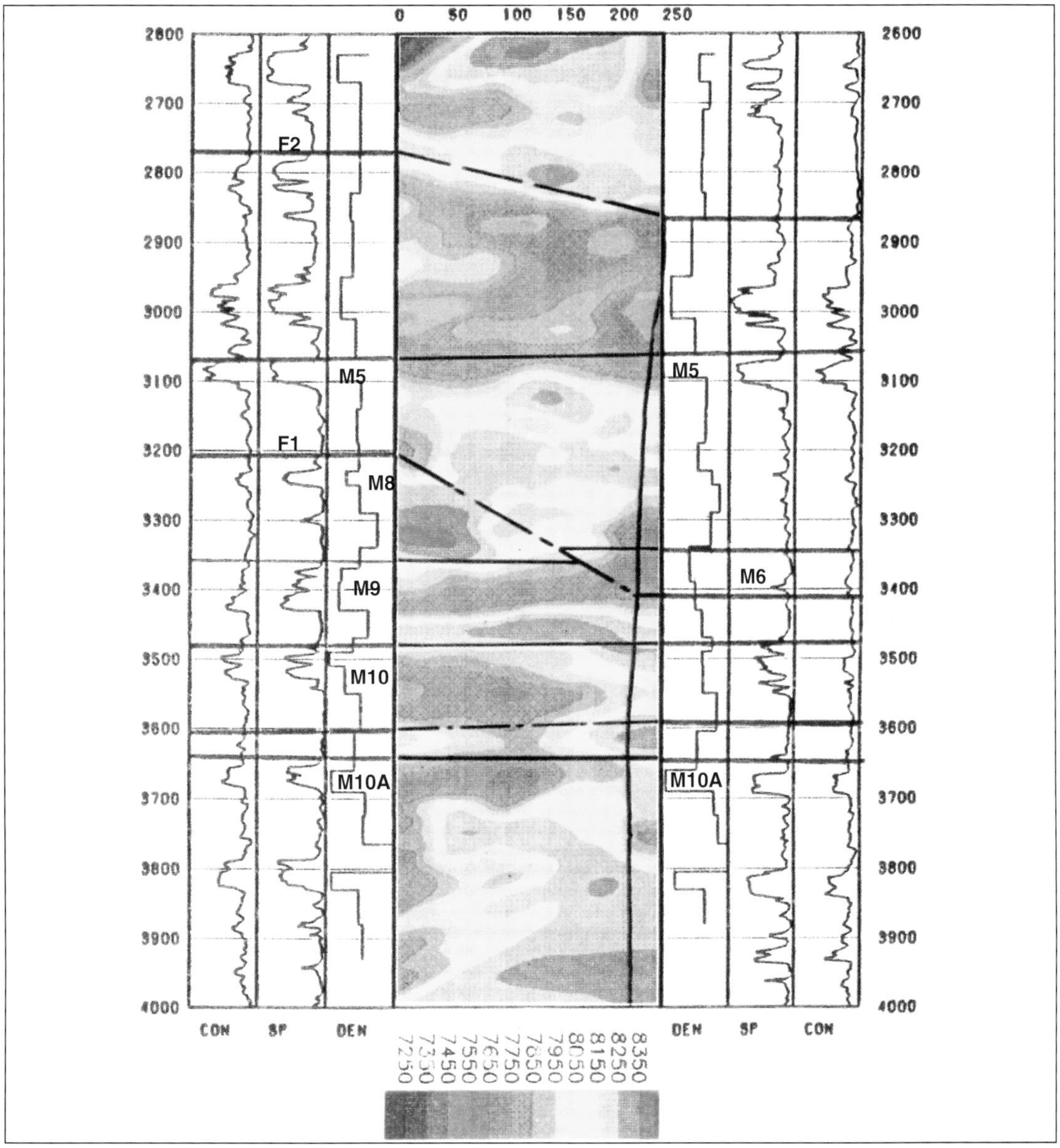

Figure 15–16. After Lines et al., 1991; courtesy CSEG Recorder.

Monitoring gas production

The figure below shows an example of a borehole gravity tool that succeeded where conventional open-hole and cased-hole logging methods had failed. In the upper part of the log, the gamma-gamma density log underestimates the gas saturation by about 15%. In the lower part of the log, wash-out zones are dominant, affecting the gamma-gamma log but not the BHGM log. Over these intervals, borehole gravity gives a more reliable and higher overall density measurement. The reservoir was fractured at 853 m, and a normally tight reservoir started to produce gas. The second BHGM logging run shows the lower density of the fractured, gas-filled producing interval. Shallower than 810 m, both gamma-gamma and BHGM logs agree. The borehole gravity tool was used to measure secondary gas saturation in a fractured limestone reservoir.

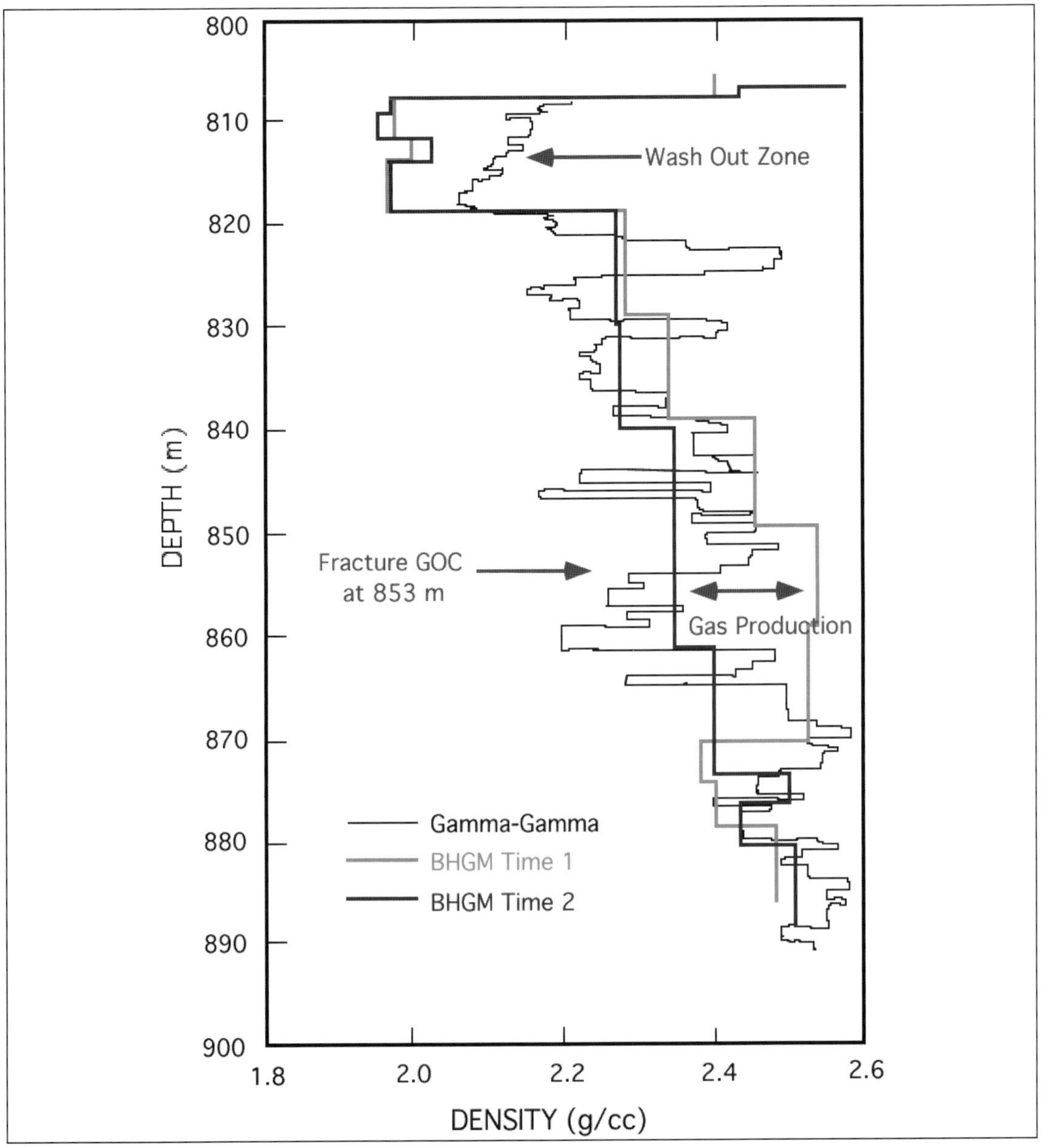

Figure 15–17. After van Popta et al., 1990; courtesy SPE.

References

Beyer, L.A., 1991, Borehole Gravity Surveys: SEG Short Course notes, June, 350 p. *Excellent source for general principles of borehole gravity. Very good figures and references.*

Chapin, D.A., 1996a, The theory of the Bouguer gravity anomaly: a tutorial: Leading Edge, May 1996, p. 361–363. *A summary of modern techniques for processing raw gravity data.*

Chapin, D.A., 1996b, A deterministic approach towards computing isostatic gravity residuals: case history from South America: Geophysics, vol. 61, no. 4, p. 1022–1033. *Details about new ways of computing isostatic residuals and computing the correct Bouguer reduction density.*

Giedt, N.R., 1990, Unity field, *in* E.A. Beaumont and N.H. Foster, eds., Treatise of Petroleum Geology Atlas of Oil and Gas Fields: AAPG Structural Traps 3, p. 177–197.

Grow, J.A., K.D. Klitgord, and J.S. Schlee, 1988, Structure and evolution of Baltimore Canyon Trough, *in* R.E. Sheridan and J.A. Grow, eds., The Geology of North America, vol. I-2: GSA, p. 269–290.

Jorgensen, G.J., and W. Bosworth, 1989, Gravity modeling in the Central African Rift system, Sudan: rift geometries and tectonic significance: J. Afri. Earth Sci., vol. 8, p. 283–306.

Lines, L.R., H. Tan, and S. Treitel, 1991, Velocity and density imaging between boreholes: CSEG Recorder, vol. 16, no. 6, p. 9–14. *A unique case study that integrates borehole gravity with the processing and interpretation of cross-well tomography.*

Millegan, P.S., 1990, Aspects of the interpretation of Mesozoic rift basins in northern Sudan using potential fields data: Expanded abstracts with biography, SEG 60th Annual Meeting, p. 605–607.

McCulloh, T.H., J.R. Kandle, and J.E. Schoellhamer, 1968, Application of gravity measurements in wells to problems of reservoir evaluation: Transactions of the 9th Annual SPWLA Logging Symposium. *Fundamental work describing the distance of sources seen by the borehole gravity meter.*

Rasmussen, N.F., 1975, The successful use of the borehole gravity meter in northern Michigan: The Log Analyst, September–October, p. 1–10.

Sheridan, R.E., J.A. Grow, and K.D. Klitgord, 1988, Geophysical data, *in* R.E. Sheridan and J.A. Grow, eds., The Geology of North America, vol. I-2: GSA, p. 177–196.

van Popta, J., J.M.T. Heywood, S.J. Adams, and D.R. Bostock, 1990, Use of borehole gravimetry for reservoir characterisation and fluid saturation monitoring: Expanded Abstracts, SPE Europec 90 Conference, p. 151–160. *Use of time-lapsed borehole gravity logging to monitor fluid movement away from the borehole.*

Annotated Bibliography

General information

Alixant, J.L., and E. Mann, 1995, In-situ residual oil saturation to gas from time-lapse borehole gravity: Proceedings of the annual SPE Conference, p. 855–869. *Use of reservoir monitoring technique in the Rabi-Kounga field, Gabon.*

Blakely, R.J., 1995, Potential Theory in Gravity & Magnetic Applications: Cambridge, Cambridge Univ. Press, 441 p. *The state-of-the-art in modern potential field theory. Good sections on the various gravity corrections with models to show the effect and an excellent description of Fourier filtering.*

Brady, J.L., D.S. Wolcott, and C.L.V. Aiken, 1993, Gravity methods: useful techniques for reservoir surveillance: Proceedings of the SPE Western Regional Conference, p. 645–658. *Predicted use of borehole gravity in reservoir monitoring of the Prudhoe Bay and Kuparuk fields, Alaska.*

Chapin, D.A., and M.E. Ander, 1999, New life for borehole gravity?: AAPG Explorer, vol. 20, no. 2, p. 24–29. *A description of the borehole gravity method for the nonspecialist.*

Dehlinger, P., 1978, Marine Gravity: Amsterdam, Elsevier Scientific Publishing Co., 322 p. *A thorough discussion of methods and interpretation of gravity with special emphasis on the stabilized platform meter and navigational methods.*

Dobrin, M.B., 1976, Introduction to Geophysical Prospecting: New York, McGraw-Hill Book Co., 630 p. *Excellent source; complementary to Nettleton (1976).*

Edcon, 1977, Borehole Gravity Meter Operation and Interpretation Manual: Denver, Edcon, 110 p. *Excellent source for general principles of borehole gravity. Has very good figures.*

Gournay, L.S., and W.D. Lyle, 1984, Determination of hydrocarbon saturation and porosity using a combination borehole gravimeter (BHGM) and deep investigating electric log: Proceedings of the 25th Annual Meeting of SPWLA, p. WW1–WW14. *Methodology to detect bypassed hydrocarbons by comparing borehole gravity with electric logs.*

Heiskanen, W.A., and F.A. Vvening-Meinesz, 1958, The Earth and Its Gravity Field: New York, McGraw-Hill Book Co., 470 p. *A classic. Contains theory and techniques for dealing with large-scale gravity data sets.*

Jageler, A.H., 1976, Improved hydrocarbon reservoir evaluation through use of borehole-gravimeter data: Journal of Petroleum Technology, vol. 28, no. 6, p. 709–718. *A good review of the borehole gravity method.*

LaCoste, L.J.B., 1967, Measurement of gravity at sea and in the air: Reviews of Geophysics, vol. 5, no. 4, p. 477–526. *A complete and extensive review of the development and use of the stabilized platform meter for shipborne and airborne acquisition. Also contains a useful discussion of the water-bottom gravity meter.*

LaFehr, T.R., 1983, Rock density from borehole gravity surveys: Geophysics, vol. 48, no. 3, p. 341–356. *How to compute whole-rock apparent densities from borehole gravity data.*

General information (continued)

Maute, R.E., and L.S. Gournay, 1985, Determination of residual oil saturation with the borehole gravity meter: SPE Middle East Oil Techology Conference, p. 185–188. *How to compute oil saturation from borehole gravity logs.*

Nettleton, L.L., 1976, Gravity and Magnetics in Oil Prospecting: New York, McGraw-Hill Book Co., 464 p. *Excellent source, particularly for acquisition and historical methods. Slightly out of date with current methods. Highly readable.*

Smith, N.J., 1950, The case for gravity data from boreholes: Geophysics, vol. 15, no. 4, p. 605–636. *Groundbreaking paper that describes the modern concepts for use of a borehole gravimeter.*

Telford, W.M., L.P. Geldart, R.E. Sheriff, and D.A. Keys, 1976, Applied Geophysics: Cambridge, Cambridge Univ. Press, 860 p. *Very complete. Contains a lot of theory.*

Interpretation—general concepts

Al-Chalabi, M., 1971, Some studies relating to nonuniqueness in gravity and magnetic inverse problems: Geophysics, vol. 36, no. 5, p. 835-855. *Potential field ambiguity as proven by model studies.*

Ervin, C.P., 1977, Short note: theory of the Bouguer anomaly: Geophysics, vol. 42, no. 7, p. 1468. *An important paper reiterating basic concepts.*

Pawlowski, R.S., 1992, Tutorial: gravity anomalies for nonspecialists: Leading Edge, Sept. 1992, p. 41–43. *A nice review of what gravity anomalies really are, based upon models.*

Romberg, F.E., 1958, Key variables of gravity: Geophysics, vol. 23, no. 4, p. 684–700. *A highly readable article outlining many basic interpretation concepts.*

Skeels, D.C., 1947, Ambiguity in gravity interpretation: Geophysics, vol. 12, no. 1, p. 43–56. *Proof that gravity cannot be interpreted uniquely.*

Interpretation—residuals

Coons, R.L., J.W. Mack, and W. Strange, 1964, Least-square polynomial fitting of gravity data and case histories, *in* G.A. Parks, ed., Computers in the Mineral Industries: Stanford Univ. Publications, vol. 9, no. 2, p. 498–519. *Discussion and use of the polynomial residual method.*

Elkins, T.A., 1951, The second derivative method of gravity interpretation: Geophysics, vol. 16, no. 1, p. 39–56. *Development and use of the second derivative method using grid convolution operators.*

Fuller, B.D., 1967, Two-dimensional frequency analysis and design of grid operators, *in* Mining Geophysics, vol. II: Tulsa, SEG, p. 658–708. *A landmark paper comparing frequency domain operations to space domain operations.*

Kanasewich, E.R., 1981, Time Sequence Analysis in Geophysics, 3rd ed.: Edmonton, University of Alberta, 480 p. *An excellent, modern and complete source for frequency domain theory, written mainly for seismic applications.*

Interpretation—residuals (continued)

Nettleton, L.L., 1954, Regionals, residuals, and structures: Geophysics, vol. 19, p. 1–22. *A fairly complete discussion about the use of grid residuals.*

Skeels, D.C., 1967, What is residual gravity?: Geophysics, vol. 32, p. 872–876. *A discussion of regional/residual separation.*

Interpretation—modeling

Bhattacharyya, B.K., 1978, Computer modeling in gravity and magnetic interpretation: Geophysics, vol. 43, p. 912–929. *A review of the theory of various modeling schemes.*

Cady, J.W., 1980, Calculation of gravity and magnetic anomalies of finite-length right polygonal prisms: Geophysics, vol. 45, p. 1507–1512. *A modified version of Talwani et. al. 1959 method of gravity modeling for a 2-D geometry. Caution: there are numerous errors in this paper. This is the method used in most current modeling programs.*

Parker, R.L., 1972, The rapid calculation of potential anomalies: Geophys. Jour. of the Royal Astronomical Society, vol. 31, p. 447–455. *Development of the theory to calculate gravity or magnetic anomalies in the frequency domain, which can be applied to modeling or inversion techniques.*

Talwani, M., J.L. Worzel, and M. Landisman, 1959, Rapid gravity computations for two-dimensional bodies with application to the mendocino submarine fracture zone: Journal of Geophysical Research, vol. 64, no. 1, p. 40–59. *Landmark paper for forward-type 2-D polygonal gravity modeling.*

Interpretation—miscellaneous concepts

Chandler, V.W., J.S. Koski, W.J. Hinze, and L.W. Braile, 1981, Analysis of multisource gravity and magnetic anomaly data sets by moving-window application of Poisson's theorem: Geophysics, vol. 46, no. 1, p. 30–39. *Use of Poisson's relationship to identify joint magnetic and gravity sources.*

Hammer, S., 1983, Airborne gravity is here!: Geophysics, vol. 48, no. 2, p. 213–223. *A controversial presentation of the airborne gravity method with examples of recent usages. A sales pitch for Carson Geoscience, it is also worthwhile to read discussions in the March and April 1984 issues of Geophysics by N.C. Steenland, A.T. Herring, and W.C. Pearson and January 1985 by M.J. Hall.*

LeFehr, T.R., 1965, The estimation of the total amount of anomalous mass by Gauss's theorem: Journal of Geophysical Research, vol. 70, p. 1911–1919. *How to analyze the gravity anomaly to compute the amount of anomalous mass.*

Chapter 16

Applying Magnetotellurics

by

Arnie Ostrander

Arnie Ostrander

Arnie Ostrander is an oil and gas exploration consultant specializing in the integration of magnetotelluric methods and surface geochemistry in frontier basin exploration and in underdeveloped stratigraphic plays in producing basins. He earned his B.A. in geology in 1974 from the University of Montana. He began his professional career with Zonge Engineering and Research Organization from 1975 to 1985, was with Phoenix Geoscience, Inc. from 1988 to 1991, and has been an independent consultant since 1991.

Overview

Introduction

This chapter discusses the nature and uses of magnetotellurics (MT), a method of surveying the subsurface from the surface. Although MT cannot provide the resolution of seismic surveys, it is less expensive and, more importantly, can be used in places where seismic is impractical or gives poor results.

In this chapter

This chapter contains the following topics.

What is Magnetotellurics (MT)?

Definition

Magnetotellurics is an electrical geophysical technique that measures the resistivity of the subsurface. This is the same physical parameter that is measured in a borehole resistivity log.

How MT differs from electric logs

MT differs from an inductive electric log in three major ways:

Magnetotellurics Measurements	Electric Log Measurements
Made from the surface	Made subsurface from inside a borehole
Depth of investigation is a function of both frequency at which the measurement is taken and the average resistivity of the subsurface	Depth of investigation is the depth of the borehole measuring device below the surface
Respond only to changes in average bulk resistivity	Respond to individual rock layers along the wall of the borehole

The figure below shows the simplified relationship between a lithologic log, an electric log, an MT sounding, and an inversion run using the MT sounding data.

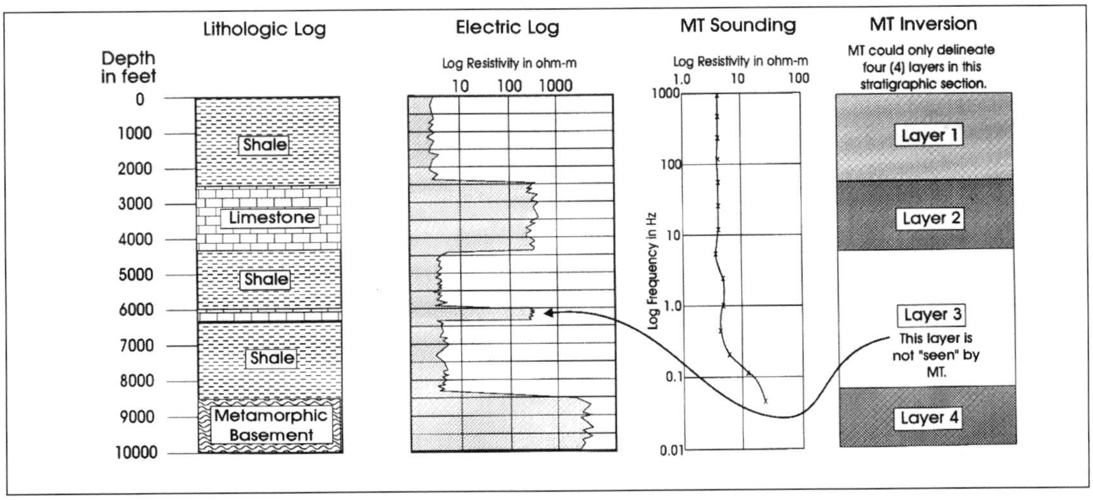

Figure 16–1.

We can also take electric log data and run a forward MT model to produce an MT sounding curve.

Subsurface layers resolved

Subsurface layers are resolved by inverse modeling of MT data acquired across a spectrum of frequencies, as illustrated in Figure 16–1.

MT resolution

The rule-of-thumb for MT resolution for depth of burial vs. layer thickness is 10:1. For example, to "see" a layer at a depth of 1,500 m (5,000 ft), the thickness of the layer needs to be approximately 150 m (500 ft) or more. Low-resistivity layers are more easily delineated than high-resistivity layers. It is difficult for MT to resolve more than three or four subsurface layers.

What Does an MT Survey Measure?

What is measured?

Two basic alternating current (AC) measurements are taken in an MT survey: a horizontal magnetic field (H-field) measurement and an electrical field (E-field) measurement. The E-field is always measured perpendicular to the H-field data.

The H-field

The H-field is the "source" signal, or the primary field. It propagates across the surface of the earth. Because it does not travel in the subsurface, the H-field data do not provide information about the subsurface geology.

Very limited information about the subsurface geology can be interpreted from the **vertical H-field** if this component is measured. The vertical H-field is called the *tipper*.

The **horizontal H-field** is measured with a horizontally oriented magnetic coil. The tipper is measured with a vertically oriented coil.

Be careful not to confuse an MT survey with a magnetic survey. An MT survey does not measure the magnetic properties of the subsurface rocks, as does a magnetic survey.

The E-field

The E-field is the secondary field, generated by the H-field propagating across the surface. Each time the primary H-field (an AC signal) switches polarity, a secondary E-field (current flow) is generated in the subsurface. Thus, the horizontal E-field data provides information about the subsurface geology.

This is the same physical principle as the alternator in a car. An alternating or spinning magnetic field (H-field) sets up current flow in the wire windings in the alternator, which in turn charges the battery. In the case of an MT survey, the "wire" is the earth.

The E-field is measured with a grounded dipole typically 50–200 m long. All subsurface geology information is contained in the E-field data. However, without the H-field data, we cannot calculate resistivity.

The figure at right shows the relationship between the E- and H-fields.

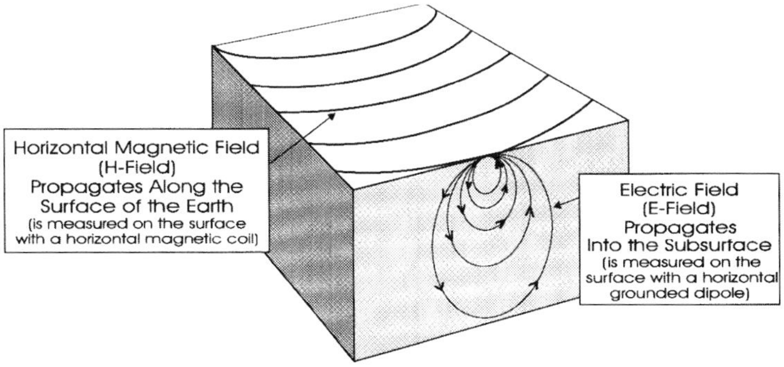

Figure 16–2.

Resistivity calculation

The resistivity calculation is a simple ratio of the primary source signal (H-field) and the secondary current flow in the earth (E-field), with a modifier for the frequency at which the data were acquired:

$$\text{Apparent Resistivity} = \left(\frac{E}{H}\right)^2 \times \frac{1}{5f}$$

where:

E = magnitude of the E-field
H = magnitude of the H-field
f = frequency

How Are MT Data Acquired?

Acquisition instrumentation

The data are collected using a microprocessor-controlled voltmeter. The voltmeter is in fact a system of complex hardware/software devices that includes amplification, filtering, A/D conversion, stacking and averaging, and various data-enhancement algorithms.

Types of surveys

There are two types of MT surveys: natural source (Vozoff, 1972) and controlled source (Goldstein and Strangway, 1975). The equipment and the operational procedures for these two types differ considerably.

Natural-source surveys

The natural-source data-acquisition system typically measures four components: E_x, E_y, H_x, and H_y. The E_x component is oriented perpendicular to the E_y component. This is also true for the H-field components.

The predominant low-frequency (< 1.0 Hz) signal source for natural-source data is sunspot activity. The dominant high-frequency (> 1.0 Hz) source is equatorial thunderstorm activity.

Although H-field data do not provide information on the subsurface geology (when only H_x and H_y components are measured), the vertical H-field component—if measured—provides information on the surface geology.

The figure below shows a typical MT setup for a natural-source survey.

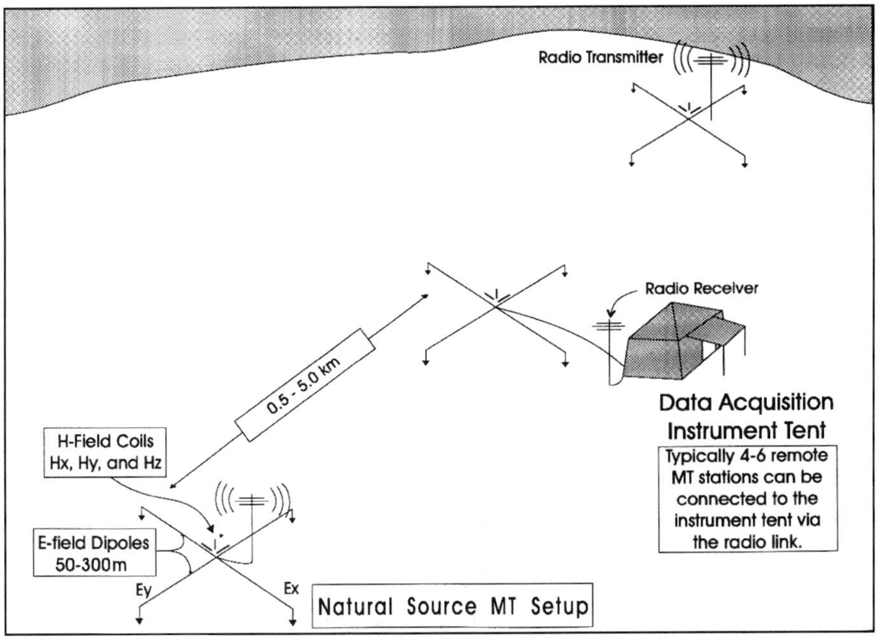

Figure 16–3.

Controlled-source surveys

The controlled-source system uses a high-power transmitter and motor/generator set to transmit a discrete AC waveform. This signal is transmitted into a grounded dipole typically 600–1,200 m (2,000–4,000 ft) long. The transmitter is normally located 3–6 km (2–4 mi) from the survey line.

Controlled-source surveys (continued)

Normally, only the E_x (parallel to the transmitter dipole) and H_y components are measured.

The figure below shows a typical MT setup for a controlled-source survey.

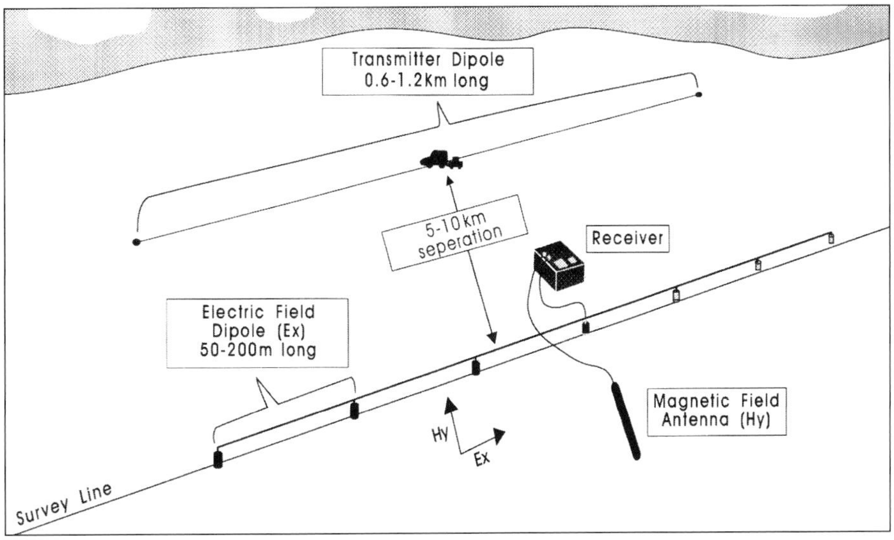

Figure 16–4.

Which method is better?

The choice of MT method depends on the survey objectives. Natural-source data are best suited for regional surveys where the stations are widely spaced (e.g., frontier basin analysis). Controlled-source data are best suited for mapping structural detail where the stations lie along a continuous profile at 100–200-m (300–600-ft) spacings. The maximum depth of exploration for the controlled-source method is 3,000–4,500 m (10,000–15,000 ft) in a typical volcanic, carbonate, or granite overthrust terrain. Natural-source data have considerably deeper penetration but poorer resolution at shallower depths.

Where to use MT

MT can be valuable in areas that yield poor-quality seismic data and where acquiring seismic data is very expensive. The following table indicates where to use MT and the reasons for using it.

Locations	Reasons for Using MT
Carbonate terrains	Poor-quality seismic data
Volcanic terrains	Poor-quality seismic data
Granite overthrusts	Poor-quality seismic data
Regional surveys	Less expensive than seismic; generates prospects to detail with seismic
Remote areas	Less expensive than seismic
Rugged terrains	Less expensive than seismic
Fracture zones	Excellent tool for mapping

Case History: Frontier Basin Analysis (Amazon Basin, Colombia)

Introduction

A regional exploration program to study a large unexplored area in the Colombian Amazon basin was conducted by Amoco Production Company in 1987 and 1988 (Burgett et al., 1992). This study area was very large [approximately 300,000 km^2 (115,000 mi^2)] and remote with dense jungle cover, rugged terrain, and limited road access.

The first phase of the program consisted of 31,700 km (19,700 mi) of airborne gravity and magnetics. The large-scale structures delineated in these surveys were then further investigated by MT. The MT survey was feasible with a light helicopter because the crew was small and equipment was light and compact. Data were collected from 43 sites, with a typical spacing of 10–20 km (6–12 mi).

Survey results

The MT data clearly delineated a thick sedimentary section with internal units that could be correlated from site to site. Three resistivity "packages" were observed:

- 40–100 ohm-m (sedimentary)
- 150–250 ohm-m (sedimentary)
- >1000 ohm-m (crystalline basement)

The figure below shows a simulated cross section in the Amazon basin based on MT data.

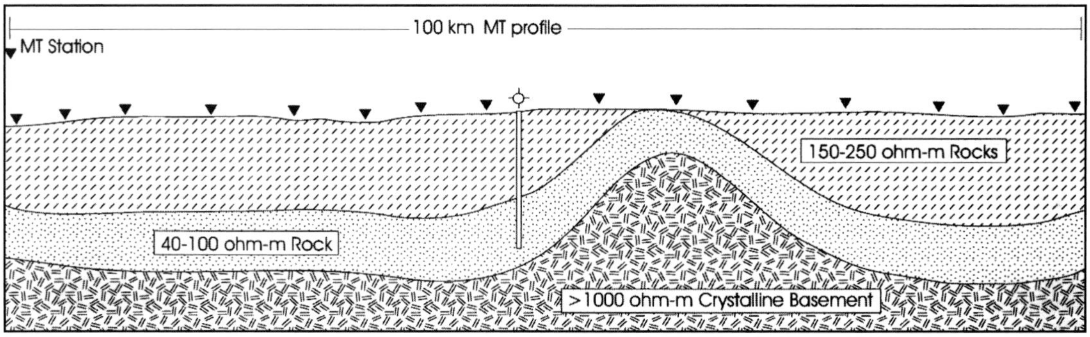

Figure 16–5. Drafted from data in Burgett et al., 1992.

Post-MT program

Encouraged by the evidence from the MT survey, Amoco decided to shoot a small seismic program and drill a shallow stratigraphic test. This program was positioned on the edge of a subbasin defined in the MT data. There generally was good agreement between the MT data, the seismic data, and the borehole geology.

The airborne gravity and magnetic data, followed by the surface MT survey, provided a very cost-effective means of regional basin definition and led directly to a well-positioned seismic survey and well site.

Case History: Rugged Carbonate Terrain (Highlands of Papua New Guinea)

Introduction

The Papuan thrust belt is both an expensive and difficult area in which to acquire seismic data. The area is typified by rugged mountainous terrain, dense equatorial jungle, and thick, heavily karstified limestone. The karstified limestone in some areas is also overlain by heterogeneous volcanics. The few coherent seismic reflectors are lacking in character and continuity, and the data in general are extremely noisy.

The sedimentary section in this area, however, is an excellent MT target (Billings and Thomas, 1990). This sequence observed in MT data is a simple three-layer package. The upper layer is the high-resistivity Darai Limestone, the middle layer is low-resistivity Leru Formation clastics, and the third layer is high-resistivity basement rocks. Therefore, the MT data provide a subsurface map of the base of the Darai and the top of the basement. The addition of an upper high-resistivity volcanic layer in some areas usually does not complicate this interpretation, except that it may not be possible to differentiate the base of the volcanics from the top of the Darai.

Survey results

More than 2,500 MT sites have been acquired in Papua New Guinea by numerous companies involved in exploration in the region (Mills, personal communication, 1994). BP Exploration (Hoversten, 1992) acquired MT data over both the Angore anticline and the Hides anticline. The interpreted models from these two data sets provide depth estimates of the base of the Darai Limestone to within 10% of the measured depth in the Angore 1 well. In both cases, the seismic data aided the interpretation.

The figure below shows the 2-D MT model beneath the Angore-1 well and the base of the Darai Limestone as observed in the well.

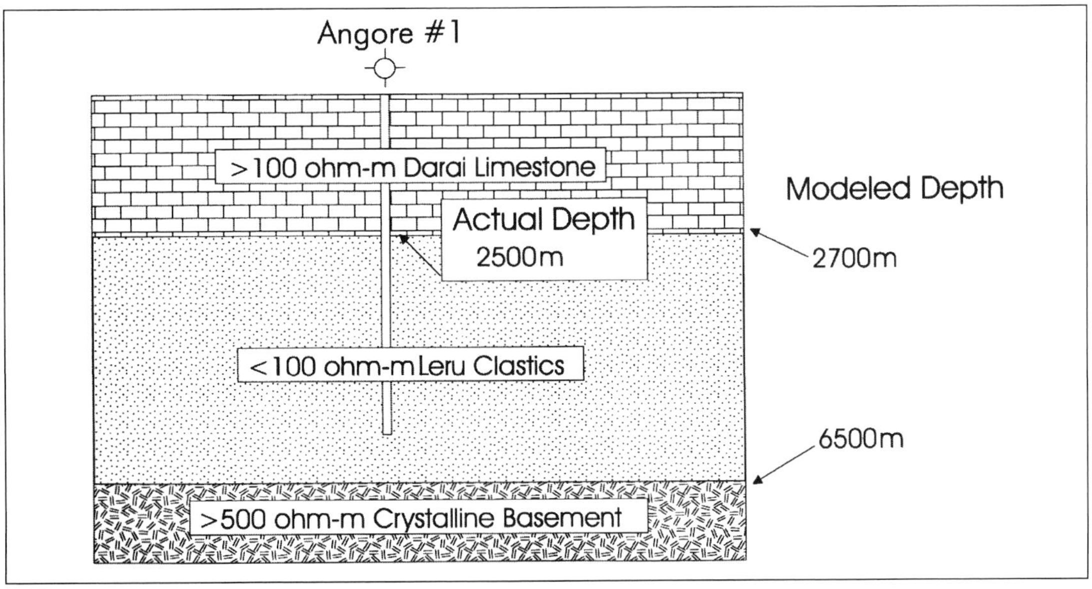

Figure 16–6. Drafted from data in Hoversten, 1992.

Case History: Precambrian Overthrust (Northwestern Colorado)

Introduction

MT can be used in an overthrust environment to delineate conductive sediments beneath a resistive thrust plate. It is often difficult to acquire good-quality seismic data in an overthrust area where high-velocity (high-resistivity) rocks overlie low-velocity (low-resistivity) sediments.

The Precambrian overthrust in the Bear Springs area of northwestern Colorado is an example (Mills, 1994).

Survey results

The MT station near the drill hole (see diagram below) shows a thin, near-surface conductor on top of the resistive Precambrian thrust sheet. This is a wedge of Quaternary and Tertiary sediments. Beneath the thrust, a thick conductive section of Cretaceous sediments is observed.

The figure below is an 11-station MT profile across the thrust.

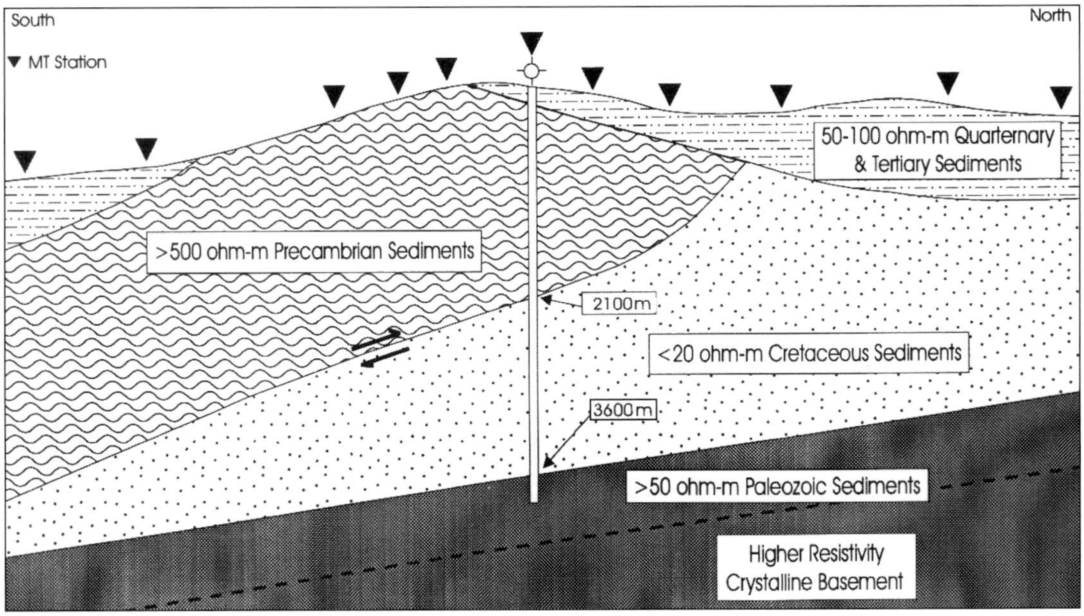

Figure 16–7. Drafied from data from Mills, 1994.

Structural details

These data provide the following structural details:

- Thickness of Quaternary and Tertiary cover
- Thickness of Precambrian thrust sheet
- Thinning of Cretaceous sediments to the south
- Depth to top of Paleozoic sediments
- No differentiation between Paleozoic and basement

A very detailed subsurface structural map could be obtained in this area using a 3-D grid, controlled-source MT survey depicting the Precambrian/Cretaceous thrust contact and the top of the Paleozoic section.

Case History: Volcanic Terrain (Columbia River Plateau)

Introduction

Seismic methods do not work well in areas covered by volcanics because of the dispersive nature of the volcanics and because of the decrease in acoustic velocity at the base of the volcanics.

Volcanic terrain, however, is an ideal environment for MT because it is a simple, three-layer stratigraphic package: resistive basalts over conductive sediments, which in turn overlie resistive metamorphic or granitic basement rocks.

Survey results

The cross section below is a 13-station MT natural source survey profile. This east–west section begins near the Idaho–Washington border and extends approximately 75 mi (120 km) to the west (Mills, personal communication, 1994).

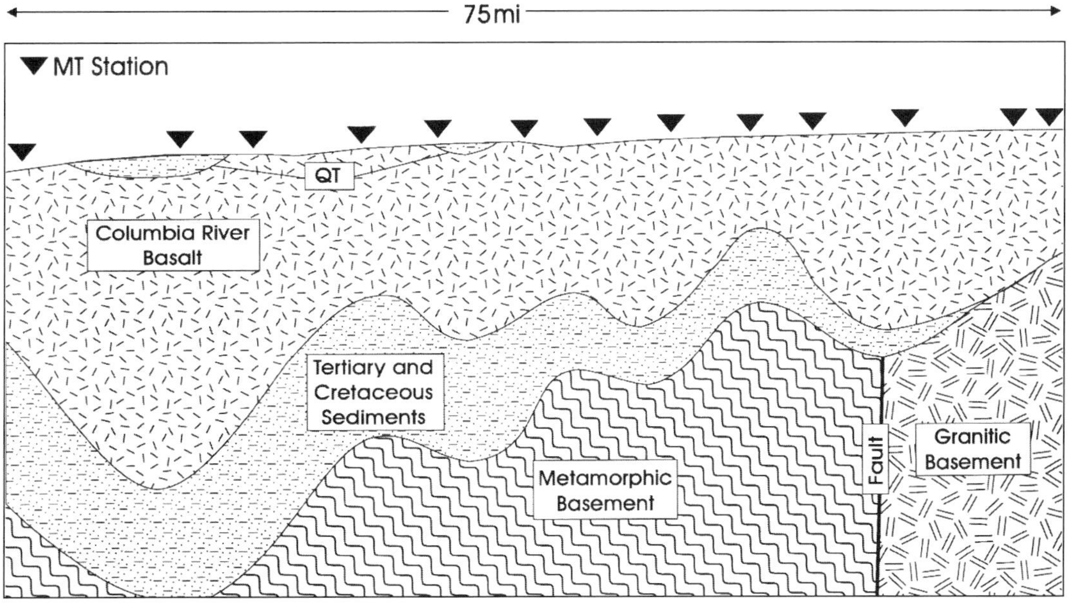

Figure 16–8. Drafted from data from Mills, 1994.

Structural details

These data provided the following structural details:

- Considerable variation on the thickness of the volcanics
- Considerable variation in the depth to top of basement
- Basalts thin to the east
- Sediments thin to east and eventually disappear
- Basement resistivities are an order-of-magnitude higher on the east end of the profile

Controlled-source MT data could provide 3-D imaging of individual prospects.

References

Billings, A.J., and J.H. Thomas, 1990, The use and limitations of non-seismic geophysics in the Papuan thrust belt, *in* C.J. Carman and Z. Carman, eds., Proceedings of the First PNG Petroleum Convention: Port Moresby, New Guinea, p. 51–62.

Burgett, W.A., A. Orange, and R.F. Sigal, 1992, Integration of MT, seismic, gravity, and magnetic data for reconnaissance of the Colombian Amazon: 54th meeting, European Association of Exploration Geophysicists, Expanded Abstracts, p. 428–499.

Goldstein, M.A., and D.W. Strangway, 1975, Audio-frequency magnetotellurics with a grounded electrical dipole source: Geophysics, vol. 40, p. 669–683.

Hoversten, G.M., 1996, Papua New Guinea MT: looking where seismic is blind: Geophysical Prospecting, vol. 44, p. 935–961.

Mills, A., 1994, Zephyr Geophysical Services, personal communication.

Vozoff, K., 1972, The magnetotelluric method in the exploration of sedimentary basins: Geophysics, vol. 37, no. 1, p. 98–141.

Chapter 17

Applied Paleontology

by

Robert L. Fleisher

and

H. Richard Lane

Robert L. Fleisher

Bob Fleisher is a biostratigraphic consultant in Houston. He was formerly a staff biostratigrapher for Chevron USA Production Company in Houston, specializing in foraminifera of California and the Gulf Coast. He received a BA degree (1966) from Amherst College and a Ph.D. (1975) from the University of Southern California. Dr. Fleisher has also worked for Exxon Production Research Company, Gulf Oil, and Chevron Overseas Petroleum Inc. He has served as Treasurer and President of the North American Micropaleontology Section of SEPM (Society for Sedimentary Geology).

H. Richard Lane

H. Richard Lane is a project manager at the National Science Foundation in Arlington, Virginia. He is the former Director of the Biostratigraphic Support and Development section at Amoco Production in Houston. He received a BS degree in geology from the University of Illinois and Masters and Ph.D. degrees in geology/paleontology from the University of Iowa. Except for $1^1/_2$ years as an Alexander von Humboldt Fellow in Marburg, Bonn, and Krefeld, Germany, Lane was a paleontologist/stratigrapher with Amoco. His specialty is mid-Paleozoic conodonts and stratigraphy. Lane has chaired the International Committee of Stratigraphy's Mid-Carboniferous Boundary group and is a titular member of the Subcommission on Carboniferous Stratigraphy.

Overview

Introduction

This chapter reviews how paleontology can help solve exploration, exploitation, and production problems. It is not, however, a manual; paleontology is a diverse and highly specialized discipline, and no earth scientist will learn how to apply these paleontological approaches merely by reading this chapter. The authors, listed within the sections they helped write, have summarized several complex and specialized subdisciplines, with emphasis on conveying a sense of the potential paleontological applications rather than an exhaustive or detailed treatment. Ideally, earth scientists involved in hydrocarbon recovery will recognize from these discussions the variety of contributions which paleontological approaches can make to geologic problem-solving and will seek assistance from a practitioner.

Paleontological process

A simple three-part process is the basis for applied paleontology.

Step	Action
1	Location and extraction of fossils is essential because this is the source of paleontologic data. Most new discoveries and applications are based on newly available fossils.
2	The central, vital step is analyzing and archiving fossil specimens. Fundamental to the analysis, for both effective use of the scientific literature and communication with other paleontologists, is careful taxonomic practice in identifying and naming species.
3	Paleontologists must apply the results to the task of solving geological problems. The quality of these solutions depends heavily on the skill with which the first two steps are performed.

In this chapter

This chapter contains the following sections.

Section A

Paleontology and Microfossils

Authors

H. Richard Lane, Merrell A. Miller, Lori B. Glassgold, John F. Baesemann, Lisanne A. Balcells-Baldwin, James A. Bergen, Kevin J. Crotty, Thomas D. Demchuk, James H. Gamber, Alfred F. Geen, William N. Krebs, Brian J. O'Neill, Ralph A. Salomon, Jeffrey A. Stein, Herbert J. Sullivan, Donald S. Van Nieuwenhuise, and Gordon D. Wood

Definitions

Applied paleontology is the study of the fossil remains of ancient organisms, both megascopic and microscopic in size, as applied to solving geological and geophysical problems. Fossils occur very sparingly in Proterozoic rocks and more abundantly in Phanerozoic rocks. The focus of paleontologic studies in the petroleum industry is mainly on microfossils—fossils so small that they are studied with a microscope. **Biostratigraphy**, a term often used synonymously with applied paleontology, is here restricted to stratigraphic applications related to correlation and age determination.

In this section

The following topics are discussed in this section.

Microfossils in Exploration

Introduction

Durable microscopic fossils have a wide distribution in time and space, and their rapid and irreversible evolution and morphologically distinctive evolutionary stages make them excellent tools for measuring relative geologic time. They are particularly useful in hydrocarbon exploration because they can be recovered from both cuttings and cores. Microfossil groups that are too rare in most sedimentary rocks, too limited in overall stratigraphic or paleoenvironmental range, or too poorly understood to be broadly useful in industrial application are not considered in this section.

Utility of microfossils in exploration

In an operational environment, microfossils can be examined shortly after being brought to the surface in ditch samples. Well-site analysis permits immediate identification of stratigraphic levels and drilling objectives, minimizing drilling time. Microfossils can also be used to accurately predict overpressured zones in advance of the drill bit.

In the office, microfossil studies allow precise local, regional, and global time–stratigraphic correlations that help in hydrocarbon prospect and trend delineation, regional stratigraphic and geologic studies, and exploitation evaluations. Analysis of microfossils helps scientists recognize paleoenvironmental distributions, which in turn helps us interpret sequence stratigraphy and reconstruct the paleogeography and paleoclimate. Some microfossils function as "paleothermometers" by undergoing irreversible color changes with postburial heating. As such, they indicate hydrocarbon maturity levels.

Principal microfossils

Microfossils useful in hydrocarbon exploration can be divided into five principal microfossil groups based on the composition of the shell (test) or hard parts. The table below shows the principal microfossil groups.

Composition	Fossil Group
Calcareous	Foraminifera, Ostracodes, Calcareous Nannofossils
Agglutinated	Foraminifera
Siliceous	Radiolarians, Diatoms, Silicoflagellates
Phosphatic	Conodonts
Organic walled	Chitinozoans, Pollen, Spores, Acritarchs, Dinoflagellates (collectively, Palynomorphs)

Calcareous Microfossils

Introduction

Calcareous microfossils have shells composed of calcite or aragonite. These organisms are present in most marine and in some nonmarine environments. At great oceanic depths characterized by low temperature and high hydrostatic pressure, however, calcareous remains are largely or completely dissolved. The depth below which this occurs, which varies in different oceanographic settings, is termed the **carbonate compensation depth** (CCD).

There are three principal types of calcareous microfossils: calcareous foraminifera, ostracodes, and calcareous nannofossils.

Calcareous foraminifera

Calcareous foraminifera are a group of unicellular organisms (protists) that secrete a rigid calcite or aragonite shell (or test). Fossils of these forms are found in sediments of brackish to marine origin from Silurian to Holocene in age. Most are benthic (bottom dwelling), but a significant group in the late Mesozoic and Cenozoic are planktonic (floating) forms.

Some stratigraphically important foraminifera developed complex internal structures and, frequently, large test size. Studied primarily in thin section, these include the fusulinids (Pennsylvanian to Permian) and several groups of so-called larger foraminifera (Triassic to Holocene). They occur primarily in carbonate or fine-grained clastic rocks and are excellent time markers.

Because many species have limited and well-known environmental ranges, they are excellent paleobathymetric and paleoenvironmental indicators, especially in younger Phanerozoic rocks.

The illustration below shows some typical calcareous foraminifera.

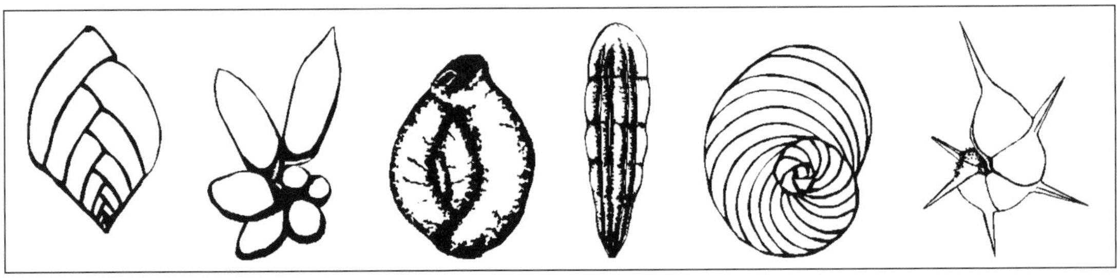

Figure 17–1.

Ostracodes

Ostracodes are microscopic crustaceans whose fossils are found in Cambrian to Holocene rocks. They occur in most marine and nonmarine depositional environments and are generally excellent environmental indicators. The paleontologic application of ostracodes is limited because (1) they are rare in many sections and (2) many species are endemic to local basins, so their age and environmental ranges are poorly understood. Ostracodes typically have rapid evolutionary rates and are useful biostratigraphic tools in some situations:

- In Paleozoic sequences
- In marine environments where wide-ranging species are present

Ostracodes (continued)

- For local stratigraphy in basins of limited extent
- In lacustrine environments, where they are frequently one of the few microfossils present

Ostracodes may also indicate thermal maturation of source rocks (see "Thermal Maturation").

The illustration below shows some typical ostracodes.

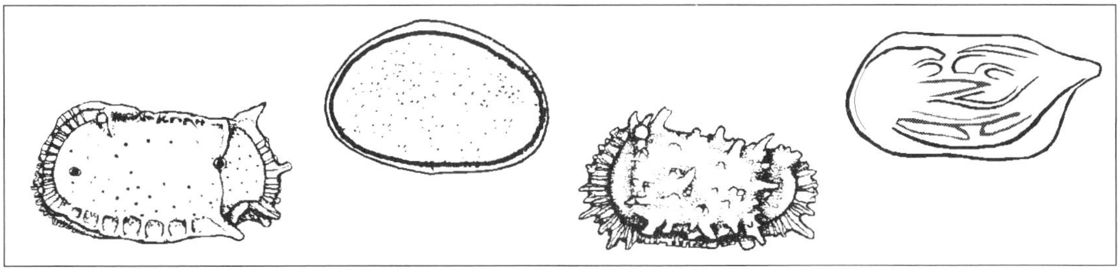

Figure 17–2.

Calcareous nannofossils

The term *calcareous nannofossils* includes both fossil coccoliths and nannoliths. **Coccoliths** are minute (< 25 μm) calcite objects produced by unicellular marine plants (golden-brown algae). The origin of nannoliths is uncertain, but these calcite bodies are associated with fossil coccolith assemblages in marine sediments and are also organically derived.

Calcareous nannofossils are an excellent biostratigraphic tool because of their rapid evolution and geographic dispersal (i.e., their entire life cycle is in the photic zone of the ocean) as well as their varied and distinct morphologies. The oldest known calcareous nannofossils are Late Triassic; they are a crucial microfossil group in calibrating the Jurassic–Holocene marine record. Relatively little has been published about the paleogeographic distributions of calcareous nannofossils; less is known about their exact paleoenvironmental preferences, although they have been shown occasionally to penetrate into shallow marine environments. Their main industrial application is their calibration to published time scales and sequence stratigraphic records, especially the association of high abundance with condensed marine sections.

The illustration below shows some typical calcareous nannofossils.

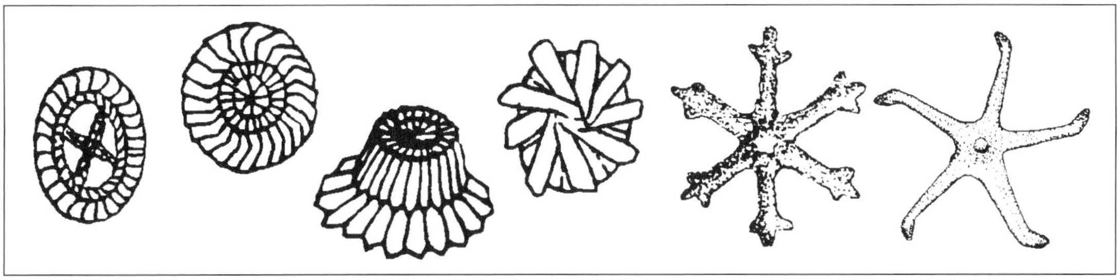

Figure 17–3.

Agglutinated Microfossils

Introduction

Agglutinated, or arenaceous, microfossils have tests (shells) constructed from sedimentary particles bound together by organic, calcareous, siliceous, or ferruginous cement. There is only one type of stratigraphically significant agglutinated microfossil: agglutinated, or arenaceous, foraminifera.

Agglutinated foraminifera

Agglutinated foraminifera are benthic microfossils found in rocks of Cambrian through Holocene age and in most marine and brackish environments, particularly in clastic facies. They construct their tests by gluing sedimentary grains together, in contrast to the other types of foraminifera, which secrete their tests. The sedimentary particles used by these forms may include silt or sand grains, glauconite, sponge spicules, or even other foraminiferal tests. Some species are highly selective in the material used and in its arrangement.

Although they are sometimes useful in age determination, agglutinated foraminifera are especially valuable as paleoenvironmental indicators because they are particularly characteristic of very shallow marine to brackish environments and very deep marine environments. Recent studies by Alve and Murray (1995) and Kaminski and Kuhnt (1995) suggest they may be useful in interpreting other paleoenvironments as well. Agglutinated foraminifera are the dominant and distinctive microfauna in Cretaceous and Tertiary flysch facies.

The color of agglutinated foraminifera has recently been shown to alter irreversibly with heating, both naturally within buried sediments and experimentally (see "Thermal Maturation").

The illustration below shows some typical agglutinated foraminifera.

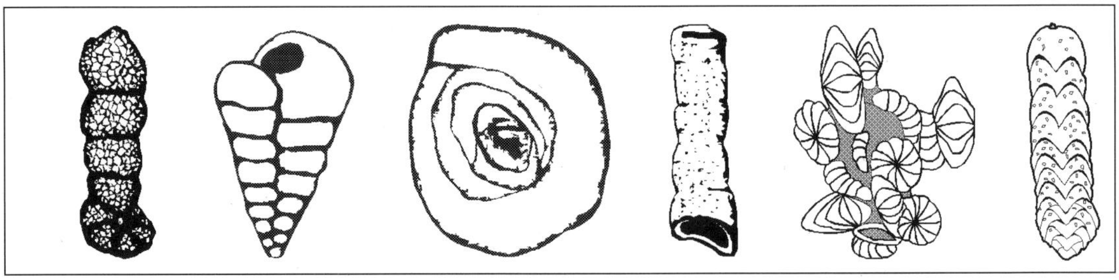

Figure 17–4.

Siliceous Microfossils

Introduction

Siliceous microfossils are protists with shells constructed of opaline (amorphous) silica. There is no intense dissolution of siliceous remains in the deep ocean. Sediments deposited below the carbonate compensation depth are commonly enriched in silica by removal of the carbonate, sometimes to the point of forming siliceous oozes. With subsequent remobilization of the silica, deep-sea cherts may be formed. Siliceous microfossils are subject to burial diagenesis and become rare at great well depths except when recrystallized, preserved in nodules or concretions, or replaced by pyrite or calcite.

There are three major groups of siliceous microfossils: radiolarians, diatoms, and silicoflagellates.

Radiolarians

Radiolarians are planktonic protists that occur primarily in open marine, deep-water settings. They are useful time indicators and are found in rocks of Cambrian to Holocene age. They may be the only common microfossils in abyssal environments, commonly forming radiolarian oozes. Radiolarian chert, the product of silica diagenesis, is fairly widespread in the geologic record. Radiolarians are common in some marine source rocks.

The illustration below shows some typical radiolarians.

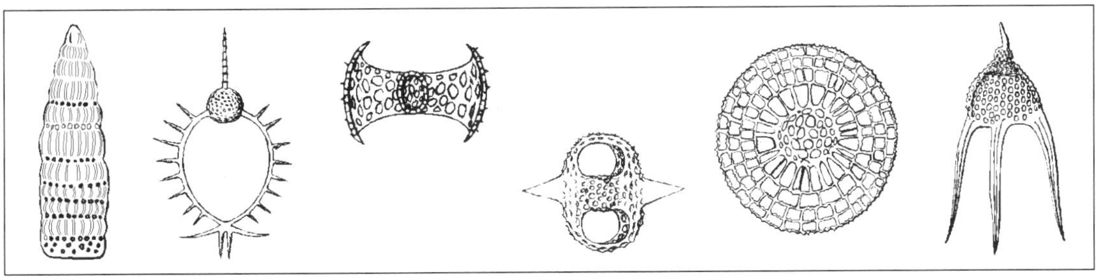

Figure 17–5.

Diatoms

Diatoms are photosynthesizing protists that occur in both marine and nonmarine environments. Marine diatoms range from Late Jurassic or Early Cretaceous to Holocene and are particularly useful for age and environmental determinations in the late Cenozoic. Nonmarine diatoms range from Eocene to Holocene and also are useful in the late Cenozoic. These microfossils can be a major rock-forming group, forming sedimentary rock (diatomites) consisting primarily of diatoms. Diatomaceous sediments, when altered by burial diagenesis, are converted to siliceous shale, porcelanite, and chert. Such rocks can serve as sources and fractured reservoirs for hydrocarbons (e.g., Monterey Formation of California). The changes in rock properties associated with silica diagenesis permit seismic definition of silica-phase transformation zones in the subsurface (e.g., bottom-simulating reflector).

Diatoms (continued)

The illustration below shows some typical diatoms.

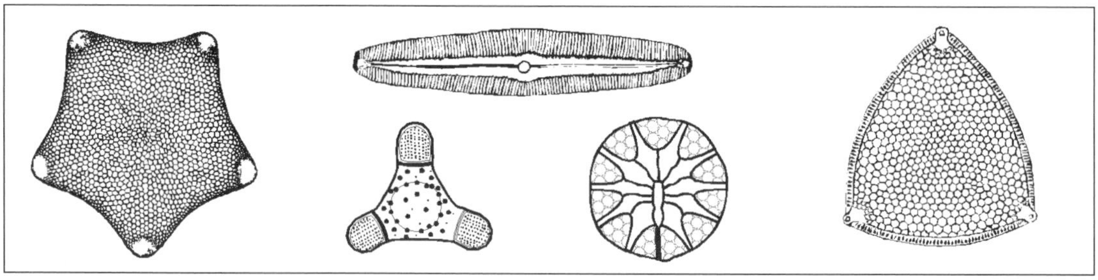

Figure 17–6.

Silicoflagellates

Silicoflagellates are another group of planktonic photosynthesizing marine protists; they commonly occur with diatoms. Silicoflagellates range in age from Cretaceous to Holocene. Although not as common as diatoms, they are useful time indicators, particularly in the late Cenozoic. As a group, they were much more abundant during the early and middle Cenozoic than today. They have been used to estimate marine paleotemperatures in the late Tertiary and Quaternary.

The illustration below shows some typical silicoflagellates

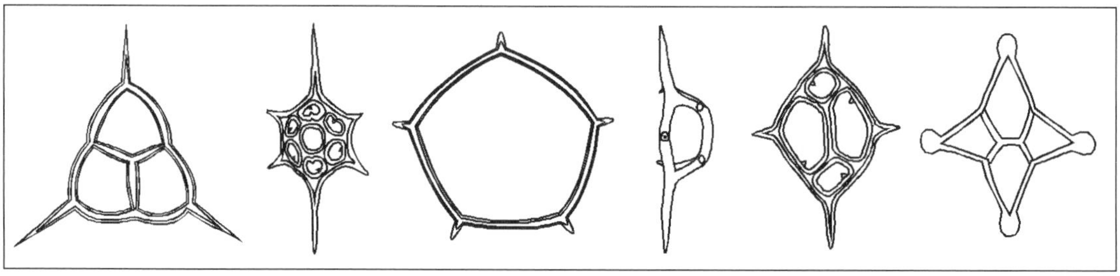

Figure 17–7.

Phosphatic Microfossils

Introduction

Phosphatic microfossils, notably conodonts, are composed of crystallites of calcium phosphate (apatite) embedded in an organic matrix. There is one type of stratigraphically significant phosphatic microfossils (conodonts); but fish teeth, of less practical utility, are found in some marine strata.

Conodonts

Conodonts are extinct toothlike microfossils composed of calcium phosphate whose biological affinities, while poorly understood, lie with chordates. Conodonts are widely distributed in marine rocks of Cambrian through Triassic age. They are excellent indicators of time and thermal maturity—especially in carbonates, where other methods of evaluating organic thermal maturity are less successful. Conodonts are commonly used as zonal indices for the latest Cambrian through Triassic because they were abundant, evolved rapidly, and were widespread geographically (Sweet, 1988). Although found in most marine rocks, conodonts are most efficiently recovered from the insoluble residues of carbonates dissolved in weak acids or from easily disaggregated shales.

Individual conodonts vary greatly in morphology, and taxonomy was originally based on the morphology of these individual specimens. While conodonts are common, the preserved remains of the soft-bodied animal that bore them are extremely rare. Based on a few preserved whole-animal specimens discovered recently (e.g., Gabbott et al., 1995), conodonts appear to have been located in the cephalic area and may have functioned as teeth (Purnell, 1995). However, the conodont animal apparently bore many conodonts of differing shapes and morphologies, based on the study of the very rare whole-animal specimens and rare bedding-plane groupings of conodonts representing individual animals. This recent information has led to more accurate multielement species concepts.

The illustration below shows some typical conodonts.

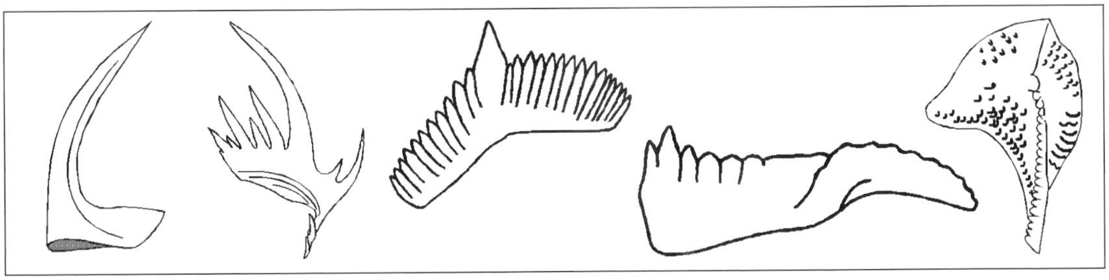

Figure 17–8.

Organic-Walled Microfossils

Introduction

Organic-walled microfossils are composed of entirely unmineralized proteinaceous material. There are four types of organic-walled microfossils: chitinozoans, spores and pollen, acritarchs, and dinoflagellates.

Chitinozoans

Chitinozoans are marine organic-walled, flask-shaped microfossils (50 µm to 2 mm in size) that occur in rocks of Ordovician to Devonian age. The biological affinities of chitinozoans are poorly understood, but they may be eggs of marine metazoans. They are excellent biostratigraphic indices and useful paleoenvironmental markers. They also have potential as thermal maturity indices (see "Thermal Maturity").

The illustration below shows some typical chitinozoans.

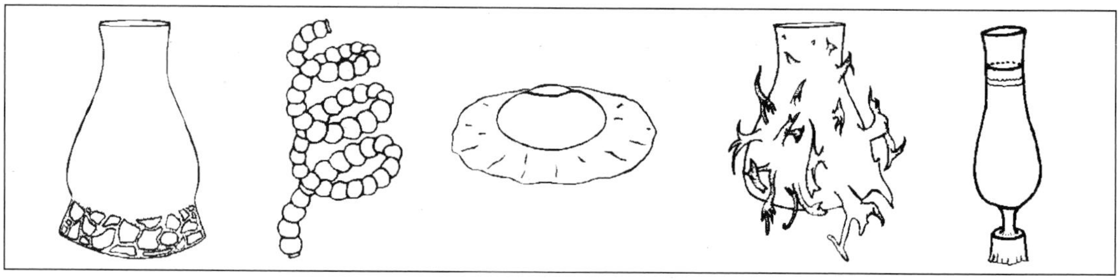

Figure 17–9.

Spores and pollen

Spores and pollen are parts of the reproductive cycle of plants and range in age from Late Ordovician and Carboniferous, respectively, to Holocene. Although land derived, the grains can be carried by wind and water currents into marine and nonmarine (particularly lacustrine and fluviatile) environments. The type and relative abundance of spores and pollen provide useful paleoenvironmental and paleoclimatic information, and they are widely used for basinal and regional stratigraphic correlation. Spores and pollen are also very useful in estimating thermal maturity, especially at temperature levels associated with hydrocarbon generation (see "Thermal Maturity").

The illustration below shows some typical spores and pollen. The first, second, and last drawings are pollen; the third is fungal (spore); and the fourth is fern (spore).

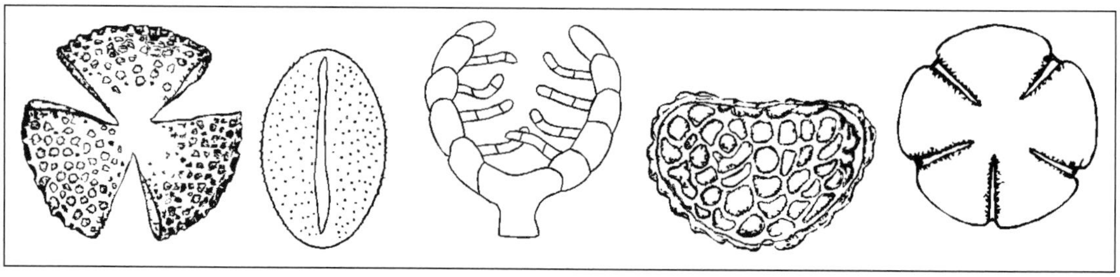

Figure 17–10.

Organic-Walled Microfossils, continued

Acritarchs

Acritarchs are marine microplankton of unknown biological affinity, ranging from Precambrian to Holocene in age. They are excellent biostratigraphic indices for Proterozoic through Devonian strata but are less important in the Mesozoic and Cenozoic. Acritarchs occur abundantly in fine-grained rocks and are geographically widespread. They have been used for paleoecology, paleogeography, and thermal maturity.

The illustration below shows some typical acritarchs.

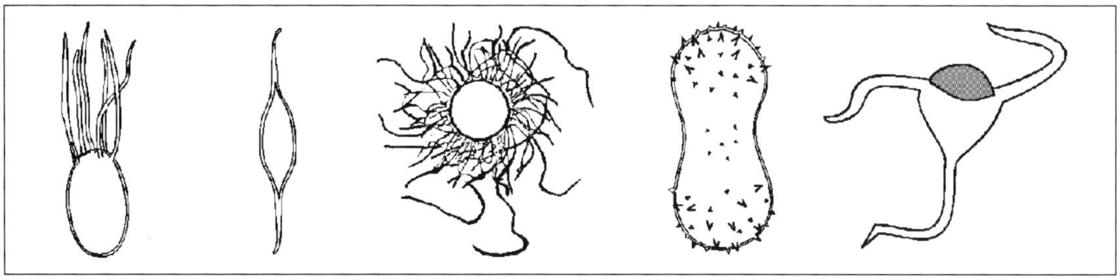

Figure 17–11.

Dinoflagellates

Dinoflagellates are the resting cysts of marine, unicellular red algae. They occur abundantly in Upper Triassic to Holocene sediments and are excellent biostratigraphic indices because of their rapid evolution and widespread geographic distribution. Dinoflagellate cysts occur predominantly in marine rocks but also are present in Cretaceous and Cenozoic lacustrine facies. The morphology and diversity of dinoflagellate assemblages can be used to differentiate marine environments.

The illustration below shows some typical dinoflagellates.

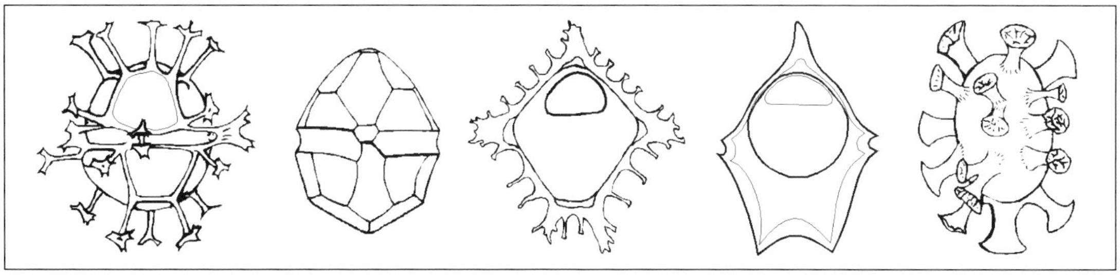

Figure 17–12.

Section B

Sample Collection and Treatment

Authors Brian J. O'Neill, Stephan A. Root, Kirby Rodgers, and Merrell A. Miller

Introduction The pattern of sample collection, the type of sample from which microfossils are recovered, and the sample processing technique strongly affect the utility of paleontologic data. This section discusses important considerations about sample collection and archiving and describes the manner in which paleontologic data are generated.

In this section The following topics are discussed in this section.

Sampling for Paleontology

Introduction

The quality of the interpretations made by a paleontologist can be strongly influenced by the quality of the samples and their preparation. Many factors, therefore, are affected by the actions of the sample collector and processor. Controlling those factors can have a significant impact on the utility and application of paleontologic data.

Drill cuttings

Most paleontologic analyses for the petroleum industry are performed on drill cuttings (fragments of rock cut by the drill bit and circulated to the surface by the mud system). Often, a sample of the drill cuttings is collected for each joint of drill pipe added to the drill string (i.e., every 30 ft, or 9 m) and represents an amalgamated sample of the rocks penetrated in that interval.

Advantages of using cuttings

Although the use of cuttings is less precise than conventional or sidewall cores, this method of sampling can yield surprisingly robust paleontologic results at a reasonable cost. Biostratigraphic analyses can be performed on cuttings at the well site, providing significant economic benefit in picking core points, casing points (which may prevent blowouts), and stopping points (to prevent unnecessary drilling below the objective section).

Disadvantages of using cuttings

Certain shortcomings are inherent in analyses based upon drill cuttings:

- Samples can contain a mix of the different lithologies penetrated.
- Downhole contamination (caving from rocks above the sample interval) can occur.
- Stratigraphic resolution can be no finer than the sampling interval.
- Lost-circulation material added to the mud system can so dilute the system that little or no formation material is contained in the "sample."

Sampling program

To obtain good samples for paleontologic studies, the following points in the sampling program should be considered.

- Begin in the planning stage and work with the engineer/geologist in charge. Clearly define the responsibility for sample collection, and specify the importance of accurate collection and labeling. Rig personnel/mud loggers have been known to gather many samples at one time but to label them as having come from different depths.
- Plan the sampling program to include fine-grained rocks because lithologies conducive to the recovery of microfossils are normally not reservoir facies.
- Specify depths (beginning and end) at which cuttings should be collected.
- Specify frequency of cuttings collection. Commonly a sample is collected every 10 ft (3 m) and composited into 30-ft (9-m) intervals for each joint of drill pipe added to the drill string (i.e., every 30 ft, or 9 m). However, the geologist can specify a different interval if necessary.
- Clearly label samples with waterproof marker as to whether they have been "lagged" (i.e., depths corrected for circulation time).

Sampling program (continued)

- Clearly define the responsibility for sample collection and specify the importance of accurate collection and labeling.
- Adjust sampling size to the fossil group being used. The following chart gives rough approximations of the quantity needed.

Fossil Group	Quantity
Nannofossils	pea to teaspoon size
Foraminifera	1–2 cups
Palynomorphs	1–2 cups
Conodonts	5 cups

Pitfalls to avoid

To obtain good samples for paleontologic studies, several pitfalls should be avoided when collecting samples:

- Avoid reusing drilling mud from other wells to preclude contamination with microfossils from the previous drill site.
- Remember that drilling muds made from naturally occurring materials may include microfossils (e.g., pollen and spores in lignite, dinoflagellates in bentonites). If unrecognized, these can distort the biostratigraphic signal.
- Monitor the mechanical effects of different bit types. In particular, diamond and composite (polycrystalline diamond composite, or PDC) bits can metamorphose the cuttings, destroying the fossils contained in them.

Laboratory techniques

Finally, workers must use proper handling techniques in the laboratory to obtain good samples for paleontologic studies:

- Use the least destructive technique for processing samples. This can be accomplished by mechanical (detergent, Varsol®, blender, etc.) and chemical (H_2O_2, various acids, bases, etc.) techniques. Overprocessing damages or destroys fossils, reducing the usefulness of the sample. Indurated rocks may require thin section.
- Carefully monitor the laboratory sample processing techniques that extract microfossils from the sediment. To obtain high-quality residues, try the following:
  - — Stain sieves between samples with methyl blue.
  - — Clean utensils between samples.
  - — Clearly label containers.
  - — Eliminate contamination from sediment "popping" during boiling by appropriate vessel spacing.

For specific processing techniques, see Kummel and Raup (1965) or Feldmann et al. (1989).

Sampling for Paleontology, continued

Other sample types

Despite the emphasis on cuttings, other sample types are used for paleontologic analysis. Cores are particularly useful in carbonate plays. Analysis of sidewall cores (especially of nonreservoir rock) can reliably identify lowest occurrence horizons because they avoid sampling caved material. The rise of international exploration has led to increased analysis of outcrop material; outcrop samples should be unweathered and "clean" to avoid contamination and leaching. Megafossils, which can be collected in many outcrop sections, may define the known local stratigraphic framework.

Sample preparation

A wide variety of techniques is available for preparing samples for paleontologic analysis. Most of these involve methods of freeing fossils from sediment and concentrating them for ease of examination. The choice of preparation process depends upon the lithology and the type of fossil; the essentially mechanical techniques used to extract foraminifera from clastic sediments are totally different from the chemical methods used to free palynomorphs or to extract conodonts from limestone. Kummel and Raup (1965) and Feldmann et al. (1989) describe many of the preparation techniques in detail.

Approaches to Data Generation

Basic paleontologic data

The basic data for applied paleontology consist of records of species occurrences in samples. Sample data can be arrayed in stratigraphic sequences for biostratigraphic analysis or in a geographic array for evaluating paleoenvironments. The two approaches are frequently combined. In order of increasing precision, fossil occurrences can be expressed in terms of the following:

- Records of species present or absent
- Relative abundances, usually expressed as categories (e.g., rare, common, abundant)
- Actual counts of individual specimens for each species

Other types of data

Paleontologic data of other sorts may be useful in applied studies. These include, among others, assigned color scale values for evaluating thermal maturation based upon conodonts or organic-walled microfossils (see "Thermal Maturation"); vitrinite reflectance (R_o) values; and observations on, or measurements of, significant specific morphologic characters of the fossils (see "Morphometric and Particle Analysis").

Sample and Data Archiving

Samples

Properly preparing and cataloging samples and slides (e.g., foraminiferal, nannofossil, and palynology slides; thin sections) for long-term storage is important; it prevents deterioration and ensures availability for future use. Large numbers of samples and slides stored in a centralized facility are most efficiently handled with a computerized inventory system. This permits easy inventory documentation and assists in rapid sample retrieval.

Data

Although interpretations are the desired results of paleontological analyses, it is important to preserve the raw data upon which these interpretations are based: species identification and abundances. Data entry systems designed for personal computers have proliferated, but ideally the data should be stored on a larger computer capable of searching and comparing large volumes of data. Relational databases are well suited for this task, and many of the major oil companies maintain large electronic databases that allow manipulation, mapping, and graphic display of these data.

Section C
Stratigraphic and Geographic Distribution of Fossils

Authors Gregg H. Blake, Allen R. Ormiston, and Robert W. Scott

Introduction

In essence, paleontologic analysis is based on knowing the distribution of fossil species in time and space. All fossil species persisted for a limited geologic duration and were restricted in habitat to specific paleoenvironments characterized by a range of ecological parameters such as temperature, salinity, dissolved oxygen, and food availability. Because several important parameters vary somewhat systematically with water depth in marine environments, benthic fossils commonly are used to estimate paleobathymetry for basin modeling and sequence stratigraphy. This chapter discusses the temporal and paleogeographic distribution of fossils and the effects introduced by postmortem redistribution.

In this section

The following topics are discussed in this section.

Temporal and Environmental Distribution of Microfossils

Introduction

Since a species persists only for a limited amount of geologic time and only in a specific environment, microfossils can be used to date the rocks in which they are found (biostratigraphy) and to indicate the environment in which the sediment was deposited (paleoecology).

Biostratigraphic utility of microfossil groups

The chart below shows the geologic periods in which various microfossil groups existed and those periods for which the groups are most useful for dating.

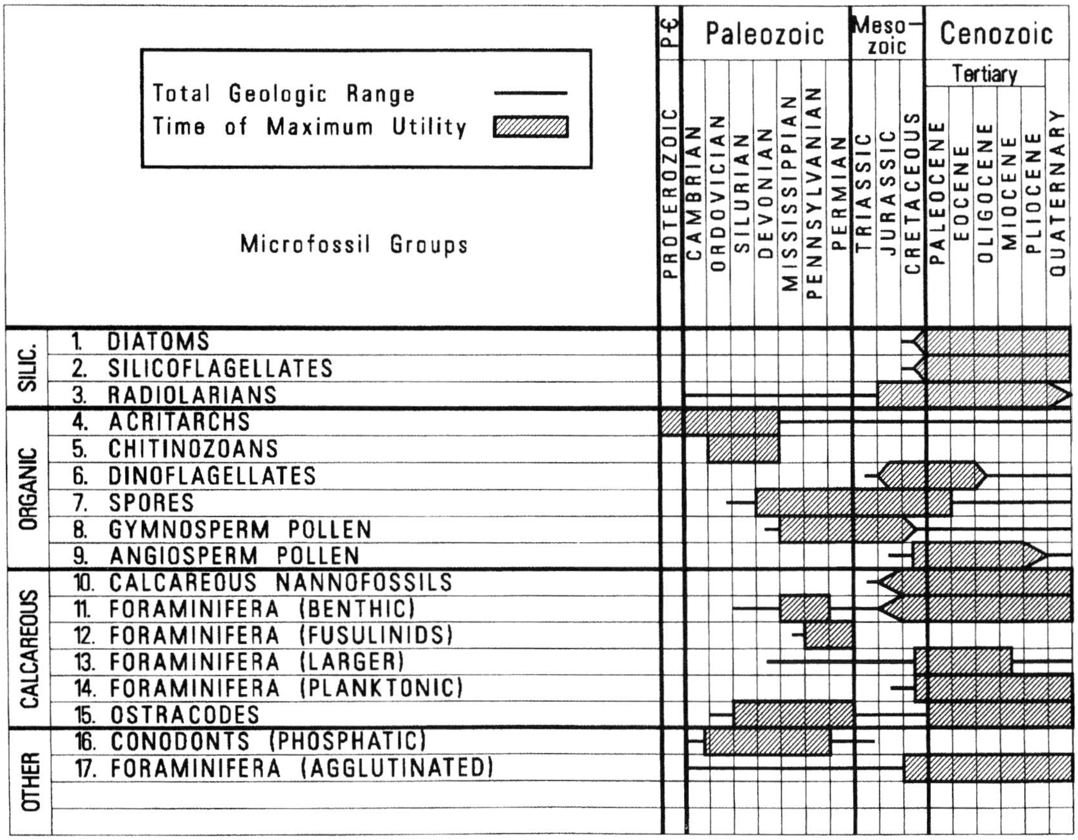

Environmental distribution of microfossil groups

The chart below shows the paleoenvironments of various microfossil groups. The width of the bar represents the relative importance of each microfossil group.

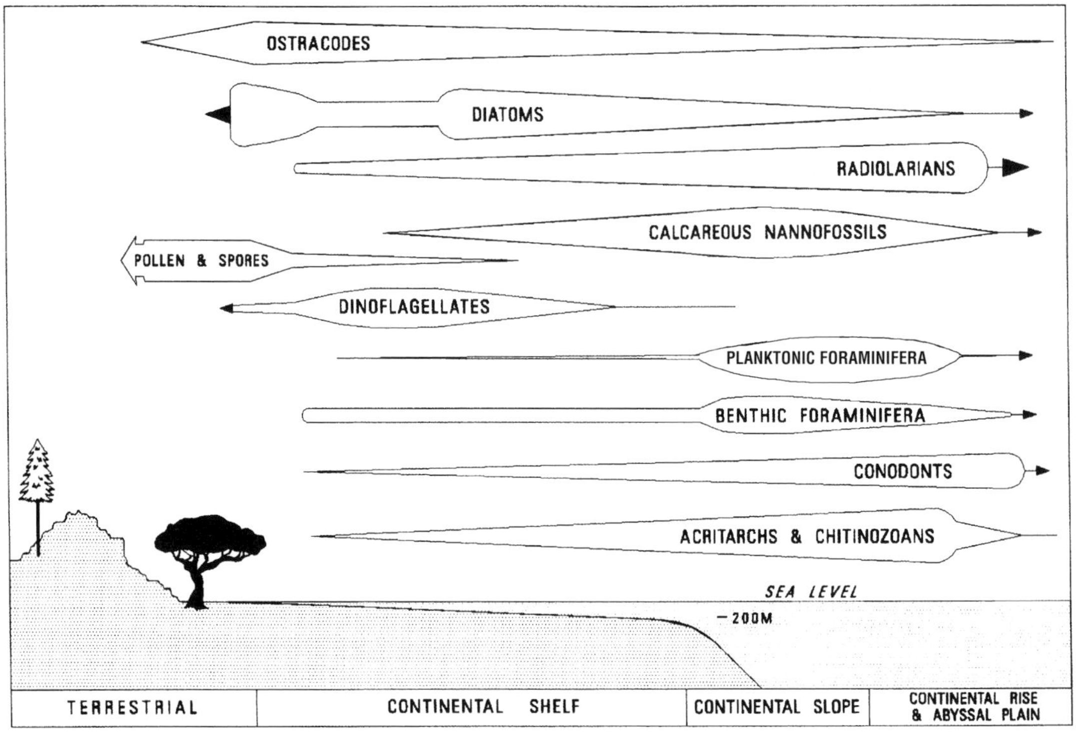

Figure 17–13.

Biogeography

Definition

Biogeography is the study of patterns of the spatial distribution of organisms and their changes with time.

Applications

Major paleogeographic and climatic shifts through the Phanerozoic have produced frequent changes in biogeographic patterns of plant and animal distribution. The resulting biogeographic arrays can be used in two ways:

- To constrain paleogeographic reconstructions
- To interpret the nature of climatic change

Paleogeography

Paleogeographic reconstructions based on geologic or geophysical evidence can be tested using patterns in the distribution of organisms. Analyzing the biogeographic patterns of fossils provides a basis for the proposal of new, and the evaluation of existing, paleogeographic reconstructions.

Examples of paleogeography

The occurrence of Early Triassic reptiles and amphibians of the *Lystrosaurus* fauna in Antarctica, southern Africa, and India is strong confirmation that the Early Triassic Gondwana reconstruction, which placed Antarctica in contact with southern Africa and India, must be correct. Terrestrial vertebrates require dry-land connections to complete such a pervasive migration (Colbert, 1972).

Australia's eventual separation from Gondwana to become an island continent about 43 Ma is also reflected in biogeographic patterns. The fossils and living marsupials of Australia are significantly different from those elsewhere because they evolved in isolation (Jardine and McKenzie, 1972).

Climate

The distribution of benthic marine organisms can help us constrain latitudinal sea-surface temperature gradients and quantitative paleoclimate models.

Examples of climate

The total paleolatitudinal range of ancient reefs has been used as a guide to rate of change of sea-surface temperature with paleolatitude. This is based on a broad analogy with the distribution of modern reef corals. Because of the Late Ordovician Gondwana glaciation, the Early Silurian reefs are asymmetrically distributed (Copper and Brunton, 1990). They did not reach as far south as 30°S paleolatitude but extended north of 30°N, reflecting the existence of a colder south polar region in the Early Silurian. This conclusion is also supported by the development of a cold-water *Clarkeia* province in the Early Silurian of Gondwana (Cocks, 1972), which is supplanted at lower latitudes by other faunal provinces.

Published interpretations of interior Australian surface temperatures during the Permian, reaching values as high as 50°C, cannot be reconciled with the existence of terrestrial vertebrates in the same area because such temperatures would have been lethal. A reassessment of this quantitative model is needed.

Problems

Problems such as the following can adversely affect biogeographic interpretations:

- Inconsistent taxonomic identifications by practitioners, impairing the validity of the basic data
- Difficulty in distinguishing local differences in the composition of fossil communities from those produced by geographic separation
- Development of accreted terranes, which may tectonically juxtapose contrasting biogeographic entities that were not naturally contiguous

Paleoclimatology

Definition

Paleoclimate can be operationally defined as those factors of climate, weather, and atmospheric and oceanic circulation that influence biotic distribution and the rate and locus of clastic, evaporite, and carbonate deposition.

Utility of fossils in paleoclimatology

Fossils have been used in an *ad hoc* manner to interpret climate since the beginnings of geology as a science, but a systematic methodology for using fossils to assess climate is still lacking. The following elements can contribute to such a methodology:

- Biostratigraphic correlation
- Adaptive morphology of animals and plants
- Isotopic "paleothermometers"
- Quantitative paleoclimate models

Biostratigraphic correlation

Because climate is a global phenomenon, the various lithofacies and biofacies that reflect climate in the time interval of interest must be correlated accurately. Climates may change abruptly, and biostratigraphy provides the only practical means to demonstrate the contemporaneity, or lack of it, of contrasting climates.

Adaptive morphology

Living organisms adapted to distinctive climates or environments may have distinctive characteristics, or **morphologies**. Recognizing these features in fossils can provide information about ancient climates.

For example, many plants of the tropical rain forest have drip points on their leaves to facilitate rainwater drainage; similar features on fossil leaves can be taken to suggest a similar paleoenvironment.

This approach can be used even when the significance of the adaptive form is unclear; Wolfe (1979), for example, suggests that quantification of angiosperm leaf characteristics (i.e., the percentage of entire-margined leaves) helps us determine Tertiary temperatures to within 1°C.

Isotopic paleotemperature

An analysis of the ratios of oxygen isotopes in fossil shell material yields estimates of ancient temperatures. Oceanic paleotemperatures based on analysis of fossil calcareous foraminiferal tests are widely used to interpret Cenozoic paleoclimate and paleoceanography (see "Stable Isotope Stratigraphy").

Quantitative paleoclimate models

Quantitative paleoclimate models often produce unique solutions to the paleoclimatic interpretation of geologic and paleontologic data.

A quantitative community climate model (CCM_1) at the National Center for Atmospheric Research was used by Amoco Production Research to investigate possible causes of Late Devonian extinctions. The results (Ormiston and Klapper, 1992) suggest two things:

1. There was no perennial snow cover and, hence, no glaciation in the Austral regions.
2. Simulated sea-surface temperatures in the tropics ranged from 27°–34°C—high enough to kill reefs (Thompson and Newton, 1989).

These results support a climatic cause for the extinctions.

Taphonomy and Provenance

Introduction

Because the hard parts of dead organisms may act as sedimentary particles, fossils provide evidence of sedimentary processes, tectonic events, sediment source areas, burial processes, and diagenesis. Reworked fossils, however, may be difficult to recognize in cuttings or even in cores and outcrops.

Definition

Taphonomy is the study of the effect of sedimentary processes and diagenesis on the postmortem redistribution and preservation of the hard parts of organisms. A taphonomic study can help identify variations in *provenance*, or source area, of fossil-bearing sediments (Lawrence, 1979).

Clues to reworking

Several characteristics of fossil deposits are clues to erosion, transport, and reworking of older fossils into younger basin fill (Brett, 1990):

- Presence of species whose stratigraphic ranges do not overlap
- Presence of fossils from significantly different environments
- Significant differences in the quality and mode of fossil preservation
- Presence of organic matter with more than one level of maturation
- Presence of fossils in "transported" lithologies (e.g., turbidites)
- Significant differences in the mineralogy and alteration of hard parts
- Orientation of shells, particularly of megafossils, reflecting displacement from the original habitat

Applications of taphonomy

The recognition of reworked fossils helps to (1) assess reservoir continuity and (2) interpret depositional models of the source area and of the depositional environment of the source rock. Applications include the following:

- Recognizing unconformities
- Recognizing condensed sections
- Identifying facies and depositional environments
- Determining ages of sediment source terranes
- Determining timing of uplift and erosion
- Interpreting contemporaneous geology of source areas
- Recognizing contamination by drilling mud or cavings
- Generating paleocurrent models for sand transport

Section D
Applications

Authors

Sheila C. Barnette, Gregg H. Blake, Denise M. Butler, Julie A. d'Ablaing, Thomas D. Demchuk, Roy J. Enrico, Martin B. Farley, Robert L. Fleisher, Lori B. Glassgold, Rome G. Lytton III, Peter P. McLaughlin, Hilary C. Olson, Brian J. O'Neill, Mark A. Pasley, Robert W. Scott, Jeffrey A. Stein, Gordon W. Wood

Introduction

Paleontologists have traditionally used fossil data to provide information about the relative age, stratigraphic correlation, and paleoenvironment (notably paleobathymetry) of sedimentary strata. The importance of these tasks remains high, but new approaches and technology have extended the applicability of biostratigraphic data to analyzing thermal maturation and sequence stratigraphy.

In this section

The following topics are discussed in this section.

Biostratigraphic Correlation and Age Determination

Correlation of "tops"

Species extinctions, often referred to as "tops," are used as horizons of correlation. The first downhole occurrence ("+" in the illustration below) in a well section is the datum most commonly used. The inception ("*" in the illustration below), or lowest occurrence of a species or lineage, is a reliable datum only in core or outcrop samples because caving is virtually unavoidable in cutting samples; however, it can help refine the stratigraphy. The overlap of species extinctions and inceptions allows the development of range zones (see figure below), which can be correlated from site to site.

A biostratigraphic zone is a body of rock defined or characterized by its fossil content (North American Commission on Stratigraphic Nomenclature, 1983). The clustering of fossil extinctions often represents missing or condensed sections. Correlation of tops is the most rapid and economical biostratigraphic technique and is the one most commonly used.

The illustration below shows how the overlap of species' ranges (between inception and extinction) is used to define zones.

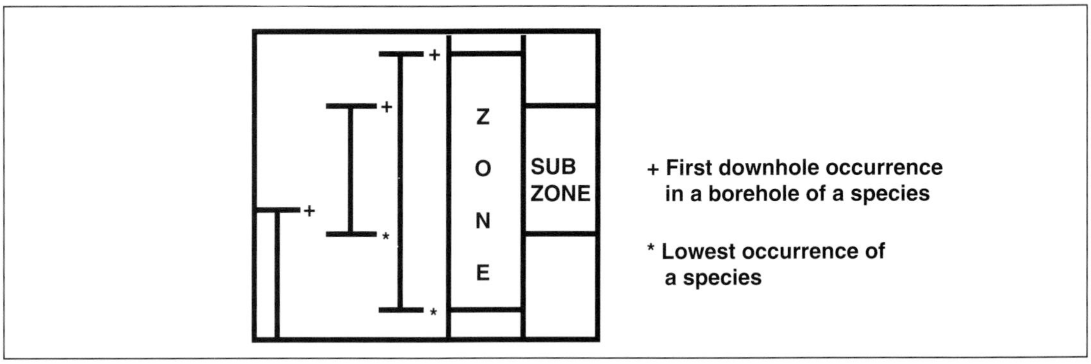

Figure 17–14.

Planktonic vs. benthic "tops"

Planktonic (floating) and nektonic (swimming) organisms are generally less affected by local environmental factors such as water depth, physical obstacles, or changes in substrate than are benthic species (bottom dwellers). This characteristic makes the fossils of planktonic forms—particularly calcareous nannofossils, planktonic foraminifera, dinoflagellates, and graptolites—and nektonic organisms such as conodonts excellent regional and even worldwide time markers in marine strata. Summaries of zonations based on the ranges of planktonic microorganisms include Blow (1979), Kennett and Srinivasan (1983), Bolli et al. (1985), Berggren and Miller (1988), and Berggren et al. (1995).

Benthic taxa are most useful for detailed local correlations and paleoenvironments. Many are too environmentally sensitive, however, to be good regional markers. Distribution of benthic forms is frequently restricted by basin configuration or other barriers to migration.

Changes in abundance or composition

Changes in the abundance or species composition of fossil assemblages within a biostratigraphic zone are useful in refining correlations.

The illustration below shows how variations in the relative proportion of individual species within assemblages can be used to characterize correlatable fossil "populations."

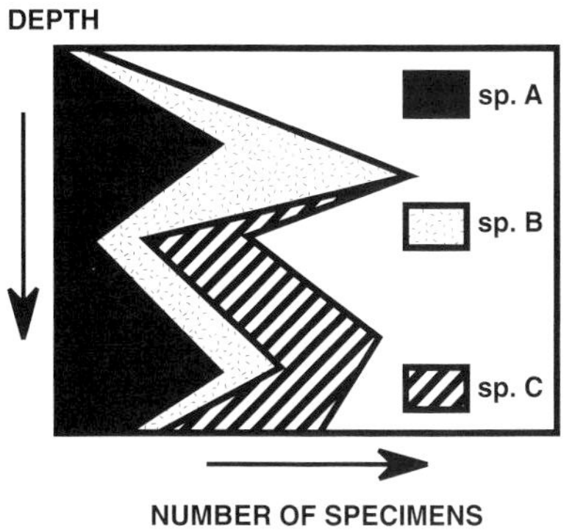

Figure 17–15.

Ratios of in situ vs. reworked species

Ratios or percentages of in situ vs. reworked calcareous nannofossil or palynomorph species may differentiate among distinct sediment packages.

The figure below shows how a comparison of the presence and abundance of different components of the assemblage (e.g., in situ vs. reworked faunas and floras) may enhance local correlations and help us identify sediment source. Generally, where in situ fossils are relatively abundant, reworked fossils are less common.

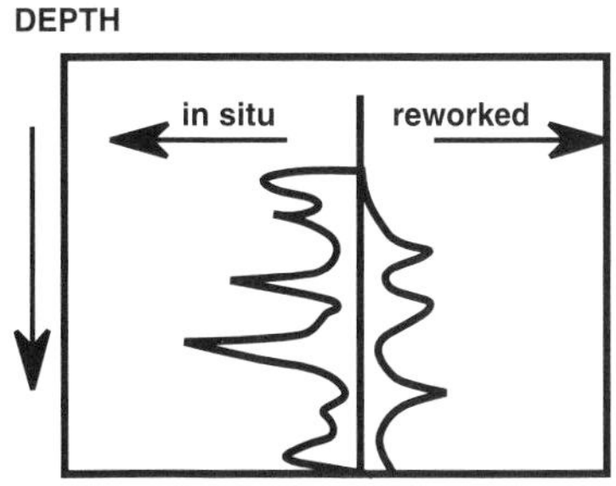

Figure 17–16.

High-resolution biostratigraphy

High-resolution methods are quantitative approaches that, in addition to species ranges, use subtle paleontological changes (e.g., fossil abundance and diversity peaks). These data can be generated from actual counts of species abundance or from estimates of relative abundance. This detailed, time-consuming approach provides closely spaced correlations that are particularly effective for sequence stratigraphy studies (Armentrout et al., 1990), local or field correlation of reservoir units, or any problem where detailed resolution is vital. The use of multiple fossil groups in the same sections can greatly increase both the resolution and the level of confidence in the analysis.

Correlation of assemblages

In the absence of index fossils (e.g., within areas of high clastic dilution or when extending a chronostratigraphic horizon across environmental boundaries), correlation methods other than the traditional use of fossil extinctions play an important role. These frequently involve characteristics of the assemblage as a whole:

- Changes in the abundance or species composition of fossil assemblages within a biostratigraphic zone
- Ratios or percentages of in situ vs. reworked calcareous nannofossil or palynomorph species

An example of the first type is the thin interval in the Lower Pliocene characterized by high abundances of the planktonic foraminiferal genus *Sphaeroidinellopsis* spp., which represents a set of paleoceanographic conditions that can be correlated in many areas of the Mediterranean (Cita, 1975; Iaccarino, 1985).

Assemblage data can also help us recognize diagnostic elements of stratigraphic sequences.

Absolute ages

Determining absolute ages through physical or chemical techniques such as radioisotope analysis, magnetostratigraphy, or fission-track dating is not, by itself, a paleontologic application. Approximate absolute ages can be derived for fossil assemblages in strata; a number of time scales have been published relating absolute age to the established sequence of (primarily planktonic) fossil events. Three of the most commonly used scales are Berggren et al. (1985a,b; 1992; 1995), Haq et al. (1988), and Harland et al. (1990).

Time scales are revised and updated in the literature as new data become available (e.g., Berggren et al., 1995; Gradstein et al., 1995). These time scales differ somewhat in the absolute ages assigned to the various fossil events (inceptions and extinctions). In most applications, the consistent use of a single time scale is more important than the choice of scale. Although absolute ages are not necessarily critical for well correlations, they are vital in studies that rely on determinations of geologic rates.

Paleoenvironmental Analysis

Introduction

The aim of paleoenvironmental analysis, or paleoecology, is to reconstruct the biological, chemical, and physical nature of the environment at the collection site at the time of deposition, based on the rock's paleontological record. Information can be reconstructed for depositional environments, paleobathymetry, positions of ancient shorelines, paleoclimate, degree of oxygenation of the bottom water and sediment, and salinity of the waters (see "Paleoclimatology," "Paleobathymetry," and "Palynofacies and Kerogen Analysis").

Procedures

The three basic steps involved in paleoenvironmental analysis are data collection, data interpretation, and integration with other data sources.

Data collection

The kind of paleoenvironmental question to be answered determines the type of paleontological data that must be collected. The following table shows some questions asked and the data needed to answer them.

What was the . . . ?	Data needed
Depositional environment/shoreline position	Presence, abundance, and relative species proportions of palynomorphs, foraminifera, and ostracodes
Paleoclimate/paleoceanography	Species distribution and abundance of climatically or oceanographically sensitive fossils: calcareous nannofossils, planktonic and benthic foraminifera, spores and pollen (e.g., bisaccate conifer pollen, tropical angiosperm pollen), and oxygen isotope analysis of foraminifera
Oxygen and salinity	Occurrence and species distribution of foraminifera, ostracodes, diatoms, and salinity-sensitive algae (e.g., *Botryococcus, Pediastrum*)

Data interpretation

Paleoenvironmental knowledge is established by (1) using the known tolerances of taxa or their nearest living relatives in modern environments and (2) studying the distribution of fossil taxa in well-controlled ancient examples. The data are interpreted on the basis of this established paleoenvironmental knowledge.

Examples of data interpretation

Traverse (1988) provides a general review of the methods of palynological paleoenvironmental analysis. He discusses the use of palynomorphs as paleoclimate indicators and the methods by which sedimentation of palynomorph assemblages help infer depositional environments in both marine and nonmarine settings. Additionally, Lipps (1993) provides a similar general review of paleoenvironmental approaches for micropaleontology. Following are three examples of paleoenvironmental information deduced from micropaleontology.

Species distribution and oxygen concentration

Lagoe (1987) recognizes four biofacies of benthic foraminiferal species in the upper Miocene Stevens Sandstone of the southern San Joaquin Valley. He demonstrates that the biofacies distribution was largely controlled by changes in oxygen concentration caused by fluctuations in the position and intensity of low-oxygen water within the oxygen minimum zone.

In the figure below, biofacies associations reflect different and distinctive populations living in different paleoenvironments. Biofacies are arranged from left to right in order of inferred increasing oxygen concentration. The stratigraphic distribution strongly suggests systematic shifts in oxygen concentration.

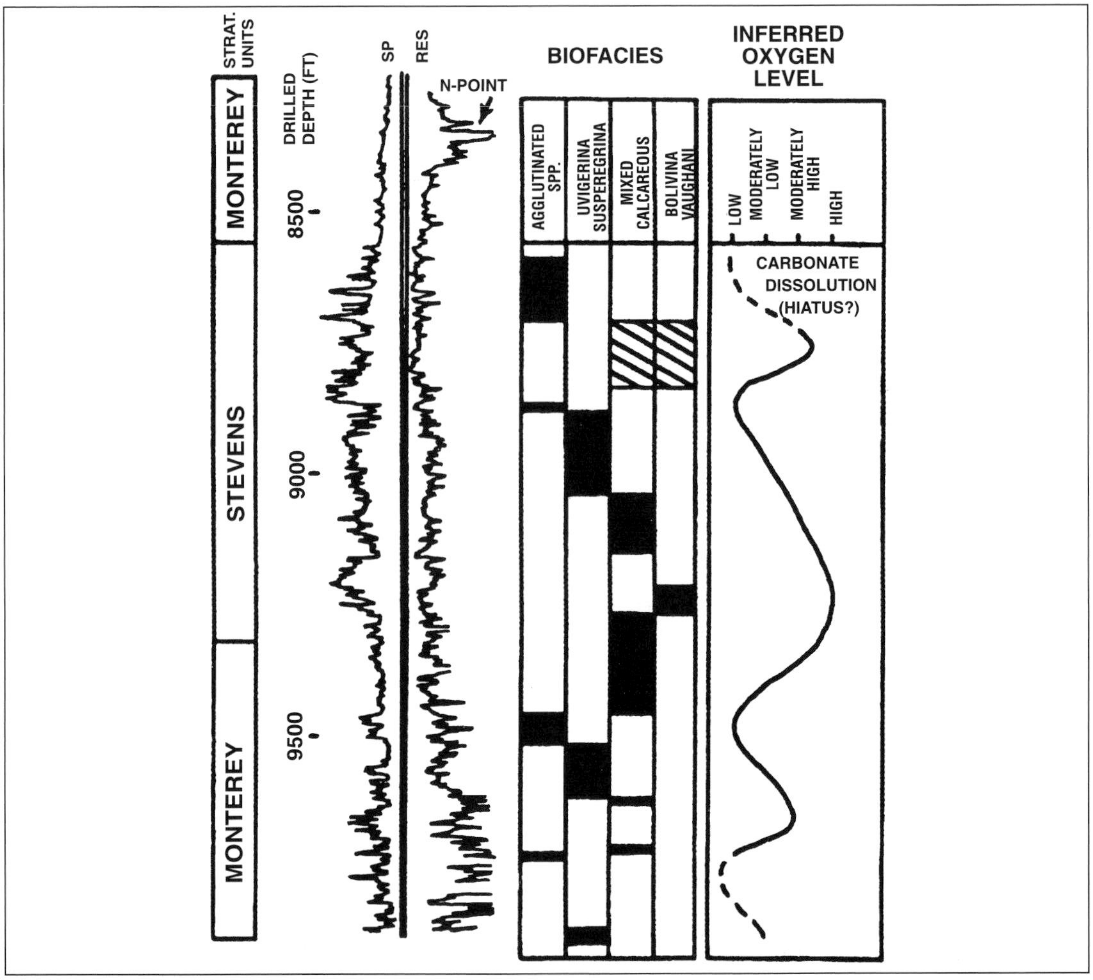

Figure 17–17. From Lagoe, 1989; courtesy Palaios.

Test shape and oxygen concentration

Test morphologies of some closely related species of the foraminiferal genus *Bolivina* differ in patterns apparently related to oxygen concentration (Douglas, 1979, 1981) in modern environments along the California continental margin. Compressed, relatively large species (*B. argentea*) are typical of low-oxygen environments.

In the figure below, species inhabiting high-oxygen environments (e.g., shelf depth) are small, prolate forms; those in low-oxygen environments (e.g., basin depths) are large, lanceolate forms.

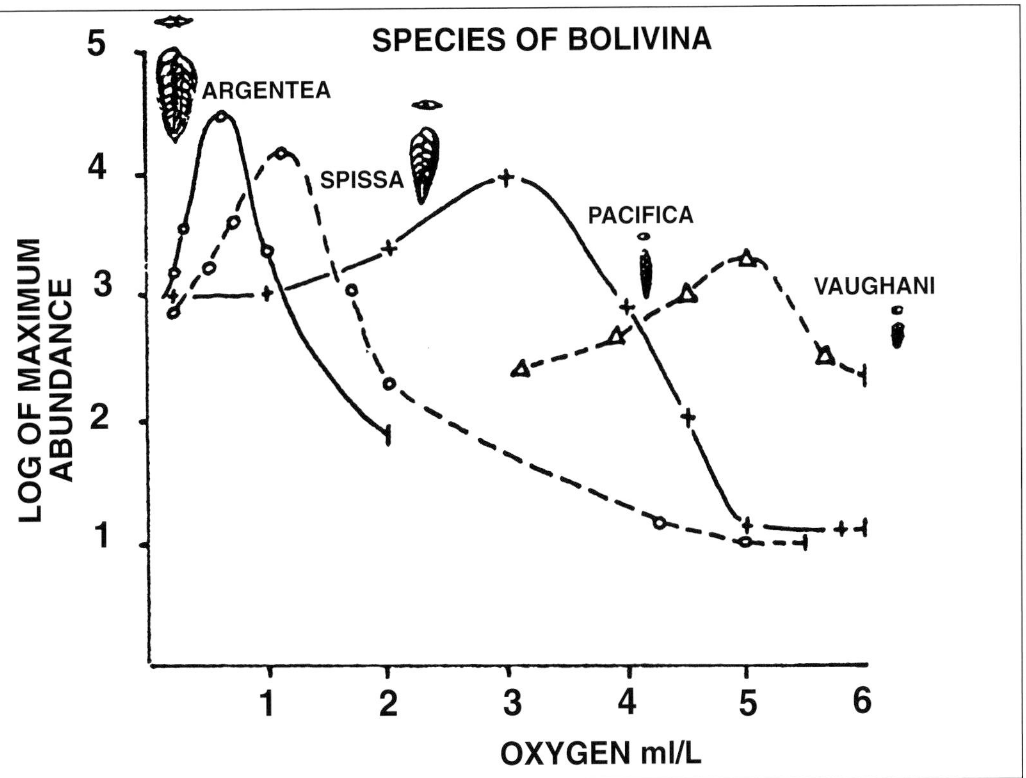

Figure 17–18. From Douglas, 1979; courtesy SEPM.

Distribution of palynomorph types

Whittaker et al. (1992) provide an industrial example in the Brent Group (Jurassic), North Sea, in which the distribution of palynomorph types is used to infer the depositional environments and extent of delta progradation during brief intervals of the Jurassic. The figure below illustrates the nonmarine (fluvial and marsh), lagoon, barrier, and marine environments and the interpreted sediment transport direction (large arrow) during one time interval. This information can help identify regions of greater potential for fluvial reservoir sands.

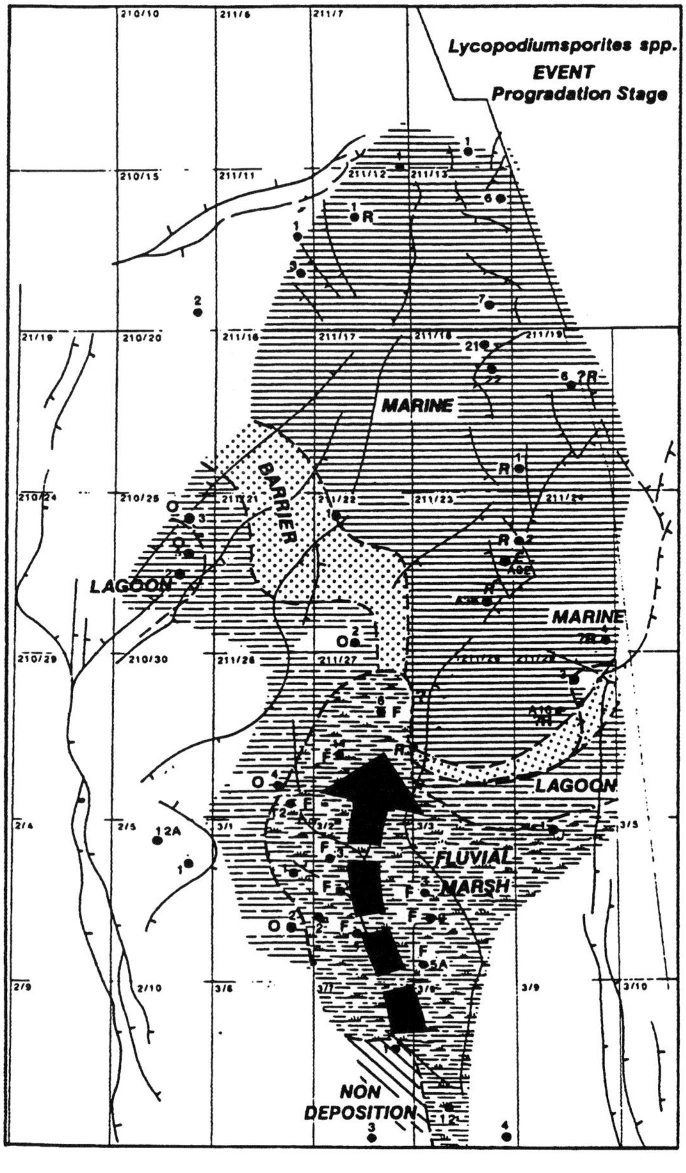

Figure 17–19. From Whittaker et al., 1992; courtesy Geological Society.

Oboh (1992) develops a paleoenvironmental model of Middle Miocene reservoir units from the Niger Delta, which uses palynomorphs and organic matter to interpret more precisely the depositional environments. This improves the understanding of the lateral continuity of the reservoir and its susceptibility to diagenetic changes.

Integrated paleoenvironmental interpretation

Figure 17–20 shows an integrated paleoenvironmental interpretation of the E2.0 reservoir (Middle Miocene, Niger Delta). Lithofacies range from pebbly sandstones (S1) to mudstones (M2). The palynofacies are composed of the following substances:

(A) Wood and amorphous organic matter

(B) Black debris (intertinite) and land plant resins

(C) Wood with slight amounts of amorphous organic matter

(D) Black debris with wood and amorphous organic matter

Integrated paleoenvironmental interpretation (continued)

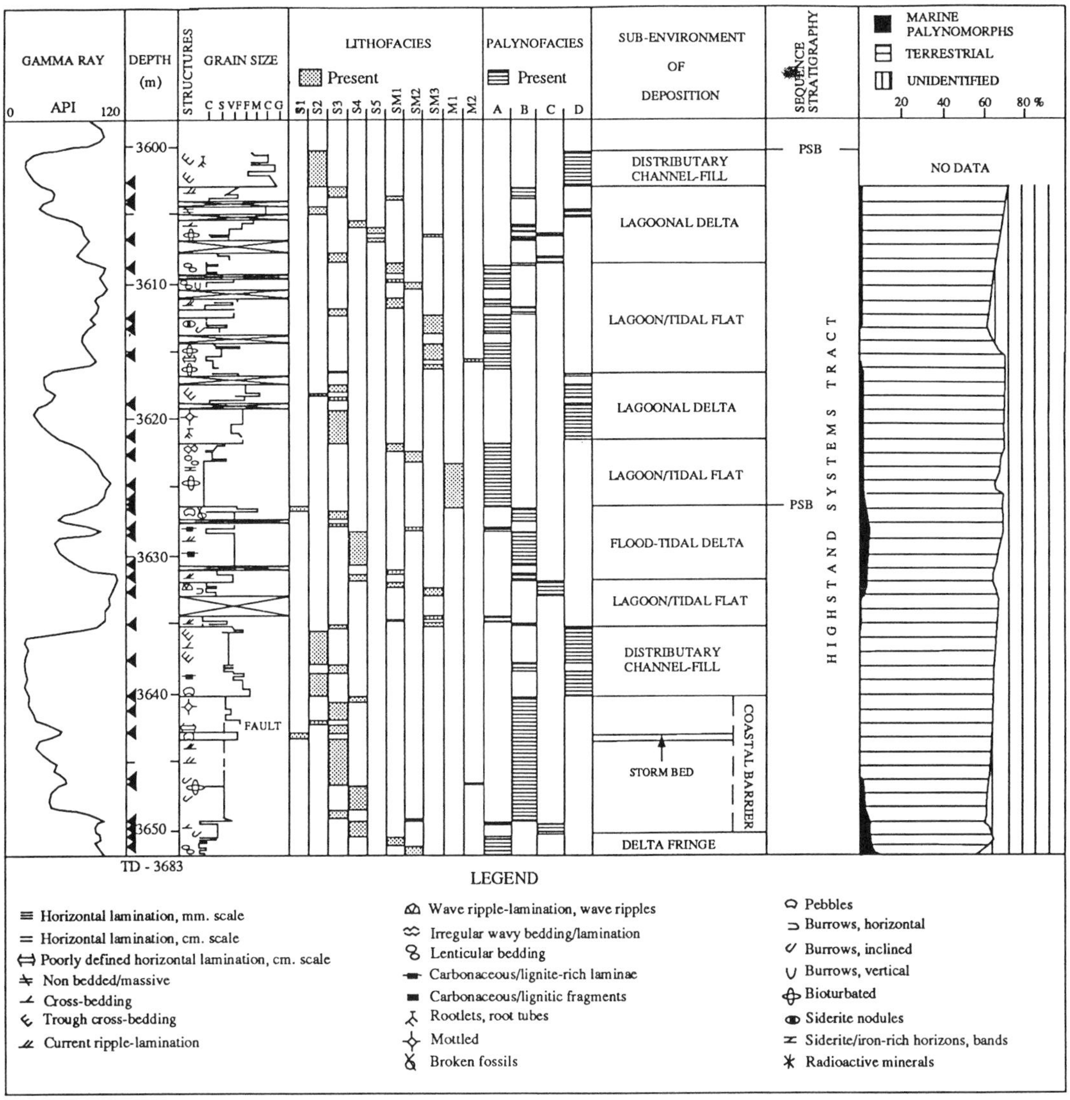

Figure 17–20. From Oboh, 1992; courtesy Palaios.

The paleoenvironmental interpretation should be integrated with interpretations based on other data sources (e.g., sedimentology, well log analysis, seismic) and plotted on wells or cross sections.

Limitations

Paleoenvironmental analysis can be limited by the ambiguity of the paleoecological significance of the fossils recorded. In general, reconstructions of paleoenvironment become less precise and less reliable with increasing geologic age as the affinities of ancient to modern forms become very distant.

Paleobathymetry

Introduction

Paleobathymetry—the determination of ancient water depth (paleodepth)—is the paleoenvironmental interpretation most widely used in petroleum exploration because of its value in determining the depositional history of a basin. Benthic foraminifera are usually used for this purpose. As bottom dwellers, they provide information about conditions at the sea floor. Many species live within a relatively limited range of water depths in patterns normally related to water mass distribution within the basin rather than directly to bathymetry. Other marine microfossils are occasionally used for more generalized paleodepth determinations.

Method

By observing modern foraminiferal populations and the distribution of modern species, paleontologists can predict (or extrapolate) the water depth ranges of their ancestors. This method, based on widespread studies of living forms, relies on the concept of *taxonomic uniformitarianism*, which assumes most modern organisms have the same, or very similar, environmental restrictions as their fossil relatives (Dodd and Stanton, 1981). Most Pleistocene, Pliocene, and Miocene foraminiferal species either are still living or have very close living relatives in modern oceans. In practice, this evolutionary stability lets us accurately estimate paleobathymetry as far back as the middle Miocene (about 14.5 Ma). The accuracy of this method decreases with geologic age but is generally accepted to be broadly useful within the Cenozoic.

Limits on reliability of interpretation

Depth is merely the vertical component of the site location relative to sea level—an arbitrarily defined point in space. Unlike temperature or salinity, depth is not a true environmental parameter because it does not directly influence the morphology, distribution, or biological processes of marine organisms. However, foraminifera can help us estimate paleodepth because many environmental factors influencing their distribution (notably ambient light, oxygen, and temperature) change systematically with increasing water depth.

Modern foraminiferal distributions reflect oceanographic patterns in a glacial world ocean that originated in the middle Miocene; they are less accurate in estimating paleobathymetry for the preglacial early and middle Tertiary. Early Tertiary and Mesozoic oceans were much warmer and less stratified than at present, and accurate paleodepth estimates must be based on recalibrated early Paleogene and Cretaceous distributions (e.g., Sliter and Baker, 1972; Olsson and Nyong, 1984).

Depth zones

A commonly accepted classification of marine environments is the zonation of Tipsword et al. (1966), shown in the illustration below.

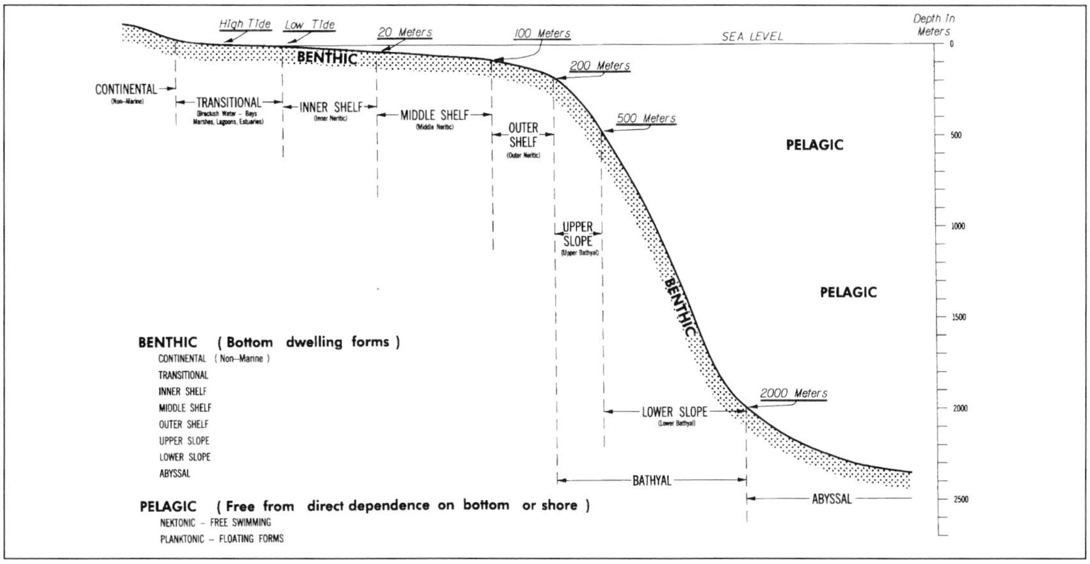

Figure 17–21. From Tipsword et al., 1966; courtesy Gulf Coast Assoc. of Geological Societies.

Zone distinctions

The continental margin profile is divided into zones that can be distinguished by distinct assemblages of microorganisms. The following table shows the depth zones and microorganisms found there.

Depth zone	Microorganisms found there
Continental (or nonmarine)	Presence of nonmarine ostracodes and diatoms; spores, pollen, and terrigenous plant debris. Absence of marine fossils.
Transitional (or marginal marine)	Low-diversity population of hyposaline-tolerant foraminifera, algae, dinoflagellates, and ostracodes.
Marine • Neritic (continental shelf) • Bathyal (continental slope) • Abyssal (sea floor)	Characteristic benthic foraminiferal faunas; in general, planktonic organisms increase in relative abundance with depth and distance from shore and usually dominate fossil populations in pelagic environments.

Regional paleobathymetric zonations

Foraminifera, particularly benthic species, may be strongly provincial, and faunas from widely separated regions may include very different assemblages of species. We need to understand the modern depth-related species distribution prevailing in a region before we can estimate paleobathymetry for ancient sediments.

Examples

Douglas and Heitman (1979) summarize foraminiferal depth distributions in the modern offshore California borderland; data of this sort enable Ingle (1980) to propose bathymetric zonations for the Tertiary of coastal California.

Quantitative Paleoenvironmental Analysis

Introduction

Benthic foraminifera have been used as paleoenvironmental indicators in the petroleum industry for forty years—most particularly as a basis for subjective estimates of paleobathymetry based on the presumed water depth range of species in the samples (see "Paleobathymetry"). Recent studies have shown that computer-based quantitative techniques such as clustering, principal component analysis, and discriminate analysis result in the following advantages:

- Permit the use of large data sets
- Increase the objectivity, reliability, and reproducibility of interpretations
- Clarify the definition of significant assemblages

Cluster analysis

One of the most popular methods of recognizing biofacies assemblages is cluster analysis. This method arranges the species into a hierarchical classification called a *dendrogram*. Dendrograms are constructed from the statistical distance or similarity between samples, based on their species composition. The species having the highest degree of similarity are clustered first, then others in successive order, until all species are paired into clusters. The results of the cluster analysis show faunal groupings, or *biofacies*, which are often characteristic of specific environments. The figure below is an example of weighted interfossil distances for Neogene benthic foraminifera of offshore California.

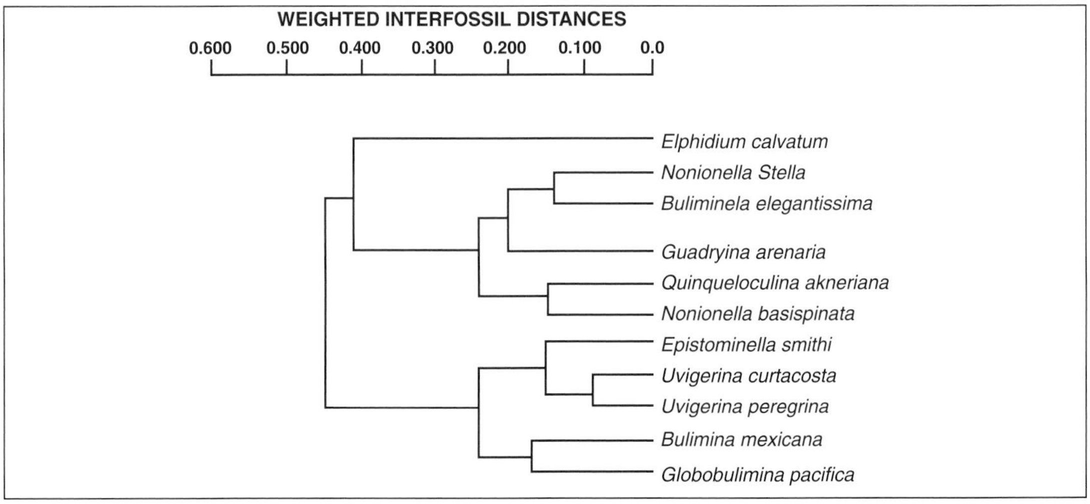

Figure 17–22.

Principal component analysis

The patterns, or *factor plots*, displayed in principal component analysis represent groupings of species based on the similarity or dissimilarity of their distribution. These groupings may represent various environments and can be integrated with other geologic data to determine or evaluate specific paleoenvironmental zones or settings.

Discriminate analysis

In discriminate analysis, paleoenvironmental zones are established and then tested against known environmental models to check the level of reliability in recognizing these biofacies. The results indicate which biofacies are distinct and statistically recognizable. The biofacies so determined can be used to interpret the paleoenvironment of well sections, cores, or outcrop sections.

Palynofacies and Kerogen Analysis

Definition of palynofacies

Combaz (1964) introduced the term *palynofacies* to describe the total organic content of a palynological assemblage (e.g., tracheids, woody tissue, microplankton, microforaminiferal linings). The relationship of these organic types to hydrocarbon generation is broached by Staplin (1969) and expressed geochemically by Tissot and Welte (1984). Amorphous and structured algal-derived detritus is considered oil prone, whereas structured terrestrially sourced organic material is associated primarily with gas generation.

Palynofacies applications

Palynofacies is a powerful analytical tool when used in conjunction with geological and geophysical information. Determination of kerogen types, abundance, and ratios of continental- vs. marine-derived components provide clues concerning depositional environment and hydrocarbon-generating potential (e.g., type and amount). Palynofacies data can be combined with ancillary biostratigraphic information in a sequence-stratigraphic framework to help recognize reservoir–source rock geometry.

Two major works integrate the geological and biological aspects of palynofacies research. Traverse (1994) includes several papers ranging from general overviews to detailed sequence-stratigraphic studies. This is complemented by Tyson's (1995) summation of the geochemical aspects of organic facies analysis. These two volumes should be the points of reference for designing any palynofacies study.

Kerogen analysis

The classification of dispersed kerogen constituents is based primarily on their appearance, in an unoxidized state, using transmitted light with ancillary observation employing reflected fluorescent and ultraviolet methods. Many classification strategies have been proposed (Burgess, 1974; Batten, 1981, 1982; Batten and Morrison, 1983; Whittaker, 1984; Boulter and Riddick, 1986; Hart, 1986) based on degradational state and biological derivation (i.e., plant vs. animal origin). However, sample processing schemes are not standardized between studies. This makes comparison between studies difficult unless applied to strata of the same age from the same basin. Classification and processing procedures are under scrutiny for standardization, and quantitative measurements are being assessed using optical scanners (Lorente, 1990a,b; Highton et al., 1991).

Thermal Maturation

Introduction

Many of the elements of basin modeling programs—maturation of source rocks, reservoir diagenesis, and porosity evolution—are affected by thermal and burial history (van Gizjel, 1980; Pradier et al., 1991). Thermal maturation data used to model these parameters are usually derived from fossils.

The following table shows which fossil material changes appearance due to thermal stress and therefore can be used as organic geothermometers.

Fossil Material	Thermal Maturation Scale
Vitrinite	Vitrinite reflectance (V_r or R_o)
Pollen and spores	Thermal Alteration Index (TAI)
Ostracodes	Ostracode Alteration Index (OAI)
Conodonts	Conodont Alteration Index (CAI)
Foraminifera	Foraminifera Alteration Index (FAI)
Graptolites	Calibrated to R_o scale
Scolecodonts	Calibrated to R_o scale
Chitinozoans	Calibrated to R_o scale

Vitrinite

Vitrinite is a coaly organic maceral derived from the connective tissue of vascular plants. The reflectance of vitrinite changes with heat. Vitrinite reflectance (V_r or R_o), the most commonly used thermal indicator, is the benchmark for maturation studies in the petroleum and coal industries (Dow and O'Connor, 1982). This technique is primarily useful for Devonian and younger clastic sediments and coals.

Pollen and spores

Pollen and spores are the organic-walled microfossils most commonly used for gauging paleotemperature. Fossil color, which changes with heating, is used to estimate a Thermal Alteration Index, or TAI (Staplin, 1969; Lerche and McKenna, 1991; Marshall, 1991). The use of pollen and spores lets us examine in situ fossils rather than evaluate an aggregate "kerogen soup." Other organic-walled fossils [acritarchs, chitinozoans, graptolites, scolecodonts (annelid worm jaws), and dinoflagellates] have been examined for their visual and reflected values, but these fossil groups have not been rigorously calibrated to the standard vitrinite reflectance scale (Bertrand and Heroux, 1987).

Thermal Maturation, continued

Other microfossils

Fossils composed of phosphate (conodonts), carbonate (ostracodes), and agglutinated grains (agglutinated foraminifera) are also used for geothermometry. The organic framework of these fossils responds to thermal stress with color change. Of these, conodonts (Conodont Alteration Index, or CAI) are the most widely used (Epstein et al., 1977), and conodont alteration values are calibrated to the vitrinite reflectance scale. The use of ostracodes (Ainsworth et al., 1990) and foraminifera (McNeil and Issler, 1992) is a newly emerging approach and is not yet calibrated to vitrinite reflectance standards. The potential of these fossils is important because they commonly occur in lithologies devoid of organic-walled fossil remains (e.g., limestones, dolomites, fine-grained sands).

Whole kerogen analysis

Geochemists use a wide variety of organic compounds, derived from both terrestrial (land and aquatic) and marine organisms, to determine depositional environments and thermal maturation. These analyses assay whole kerogen assemblages and include elemental analyses (gas chromatography–mass spectrometry, or GC-MS), Fourier transform infrared spectroscopy (FTIR), biomarkers, spectral fluorescence, and Rock-Eval pyrolysis.

Use of multiple techniques

Since none of these techniques is infallible in quantifying thermal maturation history for all conditions, two or more should be used when possible as a cross-check of the maturation data (Nuccio, 1991). Caution is necessary, however, when equating thermal values to petroleum generation windows because different organic materials generate at different times during thermal exposure (e.g., early generators vs. late generators). This affects transformation ratios used in hydrocarbon systems modeling.

Sequence Stratigraphy

Introduction

Sequence stratigraphy is the study of genetically related facies within a framework of chronostratigraphically significant surfaces (Van Wagoner et al., 1990). Paleontologic data, integrated with seismic and well log data, are an integral part of sequence stratigraphic analysis. Paleontology provides two critical types of data:

- Age control for chronostratigraphic horizons, especially sequence boundaries
- Paleoenvironmental control for systems tract interpretations

Age control

Among chronostratigraphically significant surfaces, the sequence boundary and the maximum flooding surface (i.e., downlap surface on seismic profiles) are of particular importance. Paleontology provides two important constraints on these surfaces:

- Chronostratigraphic correlation controls (Baum and Vail, 1987)
- Numerical ages for rate-dependent analyses

Chronostratigraphic correlation

The sequence stratigraphy model postulates a worldwide succession of depositional events such as coastal onlap and oceanic anoxic events (Arthur and Dean, 1986), primarily reflecting global cyclic changes in eustatic sea level. This succession ideally is represented by a sea level onlap-offlap curve such as the Haq et al. (1988) cycle chart.

One problem frequently confronted in sequence studies is determining which of these worldwide events is represented in the section of interest. Correlating a local section to the global cycles requires accurate and precise biostratigraphy, either through zonal age determination or by providing the necessary age constraints on magnetostratigraphic or isotope stratigraphic interpretations. When based on reliable age control, correlation with the succession of global processes can be a valuable predictive stratigraphic tool for understanding the temporal and areal distribution of reservoir, source, and seal rocks.

Biostratigraphic correlation between sections separated by a fault zone or other major geologic feature is frequently much more reliable than seismic reflectors or well log picks. Correlation across growth faults, where stratal thickness and character can vary greatly from the high to the low side, is a notable example.

Sequence Stratigraphy, continued

Stratigraphic distribution of onlap events

The figure below illustrates the stratigraphic distribution of onlap events, tectonic episodes ("s"-shaped arrows), oceanic anoxic events (OAE), and "crises" of the shallow water biota (BC) in various parts of the world during part of the Mesozoic (after Simo et al., 1993). Landward is toward the right in each column.

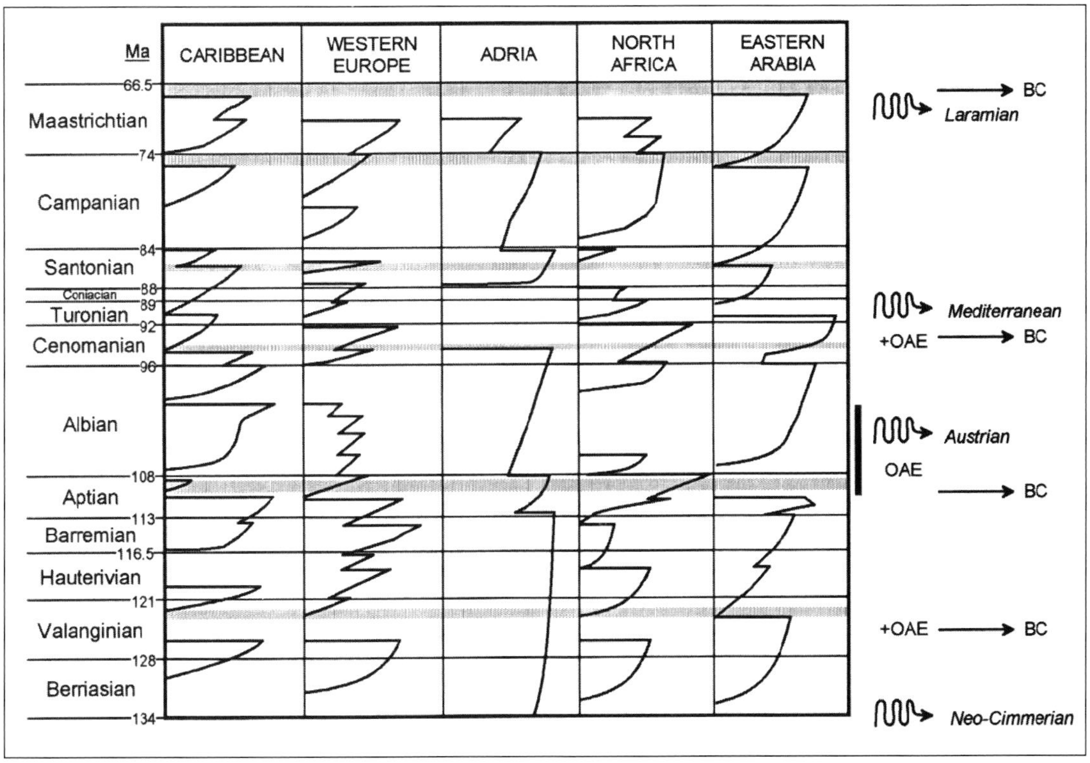

Figure 17–23. After Simo et al., 1993; courtesy AAPG.

Numerical ages

Rate-dependent analyses such as subsidence analysis, deposition rate, and maturation modeling require age–depth pairs as input data. Numerical ages are critical to accurate analyses and ideally should be based on high-resolution biostratigraphic control calibrated to a standard geochronology, such as Harland et al. (1990), Berggren et al. (1995), or Gradstein et al. (1995).

Systems tract interpretation

A systems tract (ST) is a linkage of contemporaneous, three-dimensional arrays of lithofacies (Fisher and McGowen, 1967; Brown and Fisher, 1977). The figure below shows depositional systems tracts and the bounding surfaces of a stratigraphic sequence depositional model.

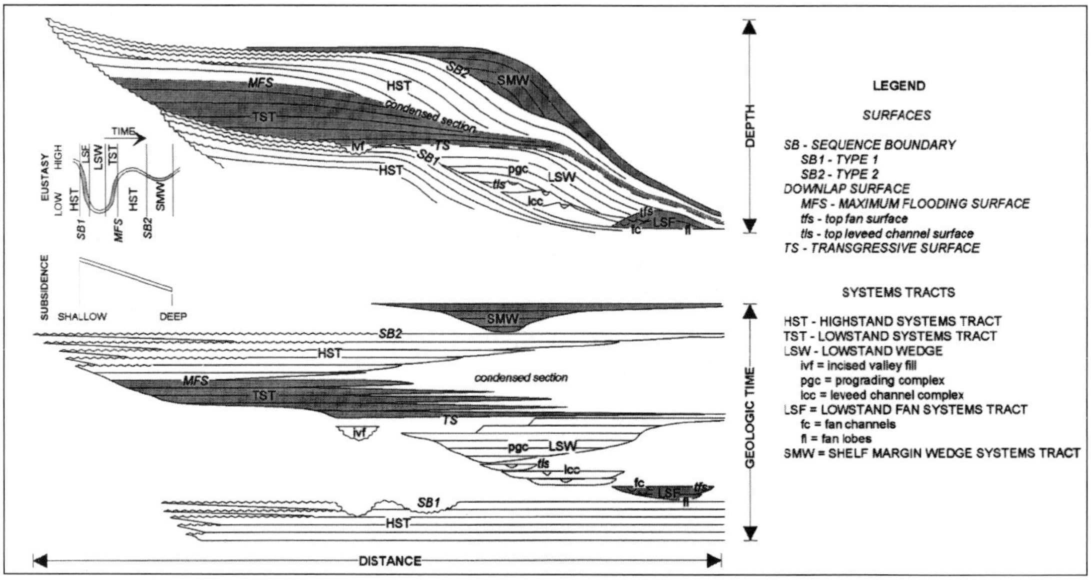

Figure 17–24. From Haq et al., 1988; courtesy SEPM.

Fossil assemblages in the systems tract

In addition to the lithological features, systems tracts can possess distinctive fossil assemblages, although the composition of the population varies, depending on the sample location relative to the ST profile. The vertical succession of STs can be delineated by trends in the distribution, abundance, and diversity of fossil taxa and morphologic groups. Environmental changes within and between systems tracts may reflect changes in sea level, sedimentation, and tectonics. The general paleontological characteristics of systems tracts are as follows.

Systems Tract	Characteristics
Lowstand fan (basin floor fan)	Basin to slope, with a strong component of terrigenous input; fossils commonly include specimens that have been reworked or redeposited from upslope, with pelagic forms typically in shales between stacked lobes
Lowstand wedge (slope fan and prograding complex)	Shallow environment compared to underlying strata; upward shoaling and increasing terrestrial input, with reworked and redeposited fossils
Shelf-margin wedge	Shallower environment than underlying strata with little vertical environmental change within the systems tract
Transgressive	Increasing water depth and decreasing terrestrial influence upward to the maximum flooding surface at the top of this systems tract
Highstand	Progressive decrease in water depth; marine fossils upsection shallower than underlying strata; assemblages commonly shallow to inner shelf, marginal marine, or continental except in basinal locations

Paleoenvironmental trends

In addition to seismic, lithofacies, and well log signatures (Van Wagoner et al., 1990), sequence stratigraphic surfaces and systems tracts can be recognized from paleoenvironmental trends evident from several types of paleontologic analyses:

- **Paleobathymetry**—changes in benthic faunal composition can help identify relative sea level changes, e.g., benthic foraminiferal biofacies (Armentrout, 1987)
- **Distance from shoreline**—changes in the relative abundance of marine vs. land-derived forms (e.g., dinoflagellate–pollen ratios) may reflect shoreline advances and retreats
- **Climatic cycles**—fluctuations of warm- and cold-water indicators in marine environments [e.g., calcareous nannofossils (Shaffer, 1987) or planktonic foraminifera (Martin et al., 1993)] may reflect sea level changes during periods of glacio-eustasy. Variations in arid vs. wet climates reflected in land-based flora (e.g., palynomorphs) or lacustrine fauna (e.g., ostracodes) help identify climatic changes that control the development of stratigraphic sequences.

The figure below illustrates the utility of variations in palynological assemblages, reflecting differing paleoenvironmental settings, when differentiating and identifying systems tracts.

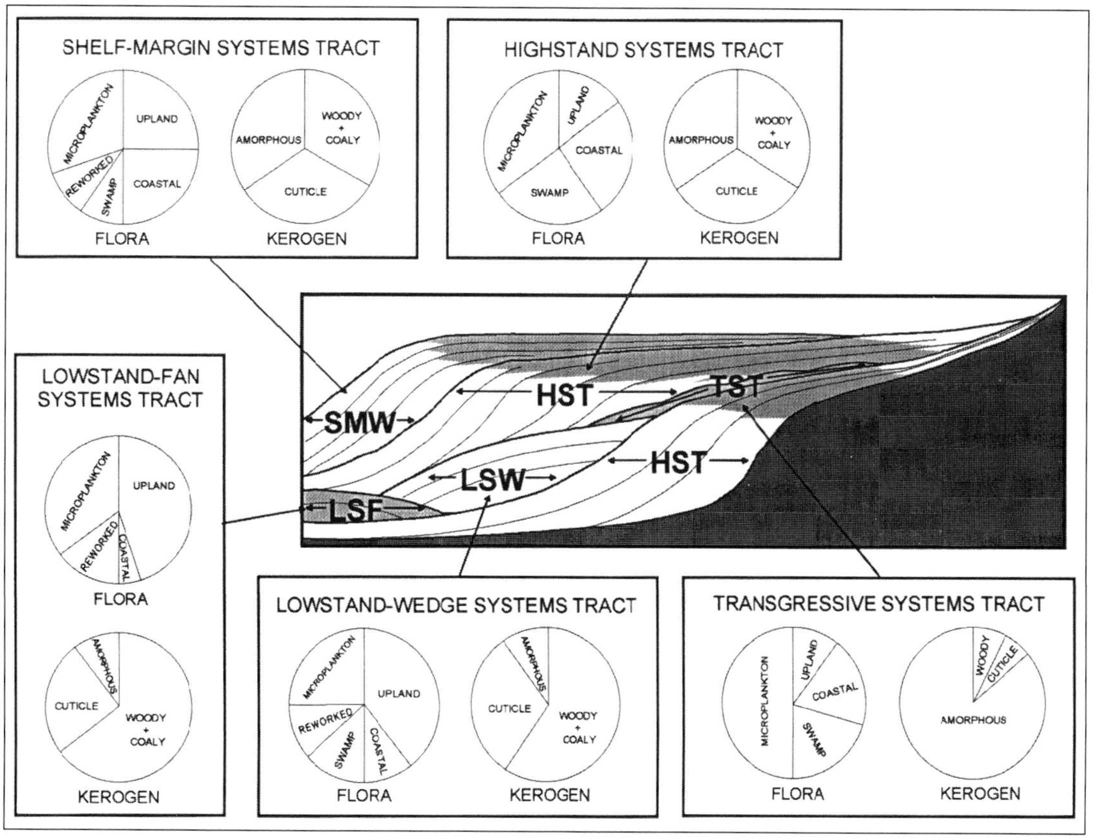

Figure 17–25. Published with the permission of Exxon.

Maximum flooding surfaces and condensed sections

The maximum flooding surface (which may in fact be a thin stratigraphic interval) marks the turn-around point from an overall deepening to an overall shallowing trend. Associated with this horizon may be a major condensed section, marked by the lowest terrigenous input, the greatest water depth (approximately), and organic enrichment. This condensed section can provide important fossil age data on continental margins (Loutit et al., 1988) because it usually contains the greatest abundance of microfossils and the highest concentration of pelagic forms, such as planktonic foraminifera and calcareous nannofossils. Other condensed sections are also (but less commonly) found (1) at the top of depositional cycles within the lowstand wedge and (2) overlying individual lowstand fans.

The figure below illustrates paleontologic and paleoenvironmental variables across a condensed section in the Upper Eocene at St. Stephens Quarry, Alabama. The condensed section corresponds to the unnamed blue clay. Overlying Eocene Red Bluff and Bumpnose Formations are highstand systems tract deposits; the Pachuta and Shubuta Formations represent shelf margin and transgressive systems tracts.

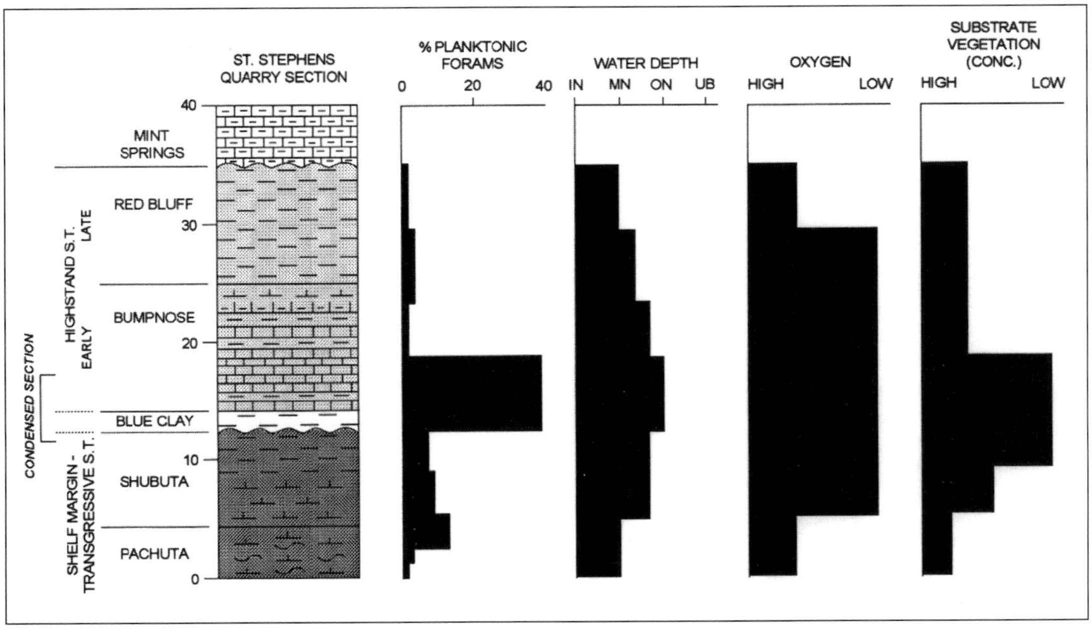

Figure 17–26. From Loutit et al., 1988; courtesy SEPM.

Section E

New Directions

Authors

Paul E. Belanger, Gregg H. Blake, Charles E. Cline, Anthony C. Gary, Garry D. Jones, Norman Macleod, Kenneth G. Miller, Allen R. Ormiston, Robert W. Pierce, Jeffrey A. Stein, Ron F. Waszczak, V. Eileen Williams

Introduction

In recent years, new approaches and new technology have been applied to the study of fossils, above and beyond the traditional studies. Many of these new techniques have significantly extended the range of interpretations that can be made from fossils and the value of the applications based on them.

In this section

The following topics are discussed in this section.

Quantitative Biostratigraphy

Introduction

Advances in statistical methods and computer technology provide paleontologists with a variety of techniques for collecting, managing, and evaluating large volumes of biostratigraphic data. Several quantitative methods have been developed to define an optimum sequence of biostratigraphic events, compositing data from many different stratigraphic sections to serve as a reference standard that will overcome inconsistencies that may be encountered in the fossil record at particular locales.

Graphic correlation

Graphic correlation (Shaw, 1964) is a widely accepted deterministic technique for ranking fossil occurrences according to the geological time represented in a set of reference sections. This approach has broad applications to solving biostratigraphic and sedimentologic problems (see Mann and Lane, 1995).

The format for a graphic correlation is an x–y crossplot on which biostratigraphic data (tops, bases, abundance/diversity events) recorded by measured stratigraphic position in one section (y-axis) may be matched to like occurrences in another section or a composite standard (x-axis; see Figure 17–27). Based on the array of data points, a preferred overall correlation can be defined by one or more line segments. Points falling on the line(s) of correlation are interpreted to be synchronous markers; those off the line(s), diachronous.

The illustration below shows a graphic correlation of two sections.

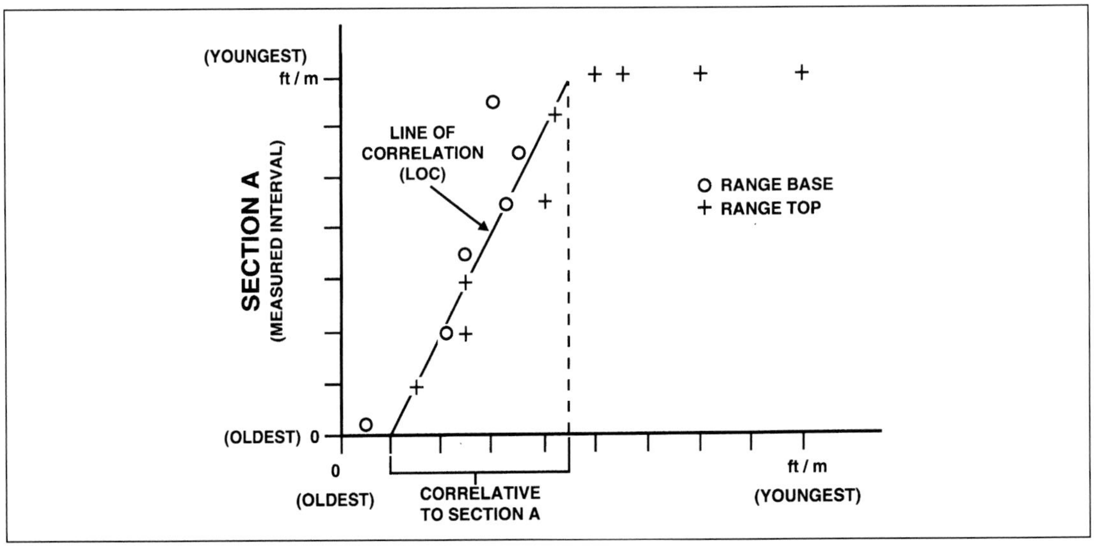

Figure 17–27.

Composite standards

An optimum sequence can be derived by graphically correlating a series of sections and establishing a composite standard—a database of the maximum time–stratigraphic ranges for a particular area under study. A composite standard should provide a relatively complete biostratigraphic representation of geologic time. On graphic correlation plots, apparent hiatuses are defined and quantified in time (composite standard units) by horizontal terraces. Fossil ranges in a composite standard are subject to alteration with each new graphic correlation, making it a complex, evolving database that usually requires computerized data management and applications.

Composite standards (continued)

As applied to geologic interpretation, a composite standard (1) unifies biostratigraphic data into a high-resolution time correlation framework and (2) provides a quantitative basis for defining the time significance of faults, unconformities, and other sequence stratigraphic boundaries.

The figure below is a graphic correlation interpretation of well data (tops only).

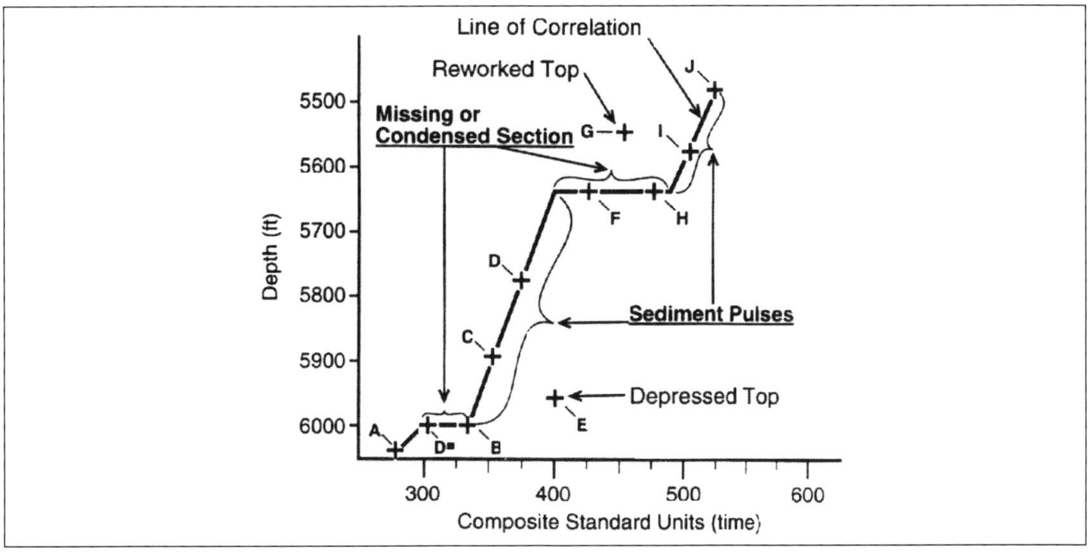

Figure 17–28.

Probabilistic correlations

The sequence of biostratigraphic events (i.e., highest and lowest occurrences) is frequently different, to a greater or lesser degree, between even nearby wells or outcrop sections. *Probabilistic biostratigraphy* is a statistical technique that determines the probability a sequence of biostratigraphic events will occur in a specific order. Probabilistic correlations, accordingly, are based on the sequence of events and not on the stratigraphic intervals or distances between them.

Probabilistic techniques can help us recognize objectively the most probable sequence of events and therefore can be used in (1) constructing interval zones and zonations and (2) evaluating the reliability of particular biostratigraphic events in local or regional settings.

Probabilistic methodology

The sequence of biostratigraphic events [i.e., highest occurrences, or last-appearance datums (LAD), and lowest occurrences, or first-appearance datums (FAD)] is determined for each section to be used in a study. The most complete is taken as a hypothetical most probable sequence and is statistically compared with all the other sequences in the study. The original hypothetical sequence is revised based on this analysis; the result is the most probable sequence of biostratigraphic events and an indication of their chronostratigraphic reliability. A high frequency of crossovers (mismatches) for a pair of species in the sections under study suggests the biostratigraphic events are closely spaced in relative time; few crossovers suggest a wider time spacing.

Stable Isotope Stratigraphy

Introduction

The shells of some carbonate-secreting marine organisms reflect the isotopic composition of the seawater in which they live. Technical advances in micromass spectrometry and the advent of deep-ocean hydraulic piston coring have permitted, through analysis of fossil carbonate shells, a rapid, cost-effective, and precise estimation of the isotopic composition of seawater through geologic time.

Isotopic correlation

Comparison of curves representing isotopic values through time can provide a basis for regional or even worldwide correlations. Although biotic and diagenetic effects must be considered when evaluating and using isotopic data, isotopic techniques can significantly augment the resolution of existing biostratigraphic zonations and provide accurate correlations within basins. Two useful stable isotopic techniques involve measuring the ratios of isotopes of oxygen ($^{18}O/^{16}O$) and strontium ($^{87}Sr/^{86}Sr$).

Oxygen isotope model

Glacial–interglacial climatic fluctuations during the late Paleogene and Neogene have been causally related to Milankovitch orbital parameters (eccentricity, obliquity, and precession). During colder glacial climates the oceans become enriched in ^{18}O relative to ^{16}O because the lighter ^{16}O molecule is more easily evaporated from seawater and becomes locked on land in the form of ice. During warmer intervals the reverse is true.

Figure 17–29 illustrates a typical oxygen isotope record (expressed as delta oxygen-18 values) for the middle Tertiary, showing standard Oligocene and Miocene isotope stages.

This record is for the middle Tertiary and shows standard Oligocene and Miocene isotope stages (Oi 1 = Oligocene isotope stage 1; Mi 1 = Miocene isotope stage 1; etc.). Oxygen isotope data are based on analyses of benthic foraminifera recovered from cores taken at seven Atlantic and Southern Ocean sites of the Ocean Drilling Program. The curve has been fitted through the data using statistical filter and smoothing techniques.

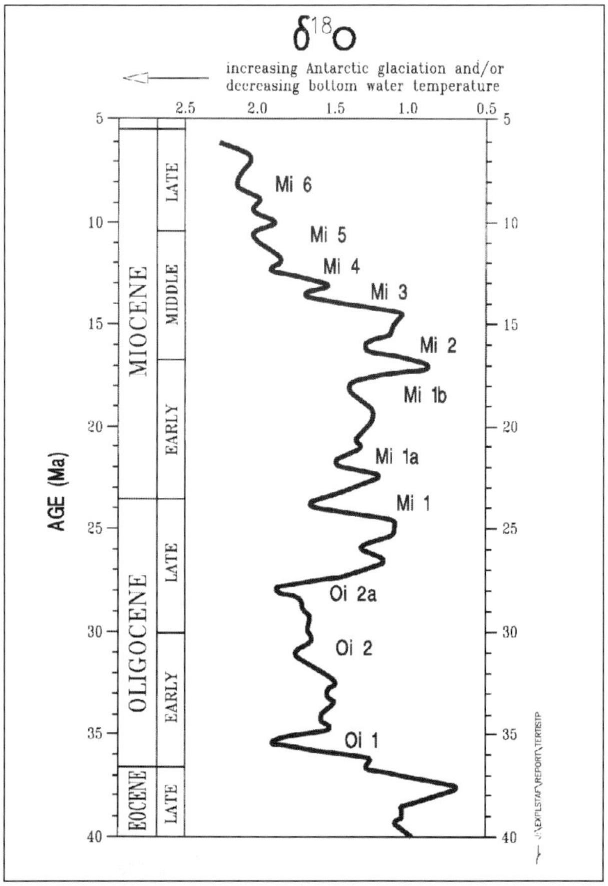

Figure 17–29. From Wright and Miller, 1993; courtesy American Geophysical Union. Time scale adapted from Berggren et al., 1985a,b.

Oxygen isotope correlation

Statistical stacking of detailed records of oceanic $^{18}O/^{16}O$ ratios, based primarily on the analysis of foraminifera from numerous deep-ocean cores and calibration to the geologic time scale, lets us construct standard oxygen isotope chronologies for the Pliocene–Pleistocene (Ruddiman et al., 1989; Shackleton et al., 1990) and the Miocene and Oligocene (Wright and Miller, 1993). Thus the oceanic $^{18}O/^{16}O$ record provides a precise correlative tool based on worldwide fluctuations in climate. Isotopic analysis of well-preserved foraminifera from core or outcrop samples or from well cuttings in areas of relatively high sedimentation rate may help us recognize worldwide oxygen isotope stages. Isotope studies can be useful locally in enhancing the stratigraphic resolution of existing biostratigraphy.

The illustration below shows correlation of a Pleistocene section between two wells in the offshore Gulf of Mexico using biostratigraphic control and the identification of standard oxygen isotope stages.

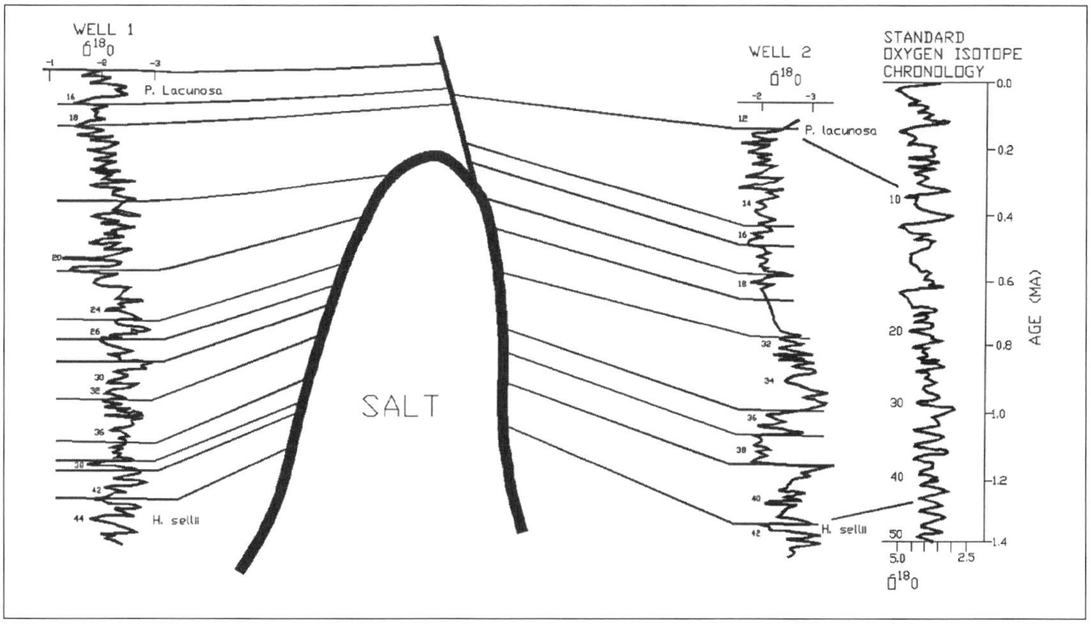

Figure 17–30. From Ruddiman et al., 1989. Reprinted with permission from Unocal; previously modified.

Strontium isotope stratigraphy

An extensive database of $^{87}Sr/^{86}Sr$ measurements on marine carbonate, evaporite, and phosphate samples compiled at Mobil and elsewhere has permitted construction of a $^{87}Sr/^{86}Sr$ "curve" for the Phanerozoic (see illustration below). During intervals when the $^{87}Sr/^{86}Sr$ curve is relatively linear and steep with respect to time (e.g., during the Permian, Jurassic, Late Cretaceous, and several intervals within the Late Eocene to Holocene), the strontium curve can be used as a chronometer because any given ratio along the line can be associated with a unique numerical age. The accuracy of the resulting age estimates approaches ±1.0 m.y. for the Cenozoic intervals.

The illustration below shows evolution of the $^{87}Sr/^{86}Sr$ ratio in seawater through the Phanerozoic.

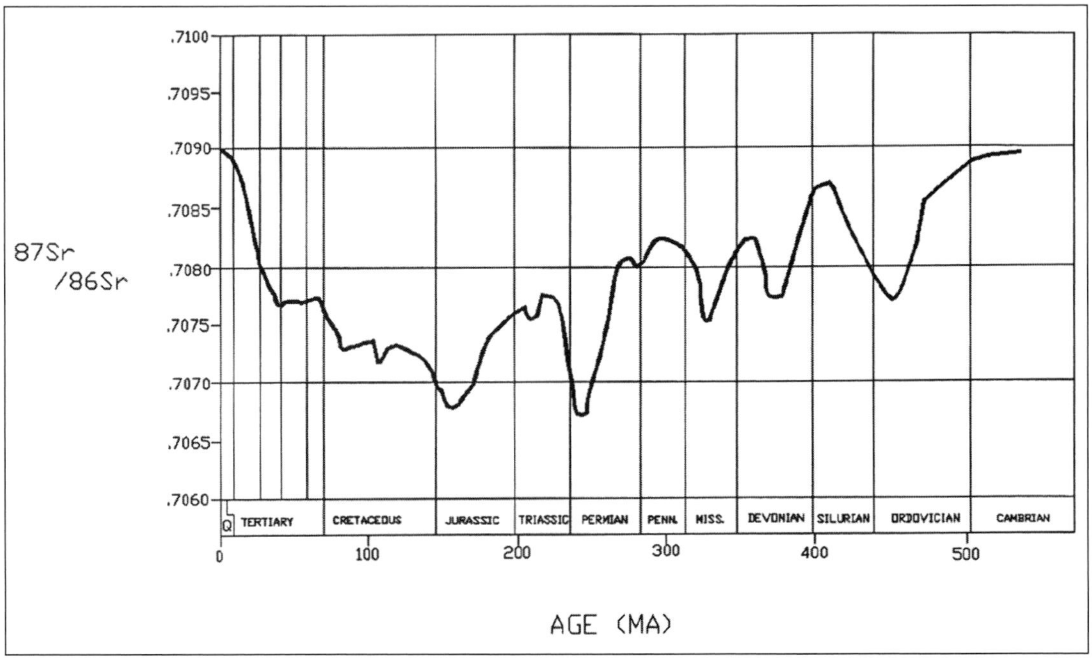

Figure 17–31. After Burke et al., 1982; courtesy Geology.

High-latitude example

The strontium isotope technique is especially useful in high-latitude and shallow-water marine sections of middle to late Tertiary age where biostratigraphic zones have relatively long durations and diagnostic calcareous taxa are often absent or difficult to identify.

The illustration below shows $^{87}Sr/^{86}Sr$ age estimates based on isotopic analysis of fossil calcareous shell material for a section of a high-latitude exploration well. Age estimates for each sample represent the mean of ages derived using the $^{87}Sr/^{86}Sr$ age relationships of DePaolo and Ingram (1985), Kopenick et al. (1985), and DePaolo (1986). Analytical error associated with each data point yields age estimate errors of approximately ±1.0 m.y.

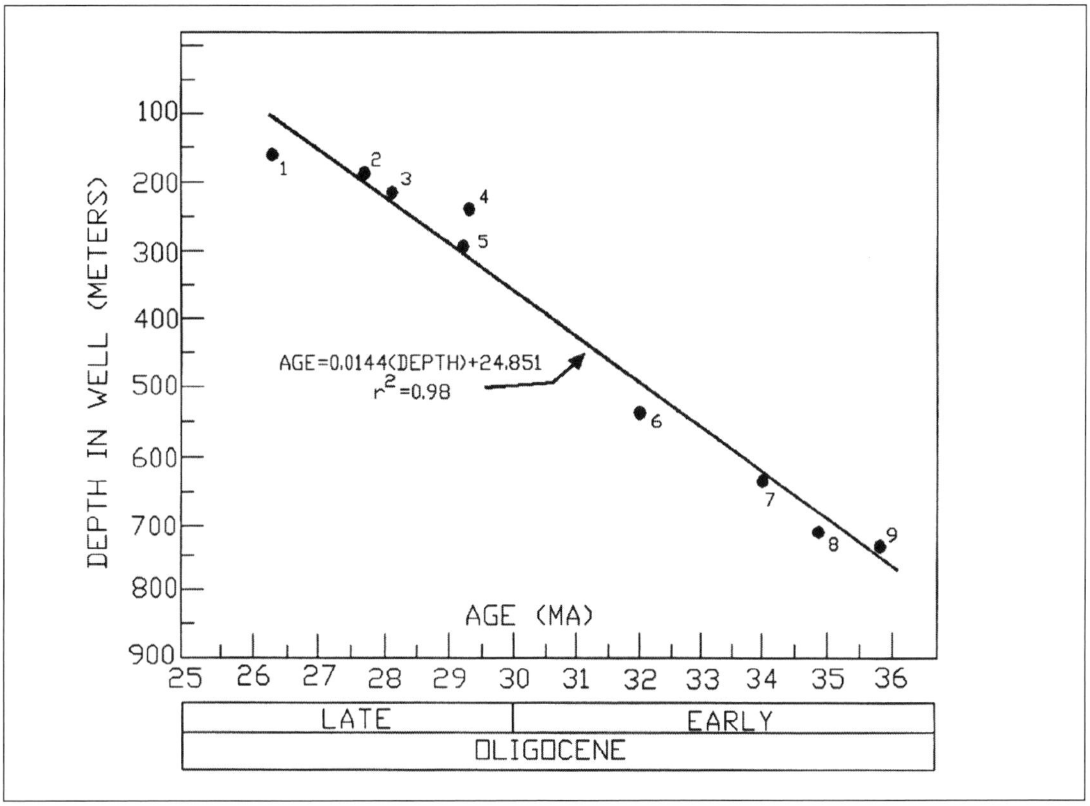

Figure 17–32. Printed with permission of Unocal; time scale after Berggren et al., 1985a.

Molecular Fossils

Definition

Molecular fossils include any distinctive organic molecule or molecular fragment recovered from rocks, sediments, fossils, or oils that can be reliably associated with one or a few biotic antecedents. The term "molecular fossil" is limited here to compounds used to identify source organisms and to interpret corresponding paleoenvironments; it is not synonymous with "biomarker."

Utility of molecular fossils

Some molecular fossils can be correlated with source organisms that were restricted to a limited range of environments. Recognizing these molecules in sediments or in oil provides information about the paleoenvironment of the sediment or source.

Recognition of biotic antecedent

Extracting high abundances of specific molecular fossils from source rocks dominated by a single type of organism is a reliable means of demonstrating connection (Azevedo et al., 1992). A less certain approach, apparently valid in select cases, is based on analogy: we can infer a molecular fossil in a modern organism, identical to a compound from ancient strata, was derived from a closely related ancient organism.

Limitations

The match of molecular fossil to biotic antecedent and the use of this knowledge for paleoenvironmental interpretation is often a challenge.

- Data are dispersed in the literature of diverse scientific disciplines.
- Modern gas chromatograph–mass spectrometer analyses are not available for many important groups of living organisms.
- Only a few molecular fossils can be correlated to biotic antecedents confined to a narrow range of environments.

Thus, Treibs' (1934) discovery that derivatives of chlorophyll are widespread in oils is not useful in defining paleoenvironments because chlorophyll is environmentally ubiquitous. Volkman (1986) dispells an earlier concept that an abundance of C_{29} sterols is evidence of terrigenous organic matter by finding abundant C_{29} sterols in lacustrine environments.

Methodology

Molecular fossils useful in diagnosing paleoenvironments in select cases include those that reflect fundamental metabolic processes and have a unique biotic antecedent. Some of these molecular fossils show great durability in terms of geologic time and can be recognized from oils and rocks as old as Precambrian. Three groups of molecular fossils meet these criteria:

- Sterols
- Phytanyl glycerol ethers
- Carotenoids

Biochemical evolution

Major evolutionary changes in the biosphere have had geochemical expression. For this reason, the molecular fossil content of many Paleozoic oils stands in distinct contrast to that of younger oils, and oils from some geological intervals are characterized by distinctive molecular fossil associations.

Molecular Fossils, continued

Application

Molecular fossils can be particularly useful in discriminating among marine, lacustrine, and terrestrial source rocks.

- **Marine** source rocks are typified by a high diversity of molecular fossils, particularly sterols. Certain carotenoids, ketones, and alkenes are only known to occur in marine plankton.
- **Lacustrine** sources are characterized by the presence of botryococcane, which originates in the lacustrine alga *Botryococcus,* and of abundant carotenoids and cyanobacterial products.
- **Terrestrial** molecular fossils are derived from terrestrial plants, particularly as part of the durable cutin and associated waxes in plant leaves.

Morphometric and Particle Analysis

Introduction

Evolutionary change within fossil lineages and the morphologic (i.e., size and shape) adaptation of fossil species to different ancient environments can only be inferred from morphologic analysis of fossil populations (Scott, 1980). Until the early 1970s the morphologic study of microfossils involved tedious "eyeball" measurements of large numbers of specimens from many samples, precluding use of the technique in industrial application. Rapid advances in computer, video, and multivariate statistical techniques have greatly reduced the time required to collect quantitative measurements on large numbers of shells.

Morphometric procedure

Morphometric analysis involves collecting the measurements of two or three dimensions of fossil form, typically either an outline (silhouette) or the coordinate positions of a morphologic "landmark." Once a sufficient data set is collected, multivariate methods are used to break out fossil "shape components" statistically and to relate component variability to chronostratigraphic or paleoenvironmental indices (Davis, 1986). When the relationship between change in fossil shape and environmental and stratigraphic data is established, fossil morphology can increase confidence in geologic correlation and paleoenvironmental inference (Reyment et al., 1984; Rohlf and Bookstein, 1990).

Applications

Morphometric analysis of microfossils from stratigraphic sections can augment the resolution of existing biostratigraphic zonations (Reyment, 1980). The illustration to the right shows changes vs. age in the average morphometrically defined shape of tests in populations of the planktonic foraminifera *Globoquadrina altispira.*

Data for the illustration were compiled from cores taken in the DeSoto Canyon area, eastern Gulf of Mexico. Significant shifts in shape (such as at 7.5 Ma) can augment the resolution of existing biostratigraphic zonations. In addition to analysis from stratigraphic sections, refined paleoenvironmental interpretations can be obtained by comparing morphometric results from fossil populations (e.g., benthic foraminifera) with results obtained from analysis of existing species from known environments.

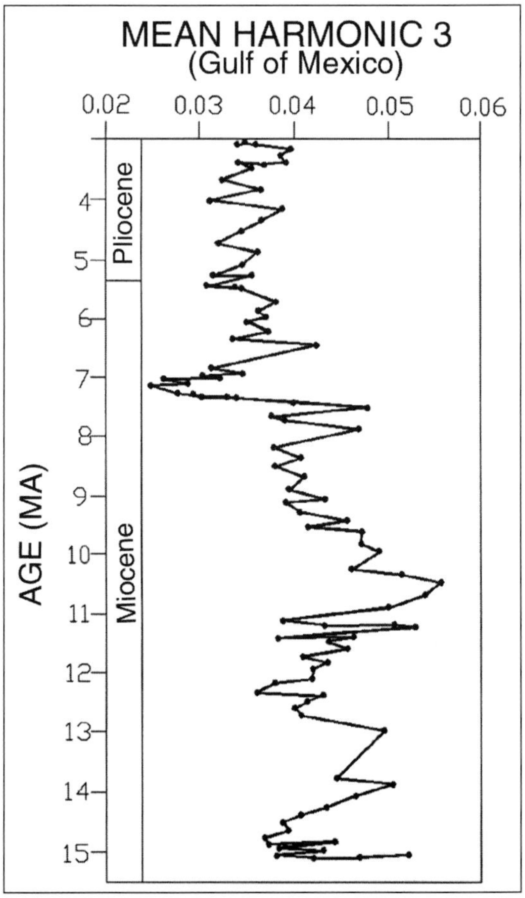

Figure 17–33. Printed with permission of N. Healy-Williams, University of South Carolina.

Systematic changes vs. water depth

The illustration below shows systematic changes vs. water depth in the outline shape (lobateness) of the benthic foraminifera *Bolivina albatrossi* as defined by morphometric analysis. Data for this illustration were collected from a transect of bottom samples from the present-day Gulf of Mexico. Similar analyses of *B. albatrossi* specimens from Neogene sections can be compared with the modern relationship to obtain paleobathymetric estimates.

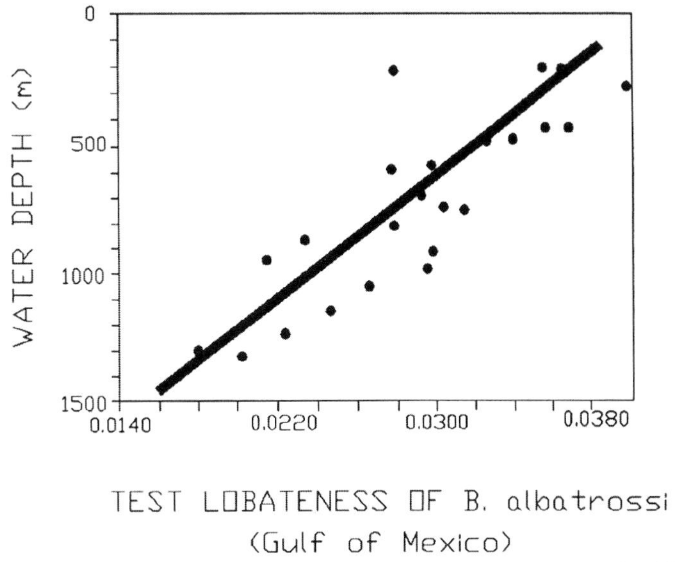

Figure 17–34. After Gary et al., 1989; courtesy Journal of Foraminiferal Research.

Particle analysis

Particle analysis involves computer-assisted automated measurement and classification of size and color information of fossils and outline shape. To date, analysis of particle images has been applied largely to kerogen particles in transmitted, reflected, and fluorescent light. The results show promise for interpreting paleoenvironments, identifying source rock intervals, estimating thermal maturity of sediments, and refining biostratigraphic correlation.

Section F
References

Ainsworth, N.R., R.D. Burnett, and M. Kontrovitz, 1990, Ostracod colour change by thermal alteration, offshore Ireland and Western UK: Marine and Petroleum Geology, vol. 7, p. 288–297.

Alve, E., and J.W. Murray, 1995, Experiments to determine the origin and palaeoenvironmental significance of agglutinated foraminiferal assemblages, *in* M.A. Kaminski, S. Geroch, and M.A. Gasiński, eds., Proceedings of the Fourth International Workshop on Agglutinated Foraminifera: Grzybowski Foundation Special Publication 3, p. 1–11.

Armentrout, J.M., 1987, Integration of biostratigraphy and seismic stratigraphy: Pliocene–Pleistocene, Gulf of Mexico, *in* Innovative Biostratigraphic Approaches to Sequence Analysis: New Exploration Opportunities: Selected Papers and Illustrated Abstracts of the Eighth Annual Research Conference of the Gulf Coast Section of the Society of Economic Paleontologists and Mineralogists Foundation, p. 6–14.

Armentrout, J.M., R.J. Echols, and T. Lee, 1990, Patterns of foraminiferal abundance and diversity: implications for sequence stratigraphic analysis, *in* J.M. Armentrout and B.F. Perkins, eds., Sequence Stratigraphy as an Exploration Tool: Concepts and Practices in the Gulf Coast: Program and Extended and Illustrated Abstracts of the Eleventh Annual Research Conference of the Gulf Coast Section of the Society of Economic Paleontologists and Mineralogists Foundation, p. 53–59.

Arthur, M.A., and W.E. Dean, 1986, Cretaceous paleoceanography, *in* B.E. Tucholke and P.R. Vogt, eds., Decade of North American Geology, Western North Atlantic Basin Synthesis Volume: Geological Society of America, p. 617–630.

Azevedo, D., F. Aquino Mato, B. Simoneit, and A. Pinto, 1992, Novel series of tricyclic aromatic terpanes characterized in Tasmanian tasmanite: Organic Geochemistry, vol. 18, no. 2, p. 9–16.

Batten, D.J., 1981, Palynofacies, organic maturation and source potential for petroleum, *in* J. Brooks, ed., Organic Maturation Studies and Fossil Fuel Exploration: London, Academic Press, p. 201–223.

______, 1982, Palynofacies, palaeoenvironments and petroleum: Journal of Micropalaeontology, vol. 1, p. 107–114.

______ and J. Morrison, 1983, Methods of palynological preparation for paleoenvironmental source potential and organic maturation studies, *in* L. Costa, ed., Palynology–Micropaleontology: Laboratories, Equipment and Methods: Bulletin of the Norwegian Petroleum Directorate, vol. 2, p. 35–53.

Baum, G.R., and P.R. Vail, 1987, Sequence stratigraphy, allostratigraphy, isotope stratigraphy, and biostratigraphy: putting it all together in the Atlantic and Gulf Paleogene, *in* Innovative Biostratigraphic Approaches to Sequence Analysis: New Exploration Opportunities: Selected Papers and Illustrated Abstracts of the Eighth Annual Research Conference of the Gulf Coast Section of the Society of Economic Paleontologists and Mineralogists Foundation, p. 15–23.

Berggren, W.A., and K.G. Miller, 1988, Paleogene tropical planktonic foraminiferal biostratigraphy and magnetobiochronology: Micropaleontology, vol. 34, no. 4. p. 362–380.

———, D.V. Kent, and J.J. Flynn, 1985a, Paleogene geochronology and chronostratigraphy, *in* N.J. Snelling, ed., The Chronology of the Geological Record: Geological Society of London Memoir 10, p. 141–195.

———, ———, and J.A. van Couvering, 1985b, Neogene geochronology and chronostratigraphy, *in* N.J. Snelling, ed., The Chronology of the Geological Record: Geological Society of London Memoir 10, p. 211–260.

———, ———, J.D. Obradovich, and C. Swisher, 1992, Towards a revised Paleogene geochronology, *in* D.R. Prothero and W.A. Berggren, eds., Eocene-Oligocene Climatic and Biotic Evolution: Princeton, Princeton University Press, p. 29–45.

———, ———, C. Swisher, and M.-P. Aubry, 1995, A revised Cenozoic geochronology and chronostratigraphy, *in* W.A. Berggren, D.V. Kent, M.-P. Aubry, and J. Hardenbol, eds., Geochronology, Time Scales, and Global Stratigraphic Correlation: Society for Sedimentary Geology (SEPM) Special Publication 54, p. 127–208.

Bertrand, R., and Y. Heroux, 1987, Chitinozoan, graptolite and scolecodont reflectance as an alternative to vitrinite and pyrobitumen reflectance in Ordovician and Silurian strata, Anticosti Island, Quebec, Canada: AAPG Bulletin, vol. 41, p. 951–957.

Blow, W.H., 1979, The Cainozoic Globigerinida: Leiden, E.J. Brill, 1413 p.

Bolli, H.M., J.B. Saunders, and K. Perch-Nielsen, 1985, Plankton Stratigraphy: Cambridge, Cambridge University Press, 1032 p.

Boulter, M.C., and A. Riddick, 1986, Classification and analysis of palynodebris from the Paleocene sediments of the Forties Field: Sedimentology, vol. 33, p. 871–886.

Brett, C.E., 1990, Destructive taphonomic processes and skeletal durability, *in* D.E.G. Briggs, and P.R. Crowther, eds., Palaeobiology: A Synthesis: Oxford, Blackwell Scientific Publications, p. 223–226.

Brown, L.F., and W.L. Fisher, 1977, Seismic–stratigraphic interpretation of depositional systems: examples from Brazil rift and pull-apart basins, *in* C.E. Payton, ed., Seismic Stratigraphy—Applications to Hydrocarbon Exploration: AAPG Memoir 26, p. 213–248.

Burgess, J.D., 1974, Microscopic examination of kerogen (dispersed organic matter) in petroleum exploration: GSA Special Paper 153, p. 19–30.

Burke, W.R., R.E. Denison, E.A. Hetherington, R.B. Koepnick, H.F. Nelson, and J.B. Otto, 1982, Variation of seawater $^{87}Sr/^{86}Sr$ throughout Phanerozoic time: Geology, vol. 10, p. 516–519.

Cita, M.B., 1975, The Miocene/Pliocene boundary: history and definition, *in* T. Saito and L.H. Burckle, eds., Late Neogene Epoch Boundaries: New York, Micropaleontology Press Special Publication 1, p. 1–30.

Cocks, L., 1972, The origin of the Silurian *Clarkeia* shelly fauna of South America, and its extension to West Africa: Palaeontology, vol. 15, p. 623–630.

Colbert, E., 1972, Antarctic fossils and the reconstruction of Gondwanaland: Natural History, vol. 12, p. 67–72.

Combaz, A., 1964, Les palynofaciès: Revue de Micropaléontologie, vol. 7, p. 205–218.

Copper, P., and O. Brunton, 1990, A global review of Silurian reefs: The Palaeontological Association, London, Special Papers in Palaeontology 44, p. 225–259.

Davis, J.C., 1986, Statistics and data analysis in geology: New York, John Wiley, 646 p.

DePaolo, D.J., 1986, Detailed record of the Neogene Sr isotopic evolution of seawater from DSDP Site 590B: Geology, vol. 14, p. 103–106.

——— and B.L. Ingram, 1985, High-resolution stratigraphy with strontium isotopes: Science, vol. 227, p. 938– 941.

Dodd, J.R., and R.J. Stanton, 1981, Paleoecology, concepts and applications: New York, John Wiley, 559 p.

Douglas, R.G., 1979, Benthic foraminiferal ecology and paleoecology: a review of concepts and methods, *in* J.H. Lipps, ed., Foraminiferal Ecology and Paleoecology: SEPM Short Course 6, p. 21–53.

———, 1981, Paleoecology of continental margin basins: a modern case history from the borderland of southern California, *in* Depositional Systems of Active Continental Margin Basins: Pacific Section of Society of Economic Paleontologists and Mineralogists Short Course Notes, p. 121–156.

——— and H.L. Heitman, 1979, Slope and basin benthic foraminifera of the California borderland, *in* L.J. Doyle and O.H. Pilkey, eds., Geology of Continental Slopes: SEPM Special Publication 27, p. 231–246.

Dow, W.G., and D.I. O'Connor, 1982, Kerogen maturity and type by reflected light microscopy applied to petroleum generation, *in* How To Assess Maturation and Paleotemperatures: SEPM Short Course Notes, p. 79–99.

Epstein, A. G., J. B. Epstein, and L. D. Harris, 1977, Conodont color alteration—an index to organic metamorphism: U.S. Geological Survey Professional Paper 995, p. 1–27.

Feldmann, R.M., R.E. Chapman, and J.T. Hannibal, eds., 1989, Paleotechniques: Paleontological Society Special Publication 4, 358 p.

Fisher, W.L., and J.H. McGowen, 1967, Depositional systems in the Wilcox Group of Texas and their relationship to occurrence of oil and gas: Transactions of the Gulf Coast Association of Geological Societies, vol. 17, p. 105–125.

Gabbott, S.E., R.J. Aldridge, and J.N. Theron, 1995, A giant conodont with preserved muscle-tissue from the Upper Ordovician of South Africa: Nature, vol. 374, p. 800–803.

Gary, A.C., N. Healy-Williams, and R. Ehrlich, 1989, Water–mass relationships and morphologic variability in the benthic foraminifer *Bolivina albatrossi* Cushman, northern Gulf of Mexico: Journal of Foraminiferal Research, vol. 19, no. 3, p. 210–221.

Gradstein, F.M., F.P. Agterberg, J.G. Ogg, J. Hardenbol, P. Van Veen, J. Thierry, and Z. Huang, 1995, A Triassic, Jurassic, and Cretaceous time scale, *in* W.A. Berggren, D.V. Kent, M.-P. Aubry, and J. Hardenbol, eds., Geochronology, Time Scales, and Global Stratigraphic Correlation: Society for Sedimentary Geology (SEPM) Special Publication 54, p. 93–125.

Haq, B.U., J. Hardenbol, and P.R. Vail, 1988, Mesozoic and Cenozoic chronostratigraphy and cycles of sea-level change, *in* C.K. Wilgus, B.S. Hastings, C.G. St. C. Kendall, H.W. Posamentier, C.A. Ross, and John C. Van Wagoner, eds., Sea-level Change: An Integrated Approach: SEPM Special Publication 42, p. 71–108.

Harland, W.B., R.L. Armstrong, A.V. Cox, L.E. Craig, A.G. Smith, and D.G. Smith, 1990, A Geologic Time Scale—Revised Edition: Cambridge, Cambridge University Press, 263 p.

Hart, G.F., 1986, Origin and classification of organic matter in clastic systems: Palynology, vol. 10, p. 1–23.

Highton, P.J.C., C.A. Pearson, and A.C. Scott, 1991, Palynofacies and palynodebris and their use in Coal Measure palaeoecology and palaeoenvironmental analysis: Neues Jahrbuch für Geologie und Paläontologie, Abhandlung, vol. 183, no. 1–3, p. 135–169.

Iaccarino, S., 1985, Mediterranean Miocene and Pliocene planktic foraminifera, *in* H.M. Bolli, J.B. Saunders, and K. Perch-Nielsen, eds., Plankton Stratigraphy: Cambridge, Cambridge University Press, p. 283–314.

Ingle, J.C., Jr., 1980, Cenozoic paleobathymetry and depositional history of selected sequences within the Southern California continental borderland, *in* W.V. Sliter, ed., Studies in Marine Micropaleontology and Paleoecology: A Memorial Volume to Orville L. Bandy: Cushman Foundation for Foraminiferal Research Special Publication 19, p. 163–195.

Jardine, N., and D. McKenzie, 1972, Continental drift and the dispersal and evolution of organisms: Nature, vol. 235, p. 20–25.

Kaminski, M.A., and W. Kuhnt, 1995, Tubular agglutinated foraminifera as indicators of organic carbon flux, *in* M.A. Kaminski, S. Geroch, and M.A. Gasiński,, eds., Proceedings of the Fourth International Workshop on Agglutinated Foraminifera: Grzybowski Foundation Special Publication 3, p. 141–144.

Kennett, J.P., and M.S. Srinivasan, 1983, Neogene Planktonic Foraminifera: A Phylogenetic Atlas: Stroudsburg, Pennsylvania, Hutchinson Ross, 265 p.

Kopenick, R.B., W.H. Burke, R.E. Denison, E.A. Hetherington, H.F. Nelson, J.B. Otto, and L.E. Waite, 1985, Construction of the seawater $^{87}Sr/^{86}Sr$ curve for the Cenozoic and Cretaceous: supporting data: Chemical Geology (Isotope Geoscience Section), vol. 58, p. 55–81.

Kummel, B., and D. Raup, eds., 1965, Handbook of Paleontological Techniques: San Francisco, W.H. Freeman, 851 p.

Lagoe, M.B., 1987, The stratigraphic record of sea-level and climatic fluctuations in an active-margin basin: the Stevens Sandstone, Coles Levee area, California: Palaios, vol. 2, no. 1, p. 48–68.

Lawrence, D. R., 1979, Taphonomy, *in* R.W. Fairbridge and D. Jablonski, eds., The Encyclopedia of Paleontology: Stroudsburg, Pennsylvania, Dowden, Hutchinson and Ross, p. 793–799.

Lerche, I., and T.C. McKenna, 1991, Pollen translucency as a thermal maturation indicator: Journal of Petroleum Geology, vol. 14, no. 1, p. 19–36.

Lipps, J.H., ed., 1993, Fossil Prokaryotes and Protists: London, Blackwell Scientific, 342 p.

Lorente, M.A., 1990a, Digital image analysis: an approach for quantitative characterization of organic facies and palynofacies, *in* W.J.J. Fermont and J.W. Weegink, eds., International Symposium in Organic Petrology: Mededlingen Rijks Geologie Dienst, vol. 45, p. 103–109.

______, 1990b, Textural characteristics of organic matter in several subenvironments of the Orinoco Upper Delta: Geologie en Mijnbouw, vol. 69, p. 263–278.

Loutit, T.S., J. Hardenbol, P.R. Vail, and G.R. Baum, 1988, Condensed sections: the key to age determination and correlation of continental margin sequences, *in* C.K. Wilgus, B.S. Hastings, C.G. St. C. Kendall, H.W. Posamentier, C.A. Ross, and J.C. Van Wagoner, eds., Sea-Level Changes: An Integrated Approach: SEPM Special Publication 42, p. 183–213.

Mann, K.O., and H.R. Lane, eds., 1995, Graphic Correlation: SEPM (Society for Sedimentary Geology) Special Publication 53, 263 p.

Marshall, J.E.A., 1991, Quantitative spore colour: Journal of the Geological Society of London, vol. 148, p. 223–233.

Martin, R.E., E.D. Neff, G.W. Johnson, and D.E. Krantz, 1993, Biostratigraphic expression of Pleistocene sequence boundaries, Gulf of Mexico: Palaios, vol. 8, no. 2, p. 155–171.

McNeil, D.H., and D.R. Issler, 1992, Correlation of foraminiferal coloration (FCI) and time-temperature (TTI) indices from Beaufort Sea exploration data: AAPG Annual Convention Abstracts, p. 87.

North American Commission on Stratigraphic Nomenclature, 1983, North American Stratigraphic Code: AAPG Bulletin, vol. 67, p. 841–875.

Nuccio, V.F., 1991, Combining methods yields best source rock maturity: World Oil, vol. 212, no. 9, p. 63–72.

Oboh, F.E., 1992, Multivariate statistical analysis of palyno debris from the Middle Miocene of the Niger Delta and their environmental significance: Palaios, vol. 7, p. 559–573.

Olsson, R.K., and E.E. Nyong, 1984, A paleoslope model for Campanian–lower Maestrichtian foraminifera of New Jersey and Delaware: Journal of Foraminiferal Research, vol. 14, no. 1, p. 50–68.

Ormiston, A.R., and G. Klapper, 1992, Paleoclimate, controls on Upper Devonian source rock sequences and stacked extinctions (abs.), *in* S. Lidgard and P.R. Crane, eds., Fifth North American Paleontological Convention Abstracts and Programs: Paleontological Society Special Publication 6, p. 227.

Pradier, B., P. Bertrand, L. Martinez, and F. Laggoun-Defarge, 1991, Fluorescence of organic matter and thermal maturity assessment: Organic Geochemistry, vol. 17, no. 4, p. 511–524.

Purnell, M. A., 1995, Microwear on conodont elements and macrophagy in the first vertebrates: Nature, vol. 374, p. 798–800.

Reyment, R.A., 1980, Morphometric methods in biostratigraphy: London, Academic Press, 168 p.

______, R.E. Blackith, and N.A. Campbell, 1984, Multivariate Morphometrics, 2d ed.: London, Academic Press, 233 p.

Rohlf, F.J., and F.L. Bookstein, eds., 1990, Proceedings of the Michigan Morphometrics Workshop: University of Michigan Museum of Zoology Special Publication 2, 380 p.

Ruddiman, W.F., M.E. Raymo, D.G. Martinson, B.M. Clement, and J. Backman, 1989, Pleistocene evolution: Northern Hemisphere ice sheets and North Atlantic Ocean: Paleoceanography, vol. 4, p. 353–412.

Scott, G.H., 1980, The value of outline processing in the biometry and systematics of fossils: Palaeontology, vol. 23, p. 757–768.

Shackleton, N.J., A. Berger, and W.R. Peltier, 1990, An alternate astronomical calibration of the lower Pleistocene time scale based on Ocean Drilling Program Site 677: Transactions of the Royal Society of Edinburgh, Earth Sciences, vol. 81, p. 251–261.

Shaffer, B.L., 1987, The potential of calcareous nannofossils for recognizing Plio–Pleistocene climatic cycles and sequence boundaries on the shelf, *in* Innovative Biostratigraphic Approaches To Sequence Analysis: New Exploration Opportunities: Selected Papers and Illustrated Abstracts of the Eighth Annual Research Conference of the Gulf Coast Section of the Society of Economic Paleontologists and Mineralogists Foundation, p. 142–145.

Shaw, A.B., 1964, Time in Stratigraphy: New York, McGraw-Hill, 365 p.

Simo, J.A.T., R.W. Scott, and J.-P. Masse, 1993, Cretaceous carbonate platforms: an overview, *in* J.A.T. Simo, R.W. Scott, and J.-P. Masse, eds., Cretaceous Carbonate Platforms: AAPG Memoir 56, p. 1–14.

Sliter, W.V., and Baker, R.A., 1972, Cretaceous bathymetric distribution of benthic foraminifers: Journal of Foraminiferal Research, vol. 2, no. 4, p. 167–183.

Staplin, F.L., 1969, Sedimentary organic matter, organic metamorphism, and oil and gas occurrence: Bulletin of Canadian Petroleum Geology, vol. 17, no. 1, p. 47–66.

Sweet, W.C., 1988, The Conodonta: morphology, taxonomy, paleoecology, and evolutionary history of a long-extinct animal phylum: Oxford [University Press] Monographs on Geology and Geophysics 10, 212 p.

Thompson, J., and C. Newton, 1989, Late Devonian mass extinction: episodic cooling or warming?, *in* N. McMillan, A. Embry, and D. Glass, eds., Devonian of the World: Canadian Petroleum Society Memoir 14, vol. 3, p. 29–34.

Tipsword, H.L., F.M. Setzer, and F.L. Smith, Jr., 1966, Interpretation of depositional environment in Gulf Coast petroleum exploration from paleoecology and related stratigraphy: Transactions of the Gulf Coast Association of Geological Societies, vol. 16, p. 119–130.

Tissot, B.P., and O.N. Welte, 1984, Petroleum Formation and Occurrence: Berlin, Springer-Verlag, 233 p.

Traverse, A., 1988, Palaeopalynology: London, Unwin Hyman, 600 p.

______, 1994, Sedimentation of organic particles: Cambridge, Cambridge University Press, 547 p.

Treibs, A., 1934, On the occurrence of chlorophyll derivates in an oil shale of the Upper Triassic Period: Annales Chimie 509, p. 103–114.

Tyson, R. A., 1995, Sedimentary organic matter—organic facies and palynofacies: London, Chapman & Hall, 651 p.

van Gizjel, P., 1980, Characterization and identification of kerogen and bitumen and determination of thermal maturation by means of qualitative and quantitative microscopical techniques, *in* How to Assess Maturation and Paleotemperatures: SEPM Short Course Notes, p. 1–56.

Van Wagoner, J.C., R.M. Mitchum, K.M. Campion, and V.D. Rahmanian, 1990, Siliciclastic sequence stratigraphy in well logs, cores, and outcrops: AAPG Methods in Exploration 7, 55 p.

Volkman, J.K., 1986, A review of sterol markers for marine and terrigenous organic matter: Organic Geochemistry, vol. 9, p. 83–99.

Whittaker, M. F., 1984, The usage of palynostratigraphy and palynofacies in definition of Troll field geology: Norwegian Petroleum Society Offshore North Seas Conference, paper 66, p. 1–50.

______, M.R. Giles, and S.J.C. Cannon, 1992, Palynological review of the Brent Group, UK sector, North Sea, *in* A.C. Morton, R.S. Haszeldine, M.R. Giles, and S. Brown, eds., Geology of the Brent Group: Geological Society Special Publication 61, p. 169–202.

Wolfe, J. A., 1979, Temperature parameters of humid to mesic forests of eastern Asia and relation to forests of other regions of the northern hemisphere and Australia: U.S. Geological Survey Professional Paper 1106-K, 37 p.

Wright, J.D., and K.G. Miller, 1993, Southern Ocean influences on late Eocene to Miocene deep-water circulation: American Geophysical Union Antarctic Research Series, vol. 60, p. 1–25.

Section G
Contributors

Introduction

Many individuals were involved in creating this chapter. They are listed below by section, including their corporate affiliation at the time of printing.

John F. Baesemann (Amoco E&P Technology Group [retired], Houston)
Lisanne A. Balcells-Baldwin (Consultant, Houston)
Sheila C. Barnette (BP Amoco, Houston)
Paul E. Belanger (Consultant, Houston)
James A. Bergen (Amoco E&P Technology Group, Houston)
Gregg H. Blake (Unocal, Sugar Land)
Denise M. Butler (Pennzenergy, Houston)
Charles E. Cline (Marshall Miller & Assoc., Bluefield, VA)
Kevin J. Crotty (Amoco Worldwide Exploration Group, Houston)
Julie A. d'Ablaing (BP Amoco, Houston)
Thomas D. Demchuk (Conoco, Houston)
Roy J. Enrico (Mobil Research and Development, Dallas)
Martin B. Farley (Exxon Exploration Co., Houston)
Robert L. Fleisher (Consultant, Houston)
James. H. Gamber (Amoco E&P Technology Group, Houston)
Anthony C. Gary (University of Utah, Salt Lake City)
Alfred F. Geen (Amoco E&P Technology Group [retired], Houston)
Lori B. Glassgold (Shell, Houston)
Garry D. Jones (Spirit Energy 76, Lafayette, Louisiana)
William N. Krebs (Amoco E&P Technology Group, Houston)
H. Richard Lane (National Science Foundation, Arlington, Virginia)
Rome G. Lytton III (Texaco, New Orleans)
Norman Macleod (The Natural History Museum, London)
Peter P. McLaughlin (Exxon Exploitation Co., Houston)
Kenneth G. Miller (Rutgers University, Piscataway, NJ)
Merrell A. Miller (Amoco E&P Technology Group, Tulsa)
Hilary C. Olson (University of Texas, Austin)
Brian J. O'Neill (Shell Offshore Inc., New Orleans)
Allen R. Ormiston (Pennwell, Geneva, Switzerland)
Mark A. Pasley (Amoco Worldwide Exploration Group, Houston)
Robert W. Pierce (Amoco E&P Technology Group, Houston)
Kirby Rodgers (Globat Biostrat Services, Dallas)
Stephan A. Root (Globat Biostrat Services, Dallas)
Ralph A. Salomon (Amoco E&P Technology Group, Houston)
Robert W. Scott (Precision Biostragraphy Assoc., Tulsa)
Jeffrey A. Stein (BP Amoco, Houston)
Herbert J. Sullivan (Amoco Production Co. [retired], Calgary)
Donald S. Van Nieuwenhuise (Amoco E&P Technology Group, Houston)
Ron F. Waszczak (Conoco, Houston)
V. Eileen Williams (Unocal, Sugar Land)
Gordon W. Wood (Amoco E&P Technology Group, Houston)

Chapter 18

Surface Geochemical Exploration for Petroleum

by

Dietmar Schumacher

Dietmar Schumacher

Dietmar "Deet" Schumacher is Director of Geochemistry at Geo-Microbial Technologies, Inc., in Ochelata, Oklahoma. He received his B.S. and M.S. degrees in geology from the University of Wisconsin and his Ph.D. from the University of Missouri. Deet taught at the University of Arizona before joining Phillips Petroleum in 1977. He held a variety of positions at Phillips, including Research Supervisor for petroleum geology and Senior Geological Specialist. Deet joined Pennzoil in 1982 and served as manager of geology/geochemistry before transferring to assignments with Pennzoil International, Pennzoil Offshore, and Pennzoil Technology Group. From 1994 to 1996, he was a Research Professor with the Earth Sciences and Resource Institute at the University of Utah.

Deet has a longstanding interest in the exploration and development applications of petroleum geochemistry, particularly surface exploration methods. He is editor, with Mike Abrams, of the recently published AAPG Memoir 66, *Hydrocarbon Migration and Its Near-Surface Expression.* He and Len LeSchack are now working on a follow-up volume for AAPG, *Surface Exploration Case Histories.* Deet is a Certified Petroleum Geologist (CPG-4301), a member of AAPG and GSA, and a past president of the Houston Geological Society.

Overview

Introduction

Surface indications of oil and gas seepage have been noted for thousands of years, and such seeps have led to the discovery of many important petroleum producing areas. Over the past sixty years, numerous geochemical and nonseismic geophysical surface exploration methods have been developed. The application of these geochemical prospecting methods to oil and gas exploration has resulted in varied success and occasional controversy. Few question the fact that hydrocarbons migrate to the surface in detectable amounts, but many remain uncertain of how such information can best be integrated into conventional exploration and development programs. This chapter examines surface geochemical prospecting technology and discusses its application.

In this chapter

This chapter contains the following sections.

Section A
Principles of Surface Geochemical Exploration

Introduction

Geochemical exploration for petroleum is the search for chemically identifiable surface or near-surface occurrences of hydrocarbons and their alteration products, which serve as clues to the location of undiscovered oil and gas accumulations. All surface geochemical methods assume that hydrocarbons generated and trapped at depth leak in varying but detectable quantities to the surface.

Geochemical exploration techniques can be direct or indirect. Direct techniques analyze small quantities of hydrocarbons that occur in the pore space of soil, that are adsorbed on the fine-grained portion of soil, or that are incorporated in soil cements. Indirect geochemical methods detect seepage-induced changes to soil, sediment, or vegetation.

Geological exploration data have found their greatest utility when integrated with geological and geophysical data. Poorly applied, the combination of surface and subsurface exploration methods leads to better prospect evaluation and risk assessment.

In this section

This section contains the following topics.

Basics

Definition

Geochemical exploration for petroleum is the search for chemically identifiable surface or near-surface occurrences of hydrocarbons and their alteration products, which serve as clues to the location of undiscovered oil and gas accumulations.

Surface geochemical principles

The past decade has seen a renewed interest in surface geochemical exploration. Coupled with developments in analytical and interpretive methods, this interest has produced a new body of data and insights, many of which are summarized in AAPG Memoir 66 (Schumacher and Abrams, 1996). There is now consensus with the following points:

- All petroleum basins exhibit some type of near-surface hydrocarbon leakage.
- Petroleum accumulations are dynamic and their seals are imperfect.
- Hydrocarbon seepage can be active or passive and is visible (macroseepage) or only detectable analytically (microseepage).
- Hydrocarbons move vertically through thousands of meters of strata without observable faults or fractures in a relatively short time (weeks to years).
- Migration is mainly vertical but can also occur over great distances laterally.
- Relationships between surface anomalies and subsurface accumulations range from simple to very complex.

Significance of anomalies

Surface indications of oil and gas seepage have been noted for thousands of years; such seeps have led to the discovery of many important petroleum producing areas. Although the discovery of a surface geochemical anomaly does not guarantee the discovery of commercially significant petroleum, it does establish the presence of hydrocarbons in the area of interest. Hydrocarbon seeps at the surface represent the end of the migration pathway. Traps and structures along such pathways should be considered significantly more prospective than those not associated with such anomalies.

Benefits

The potential benefits of a successful geochemical exploration program are many and include the following:

- Directly detect hydrocarbons and/or hydrocarbon-induced changes in soils, near-surface sediments, and/or on the sea floor.
- Document the presence of a working petroleum system in the area of interest.
- Permit high-grading of basins, plays, or prospects prior to acquiring leases or before conducting detailed seismic surveys.
- Permit postseismic high-grading of leads and prospects; generate geochemical leads for further geological or geophysical evaluation.
- Use geochemical data to infill between seismic lines and constrain mapping of AVO/amplitude anomalies between lines.
- Evaluate areas where seismic surveys are impractical or are ineffective due to geological or environmental factors.
- Provide methods applicable to both stratigraphic traps and structural traps, with the ability to locate traps invisible or poorly imaged with seismic data.
- Have little or no negative environmental impact (most surface geochemical methods).

Assumptions

Traps leak

The underlying assumption of all near-surface geochemical exploration techniques is that hydrocarbons are generated and/or trapped at depth and leak in varying but detectable quantities to the surface. This has long been established as fact, and the close association of surface geochemical anomalies with faults and fractures is well known (Horvitz, 1939, 1985; Jones and Drozd, 1983; Price, 1986). The surface expression of hydrocarbon seeps is best developed in areas with numerous well-developed migration pathways and an active petroleum system.

Anomalies relate to traps

A further assumption is that the anomaly at the surface can be related reliably to a petroleum accumulation at depth. The success with which this can be done is greatest in areas of relatively simple geology and becomes increasingly difficult as the geology becomes more complex. The geochemical or microbial anomaly at the surface represents the end of a petroleum migration pathway, a pathway that can range from short-distance vertical migration at one end of the spectrum to long-distance lateral migration at the other extreme (Thrasher et al., 1996b). Relationships between surface geochemical anomalies and subsurface accumulations can be complex; proper interpretation requires integrating seepage data with geological, geophysical, and hydrologic data. Understanding geology—and, hence, petroleum dynamics—is the key to using seepage data in exploration.

Seepage styles

The figure below shows examples of contrasting seepage styles and migration pathways from the Gulf of Mexico and the North Sea.

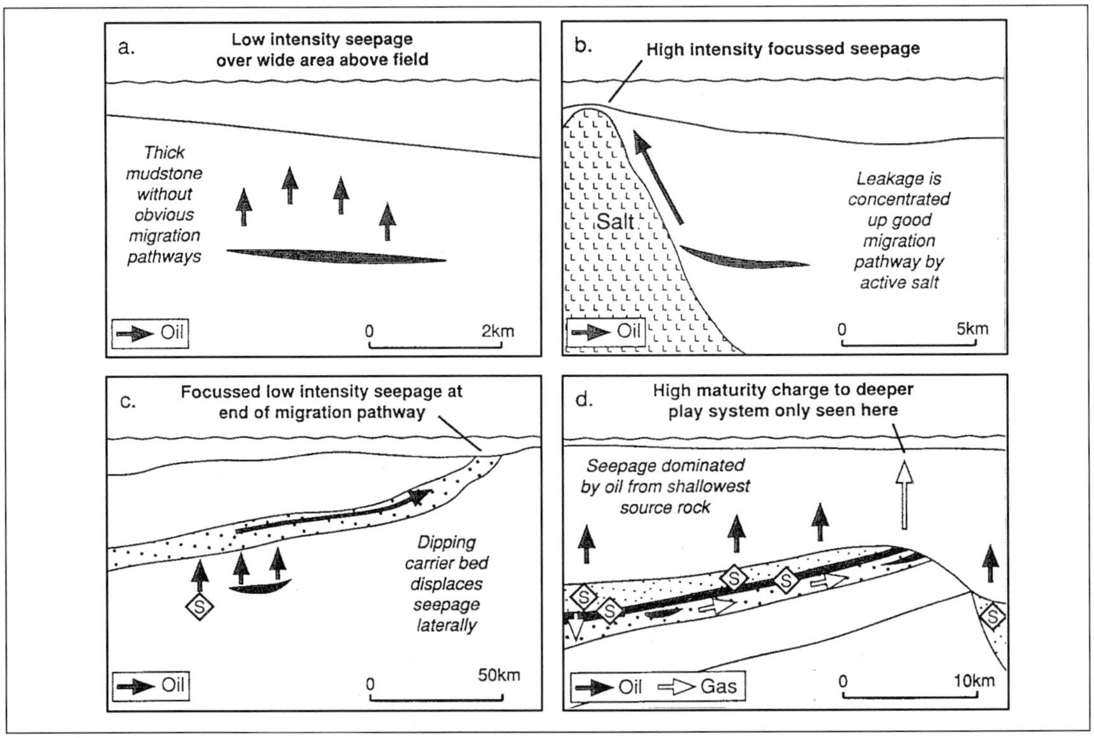

Figure 18–1. Modified from Thrasher et al., 1996b; courtesy AAPG.

Limitations and Uncertainties

Introduction

While the potential benefits of a successful surface geochemical exploration program are very real and can significantly affect the economics of an exploration or development program, the user must be aware of limitations associated with geochemical exploration methods. Some limitations of surface geochemical exploration are related to geology; others are related to the method itself.

Limitations related to geology

The following are limitations of surface geochemical prospecting related to geology:

- The geochemical expression of seepage is complex and varied.
- There is generally no simple one-to-one correlation between a surface anomaly and a subsurface accumulation. Some anomalies approximate the productive limits of an accumulation, but many do not.
- Successful integration of surface geochemical data with subsurface geology becomes increasingly difficult as the geology becomes more complex.
- False seep anomalies can be caused by reworked hydrocarbons and/or reworked source rocks.
- Reservoirs that are significantly underpressured or contain heavy oil may not be detected by some surface geochemical methods.

Limitations related to the method

The following are limitations of surface geochemical prospecting related to the method:

- No single method works everywhere; there are many methods to choose from.
- A surface anomaly generally cannot be related to a specific source reservoir or depth; however, compositional fingerprinting techniques can sometimes discriminate seepage from different reservoir zones.
- Undersampling and/or use of improper sampling techniques causes ambiguity that leads to interpretation failures.
- Discovery of a surface geochemical anomaly does not guarantee discovery of commercially significant volumes of hydrocarbon.
- Geochemical exploration methods cannot replace existing exploration technology; however, they can add value to existing geological and geophysical exploration data.

Seepage Activity

Types of seepage activity

Seepage activity refers to the relative rate of hydrocarbon seepage. Abrams (1992, 1996a) defines two distinct end members of seepage activity: active and passive.

Active seepage

The term **active seepage** refers to areas where subsurface hydrocarbons seep in large concentrations into shallow sediments and soils and into the overlying water column. Active seeps often display acoustic anomalies on conventional or high-resolution seismic profiles. Active seepage occurs in basins now actively generating hydrocarbons or that contain excellent migration pathways. These seeps are easily detected by most sampling techniques.

Passive seepage

Areas where subsurface hydrocarbons are not actively seeping are referred to as characterized by **passive seepage.** Such seeps usually contain low-molecular-weight hydrocarbons and volatile high-molecular-weight hydrocarbons above background levels. Acoustic anomalies may be present, but water column anomalies are rare. Anomalous levels of hydrocarbon seepage may only be detectable near major leak points or below the zone of maximum disturbance.

Zone of maximum disturbance

The **zone of maximum disturbance,** defined by Abrams (1992, 1996a), is a near-surface zone of variable depth and thickness in which sedimentary and biological processes alter or destroy volatile hydrocarbons. Anomalous concentrations of hydrocarbons may not be detectable if samples are not obtained from below the zone of maximum disturbance. The figure below illustrates the zone of maximum disturbance in shallow marine sediments. Deeper sampling may be required in areas of passive seepage.

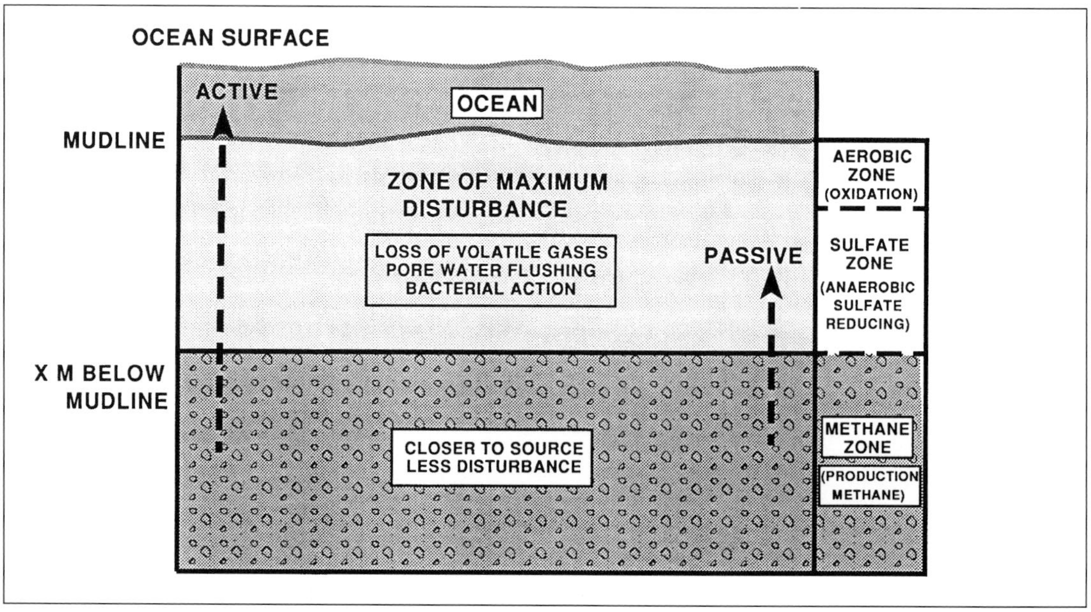

Figure 18–2. From Abrams, 1996a; courtesy AAPG.

Macroseepage vs. Microseepage

Macroseeps

There is a seepage continuum from the smallest detectable levels to visible oil and gas seeps. The term **macroseepage** refers to visible oil and gas seeps. Macroseeps are very localized areas containing large concentrations of light hydrocarbons as well as, if available, high-molecular-weight hydrocarbons. They are localized at the termination of faults, fractures, and outcropping unconformities or carrier beds. These visible seeps have led to the discovery of many of the world's important oil and gas producing areas (Link, 1952; Macgregor, 1993).

Microseeps

Microseepage is defined as high concentrations of analytically detectable volatile or semivolatile hydrocarbons in soils, sediments, or waters. These invisible seeps are recognized only by the presence of anomalous concentrations of the following:

- Light hydrocarbons (principally C_1–C_5)
- Volatile or semivolatile high-molecular-weight hydrocarbons (such as 2–4 ring aromatics)
- Hydrocarbon-oxidizing microbes
- Hydrocarbon-induced alteration products

High-molecular-weight hydrocarbons may be present in ever-wet or intermittently wet environments; however, only volatile or semivolatile hydrocarbons are expected above the water table. Most surface geochemical methods, including both direct and indirect methods, were developed to detect microseepage.

Microseepage evidence

The existence of microseepage is supported by a large body of empirical evidence (Price, 1986; Klusman, 1993; Klusman and Saeed, 1996; Matthews, 1996a). This includes the following:

- Increased concentration of light hydrocarbons and hydrocarbon-oxidizing microbes in soils and sediments above hydrocarbon reservoirs.
- Increased key light hydrocarbon ratios in soil gas over oil and gas reservoirs.
- Sharp lateral changes in these concentrations and ratios at the edges of the surface projections of these reservoirs.
- Similarity of stable carbon isotopic ratios for methane and other light hydrocarbons in soil gases to those found in underlying reservoirs.
- The disappearance and reappearance of soil gas and microbial anomalies in response to reservoir depletion and repressuring.

Microseep migration

Research and field studies suggest that the dominant migration medium is as a continuous-phase, buoyancy-driven gas flow within carrier and reservoir rocks and capillary imbibition in the transition from sources and seals into carrier rocks. Hydrocarbon microseepage is predominantly vertical and is dynamic; migration rates range from less than 1 meter per day to tens of meters per day (Arp, 1992; Klusman and Saeed, 1996; Matthews, 1996a).

Surface Expression

Geochemical evidence of seepage

The surface geochemical expression of petroleum seepage can take many forms:

- Anomalous hydrocarbon concentrations in sediment, soil, water, and even the atmosphere
- Microbiological anomalies and the formation of paraffin dirt
- Anomalous nonhydrocarbon gases such as helium and radon
- Mineralogical changes such as the formation of calcite, pyrite, uranium, elemental sulfur, and certain magnetic iron oxides and sulfides
- Clay mineral alterations
- Radiation anomalies
- Geothermal and hydrologic anomalies
- Bleaching of red beds
- Geobotanical anomalies
- Altered acoustical, electrical, and magnetic properties of soils and sediments

Oxidation reduction zones

Bacteria and other microbes play a profound role in the oxidation of migrating hydrocarbons. Their activities are directly or indirectly responsible for many of the diverse surface manifestations of petroleum seepage. These activities, coupled with long-term migration of hydrocarbons, lead to the development of near-surface oxidation-reduction zones that favor the formation of this variety of hydrocarbon-induced chemical and mineralogical changes. This seep-induced alteration is highly complex, and its varied surface expressions have led to the development of an equally varied number of geochemical exploration techniques. Some detect hydrocarbons directly in surface and seafloor samples, others detect seep-related microbial activity, and still others measure the secondary effects of hydrocarbon-induced alteration (Schumacher, 1996; Saunders et al., 1999). The figure below shows a generalized model of hydrocarbon microseepage and hydrocarbon-induced effects on soils and sediments.

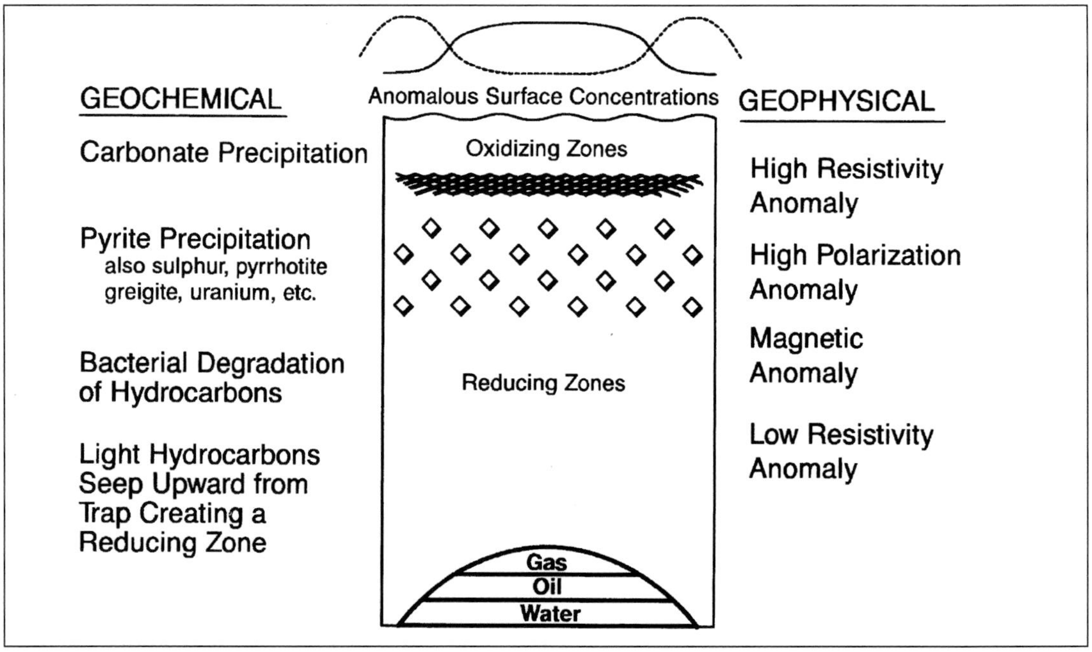

Figure 18–3. From Schumacher, 1996; courtesy AAPG.

Section B

Designing Surface Geochemical Surveys

Introduction

Survey design and sampling strategy for geochemical surveys must be dictated by the exploration objectives, expected target size, and logistical consideration. Best results are realized when surface geochemical survey design is integrated with all available geological and geophysical data. This section reviews methods available for surface geochemical surveys and discusses how to design a survey for maximum effectiveness.

In this section

This section contains the following topics.

Hydrocarbon Detection Methods

Direct methods

Direct detection methods are geochemical exploration methods designed to detect the presence of hydrocarbons in soils, near-surface sediments, seafloor sediments, and waters.

Detection of light hydrocarbons

The analysis of light hydrocarbons (chiefly methane through pentane) in soils and soil gases represents one of the earliest surface geochemical methods used and is one of the most researched and tested geochemical survey approaches. Light hydrocarbons can reside in soils and shallow sediments in a number of ways:

- Free gas in the effective porosity
- Interstitial gas occluded in pore spaces between grains
- Gas adsorbed onto sedimentary particles or trapped within carbonate cements
- Gas dissolved in water or present in the atmosphere

Detection of heavier hydrocarbons

Volatile and semivolatile heavier hydrocarbons such as aromatic compounds, gasoline-range hydrocarbons, and even normal or biodegraded oils can also be found, particularly where migration occurs along fault and fracture pathways. These different manifestations have led to the development of different techniques for sampling and analyzing hydrocarbons. It is beyond the scope of this chapter to discuss the advantages and limitations of specific methods or sampling procedures; however, such information is available in publications by Abrams (1996a), Barwise and Hay (1996), Brooks et al. (1986), Horvitz (1985), Jones and Drozd (1983), Klusman (1993), Price (1986), Richers and Maxwell (1991), Schiemer et al. (1985), and Schumacher and Abrams (1996).

Indirect methods

Indirect methods for detecting hydrocarbon seepage and microseepage are based on what are assumed to be seepage-induced soil and sediment alteration. Indirect detection methods include the following:

- Microbial
- Helium
- Radiometrics
- Iodine
- Soil alteration
- Trace elements
- Electrical
- Magnetics
- Biogeochemical
- Geobotanical

Indirect detection of hydrocarbons

Some indirect detection methods are better understood and more consistently reliable than others. Microbial methods, for example, detect the presence of hydrocarbon-oxidizing microbes in soils and sediments. These microbes would not be expected to be present in significant concentrations if there were no hydrocarbon source present, such as from a hydrocarbon seep or microseep. Helium, by contrast, is not uniquely associated with petroleum. However, it is a common constituent of petroleum accumulations and due to its mobility, chemical inertness, and abiogenic nature forms a very good indirect geochemical marker.

Hydrocarbon Detection Methods, continued

Indirect detection of hydrocarbons (continued)

The formation of radiation anomalies and other secondary alteration anomalies (soil carbonate, iodine, trace metal, Eh, pH, electrical, magnetic, geobotanical, etc.) is less well understood. The cause of these altered soils and sediments may well be seepage related, but migrating hydrocarbons are an indirect cause at best and not always the most probable cause. Even if due to hydrocarbons, the cause could be shallow biogenic gas and thus unrelated to leakage from deeper oil and gas accumulations.

Additional information about these various indirect geochemical methods can be found in Al Shaieb et al. (1994; general), Beghtel et al. (1987; microbial), Cunningham et al. (1987; helium), Curry (1984; radiometrics), Duchscherer (1984; soil carbonate), Foote (1996; magnetics), Klusman (1993; general), Machel (1996; magnetics), Price (1993; microbial), Rock (1984; geobotany), Saunders et al. (1999; general); Schumacher (1996; general), Schumacher and Abrams (1996; general), Sternberg (1991; electrical), Tedesco (1995; iodine), and Weart and Heimberg (1981; radiometrics).

Geochemical Survey Objectives

Principal objectives

The principal objectives of a geochemical exploration survey are to

(1) establish the presence, distribution, and composition of hydrocarbons in the area of exploration or development interest and
(2) determine the probable hydrocarbon charge to specific exploration leads and prospects.

Reconnaissance objectives

The objective of a reconnaissance survey is to find seeps and microseeps that provide direct evidence that thermogenic hydrocarbons have been generated, i.e., they document the presence of a working petroleum system. Additionally, the composition of these seeps can indicate whether a basin or play is oil prone or gas prone (Jones and Drozd, 1983). Hydrocarbons from surface and seafloor seeps can be correlated with known oils and gases to identify the specific petroleum system(s) present. Seepage data allow the explorationist to screen large areas quickly and economically, determining where additional and more costly exploration is warranted. For example, results of preseismic geochemical surveys can guide the location and extent of subsequent seismic acquisition by ensuring that areas with significant hydrocarbon anomalies are covered by seismic data.

Published examples of reconnaissance surface geochemical surveys include Abrams (1992), Piggot and Abrams (1996), Schiemer et al. (1995), Thrasher et al. (1996a), and Williams et al. (1995).

Evaluating leads and prospects

If the objective is to evaluate individual exploration leads and prospects, the results of geochemical surveys can identify those leads associated with strong hydrocarbon anomalies and thereby enable high-grading prospects on the basis of their association with hydrocarbon indicators. Regional geochemical surveys can help determine which leases should be renewed and which ones do not warrant additional expense. Detailed seepage surveys can also generate geochemical leads for evaluation with geologic and seismic data—leads that might otherwise go unnoticed. Published examples of these kinds of applications include Foote (1996), Lopez et al. (1994), Potter et al. (1996), Rice (1989), and Saunders et al. (1993).

Evaluating development projects

For development projects, detailed microseepage surveys can help evaluate infill or step-out drilling locations, delineate productive limits of undeveloped fields, and identify bypassed pay or undrained reservoir compartments. Hydrocarbon microseepage surveys have the potential to add value to 2-D and 3-D seismic data by identifying those features or reservoir compartments that are hydrocarbon charged. Published studies of development applications are few but include Belt and Rice (1996), Rice (1986), Schumacher et al. (1997), and Tucker and Hitzman (1994).

Selecting a Survey Method

Introduction

How does one select a method(s) for a surface geochemical exploration program? The choice of method(s) depends on the kinds of questions you hope the survey results will answer.

- What are the objectives of the survey—to demonstrate the presence of an active petroleum system in a frontier area, to high-grade previously defined exploration leads and prospects, or to determine the type of petroleum (i.e., oil vs. gas) likely to be encountered?
- What other data are presently available for the area of interest (satellite imagery, aeromagnetics, gravity, seismic, etc.)?
- What geochemical methods have previously been used successfully in the area of interest or in a geologic analog area?
- What limitations are imposed by the survey area (onshore or offshore, deep water or shallow, jungle or desert, mature basin or remote area, budget and personnel constraints)?

Direct vs. indirect methods

As a generalization, direct hydrocarbon methods are preferred over indirect methods because they can provide evidence of the very hydrocarbons we hope to find in our traps and reservoirs. Additionally, chemical and isotopic analysis of these hydrocarbons, especially the high-molecular-weight hydrocarbons, can provide insight into the nature and maturity of the source rock that generated these hydrocarbons.

Offshore methods

The table below lists the principal geochemical methods used for offshore exploration.

Medium to be Sampled	Target to be Analyzed	Methods
Atmosphere	Hydrocarbons	Radar or laser
Water surface	Oil slicks or sheens	Satellite, airborne sensors (radar, multispectral, hyperspectral, laser, fluorescence), or direct sampling
Water	Dissolved hydrocarbons (LMW, HMW, or aromatics)	Marine sniffer, water analysis
Sea bottom	Hydrocarbon macro- or microseepage	High-resolution seismic, side-scan sonar, direct sampling (gravity core, vibro-core, piston core, jet core, etc.)
	Hydrocarbon-induced alteration	Topographic, acoustic, and temperature contrasts; sediment sampling for microbial or geochemical indicators

Selecting a Survey Method, continued

Onshore methods

The table below lists the principal geochemical methods used for onshore exploration.

Medium to be Sampled	Target to be Analyzed	Methods
Land surface	Oil and gas macroseeps,stains, impregnations	Geologic mapping; historical records; satellite and airborne sensors (multispectral, hyperspectral); direct sampling of seeps, stains
	Hydrocarbon microseeps	Soil/sediment sampling for hydrocarbon analysis
	Hydrocarbon-induced alteration	Soil/sediment sampling for indirect microbial or geochemical indicators, aeromagnetic, electrical, or radiometric
Soil air	Light hydrocarbons	Probe or adsorptive collectors
	Nonhydrocarbons	Probe or adsorptive collectors
Soil/sediment	Light hydrocarbons, aromatics	Sample disaggregation and/or acid extraction for chromatography, UV-fluorescence
	Nonhydrocarbons or diagenetic anomalies	Hydrocarbon-oxidizing microbes, soil salts (i.e., carbonates, chloride, iodine, sulfate, etc.); clay minerals; trace metals; magnetic susceptibility, aeromagnetics, ground magnetics; electrical (IP, CSAMT, resistivity, MT); radiometrics

Recommendations

Whenever possible, use more than one geochemical survey method, for example, combine a direct method with an indirect method. The use of multiple methods can reduce interpretation uncertainty because seepage-related anomalies tend to be reinforced while random highs and lows tend to cancel each other. If surface conditions or budgetary constraints preclude the use of direct hydrocarbon detection methods, the next best choice is the indirect method most closely linked to hydrocarbons and hydrocarbon accumulations (microbial, helium, and perhaps certain magnetic and radiometric methods).

Designing a Geochemical Survey

Design considerations

Survey design and sampling strategy for geochemical surveys should be flexible and must be dictated by the following:

- Exploration objectives
- Geologic setting
- Basin hydrodynamics
- Anticipated target size and shape of the anomaly (or geologic target)
- Ability to sample along (and/or between) key seismic lines
- Logistical considerations
- Expected natural variation in surface measurements
- Probable signal-to-noise ratio (Matthews, 1996b)

Procedure

Use the table below as a guide for designing a surface geochemical survey.

Step	Action
1	Research the method(s); investigate contractor, past clients.
2	Use more than one geochemical survey method when possible.
3	Be guided by past experience in the basin or exploration trend.
4	Base the geochemical sample program on the target's size, geology.
5	Conduct a calibration survey(s) over an analog field or recent discovery.
6	Integrate available geological and geophysical data to achieve the most meaningful results.

Sample locations

In frontier areas, geochemical exploration often begins with a search for, and analysis of, visible oil and gas seeps. Additional geochemical data may then be acquired along the trace of existing seismic lines or along regional geochemical traverses located to cross features of geologic and structural significance. Depending on survey objectives, sample spacing for geochemical surveys may vary from 500–1,000 m at one extreme to 50–100 m at the other. Sampling along geochemical grids is recommended for small exploration targets and/or 3-D seismic programs; however, grids are not cost effective for large reconnaissance surveys.

Analogs

Whenever possible, it is advisable to acquire surface geochemical data over a nearby geologic analog or recent discovery. A dry hole can be as valuable an analog as a recent discovery if the well penetrated the target horizon and found it water wet (or lacking the reservoir facies).

Seeps

Oil and gas seeps, if present, are also valuable analogs because they permit direct correlation of seeping hydrocarbons with soil gas and fluorescence data as well as other microbial or geochemical data. Old producing fields may not provide good analogs since production and pressure decline may have reduced or even eliminated their surface geochemical expression (Horvitz, 1969).

Sample density

Hydrocarbon microseepage data, whether soil gas or microbial or other geochemical measurements, are inherently noisy and require adequate sample density to distinguish between anomalous and background areas. Matthews (1996b) reviews the importance of sampling design and sampling density in target recognition. He states that undersampling is probably the major cause of ambiguity and interpretation failures involving surface geochemical studies.

Recognizing anomalies

Defining background values adequately is an essential part of anomaly recognition and delineation; Matthews (1996b) suggests that as many as 80% of the samples collected be obtained outside the area of interest. This is a good recommendation for reconnaissance and prospect evaluation surveys. However, for very small targets such as pinnacle reefs or channel sandstones, optimum results are obtained when numerous samples are collected in a closely spaced grid pattern, (100–160-m sample interval or less) over the feature of interest (Schumacher et al., 1997).

Example

The recognition of surface geochemical anomalies improves by increasing sample number and reducing sample spacing. The example below from Oklahoma illustrates the value of geochemical grids over geochemical traverses for anomaly recognition.

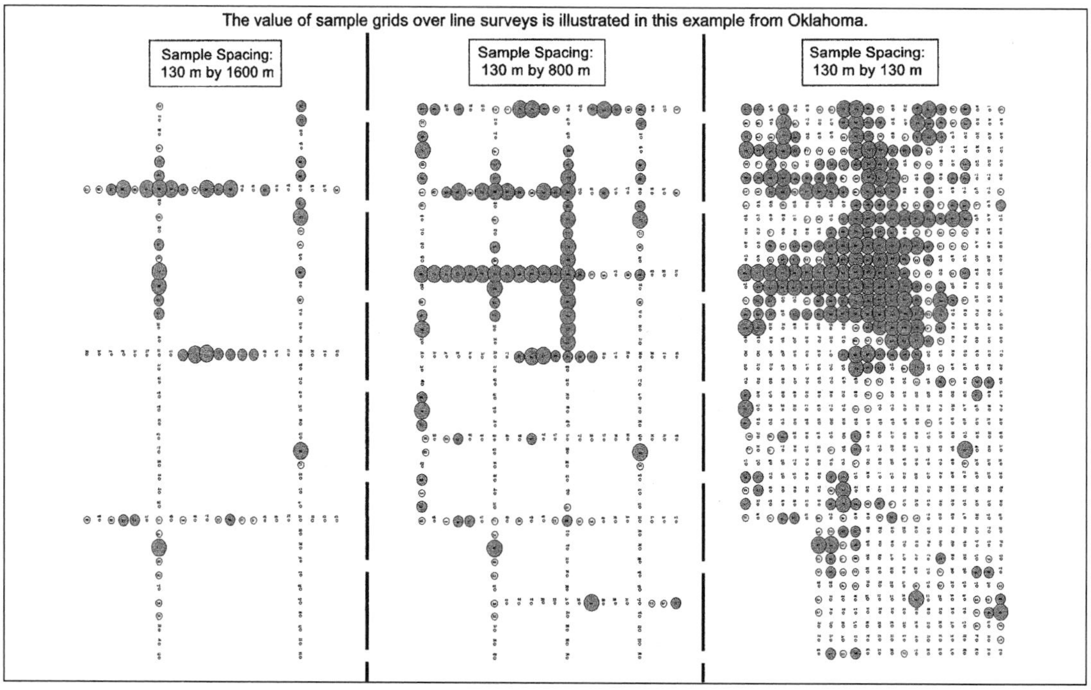

Figure 18–4. Courtesy Geo-Microbial Technologies, Inc.

Interpretation Guidelines

Introduction

The presence of hydrocarbon macroseeps or microseeps in the area of a geochemical survey is direct evidence that petroleum has been generated. Hydrocarbon seepage at the surface represents the end of a petroleum migration pathway. These hydrocarbons may represent hydrocarbon leakage from an accumulation or leakage along a carrier bed or other migration pathway. Anomalies defined by multiple samples from one or more survey lines may indicate the location of discrete structural or stratigraphic targets within the survey area.

Anomalies and vertical migration

If the basin or play is characterized by predominantly vertical migration, then the correlation of a strong geochemical anomaly at the surface with a possible trap at depth suggests that the trap is charged with hydrocarbons. Conversely, if the trap is not associated with a positive geochemical anomaly, we assume the trap is not charged with hydrocarbons.

Anomalies and lateral migration

If the structural or geologic setting of the area suggests that microseepage may be predominantly lateral or pathway selective, such as along dipping stratigraphic surfaces and unconformities, the interpretation will be more difficult since geochemical anomalies may then not be located vertically above a trap. Which of these migration scenarios is more likely in your area of investigation? What is the relationship of the anomalies to outcrop geology, mapped structural closures, stratigraphic pinch-outs, faults, or basement highs? Because relationships between surface geochemical anomalies and subsurface accumulations can be complex, proper interpretation requires integration of surface geochemical data with geologic, geophysical, and hydrologic data. The importance of such integration cannot be overstated (Thrasher et al., 1996b).

Hydrocarbon composition from macroseeps

Hydrocarbon seep composition can play an important role in evaluating the exploration potential of a basin, play, or prospect. Petroleum in most visible oil and gas seeps (i.e., macroseeps) generally has been altered by processes such as biodegradation, water washing, and evaporative loss of volatile components. Despite these changes, chemical and isotopic analysis of such seeps can enable inferences about the nature of the source rock facies and maturity as well as permit correlation with known source rocks and reservoired petroleum.

Hydrocarbon composition from microseeps

Obtaining compositional information from the analysis of hydrocarbon microseeps is more difficult because microseeps generally consist of only light hydrocarbons (methane through pentane). Sometimes, however, the heavier gasoline-range and aromatic hydrocarbons are also present. One can infer the composition of the migrating petroleum from these light hydrocarbons from soil gas/hydrocarbon ratios, carbon isotopic composition of soil gases, fluorescence characteristics of soil or sediment extracts, and chromatographic analysis of such extracts. A detailed discussion of these methodologies is beyond the scope of this article, but published examples of such analyses and their interpretations include Abrams (1996b), Barwise and Hay (1996), Belt and Rice (1996), Brooks et al. (1986), Horvitz (1985), Jones and Drozd (1983), Kornacki (1996), Piggot and Abrams (1996), Schiemer et al. (1985), Stahl et al. (1981), and Thrasher et al. (1996a).

Section C
Case Histories

Introduction

The case histories presented in this section document the effectiveness of geochemical surveys.

In this section

This section contains the following topics.

Case History 1: Structural Traps

Introduction

Meyer et al. (1983) published an excellent but little-known case history documenting vertical migration and microseepage from undisturbed structural traps. In the early 1980s, a series of microseepage surveys were conducted over 49 proposed well locations in Kansas and Colorado.

Sampling

Soil samples were collected at one-tenth-mile intervals within one-half mile of each proposed drilling site and analyzed for the presence of hydrocarbon-oxidizing microbes. All samples were collected and analyzed prior to drilling, and the results were placed in escrow until after the wells were drilled.

Survey vs. drilling results

When compared with the subsequent drilling results, the soils overlying productive reservoirs contained microbial populations that were readily distinguishable from those of samples that were collected from nonproductive sites. The 39 wells subsequently drilled yielded three producers, three wells with uncommercial shows, and 33 dry holes. The microbial survey correctly predicted all 33 dry holes and identified the three producing wells and two of the three wells with uncommercial shows. The one show well that was not recognized tested 9 BO/D with a very low GOR.

The figure below illustrates ten representative seismic prospects surveyed and later drilled. Each prospect displays good four-way dip closure on a Cretaceous horizon, and each is located in a productive basin. Only one was associated with a surface geochemical anomaly; it was the only one of the ten shown that resulted in a commercial discovery.

Figure 18–5. Based on Meyer et al., 1983; courtesy Barringer Technologies Inc.

Case History 2: Stratigraphic Trap

Introduction

In this case history, the client conducted a soil gas hydrocarbon survey along the trace of the seismic line to look for evidence of hydrocarbon microseepage from a seismically defined trap at CDP 1070 (Figure 18–6, left). Propane soil gas anomalies were detected at CDP 1070 and 1096. The wildcat well drilled at CDP 1070 resulted in a new field discovery. The geochemical lead at CDP 1096 was reevaluated seismically. After additional processing, a revised interpretation (right) also predicted porosity development there and coincident with the surface geochemical anomaly. A second productive well was drilled at CDP 1096.

This is a good example, illustrating how we can use surface geochemical data to evaluate a geophysical lead and a geochemical lead.

Anomaly map

The figure below is a seismic section and soil gas profile of a stratigraphic trap located at approximately 5,600 ft (1.5 sec) in the Cretaceous Escondido Sandstone in La Salle County, Texas.

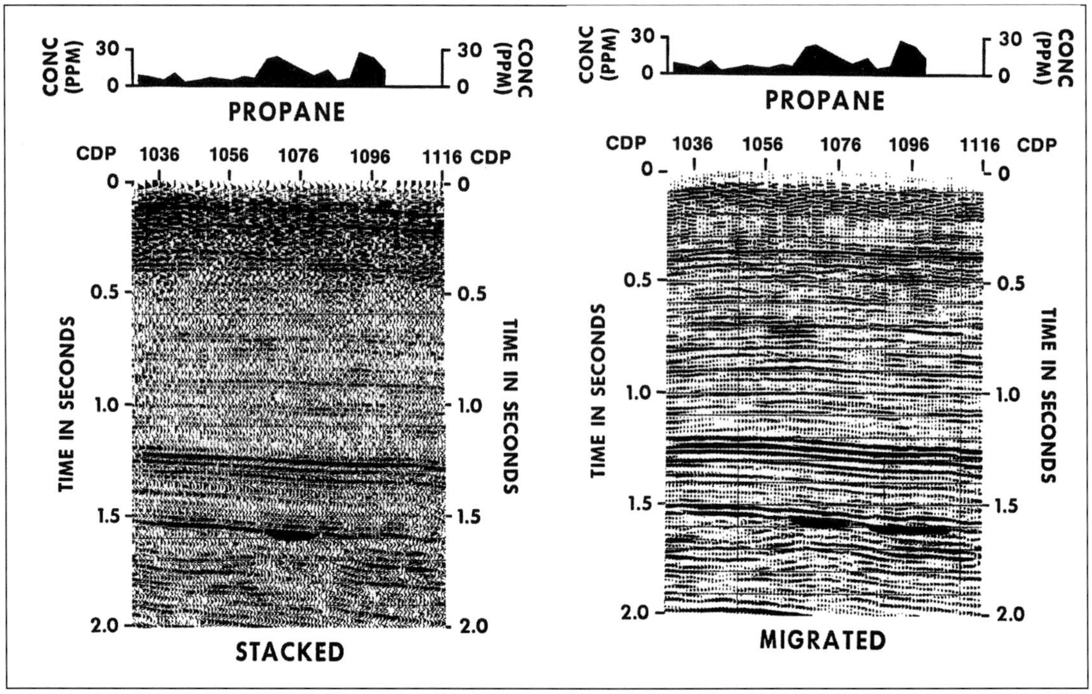

Figure 18–6. Modified from Rice, 1989; courtesy Oil & Gas Journal.

Case History 3: Predrilling/Postdrilling Comparison

Introduction

The significance of surface geochemical anomalies in hydrocarbon exploration are often difficult to quantify. Potter et al. (1996) summarize one company's experience with a soil gas geochemical method. Their exploration program involved geochemical surveys of 139 prospects located in both mature basins and frontier basins, onshore and offshore, in a wide variety of environments. Targets ranged in depth from 1,000–15,000 ft (305–4,572 m) and covered the full spectrum of trap styles; survey areas ranged from as small as a few hundred acres to regional programs covering 1,000 mi^2 (2,590 km^2).

Results

The 139 surveys led to the drilling of 141 wells in previously undrilled prospects. A total of 43 wells were drilled in negative geochemical anomalies, and 41 of these encountered no hydrocarbons. Of the 98 wells drilled in positive geochemical anomalies, 92% encountered reservoired hydrocarbons and 76% were completed as producers. This company's experience is fairly typical and documents that integration of seismic data and geochemical data yields greater definition of exploration targets than provided by either method separately.

Conclusion

Although the discovery of a surface geochemical anomaly does not guarantee the discovery of commercially significant hydrocarbons, it does establish the presence of hydrocarbons in the area of exploration interest. Seeps and microseeps at the surface represent the end of a petroleum migration pathway. Traps and structures along such migration pathways should be considered significantly more prospective than those not associated with hydrocarbon anomalies.

Surface geochemical exploration methods cannot replace conventional exploration methods, but they can be a powerful complement to them. Geochemical and other surface methods have found their greatest utility when used in conjunction with available geological and geophysical information. The need for such an integrated approach cannot be overemphasized. Properly applied, the combination of surface and subsurface methods will lead to better prospect evaluation and risk assessment.

Section D
References

Abrams, M.A., 1992, Geophysical and geochemical evidence for subsurface hydrocarbon leakage in the Bering Sea, Alaska: Marine and Petroleum Geology Bulletin, vol. 9, p. 208–221.

______ 1996a, Distribution of subsurface hydrocarbon seepage in near-surface marine sediments, *in* D. Schumacher and M.A. Abrams, eds., Hydrocarbon Migration and Its Near-Surface Expression: AAPG Memoir 66, p. 1–14.

______ 1996b, Interpretation of methane carbon isotopes extracted from surficial marine sediments for detection of subsurface hydrocarbons, *in* D. Schumacher and M.A. Abrams, eds., Hydrocarbon Migration and Its Near-Surface Expression: AAPG Memoir 66, p. 309–318.

Arp, G.K., 1992, Effusive microseepage: a first approximation model for light hydrocarbon movement in the subsurface: Assoc. Petroleum Geochemical Explorationists Bulletin, vol. 8, p. 1–17.

Al Shaieb, Z., J. Cairns, and J. Puckette, 1994, Hydrocarbon-induced diagenetic aureoles: indicators of deeper, leaky reservoirs: Assoc. of Petroleum Geochemical Explorationists Bulletin, vol. 10, p. 24–48.

Barwise, T., and S. Hay, 1996, Predicting oil properties from core fluorescence, *in* D. Schumacher and M.A. Abrams, eds., Hydrocarbon Migration and Its Near-Surface Expression: AAPG Memoir 66, p. 363–371.

Beghtel, F.W., D.O. Hitzman, and K.R. Sundberg, 1987, Microbial oil survey technique (MOST) evaluation of new field wildcat wells in Kansas: Assoc. of Petroleum Geochemical Explorationists Bulletin, vol. 3, p. 1–14.

Belt, J.Q., and G.K. Rice, 1996, Offshore 3D seismic, geochemical data integration, Main Pass project, Gulf of Mexico: Oil & Gas Journal, vol. 94, no. 14, p. 76–81, and vol. 94, no. 15, p. 100–102.

Brooks, J.M., M.C. Kennicutt, and B.D. Carey, 1986, Offshore surface geochemical exploration: Oil & Gas Journal, October 20, p. 66–72.

Cunningham, K.I., A.A. Roberts, and T.J. Donovan, 1987, Horizontal-gradient magnetic and helium surveys, in K.J. Bird and L.B. Magoon, eds., Petroleum Geology of the Northern Part of the Arctic National Wildlife Refuge, Alaska: USGS Bulletin 1178, p. 209–218.

Curry, W.H., III, 1984, Evaluation of surface gamma radiation surveys for petroleum exploration in the deep Powder River basin, Wyoming, in M.J. Davidson, ed., Unconventional Methods in Exploration for Petroleum and Natural Gas III: Dallas, Southern Methodist Univ. Press, p. 25–39.

Duchscherer, W., Jr., 1984, Geochemical hydrocarbon prospecting, with case histories: Tulsa, PennWell Publishing Co., 196 p.

Foote, R. S., 1996, Relationship of near-surface magnetic anomalies to oil- and gas-producing areas, *in* D. Schumacher and M. A. Abrams, eds., Hydrocarbon Migration and Its Near-Surface Expression: AAPG Memoir 66, p. 111–126.

Horvitz, L., 1939, On geochemical prospecting: Geophysics, vol. 4, p. 210–228.

______ 1969, Hydrocarbon prospecting after thirty years, *in* W.B. Heroy, ed., Unconventional Methods in Exploration for Petroleum and Natural Gas: Dallas, Southern Methodist Univ. Press, p. 205–218.

______ 1985, Geochemical exploration for petroleum: Science, vol. 229, p. 821–827.

Jones, V.T., and R.J. Drozd, 1983, Predictions of oil or gas potential by near-surface geochemistry: AAPG Bulletin, vol. 67, p. 932–952.

Klusman, R.W., 1993, Soil gas and related methods for natural resource exploration: New York, John Wiley & Sons, 483 pp.

______ and M.A. Saeed, 1996, Comparison of light hydrocarbon microseepage mechanisms, *in* D. Schumacher and M. A. Abrams, eds., Hydrocarbon Migration and Its Near-Surface Expression: AAPG Memoir 66, p. 157–168.

Kornacki, A.S., 1996, Petroleum geology and geochemistry of Miocene source rocks and heavy petroleum samples from Huasna Basin, California, *in* D. Schumacher and M. A. Abrams, eds., Hydrocarbon Migration and Its Near-Surface Expression: AAPG Memoir 66, p. 413–430.

Link, W.K., 1952, Significance of oil and gas seeps in world oil exploration: AAPG Bulletin, vol. 36, p. 1505–1541.

Lopez, J.P., D.C. Hitzman, and J.D. Tucker, 1994, Combined microbial, seismic surveys predict oil and gas occurrences in Bolivia: Oil & Gas Journal, October 24, p. 68–70.

Macgregor, D.S., 1993, Relationships between seepage, tectonics, and subsurface petroleum reserves: Marine and Petroleum Geology, vol. 10, p. 606–619.

Machel, H.G., 1996, Magnetic contrasts as a result of hydrocarbon seepage and migration, *in* D. Schumacher and M.A. Abrams, eds., Hydrocarbon Migration and Its Near-Surface Expression: AAPG Memoir 66, p. 99–109.

Matthews, M.D., 1996a, Migration a view from the top, *in* D. Schumacher and M. A. Abrams, eds., Hydrocarbon Migration and Its Near-Surface Expression: AAPG Memoir 66, p. 139–155.

______ 1996b, Importance of sampling design and density in target recognition, *in* D. Schumacher and M.A. Abrams, eds., Hydrocarbon Migration and Its Near-Surface Expression: AAPG Memoir 66, p. 243–253.

Meyer, W.T., J.S. Lovell, and M. Hale, 1983, Detection of concealed mineral and energy resources by vapor geochemistry, *in* I. Thornton and R. J. Howarth, eds., Applied Geochemistry in the 1980s: London, Graham and Trotman, p. 86–102.

Piggott, N., and M.A. Abrams, 1996, Near-surface coring in the Beaufort and Chukchi Seas, northern Alaska, *in* D. Schumacher and M.A. Abrams, eds., Hydrocarbon Migration and Its Near-Surface Expression: AAPG Memoir 66, p. 385–399.

Potter, R.W., II, P.A. Harrington, A.H. Silliman, and J.H. Viellenave, 1996, Significance of geochemical anomalies in hydrocarbon exploration: one company's experience, *in* D. Schumacher and M. A. Abrams, eds., Hydrocarbon Migration and Its Near-Surface Expression: AAPG Memoir 66, p. 431–439.

Price, L. C., 1986, A critical overview and proposed working model of surface geochemical exploration, *in* M. J. Davidson, ed., Unconventional Methods in Exploration for Petroleum and Natural Gas IV: Dallas, Texas, Southern Methodist Univ. Press, p. 81–129.

_____ 1993, Microbial soil surveying: preliminary results and implications for surface geochemical oil exploration: Assoc. Petroleum Geochemical Explorationists Bulletin, vol. 9, p. 81–129.

Rice, G., 1986, Near-surface hydrocarbon gas measurement of vertical migration, *in* M. J. Davidson, ed., Unconventional Methods in Exploration for Petroleum and Natural Gas IV: Dallas, Southern Methodist Univ. Press, p. 183–200.

_____ 1989, Exploration enhancement by integrating near-surface geochemical and seismic methods: Oil & Gas Journal, v. 87, no. 14 (April 3), p. 66–71.

Richers, D.M., and L.E. Maxwell, 1991, Application and theory of soil gas geochemistry in petroleum exploration, *in* R.K. Merrill, ed., Source and Migration Processes and Techniques: AAPG Treatise of Petroleum Geology, Handbook of Petroleum Geology, p. 141–158.

Rock, B.N., 1984, Remote detection of geobotanical anomalies associated with hydrocarbon microseepage using Thematic Mapper Simulation (TMS) and Airborne Imaging Spectrometer (AIS) data: International Union of Geological Sciences and UNESCO, BRGM document no. 82, p. 299–309.

Saunders, D.F., K.R. Burson, J.J. Brown, and C.K. Thompson, 1993, Combined geological and surface geochemical methods discovered Agaritta and Brady Creek fields, Concho County, Texas: AAPG Bulletin, vol. 77, p. 1219–1240.

_____, _____, and C.K. Thompson, 1999, Model for hydrocarbon microseepage and related near-surface alterations: AAPG Bulletin, vol. 83, p. 170–185.

Schiemer, E.J., G. Stober, and E. Faber, 1985, Surface geochemical exploration for hydrocarbons in offshore areas—principles, methods and results, *in* Petroleum Geochemistry in Exploration of the Norwegian Shelf: London, Graham and Trotman, p. 223–238.

Schumacher, D., 1996, Hydrocarbon-induced alteration of soils and sediments, *in* D. Schumacher and M.A. Abrams, eds., Hydrocarbon Migration and Its Near-Surface Expression: AAPG Memoir 66, p. 71–89.

______ and M.A. Abrams, eds., 1996, Hydrocarbon Migration and Its Near-Surface Expression: AAPG Memoir 66, 445 p.

______, D.C. Hitzman, J. Tucker, and B. Roundtree, 1997, Applying high-resolution surface geochemistry to assess reservoir compartmentalization and monitor hydrocarbon drainage, *in* R.J. Kruizenga and M.W. Downey, eds., Applications of Emerging Technologies: Unconventional Methods in Exploration for Oil and Gas V: Dallas, Texas, Southern Methodist Univ. Press, p. 309–322.

Stahl, W., E. Faber, B.D. Carey, and D.L. Kirksey, 1981, Near-surface evidence of migration of natural gas from deep reservoirs and source rocks: AAPG Bulletin, vol. 65, p. 1543–1550.

Sternberg, B.K., A review of some experience with the induced polarization/resistivity method for hydrocarbon surveys: successes and limitations: Geophysics, vol. 37, p. 1522–1532.

Tedesco, S.A., 1995, Surface Geochemistry in Petroleum Exploration: New York, Chapman and Hall, Inc., 206 p.

Thrasher, J.A., D. Strait, and R.A. Lugo, 1996a, Surface geochemistry as an exploration tool in the South Caribbean, *in* D. Schumacher and M.A. Abrams, eds., Hydrocarbon Migration and Its Near-Surface Expression: AAPG Memoir 66, p. 373–384.

______, A.J. Fleet, S.J. Hay, M. Hovland, and S. Duppenbecker, 1996b, Understanding geology as the key to using seepage in exploration: the spectrum of seepage styles, *in* D. Schumacher and M.A. Abrams, eds., Hydrocarbon Migration and Its Near-Surface Expression: AAPG Memoir 66, p. 223–241

Tucker, J., and D.C. Hitzman, 1994, Detailed microbial surveys help improve reservoir characterization: Oil & Gas Journal, vol. 92, no. 23, p. 65–68.

Weart, R.C., and G. Heimberg, 1981, Exploration radiometrics: post-survey drilling results, *in* M.J. Davidson and B.M. Gottlieb, eds., Unconventional Methods in Exploration for Petroleum and Natural Gas II : Dallas, Southern Methodist Univ. Press, p. 116–123.

Williams, A., A. Kloster, R. Duckworth, and N. Piggott, 1995, The role of the Airborne Laser Fluorosensor (ALF) and other seepage detection methods in exploring frontier basins, *in* S. Hansjien, ed., Petroleum Exploration and Exploitation in Norway: NPF Special Publication 4, p. 421–431.

Acknowledgments I am indebted to Michael Abrams, Gary Rice, and Daniel Hitzman for review of this chapter and their many helpful suggestions. Thanks are also extended to Ted Beaumont and Kathy Pile for their editorial efforts.

Chapter 19

Value of Geological Fieldwork

by

Denise M. Stone

Denise M. Stone

Denise Stone works for BP Amoco, based in Houston, where she has worked on various international exploration and production projects. She earned a B.S. degree in geology from Texas Christian University in Fort Worth, Texas, and an M.S. in geology from Memphis State University, Memphis, Tennessee. Ms. Stone began her career working for Union Oil of California in 1977 as an assistant geologist. Following completion of her Master's degree, she joined Superior Oil International in Houston, which was acquired by Mobil in 1984. She left Mobil in 1985 to work for Amoco Production Co., where she has done geological fieldwork in the U.S., U.K., Kenya, Burundi, Tanzania, Egypt, and Colombia. She is an active member of the Houston Geological Society, the Geological Society of America, and AAPG.

Overview

Introduction

Geological fieldwork is an important tool in finding oil and should be included in the broad range of available technologies that assess technical risks in an exploration play. Essential to the success of any geologic field effort is the time-efficient gathering of data relevant to exploration objectives. The key is identifying the main exploration questions and determining if and where a field might contain the answers. Fieldwork does not necessarily lower exploration risk, but it may improve how risk is defined. Good planning and logistics are required for any successful field program.

The how and why of doing fieldwork differs for every basin. This chapter attempts to synthesize the concerns and practices common to any area being explored. It is a thought-provoking tool for geoscientists considering fieldwork as part of a hydrocarbon exploration program. The material is a how-to approach for assessing the value of fieldwork in any basin, helping us to assess technical risks and improve subsurface interpretation.

In this chapter

Section A
Why Conduct Geological Fieldwork?

Introduction

This section explains what geological fieldwork is and what it can do for an exploration program. It also answers some of the objections to conducting geological fieldwork.

In this section

This section contains three subsections.

Subsection A1

Definition and Benefits of Geological Fieldwork

Definition

The following tasks are associated with fieldwork:

- Sampling rocks for analysis
- Describing and measuring stratigraphic sections
- Mapping surface features
- Interpreting the significance of relationships observed

In this subsection

This subsection contains the following topics.

Types of Geological Fieldwork

Introduction

There are two types of geological fieldwork: direct and indirect.

Direct geological fieldwork

Direct geological fieldwork is conducted in the basin being explored, where the outcropping formations studied are also present in the subsurface.

Where there are outcrops, an outcropping interval is the best source of information about the equivalent interval in the subsurface. Results of direct geological fieldwork typically are extrapolated into the subsurface interpretation. Interpreters of direct field data must know whether a particular formation varies laterally in the distance from surface to subsurface, sometimes ranging from kilometers to hundreds of kilometers.

Indirect geological fieldwork

Indirect geological fieldwork is conducted outside the immediate basin being explored. It applies where other well-studied areas are used as analogs, guides to interpretation, and predictive models.

Indirect geological fieldwork employs the concept that if two or more geographically distant locations (e.g., one at the surface and one in the subsurface) have like geological attributes, the well-understood area may serve as a model for interpreting the less-understood area. Examples of attributes are the depositional environment of a formation, the thermal history of the basin, and the lateral distribution of a source rock.

Indirect geological fieldwork can be particularly valuable when applied to production geology and exploitation. Understanding the reservoir facies distribution and scale can help locate development wells.

Guiding Principles

Introduction

The following table contains some of the guiding principles to use when planning geological fieldwork.

Table of principles

Principle	Explanation
There is still a lot of uncollected data out there.	In basin areas around the world, a wealth of surface data waits to be collected through observation, sampling, and measurement. This data has the potential to contribute value to an exploration effort in petroleum provinces in all stages (frontier, emerging, and mature) and can provide competitive advantage to explorers willing to invest the time, money, and personnel in the effort.
The past is only prologue.	A lot of oil has been found using geological fieldwork, and a lot remains to be found using geological fieldwork. In the past, drilling of anticlines and surface anomalies based solely on geological fieldwork led to many exploration successes. Today, however, most obvious anticlinal features have been drilled and hydrocarbons have become harder to find; so field objectives must be more varied and, frequently, more specialized.
Old maps may not satisfy new needs.	Most parts of the world have been mapped to some level of detail, and few unstudied areas exist any more. Although earlier mappers may have covered the ground well, they might not have been looking for the specific facies changes or subtle unconformities that guide the modern explorer looking for a play.
Integrate other data sets with field data.	Field data is not the only type of data used to decide where to drill. Results of geological fieldwork must be integrated with other data sets with the goal of developing a broader understanding of the components that make up a hydrocarbon system.
Usefulness is the goal.	Like any other technique used in exploration for hydrocarbons, geological fieldwork should be evaluated for its usefulness at helping answer key exploration questions and assessing technical risk.

Benefits of Geological Fieldwork

Introduction

The major benefits of doing geological fieldwork include the following:

- Cost effectiveness
- Competitive advantage
- First-order data
- Integration of data
- Confidence boosting
- Marketing tool
- New ideas

Cost effectiveness

Geological fieldwork can be a cost-effective tool for assessing technical exploration risk. Compared with more sophisticated exploration techniques, the cost of a field program is a bargain. Acquiring, processing, and interpreting seismic data, for example, costs orders of magnitude more.

Competitive advantage

Geological fieldwork can provide a competitive advantage. Fieldwork results can advance specific business recommendations on how to proceed with exploration or manage technical risk.

For example, geological fieldwork was applied successfully to an exploration program by Exxon in the Rover Boy days to high-grade worldwide basin areas (Kingston, 1992). Understandably, specific objectives and results of these and other exploration field efforts rarely become public; they reside in company files due to their proprietary nature. Similarly, in the literature, results of exploration field efforts are not specifically stated as such but tend to be buried in the broader results published.

First-order data

Geological fieldwork lets us acquire first-order data. Current maps and data may not be valid. And it isn't always safe to assume the other guy did it correctly—particularly when spending exploration money is involved.

We must know what portion of previous fieldwork is known from direct observation vs. interpretation. With maps, this distinction isn't clear most of the time. A perfect example of this is the concept of the "state-line fault," resulting when two different geologists mapping two adjacent areas disagree on how the maps join.

Data integration

Geological fieldwork can integrate data because it crosses discipline boundaries. A set of shale samples, for example, when analyzed for age, organic richness, and acoustic velocity can advance the understanding of basin history, the source rock facies, and the seismic interpretation. Each data set furthers the work of paleontologists, geochemists, and geophysicists working the basin.

Geological fieldwork can also provide a tighter tie between the rocks themselves and the technologies (logs, seismic surveys, etc.) used to evaluate the rocks indirectly.

Benefits of Geological Fieldwork, continued

Confidence boosting

Geological fieldwork boosts the confidence of the explorationist. A sense of the lay-of-the-land, the quality of the outcrops, and the rigor of previous interpretations—all are critical ingredients to the confidence an explorationist has in his or her work. In presentations to management or investors, that "been-there" confidence shows through.

Furthermore, showing representative samples of source or reservoir rock in a presentation can be very impressive. Rocks on a conference room table always generate interest.

Marketing tool

Geological fieldwork can be a valuable marketing tool. A tour of key outcrops is useful for building the interest of management, partners, or investors. Explorationists should develop the field knowledge and confidence necessary to lead a quick tour of the key locations of the area.

If such a tour isn't possible, consider making a well-narrated video in the field to emphasize key points. A video can be a powerful tool to show the field environment, logistics, and outcrops to those who cannot visit the site.

New ideas

Geological fieldwork helps explorationists generate new ideas. It provides a setting for discussion and allows the application of new concepts. The rocks don't change; what changes is the way we view them.

In the field, observations can be discussed and new doors opened to collaboration. Offices don't provide the same opportunity. Most of us like fieldwork; it's why we entered the profession.

Subsection A2

Fieldwork and Your Exploration Program

Introduction

To improve the assessment of technical risk, geological fieldwork is a valuable tool for uncovering new information or evaluating existing information.

Determining whether geological fieldwork would be valuable to a project requires a thorough understanding of all existing exploration data.

In this subsection

This subsection details the following step-by-step procedure to help answer the question, "Would geological fieldwork be valuable in this exploration program?"

Step	Action	Topic	Page
1	Know the seven critical elements necessary for a subsurface hydrocarbon accumulation to occur.	The Seven Critical Elements	19–11
2	Determine what is known about each of the seven critical elements in the basin being explored.	Applying the Seven Critical Elements	19–13
3	Determine what risks are associated with each critical element. Rank the risks, and determine what will reduce or further assess key risks.	Assessing Risk	19–16
4	In light of the risks identified, determine whether geological fieldwork might provide the information needed.	How Geological Fieldwork Fits In	19–17

The Seven Critical Elements

Introduction

Seven critical elements are necessary for subsurface hydrocarbon accumulations to occur:

1. Reservoir rock
2. Source rock
3. Seal
4. Thermal history
5. Migration and trapping of hydrocarbons
6. Geologic history of the basin
7. Structural history and style

Criticality

Exploration risk is best understood by studying historically what has and has not been successful in a basin. In other words, what combination of the seven critical elements occurred to form existing fields and, conversely, what are the main reasons for the dry holes in that same basin? Is a common element responsible for the dry holes?

The goal of an exploration effort is to use all the data available to identify fully the technical risks and recommend the best course of action and investment. Action following a field project might range from no action, to acquiring more data in key areas, to drilling a well.

Critical element checklist

The following checklist summarizes key attributes of the seven critical elements. The working explorer should have a general understanding of these attributes in the basin studied.

Reservoir Rock

General 3-D definition

- ❑ Sedimentary rock type(s)
- ❑ Gross thickness range
- ❑ Lateral continuity (faulted?)
- ❑ Mappability
- ❑ Depth of burial: structural relief of reservoir top
- ❑ Outcrop occurrences

Character of upper and lower boundaries

- ❑ Origin: erosional vs. depositional
- ❑ Nature: abrupt vs. gradational
- ❑ Seismic reflectivity
- ❑ Conformability

Diagnostic features

- ❑ Depositional environment
- ❑ Facies distribution
- ❑ Provenance
- ❑ Internal stratigraphic subdivisions
- ❑ Age diagnostic criteria: fossils, intrusives, marker horizons
- ❑ Electric log responses
- ❑ Pay distribution: vertical, lateral
- ❑ Sedimentary structures

Petrographic characteristics

- ❑ Composition: framework grain mineralogy, crystallinity
- ❑ Texture: grain size, sorting, roundness, crystallinity
- ❑ Degree of cementation
- ❑ Diagenetic alteration
- ❑ Microfossils
- ❑ Fractures
- ❑ Porosity
- ❑ Permeability

The Seven Critical Elements, continued

Source Rock

- ❑ Age
- ❑ Thickness
- ❑ Lateral continuity
- ❑ Organic richness
- ❑ Thermal maturity
- ❑ Kerogen type
- ❑ Depositional environment
- ❑ Facies
- ❑ Mappability
- ❑ Carbonate vs. clastic
- ❑ Depth of burial

Seal

- ❑ Vertical seals
- ❑ Lateral seals
- ❑ Lithology of potential seals
- ❑ Capillary pressure
- ❑ Lateral continuity of sealing formations
- ❑ Presence of evaporates
- ❑ Fracture systems

Thermal History

- ❑ Rates of deposition
- ❑ Rates of burial
- ❑ Paleogeothermal gradient
- ❑ Tectonic history
- ❑ Location of kitchen areas

Migration and Trapping

- ❑ Fault juxtaposition
- ❑ Fractures
- ❑ Lateral permeability and porosity
- ❑ Controls on migration

Geologic History

- ❑ Main tectonic events: compressional, tensional, wrench
- ❑ Structural overprinting
- ❑ Depositional history: continental, marine
- ❑ Episodes of subsidence: regional, local
- ❑ Controls on subsidence
- ❑ Unconformities
- ❑ Significant episodes of volcanism, subsidence, uplift, erosion
- ❑ Rates of deposition
- ❑ Paleotopography
- ❑ Paleoshoreline
- ❑ Paleoclimate
- ❑ Chronostratigraphy

Structural History and Style

- ❑ Compressional vs. tensional basin
- ❑ Main structural elements
- ❑ Tectonic development
- ❑ Sequence of events
- ❑ Structural overprinting
- ❑ Fault trends: major and minor
- ❑ Basin boundary faults
- ❑ Major faults vs. minor faults
- ❑ Zones of weakness
- ❑ Dip domains
- ❑ Outcrop patterns
- ❑ Dip and strike trends
- ❑ Average throw on faults

Applying the Seven Critical Elements

Introduction

Determining our *state of understanding*—what we know—of each of the seven critical elements in the basin being explored forces us to identify what is known and unknown about the basin. What are the certainties and uncertainties about each element? What element is the least understood, and why? The answers to these questions tell us whether we need to conduct geological fieldwork.

Determining the state of understanding

To determine the state of understanding of the seven critical elements, complete all of the following:

- Examine previous work
- Determine the exploration state of the basin
- Make a stratigraphic column

Examine previous work

The first step is to study previous exploration work. Look at as many recommendations, reports, maps, seismic sections, cross sections, field studies, and surveys as possible. Distill the results into a summary for each critical element.

Determine the exploration state

While examining previous work, determine if the basin is frontier, emerging, or mature with respect to hydrocarbon exploration. In general, frontier basins where no hydrocarbons have been found tend to benefit the most from geological fieldwork because critical elements in frontier basins are not well understood and have not been proven by hydrocarbon discovery. But remember that emerging and mature basins can benefit from fieldwork as well.

Figure 19–1 summarizes the state of understanding of each of the seven critical elements of a hydrocarbon system with respect to the exploration maturity of the basin. It provides a framework to delve deeper into the reasons for either lack of drilling or dry holes and directs us toward the next step in the project.

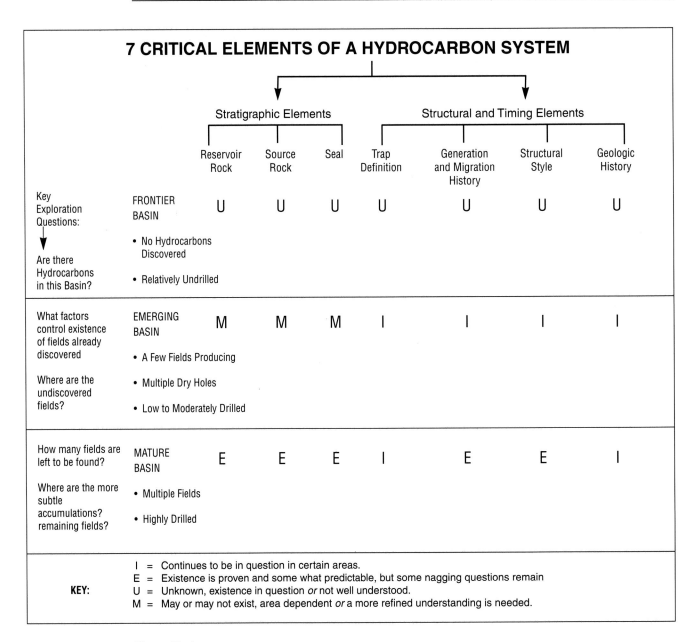

7 CRITICAL ELEMENTS OF A HYDROCARBON SYSTEM

Key Exploration Questions		Stratigraphic Elements			Structural and Timing Elements			
		Reservoir Rock	Source Rock	Seal	Trap Definition	Generation and Migration History	Structural Style	Geologic History
Key Exploration Questions: ↓ Are there Hydrocarbons in this Basin?	FRONTIER BASIN • No Hydrocarbons Discovered • Relatively Undrilled	U	U	U	U	U	U	U
What factors control existence of fields already discovered Where are the undiscovered fields?	EMERGING BASIN • A Few Fields Producing • Multiple Dry Holes • Low to Moderately Drilled	M	M	M	I	I	I	I
How many fields are left to be found? Where are the more subtle accumulations? remaining fields?	MATURE BASIN • Multiple Fields • Highly Drilled	E	E	E	I	E	E	I

KEY:
I = Continues to be in question in certain areas.
E = Existence is proven and some what predictable, but some nagging questions remain
U = Unknown, existence in question *or* not well understood.
M = May or may not exist, area dependent *or* a more refined understanding is needed.

Figure 19–1.

Make a stratigraphic column

The last step is to make a stratigraphic column, showing what is known about each of the seven critical elements. By doing this, you summarize the state of understanding in an illustration which, when combined with a surface geology map, is useful for presenting field objectives and results.

A stratigraphic column and a surface geology map can show the following:

- Vertical arrangement of formations
- Relative formation thicknesses
- Where formations outcrop
- Exploration significance of each formation
- Succinct summary of what is known about the subsurface
- How the surface and subsurface tie together

The following figure is an example of such a stratigraphic column.

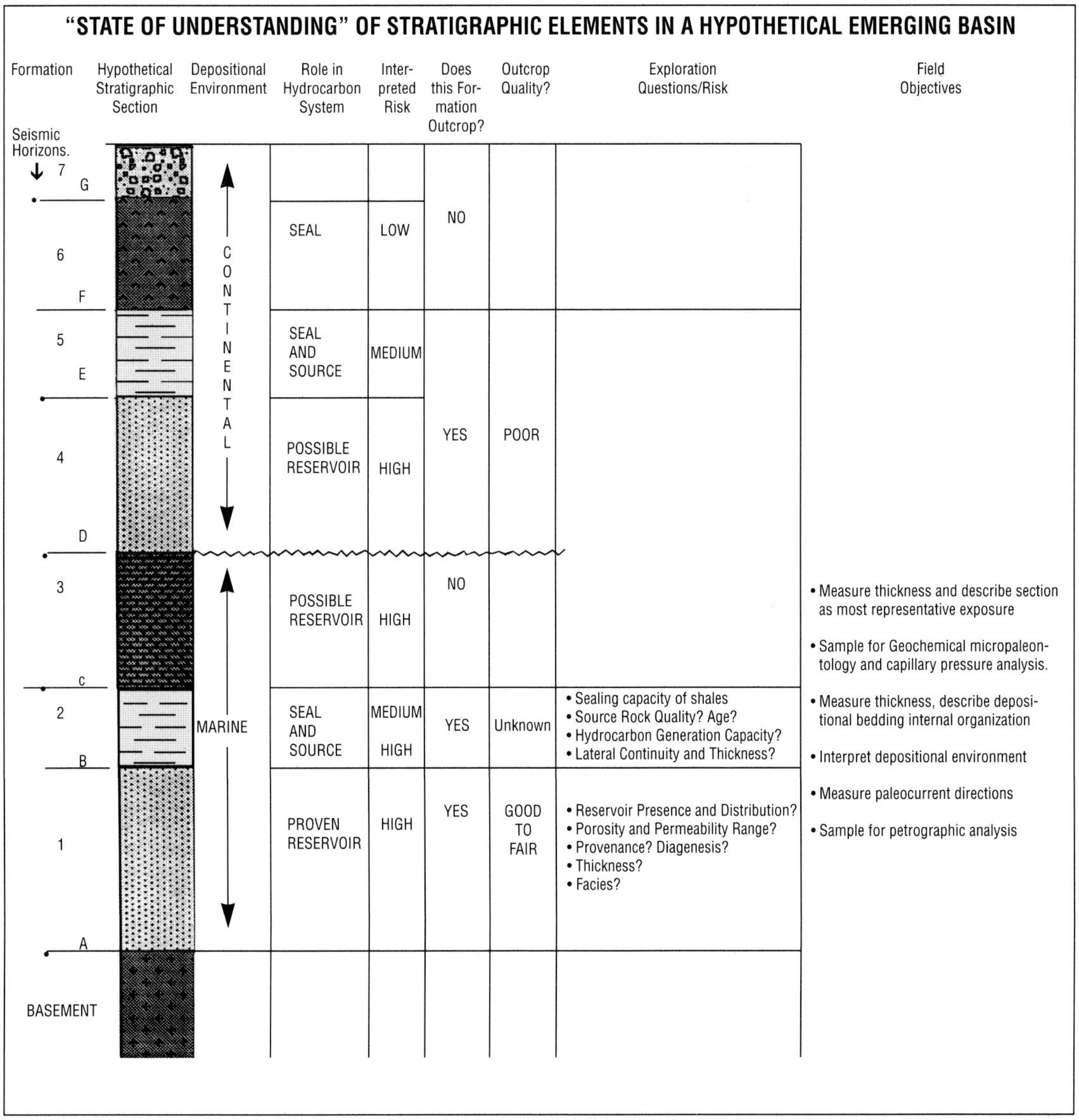

Figure 19–2.

Assessing Risk

Introduction

As used here, *risk* is exposure to an undesirable outcome or chance at loss. In the case of exploration, it is exposure to the occurrence of an all-too-common dry hole where no hydrocarbons are found and the well is plugged and abandoned.

Determining risk

The first step is to determine which risks are associated with each critical element. For reservoir rock, the main risk might be thickness and porosity preservation. For source rock, the main risk might be organic richness and thermal maturity.

Ranking risk

Next, rank the risks in order of greatest to least concern. In one basin, the risks might rank as follows:

1. Reservoir porosity
2. Source rock maturity
3. Reservoir thickness

The highest ranked risks are the *key risks*—the ones to be most concerned about.

Reducing risk

The final step is to determine the information needed to reduce or further assess key risks. This step promotes free thinking and lets us visualize success. For example, if you had the choice of any field data to address the issue of reservoir porosity, what would they be? Designing a method to address the questions you have about the key risks is the most important step of any field project. Once this is done, the objectives of the field program fall into place.

How Geological Fieldwork Fits In

Is geological fieldwork needed?

Once you identify the risks in a basin being explored, you must determine if conducting geological fieldwork will improve risk assessment.

A field program to address questions about reservoir risk, for example, might include a sampling program at representative outcrops of the reservoir rock. Samples collected would be studied petrographically for their composition, texture, and porosity to better assess the fluid-holding capacity of the rock. The outcrops in question may have been described in the literature, but perhaps not petrophysically.

Field data are the foundation of a geologic interpretation from a regional to a microscopic scale. Field data provide the information from which to calibrate and build a multiscale model of how to envision the subsurface. This essential understanding can be extracted from the in situ surface rocks.

Caveat

Of all the steps in this process, deciding if you need to do geological fieldwork (and, if so, what to concentrate on) is the least straightforward. Since it takes a critical review of what is known before recommending specific geological fieldwork, you may require time to talk with experts and review the literature before you can make an informed decision. Nevertheless, this is time well spent if it saves work, time, and money in the long run. Drilling is expensive, but drilling dry holes is even more expensive.

Subsection A3
Objections to Geological Fieldwork

Introduction

Not everyone accepts the usefulness of geological fieldwork. As McPhee (1986) notes, "Black-box geologists—also referred to as office geologists and laboratory geologists—have been known to say that field work is an escape mechanism by which their colleagues avoid serious scholarship. Their remarks may rarely be that overt, but the continuing relevance of field geology is not—to say the least—universally acknowledged."

Killer phrases

Many people disregard the benefits of geological fieldwork and use "killer phrases" to dismiss it. Some objections may be valid, but many are not. If you think geological fieldwork is important to your exploration project, take a few minutes to read through the following table of killer phrases and learn how to counter the objections you may meet.

Killer Phrase	Counter-argument
All geological fieldwork has already been done. There's nothing new to do.	This is a major misconception. People believe this because previous work seems so complete or was done by an "expert." But have the newest (or even new) techniques and concepts been applied to well-studied areas? The answer frequently is "No." In the field, the tendency is to see only what we have learned to see. New ideas and open minds lead to new reserves.
The field data and surface maps we have now are good enough.	That's what everyone told Christopher Columbus. How do we judge if the maps are "good enough" if we haven't tested them?
Other activities have higher priority than geological fieldwork.	This may be true. But is there enough information to fairly prioritize geological fieldwork? Priorities based on no information (or, worse, on misinformation) can be dangerous.
There are no outcrops in my area.	This is true for many areas, such as offshore basins. Try using analogs (modern, ancient, or both) as predictive tools and guides to interpretation. If you are working from a model, be sure you understand the model you are applying.
The ultimate outcome of a field program is uncertain.	Uncertainty is the case with most things in life. It should not guide your thinking, or you may never do anything.
None of the geologists working on the project has field experience.	A great training opportunity awaits the inexperienced. Team up field veterans and novices. Otherwise, the number of those with field experience will continue to decline.
The method is too low tech and old fashioned to be significant today.	Office geologists dangerously rely on second- and third-hand data for interpretations and models. They then feed these data into a computer and hope the results make sense. But as the saying goes, "Garbage in, garbage out." You need the best data as input. The key is quality data—not how the data were obtained—and frequently the only way to make sure of quality is old-fashioned geological fieldwork.

Objections to Geological Fieldwork, continued

Killer phrases (continued)

Killer Phrase	Counter-argument
It costs too much money.	What might it cost *not* to get the information needed?
It's just another boondoggle.	Yes, some geologists return from fieldwork talking more about the good time they had than the data they collected, creating the impression they were vacationing instead of working. The truth, however, is less glamorous: not all geological fieldwork is easy. One needs to be in good physical shape and able to tolerate adverse conditions, enjoy challenges, and, most importantly, incorporate results into the overall exploration effort. Not all geologists have this mix of abilities.

Summary

Geological fieldwork is an exploration tool available to explorers with the technical objectives, desire, and access to the field. Geological fieldwork is never really prohibited from an exploration program as much as it may be omitted from consideration in favor of other exploration tools. But if serious exploration questions arise that geological fieldwork may address, consider fieldwork as an important—and sometimes the only—way to answer those questions.

Section B

Necessary Considerations

Introduction

This section discusses how to prepare before you go into the field, what kind of planning and logistical preparation you need for a specific field party, and which field practices are most helpful.

In this section

This section contains the following subsections.

Subsection B1

Preparing to Go to the Field

Introduction

This subsection discusses the general geological preparation you need to do before embarking on geological fieldwork. As shown in the following figure, planning and logistics are key components for the success of any field party.

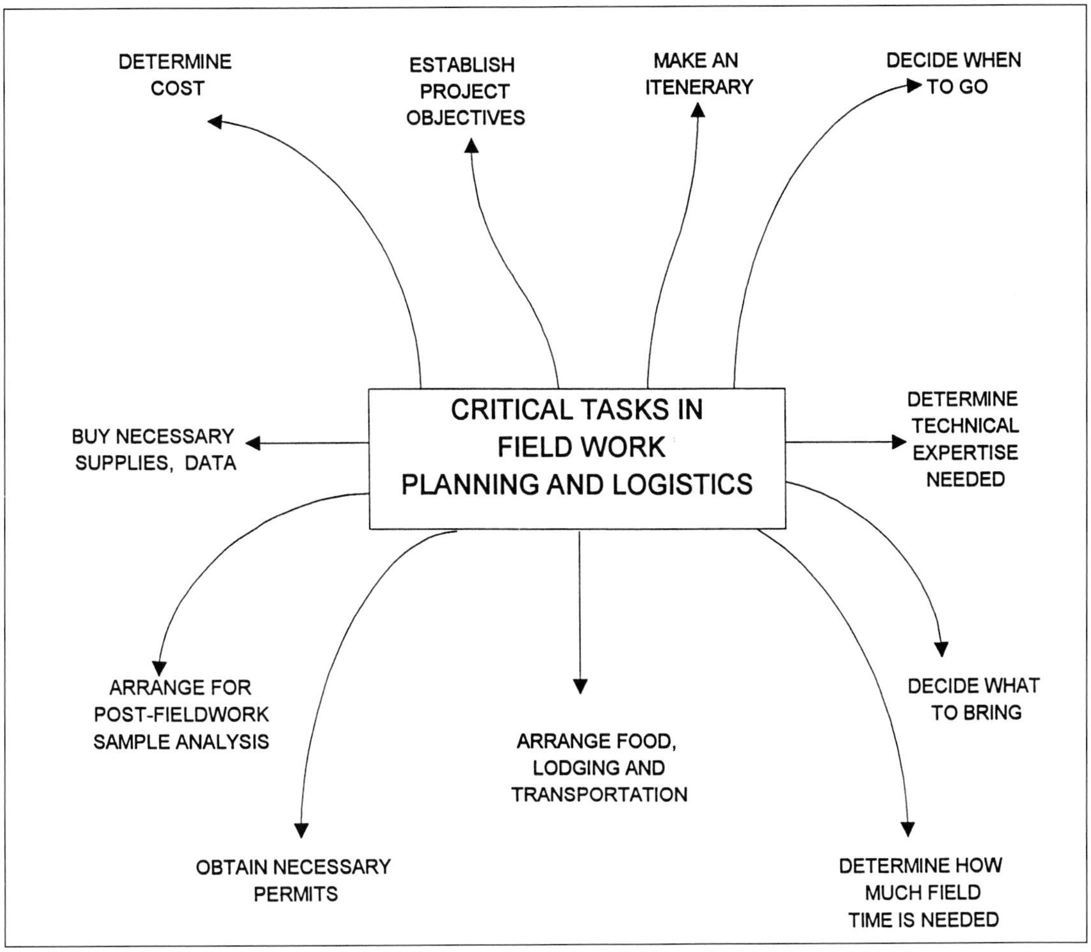

Figure 19–3.

In this subsection

This subsection contains the following topics.

When to Go

Introduction

Timing is an important consideration in fieldwork. We need to consider the time available and then plan around the field objectives.

Consider the time frame

In determining when to conduct fieldwork, plan within the time frame of the large-scale exploration effort.

Conduct the fieldwork at a time in the program when the results will have the greatest impact on exploration decisions. A good time for geological fieldwork is during seismic data acquisition. By the time the lines are shot, processed, and ready to be interpreted, the field data will be compiled and ready to be incorporated into the interpretation. Also, the seismic camp might be able to provide accommodations for the field party. In remote areas, this can significantly ease field logistics.

Plan around field objectives

The field objectives should dictate how time is spent in the field and what localities are studied and sampled.

What to Look At

Introduction

Before going into the field, determine the scale of the objectives and examine geologic maps and remote-sensing imagery. Finally, evaluate the quality of the outcrops.

Determine the scale of the objectives

A critical task is to spend field time focusing on the scale suitable to the project's objectives (tectonic through microscopic). If a main field objective is to interpret the structural style, for example, then gain perspective on some of the large-scale features. Use aerial photographs as opposed to hand lenses.

Examine geologic maps

Another important task is to examine existing geologic maps of your area. Then ask yourself these questions:

- Are you comfortable with and confident in the maps?
- Do the maps make sense? If not, why not?
- Are there accessible outcrops of subsurface formations?
- How abundant are exposures in the study area?
- How much study has been done and with what objective in mind?

The maps used must have integrity. Recommendations and interpretations must build on reliable information.

Acquire remote-sensing imagery

Aerial photographs and Landsat, SPOT (Systeme Probatorie d'Observation de la Terre), and SLAR (Side-Looking Airborne Radar) images are very useful in evaluating surface geology. Remote-sensing imagery can be extremely useful for a preliminary analysis of a field area. It has the following virtues:

- Provides a bird's eye look at the study area
- Helps evaluate existing geologic maps
- Influences field itinerary planning
- Shows outcrop patterns
- Displays drainage in relation to the outcrop patterns
- Exhibits the role vegetation plays in a program
- Gives a view of structural lineaments, faults, and fractures
- Reveals anomalies to investigate

Evaluate quality of outcrops

The quality of the outcrops probably will be influenced heavily by the climate. Desert areas, for example, tend to have good-quality exposures because minimum vegetation obscures the outcrops. Tropical areas with abundant rainfall tend to be vegetated with a thick weathering profile and poor outcrops. If you have no idea about outcrop quality in the area, consult experts. Know before you go, and save time and effort.

Reviewing Previous Work

Introduction

An important prefield step is to review previous work. This includes finding and evaluating previous geological fieldwork, learning about the formations in the study area—even driving the seismic lines or flying over the area.

Research previous geological fieldwork

Seek and evaluate previous geological fieldwork done in the study area. Good sources for previous fieldwork are government agencies, geological surveys, mining authorities, universities in the area, consulting companies, and published geological literature.

When using previous geological fieldwork, be critical. Ask yourself question such as the following:

- What were the objectives of previous field projects? Were they achieved? Was anything done or not done that you should do?
- Were the previous field projects looking for hydrocarbons? If so, can you use the data? If not, are the data still useful?
- Does the previous geological fieldwork provide some of the answers you need, or does it pose more questions? If it poses more questions, what are the question? Asking the right question is the first step to obtaining the right answer.

Know type sections in the study area

Another area to review is the information on formation type sections that is available in the literature. At what localities were the formations in your study area first described? Who first described them and why? The more you learn before you go into the field, the better you can focus on your objectives.

Drive the seismic lines

If possible, drive all of the seismic lines and document the outcrops by shotpoint number. Measure strike and dip of features. Observe what is present along the entire length of the line, ranging from vegetation to outcrop quality. These data are a useful control for seismic line interpretation.

Consider an overflight

An overflight in a small aircraft is an excellent way to get a sense of the land and the scale of the area and to evaluate outcrop quality, access routes, etc. Traveling by air can be much faster and more efficient than traveling by land, especially if you are unfamiliar with the area. Low-angle oblique photographs taken in flight are a great way to illustrate ideas about an area, especially large-scale features that cannot be photographed from the ground.

Final Reminders

Introduction

The following items are very important but easy to overlook. Remembering them will make your job easier and possibly more productive.

Have a sampling strategy

Answering questions like the following before you travel to the field is essential. Plan ahead as much as possible.

- What samples need to be collected and for what purpose?
- Who will collect the samples, and how should the samples be selected?
- Will weathering of samples be a factor?
- Will multiple sets of samples be taken for analysis? If so, how many?
- In what containers should samples be transported (bags, jars, etc.)? Will any special precautions be necessary to prevent breakage or contamination?

Seek out anomalies

Seek out anomalies such as seeps, hot springs, and topographic irregularities. Why do these occur where they do? What do they describe about the geology of your area? Do they pose questions to be answered?

Use analogs

If your basin is offshore or has poor to no outcrops, all is not lost. Is there an analogous area or formation to use as a predictive model or guide for interpretation? Will a modern or ancient analog be more useful?

Also, use "classic localities" worldwide in your quest for data. For example, if carbonates are your exploration target, the modern reefs in the Bahamas or the ancient Permian reef complex of West Texas could be a valuable guide to interpretation.

Analogs are worthwhile even if your study area is rich in outcrops. What other geologists have learned about areas similar to yours can help guide study or save work.

Subsection B2

Planning for a Field Party

Introduction

Geological fieldwork isn't conducted the same way in any two areas. Methods, itineraries, and logistics vary. But what remains common to any field program is the need for planning around technical objectives and using available resources to the maximum benefit. Be reasonable; plan a do-able program.

This subsection helps you organize the main technical objectives of the field program. Good field logistics and planning are absolutely essential to a successful field program. Without careful prefield planning, field objectives may not be met.

Issues covered in this subsection are generally dealt with simultaneously in no set order.

In this subsection

This subsection contains the following topics.

How Much Will It Cost?

Introduction

The following list of the general cost components of a field program is a guide for planning. It is not exhaustive and varies, depending on the project and objectives.

Geological fieldwork costs

Be sure to budget for all of the following:

- Data purchases
- Equipment purchases
- Salaries of participants
- Transportation to the field for personnel and equipment
- Transportation while in the field for personnel and equipment
- Repairs to vehicles and/or equipment
- Food, water, etc.
- Nightly accommodations for the field party
- Insurance for accident or injury
- Communication between field and office
- Special analyses of data and/or samples collected
- Final report preparation and distribution

Where Will You Go?

Introduction

It is important to plan as much as possible how you will spend field time. A daily itinerary is a useful planning tool.

Good itinerary planning

An itinerary may change and improve as the fieldwork proceeds; however, begin with a plan that includes places and time. On departure for the field, give a copy to anyone who may need to reach members of the field party. Remember the keys to good itinerary planning:

- Know the exploration objectives and plan around them.
- Put dots on a map, showing the localities to be studied, and note approximately how much time to spend at each.
- Realize that field plans can't always be specific. If the best you can do is say "We need to spend a day in this area to see what's there," that's fine.
- Make overnight arrangements as close to the outcrops as possible. By doing this, you maximize field time and minimize transportation time.
- Know access routes to the outcrops and roads, and know how long it will take to travel from point A to point B.
- Know the general topography, drainage, and culture of the study area (i.e., the landmarks).
- Get input for the itinerary from the rest of the field party. Take everyone's field concerns into account.
- Allow for bad weather and the unexpected.

Whom Will You Take?

Introduction

You will need to decide whom to take to the field. You also need to remember that fieldwork offers opportunities to cross-train those in peripheral fields, e.g., engineering, environmental geology. Consider the technical expertise needed for the project and whether trainees or more experienced geologists would be more appropriate.

Technical expertise needed

Determine what level of expertise the project needs. For example, it may require a carbonate sedimentologist, a structural geologist, and a geochemist. Each should have an understanding of the field objectives and a specific contribution to make. If you don't know anyone with the required expertise, consult experts. Experts can be identified from the literature, local geological societies, mining authorities, and universities.

Local geologists

There is a great difference between struggling on your own and having a local guide to show you the current interpretation. A local field geologist can be an extremely valuable addition to your field party. He or she knows the outcrops, and you can share ideas and save field time.

Field party leader

Appoint a field party leader who is responsible for ensuring the project is planned properly, objectives are met, field time is used effectively, and the results of the effort are organized into a final report and integrated into the existing data set.

When Should You Go?

Introduction

Before going to the field, determine the company's or client's business needs, local conditions, and scheduling situations such as project phases and duration.

Business needs

Know what exploration issue(s) is driving the field effort. For example, is there a drilling commitment or an evaluation deadline? Conduct the geological fieldwork when results will contribute most to upcoming business decisions.

Local conditions

Determine the optimum time of year to conduct geological fieldwork in the area, and do the work then if possible. Seasonal conditions such as rain, snow, heat, foliage, and insects can foil the project. Work around them.

Fieldwork phases

Decide if the geological fieldwork will be done all at once or in phases. For example, a project might be conducted in three phases:

I Initial reconnaissance phase—determine access and feasibility

II Data-gathering phase—conduct detailed work

III Final phase— check quality of work, take additional samples, and tie up loose ends

Given a project's objectives, only one or two phases may be necessary.

Duration

Time requirements vary. You may need to spend days or weeks in the field. This depends on factors such as the number of people doing the work, the size of the area, and the number of outcrops to be studied.

Time management techniques

In the field, use good time management techniques and tools. Communicate the plan to sponsors before the team departs, perhaps utilizing a software tool such as Microsoft® Project. Use time/project management tools to report and monitor progress. Once the fieldwork is completed, appraise the field program's effective (or ineffective) use of time.

What Should You Bring?

Introduction

You don't want to arrive at a remote site and realize you've left something important behind—like sample containers. Early on, determine how you're going to get the field team to the site and create a checklist of what they need to bring with them.

Transportation

Decide how people will move about in the field.

- Will they be in trucks? Jeeps? Helicopters? Boats?
- How many people will be on the team, and what equipment will they be carrying?
- Are fuel and repair services available for the vehicles?
- Will the field party always remain together, or will they split up to work in separate areas during the project? From a practical and safety standpoint, no one should ever work alone.

Field party transportation must be well planned. Without dedicated, reliable, timely transportation, field progress suffers.

Equipment

Following is a checklist of suggested equipment to take to the field.

- ❏ Laptop computer with extra batteries
- ❏ Video camera
- ❏ Hand-held tape recorder
- ❏ Waterproof field notebooks and markers
- ❏ Brunton compass; inclinometer
- ❏ Latitude/longitude locator for GPS positioning; magellan
- ❏ Surveyor's tape for marking locations
- ❏ Rock hammer, chisels, and shovels
- ❏ Rod; tape measure
- ❏ Sample containers (e.g., cloth bags, jars, large trash bags)
- ❏ Waterproof markers for labeling
- ❏ Measurement devices (e.g., gravimeter, scintillation counter, magnetometer)
- ❏ Portable radios for in-field communication
- ❏ Stereoscope, hand lens
- ❏ Camera and film
- ❏ Binoculars
- ❏ First aid kit
- ❏ Snake bite kit
- ❏ Bug spray
- ❏ Gloves
- ❏ Portable radio
- ❏ Cellular phone
- ❏ Flares
- ❏ Matches/lighter

What Should You Bring? continued

Data and references

The following is a checklist of suggested data and references to take to the field.

- ❏ Reference and discussion materials
- ❏ Key cross sections
- ❏ Key seismic lines
- ❏ Key maps
- ❏ Stratigraphic columns
- ❏ Aerial photographs and other remote-sensing imagery
- ❏ Topographic maps
- ❏ Existing field guidebooks

Be Prepared

Introduction

Remember the old scouting motto, "Be Prepared." Know where you are going, identify potential problems, and devise a way to stay in touch with your colleagues in the office.

Know the study area

Learn the basics about the local area, including customs, language, and food, if different from your own. In central Africa, laughing is considered a sign of embarrassment; in Saudi Arabia, crossing your legs and exposing the soles of your shoes is considered rude. Read up about the distinguishing cultural traits of the area you will visit.

Get the necessary permissions

Obtain the necessary permissions from owners and/or authorities to access land or airspace. It's a good idea to get permissions in writing and carry them with you.

Identify potential hazards

Identify potential hazards in the field. These include wildlife, hunters, military maneuvers, minefields, and ordinance depots.

Carry first aid equipment and a snake bite kit, and know where to get the nearest medical help. Also be sure you know any specific medical conditions of your team members, such as allergies to food, medicines, or insects. Be sure that all members of the field party have the physical fitness required to do the work.

Stay in touch with the office

Have a plan for staying in communication with the office while you are in the field. Staying in communication is critical, particularly if the field work is done in a remote, unpopulated area. Periodic contact will allow for status reports, idea sharing, and help in the event of injury or emergency. Also plan for a way that members of the field party can be reached.

Subsection B3

Helpful Field Practices

Introduction

Once you're out in the field, follow the recommendations in this subsection to improve the quality of your work.

In this subsection

This subsection contains the following topics.

Gathering Data

Introduction

Gathering data is one of the most important techniques in the field. Have a system for capturing and recording it.

Capture data daily

Beyond just keeping field notes and recording observations, write down at each day's end your main ideas and interpretations. These will build and evolve as the project work is accomplished and will simplify preparing the final report.

List all samples

Keep a master list or spreadsheet of all samples collected. A laptop computer in the field is great for this, but a field notebook will work fine. Useful information on the sample master list should include the following:

- Stop number where the sample was collected
- Analyses planned for that sample
- Number of duplicate samples taken, if any
- Latitude–longitude coordinates where the sample was taken, if available

Label all samples

Devise an informative sample labeling system for the sample bags or containers. An effective system might include the date, stop number, and sample number. Write these on the outside of the sample bag or container with a permanent marker. This information ties back to the field notes by date to facilitate reference long after the field effort is complete.

Example: 4/23-5-22G

Translation: This sample was taken on April 23 at stop 5; it was the 22nd sample collected that day; on return from the field, it will be sent for Geochemical analysis.

Determine sample sizes

Know how much sample to collect and how it should be preserved for optimum analytical results. For example, loosely consolidated sandstones for petrographic study should be handled carefully to avoid breakage.

If duplicate samples are needed, it is always easier to collect them at the outcrop rather than split the sample after returning from the field.

Know where you are

Take whatever you need to the field to keep a sense of direction and location. It is essential to know where you are in the field at all times with respect to a reference point(s) (e.g., north, visible landmarks, a shoreline). A magellan, Brunton compass, maps, or aerial photographs can help you stay located.

Staying located can be particularly challenging when on foot in dense vegetation. For additional information, refer to Talbot and Carman (1990), Carey (1990), and Carman (1990).

Gathering Data, continued

Keep a photo log

If photographs are planned, keep a photo log, recording the date, subject, and location where the photograph was taken. This is particularly useful if the project is long and many localities are studied.

Decide ahead of time whether slides or prints will be more useful.

Use a tape recorder

Consider using a tape recorder, particularly during overflights when writing reduces observation time.

Special Field Techniques

Magellans and GPS positioning

Magellans and GPS positioning devices offer a handy way to find your location with respect to surface maps. Latitude and longitude coordinates are read from a lightweight, hand-held device that determines position by triangulating with functioning satellites overhead. Coordinates are particularly useful when making numerous road stops and can be input into a computer for plotting.

Outcrop gamma-ray logging

Outcrop gamma-ray logging can be a valuable technique for stratigraphic correlation. It allows a quantitative tie between surface and subsurface using a measurement common to both: the gamma-ray curve. This kind of tie can be more credible than "jump correlating" (identifying events on noncontiguous seismic records or lithologic horizons on well logs, separated by distance, as the same or correlative interfaces in the earth), particularly when significant distance is involved.

Two methods of outcrop gamma-ray logging are currently in use:

- Truck-mounted gamma-ray sonde
- Hand-held scintillometer

These tools measure the surface gamma radiation signature emitted by sedimentary outcrops. The data collected can be used to compare and correlate to subsurface sedimentary sections whose radiation signature is measurable only with sophisticated downhole wireline logging tools. Gamma radiation is the most commonly used data set to correlate stratigraphy laterally.

Shallow coring

Surface outcrop samples of a given formation are assumed to be the best available example of that same formation at depth. If this isn't the case, though, another approach exists. A shallow coring program is a cost-effective way to obtain surface geologic data in areas of limited outcrops, severe surface weathering, thick vegetation, and/or thin alluvial cover. A seismic shot hole or water well drilling rig can be strategically positioned for collecting such samples.

Influencing Decisions

Introduction

On return to the office, the field party should do the following:

- Review the actual itinerary with management
- Summarize the data collected
- Begin analyzing samples
- Formulate preliminary recommendations
- Estimate when the final analysis and recommendations will be completed

The fieldwork should result in business recommendations that focus on technical risk. Field results can influence the course of exploration in three ways:

- Improving or refining subsurface interpretation
- Indicating whether further data should be acquired or new technology applied
- Guiding operation planning

Improving subsurface interpretation

Data from geological fieldwork can improve or refine subsurface interpretation.

For example, one finding from geological fieldwork might be that a surface outcrop of a basin-wide but variable-quality seismic reflector was identified on line XXX to be the boundary between sequence A and sequence B of Formation Z. Or palynologic analysis of shale field samples from Formation Y indicates the formation is actually Eocene and not Cretaceous, as implied in the literature.

Need for data or technology

Geological fieldwork may indicate further data should be acquired or new technology applied.

For example, geological fieldwork might indicate a need for more seismic surveys, a gravity survey, a magnetic survey, shallow core holes, or an exploratory well.

Operational planning

Geological fieldwork can guide operational planning. It might indicate the need to shoot seismic lines at 90° to regional strike or indicate seismic acquisition parameters. It might also help in bit selection for exploration wells.

Avoiding Problems

Why field projects fail

When field projects fail, it can be for any of the following reasons—and this list is not exhaustive:

- Bad weather
- Poor data collecting
- Poor sampling strategy
- Bad planning
- Unrealistic objectives
- Poorly documented or unclear results

Some of these factors are within the control of field geologists, and some are not. The key is to focus on what is within your control. Know the limitations and capabilities of the field party. And manage time effectively, be realistic, and plan. Getting geologists to an outcrop can take a lot of time, effort, and money. So when you're there, make the most of the moment. Know exactly what information you want to extract from each outcrop before you arrive, and document your observations so they can be communicated clearly to others.

Plan and anticipate

You have no control over the weather, but you can control most of the situations that might arise. The key to preventing failure is to complete the maximum amount of planning and anticipate what will be required for success.

Section C

Some Thoughts About Geological Fieldwork

Introduction

Geology requires thinking as well as doing. I hope the quotations that follow will stimulate you to further thought.

Thoughts

"We need to examine the source of our data, lest we fall prey to preconceived ideas." (Carey, 1990)

"The use of traveling is to regulate imagination by reality, and instead of thinking of how things may be, to see them as they are." —English author Samuel Johnson (1709–1784), who might as well have been writing about geological fieldwork

"You can't look at satellite photos for everything. You've got to have high resolution basic-mapping. You have to keep your hand in the real stuff. When the solid foundations aren't there geologists are talking complete mush." (McPhee, 1986, p. 144)

"... we see misinterpretations because of lack of knowledge of field relationships. Many of the mega-thinkers are doing their interpretations on the basis of second and third hand information. The name of the game now is "modeling" ... how can you write or talk authoritatively about something if you haven't seen it? It isn't adequate to trust that the other guy is correct. You should be able to evaluate things in your own right." (McPhee, 1986, p. 148)

Section D
References

References cited

Carey, S.W., 1990, Fifty years of oil search, *in* G. J. Carman and Z. Carman, eds., Petroleum Exploration in Papua New Guinea: Proceedings of the First PNG Petroleum Convention, p. 17–26.

Carman, G.J., 1990, Geofinder traversing and data computation, *in* G. J. Carman and Z. Carman, eds., Petroleum Exploration in Papua New Guinea: Proceedings of the First PNG Petroleum Convention, p. 27–32.

Kingston, D.R., 1992, The Rover Boys and other stories, *in* A. G. Hatley, Jr., ed., The Oil Finders: A Collection of Stories about Exploration: Tulsa, AAPG, p. 1–13.

McPhee, J., 1986, Rising from the Plains: New York, Farrar-Straus-Giroux, 214 p.

Talbot, N.C., and G.J. Carman, 1990, Application of the global positioning system to PNG petroleum exploration, *in* G. J. Carman and Z. Carman, eds., Petroleum Exploration in Papua New Guinea: Proceedings of the First PNG Petroleum Convention, p. 73–82.

Additional references

Chew K.J., and H. Stephenson, 1986, Exploration success offshore Norway compared with the remainder of the North Sea graben system and with other hydrocarbon provinces, *in* Habitat of Hydrocarbons on the Norwegian Continental Shelf: London, Graham and Trotman, p. 61–74.

Denham, L. R., H. N. Reeves, and R. E. Sheriff, 1980, How geologic objectives should determine seismic field design (abs.): AAPG Bulletin, vol. 64, no. 5, p. 698.

Dietrich, R.V., J.T. Dutro, Jr., and R.M. Foose, compilers, 1982, AGI Datasheets for Geology in the Field, Laboratory and Office: Washington, American Geological Institute, various pages.

Halbouty, M. T., 1980, Geological significance of Landsat data for 15 giant oil and gas fields, *in* M. T. Halbouty, ed., Giant Oil and Gas Fields of the Decade 1968–1978: AAPG Memoir 30, p. 7–38.

Kerans, C., F. J. Lucia, and R. K. Senger, 1994, Integrated characterization of carbonate ramp reservoirs using Permian San Andres Formation outcrop analogs: AAPG Bulletin, vol. 78, no. 2, p. 181–216.

Knowles, R. S., The Greatest Gamblers—The Epic of American Oil Exploration: Norman, Oklahoma, University of Oklahoma Press, 376 p.

Levorsen, A. I., 1943, Discovery thinking: AAPG Bulletin, vol. 27, p. 887–928.

Martini, A.V., with J. L. Payne, 1992, Beyond Kartoum: petroleum exploration and discovery, interior Sudan, 1973–1980, *in* A. G. Hatley, Jr., ed., The Oil Finders: A Collection of Stories about Exploration: Tulsa, AAPG, p. 77–93.

McClay, K.R., 1987, The Mapping of Geological Structures: London, Geological Society of London Handbook, 161 p.

References, continued

Additional references (continued)

Setio, N., W. Suwarlan, and R. Latief, 1989, The integration of borehole, seismic data, geological fieldwork, paleontological data, and SAR in a thrusted area of East Kalimantan: Proceedings of the Indonesian Petroleum Association, October, p. 17–30.

Slatt, R.M., D.W. Jordan, A.E. D'Agostino, and R.H. Gillespie, 1992, Outcrop Gamma-Ray Logging to Improve Understanding of Subsurface Well Log Correlations: Geological Society of London Special Publication 65, p. 3–19.

Wise, D., 1992, Dip domain method applied to the Mesozoic Connecticut Valley rift basins: Tectonics, vol. 11, no. 6, p. 1357–1368.

Acknowledgments The author thanks the following field geologists for their thoughtful review of the manuscript: Ted Beaumont, Robert Raynolds, Richard Hutson, Sandy Serra, and Ron Brogden. Their suggestions for improvement in readability and organization, plus their extensive field experience, greatly added to the final product.

Chapter 20

Exploring for Structural Traps

by

R.A. Nelson,

T.L. Patton,

and

S. Serra

R.A. Nelson

Ronald Nelson is currently a Geology Discipline Coach in Amoco Corporation's Exploration and Technology Group in Houston. His research interests include fractured reservoir analysis and predictions, rift tectonics and sedimentation, and quantification of trap definition risk. He holds geology degrees from Northern Illinois University (B.A.) and Texas A&M University (M.S., Ph.D.).

T.L. Patton

Tom Patton is a geologist with Amoco Corporation. He has participated in exploration programs for structural traps in the North American Cordillera, the Middle East, and Africa. His research interests include mathematical and laboratory models of structures and their application to the interpretation of subsurface traps.He holds geology degrees from Muskingum College (B.S.), University of Alaska (M.S.), and Texas A&M University.

S. Serra

Sandro Serra is currently a geological associate in Amoco Corporation's Exploration and Technology group in Houston. He is involved in structural geology consulting, specializing in thrust terranes, physical modeling, restoration and balancing of structure cross sections, and 3-D computer-aided vusualization of complex structures. He holds geology degrees from City College of New York (B.S.), Syracuse University (M.S.), and Texas A&M University (Ph.D.).

Overview

Introduction

Structural traps are the most prolific and varied of all trap types; they account for most of the world's hydrocarbon reserves. They range from very large [e.g., Ghawar, Saudi Arabia (560,000 ac)] to small [Major County, Oklahoma, U.S.A. (160 ac or less)]. (J. Coughlon, personal communication, 1996). To effectively prospect at all scales in this size continuum, we must apply a wide variety of techniques, tools, and approaches.

Deformation, including sedimentary (diagenetic) processes of compaction, creates folds and faults, which can result in structural traps, anticlines, and fault closures. This chapter discusses how to predict these by applying structural geology principles to find and develop oil and gas traps.

In this chapter

This chapter contains the following sections.

Section A

Basic Structural Approach

What is a structural trap?

In a structural trap, closure of the reservoir rock and seal are defined entirely by various structural or deformational elements, such as folds or faults. In Chapter 4, a structural trap is defined as a "hydrocarbon accumulation in which the trapping element is post- or syndepositional deformation displacement of reservoir and/or sealing units."

Structural maps and sections

The structural maps and structural cross sections we create are more than just 2-D spatial representations of subsurface data. They are shorthand visual depictions of our views of geological history as well. Structural maps and sections display our understanding of the geology, showing the known facts as well as the implied sequence of events within the context of current geoscience paradigms and approaches. The more thorough our knowledge of the geology of a structural play or prospect, the easier it is to evaluate.

In this section

This section covers the following topics.

Structural Maps and Cross Sections

Basic tools of a structural play

Four basic tools must be put together in a structural play or prospect, regardless of local structural style, level of structural complexity, or exploration maturity:

- A structure contour map on top of the reservoir.
- An isopach map of the target reservoir—especially important if the reservoir displays significant stratigraphic thickness variation or has behaved in a ductile or compactive manner during deformation.
- Two or more structural cross sections incorporating all surface and subsurface control (wells and seismic) projected into the line of section in both the strike and dip directions.
- Fault-surface maps (structural contours on the fault plane), made for all faults critical to closure at the top of the reservoir.

Guidelines for making maps and sections

Follow these guidelines when making maps and cross sections of a structural play.

- Construct maps using interpretive, not mechanical, mapping techniques.
- Make maps and sections at the same scale—in depth, not seismic time (if possible)—and internally consistent to one another.
- Use a 1:1 vertical to horizontal scale for sections. If this is impractical, construct sections with as little vertical exaggeration as possible to minimize distorting the true shape of the structures.
- For control, project wells into sections parallel to the structural contours.
- Check sections for geometric feasibility (i.e., balanced or restored) where appropriate.
- Integrate the contours of reservoir tops and fault surfaces to honor vertical separation along faults.
- Depict "known" vs. "inferred" or interpreted geometry on sections and maps. Display the relative subjective quality of interpreted geometry (low, medium, high). As shown in Figure 19–1, displaying the data in this manner allows the viewer to know where it is well and poorly constrained.

Integrating maps and sections The schematic figure below represents how to integrate different maps and cross sections in a structural geology play. It also shows how to display levels of confidence of interpretation. (More control points are depicted than would normally be present in a prospect.)

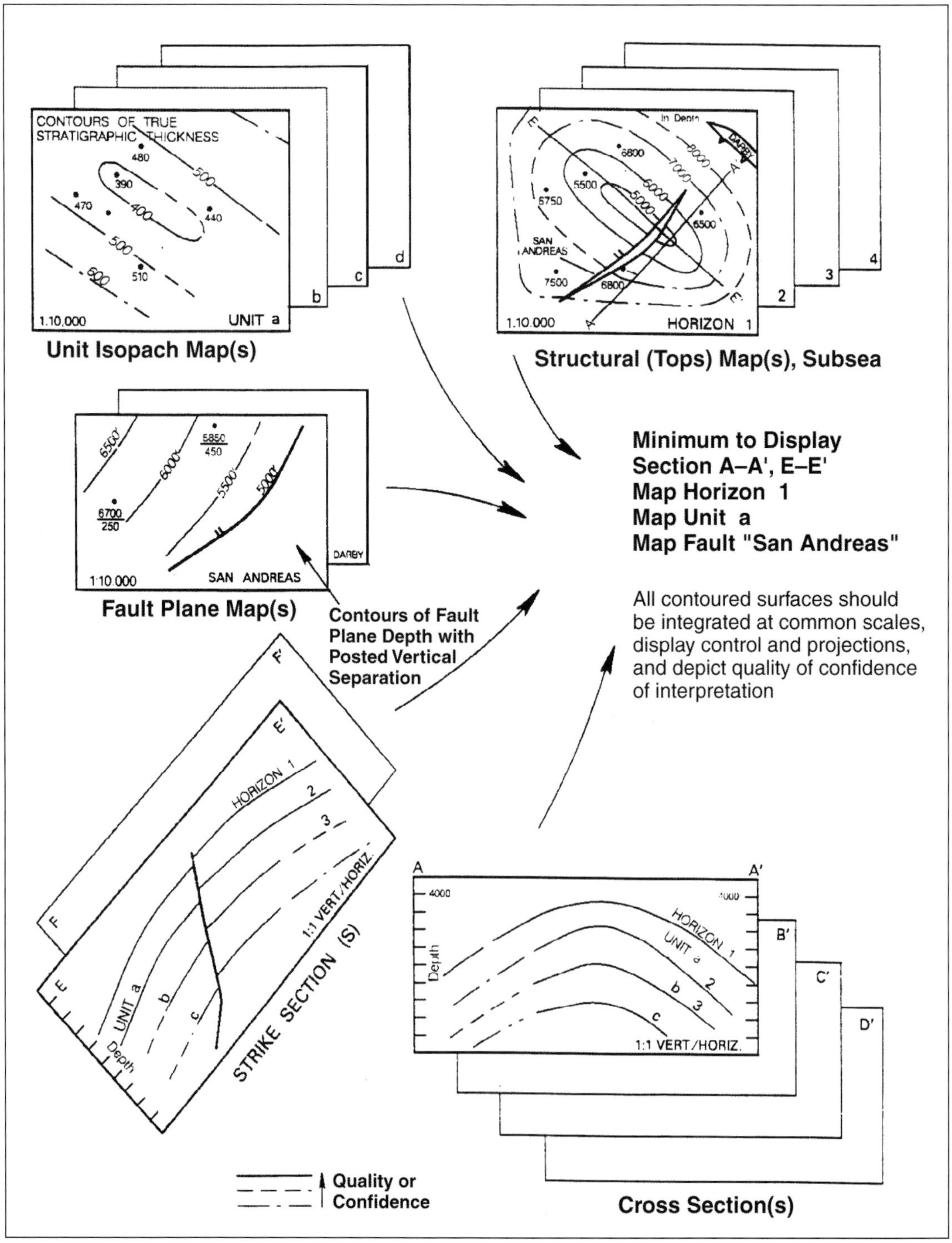

Figure 20–1.

Understanding the Geology of a Structural Play

Structural elements

To build a structural play and create the necessary factual/interpretive displays, we must analyze four structural elements of the play:

- The structural geometry of the play in three dimensions, including relative attitudes of formation and fault surfaces
- Deformation or physical diagenesis of reservoirs and seals (trap integrity)
- Timing of structural development and trap formation, and its relation to important petroleum system events
- Trap genesis in terms of structural process and/or tectonic context

Too often we focus only on structural geometry and ignore the other three elements. Timing, seal, reservoir, and process are what relate structural geometry to the petroleum system.

Unraveling structural geometry

To describe adequately the structural geometry of the subsurface trap, we must integrate subsurface data into a cohesive whole. Data include well logs, 2-D and 3-D seismic images (in both time and depth), gravity surveys, magnetics, and surface geology. These data are integrated with our understanding of the geometric possibilities for the structural style expected or demonstrated to exist in the area.

A structural style is a group of structures that often occur together in a particular tectonic setting. The following table from Harding and Lowell (1983) lists the characteristics of the primary structural styles. Figure 20–2 illustrates schematic cross sections of hydrocarbon traps (black areas) most commonly associated with the major structural styles.

Understanding the Geology of a Structural Play, continued

Structural Style	Dominant Deformational Force	Typical Transport Mode	Plate-Tectonic Habitats: Primary	Plate-Tectonic Habitats: Secondary
		BASEMENT INVOLVED		
Wrench-fault assemblages	Couple	Strike slip of subregional to regional plates	Transform boundaries	Convergent boundaries: 1. Foreland basins 2. Orogenic belts 3. Arc massif Divergent boundaries: 1. Offset spreading centers
Compressive fault blocks and basement thrusts	Compression	High to low-angle convergent dip slip of blocks, slabs, and sheets	Convergent boundaries: 1. Foreland basins 2. Orogenic belt cores 3. Trench inner slopes and outer highs	Transform boundaries (with component of convergence)
Extensional fault blocks	Extension	High to low-angle divergent dip slip of blocks and slabs	Divergent boundaries: 1. Completed rifts 2. Aborted rifts; aulacogens Intraplate rifts	Convergent boundaries: 1. Trench outer slope 2. Arc massif 3. Stable flank of foreland and fore-arc basins 4. Back-arc marginal seas (with spreading) Transform boundaries: 1. With component of divergence 2. Stable flank of wrench basins
Basement warps: arches, domes, sags	Multiple deep-seated processes (thermal events, flowage, isostacy, etc.)	Subvertical uplift and subsidence of solitary undulations	Plate interiors	Divergent, convergent, and transform boundaries Passive boundaries
		DETACHED		
Decollement thrust-fold assemblages	Compression	Subhorizontal to high-angle convergent dip slip of sedimentary cover in sheets and slabs	Convergent boundaries: 1. Mobile flank (orogenic belt) of forelands 2. Trench inner slopes and outer highs	Transform boundaries (with component of convergence)
Detached normal fault assemblages ("growth faults" and others)	Extension	Subhorizontal to high-angle divergent dip slip of sedimentary cover in sheets, wedges, and lobes	Passive boundaries (details)	
Salt structures	Density contrast Differential loading	Vertical and horizontal flow of mobile evaporites with arching and/or piercement of sedimentary cover	Divergent boundaries: 1. Completed rifts and their passive margin sags 2. Aborted rifts; aulacogens	Regions of intense deformation containing mobile evaporite sequence
Shale structures	Density contrast Differential loading	Dominantly vertical flow of mobile shales with arching and/or piercement of sedimentary cover	Passive boundaries (deltas)	Regions of intense deformation containing mobile shale sequence

Unraveling structural geometry (continued)

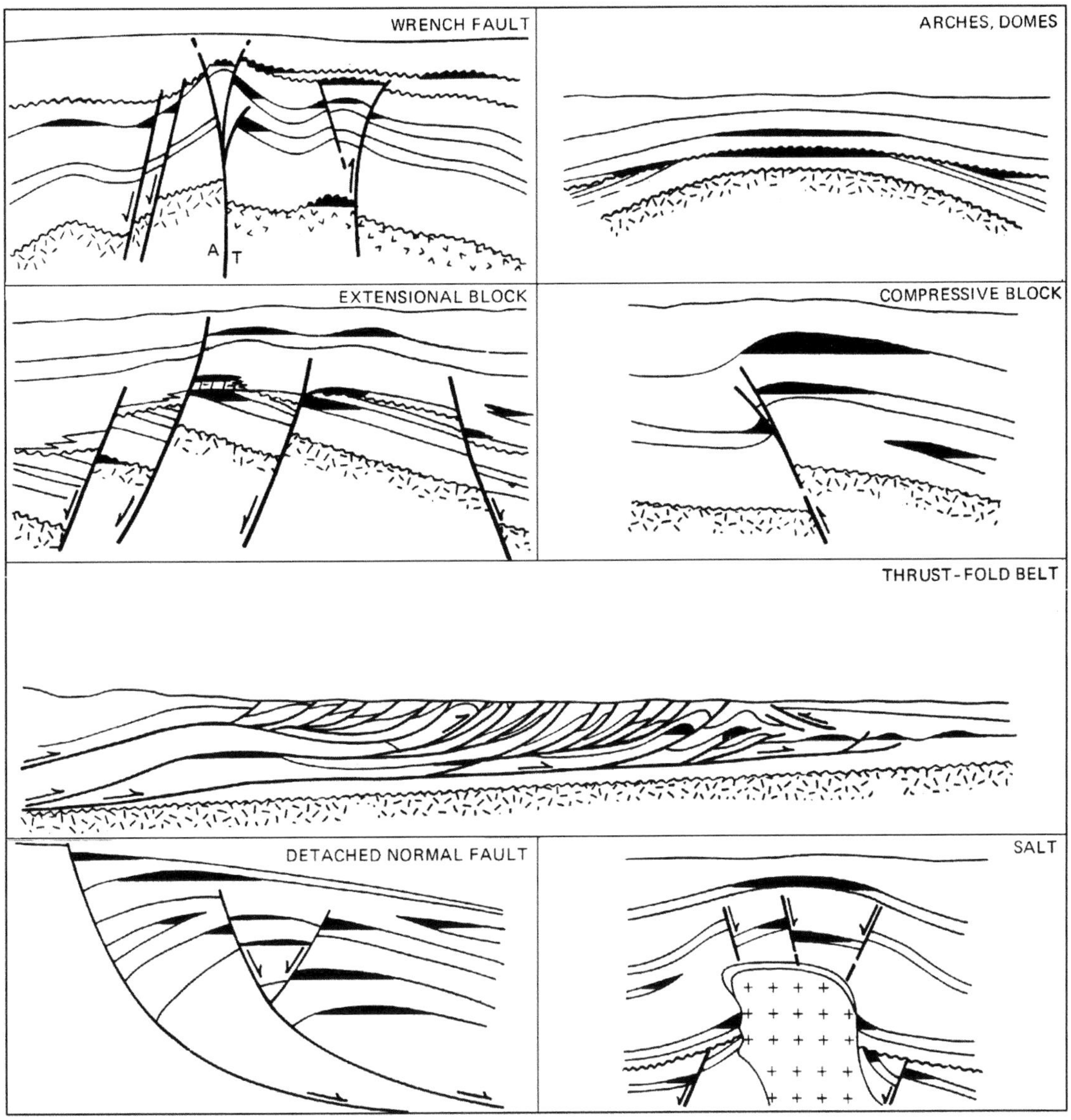

Figure 20–2. After Harding and Lowell, 1983; courtesy AAPG.

Creating a concept

Using these data, we create a concept of the structural geometry of the play, following the steps in the table below.

Step	Task	Why
1	Through stratigraphic correlation, determine/delineate "structural tops" for several mappable horizons from well and/or seismic data. The number of horizons depends on the quality of the data and the complexity of the structural style.	Changes in structural form with depth vary with structural style, mode of origin, and the operative deformational mechanisms.
2	Determine the relative attitude and thickness of units on fold limbs (dip panels) and/or units within fault blocks.	Given a deformational style, limb angles and thicknesses can be used to estimate fault and axial plane dip, and vice versa.
3	Determine the tightness of fold hinges with depth and the 3-D orientation of axial surfaces.	These features vary substantially with fold origin and are critical to predicting well paths.
4	Determine the position and offsets (throw, heave, separation, etc.) on faults and map their variation along the fault surface(s) (contour integration).	In any structural trap where faults play an important part in closure, the fault surface(s) must be contoured in order to accurately contour the top of the reservoir near the fault trace on that reservoir.
5	Determine closure (dip and/or fault) in all 2-D map directions.	Closure is the key element in all structural plays and must be evaluated at all appropriate horizons to look for vertical continuity and variation.

Timing structural development

In the petroleum systems approach to exploration, the relative timing of major events, such as trap formation, is critical. Timing of structural trap development is difficult to determine and usually must be inferred. The techniques for determining timing are often integrated with one another using sequential restored sections (by hand or computer) that either back-strip the sedimentary layers by "flattening" to their depositional surface or palinspastically restore them to predeformational geometries by removing displacement on the faults and unfolding the folds (Nelson et al., 1996). In simplified structural settings, isopach maps of successive stratigraphic units may be regarded as paleostructural maps.

Determining timing

Following are tables of primary, secondary, and tertiary techniques that can be applied to determine structural trap timing, with primary techniques being the most useful.

Understanding the Geology of a Structural Play, continued

Primary techniques

The following techniques are the most useful in determining structural trap timing.

Technique	Function
Isopachs of time-specific intervals	Isopach maps are a basic subsurface tool. Thicks and thins displayed in those maps are assumed to be depositional variations related to vertical components of structural relief and/or movement.
Unconformity studies • Missing time/section • Relations to eustacy • Sequence stratigraphy • Angular discontinuities	The ages of surfaces of erosion, nondeposition, condensed section, or angular discordance can be used to time the structural motion that caused them.
Facies/isolith distributions	Often structural motion or relief does not cause interval isopaching but does cause facies or environment of deposition changes due to subsidence rate differences or sediment pathways.
Fault terminations • Up-section termination horizons • Lower detachment planes	Consistent vertical termination of faults within the section can help us bracket timing relative to the ages of the section they cut and do not cut.
Relative crosscutting relations of faults	The crosscutting nature of discrete fault sets can help us infer the relative timing of motion of those sets.
Subsidence profiles	Changes in subsidence rate as shown in time/thickness profiles imply times of uplift and subsidence.
Thermal maturity profiles	Inflections in curves of maturity vs. depth depict burial/uplift history and can help us model structural development.

Secondary techniques

The following techniques are useful in determining structural trap timing.

Technique	Function
Vertical and lateral distribution of depositional environments to document uplift and subsidence	Tectonic activity can cause changes in sediment source terrances, bathymetry, and depositional environment, resulting in structurally controlled facies variations.
Radiometric dates of crosscutting intrusives and capping volcanics	Absolute age dating of these units can help to constraint the age of deformation of the host sedimentary rocks.
Unroofing sequences/ clastic lithology studies	The age of deposits shed off erosional highs relative to the age of the rock(s) being eroded implies the time of uplift.
Outcrop studies of kinematic indicators	Tectonic fabrics showing crosscutting or overprinting relationships suggest the sequence of deformation events.

Tertiary techniques

The following techniques are the least useful in determining structural trap timing.

Technique	Function
Fission-track thermal history modeling	These data help us model the temperature history of a rock from the time it cooled below a threshold temperature, thereby helping to date uplift and erosional events.
Inflections in shale compaction curves and velocity profiles	Vertical changes in percent compaction in shales inferred from logs can document changes in depth and/or rate of burial.
Paleoseismic indicators due to fault motion	The presence of synsedimentary or soft sediment deformation may indicate paleoseismic activity and date the tectonic motions responsible, in a relative sense.
Geochemical and geophysical investigations of fault zones • Rb-Sr, Ar-Ar, and K-Ar dating of fault zone material • Electron spin resonance techniques • Fracture fabric sequencing in fault zones	Fabric analysis and relative dating of fault zone diagenesis can be used in some cases to date periods of fault motion.

Reservoir and seal deformation

The table below describes the procedure for determining the relative deformation of seals and reservoirs in a structural trap.

Step	Task	Explanation
1	Based on outcrop studies and subsurface data, subdivide the stratigraphic section according to the relative mechanical strength of the units.	In all structural styles, the mechanical makeup of the stratigraphic package has a strong and often predictable effect on structure geometry.
2	Determine the mechanical properties (brittle vs. ductile) of the individual reservoir and seal rocks using the following: • Mechanical tests • Resistivity logs (in shales) • Composition–porosity–grain size predictions	These properties help predict the deformation mechanisms activated during deformation. In siliciclastic reservoirs, these mechanisms may result in deformation-induced dilatant or compactive changes which in turn may have a large impact on reservoir quality.
3	Interpret equivalent strain maps derived from curvature analysis, such as Gaussian curvature.	These maps determine possible compactive zones and predict fractured reservoir properties, such as fracture permeability.
4	Define deformation mechanisms (fracture, cataclasis, intracrystalline flow, pressure solution, etc.) in seal and reservoir rocks at appropriate depths, and relate them to capillary pressure for sealing capabilities.	These mechanisms help us predict deformation-related changes in seal and reservoir rock properties.
5	If needed, create equivalent plastic strain maps or sections (numerical mechanical modeling, e.g., boundary value problems and finite element modeling).	Numerical mechanical modeling can predict and map (1) deformation mechanisms and (2) reservoir and seal property changes related to deformation

Reservoir and seal changes

Structural deformation changes the petrophysical properties of the reservoir and seal facies. This physical diagenesis of reservoirs and seals in structural traps can take the form of compaction (reduction in porosity, permeability, and/or pore size) or dilatancy (increase in permeability by fracturing). These deformation-related changes should be either documented or predicted to estimate and risk reservoir and seal properties accurately in a structural trap.

Selling a Structural Play

Explaining the concept

For a structural play to be accepted, we must construct a coherent explanation of the mechanics or tectonics responsible for creating the play. Such explanations can be any of the following:

- The sequential development of the structure
- How the structure fits spatially and temporally within the regional tectonic fabric
- Appropriate physical and/or mechanical models that clarify the structure's development

Once constructed, these explanations give us greater confidence in our interpretations and a higher level of predictability in poorly constrained areas.

The table below describes the procedure for constructing such an explanation.

Step	Task	Explanation
1	Relate the play to published or in-house regional tectonic reconstructions and paleogeographic maps of the time periods over which the play's structural movement(s) occurred. Determine if your concept of the structural genesis of the play on the local scale is consistent with these regional scale models. Also consider whether to modify the local structural model or the tectonic model.	Provides a context in which to place the deformation that is consistent with regional data.
2	Determine whether results from considering structural timing and reservoir and seal quality are consistent with current mechanical models of fold and fault generation or with current knowledge of structural styles.	Provides a check with respect to the rules of mechanics and our knowledge of general structural form.
3	If the structural prospect is either quite complicated or ill constrained by the data, consider physical or numerical modeling to help define geometry and probable mode of origin.	Modeling provides a heuristic approach to predicting type and position of deformational features that can then be tested in outcrop or with subsurface data.

Selling a Structural Play, continued

Testing the play

If we have created the minimum play requirements, then we must convince someone—either management or investors—to test the play concept. Gaining consensus from peer review bodies, risk panels, management committees, and financial advisors can require a variety of presentation formats. Whereas the presentations all share some common aspects, differences exist because of the varied focus of these groups in today's exploration environment. The table below lists suggestions for the style of presentation appropriate for various groups.

Target Group	Style of Presentation
All groups	Control quality of all displays. This includes proper position of control and interpretive "picks" and consistency of dipping fault plane and axial surfaces between mapped horizons. One mistake can destroy the reviewer's faith in the entire project. Openly discuss strengths and weaknesses of the play. And be enthusiastic without equating approval to your own emotional well-being.
Peer review	Lead a discussion rather than make a presentation. Present negatives of the play up front to draw out helpful suggestions. Discuss detailed technical approaches and arguments early in the presentation. The goal is to solicit help solving problems.
Risk review panel (major company)	Emphasize the technical details. Present the positive and negative aspects in a more balanced manner than in the peer "problem-solving" review. Use all supportive illustrations and approaches to make a fair and accurate depiction of technical risk. The goal is technical calibration with other prospects within the exploration portfolio.
Management committee	Focus on technical conclusions and implications of the play to company exploration strategy. Emphasize the advantages of the play, but also disclose any technical details that increase the play's risk over other plays. The goal is to illustrate the strategic fit or importance of the play in the company's exploration portfolio.
Outside investors	Focus on generalities and play concepts. Check all data for accuracy. The goal is to gain commitment of capital early in the exploration process.

Section B
Structural Interpretation Techniques and Tools

Introduction

A variety of techniques and tools are available to explorationists for analyzing various aspects of a structural play. These cover a broad range, both in scale and type, from plate tectonic studies to microscopic examination of grain-scale structures and from outcrop studies to computer-intensive numerical modeling.

In this section, each technique or tool is discussed, emphasizing the following:

- The information it provides
- How to get that information
- When, where, or how to use the information
- Examples in the literature

In this section

This section contains two subsections:

Subsection B1

Scoping Techniques and Tools

In this subsection

This subsection discusses techniques that are primarily scoping in character and are frequently applied to large geographical areas. They often require little in monetary expenditure and are most appropriate for frontier basins. However, they can also be useful to companies seeking an entry position in a basin with established production and a competitive business environment.

Plate Tectonic Studies

Information provided

Plate tectonic studies provide the following kinds of information:

- Regional geologic framework
- Types of major structures expected in the play
- Whether the area may have been affected by more than one deformation event and/or more than one deformational style
- Age and relative timing of deformation
- Relation between structural trap development and other hydrocarbon systems events, such as source, seal, and reservoir deposition

When to use it

Always use plate tectonics. Although it is most useful in frontier basins, it is helpful even in mature basins. Knowing how a structural play fits into the regional tectonic picture may yield new ideas and approaches to exploration.

How to use it

This inexpensive technique is applied directly from the following:

- Regional literature in professional journals
- Interactive computer programs showing plate positions and configurations during geologic history
- Independent or "spec" regional studies integrating all aspects of the petroleum geology of a large region

Examples of use

Beydoun, Z.R., 1991, Arabian Plate Hydrocarbon Geology and Potential—A Plate Tectonic Approach: AAPG Studies in Geology 33, 77 p.

Busby, C.J., and R.V. Ingersoll, eds., 1995, Tectonics of SedimentaryBasins: Cambridge, Mass., Blackwell Scientific, 570 p.

Dickinson, W.R., and H. Yarborough, 1978, Plate Tectonics and Hydrocarbon Accumulation: AAPG Continuing Education Series 1, 148 p.

Harding, T.P., and J.D. Lowell, 1979, Structural styles, their plate-tectonic habitats and hydrocarbon traps in petroleum provinces: AAPG Bulletin, vol. 63, p. 1016–1058.

Pindell, J.L., and S.F. Barrett, 1990, Geological evolution of the Caribbean region: a plate-tectonic perspective, *in* G. Dengo and J.E. Case, eds., The Caribbean Region (vol. H of the Geology of North America series): Boulder, Colorado, Geological Society of America, p. 405–432.

Redfern, P., and J.A. Jones, 1995, The interior rifts of Yemen-analysis of basin structure and stratigraphy in a regional plate tectonic context: Basin Research, v. 7, p. 337–356.

Watson, M.P., A.B. Hayward, D.N. Parkinson, and Z.M. Zhang, 1987, Plate tectonic history, basin development and petroleum source rock deposition onshore China: Marine and Petroleum Geology, vol. 4, p. 205–225.

Yin, A., and S. Nie, 1996, A Phanerozoic palinspastic reconstruction of China and its neighboring regions, *in* A. Yin and T.M. Harrison, eds., The Tectonic Evolution of Asia: Cambridge, Mass., Cambridge University Press, p. 442–485.

Potential Fields

Information provided

The following table indicates the information provided by the three kinds of potential fields.

Field	Information Provided
Gravity	• Basin shape and depth • Constraints on diapiric origin of modeling structural geometry and depth structures
Magnetic	• Depth to basement • Basement fault trends and fault block boundaries
Magnetotelluric	• Thick-skinned vs. thin-skinned deformation • Amount of section below regional decollement

How to get it

Various scale regional gravity and magnetic surveys can be obtained from the following sources:

- Existing surveys (both ground and airborne acquired) from contractors
- Contractor-acquired data along seismic lines during seismic surveys
- Purchased surveys from government sources in the U.S. and overseas

Where to use it

Such data are extremely useful in extensional and rift terranes and as a guide in planning subsequent seismic surveys.

Examples of use

Billings, A.J., and J.H. Thomas, 1990, The use and limitations of non-seismic geophysics in the Papuan thrust belt, *in* G.J. Carman and Z. Carman, eds., Petroleum Exploration in Papua New Guinea: Proceedings of the First Papua New Guinea Petroleum Convention, Port Moresby, p. 51–62.

Christopherson, K.R., 1990, Applications of magnetotellurics to petroleum exploration in Papua New Guinea, *in* G.J. Carman and Z. Carman, eds., Petroleum exploration in Papua New Guinea: Proceedings of the First Papua New Guinea Petroleum Convention, Port Moresby, p. 63–71.

Nettleton, L.L., 1971, Elementary gravity and magnetics for geologists and seismologists: Society of Exploration Geophysicists Monograph Series 1, 121 p.

Remote Sensing

Information provided

Remote sensing data such as satellite imagery can help us examine regional structural fabrics, patterns, and contacts. Detailed mapping can be done using high-resolution satellite imagery and both high-altitude and low-level photography. The infrared bands on satellite imagery minimize the blurring effects of haze. Radar imagery removes the effects of haze and clouds.

Types

There are four types of remote sensing imagery used when exploring for structural traps:

- Satellite imagery
- High-altitude photography
- Low-level aerial photographs
- Side-looking airborne radar (SLAR) and/or sonar

The following table indicates the coverage and resolution of the various types of satellite imagery.

Type	Single Scene Coverage (km)	Resolution (m)
Landsat MSS	185 × 170	80
Landsat TM	185 × 170	30
SPOT	60 x 60	20 (color), 10 (b&w)
Soyuz	40 × 40	2

How to get it

Remote sensing imagery can be obtained from the following sources:

- Directly from vendors or foreign governments for satellite or high-altitude data or by using a contractor as an intermediary for obtaining and/or processing the imagery
- From published sources such as the proceedings from conferences and topical meetings
- Directly contracting low-altitude aerial photography or, in the U.S., obtaining existing surveys from the Department of Interior or Department of Agriculture (In foreign locations, such surveys often require local government approval and involvement.)

U.S. sources for high-altitude photography, low-level aerial photography, and SLAR are listed in the table below.

Type of Imagery	Sources
High-altitude photography	• Manned space mission photographs • U-2 photographs • National High Altitude Photography (NHAP)
Low-level aerial photographs	• Black and white or color, vertical or oblique photographs • Infrared (IR) photographs
Side Looking Airborne Radar (SLAR)	• Aircraft-based, low-level radar imagery • Satellite or shuttle-based radar imagery

Remote Sensing, continued

Where to use it

Remote sensing data are useful in all structural terranes but are especially important in remote areas where local topographic and geological control is absent or unobtainable.

In hydrocarbon exploration, remote sensing data is primarily used to (1) examine and map the surface geology in and around a concession area and (2) check terrain conditions and access routes for geologic fieldwork, seismic surveys, well locations, pipeline routes, and environmental hazards

Examples of use

Allenby, R.J., 1987, Origin of the Bolivian Andean orocline: a geologic study utilizing Landsat and Shuttle Imaging Radar: Tectonophysics, vol. 142, p. 137–154.

Beauchamp, W., M. Barazangi, A. Demnati, and M. El Alji, 1996, Intracontinental rifting and inversion: Missour Basin and Atlas Mountains, Morocco: AAPG Bulletin, vol. 80, p. 1459–1482.

Foster, N.H., and E.A. Beaumont, eds., 1992, Photogeology and photogeomorphology: AAPG Treatise of Petroleum Geology Reprint Series 18, 555 p.

Halbouty, M.T., 1980, Geologic significance of Landsat data for 15 giant oil and gas fields: AAPG Bulletin, vol. 64, p. 8–36.

Insley, M.W., F.X. Murphy, D. Naylor, and M. Critchley, 1996, The use of satellite imagery in the validation and verification of structural interpretations for hydrocarbon exploration in Pakistan and Yemen, *in* P.G. Buchanan and D.A. Nieuwland, eds., Modern Developments in Structural Interpretation, Validation and Modeling: Geological Society of London Special Publication 99, p. 321–343.

Prost, G.L., 1994, Remote Sensing for Geologists: A Guide to Image Interpretation: Gordon and Breach Science Publishers, 326 p.

Sabins, F.F., Jr., 1987, Remote Sensing, Principles and Interpretation: New York, W.H. Freeman Company, 449 p.

_____, 1998a, Remote sensing for petroleum exploration, part 1: overview of imaging systems: The Leading Edge, vol. 17, p. 467–470.

_____, 1998b, Remote sensing for petroleum exploration, part 2: case histories: The Leading Edge, vol. 17, p. 623–626.

Sosromihardjo, S.P.C., 1988, Structural analysis of the north Sumatra Basin with emphasis on synthetic aperture radar data: Proceedings of the Indonesian Petroleum Association, p. 187–209.

Regional Maps and Cross Sections

Information provided

Maps and cross sections provide the following kinds of information:

- Documentation/determination of structural style(s)
- Size, distribution, and spatial and age relationships of structures
- Spatial and age relationships of rock units

Types

Among the various types of maps are ...

- Maps of structural patterns and trends (fold, faults, lineaments)
- Structure contour/isopach maps
- General geological and tectonic maps

We should always compile/construct maps and cross sections using all available surface, well log, and seismic data.

How to get it

Such maps and sections can be obtained from the following sources:

- Local geological surveys and international societies
- National oil companies as part of data packages for concession offerings
- Independent regional studies within companies or by service companies on a "spec" or contract basis

Where to use it

Such data are mandatory for structural background in all structural terranes, especially in less mature basins.

Examples of use

Bally, A.W., P.L. Gordy, and G.A. Stewart, 1966, Structure, seismic data and orogenic evolution of southern Canadian Rocky Mountains: Bulletin of Canadian Petroleum Geology, vol. 4, p. 337–381.

_____, L. Burbi, C. Cooper, and R. Ghelardoni, 1986, Balanced sections and seismic reflection profiles across the central Apennines: Memorie della Societa Geologica Italiana, vol. 35, p. 257–310.

Dixon, J.S., 1982, Regional structural synthesis, Wyoming salient of the Western overthrust belt: AAPG Bulletin, vol. 66, p. 1560–1580.

Dunn, J.F., K.G. Hartshorn, and P.W. Hartshorn, 1995, Structural styles and hydrocarbon potential of the Sub-Andean thrust belt of southern Bolivia, *in* A.J. Tankard, R.S. Suarez, and H.J. Welsink, eds., Petroleum Basins of South America: AAPG Memoir 62, p. 523–543.

Dutton, S.P., A.G. Goldstein, and S.C. Ruppel, 1982, Petroleum Potential of the Palo Duro basin, Texas Panhandle: University of Texas at Austin Bureau of Economic Geology Report of Investigations 123, 87 p.

Picha, F.J., 1996, Exploring for hydrocarbons under thrust belts—a challenging new frontier in the Carpathians and elsewhere: AAPG Bulletin, vol. 80, p. 1547–1564.

Roure, F., J.O. Carnevali, Y. Gou, and T. Subieta, 1994, Geometry and kinematics of the north Monagas thrust belt (Venezuela): Marine and Petroleum Geology, vol. 11, p. 347–362.

Fieldwork

Information provided

Reconnaissance fieldwork can be used to familiarize the explorationist quickly with regional structural patterns, stratigraphy, and the distribution of rock types. It can also highlight areas where more detailed work is necessary. Existing maps should be spot-checked to determine if they can be confidently used for interpretation and as a base for additional work. In areas where geologic maps at the required scale are not available, detailed mapping and traversing may be required. Fieldwork can also be targeted to investigate specific topics such as fracture morphology and distribution, detailed fold geometry, and timing of structures.

The various types of fieldwork include the following:

- Regional reconnaissance
- Spot checks of existing maps
- Detailed mapping, traversing
- Targeted studies

When to use it

Structural fieldwork can be useful throughout an exploration program. If it is done prior to or in conjunction with the interpretation of seismic data in the area, it can help guide the interpretation. Structural fieldwork is most effective when done in conjunction with other stratigraphic and petrologic studies.

Examples of use

Dahlstrom, C.D.A., 1970, Structural geology in the eastern margin of the Canadian Rocky Mountains: Bulletin of Canadian Petroleum Geology, vol. 18, p. 332–406.

Fantozzi, P.L., 1996, Transition from continental to oceanic rifting in the Gulf of Aden: structural evidence from field mapping in Somalia and Yemen: Tectonophysics, vol. 259, p. 285–311.

Fermor, P.R., and R.A. Price, 1987, Multiduplex structure along the base of the Lewis thrust sheet in the southern Canadian Rockies: Bulletin of Canadian Petroleum Geology, vol. 35, p. 159–185.

Ghisetti, F., Mechanisms of thrust faulting in the Gran Sasso chain, southern Appenines, Italy: Journal of Structural Geology, vol. 9, p. 955–967.

McClay, K.R., 1987, The Mapping of Geologic Structures: New York, Halstead Press, 161 p.

Price, R.A., 1965, Flathead Map Area, British Columbia, Alberta: Geological Survey of Canada Memoir 336, 221 p.

Reynolds, A.D., M.D. Simmons, M.B.J. Bowman, J. Henton, A.C. Brayshaw, A.A. Ali-Zade, I.S. Guliyev, S.F. Suleymanova, E.Z. Ateava, D.N. Mamedova, and R.O. Koshkarly, 1998, Implications of outcrop geology for reservoirs in the Neogene productive series: Apsheron Peninsula, Azerbaijan: AAPG Bulletin, vol. 82, p. 25–49.

Rubey, W.W., S.S. Oriel, and J.I. Tracey, Jr., 1975, Geology of the Sage and Kemmerer 15-Minute Quadrangles, Lincoln County, Wyoming: U.S. Geological Survey Professional Paper 855, 18 p.

Stockmal, G.S., P.A. MacKay, D.C. Lawton, and D.A. Spratt, 1996, The Oldman River triangle zone: a complicated tectonic wedge delineated by new structural mapping and seismic interpretation: Bulletin of Canadian Petroleum Geology, vol. 44, p. 202–214.

Natural Analogs

How to use it

Well-documented surface or subsurface structures can be used as analogs to help constrain other structural interpretations based on sparse data. For example, if the regional tectonic setting indicates that our exploration area is in a thrust belt, but local outcrop/subsurface data do not accurately define the shape of individual structures, then we can use well-documented examples of structures from other thrust belts *with similar stratigraphy* as analogs to constrain our interpretation. However, correlation to producing structures is most valued.

Where to get it

Because one of the strongest arguments that can be used to "sell" a play in the industry is a producing analogy, such structural analogs are an important part of every structural play. These can be found in such sources as:

- Field catalogs within major companies
- Published regional field atlases from oil-producing states like California, Texas, and Louisiana
- The AAPG Treatise of Petroleum Geology, Atlas of Giant Fields, volumes on structural traps

Examples of use

Davison, I., D. Bosence, G.I. Alsop, and M.H. Al-Aawah, 1996, Deformation and sedimentation around active Miocene salt diapirs on the Tihama plain, northwest Yemen, *in* G.I. Alsop, D.J. Blundell, and I. Davison, eds., Salt Tectonics: Geological Society of London Special Publication 100, p. 23–39.

Erslev, E.A., and K.R. Mayborn, 1997, Multiple geometries and modes of fault-propagation folding in the Canadian thrust belt: Journal of Structural Geology, v. 19, 321–335.

Gabrielsen, F.H., R.J. Steel, and A. Nottvedt, 1995, Subtle traps in extensional terranes: a model with reference to the North Sea: Petroleum Geoscience, vol. 1, p. 223–235.

Halbouty, M.T., ed., 1992, Giant Oil and Gas Fields of the Decade: AAPG Memoir 54, 526 p.

Harding, T.P., 1984, Graben hydrocarbon occurrences and structural style: AAPG Bulletin, vol. 68, p. 333–362.

Hardman, R.F.P., and J. Brooks, eds., 1990, Tectonic Events Responsible for Britain's Oil and Gas Reserves: Geological Society of London Special Publication 55, 404 p.

Jackson, M.P.A., R.R. Cornelius, C.H. Craig, A. Gansser, J. Stocklin, and C.J. Talbot, 1990, Salt diapirs of the Great Kavir, central Iran: Geological Society of America Memoir 177, 139 p.

Jamison, W.R., 1987, Geometric analysis of fold development in overthrust terranes: Journal of Structural Geology, vol. 9, p. 207–219.

Lowell, J.D., 1995, Mechanics of basin inversion from worldwide examples, *in* J.G. Buchanan and P.G. Buchanan, eds., Basin Inversion: Geological Society of London Special Publication 88, p. 39–57.

Mitra, S., 1986, Duplex structures and imbricate thrust systems: geometry, structural position, and hydrocarbon potential: AAPG Bulletin, vol. 70, p. 1087–1112.

Morley, C.K., R.A. Nelson, T.L. Patton, and S.G. Munn, 1990, Transfer zones in the East African rift system and their relevance to hydrocarbon exploration in rifts: AAPG Bulletin, vol. 74, p. 1234–1253.

Natural Analogs, continued

Examples of use (continued)

Serra, S., 1977, Styles of deformation in the ramp regions of overthrust faults: Wyoming Geological Assoc. 29th Annual Field Conference Guidebook, p. 487–498.

Soule, G.S., and D.A. Spratt, 1996, En echelon geometry and two-dimensional model of the triangle zone, Grease Creek syncline area, Alberta: Bulletin of Canadian Petroleum Geology, vol. 44, p. 244–257.

Subsection B2

Prospect Delineation Techniques and Tools

In this subsection

In this subsection, we discuss techniques that refine our understanding of individual structural traps, both prior to and subsequent to drilling. The techniques may require significant monetary expenditure and are applied in smaller, more well-defined geographical areas (i.e., structural fairways) than the techniques discussed in Subsection B1.

Seismic Data

Information provided

Seismic data provide a "time picture" of subsurface structure. For accurate structural analysis, an effort should be made to convert the time data to depth.

There are three types of seismic data:

- Reflection (including 2-D and 3-D)
- Shear wave
- Refraction

2-D reflection seismic data provide cross-sectional views in both the dip and strike directions. Data on the lines are a mixture of both in-plane and out-of-plane reflectors. 2-D reflection seismic data are most important in the earlier stages of an exploration program, especially in frontier basins.

3-D reflection seismic data provide resolved cross-sectional views along any azimuth within the survey area. Time "slices" (maps) on any horizon can also be generated. The nature and location of out-of-plane features can be more accurately determined. Because of the high acquisition costs, 3-D seismic techniques normally are used only to more accurately define individual prospects.

Shear wave data, in combination with conventional compressional wave data, can provide information on lithology, fractures, and the presence of hydrocarbons.

Refraction seismic data provide a deep crustal view of gross structure (basin scale to lithosphere–upper mantle scale), which is useful when trying to understand regional tectonics.

How to use it

Although structural interpretation from seismic data is indeed a difficult endeavor and a detailed discussion is beyond the scope of this chapter, the following are hints for effective interpretation procedures.

- Interpretation on each line should proceed from well-imaged, well-constrained portions of the line toward areas of poorer constraint. Use symbols for varying quality of interpretation.
- Map multiple horizons.
- Map and contour fault surfaces critical to closure.
- Integrate fault and horizon contours.
- In thrust, rift, and extensional terranes, emphasize dip line interpretation; in foreland and wrench terranes, equally emphasize strike line interpretation.
- Generate depth conversions during iterative interpretations.

Examples of use

Badley, M.E., 1985, Practical Seismic Interpretation: Boston, International Human Resources Development Corp., 266 p.

Bally, A.W., ed., 1983, Seismic Expression of Structural Styles, A Picture and Work Atlas: AAPG Studies in Geology 15, 3 vols.

Brown, A.R., 1996, Interpretation of three-dimensional seismic data: AAPG Memoir 42, 4th ed., 424 p.

Coffeen, J.A., 1984, Interpreting Seismic Data Workbook: Tulsa, PennWell Publishing Co., 196 p.

Seismic Data, continued

Examples of use (continued)

Fraser, A.J., and R.L. Gawthorpe, 1990, Tectono-stratigraphic development and hydrocarbon habitat of the Carboniferous in northern England, *in* R.F.P. Hardman and J. Brooks, eds., Tectonic Events Responsible for Britain's Oil and Gas Reserves: Geological Society of London Special Publication 55, p. 49–86.

Sheriff, R.E., 1982, Structural Interpretation of Seismic Data: AAPG Education Course Notes 23, 73 p.

Slotboom, R.T., D.C. Lawton, and D.A. Spratt, 1996, Seismic interpretation of the triangle zone at Jumping Pond, Alberta: Bulletin of Canadian Petroleum Geology, vol. 44, p. 233–243.

Telford, W.M., L.P. Geldart, and R.E. Sheriff, 1990, Applied Geophysics: Cambridge, Cambridge University Press, 770 p.

Valderrama, M.H., K.C. Nielsen, and G.A. McMechan, 1996, Three-dimensional seismic interpretation from the triangle zone of the frontal Ouachita Mountains and Arkoma basin, Pittsburg County, Oklahoma: AAPG Bulletin, vol. 80, p. 1185–1202.

Modeling

Information provided

Models are representations of natural structures. They are used when direct analysis of various aspects of natural structures is either difficult or impossible.

There are two types of models:

- Physical (including rock mechanics models, photoelastic models, and geometry models)
- Mathematical (including mechanics models and geometry models)

Physical models

Physical models are constructed from rocks or a variety of materials including clay, sand, and putty.

- **Rock mechanics models** are designed and run to gain information on the strength and deformation mechanisms of rocks when subjected to various loads and displacements under controlled conditions of pressure, temperature, strain rate, and pore fluid pressure and chemistry. The starting configuration of these models is usually a right circular cylinder composed of the rock(s) being studied.
- **Photoelastic models** provide information on stress magnitude and orientation. They are made of transparent materials such as clear plastics or gelatins. When deformed and examined in polarized light, these materials exhibit color fringes and alternating light and dark bands. From these, we can determine the stress intensity and the orientation of the principal stresses at any point in the model.
- **Geometric models** reproduce the shape of naturally occurring structures. The starting configuration is usually a layered rectangular block or some variation thereof. Displacements are imposed at the boundaries of the block to create the desired deformation. The hope is that if we can create a good geometric analog of a natural structure under conditions we specify and control, then we will gain a better understanding of the conditions that influence the development of the natural structure. This highlights an important role of these models: they generate hypotheses or ideas regarding the development and final shape of natural structures—ideas that may not occur to us even after careful study of structures in the field.

Mathematical models

Mathematical models consist of equations that describe the interrelationship of parameters thought to be important in the development of natural structures.

- **Mechanics models** use various analytic and numerical techniques (finite element, distinct element, finite difference) to simulate deformation. Input parameters are undeformed shape, mechanical properties of the model materials, displacements, and displacement rate. The models yield information on deformed shape, displacement trajectories, and the orientation and magnitude of stress and strain in the model at various stages of displacement.
- **Geometry models** examine the development of structures, mainly in 2-D, by applying various simplified kinematic or displacement rules. These models do not provide direct information on the structural effects of environmental parameters during deformation (e.g., rock strength, overburden pressure, temperature, strain rate).

How to use it

Models offer insight into how natural structures may have developed. For structures where geometry is poorly constrained by outcrop, seismic data, or well data, models may suggest reasonable options for completing the structural interpretation.

How to use it (continued)

Quantitative data derived from a model can be confidently applied to natural structures only if the model has been accurately and completely scaled with respect to the natural counterpart. In practice, this degree of scaling may be achieved in numerical models and mechanical physical models. It is often difficult to achieve in geometrical physical models. Nevertheless, partially scaled and even nonscaled models can still help generate ideas on structure development.

"No absolute or final decision can be made about the admissibility of a given modeling technique; the decision must always depend on the interest of the experimenter, the accuracy and urgency of the required prediction, and the availability of other techniques. Often the modeling technique which most flagrantly flouts the similarity [scaling] rules is the most useful one in practice" (Spalding, 1962).

Modeling concepts

Gretener, P.E., 1981, Reflections on the value of laboratory tests on rocks, *in* N.L. Carter, M. Friedman, J.M. Logan, and D.W. Stearns, eds., Mechanical Behavior of Crustal Rocks: American Geophysical Union Monograph 24, p. 323–326.

Hubbert, M.K., 1937, Theory of scale models as applied to the study of geologic structures: Geological Society of America Bulletin, vol. 48, p. 1459–1520.

Paterson, M.S., 1987, Problems in the extrapolation of laboratory rheological data: Tectonophysics, v. 133, p. 33–43.

Patton, T.L., S. Serra, R.J. Humphreys, and R.A. Nelson, 1995, Building conceptual structural models from multiple modeling sources: an example from thrust-ramp studies: Petroleum Geoscience, v. 1, p. 153–162.

Spalding, D.B., 1962, The art of partial modeling: 9th Symposium on Combustion, p. 833–843.

Stearns, D.W., G.D. Couples, W.R. Jamison, and J.D. Morse, 1981, Understanding faulting in the shallow crust: contributions of selected experimental and theoretical studies, *in* N.L. Carter, M. Friedman, J.M. Logan, and D.W. Stearns, eds., Mechanical Behavior of Crustal Rocks: American Geophysical Union Monograph 24, p. 215–229.

Physical models

Rock mechanics models

Donath, F.A., 1970, Some information squeezed out of rock: American Scientist: vol. 58, p. 53–72.

Dunn, D.E., L.J. LaFountain, and R.E. Jackson, 1973, Porosity dependence and mechanism of brittle fracture in sandstones: Journal of Geophysical Research, vol. 78, p. 2403–2417.

Handin, J., R.V. Hager, Jr., M. Friedman, and J.N. Feather, 1963, Experimental deformation of sedimentary rocks under confining pressure: pore pressure tests: AAPG Bulletin, vol. 47, p. 717–755.

Logan, J.M., and P. Lin, 1991, The interaction of two closely spaced cracks: a rock model study: Journal of Geophysical Research, vol. 96, p. 21667–21675.

Renner, J., and F. Rummel, 1996, The effect of experimental and microstructural parameters on the transition from brittle failure to cataclastic flow of carbonate: Tectonophysics, vol. 258, p. 151–169.

Physical models (continued)

Scott, T.E., and K.C. Nielsen, 1991, The effects of porosity on the brittle-ductile transition in sandstones: Journal of Geophysical Research, v. 96, p. 405–414.

Photoelastic models

Bell, R.T., and J.B. Currie, 1964, Photoelastic experiments related to structural geology: Proceedings of the Geological Association of Canada, vol. 15, p. 33–51.

Bombolakis, E.G., 1968, Photoelestic study of initial stages of brittle fracture in compression: Tectonophysics, v. 6, p. 461–473.

Gallagher, J.J., M. Friedman, J. Handin, and G.M. Sowers, 1974, Experimental studies relating to microfractures in sandstone: Tectonophysics, vol. 21, p. 203–247.

Geometry models

Dixon, J.M., and S. Liu, 1992, Centrifuge modeling of the propagation of thrust faults, *in* K.R. McClay, ed., Thrust Tectonics: London, Chapman and Hall, p. 53–69.

Dooley, T., and K. McClay, 1997, Analog modeling of pull-apart basins: AAPG Bulletin, v. 81, p. 1804–1826.

Ge, H., M.P.A. Jackson, and B.C. Vendeville, 1997, Kinematics and dynamics of salt tectonics driven by progradation: AAPG Bulletin, v. 81, p. 398–423.

Guglielmo, G. Jr., M.P.A. Jackson, and B.C. Vendeville, 1997, Three-dimensional visualization of salt walls and associated fault systems: AAPG Bulletin, v. 81, p. 46–61.

Letouzey, J., B. Colletta, R. Vially, and J.C. Chermette, 1995, Evolution of salt-related structures in compressional settings, in M.P.A. Jackson, D.G. Roberts, and S. Snelson, eds., Salt tectonics: a global perspective: AAPG Memoir 65, p. 41–60.

McClay, K., 1996, Recent advances in analogue modelling: uses in section interpretation and validation, in P.G. Buchanan and D.A. Nieuwland, eds., Modern Developments in Structural interpretation, Validation and Modelling: Geological Society of London Special Publication no. 99, p. 201–255.

Morse, J., 1977, Deformation in ramp regions of overthrust faults: experiments with small-scale rock models: Wyoming Geological Association 29th Annual Field Conference Guidebook, p. 457–470.

Naylor, M.A., J.M. Laroque, and B.D.M. Gauthier, 1996, Understanding extensional tectonics: insights from sandbox models, in F. Roure, N. Ellouz, V.S. Shein, and I. Skvortsov, eds., Geodynamic Evolution of Sedimentary Basins: Editions Technip, p. 69–83.

Storti, F., F. Salvini, and K. McClay, 1997, Fault-related folding in sandbox analogue models of thrust wedges: Journal of Structural Geology, v. 19, p. 583–602.

Vendeville, B.C., and M.P.A. Jackson, 1992, The rise of diapirs during thin-skinned extension: Marine and Petroleum Geology, v. 9, p. 331–353.

Vendeville, B.C., and M.P.A. Jackson, 1992, The fall of diapirs during thin-skinned extension: Marine and Petroleum Geology, v. 9, p. 354–371.

Weinberg, D.M., 1979, Experimental folding of rocks under confining pressure, part VII: partially scaled models of drape folds: Tectonophysics, vol. 54, p. 1–24.

Withjack, M.O., Q.T. Islam, and P.R. LaPointe, 1995, Normal faults and their hangingwall deformation: an experimental study: AAPG Bulletin, v. 79, p. 1–18.

Mathematical models

Mechanics models

Couples, G.D., and D.W. Stearns, 1978, Analytical solutions applied to structures of the Rocky Mountain foreland on local and regional scales, *in* V. Matthews III, ed., Laramide Folding Associated with Basement Block Faulting in the Western United States: Geological Society of America Memoir 151, p. 313–335.

Crans, W., and G. Mandl, 1980, On the theory of growth faulting; part II (a): genesis of the "unit": Journal of Petroleum Geology, vol. 3, p. 209–236.

Gangi, A.F., K.D. Min, and J.M. Logan, 1977, Experimental folding of rocks under confining pressure; part IV: theoretical analysis of faulted drape folds: Tectonophysics, vol. 42, p. 227–260.

Jamison, W.R., 1996, Mechanical models of triangle zone evolution: Bulletin of Canadian Petroleum Geology, vol. 44, p. 180–194.

Johnson, A., 1977, Styles of Folding: Amsterdam, Elsevier, 406 p.

Patton, T.L., and R.C. Fletcher, 1995, Mathmatical block-motion model for deformation of a layer above a buried fault of arbitrary dip and sense of slip: Journal of Structural Geology, vol., p. 1455–1472.

Shimamoto, T., and I. Hara, 1976, Geometry and strain distribution of single-layer folds: Tectonophysics, vol. 30, p. 1–34.

Strayer, L.M., and P.J. Hudleston, 1997, Numerical modeling of fold initiation at thrust ramps: Journal of Structural Geology, vol. 19, p. 551–566.

Geometry models

Chester, J.S., and F.M. Chester, 1990, Fault-propagation folds above thrusts with constant dip: Journal of Structural Geology, vol. 12, p. 903–910.

Dula, W.F., Jr., 1991, Geometric models of listric normal faults and rollover folds: AAPG Bulletin, vol. 75, p. 1609–1625.

Groshong, R.H., Jr., 1994, Area balance, depth to detachment, and strain in extension: Tectonics, vol. 13, p. 1488–1497.

Jamison, W.R., 1987, Geometric analysis of fold development in overthrust terranes: Journal of Structural Geology, vol. 9, p. 207–219.

Marrett, R., and P.A. Bentham, 1997, Geometric analysis of hybrid fault-propagation/detachment folds: Journal of Structural Geology, vol. 19, p. 243–248.

Mitra, S., 1990, Fault-propagation folds: geometry, kinematic evolution, and hydrocarbon traps: AAPG Bulletin, vol. 74, p. 921–945.

_____ and V.S. Mount, 1998, Foreland basement-involved structures: AAPG Bulletin, vol. 82, p. 70–109.

Poblet, J., and K. McClay, 1996, Geometry and kinematics of single-layer detachment folds: AAPG Bulletin, vol. 80, p. 1085–1109.

Shaw, J.H., S.C. Hook, and J. Suppe, 1994, Structural trend analysis by axial surface mapping: AAPG Bulletin, vol. 78, p. 700–721.

Suppe, J., 1983, Geometry and kinematics of fault-bend folding: American Journal of Science, vol. 283, p. 648–721.

Balanced Cross Sections

Definition

Balanced cross sections honor all available data and are constructed and analyzed to ensure they are geometrically possible and geologically admissible, given reasonable assumptions about the predeformation setting of rocks and how rocks behave during deformation in a particular tectonic environment. "Balanced" refers to the basic assumption made in constructing these sections—that rock area (rock volume) does not change substantially as a result of deformation. Balanced cross sections are restorable. This means that, while maintaining constant area, the deformation displayed in a balanced cross section can be incrementally removed to yield a geologically plausible predeformation configuration.

The constant area (constant volume) assumption is generally valid for deformation that has occurred in upper crustal, nonmetamorphic settings, but there are important exceptions. For example, in some settings syntectonic deposition and compaction can result in substantial rock volume changes throughout the course of deformation. In these cases, approximations of the volume changes must be incorporated in the balancing process.

Balancing is an interative, trial-and-error process. If done manually, it is tedious and very time consuming. Computer programs greatly simplify the measurement and drafting aspects of cross section balancing. Some of these programs also incorporate functions and algorithms that permit some rudimentary 3-D balancing of structures.

Value of Balancing

Balanced cross sections are not necessarily correct. However, the methodical scrutiny imposed by the balancing process highlights discrepancies in interpretations, points to the types of data or alternative schemes needed to resolve the discrepancies, and generally results in more carefully constructed, defensible, and explainable cross sections.

Examples of use

Baby, P., G. Herail, R. Salinas, and T. Sempere, 1992, Geometry and kinematic evolution of passive roof duplexes deduced from cross section balancing: example from the foreland thrust system of the southern Bolivian Subandean zone: Tectonics, vol. 11, p. 523–536.

Buchanan, P.G., D.J. Bishop, and D.N. Hood, 1996, Development of salt-related structures in the central North Sea: results from section balancing, *in* G.I. Alsop, D.J. Blundell, and I. Davison, eds., Salt Tectonics: Geological Society of London Special Publication 100, p. 111–128.

_____ and D.A. Nieuwland, eds., 1996, Modern Developments in Structural Interpretation, Validation and Modelling: Geological Society of London Special Publication 99, p. 369.

Dahlstrom, C.D.A., 1969, Balanced cross sections: Canadian Journal of Earth Sciences, vol. 6, p. 743–757.

Diegel, V.A., J.F. Karlo, D.C. Schuster, R.C. Shoup, and P.R. Tauvers, 1995, Cenozoic structural evolution and tectono-stratigraphic framework of the northern Gulf Coast continental margin, *in* M.P.A. Jackson, D.G. Roberts and S. Snelson, eds., Salt Tectonics: A Global Perspective: AAPG Memoir 65, p. 109–151.

Geiser, P.A., 1988, The role of kinematics in the construction and analysis of geological cross sections in deformed terranes, *in* G. Mitra and S. Wojtal, eds., Geometries and Mechanisms of Thrusting, with Special Reference to the Appalachians: Geological Society of America Special Paper 222, p. 47–76.

Examples of use (continued)

Gibbs, A.D., 1983, Balanced cross-section construction from seismic sections in areas of extensional tectonics: Journal of Structural Geology, vol. 5, p. 153–160.

Groshong, R.H., Jr., 1990, Unique determination of normal fault shape from hanging-wall bed geometry in detached half grabens: Ecologae Geologicae Helvetiae, vol. 83, p. 455–471.

Hossack, J., 1995, Geometric rules of section balancing for salt structures, *in* M.P.A. Jackson, D.G. Roberts, and S. Snelson, eds., Salt Tectonics: A Global Perspective: AAPG Memoir 65, p. 29–40.

Marshak, S., and N. Woodward, 1988, Introduction to cross-section balancing *in* S. Marshak and G. Mitra, eds., Basic Methods of Structural Geology: Englewood Cliffs, New Jersey, Prentice Hall, p. 303–302.

Mitra, S., 1992, Balanced structural interpretations in fold and thrust belts, *in* S. Mitra and G.W. Fisher, eds., Structural Geology of Fold and Thrust Belts: Johns Hopkins University Press, Maryland, p. 53–77.

_____ and J. Namsom, 1989, Equal-area balancing: American Journal of Science, vol. 289, p. 563–599.

Moffat, D.T., L.F. Henage, R.A. Brash, R.W. Tauer, and B.H. Harahap, 1991, Lengguru, Irian Jaya: prospect selection using field mapping, balanced cross sections, and gravity modeling: Proceedings of the Indonesian Petroleum Association's 20th Annual Convention, p. 85–106.

Mount, V.S., J. Suppe, and S.C. Hook, 1990, A forward modeling strategy for balancing cross sections: AAPG Bulletin, vol. 74, p. 521–531.

Rouby, D., H. Fossen, and P.R. Cobbold, 1996, Extension, displacement, and block rotation in the larger Gullfaks area, northern North Sea: determined from map view restoration: AAPG Bulletin, vol. 80, p. 875–890.

Rowan, M.G., 1993, A systematic technique for the sequential restoration of salt structures: Tectonophysics, vol. 228, p. 331–348.

_____ and R. Kligfield, 1989, Cross section restoration and balancing as aid to seismic interpretation in extensional terranes: AAPG Bulletin, vol. 73, p. 955–966.

White, N., and G. Yielding, 1991, Calculating normal faults geometries at depth: theory and examples, *in* A.M. Roberts, G. Yielding, and B. Freeman, eds., The Geometry of Normal Faults: Geological Society of London Special Publication 56, p. 251–260.

Dipmeter Analysis

Information provided

Dipmeter logs provide data on the dip magnitude and azimuth of planar features in the well bore. These features commonly include primary bedding, cross-bedding, and faults. High-resolution dipmeters can also yield information on fractures and lithologic textural variations. Analysis of dipmeter data using statistical curvature analysis techniques (SCAT) let us more confidently extrapolate structural data away from the well bore.

Where to get it

Dipmeter and borehole imaging logs like the formation microscanner (FMS) or FMI are useful in analyzing all subsurface structural plays, regardless of origin or style.

Interpretations can be obtained from the following:

- Logging service companies as a consulting service
- SCAT-type analysis from commercially available programs and consultants.
- Independent analysis of tadpole logs via pattern recognition or by standard stereographic projections and rose diagrams from FMS workstations

Examples of use

Bengston, C.A., 1981, Statistical curvature analysis techniques for structural interpretation of dipmeter data: AAPG Bulletin, vol. 65, p. 312–332.

_____, 1982, Structural and stratigraphic uses of dip profiles in petroleum exploration, *in* M.T. Halbouty, ed., The Deliberate Search for the Subtle Trap: AAPG Memoir 32, p. 619–632.

Delhomme, J.-P., T. Pilenko, E. Cheruvier, and R. Cull, 1986, Reservoir applications of dipmeter logs: Society of Petroleum Engineers Paper 15485, 7 p.

Etchecopar, A., and J.-L. Bonnetain, 1992, Cross sections from dipmeter data: AAPG Bulletin, vol. 76, p. 621–637.

Hurley, N.F., 1994, Recognition of faults, unconformities, and sequence boundaries using cumulative dip plots: AAPG Bulletin, vol. 78, p. 1173–1185.

Morse, J.D., and C.A. Bengston, 1988, What is wrong with tadpole plots?: AAPG Bulletin, vol. 72, p. 390.

Nurmi, R. D., 1984, Geological evaluation of high resolution dipmeter data: Society of Professional Well Log Analysts' 25th Annual Logging Symposium, vol. 2, paper YY, 24 p.

Schlumberger, 1986, Dipmeter Interpretation Fundamentals: New York, Schlumberger Ltd., 76 p.

Sercombe, W.J., B.R. Golob, M. Kamel, J.W. Stewart, G.W. Smith, and J.D. Morse, 1997, Significant structural reinterpretation of the subsalt, giant October field, Gulf of Suez, Egypt, using SCAT, isogon-based section and maps, and 3D seismic: The Leading Edge, vol. 16, p. 1143–1150.

Fault Seal–Conduit Studies

Introduction

These studies try to determine if faults in a particular tectonic setting have acted as conduits or seals with respect to the migration of subsurface fluids. They use a variety of techniques, including outcrop studies of fault zones, core analysis and laboratory testing, thin-section analysis, and construction of fault-plane maps to determine the juxtaposition of rock types along faults.

Information provided

Fault seal–conduit studies predict fault seal–conduit behavior and potential hydrocarbon column height, based on fault morphology and gouge composition, lithology juxtapositions along faults, hydrocarbon type, and reservoir pressure.

How to use them

These data are important in traps where faults play an important role in the critical seal. The analysis involves blending data on fault deformation mechanisms and kinematics with petrophysics and hydrodynamics. Historical analysis of fault sealing capacity in an area is also extremely useful.

Examples of use

Alexander, L.L., and J.W. Handschy, 1998, Fluid flow in a faulted reservoir system: fault trap analysis for the Block 330 field in Eugene Island, South Addition, offshore Louisiana: AAPG Bulletin, vol. 82, p. 387–411.

Allan, U.S., 1989, Model for hydrocarbon migration and entrapment within faulted structures: AAPG Bulletin, vol. 73, p. 803–811.

Antonellini, M., and A. Aydin, 1995, Effect of faulting on fluid flow in porous sandstones: geometry and spatial distribution: AAPG Bulletin, vol. 79, p. 642–671.

Brenneke, J.C., 1995, Analysis of fault traps: World Oil, vol. 217, p. 63–71.

Finkbeiner, T., C.A. Barton, and M.D. Zoback, 1997, Relationships among in-situ stress, fractures and faults, and fluid flow: Monterey Formation, Santa Maria basin, California: AAPG Bulletin, vol. 81, p. 1975–1999.

Gibson, R.G., 1994, Fault-zone seals in siliciclastic strata of the Columbus basin, offshore Trinidad: AAPG Bulletin, vol. 78, p. 1372–1385.

Hooper, E.C.D., 1991, Fluid migration along growth faults in compacting sediments: Journal of Petroleum Geology, vol. 14, p. 161–180.

Jev, B.I., C.H. Kaars-Slijpesteijn, M.P.A.M. Peters, M.L. Watts, and J.T. Wilkie, 1993, Akaso field, Nigeria: use of integrated 3-D seismic, fault slicing, clay smearing and RFT pressure data on fault trapping and dynamic leakage: AAPG Bulletin, vol. 77, p. 1389–1404.

Knipe, R.J., 1997, Juxtaposition and seal diagrams to help analyze fault seals in hydrocarbon reservoirs: AAPG Bulletin, vol. 81, p. 187–195.

Moeller-Pederson, P., and A.G. Koestler, eds., Hydrocarbon Seals, Importance for Exploration and Production: Norwegian Petroleum Society Special Publication 7, 250 p.

Nybakken, S., 1991, Sealing fault traps—an exploration concept in a mature petroleum province: Tampen Spur, northern North Sea: First Break, vol. 9, p. 209–222.

Smith, D.A., 1980, Sealing and non-sealing faults in Louisiana Gulf Coast salt basin: AAPG Bulletin, vol. 64., p. 145–172.

Petrofabrics

Information provided

Petrofabrics is the study of deformation features in rocks, usually at the grain scale. The most commonly studied features are fractures (distribution, morphology, and orientation), twinning, pressure solution, and recrystallization fabrics.

Petrofabrics provides information on the following:

- Mechanisms of deformation
- Orientation and magnitude of principal stresses
- Deformation effects on porosity/permeability

How to use it

Structural petrofabric analysis is important in a relatively limited number of special situations. It requires oriented subsurface or surface samples and is performed only by a relatively limited number of specialists, usually at universities.

Examples of use

Allmendinger, R.W., 1982, Analysis of microstructures in the Meade plate of the Idaho–Wyoming foreland thrustbelt, U.S.A.: Tectonophysics, vol. 85, p. 221–251.

Burger, H.R., and M. Hamill, 1976, Petrofabric analysis of the Dry Creek Ridge anticline, Montana: Geological Society of America Bulletin, vol. 87, p. 555–566.

Burkhard, M., 1993, Calcite twins, their geometry, appearance and significance as stress-strain markers and indicators of tectonic regime: a review: Journal of Structural Geology, vol. 15, p. 351–368.

Friedman, M., 1964, Petrofabric techniques for the determination of principal stress directions in rocks, *in* W.R. Judd, ed., State of Stress in the Earth's Crust: New York, Elsevier, p. 451–552.

_____ and G.M. Sowers, 1970, Petrofabrics: a critical review: Canadian Journal of Earth Sciences, vol. 7, p. 477–497.

_____ and D.W. Stearns, 1971, Relations between stresses inferred from calcite twin lamellae and macrofractures, Teton anticline, Montana: Geological Society of America Bulletin, vol. 82, p. 3151–3162.

Onasch, C.M., 1990, Microfractures and their role in deformation of a quartz arenite from the central Appalachian foreland: Journal of Structural Geology, vol. 12, p. 883–894.

Fracture Analysis

Information provided

Five types of fracture analysis provide the following types of information:

Outcrop studies
- Regional-scale to prospect-scale fracture orientation, distribution, width, and spacing
- Fracture size and morphology

Curvature analysis
- Strain distribution prediction based on geometry from structural mapping (fold shape and location on fold)
- Natural fracture intensity prediction and, to a limited extent, fracture porosity, given assumptions regarding rock behavior and strain partitioning

Core analysis
- Downhole fracture distribution, orientation, size, width, spacing, and morphology
- Relationship between petrophysical properties of fractures and matrix

Log analysis
- Detection of fractures in a nonquantitative manner
- Orientation of a selected fracture population
- In some cases, determination of the fluid or mineral filling in fractures

Mathematical models
- Prediction of compactive vs. dilatant rock behavior
- Maps of fracture zones and variations in fracture intensity
- Prediction of fracture porosity, given assumptions regarding relationships between stress and strain and the fracture response of the rock

How to use it

Fracture analysis can help us define structural axes and trends or fracture-related reservoir properties. It can be applied in a variety of structural terranes and rock types, but it is especially important in brittle rock packages. To determine reservoir-property requires integrating geology, petrophysics, and reservoir engineering, and it is most often done by experienced specialists.

Examples of use

Aguilera, R., 1980, Naturally Fractured Reservoirs: Tulsa, PennWell, 703 p. Coward, M.P., T.S. Daltaban, and H. Johnson, eds., Structural Geology in Reservoir Characterization: Geological Society of London Special Publication 127, 266 p.

Jamison, W.R., 1997, Quantitative evaluation of fractures on Monkshood anticline, a detachment fold in the foothills of western Canada: AAPG Bulletin, vol. 81, 1110–1132.

Kulander, B.R., S.L. Dean, and B.J. Ward, Jr., 1990, Fractured Core Analysis: Interpretation, Logging, and Use of Natural and Induced Fractures in Core: AAPG Methods in Exploration 8, 88 p.

Laubach, S.E., 1989, Fracture Analysis of the Travis Peak Formation, Western Flank of the Sabine Arch, East Texas: University of Texas at Austin Bureau of Economic Geology Report of Investigations 185, 55 p.

_____, 1997, A method to detect natural fracture strike in sandstones: AAPG Bulletin, vol. 81, p. 604–623.

Examples of use (continued)

Narr, W., 1996, Estimating average fracture spacing in subsurface rock: AAPG Bulletin, vol. 80, p. 1565–1586.

Nelson, R.A., 1985, Geologic Analysis of Naturally Fractured Reservoirs: Houston, Gulf Publishing Co., 320 p.

_____ and S. Serra, 1995, Vertical and lateral variations in fracture spacing in folded carbonate sections and its relation to locating horizontal wells: Journal of Canadian Petroleum Technology, vol. 34, p. 51–56.

U.S. National Committee for Rock Mechanics, 1996, Rock Fractures and Fluid Flow: Washington, D.C., National Academy Press, 551 p.

Wiltschko, D.V., K.P. Corbett, M. Friedman, and J-H. Hung, 1991, Predicting fracture connectivity and intensity within the Austin Chalk from outcrop fracture maps and scanline data: Transactions of the Gulf Coast Association of Geological Societies, vol. 41, p. 702–718.

Section C

Workflow to Find a Prospect

Introduction

This section suggests a flow of tasks to help explorationists define a drill location, moving from the regional scale to the drill site. The discussion is from the perspective of a full-cycle exploration play, where we have a play concept and are looking for a drill location to test it.

In this section

This section contains the following topics.

Schematic Overview

The workflow We begin by envisioning a structural play concept based on the thrust belt play of the U.S. Rocky Mountain area. The following workflow discussion tracks this play concept from inception to drill location through a "normal" structural exploration process, as shown in the figure below.

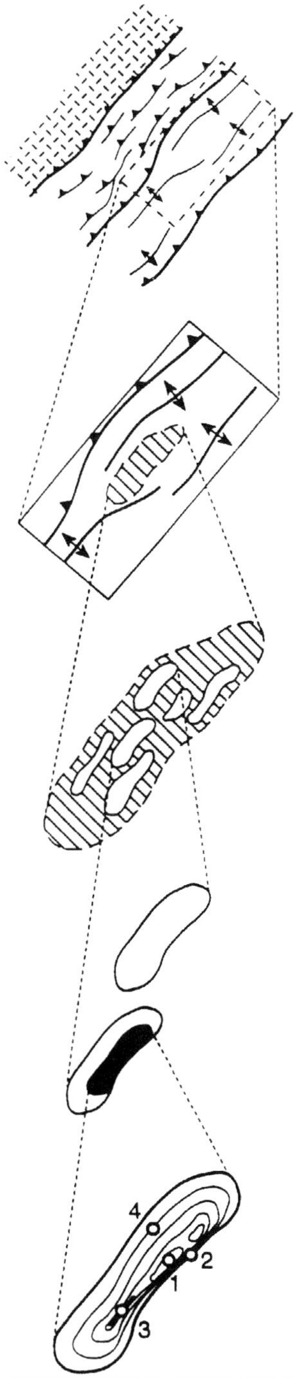

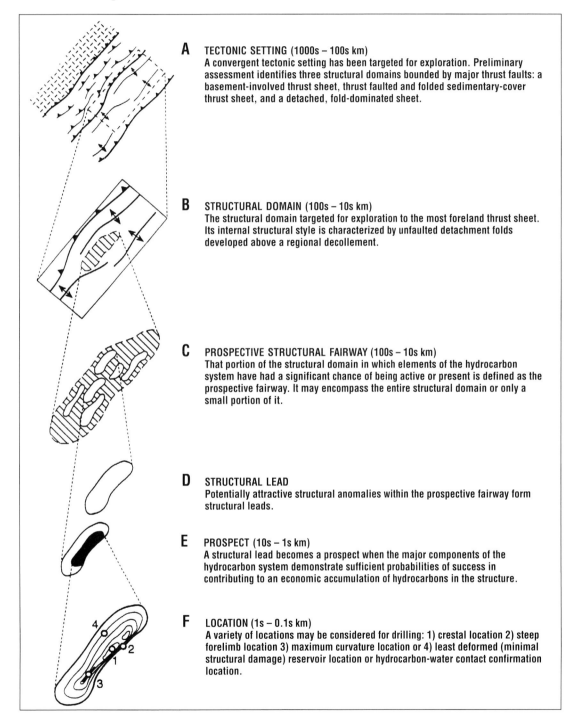

A TECTONIC SETTING (1000s – 100s km)
A convergent tectonic setting has been targeted for exploration. Preliminary assessment identifies three structural domains bounded by major thrust faults: a basement-involved thrust sheet, thrust faulted and folded sedimentary-cover thrust sheet, and a detached, fold-dominated sheet.

B STRUCTURAL DOMAIN (100s – 10s km)
The structural domain targeted for exploration to the most foreland thrust sheet. Its internal structural style is characterized by unfaulted detachment folds developed above a regional decollement.

C PROSPECTIVE STRUCTURAL FAIRWAY (100s – 10s km)
That portion of the structural domain in which elements of the hydrocarbon system have had a significant chance of being active or present is defined as the prospective fairway. It may encompass the entire structural domain or only a small portion of it.

D STRUCTURAL LEAD
Potentially attractive structural anomalies within the prospective fairway form structural leads.

E PROSPECT (10s – 1s km)
A structural lead becomes a prospect when the major components of the hydrocarbon system demonstrate sufficient probabilities of success in contributing to an economic accumulation of hydrocarbons in the structure.

F LOCATION (1s – 0.1s km)
A variety of locations may be considered for drilling: 1) crestal location 2) steep forelimb location 3) maximum curvature location or 4) least deformed (minimal structural damage) reservoir location or hydrocarbon-water contact confirmation location.

Figure 20–3.

Effects of scale

The technical tasks we identify are often related to the scale of our observation, from regional to microscopic. The following figure summarizes where the different techniques and tools described in section B can be applied. This sequence of tasks, in varying degrees, applies to any structural play.

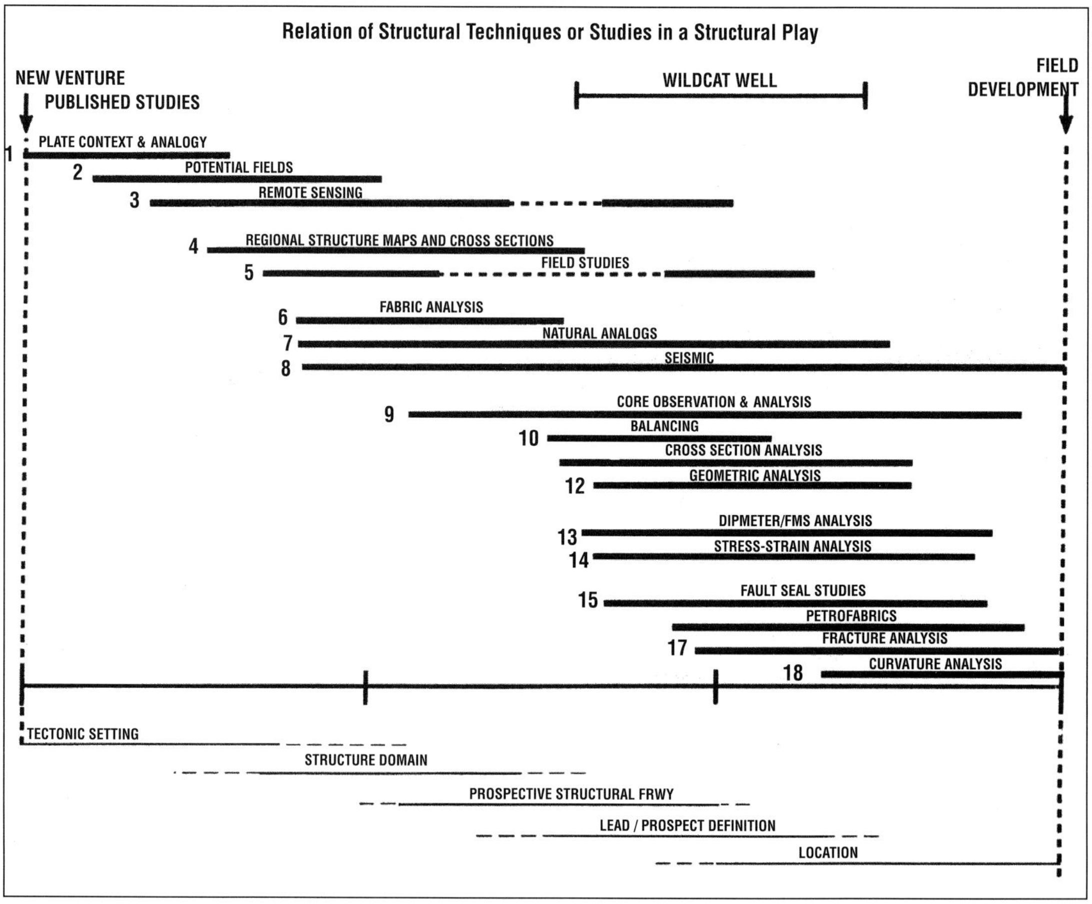

Figure 20–4.

Tectonic Setting

Determining the tectonic setting

The play concept envisioned is determined by the tectonic setting(s) in which the play can be pursued, from a structural as well as source and reservoir perspective. We identify regions with the correct tectonic setting by using the following data sources:

- Published geological studies
- Plate reconstructions and motions
- Tectonic maps
- Paleomagnetic data
- Satellite images

Assessing the area

Once regions with the appropriate tectonic setting are identified, we determine if these areas have the appropriate components to satisfy the requirements established for the play concept. Examples of issues of structure and tectonics which might be addressed include the following:

- Kinematics (e.g., oblique vs. orthogonal convergence)
- Significant changes in kinematics with time (e.g., episodic vs. continuous tectonic events)
- Duration of tectonism
- Major tectonostratigraphic terranes
- Overall complexity of the deformed belt
- Igneous activity

We then examine more closely those regions that meet the play concept criteria to determine if specific structural domains exist within these settings where we can pursue the structural play concept.

Structural Domains

Definition

A structural domain is an areally distinct region or subregion with similar structural properties (e.g., similar fold vergence or style, shortening, uplift, faulting style, etc.).

Identifying structural domains

Once a prospective tectonic setting is identified, we can determine where to focus exploration within that setting. This can be done most effectively by defining the boundaries and internal structural character of the different structural domains within the tectonic setting.

Among different tectonic settings, the number and complexity of the structural domains can vary significantly. For example, the number and character of the structural domains defined in a basin forming in the cratonic interior in a relatively quiet but long-lived tectonic setting contrast significantly to those defined in a short-lived but intense rifting event.

Tools to define structural domains

Within a particular tectonic setting, a significant number of markedly different domains may exist. Our ability to define the domains depends on the data available and the scale of observation. The following data sources can help define the boundaries and describe the internal complexity of structural domains:

- Potential fields
- Satellite imagery and/or aerial photography
- Regional surface and subsurface geologic data
- Exploration seismic data
- Deep crustal seismic data
- Reconnaissance outcrop studies

Assessing potential

Once the structural domain is defined and described, we must assess its potential to satisfy the play concept criteria. Some of the more obvious issues center around structural style:

- Fold styles
- Fault–fold relationships
- Fault spacing and interaction
- Fault fabrics
- Fault scaling
- Shortening–uplift ratios

Characterizing the structural domains lets us look at specific domains relative to the hydrocarbon system and thereby identify prospective structural fairways.

Prospective Structural Fairways

Definition

Certain structural domains or specific portions of those domains provide the greatest opportunities for exploration success. Those areas are called **prospective structural fairways.** In a prospective structural fairway, the structural history, trap configuration, and major elements of the hydrocarbon system combine to present a likely scenario for an economic accumulation of hydrocarbons.

Important considerations in identifying a prospective structural fairway are as follows:

- Structural style
- Tectonic overburden or denudation
- Trap evolution and timing
- Presence of source and reservoir facies
- Timing of hydrocarbon generation and migration

Assessing fairway prospectivity

The above considerations and their interdependencies, along with the following data sources, help us assess which structural fairways might be prospective:

- Regional geologic data (tops, sections, maps)
- Natural and productive analogs of structures
- Reconnaissance seismic data
- Potential fields
- Remote sensing data (satellite and air photo)
- Surface geologic data
- Fabric analysis
- Tectonic subsidence analysis
- Surveys for remote detection of hydrocarbons

If the structural fairway has most, if not all, of the major components needed for a viable hydrocarbon system, the next step is to identify structural leads and convert these to prospects.

Lead/Prospect Delineation

Prospect identification

A structural lead becomes a prospect once we determine that the major components of the hydrocarbon system have sufficient probabilities of success in contributing to an economic accumulation of hydrocarbons in the structure. In the table below are examples of some structural technical issues to consider when assessing the petroleum system relative to a structural lead. Many companies use a mixture of these issues to assess exploration risk, employing various numerical approaches.

Element	Factors Defining the Structural Prospect
Trap	• Trap integrity (certainty of dip closure; integrity of the closure throughout the evolution of the structure) • Area/volume under closure (present closure; structural closure during migration)
Seal	• Integrity of seals (continuity and integrity of top seal; integrity and capacity of fault seals)
Reservoir	• Storage capacity (structural degradation or enhancement effects) • Deliverability (structurally induced enhancement or degradation of permeability) • Anisotropy (flow anisotropy due to faults, folds, or fracture facies variability) • Heterogeneity (local enhancement or degradation; fault isolation or compartmentalization) • Pressures (structurally induced overpressures)
Source facies	• Maturation (structural overburden considerations; tectonic subsidence and uplift effects considered)
Expulsion/ migration	• Structural pathways (charge areas have been in effective communication with prospects) • Structural gathering areas (sufficient volumes of migrating hydrocarbons captured and diverted into appropriate pathways) • Timing (structural pathways effective throughout generation/migration event)

Assessing technical issues

The following data sources and techniques can help us assess some of these technical issues:

- Outcrop studies (interpretive analogs)
- Structure section balancing (structural geometry)
- Palinspastic restoration (migration pathways; paleostructure)
- Dipmeter and FMS analysis (structural geometry)
- Detailed seismic, 2-D and 3-D (structural geometry)
- Modeling studies (seismic; theoretical; physical; interpretive analogs)
- Hydrocarbon migration pathway analysis
- Fault-seal studies (trap integrity)
- Core analysis (fracture potential)
- Mechanical testing of rock (fracture potential)
- Petrofabric analysis
- Fracture analysis
- Curvature analysis (fracture potential)
- Mechanical testing (fracture potential)
- Special seismic processing and velocity analysis (e.g., prestack migration; amplitude vs. offset)

When a lead becomes a prospect

Once we determine that the risk in drilling for hydrocarbons on the structural anomaly is acceptable, the lead qualifies as a prospect. The next problem confronting the explorationist is picking an appropriate location on the prospect.

Location Selection

Crestal locations

Because the most important goal of exploration is economic success, locations are often chosen to provide maximum information on the economic viability of the prospect. Therefore, locations that assess the structurally highest point (crest) at the primary reservoir appear, at first, to be most attractive. However, other criteria in structural plays need to be recognized when determining prospect-assessing locations. This approach becomes critical as the structural complexity increases or the structural play concept becomes more sophisticated.

Off-crestal locations

Circumstances may occur in which it is more appropriate to select a location based on technical needs or data quality rather than optimizing the economic success of the first well. Generally, these locations provide greater certainty in evaluating data (e.g., clearly defined seismic reflectors to help define a crestal position). Other structural play concepts may require off-crestal positions to be viable.

Examples of circumstances in which it is desirable to drill a location other than the crest include the following:

- Certain fracture plays in the Rocky Mountain thrust belts of the U.S. and Canada may be sensitive to fore limb or back limb locations to provide the flow rates necessary to establish economic success.
- Tests in the offshore Netherlands have been drilled off crest and away from hinges to obtain an early assessment of matrix porosity in the reservoir.
- The position of the oil–water contact may be critical in defining the volume of hydrocarbons necessary for economic success.
- A nonoptimal acreage position may preclude access to the crestal location.
- Logistics problems (e.g., topography, environmental sensitivities) may preclude access to the crestal location.

Multiple-well locations

Well locations may be selected solely to provide information to support a second location. Such locations may be entirely off structure.

Well data programs and contingencies

There is often a tendency to plan well programs with economic success in mind. Unfortunately, an economic or technical failure is more likely, and we need to design data acquisition programs with options for that eventuality. In choosing a location and designing a well data program, we need to plan for possible failure by asking the following questions:

- Can this play be tested effectively with one well?
- What data do we need to establish a second location?
- What data do we need to determine whether to continue evaluating this play concept on this prospect?

Thrust Belt Example

Introduction

This example of structural exploration in the Laramide western Wyoming thrust belt in the late 1970s and early 1980s illustrates how the preceding tasks flow together and applies the techniques and approaches in Figure 20–4. The exploration process begins with an examination of the regional tectonic setting of the Wyoming thrust belt and gradually narrows to a study of structural features at the prospect level.

Tectonic setting

The figure below depicts the tectonic setting for the western U.S. relevant to Laramide plate tectonics. It shows where overthrusting took place, its overall geometry and vergence direction, and the interference with foreland deformation.

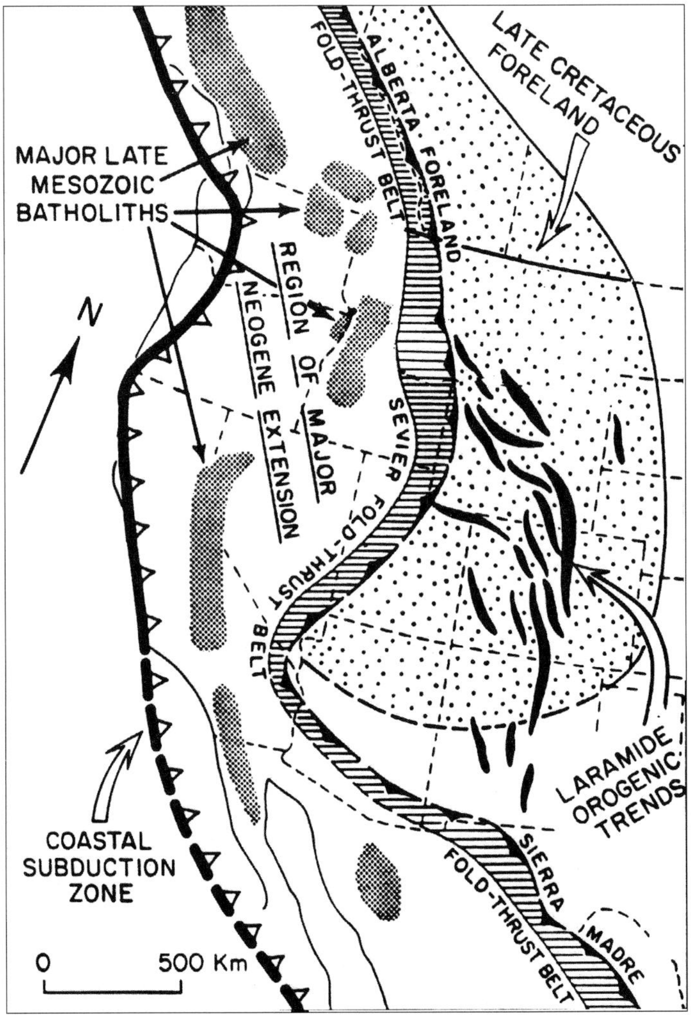

Figure 20–5. From Schwartz, 1982; courtesy Rocky Mountain Assoc. of Geologists.

Thrust Belt Example, continued

Structural domains

Structural domains within the Wyoming thrust belt were defined by the regional mapping of the U.S. Geological Survey (Rubey, 1973) and by interpreting satellite images such as the one shown in the figure below. Individual major thrust sheets were defined across the belt as well as their change in character along strike, thus defining domains on a large scale. Note that the small white rectangle in the center of the satellite image is the approximate area seen in the oblique aerial photograph in Figure 20–12.

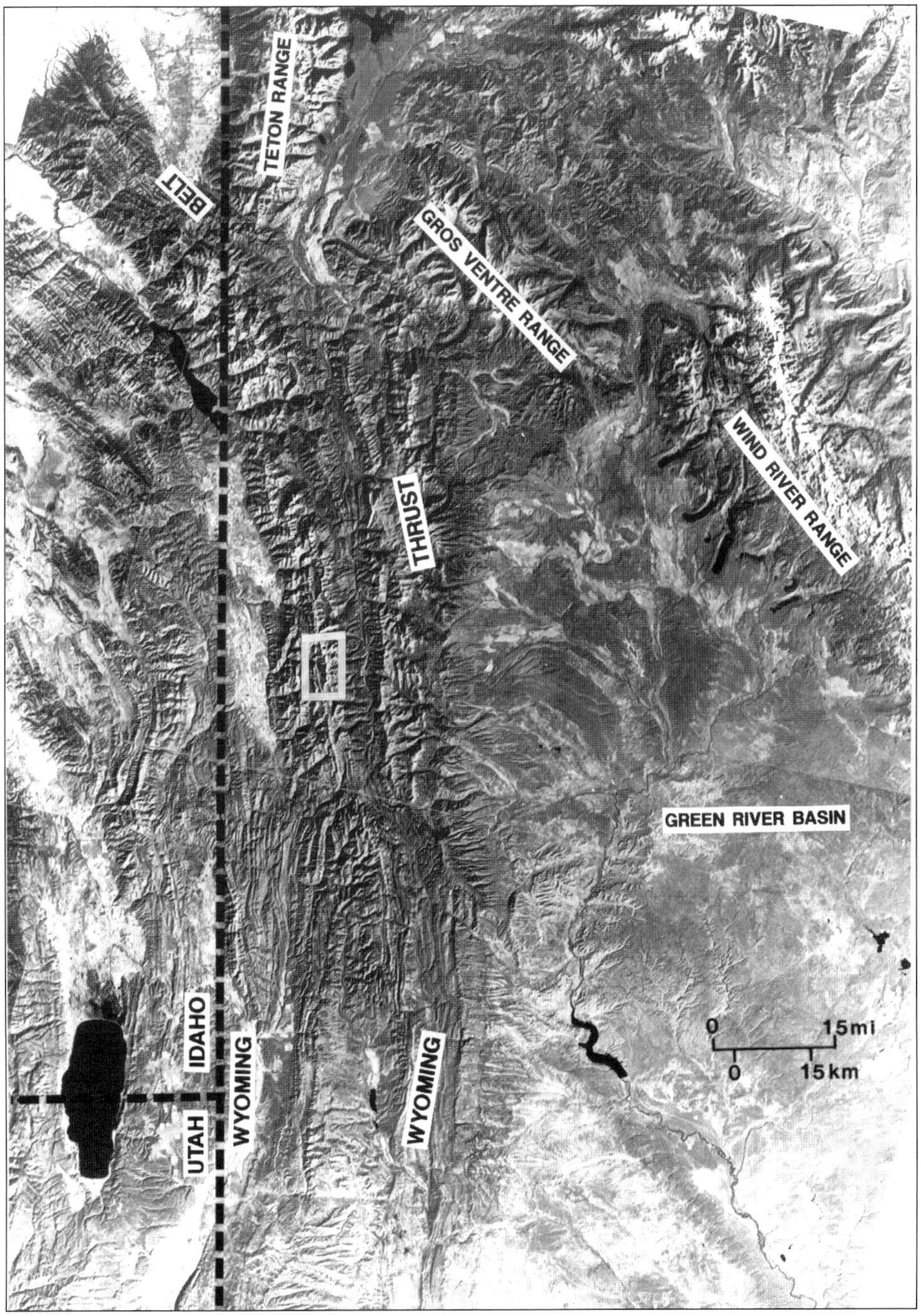

Figure 20–6.

Prospective structural fairways

Within the structural domains, regional analysis of structural style and timing were integrated with other elements of the hydrocarbon system to define prospective fairways. The figure below covers approximately the same area as the preceding satellite image and shows the location of the major thrust sheets in the Wyoming thrust belt. Note that most of the oil and gas fields occur in the southern half of the Absaroka thrust sheet.

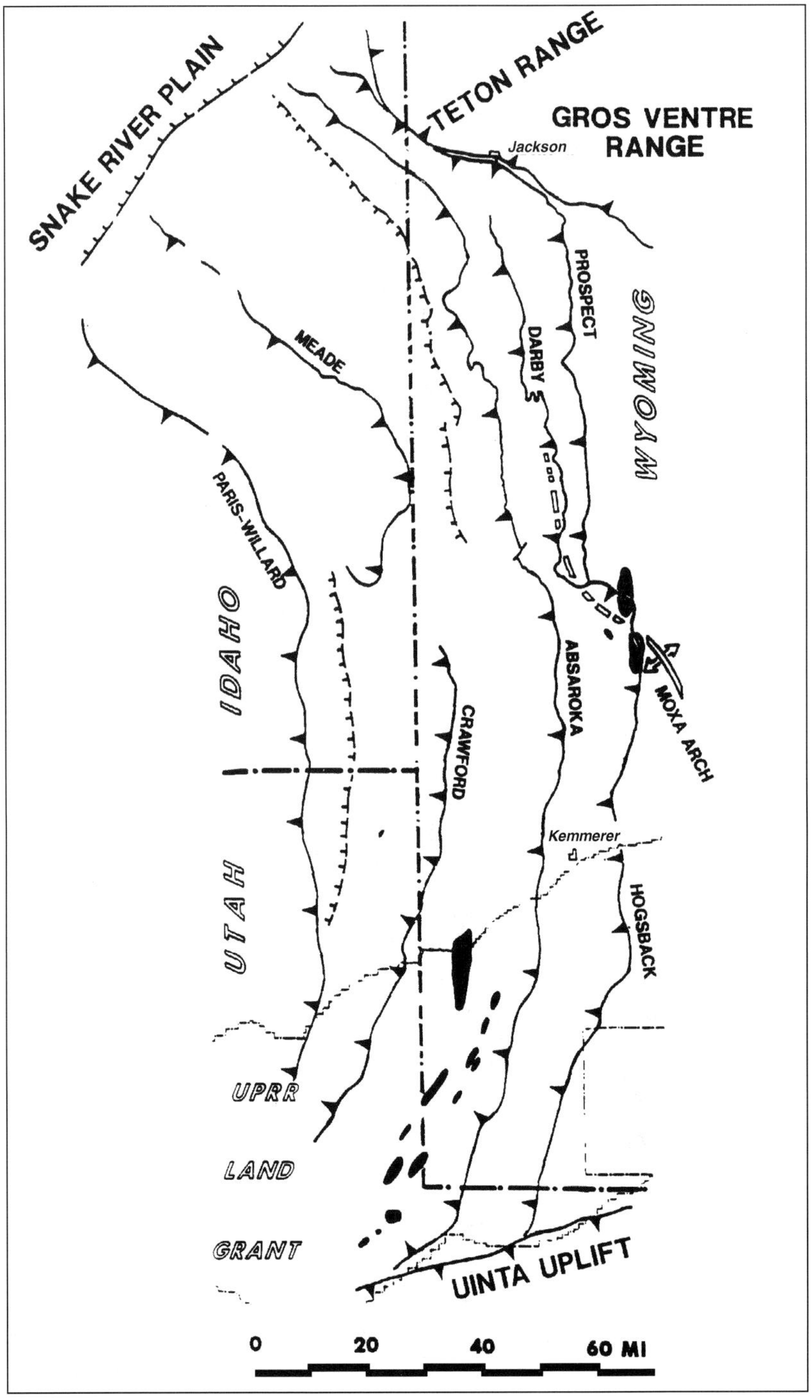

Figure 20–7. From Dixon, 1982; courtesy AAPG.

Prospective structural fairways (continued)

The figure below is a contoured fault-plane map at two different scales for the Absaroka thrust, the major thrust that contains the producing fairway.

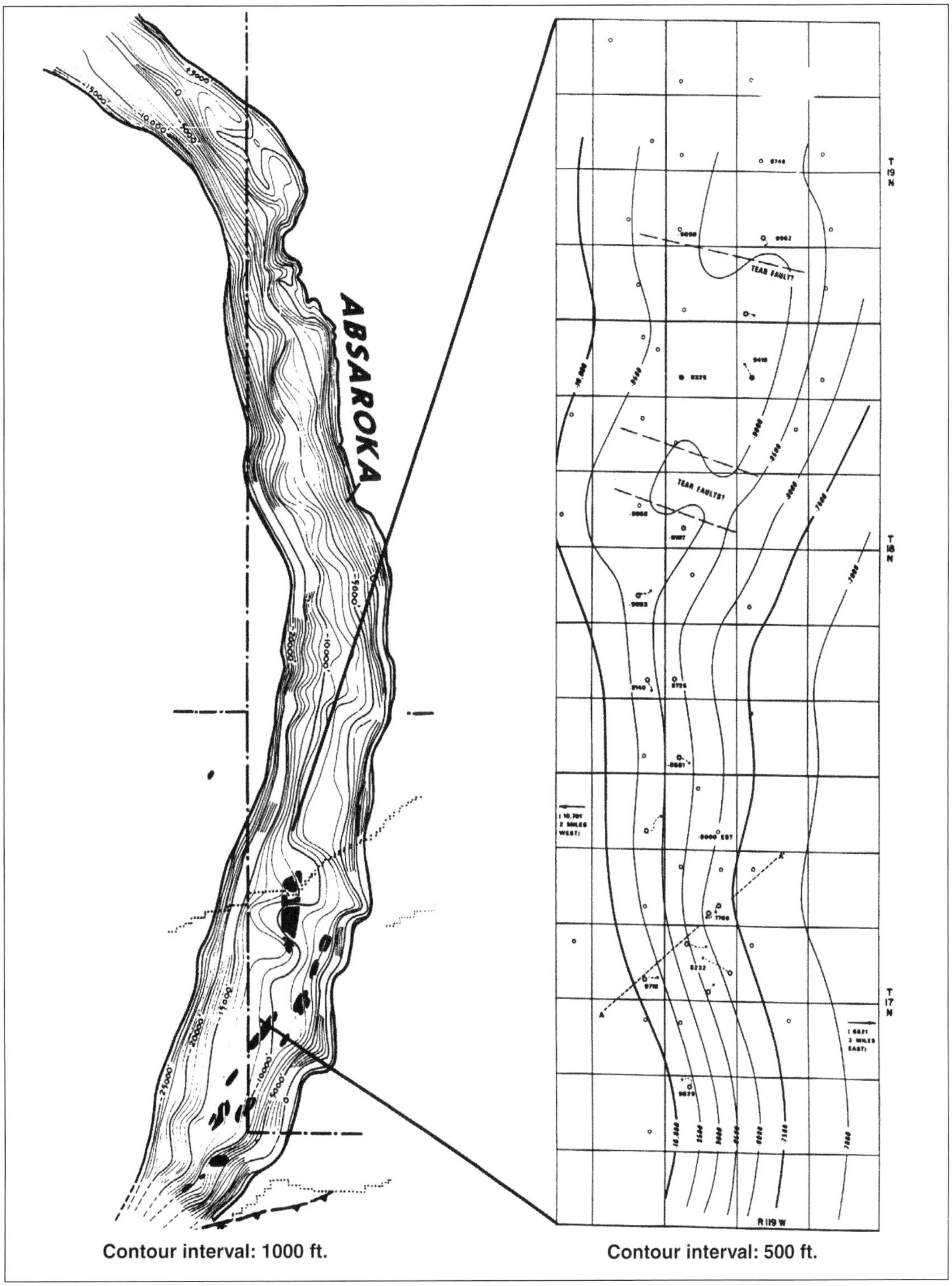

Figure 20–8. From Dixon, 1982, and Bishop, 1982; courtesy AAPG and Rocky Mountain Assoc. of Geologists, respectively.

Structural lead

Detailed analysis of the fairway proceeded using surface and subsurface data. Examples of the data used are shown below and on the next few pages.

Figure 20–11 on the opposite page shows a cross section across the Whitney Canyon and Ryckman Creek producing structures in the upper plate of the Absaroka thrust.

The figure below shows an interpreted seismic line in the approximate location of Figure 20–11.

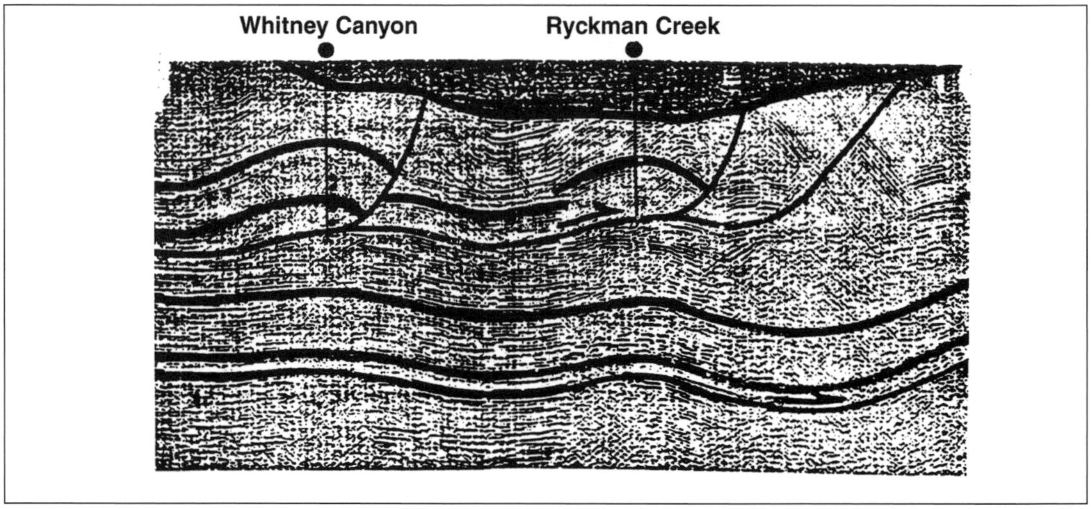

Figure 20–9.

The figure below shows restoration and balancing of a cross section through the Whitney Canyon and Ryckman Creek fields. Restoration and balancing help ensure that structures shown on cross sections are geometrically possible and geologically plausible.

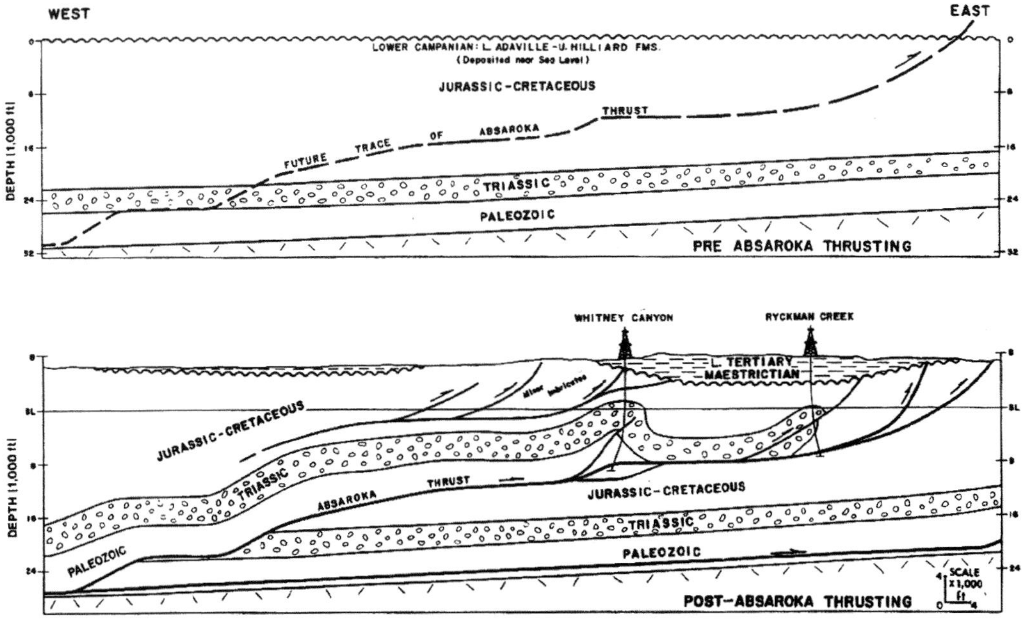

Figure 20–10. From Sieverding and Royse, 1993; courtesy AAPG.

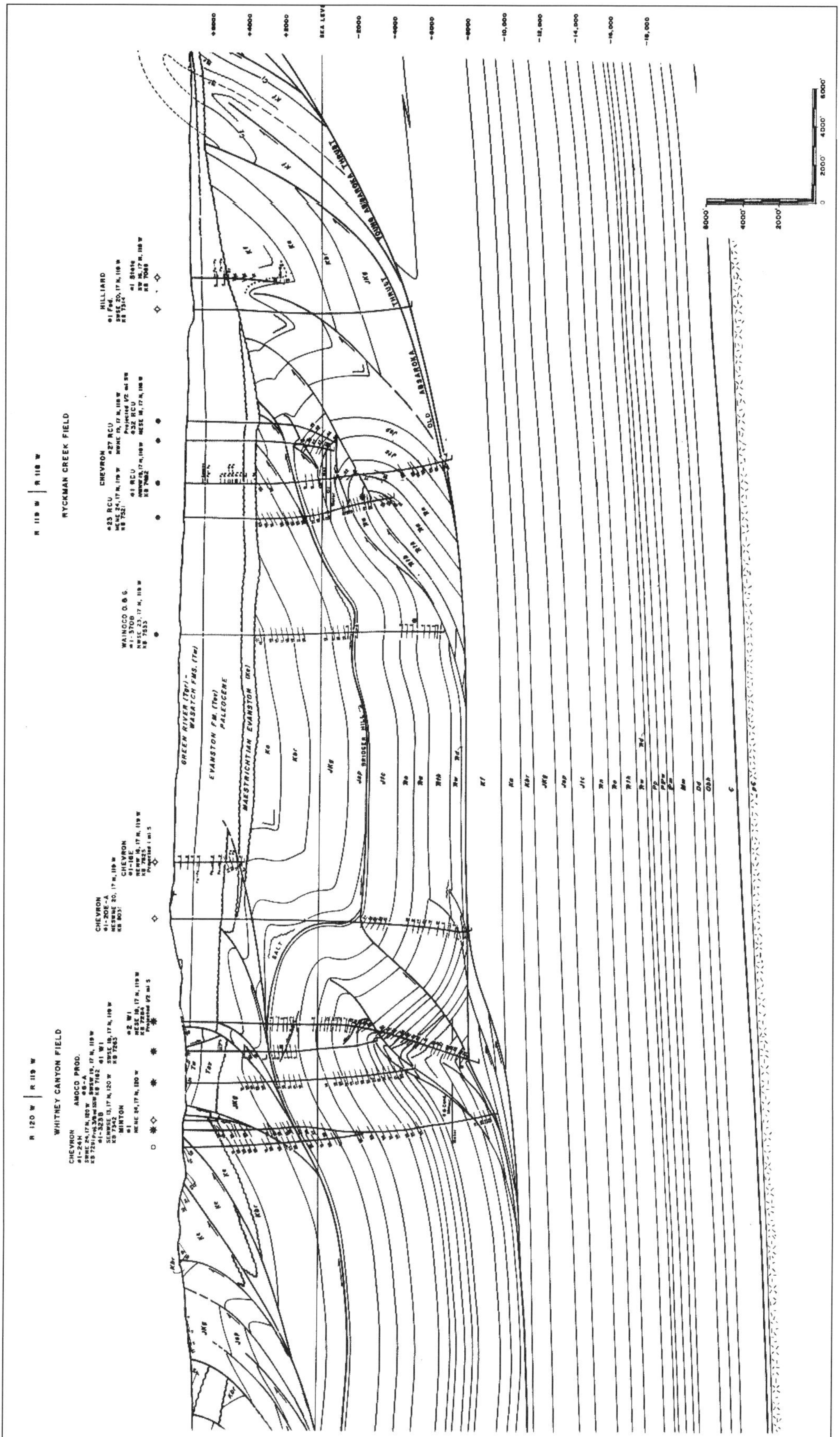

Figure 20–11. From Lamerson, 1982; courtesy Rocky Mountain Assoc. of Geologists.

Structural lead (continued)

The oblique aerial photograph below shows structures in the upper plate of the Absaroka thrust in the central Wyoming thrust belt, updip and along strike of the producing structures in the same thrust sheet to the south. (See Figure 20–6 for the location.)

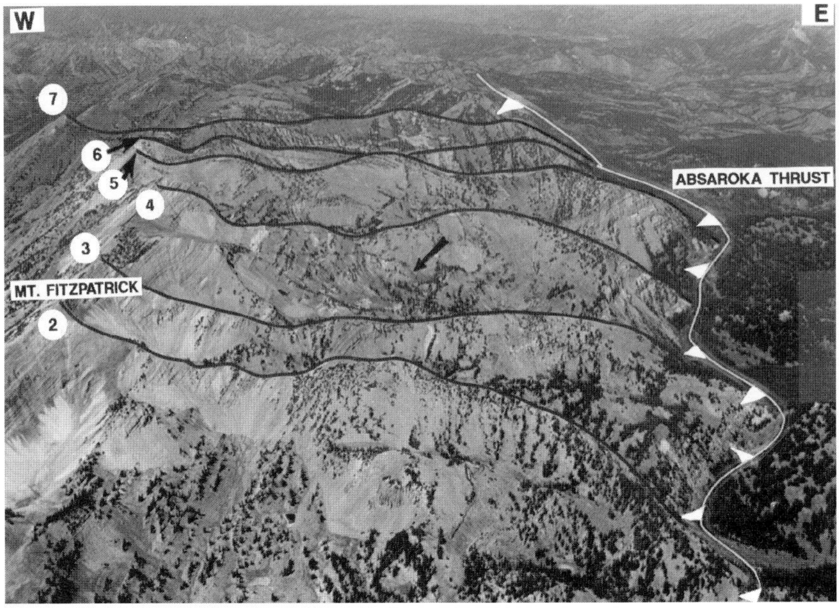

Figure 20–12.

The tectonic setting and stratigraphic section are similar to the producing trend; therefore, the deformation features of the exposed structures can be used as analogs for producing structures to the south. The numbered ridge lines in the photo provide a set of natural serial cross sections through the structures, detailed below.

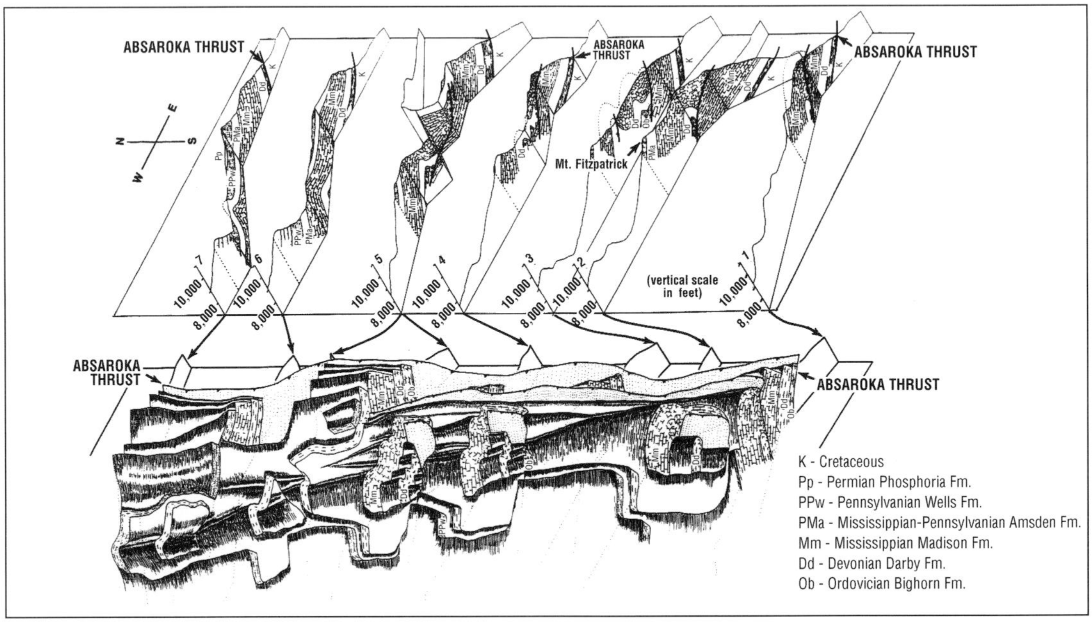

Figure 20–13.

Structural lead (continued)

The photograph below shows structures in the upper plate of the Absaroka thrust fault on the south side of ridge line 4 in Figure 20–12. The white outcrops in the valley in the left foreground are tightly folded Ordovician Bighorn dolomite.

Figure 20–14.

Prospect and location

Once leads have been defined, detailed analyses of individual well locations must take place. The figure below shows an example of detailed structural mapping at the prospect level. It is a structural map on top of the Upper Triassic Nugget Sandstone, Ryckman Creek field area, Uinta County, Wyoming. Contour interval varies from 100 ft (30 m) near the crest of the structure to 500 ft (150 m) on the flanks. The dashed contours are the oil/water and gas/oil contacts.

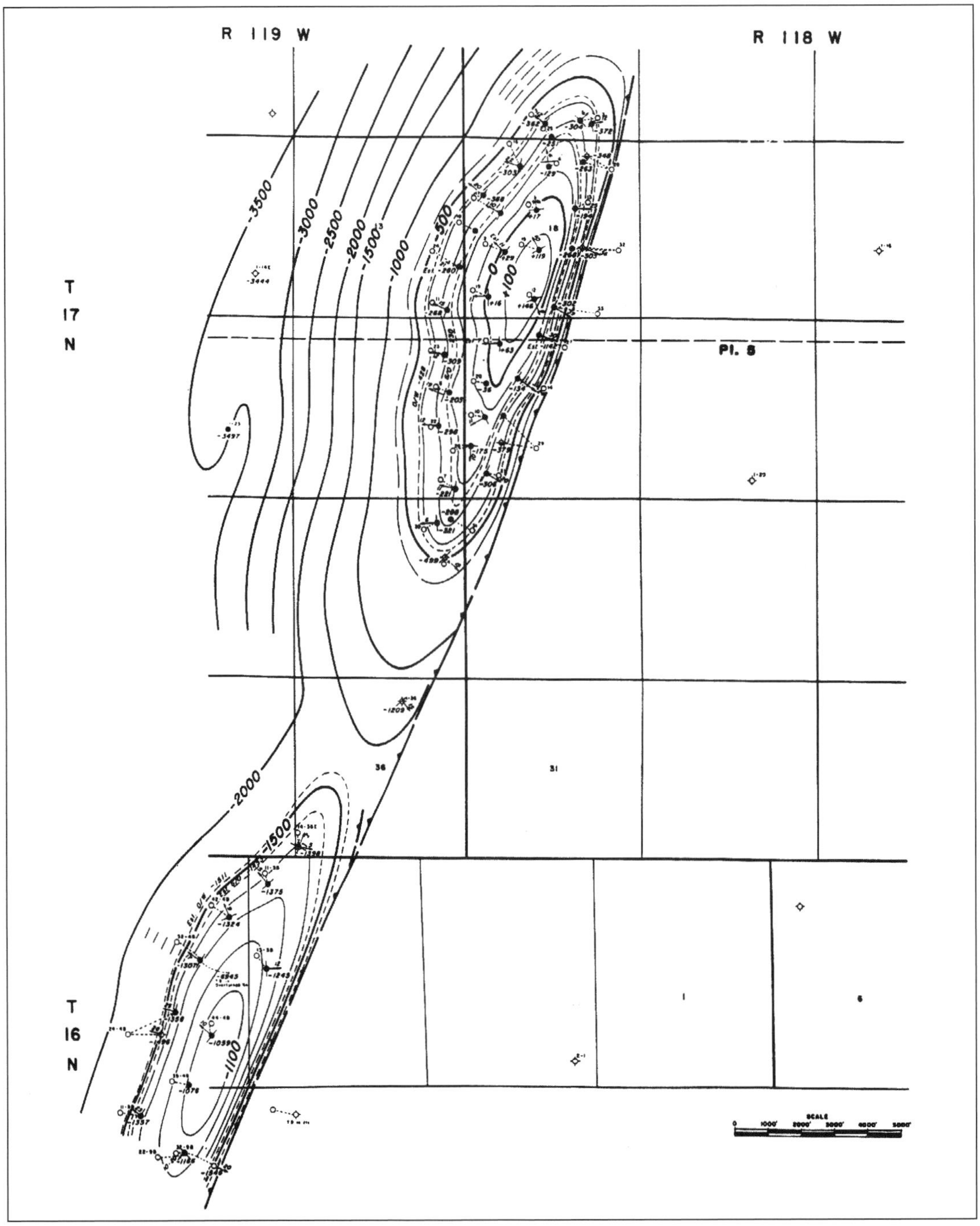

Figure 20–15. From Lamerson, 1982; courtesy Rocky Mountain Assoc. of Geologists.

Prospect and location (continued)

Physical models, such as those shown below, that display structures similar in shape to natural, prospect-scale, thrust-related structures can provide insight on the overall geometry of the prospect and the location of zones of high strain (high fracture density?) within the structure. These insights can be useful in determining optimal well locations.

These models were constructed of originally planar layers of limestone, sandstone, and granite. They were deformed in a pressure vessel at an effective overburden pressure of 15×10^3 psi (1×10^5 kPa). The top view is a photomicrograph of a model that simulates a thrust ramp. The bottom view simulates the hanging-wall geometry produced by movement along a series of bedding-parallel and ramp segments of a thrust fault.

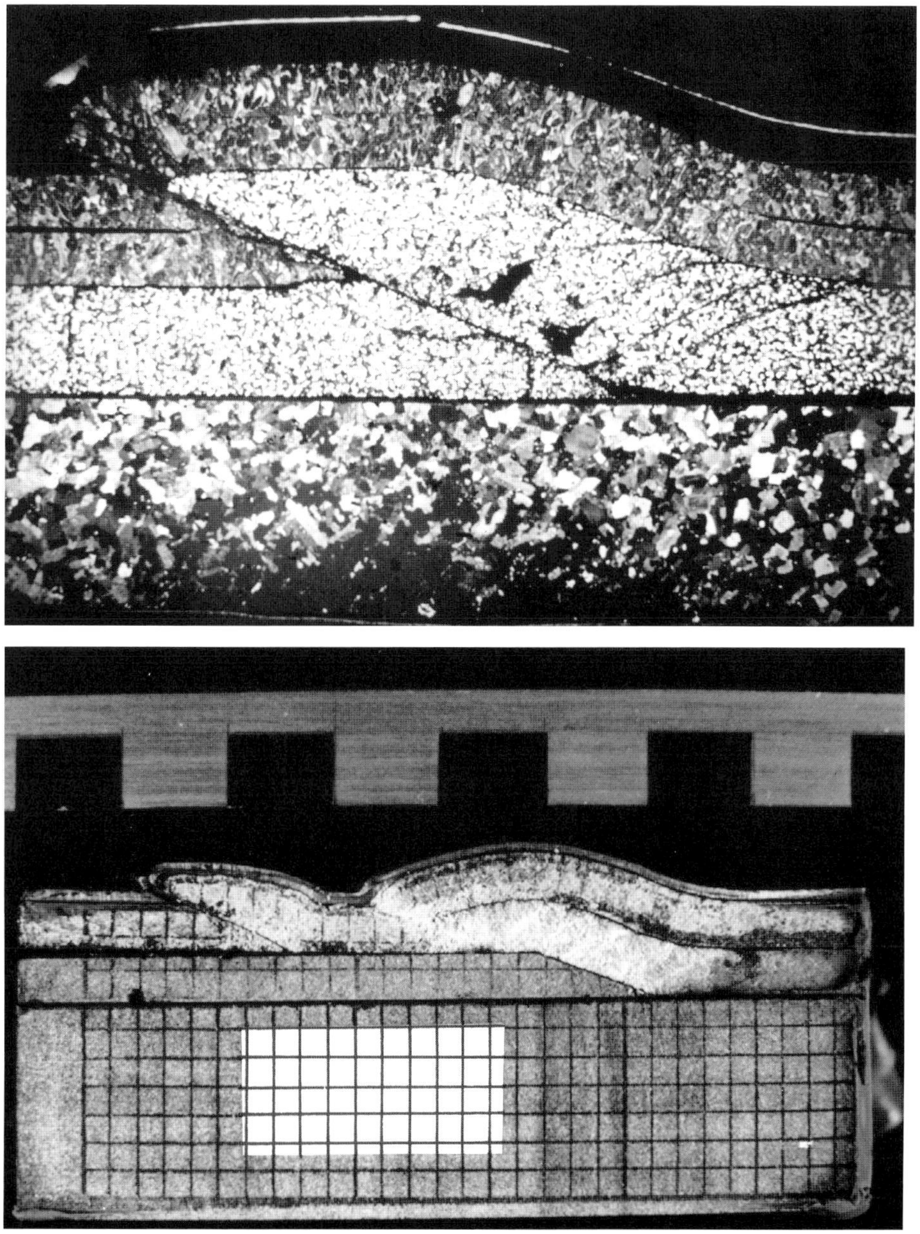

Figure 20–16. Published with permission of James Morse, Computational Geology.

Prospect and location (continued)

Data on deformation mechanisms, such as fractures and how they affect reservoir properties, are obtained by integrating outcrop fracture data and laboratory estimates of fracture aperture. This integration allows for a direct calculation of fracture porosity and fracture permeability for the reservoir.

Examples of outcrop fracture-spacing data relevant to the carbonate section of Whitney Canyon field are shown below. The photograph shows fractures in the Ordovician Bighorn dolomite in outcrops in the valley seen in Figure 20–14. (Note the inch-scale measuring tape stretched across the center of Figure 20–17.)

Figure 20–17.

Thrust Belt Example, continued

Prospect and location (continued)

The outcrop sketch below is of folds in the Devonian Darby siltstone and Ordovician Bighorn dolomite from the same location as Figure 20–17. The numbers on the sketch represent fracture intensity values expressed as the average number of fractures encountered per foot of scanline measurement at various locations on the folds. All else being equal, higher fracture intensities should be associated with zones of higher fracture porosities and permeabilities. Maps of high fracture intensities can be used to locate optimum well locations and well trajectories in prospects.

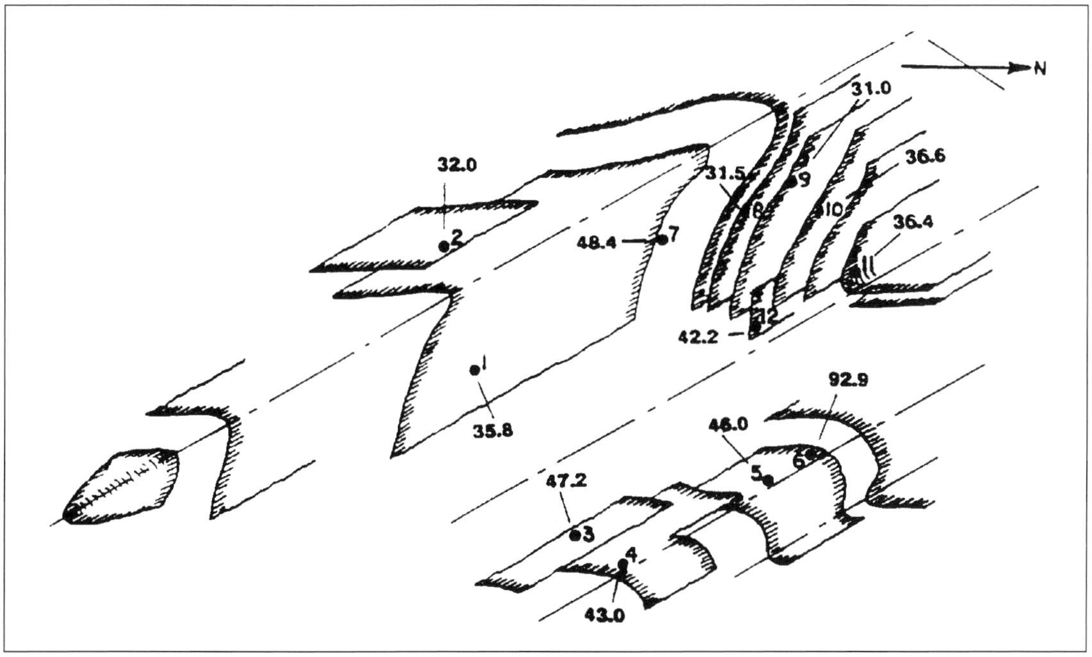

Figure 20–18. From Nelson and Serra, 1995; courtesy Journal of Canadian Petroleum Technology.

Summary

This thrust belt example has shown the structural exloration process and some of the data types, techniques, and approaches that can be used in exploring for a structural trap.

Section D

Project Planning:
The One-Minute Structural Play for Managers

Introduction

This section discusses how we might shorten or streamline the general technical application process presented in Figure 20–4 by limiting ourselves to those structural techniques most relevant to the particular project or structural play of interest. This can be done by considering the following:

- The structural style with which we are dealing
- The maturity of the area or play
- The structural philosophy dominant within the exploration team or company

In general, we strive to minimize technical application cycle time to match our original goal as described in section A and thereby maintain our competitive advantage. Increased technical quality and reduced cycle time might require outsourcing and strategic alliances to meet our goals.

In this section

This section contains the following topics.

Data and Techniques That Delineate Structural Styles

What is a structural style?

Structural styles or structural families are associations of structures that often occur together due to a common origin. For example, major foreland thrust belts usually contain a mixture of listric reverse or decollement thrust faults, large asymmetric hanging-wall folds, and late listric normal faults. These features are arranged to form an overall arcuate deformed belt. There is little or no involvement of mechanical basement in the deformation. Individual structures generally have good strike continuity and poor depth or dip continuity. Hence, in any newly discovered thrust belt, these same associations (thrust belt structural style) would be anticipated, modified somewhat by local geology. The concept of structural styles and their classification are given in Harding and Lowell (1979) and Lowell (1985).

Choosing techniques

If and when a structural style(s) is ascribed to an area, certain of the structural techniques become more important to perform than others. The list below displays those techniques (keyed to the numbers in Figure 20–4) deemed important for each major structural style.

Style	Very Important*
Thrust belts	5, 8, 10, 12
Wrench systems	1, 3, 11
Rifts and detached normal fault systems	2, 8, 10, 12, 15
Diapiric	2, 12
Foreland block folds	3, 6, 8
Basement warps and sags	2, 6, 8, 11

* Techniques 13–15 are important in all styles but in later stages of exploration.

Data and Techniques to Study Basins of Varying Maturity

Techniques to use

We limit or reduce the number of structural techniques applied by the inherent maturity of the basin or play. In general, those techniques involving data and data generation on a large or reconnaissance scale (left half, Figure 20–4) are most important to perform early in a frontier basin or play. More detailed analyses requiring more detailed data (right half, Figure 20–4) are appropriate only to more mature basins and development studies/plays.

These are depicted in the table below by a common basin/play maturity classification.

Maturity Level	Very Important*
Frontier	1, 2, 3, 7, reconnaisance 5
Emergent	4, 5, 7, 8 stratigraphic, 10
Established	6, 9, 11, 13, 14
Mature	6, 8 (rock properties), 9, 13, 15

*For number reference, see Figure 20–4.

How Different Structural Philosophies Govern Techniques

Introduction

There are several major philosophies or approaches to structural geology, and various university departments and E&P companies favor one or another in their courses and approaches to problem-solving. The major approaches can be grouped into four major categories:

- Global tectonics
- Structural styles
- Detailed geometric and/or kinematic studies
- Mechanical or dynamic approaches

The individual techniques presented in this section and highlighted in Figure 20–4 span the range of these categories. A complete E&P structural study, therefore, includes aspects of all four.

Different organizations; different philosophies

Exploration and production organizations usually display strength or focus in perhaps one or two of the above category areas or focus on different areas of the technologies timeline. For example: organizations that emphasize global tectonics (including basin analysis) and structural styles probably display particular strength in new ventures and effective concession acquisition, whereas those that emphasize mechanical structural approaches probably have great success in development geology. Those emphasizing detailed geometric analyses probably work more in the central portions of Figure 20–4 and effectively pick wildcat and first follow-up well locations.

Matching strength to strategy

Organizations should understand their strengths and areas of focus in their structural plays and supplement them in other areas by judiciously using complementary consultants, strategic alliances, and partnership agreements. Each player, then, brings the strength and focus necessary to conduct the effective structural play.

In this way, Figure 20–4 can be a tool for effective project planning when deciding which studies need to be done in-house, which ones should be done by various support organizations and partners, and when these studies should be initiated and completed.

Section E
Annotated Bibliography

Allan, U.S., 1989, Model for hydrocarbon migration and entrapment within faulted structures: AAPG Bulletin, vol. 73, p. 803–811. *Fault seal–conduit studies.*

Allenby, R.J., 1987, Origin of the Bolivian Andean orocline: a geologic study utilizing Landsat and Shuttle Imaging Radar: Tectonophysics, vol. 142, p. 137–154. *Information on remote sensing.*

Allmendinger, R.W., 1982, Analysis of microstructures in the Meade plate of the Idaho–Wyoming foreland thrustbelt, U.S.A.: Tectonophysics, vol. 85, p. 221–251. *Petrofabrics examples.*

Badley, M.E., 1985, Practical Seismic Interpretation: Boston, International Human Resources Development Corp., 266 p. *Seismic data.*

Bally, A.W., ed., 1983, Seismic Expression of Structural Styles, A Picture and Work Atlas: AAPG Studies in Geology 15, 3 vols. *Seismic data.*

Bally, A.W., P.L. Gordy, and G.A. Stewart, 1966, Structure, seismic data and orogenic evolution of southern Canadian Rocky Mountains: Bulletin of Canadian Petroleum Geology, vol. 4, p. 337–381. *Maps and sections.*

Bell, R.T., and J.B. Currie, 1964, Photoelastic experiments related to structural geology: Proceedings of the Geological Association of Canada, vol. 15, p. 33–51. *Photoelastic models.*

Bengston, C.A., 1981, Statistical curvature analysis techniques for structural interpretation of dipmeter data: AAPG Bulletin, vol. 65, p. 312–332. *Dipmeter analysis.*

_____, 1982, Structural and stratigraphic uses of dip profiles in petroleum exploration, *in* M.T. Halbouty, ed., The Deliberate Search for the Subtle Trap: AAPG Memoir 32, p. 619–632. *Dipmeter analysis.*

Beydoun, Z.R., 1991, Arabian Plate Hydrocarbon Geology and Potential—A Plate Tectonic Approach: AAPG Studies in Geology 33, 77 p. *Plate tectonic studies.*

Billings, A.J., and J.H. Thomas, 1990, The use and limitations of non-seismic geophysics in the Papuan thrust belt, *in* G.J. Carman and Z. Carman, eds., Petroleum Exploration in Papua New Guinea: Proceedings of the First Papua New Guinea Petroleum Convention, Port Moresby, p. 51–62. *Potential fields.*

Bishop, R.A., 1982, Whitney Canyon–Carter Creek gas field, SW Wyoming, *in* R.B. Powers, ed., Geological Studies of the Cordilleran Thrust Belt: Rocky Mountain Assoc. of Geologists, p. 591–599.

Burger, H.R., and M. Hamill, 1976, Petrofabric analysis of the Dry Creek Ridge anticline, Montana: Geological Society of America Bulletin, vol. 87, p. 555–566. *Petrofabrics examples.*

Christopherson, K.R., 1990, Applications of magnetotellurics to petroleum exploration in Papua New Guinea, *in* G.J. Carman and Z. Carman, eds., Petroleum exploration in Papua New Guinea: Proceedings of the First Papua New Guinea Petroleum Convention, Port Moresby, p. 63–71. *Potential fields.*

Coffeen, J.A., 1984, Interpreting Seismic Data Workbook: Tulsa, PennWell Publishing Co., 196 p. *Seismic data.*

Couples, G.D., and D.W. Stearns, 1978, Analytical solutions applied to structures of the Rocky Mountain foreland on local and regional scales, *in* V. Matthews III, ed., Laramide Folding Associated with Basement Block Faulting in the Western United States: Geological Society of America Memoir 151, p. 313–335. *Mathematical mechanics models.*

Crans, W., and G. Mandl, 1980, On the theory of growth faulting; part II (a): genesis of the "unit": Journal of Petroleum Geology, vol. 3, p. 209–236. *Mathematical mechanics models.*

Dahlstrom, C.D.A., 1969, Balanced cross sections: Canadian Journal of Earth Sciences, vol. 6, p. 743–757. *Cross section analysis.*

_____, 1970, Structural geology in the eastern margin of the Canadian Rocky Mountains: Bulletin of Canadian Petroleum Geology, vol. 18, p. 332–406. *Fieldwork.*

Delhomme, J.-P., T. Pilenko, E. Cheruvier, and R. Cull, 1986, Reservoir applications of dipmeter logs: Society of Petroleum Engineers Paper 15485, 7 p. *Dipmeter analysis.*

Dickinson, W.R., and H. Yarborough, 1978, Plate Tectonics and Hydrocarbon Accumulation: AAPG Continuing Education Series 1, 148 p. *Plate tectonic studies.*

Dixon, J.M., and S. Liu, 1992, Centrifuge modeling of the propagation of thrust faults, *in* K.R. McClay, ed., Thrust Tectonics: London, Chapman and Hall, p. 53–69. *Physical geometry models.*

Dixon, J.S., 1982, Regional structural synthesis, Wyoming salient of the Western overthrust belt: AAPG Bulletin, vol. 66, p. 1560–1580. *Maps and sections.*

Dunn, D.E., L.J. LaFountain, and R.E. Jackson, 1973, Porosity dependence and mechanism of brittle fracture in sandstones: Journal of Geophysical Research, vol. 78, p. 2403–2417. *Rock mechanics models.*

Dutton, S.P., A.G. Goldstein, and S.C. Ruppel, 1982, Petroleum Potential of the Palo Duro Basin, Texas Panhandle: University of Texas at Austin Bureau of Economic Geology Report of Investigations 123, 87 p. *Maps and sections.*

Etchecopar, A., and J.-L. Bonnetain, 1992, Cross sections from dipmeter data: AAPG Bulletin, vol. 76, p. 621–637. *Dipmeter analysis.*

Fermor, P.R., and R.A. Price, 1987, Multiduplex structure along the base of the Lewis thrust sheet in the southern Canadian Rockies: Bulletin of Canadian Petroleum Geology, vol. 35, p. 159–185. *Fieldwork.*

Foster, N.H., and E.A. Beaumont, eds., 1992, Photogeology and Photogeomorphology; AAPG Treatise of Petroleum Geology Reprint Series 18, 555 p. *Information on remote sensing.*

Fraser, A.J., and R.L. Gawthorpe, 1990, Tectono-stratigraphic development and hydrocarbon habitat of the Carboniferous in northern England, *in* R.F.P. Hardman,and J. Brooks, eds., Tectonic Events Responsible for Britain's Oil and Gas Reserves: Geological Society of London Special Publication 55, p. 49–86. *Seismic data.*

Friedman, M., 1964, Petrofabric techniques for the determination of principal stress directions in rocks, *in* W.R. Judd, ed., State of Stress in the Earth's Crust: New York, Elsevier, p. 451–552. *Petrofabrics examples.*

_____ and G.M. Sowers, 1970, Petrofabrics: a critical review: Canadian Journal of Earth Sciences, vol. 7, p. 477–497. *Petrofabrics examples.*

_____ and D.W. Stearns, 1971, Relations between stresses inferred from calcite twin lamellae and macrofractures, Teton anticline, Montana: Geological Society of America Bulletin, vol. 82, p. 3151–3162. *Petrofabrics examples.*

Gallagher, J.J., M. Friedman, J. Handin, and G.M. Sowers, 1974, Experimental studies relating to microfractures in sandstone: Tectonophysics, vol. 21, p. 203–247. *Photoelastic models.*

Gangi, A.F., K.D. Min, and J.M. Logan, 1977, Experimental folding of rocks under confining pressure; part IV: theoretical analysis of faulted drape folds: Tectonophysics, vol. 42, p. 227–260. *Mathematical mechanics models.*

Geiser, P.A., 1988, The role of kinematics in the construction and analysis of geological cross sections in deformed terranes, *in* G. Mitra and S. Wojtal, eds., Geometries and Mechanisms of Thrusting, with Special Reference to the Appalachians: Geological Society of America Special Paper 222, p. 47–76. *Cross section analysis.*

Ghisetti, F., Mechanisms of thrust faulting in the Gran Sasso chain, southern Appenines, Italy: Journal of Structural Geology, vol. 9, p. 955–967. *Fieldwork.*

Gibbs, A.D., 1983, Balanced cross-section construction from seismic sections in areas of extensional tectonics: Journal of Structural Geology, vol. 5, p. 153–160. *Cross section analysis.*

Gretener, P.E., 1981, Reflections on the value of laboratory tests on rocks, *in* N.L. Carter, M. Friedman, J.M. Logan, and D.W. Stearns, eds., Mechanical Behavior of Crustal Rocks: American Geophysical Union Monograph 24, p. 323–326. *Modeling concepts.*

Groshong, R.H., Jr., 1990, Unique determination of normal fault shape from hanging-wall bed geometry in detached half grabens: Ecologae Geologicae Helvetiae, vol. 83, p. 455–471. *Cross section analysis.*

Halbouty, M.T., 1980, Geologic significance of Landsat data for 15 giant oil and gas fields: AAPG Bulletin, vol. 64, p. 8–36. *Information on remote sensing.*

_____, ed., 1992, Giant Oil and Gas Fields of the Decade: AAPG Memoir 54, 526 p. *Natural analogs.*

Harding, T.P., 1984, Graben hydrocarbon occurrences and structural style: AAPG Bulletin, vol. 68, p. 333–362. *Natural analogs.*

_____ and J.D. Lowell, 1983, Structural styles, their plate-tectonic habitats and hydrocarbon traps in petroleum provinces: AAPG Studies in Geology series 15, vol. 1, p. 1–24. *Plate tectonic studies.*

Hardman, R.F.P., and J. Brooks, eds., 1990, Tectonic Events Responsible for Britain's Oil and Gas Reserves: Geological Society of London Special Publication 55, 404 p. *Natural analogs.*

Hooper, E.C.D., 1991, Fluid migration along growth faults in compacting sediments: Journal of Petroleum Geology, vol. 14, p. 161–180. *Fault seal–conduit studies.*

Hubbert, M.K., 1937, Theory of scale models as applied to the study of geologic structures: Geological Society of America Bulletin, vol. 48, p. 1459–1520. *Modeling concepts.*

Jackson, M.P.A., and C.J. Talbot, 1989, Anatomy of mushroom shaped diapirs: Journal of Structural Geology, vol. 11, p. 211–230. *Physical geometry models.*

Jamison, W.R., 1987, Geometric analysis of fold development in overthrust terranes: Journal of Structural Geology, vol. 9, p. 207–219. *Natural analogs and mathematical geometry models.*

Johnson, A., 1977, Styles of Folding: Amsterdam, Elsevier, 406 p. *Mathematical mechanics models.*

Kulander, B.R., S.L. Dean, and B.J. Ward, Jr., 1990, Fractured Core Analysis: Interpretation, Logging, and Use of Natural and Induced Fractures in Core: AAPG Methods in Exploration 8, 88 p. *Fracture analysis.*

Lamerson, P.R., 1982, Fossil basin area and its relationship to the Absaroka thrust fault system, *in* R.B. Powers ed., Geological Studies of the Cordilleran Thrust Belt: Rocky Mountain Assoc. of Geologists, p. 279–340.

Laubach, S.E., 1989, Fracture analysis of the Travis Peak Formation, western flank of the Sabine arch, east Texas: University of Texas at Austin Bureau of Economic Geology Report of Investigations 185, 55 p. *Fracture analysis.*

Logan, J.M., and P. Lin, 1991, The interaction of two closely spaced cracks: a rock model study: Journal of Geophysical Research, vol. 96, p. 21667–21675. *Rock mechanics models.*

Lowell, J.D., 1985, Structural Styles in Petroleum Exploration: Tulsa, OGCI, 460 p.

McClay, K.R., 1987, The Mapping of Geologic Structures: New York, Halstead Press, 161 p. *Fieldwork.*

Mitra, S., 1986, Duplex structures and imbricate thrust systems: geometry, structural position, and hydrocarbon potential: AAPG Bulletin, vol. 70, p. 1087–1112. *Natural analogs.*

_____, 1990, Fault-propagation folds: geometry, kinematic evolution, and hydrocarbon traps: AAPG Bulletin, vol. 74, p. 921–945. *Mathematical geometry models.*

_____, and J. Namsom, 1989, Equal-area balancing: American Journal of Science, vol. 289, p. 563–599. *Cross section analysis.*

Moffat, D.T., L.F. Henage, R.A. Brash, R.W. Tauer, and B.H. Harahap, 1991, Lengguru, Irian Jaya: prospect selection using field mapping, balanced cross sections, and gravity modeling: Proceedings of the Indonesian Petroleum Association's 20th Annual Convention, p. 85–106. *Cross section analysis.*

Morley, C.K., R.A. Nelson, T.L. Patton, and S.G. Munn, 1990, Transfer zones in the East African rift system and their relevance to hydrocarbon exploration in rifts: AAPG Bulletin, vol. 74, p. 1234–1253. *Natural analogs.*

Morse, J.D., and C.A. Bengston, 1988, What is wrong with tadpole plots?: AAPG Bulletin, vol. 72, p. 390. *Dipmeter analysis.*

Nelson, R.A., 1985, Geologic Analysis of Naturally Fractured Reservoirs: Houston, Gulf Publishing Co., 320 p. *Fracture analysis.*

_____ and S. Serra, 1995, Vertical and lateral changes in fracture spacing in several folded carbonate sections and its relation to locating horizontal wells: Journal of Canadian Petroleum Technology, vol. 34, p. 51–56.

_____, T.L. Patton, S. Serra, and P.A. Bentham, 1996, Delineating structural timing: Houston Geological Society Bulletin, v. 39 (1), p. 14–17. *Timing techniques.*

Nettleton, L.L., 1971, Elementary gravity and magnetics for geologists and seismologists: Society of Exploration Geophysicists Monograph Series 1, 121 p. *Potential fields.*

Nurmi, R. D., 1984, Geological evaluation of high resolution dipmeter data: Society of Professional Well Log Analysts' 25th Annual Logging Symposium, vol. 2, paper YY, 24 p. *Dipmeter analysis.*

Nybakken, S., 1991, Sealing fault traps—an exploration concept in a mature petroleum province: Tampen Spur, northern North Sea: First Break, vol. 9, p. 209–222. *Fault seal–conduit studies.*

Onasch, C.M., 1990, Microfractures and their role in deformation of a quartz arenite from the central Appalachian foreland: Journal of Structural Geology, vol. 12, p. 883–894. *Petrofabrics examples.*

Patton, T.L., and R.C. Fletcher, 1995, Mathematical block-motion model for deformation of a layer above a buried fault of arbitrary dip and sense of slip: Journal of Structural Geology, vol. 17, p. 1455–1472.

Price, R.A., 1965, Flathead Map Area, British Columbia, Alberta: Geological Survey of Canada Memoir 336, 221 p. *Fieldwork.*

Rubey, W.W., 1973, Geologic map of the Afton quadrangle and part of the big Piney quadrangle, Lincoln and Sublette counties, Wyoming: U.S. Geological Survey map I–686.

____, S.S. Oriel, and J.I. Tracey, Jr., 1975, Geology of the Sage and Kemmerer 15-Minute Quadrangles, Lincoln County, Wyoming: U.S. Geological Survey Professional Paper 855, 18 p. *Fieldwork.*

Sabins, F.F., Jr., 1987, Remote Sensing, Principles and Interpretation: New York, W.H. Freeman Company, 449 p. *Information on remote sensing.*

Schlumberger, 1986, Dipmeter Interpretation Fundamentals: New York, Schlumberger Ltd., 76 p. *Dipmeter analysis.*

Schwartz, R.T., 1982, Broken early cretaceous foreland basin in SW Montana: sedimentation related to tectonism, *in* R.B. Powers, ed., Geological Studies of the Cordilleran Thrust Belt: Rocky Mountain Assoc. of Geologists, p. 159–183.

Sheriff, R.E., 1982, Structural Interpretation of Seismic Data: AAPG Education Course Notes 23, 73 p. *Seismic data.*

Shimamoto, T., and I. Hara, 1976, Geometry and strain distribution of single-layer folds: Tectonophysics, vol. 30, p. 1–34. *Mathematical mechanics models.*

Sieverding, J.L., and F. Royse, Jr., 1993, Whitney Canyon–Carter Creek Field—USA, *in* E.A. Beaumont and N.H. Foster, eds., Treatise of Petroleum Geology, Atlas of Oil and Gas Fields, Structural Traps III: AAPG, p. 1–29.

Smith, D.A., 1980, Sealing and non-sealing faults in Louisiana Gulf Coast salt basin: AAPG Bulletin, vol. 64., p. 145–172. *Fault seal–conduit studies.*

Sosromihardjo, S.P.C., 1988, Structural analysis of the north Sumatra Basin with emphasis on synthetic aperture radar data: Proceedings of the Indonesian Petroleum Association, p. 187–209. *Information on remote sensing.*

Spalding, D.B., 1962, The art of partial modeling: 9th Symposium on Combustion, p. 833–843. *Modeling concepts.*

Stearns, D.W., G.D. Couples, W.R. Jamison, and J.D. Morse, 1981, Understanding faulting in the shallow crust: contributions of selected experimental and theoretical studies, *in* N.L. Carter, M. Friedman, J.M. Logan, and D.W. Stearns, eds., Mechanical Behavior of Crustal Rocks: American Geophysical Union Monograph 24, p. 215–229. *Modeling concepts.*

Suppe, J., 1983, Geometry and kinematics of fault-bend folding: American Journal of Science, vol. 283, p. 648–721. *Mathematical geometry models.*

Telford, W.M., L.P. Geldart, and R.E. Sheriff, 1990, Applied Geophysics: Cambridge, Cambridge University Press, 770 p. *Seismic data.*

Weinberg, D.M., 1979, Experimental folding of rocks under confining pressure, part VII: partially scaled models of drape folds: Tectonophysics, vol. 54, p. 1–24. *Physical geometry models.*

Annotated Bibliography, continued

White, N., and G. Yielding, 1991, Calculating normal faults geometries at depth: theory and examples, *in* A.M. Roberts, G. Yielding, and B. Freeman, eds., The Geometry of Normal Faults: Geological Society of London Special Publication 56, p. 251–260. *Cross section analysis.*

Wiltschko, D.V., K.P. Corbett, M. Friedman, and J-H. Hung, 1991, Predicting fracture connectivity and intensity within the Austin Chalk from outcrop fracture maps and scanline data: Transactions of the Gulf Coast Association of Geological Societies, vol. 41, p. 702–718. *Fracture analysis.*

Chapter 21

Exploring for Stratigraphic Traps

by

John C. Dolson,

Mike S. Bahorich,

Rick C. Tobin,

Edward A. Beaumont,

Louis J. Terlikoski,

and

Michael L. Hendricks

John C. Dolson

John C. Dolson is a Senior Geological Associate with BP-Amoco, currently assigned to the BP-Amoco Egypt Business Unit in Cairo. He received his B.S. in natural science from The Colorado College (1971) and an M.S. in earth science from Colorado State University (1981). He joined Amoco in 1980 and has explored for hydrocarbons in the Hugoton, Anadarko, Rocky Mountain, and Cook Inlet (Alaska) basins (U.S.A.), Caspian (Azerbaijan) and Pre-Caspian basins (Khazakhstan, Gulf of Suez, and Nile Delta. Dolson cochaired an Amoco symposium on stratigraphic trap exploration in 1989 and the Cairo '98 AAPG Hedberg Conference Integrated Structural and Sequence Stratigraphic Analysis in Rift Settings. He has a keen interest in the application of computing technology and workstations in recognizing and evaluating subtle traps. Dolson has written over 20 papers on stratigraphic traps and coedited the 1994 RMAG publication Unconformities and Hydrocarbons in Sedimentary Sequences.

Mike S. Bahorich

Mike Bahorich is currently Vice President of Exploration and Production Technology with Apache Corp. in Houston. He received a B.S. in geology (1978) from the University of Missouri and an M.S. in geophysics (1981) from VPI in Blacksburg, VA. His first decade at Amoco involved prospect generation and development. He then spent three years with Amoco Research in scientific and management positions and received patents for the Coherence Cube™ and interval/volume seismic attributes (a technology developed with Landmark Graphics and currently named PAL). He later became a resource exploration manager in the company's Mid-Continent operations. In 1996 he began his career with Apache. Bahorich was an organizing member of the 1992 Society of Exploration Geophysicists Sequence Stratigraphy Workshop. He is currently First Vice President of SEG and was recently awarded "Best Paper in Geophysics." He was also awarded the 1998 SEG Virgil Kauffman Gold Medal.

Rick C. Tobin

Rick Tobin is a senior staff geologist with BP-Amoco's Upstream Technology Group in Houston. He received geology degrees from James Madison University (B.S., 1977) and the University of Cincinnati (M.S., 1980; Ph.D. 1982). His technical specialties and current research interests include sedimentology, sedimentary petrology and diagenesis, fluid inclusion thermometry, and related thermal maturity technologies. Tobin has been actively involved in both exploration and development activities associated with reservoir quality and stratigraphic prediction worldwide. He is an active member of AAPG, SEPM, and Sigma Xi.

Edward A. Beaumont

Edward A. (Ted) Beaumont is an independent petroleum geologist from Tulsa, Oklahoma. He holds a BS in geology from the University of New Mexico and an MS in geology from the University of Kansas. Currently, he is generating drilling prospects in Texas, Oklahoma, and the Rocky Mountains. His previous professional experience was as a sedimentologist in basin analysis with Cities Service Oil Company and as Science Director for AAPG. Ted is coeditor of the Treatise of Petroleum Geology. He has lectured on creative exploration techniques in the U.S., China, and Australia and has received the Distinguished Service Award and Award of Special Recognition from AAPG.

Louis J. Terlikoski

Louis J. Terlikoski is a geophysicist with Statoil who received his B.S. degree in geology from the University of Massachusetts in 1982 and worked as an exploitation geophysicist for Gulf Oil Exploration and Production in New Orleans prior to joining Amoco in 1985. He has been exploring for turbidite reservoirs in the deepwater trend of the Gulf of Mexico since 1988. He is a member of AAPG and SEG.

Michael L. Hendricks

Michael Hendricks received his B.A. (1971) from the University of Colorado and an M.S. (1977) and Ph.D. (1982) from the Colorado School of Mines. He has worked in the petroleum industry, both as an exploration geologist and consultant. His interests include stratigraphic modeling, sequence stratigraphy, and reservoir characterization. He is currently the president of Hendricks and Associates, Inc., Englewood, CO.

Overview

Introduction

This chapter reviews methods for locating prospective stratigraphic traps. It stresses the need to use sequence stratigraphy as the framework for data integration. Discussions and examples show how to use sequence stratigraphy to integrate seismic and geologic data. The premise is that effective stratigraphic trap exploration consists of the following steps:

1. Calibrate rocks and fluids to logs and seismic.
2. Apply sequence stratigraphy.
3. Analyze seal, reservoir, and show to find and evaluate traps.

In this chapter

This chapter contains the following sections.

Section A
Stratigraphic Trap Basics

Introduction

As technology evolves and well control increases, exploration for pure stratigraphic traps becomes more and more practical. Seismic technology produces images of the subsurface with higher and higher resolution. Images and measurements of the subsurface, however detailed, still must be interpreted geologically. Effective geologic interpretation and, therefore, effective stratigraphic trap exploration integrates all data types, including seismic, well log, fluid character, fluid pressure, show, core, and cuttings. Sequence stratigraphy serves as a framework for integrating data.

In this section

This section contains the following topics.

Exploring for Stratigraphic Traps

Introduction

Historically, many stratigraphic traps were found accidentally while drilling for a structural objective. This is due to (1) an historical emphasis on structures and (2) the difficulty in seismically imaging stratigraphic trap components. Most traps are small, due to thin, single-zone pays or short columns created by unfavorable seal geometry or poor-quality seals. Data derived from AAPG memoirs (Halbouty, 1970, 1980, 1982, 1990) suggest that 7.5–12% of the world's giant fields occur in stratigraphic traps.

Definitions

Stratigraphic traps are hydrocarbon accumulations independent of structural or fault closure. **Combination traps** occur where structural nosing and/or faulting modifies the hydrocarbon distribution but is not the sole reason for the accumulation.

Suggested approach

Before sophisticated seismic technology was developed that allowed resolution great enough to image stratigraphic trapping geometry, many (if not most) stratigraphic trap discoveries were accidental. The discoveries were the result of drilling for a structural closure. With the advent of 3-D and other seismic techniques, the exploration industry became more inclined to drill wildcats for stratigraphic traps.

Sequence stratigraphy combines the strengths of seismic stratigraphy with litho- and biostratigraphy to enhance the effectiveness of stratigraphic trap exploration. An effective approach to stratigraphic trap exploration is to apply sequence stratigraphic principles to geophysical and geological data. The table below, modified from Bally (1987), details this approach.

Step	Action
1	*Analyze geometrical relationships in the data.* Break down basin stratigraphy, as displayed in detailed log cross sections and seismic sections, into genetically related sequences using unconformities and other regional correlation features.
2	*Analyze seismic facies and lithofacies.* Identify seismic facies within seismic sequences on the basis of internal and external reflection configurations. Integrate seismic facies with lithofacies interpreted from well data.
3	*Analyze the basin fill.* Make paleogeographic maps of the basin by combining seismic data with paleoenvironmental, chronostratigraphic, and sequence stratigraphic interpretations of lithologic and biostratigraphic data.
4	*Predict the quality and location of reservoir systems and seals.* Identify known and potential reservoir systems and seals.
5	*Evaluate basin for potential traps.* Place known traps in the basin in context with the information gathered in steps 1–4. Use analog traps within the basin and from other basins. Look for trapping geometries in areas with potential charge

Importance of Stratigraphic Trap Seals

Seal geometry

Most stratigraphic and combination traps require top, lateral, and bottom seals to retain a hydrocarbon accumulation. The figure below compares typical structural and stratigraphic traps and shows why bottom seals are more important to stratigraphic traps in determining accumulation size.

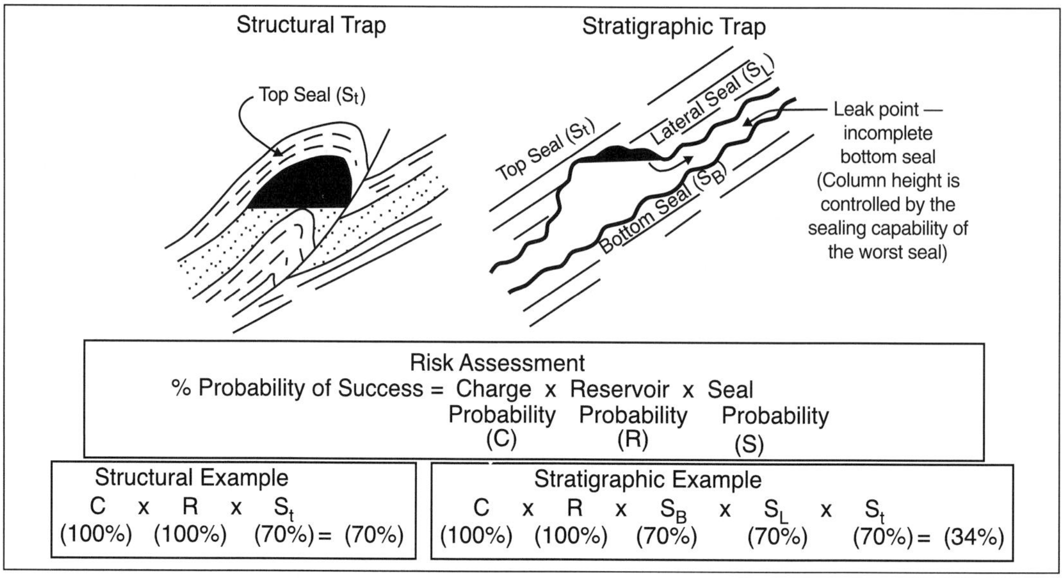

Figure 21–1.

Seal quality and dip rate

Large stratigraphic traps are most common in basins with gentle structural dip, where small hydrocarbon columns can be areally extensive. As structural dip steepens, the need for high-quality seals increases, raising the probability of trap failure (e.g., Gries et al., 1993). That is why large stratigraphic traps are most common in basins with gentle structural dip, where small hydrocarbon columns can be areally extensive. The figure below illustrates in map view how dip rate affects stratigraphic trap size.

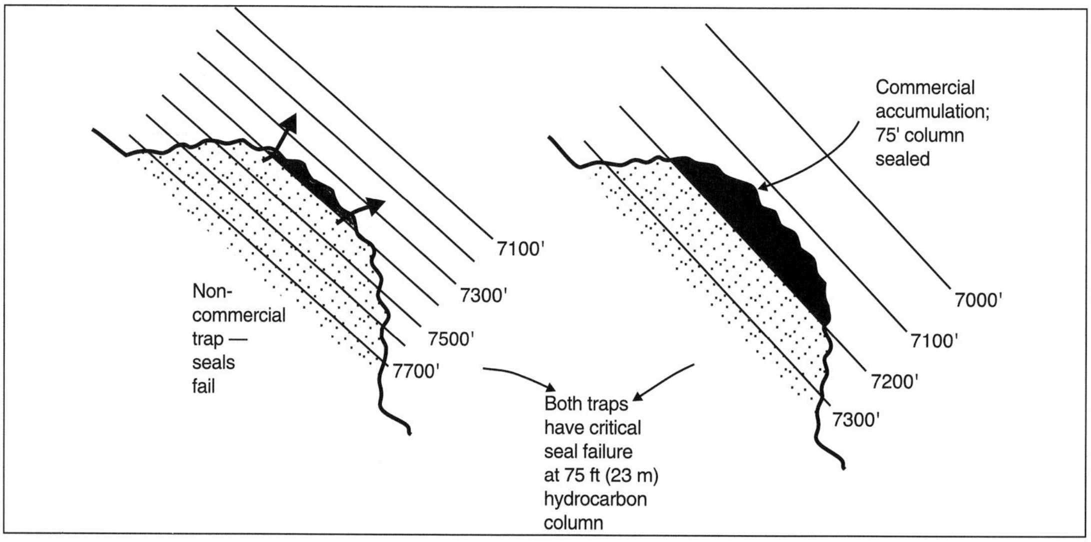

Figure 21–2.

Example

Raven Creek field (with 40 million BOE) illustrates the importance of a bottom seal. It is a paleotopographic trap in the Powder River basin of Wyoming. An unconformity overlying the "A" sandstone of the Permian Minnelusa Formation determines the primary trap geometry. This unconformity has paleotopographic relief, and the Opeche Shale red beds are sabkha deposits that infill an erosional valley forming the top and lateral seals to the "A" sandstone reservoir. The dolostone bed separating reservoir sandstones "A" and "B" provides the bottom seal.

A trap would not form if the valley fill were composed of porous sand or if the bottom-sealing dolostone were absent (from unpublished data by Ralph Thompson, 1986).

The figure below shows a map and cross section of Raven Creek field.

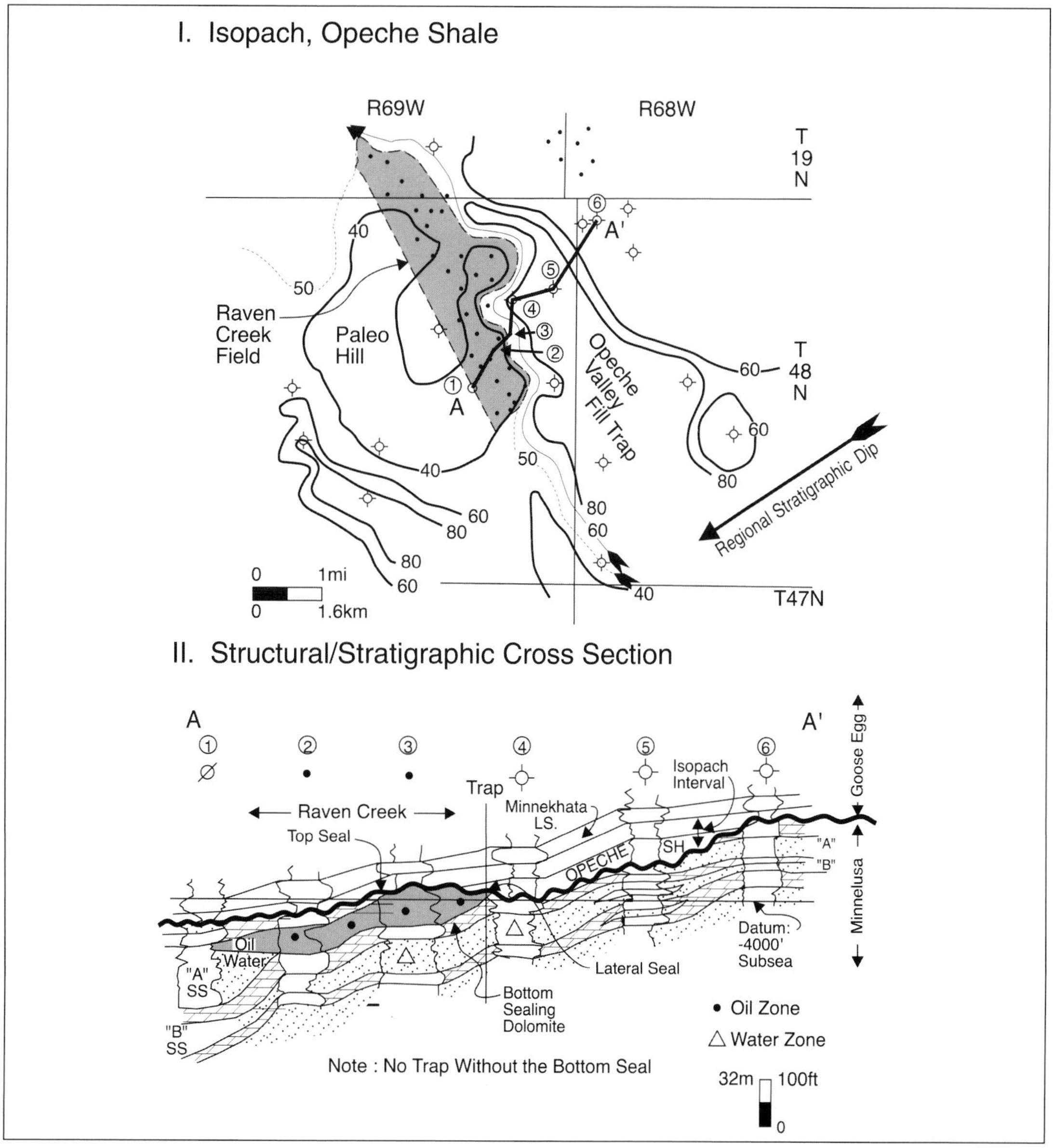

Figure 21–3.

Importance of Stratigraphic Trap Seals, continued

Reservoir quality and column height

Because of leaky seals—especially lateral seals—many stratigraphic traps have short hydrocarbon column heights. In these kinds of plays, reservoir quality can be critical. Higher quality reservoirs require less column height to drive water saturations low enough for water-free production. Lower quality reservoirs require more column height for water-free production.

For example, a trap with 100 ft (32 m) of stratigraphic closure has a maximum column height of 100 ft. If its reservoir is a mesoporous sandstone with 18% porosity and 10 md permeability, then the bottom 75 ft (20 m) of the trap will produce both oil and water in a long transition zone. Commercial production can be reached only at the top, where buoyancy pressure is sufficient to create water-free production.

Importance of Scale

Scale and data type

Correlations with well data, such as cuttings, cores, or well logs, can be done to a much higher resolution than seismic scale correlations. The scale of a seismic wavelet limits the scale of correlations within a seismic section. The geologist must refine these correlations to a higher resolution using well data to more accurately define the location of seals and reservoirs.

Scale and trap detection

Scale makes a difference in ease of detection and, hence, affects risk. In the figures below, Pennsylvanian carbonate reef margin depositional sequences from the Delaware and Paradox basins, U.S.A., are compared. Note the difference in scale and how it affects seismic interpretation. Seismic detection of the Paradox basin traps is much more difficult because of the wavelength of the seismic wave vs. the reservoir thickness.

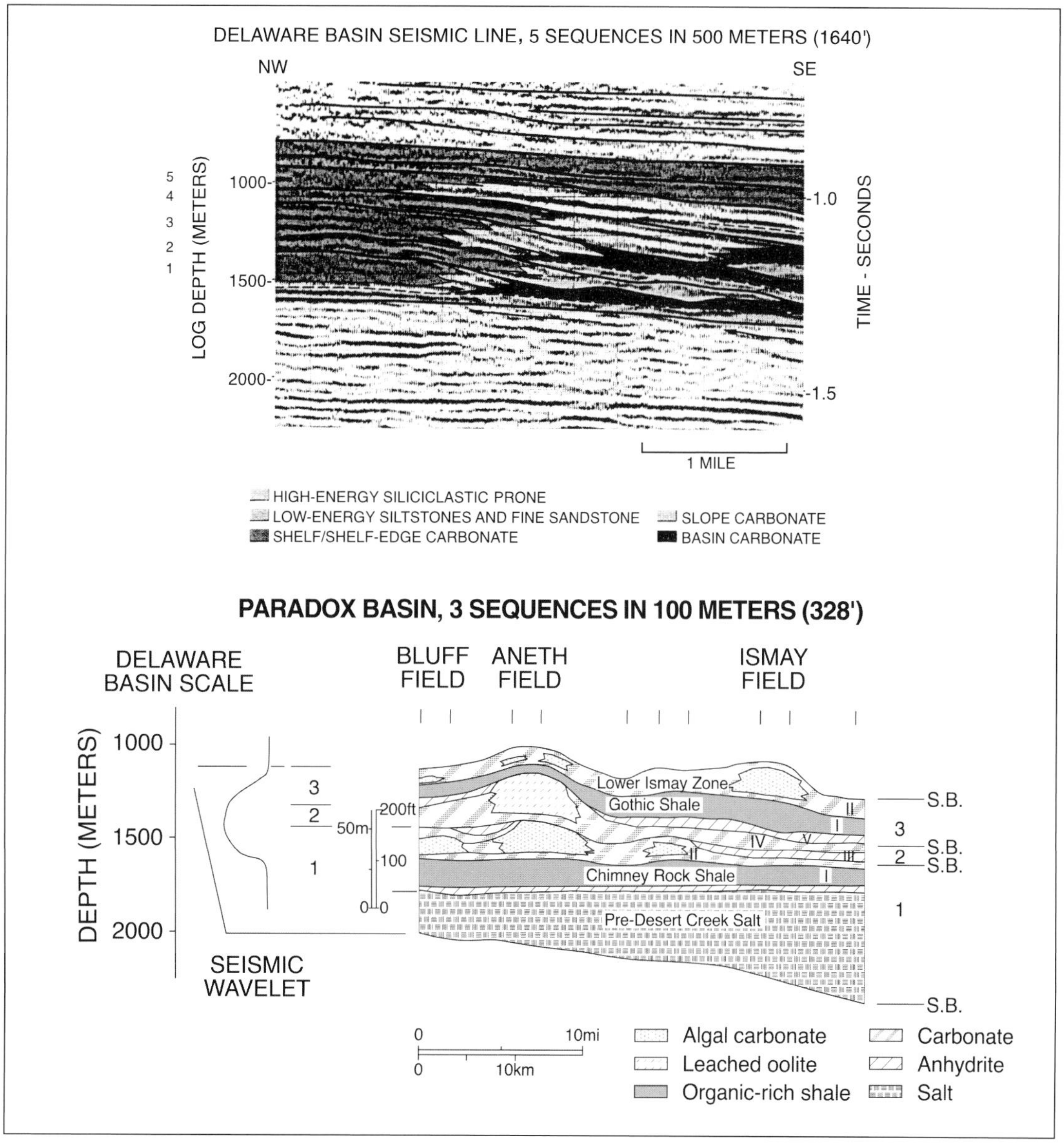

Figure 21–4. From Sarg, 1988; courtesy SEPM.

Impact of Diagenesis

Introduction

Stratigraphic trap geometries can be mapped and defined at any geologic scale from an interpretation of facies in seismic or well data, but diagenetic overprints often modify primary trapping geometries. Diagenetic changes often can be predicted and mapped reliably, especially if they follow facies or paleostructure. However, if diagenesis does not follow facies or paleostructure, then the exploration and exploitation risk increases because predicting the trap location is more difficult.

Example

Access to core, samples, and modern wireline log suites greatly facilitates subsurface interpretation. In the example below, both lateral and top seals in the dolomite reservoir were created by anhydrite cementation during early diagenesis. Primary facies changes do not control the location of the trap.

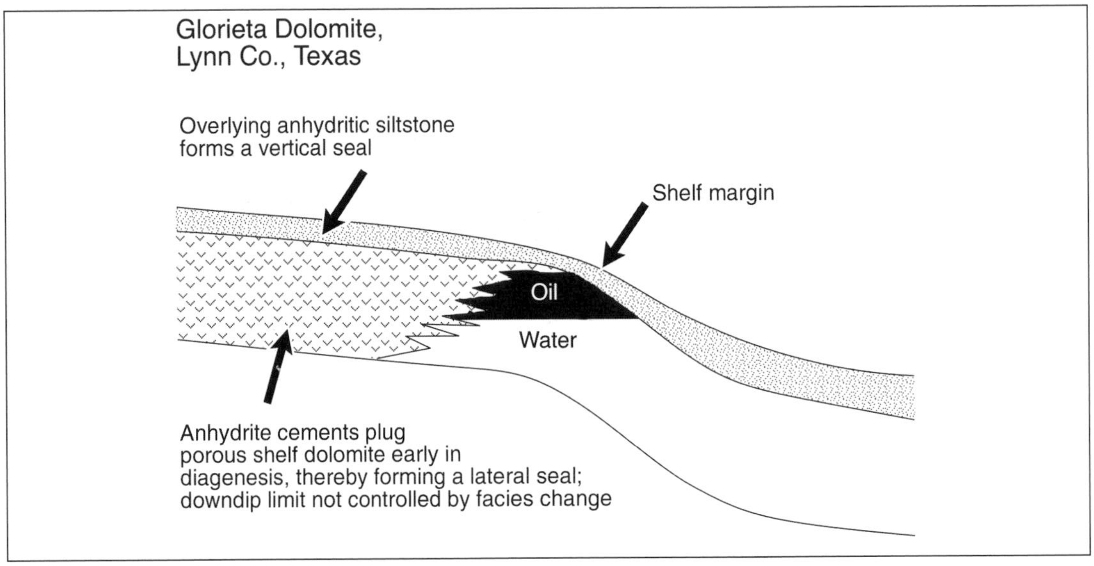

Figure 21–5. From unpublished data by R.C. Tobin, 1987.

Section B
Sequence Stratigraphy

Introduction

Applying the principles of sequence stratigraphy to petroleum exploration leads to more effective prediction of the quality and location of source, reservoir, and seal rocks. This section presents a brief review of sequence stratigraphy. For more detail refer to Wilgus et al., 1988; Van Wagoner et al., 1990; Weimer and Posamentier, 1993; Loucks and Sarg, 1993; and Read et al., 1995.

In this section

This section contains the following topics.

Basics of Sequence Stratigraphy

Introduction

Sequence stratigraphy allows an effective, systematic approach to stratigraphic trap exploration. Sequence stratigraphic concepts provide a means to classify, correlate, and map sedimentary rocks using time–stratigraphic units. Sequence stratigraphic techniques provide (1) a more effective method for evaluating reservoir system continuity and trend directions and (2) improved methods for predicting reservoir system, source, and sealing facies away from well control (Van Wagoner et al., 1990). Basic principles are reviewed below, but many important details, model variations, and examples are not included. Interested readers should review the abundant literature regarding sequence stratigraphy (see Weimer and Posamentier, 1993; Loucks and Sarg, 1993; Read et al., 1995; Van Wagoner et al., 1990; Wilgus et al., 1988) and the role of tectonics and rapid sedimentation in stratigraphic architecture (see Dolson et al., 1997; Gawthorpe et al., 1994; Ravnas and Steel, 1998; and Prosser, 1993).

Definition

Van Wagoner et al. (1990) define sequence stratigraphy as "... the study of rock relationships within a chronostratigraphic framework of repetitive, genetically related strata bounded by surfaces of erosion or nondeposition, or their correlative unconformities." Paleogeographic reconstruction of facies belts at precise moments in time is the goal of the sequence stratigrapher.

Development of sequence stratigraphy

In the late 1970s, seismic data was interpreted stratigraphically to define packages of strata hundreds of meters thick that were deposited between sea level cycles that lasted 0.5–5 m.y. During the 1980s, a finer resolution of stratigraphic analysis developed when outcrop and well data were applied to seismic stratigraphy (Van Wagoner et al., 1990). This type of analysis, termed **sequence stratigraphy**, defines a hierarchy of stratal units that range from thousands of meters to millimeters in thickness and that were deposited by events that range from tens of millions of years to days in duration.

Factors controlling sequence deposition

Four factors control sequence deposition:

- Global sea level changes (eustacy)
- Subsidence
- Sediment supply
- Climate

Other factors that influence sequence deposition (although not to the same extent) are crustal loading, dominant sediment type (i.e., siliciclastic vs. carbonate), basin type, and differential compaction.

Accommodation

Accommodation is the space made available for the accumulation of sediment that results from global sea level change and subsidence. In most cases, subsidence can be considered as constant (Posamentier and Vail, 1988). Accommodation is equal to the rate of eustatic change minus the rate of subsidence. For example, if global sea level is falling at the same rate as subsidence, then no new space is made for sediment accumulation. However, if global sea level is falling but more slowly than the basin is subsiding, then new space is created.

Accommodation (continued)

The figure below shows how, at a point on a shelf, for example, global sea level cycles combine with subsidence to produce accommodation.

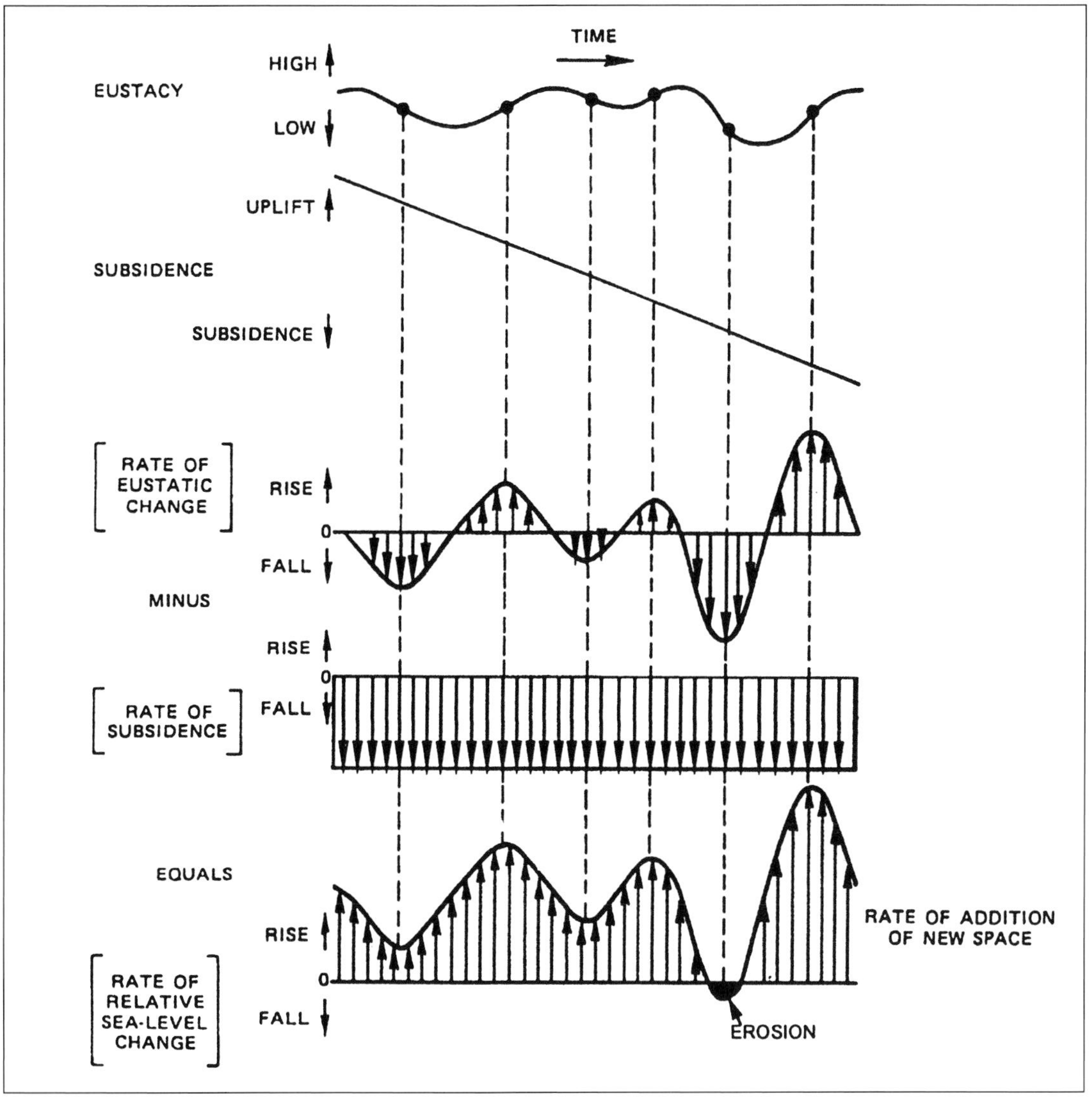

Figure 21–6. From Posamentier and Vail, 1988; courtesy SEPM.

Carbonate vs. siliciclastic deposition

Sediment supply is a greater factor in siliciclastic sequence deposition than carbonate sequence deposition because siliciclastic sediments originate from outside the basin, whereas carbonate sediments originate within the basin. Streams and rivers draining areas landward and updip from the basin deliver sediment to the basin. Organic and inorganic processes produce carbonate sediment within the basin. This plus the unique ability of carbonate sedimentation to keep pace with sea level rise is responsible for the diverse morphology of carbonate platforms, i.e., ramps, rimmed platforms, and isolated platforms. The slope angle of siliciclastic margins is generally less than carbonate margins (Handford and Loucks, 1993).

Hierarchy of Sequences

Introduction

Global sea level changes (eustacy) are cyclic phenomena. Six orders of sea level cycles are recognized from stratigraphic evidence (Van Wagoner et al., 1990). Third-, fourth-, and fifth-order sea level cycles model sequence deposition for petroleum exploration. A third-order sequence is a composite of fourth- and fifth-order sequences.

The table below shows sea level cycle frequencies, thickness ranges, and stratigraphic names for third-, fourth-, and fifth-order sequences.

Sequence Order	Cycle Frequency, m.y.	Thickness, m	Stratigraphic Name
Third	0.5–5	100–1000	Sequence
Fourth	0.1–0.5	1–10	Parasequence
Fifth	0.01–0.1	1–10	Parasequence

Superimposition of cycles

Several frequencies, representing different orders of sea level cycles, are superimposed on one another to make a composite sea level cycle curve. For stratigraphic trap exploration, cycles that impact trap location are usually third-, fourth-, and fifth-order sea level cycles. The figure below shows how adding third-, fourth-, and fifth-order cycles together will produce a composite curve.

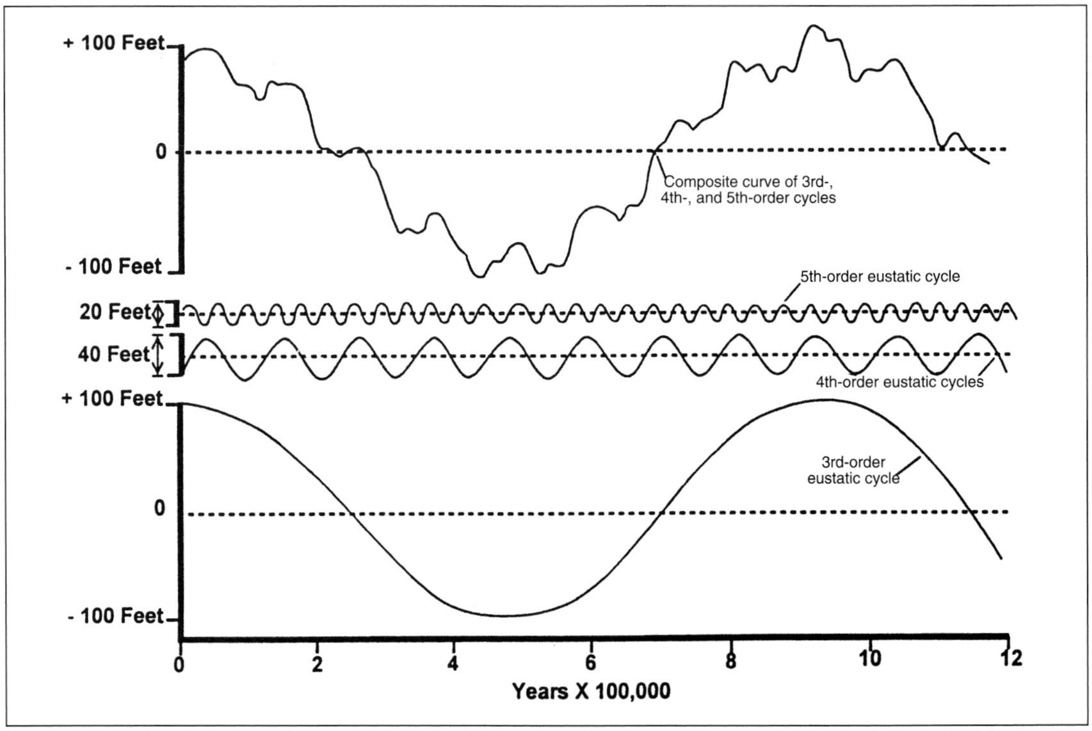

Figure 21–7. From Van Wagoner et al., 1990; courtesy AAPG.

Third-Order Sequences

Introduction

During a third-order sea level change, cycle amplitude is great enough (approximately 50–150 ft) to expose the shelf. Depositional sites range from coastal plain to deep basin. The unit of strata deposited during a third-order cycle is called a **depositional sequence**. A depositional sequence has three subdivisions: highstand systems tract (HST), transgressive systems tract (TST), and lowstand systems tract (LST). The figure below shows a schematic cross section of a third-order sequence and its various systems tracts.

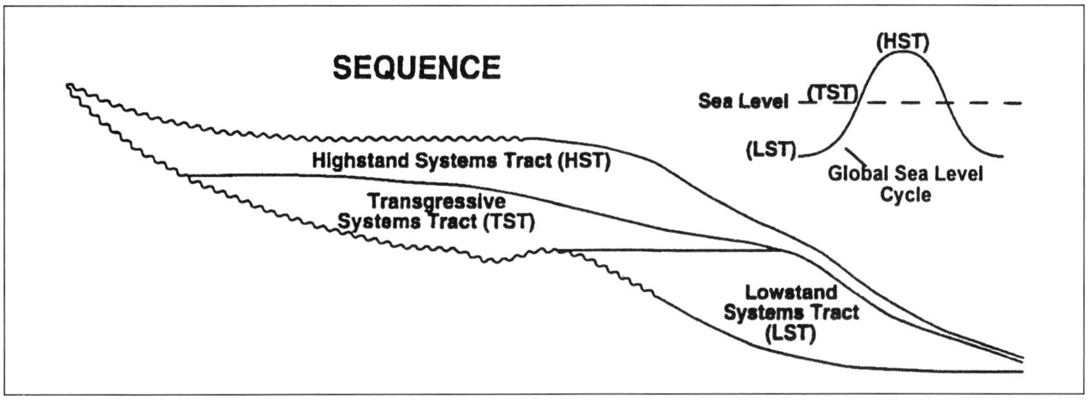

Figure 21–8. From Hyne, 1995; courtesy Tulsa Geological Society.

Third-order sequence deposition

The schematic cross section below is a third-order sequence model based on observations of the Tertiary of the Gulf of Mexico passive margin basin (Van Wagoner, 1990). Although different basin types, i.e., foreland basins or active margin basins, require adjustments to the model, the Gulf of Mexico model still is useful for understanding third-order sequence deposition.

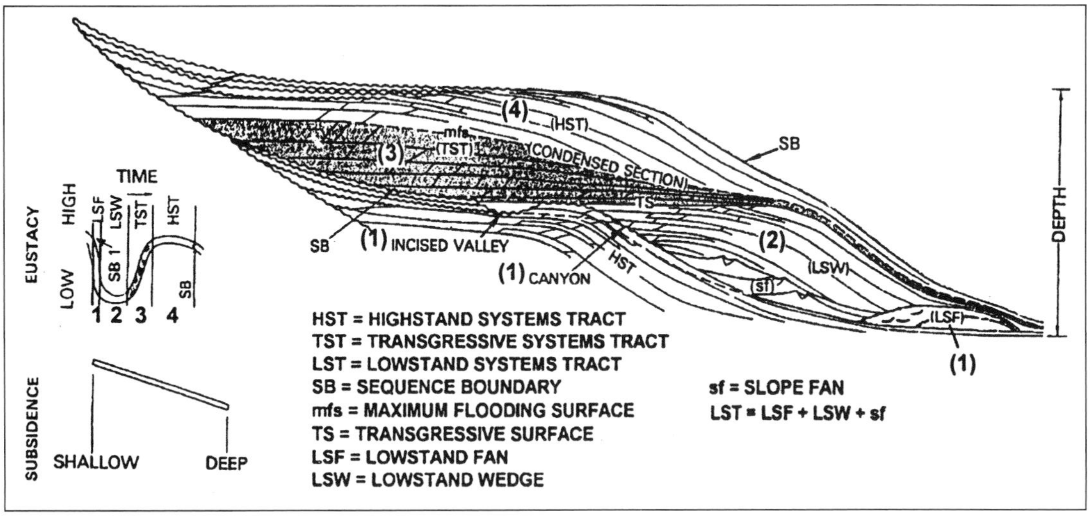

Figure 21–9. From Haq, 1988; courtesy SEPM.

Third-order sequence deposition (continued)

The order of deposition for the sequence shown in Figure 21–9 is as follows (Van Wagoner, 1990):

1. Sequence boundary formation and lowstand systems tract; fan deposition
   - Rate of eustatic fall exceeds rate of subsidence.
   - Sea level falls to shelf break, shelf is exposed, incised; canyon cut.
   - Slope-perched deltas and submarine fans are deposited.
2. Lowstand systems tract; wedge deposition
   - Rate of eustatic fall decreases, reaches a stillstand, and rises slowly.
   - Submarine fan deposition ceases.
   - Incised valleys fill with coarse-grained, low-sinuosity channel or estuarine sandstones in response to sea level rise.
   - Shale-prone wedge with thin, fine-grained turbidites forms on the slope, then downlaps the top of the submarine fan.
3. Transgressive systems tract deposition
   - Rate of rise is at a maximum.
   - During brief slowdowns in the rate of rise, parasequences (fourth-order sequences) prograde; but overall they stack in a backstepping pattern.
   - Organic-rich (condensed) section moves up onto the shelf.
   - Fluvial systems typically shift from braided to meandering pattern.
4. Highstand systems tract deposition
   - Rate of sea level rise is at a minimum; in the late highstand, it falls slowly.
   - Depositional rates exceed rate of sea level rise, causing parasequences to build basinward in aggradational to progradational parasequence sets.
   - Parasequences downlap onto the condensed section.

Third-order sequence example

The Desmoinian of the Paradox basin, Utah, shown in the figure below, is an example of a third-order depositional sequence.

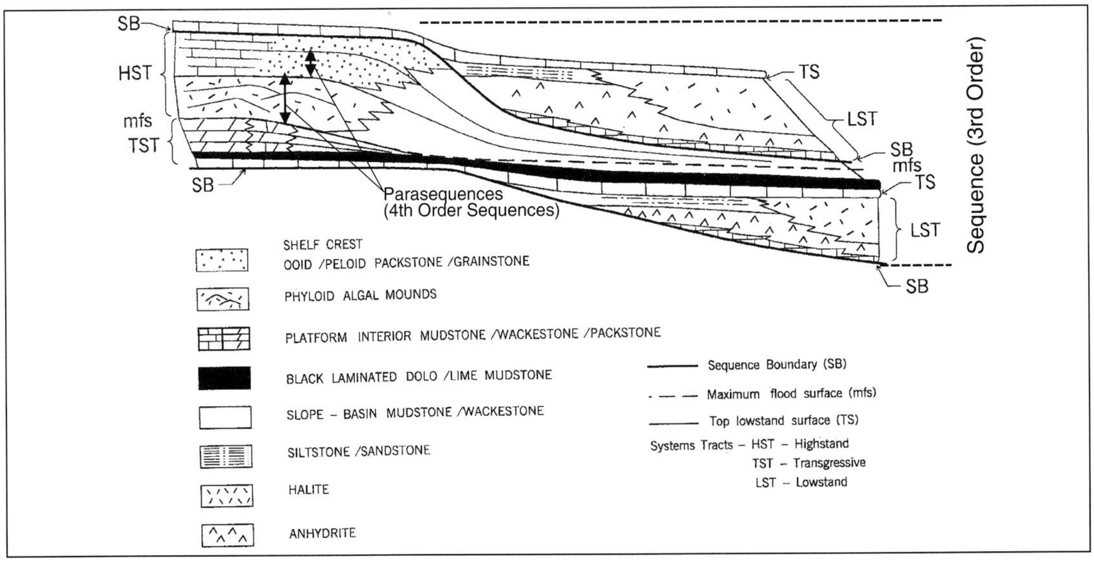

Figure 21–10. From Weber et al., 1995; courtesy SEPM.

Carbonate platform third-order sequence

The diagrams below outline the deposition of a sequence associated with a carbonate platform during a third-order sea level cycle. Sequence deposition begins with lowstand systems tract (2 and 3) and ends with the highstand systems tract (5).

1. **Highstand**
   - Rimmed shelf with accretionary slope apron pattern of progradation

2. **Forced regression**
   - Rate of eustatic fall exceeds rate of subsidence
   - Sea level is at its lowest point and the greatest area of the platform is exposed.
   - Platform eroded and sequence boundary develops
   - Submarine fans and megabreccias deposited: beginning of lowstand systems tract deposition

3. **Lowstand**
   - Rate of eustatic fall decreases, reaches stillstand, and rises slowly
   - Lowstand wedge progrades seaward

4. **Maximum flooding**
   - Most of shelf drowns as sedimentation outpaced by relative sea level rise
   - Maximum flooding surface forms
   - Condensed section develops across shelf, transgressive systems tract deposited
   - Shelf margin is scalloped due to frequent collapse.

5. **Highstand**
   - Normal shelf sedimentation resumes as rate of relative sea level rise decreases
   - Rates of deposition exceed rates of sea level rise: highstand systems tract progrades basinward.
   - Facies on shelf reflect inherited topography form the lowstand (e.g., karst) and transgression (e.g., build-ups)
   - Shallow shelf-sediments bypass slope to basin floor, which aggrades

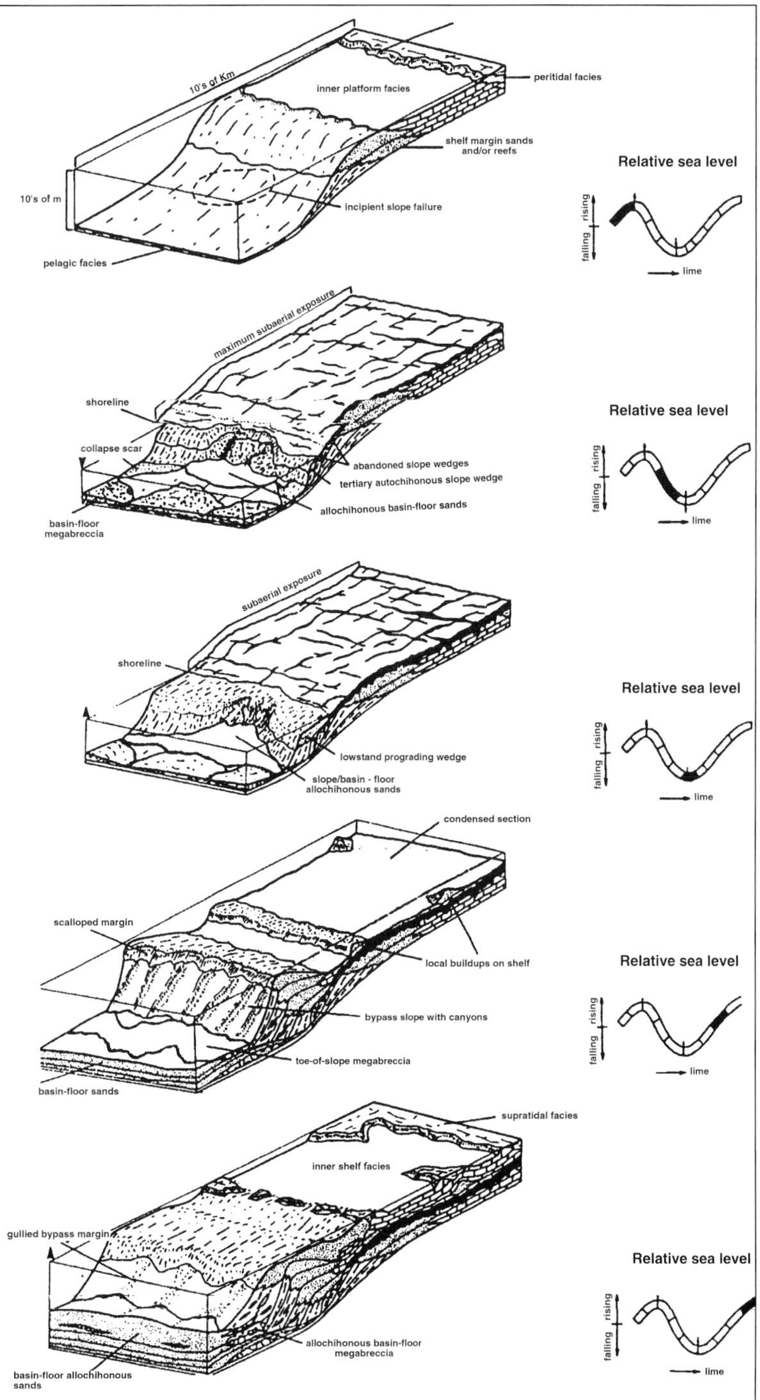

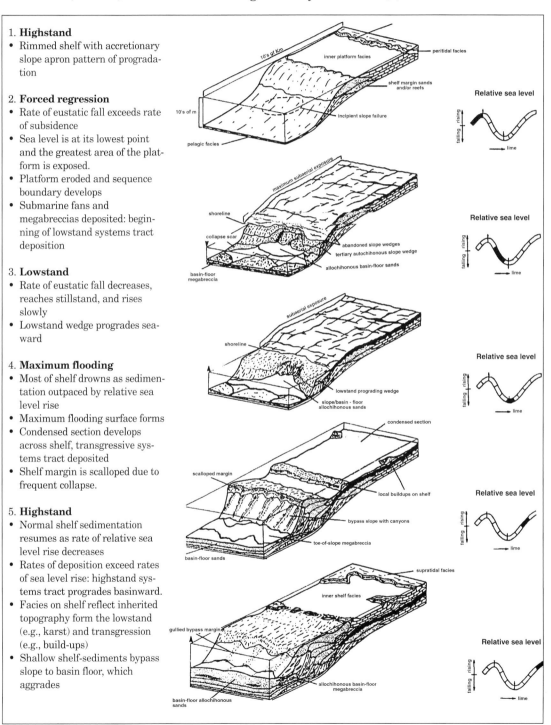

Figure 21–11. From Hunt and Tucker, 1993; courtesy AAPG.

Fourth- and Fifth-Order Sequences (Parasequences)

Introduction

Parasequences are deposited during fourth- or fifth-order eustatic cycles. They are generally progradational and have a shoaling-upward association of facies (Van Wagoner et al., 1990). In siliciclastic parasequences, grain size can either fine or coarsen upward, reflecting an upward decrease in water depth. Some workers (Van Wagoner, 1995) consider fourth-order sequences (deposited during cycles 100,000–200,000 years in duration) to be the building blocks of most reservoir or field studies.

Periodic vs. episodic parasequences

A parasequence can be either periodic or episodic (Weber et al., 1995). A **periodic parasequence** has regional continuity and forms in response to deposition during a global sea level cycle. An **episodic parasequence** has limited lateral extent and forms in response to tidal flat migration or delta lobe shifts. Episodic parasequences are of very short duration—generally less than 10,000 years. Periodic parasequences have average durations of 100,000 years.

Parasequence sets

A parasequence set is a succession of genetically related parasequences that forms a distinctive stacking pattern. A parasequence set is generally bounded by a marine flooding surface (Van Wagoner, 1995).

Upward-coarsening parasequence

The figure below shows the characteristics of an upward-coarsening parasequence formed in a deltaic environment.

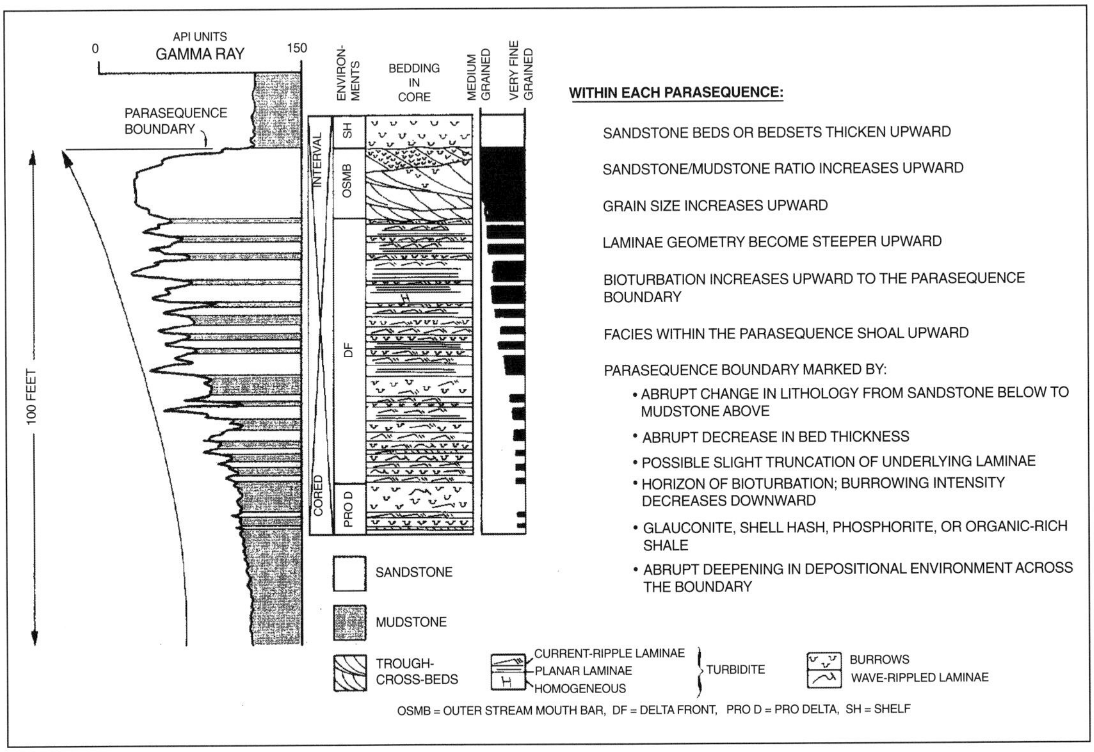

Figure 21–12. From Van Wagoner et al., 1990; courtesy AAPG.

Upward-fining parasequence

The figure below shows the characteristics of two upward-fining parasequences formed in a tidal flat to subtidal environment.

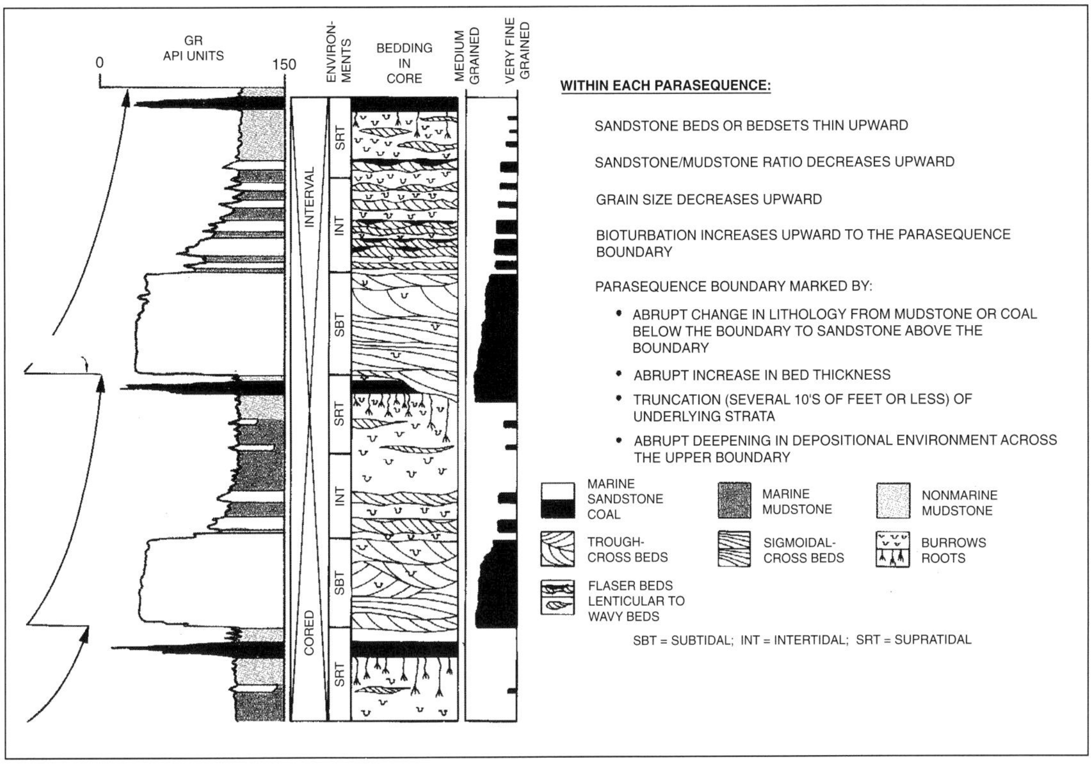
GR
API UNITS
0
150
ENVIRON-MENTS
BEDDING IN CORE
MEDIUM GRAINED
VERY FINE GRAINED
INTERVAL
CORED
SRT
INT
SBT
WITHIN EACH PARASEQUENCE:
SANDSTONE BEDS OR BEDSETS THIN UPWARD
SANDSTONE/MUDSTONE RATIO DECREASES UPWARD
GRAIN SIZE DECREASES UPWARD
BIOTURBATION INCREASES UPWARD TO THE PARASEQUENCE BOUNDARY
PARASEQUENCE BOUNDARY MARKED BY:
• ABRUPT CHANGE IN LITHOLOGY FROM MUDSTONE OR COAL BELOW THE BOUNDARY TO SANDSTONE ABOVE THE BOUNDARY
• ABRUPT INCREASE IN BED THICKNESS
• TRUNCATION (SEVERAL 10'S OF FEET OR LESS) OF UNDERLYING STRATA
• ABRUPT DEEPENING IN DEPOSITIONAL ENVIRONMENT ACROSS THE UPPER BOUNDARY
MARINE SANDSTONE
COAL
MARINE MUDSTONE
NONMARINE MUDSTONE
TROUGH-CROSS BEDS
SIGMOIDAL-CROSS BEDS
BURROWS
ROOTS
FLASER BEDS
LENTICULAR TO WAVY BEDS
SBT = SUBTIDAL; INT = INTERTIDAL; SRT = SUPRATIDAL

Figure 21–13. From Van Wagoner et al., 1990; courtesy AAPG.

Traps in a Framework of Sequence Stratigraphy

Play types

The schematic cross section below illustrates different stratigraphic play types in the context of sequence stratigraphy.

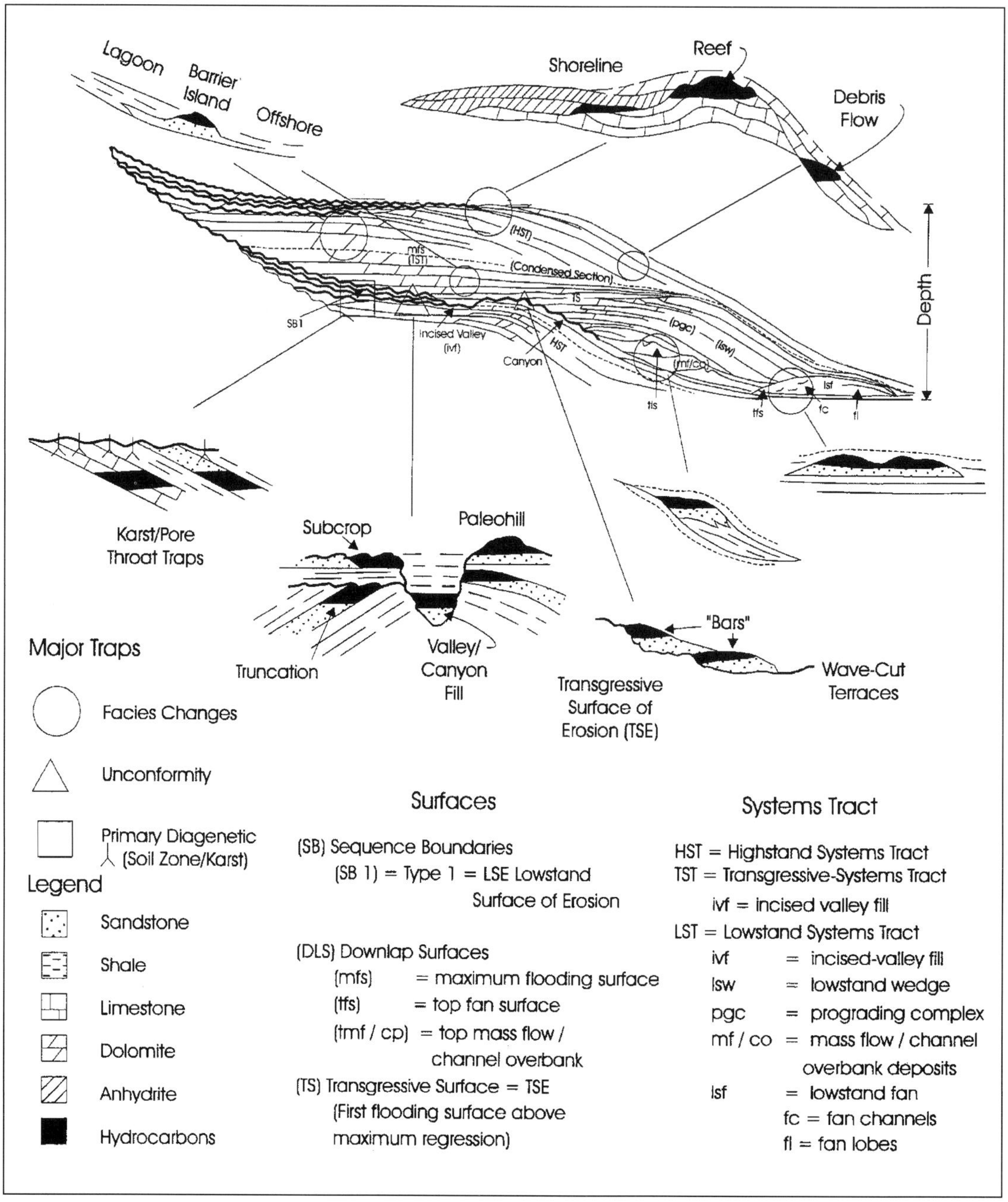

Figure 21–14. Modified from passive margin sequence stratigraphic models by Baum and Vail, 1988, and Sarg, 1988; courtesy SEPM.

Traps in a Framework of Sequence Stratigraphy, continued

Shelf-edge and ramp-type margin traps

Below are two schematic cross sections showing potential stratigraphic and combination stratigraphic–structural plays associated with sequences and parasequences on shelf-edge and ramp margins. Shelf-edge margins are found in continental margin basins. Ramp margins are found in cratonic, continental margin, or lacustrine basins. The numbers in the cross sections correspond to the numbers in the table.

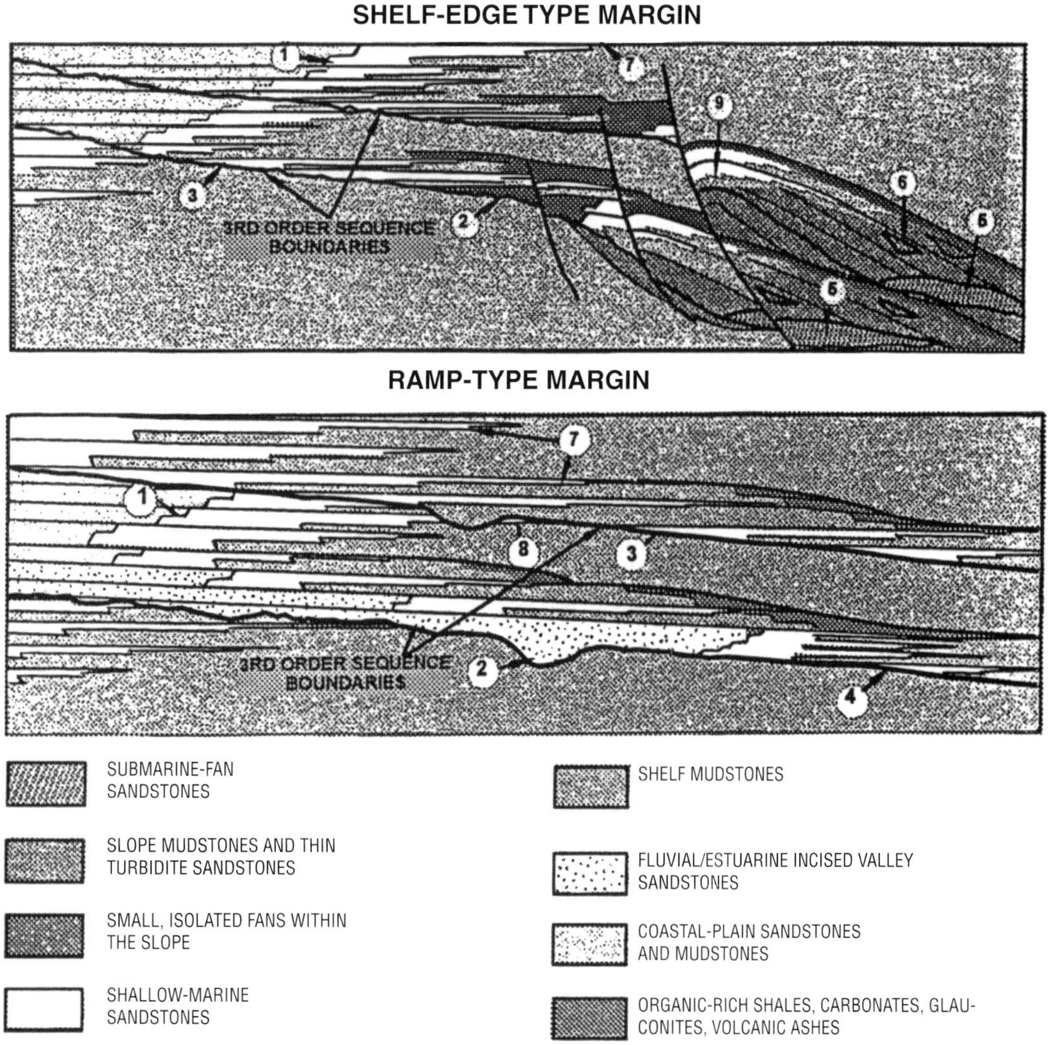

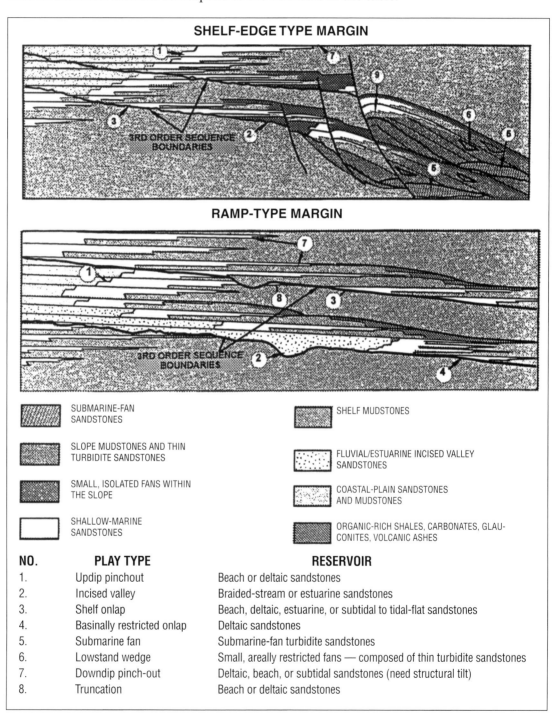

NO.	PLAY TYPE	RESERVOIR
1.	Updip pinchout	Beach or deltaic sandstones
2.	Incised valley	Braided-stream or estuarine sandstones
3.	Shelf onlap	Beach, deltaic, estuarine, or subtidal to tidal-flat sandstones
4.	Basinally restricted onlap	Deltaic sandstones
5.	Submarine fan	Submarine-fan turbidite sandstones
6.	Lowstand wedge	Small, areally restricted fans — composed of thin turbidite sandstones
7.	Downdip pinch-out	Deltaic, beach, or subtidal sandstones (need structural tilt)
8.	Truncation	Beach or deltaic sandstones

Figure 21–15. After Van Wagoner et al., 1990; courtesy AAPG.

Section C
Geometrical Analysis

Introduction

The first step in stratigraphic trap exploration is a geometrical analysis of stratigraphic components of the basin fill. A geometrical analysis consists of (1) dividing the stratigraphic section into depositional sequences, systems tracts, and parasequences and (2) mapping their thicknesses. Correlation surfaces that are genetically significant, such as unconformities, divide the stratigraphic section.

This section discusses procedures and gives examples of geometrical analysis.

Procedure for Geometrical Analysis

Introduction

A geometrical analysis is simply dividing a basin's sedimentary section into three-dimensional bodies of strata using regionally correlative surfaces or features as boundaries. The sequence stratigraphic approach uses unconformities or other genetically significant features to divide the section into depositional sequences, systems tracts, and/or parasequences. Recognizing these correlation features is key to identifying depositional sequences properly.

Procedure

The table below lists steps for a geometrical analysis of the sedimentary section of a basin in seismic sections, outcrop sections, and well log sections.

Step	Action
1	Identify unconformities (third-order sequence boundaries) in seismic sections, outcrop sections, and regional well log sections.
2	Identify other correlation features, such as maximum flooding surfaces, condensed sections, transgressive surfaces.
3	Divide the sedimentary section into depositional sequences, systems tracts, and parasequences using the following: • Seismic sequence analysis • Well data sequence analysis
4	Map the thicknesses of third-order depositional sequences, systems tracts, and important parasequences.

Identifying unconformities

Unconformities are third-order sequence boundaries. They are generally regional onlap surfaces. In *basinal settings,* they are characterized by onlap of allochthonous deposits (i.e., debris flows, slump deposits, turbidites), prograding deltas, carbonate platform deposits, or evaporites. In *shallow-water or nonmarine settings,* they are characterized by onlap of strata deposited in fluvial, deltaic, or nearshore marine or peritidal environments (Weber et al., 1995). We can identify unconformities using stratigraphic evidence and individual well evidence.

Stratigraphic Evidence

- Reflection terminations in seismic sections (onlap, downlap, toplap, or truncation)
- Bed truncation observed in detailed well log cross sections
- Missing biostratigraphic horizons
- Missing facies in a sequence, i.e., abrupt change from fluvial sandstone to marine shale
- Evidence of widespread channeling of platforms or shelves
- Abrupt vertical geochemical changes such as stable isotopes

Individual Well Evidence

- Dipmeter changes
- Gamma-ray log changes in response to increased uranium concentration at exposure surfaces

Procedure for Geometrical Analysis, continued

Identifying unconformities (continued)

- Vertical breaks in thermal maturity profiles (i.e., abrupt vertical change in vitrinite reflection values)
- Changes in lithology as seen in cores that indicate subaerial exposure or nondeposition, as evidenced by the following:
  - — Paleosols and weathered horizons
  - — Hematitic grain coatings or dissolution textures unrelated to burial diagenesis
  - — Clam-bored hardgrounds such as Toredo borings
  - — Thin lag deposits of bone, phosphate, or shell hash
- Fluid inclusion evidence for atmospheric gases (e.g., argon, helium)

Example of unconformity analysis

Cores and samples should be examined for evidence of unconformities. These unconformity surfaces should then be calibrated to logs. Logs can then be used to correlate the surfaces to seismic and to other wells. The figure below (from Dolson and Piombino, 1994) shows an example of calibrating unconformity evidence from cores to logs. The Lower Cretaceous Cutbank Sandstone unconformably overlies the Jurassic Swift Formation. A major lowstand surface of erosion (LSE) is shown at 2957 ft (901 m) and was identified using the following criteria:

- Missing biostratigraphic horizons
- Subaerial (weathered) zone beneath a channel
- Facies omission (abrupt change from marine shale to a fluvial sandstone)

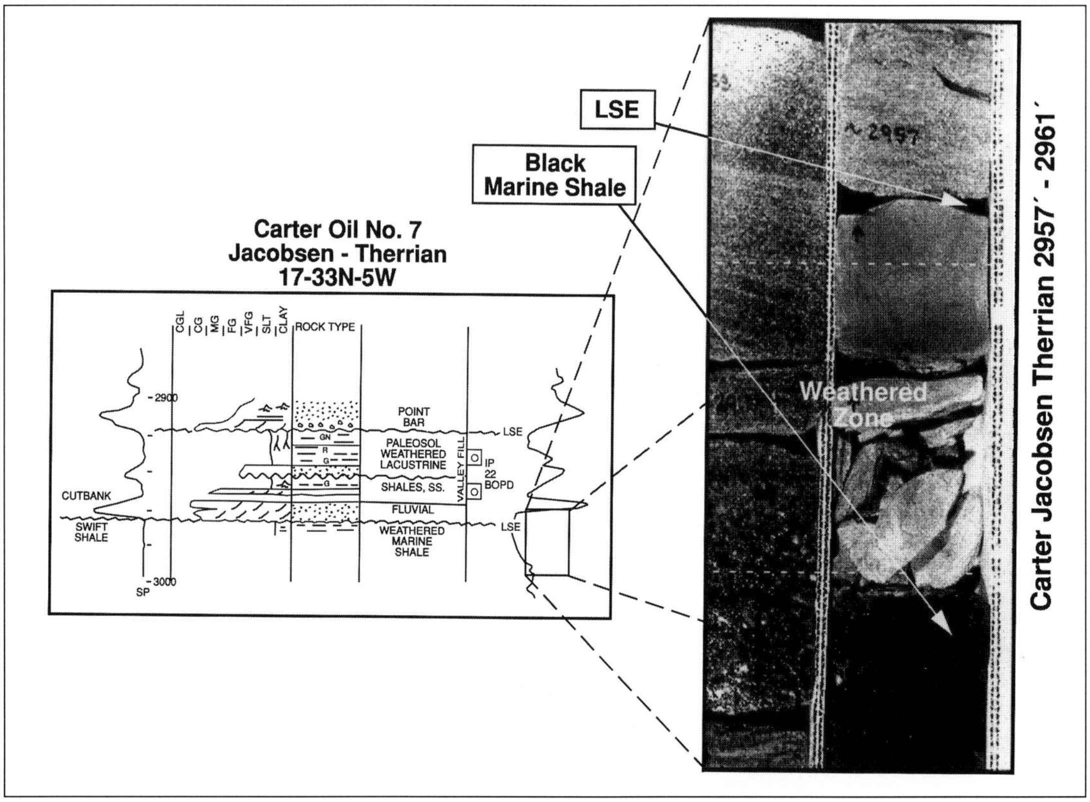

Figure 21–16. From Dolson and Piombino, 1994; courtesy Rocky Mountain Assoc. of Geologists.

Other Correlation Features

Introduction

Besides unconformities, other surfaces and stratigraphic features are useful for correlation. Unconformities serve as boundaries for first-, second-, and third-order sequences. Other correlation features—maximum flooding surfaces, condensed sections, transgressive surfaces, and downlap surfaces—subdivide the third-order sequences into systems tracts and parasequences.

Maximum flooding surface

A maximum flooding surface separates "younger from older strata across which there is an abrupt increase in water depth. This deepening is commonly accompanied by minor submarine erosion or nondeposition, but not by subaerial erosion due to stream rejuvenation or basinward shift in facies" (Van Wagoner, 1995). Submarine erosion ranges from inches to tens of feet, with several feet being common.

A maximum flooding surface represents the point of maximum shoreline transgression. It marks the "turnaround" of the sequence from transgressive to regressive events. The maximum flooding surface is the physical boundary between the transgressive system tract (TST) and the highstand systems tract (HST). In basinward positions, it is contained within the condensed section. In starved areas, it is associated with a hardground or marine dissolution surface (Weber et al., 1995). Galloway (1989) argues that maximum flooding surfaces are more easily recognized and mapped than unconformities and are an alternative method of subdividing sequences.

Condensed section

A condensed section is "a facies consisting of thin hemipelagic or pelagic sediments deposited as the parasequences step landward and as the shelf is starved of terrigenous sediment" (Van Wagoner, 1995). They are most extensive during times of regional shoreline transgressions. Condensed sections contain the greatest abundance and diversity of fauna within a third-order sequence. The section is thin because it accumulates at very slow rates.

Transgressive surface

A transgressive surface forms during a transgression. It is the physical boundary between the lowstand and transgressive systems tracts and is defined by the change from forestepping to backstepping. It merges with the basal unconformity landward of the point where the lowstand systems tract pinches out (Weber et al., 1995).

Downlap surface

A downlap surface (DLS) is a marine flooding surface onto which the toes of prograding clinoforms of the overlying highstand systems tract downlap. The surface represents a change from a retrogradational depositional pattern to an aggradational pattern. It is the surface of maximum flooding, recognized by downlap of overlying units and apparent truncation of underlying units. A downlap surface is common at the base of prograding deltas and the top of submarine fans.

Other Correlation Features, continued

Example: Identifying MFS with biostratigraphic data

In the example below from the Gulf of Suez basin, planktonic and foraminiferal data taken on a 30-ft (9.1-m) interval show abundance peaks crossing a sharp log break from a thin carbonate to marine shale. Abundance peaks such as this are a common feature of the maximum flooding surface (MFS). Seismic and well log correlations confirm that this break is an MFS overlain by a prograding clastic wedge.

The computer-generated labels on the right side post alternative sequence boundary picks. In this way, the interpreter can choose the best pick from all available well and seismic information.

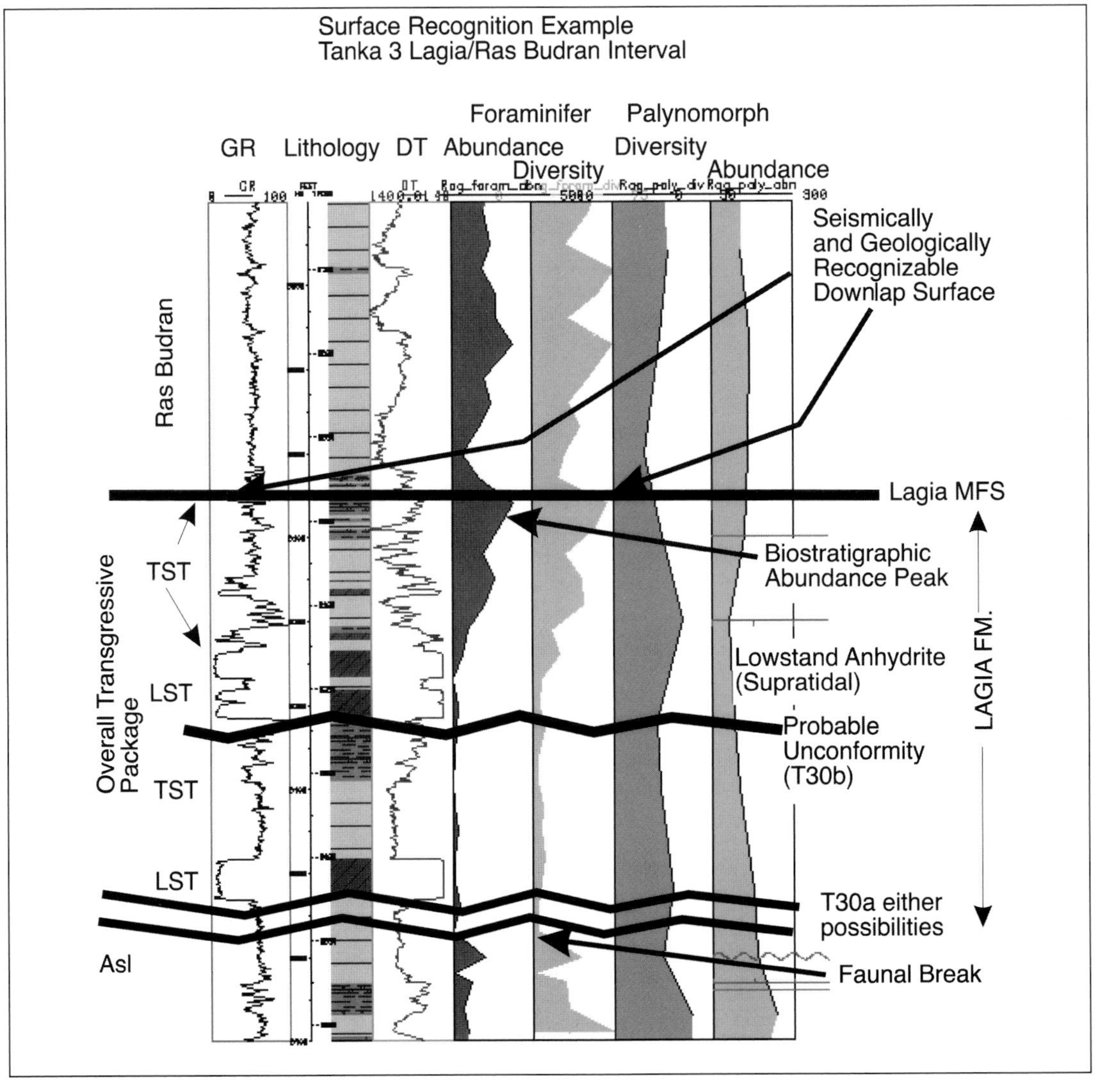

Figure 21–17.

Seismic Sequence Analysis

Objective

The objective of seismic sequence analysis is to identify depositional sequences and systems tracts on seismic sections by interpreting the location of their boundaries. Boundaries are manifested as discontinuities in seismic sections and are located mainly by finding reflection terminations (Vail, 1987).

Procedure

Follow the steps listed in the table below to perform a sequence analysis of a seismic section (adapted from Vail, 1987).

<table>
<tr><th>Step</th><th>Action</th></tr>
<tr><td>1</td><td>Look for places where two reflectors converge. Where reflectors converge, there will be terminations.</td></tr>
<tr><td>2</td><td>Mark the reflection terminations with arrows.</td></tr>
<tr><td>3</td><td>Draw in the discontinuity surface between the onlapping and downlapping reflections above, and the truncating and toplapping reflectors above. If the discontinuity surface becomes conformable, trace its position across the section by reflection correlation.</td></tr>
<tr><td>4</td><td>Continue the process described in steps 1, 2, and 3 for all the seismic lines in the grid.</td></tr>
<tr><td>5</td><td>Close all seismic grid loops by checking the loop ties for each discontinuity or its correlative equivalent.</td></tr>
<tr><td>6</td><td>Categorize each discontinuity.
<table>
<tr><th>If</th><th>Then...</th></tr>
<tr><td>It is characterized by regional onlap above and truncation below</td><td>It is probably a sequence boundary</td></tr>
<tr><td>It is characterized by regional downlap</td><td>It is most likely a downlap surface</td></tr>
</table></td></tr>
</table>

Marking a seismic section, marking

The table below shows suggested colors for marking seismic sections during sequence analysis (after Vail, 1987).

Feature	Color
Reflection terminations and reflection patterns	Red
Downlap surfaces	Green
Transgressive surfaces	Blue
Sequence boundaries	Miscellaneous

Reflection terminations

The table below groups termination patterns by position with respect to a discontinuity.

Reflection Termination Point	Pattern	Associated Discontinuity
Above a discontinuity	Onlap	Sequence boundary (unconformity)
	Downlap	Downlap surface (condensed section)
Below a discontinuity	Truncation	Sequence boundary
	Toplap	Sequence boundary
	Apparent truncation	Downlap surface

Locating reflection terminations

Locating reflection termination is a matter of finding the patterns described in the table above. The figure below shows these patterns and the associated discontinuity surfaces. HST is highstand systems tract, LST is lowstand systems tract, and TST is transgressive systems tract.

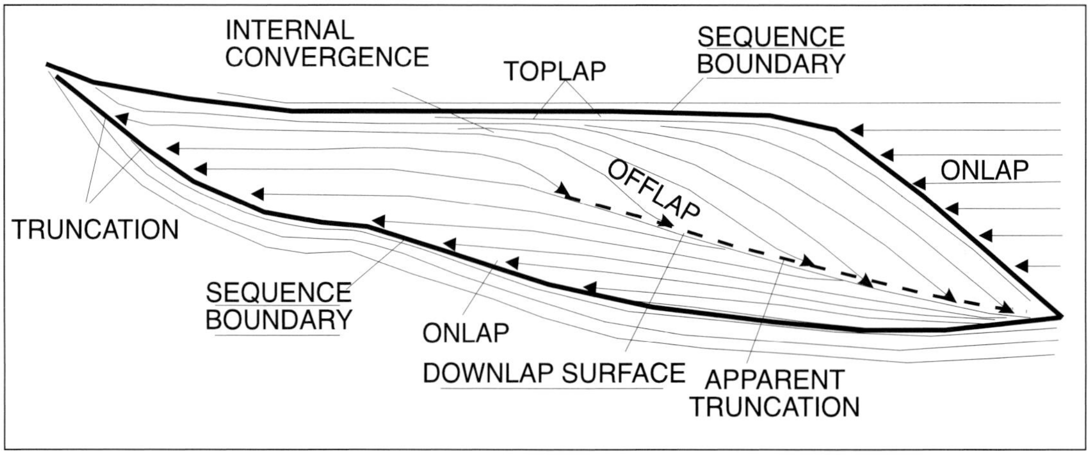

Figure 21–18. From Vail, 1987; courtesy AAPG.

Well Log Sequence Analysis

Introduction

After seismic sections have been analyzed for sequences, well logs are analyzed for sequences and systems tracts. This involves interpreting depositional lithofacies on logs using cuttings and cores and then identifying sequences and systems tracts from the interpreted logs. Stacking patterns displayed in cross sections and individual logs show accommodation space changes which help us identify sequence and systems tracts.

Procedure

The table below, modified from Vail (1987), outlines a suggested procedure for well log sequence analysis.

Step	Action
1	Interpret depositional lithofacies on logs using cores and cuttings to calibrate the log.
2	Estimate sequences and systems tracts from the interpreted lithofacies using regional cross sections with well and outcrop data.
3	Determine accommodation space changes from parasequence stacking patterns seen in well log cross sections (see below).
4	Check estimates of sequences and systems tracts: • Correlate between wells that have biostratigraphic–time correlations, well log marker-bed correlations, and the global sea cycle chart. • Correlate with seismic profiles.

Parasequence stacking patterns

Parasequences stack into three basic patterns as a result of the interaction of accommodation and rate of sediment supply:

- Progradational
- Retrogradational
- Aggradational

Parasequence stacking patterns (continued)

The diagram below shows these three stacking patterns.

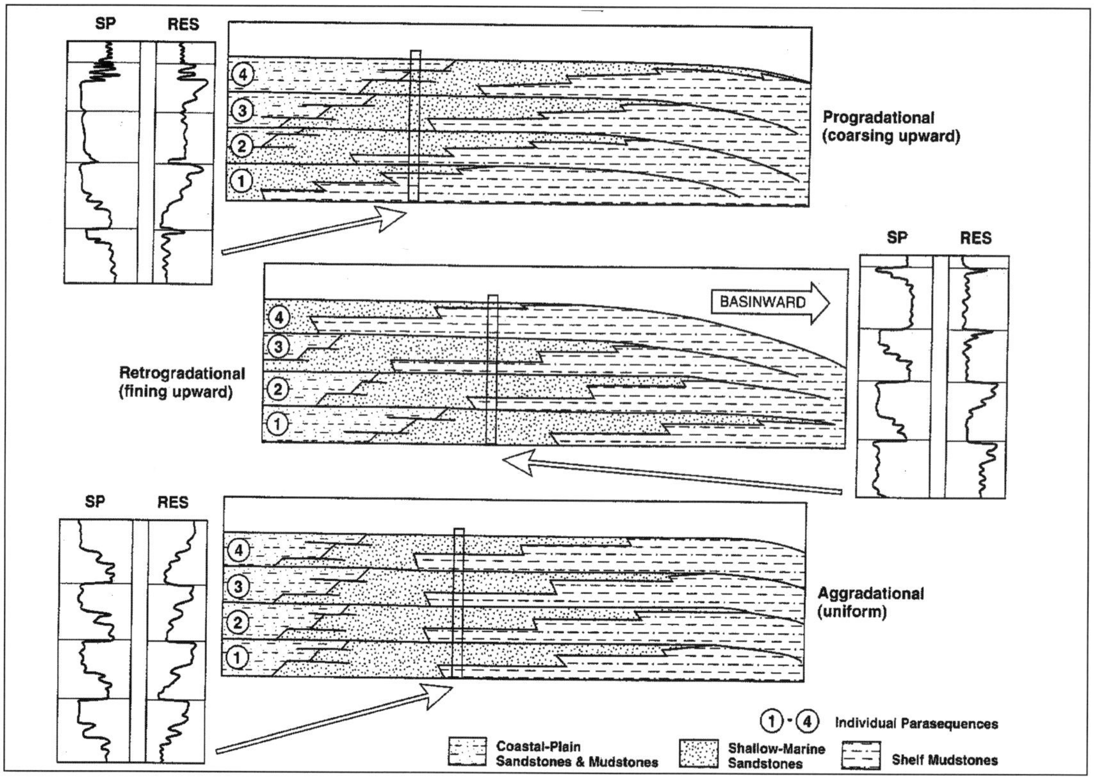

Figure 21–19. From Hyne, 1995; courtesy Tulsa Geological Society. Modified from Van Wagoner et al., 1990; courtesy AAPG.

Stacking patterns for systems tracts

Systems tracts often have characteristic parasequence stacking patterns. Stacking patterns of the basin-floor fan and slope fan, contained within the lowstand systems tract, are difficult to identify. The table below summarizes typical stacking patterns for the three systems tracts.

Systems Tract	Stacking Pattern
Lowstand • Basin-floor fan • Slope fan • Wedge	 Difficult to recognize Difficult to recognize Progradational
Transgressive	Retrogradational
Highstand • Early • Late	 Aggradational Progradational

Well Log Sequence Analysis, continued

Log patterns for systems tracts

The diagram below shows the characteristic parasequence stacking patterns for the highstand (HST), transgressive (TST), and lowstand (LST) systems tracts of a passive margin basin third-order depositional sequence.

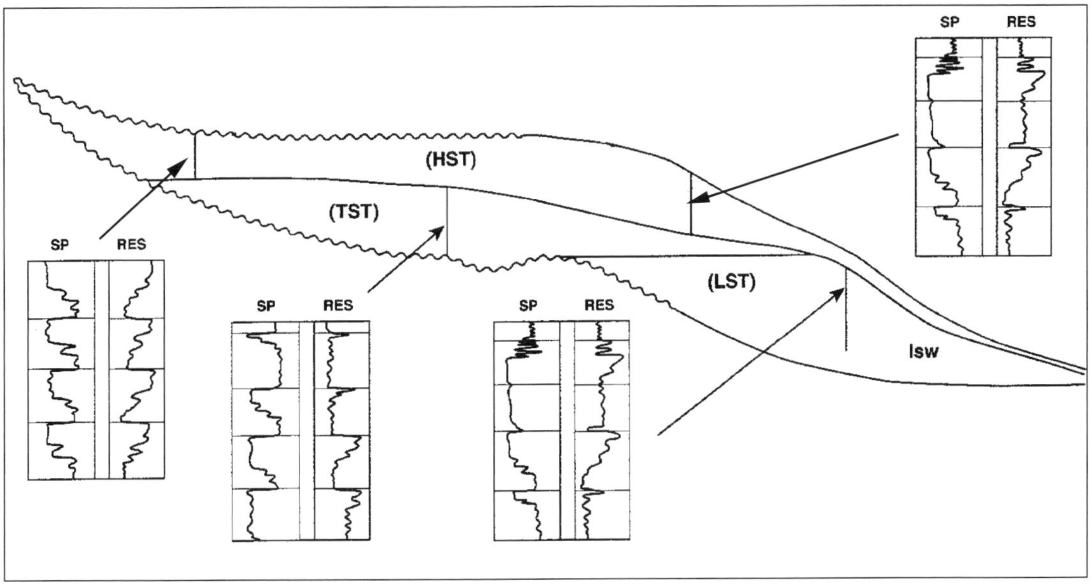

Figure 21–20. Modified from Hyne, 1995; courtesy Tulsa Geological Society.

LST example

The cross section below is from the Late Cenozoic of the Gulf of Mexico. It shows the well log responses of a lowstand systems tract (labeled as PGC, or prograding complex, on the cross section). Log A is completely basinal with a slope fan overlain by shingled turbidites. Logs B and C have deltaic and delta front sands, and midslope turbidite sands. Log D has a "classic" coarsening-upward pattern. Log E has incised valley sands.

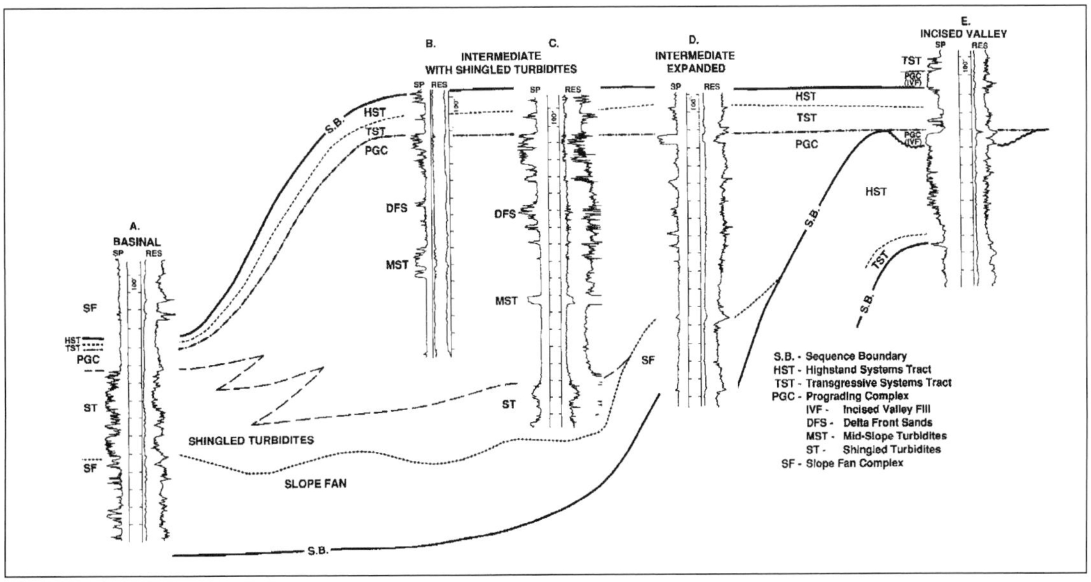

Figure 21–21. From Mitchum et al., 1993; courtesy AAPG.

Combining Well Log with Seismic Sequence Analysis

Introduction

By interpreting depositional sequences in the seismic and well log data separately, discontinuities are identified as objectively as possible on the seismic and log sections before they are tied together using the synthetic seismogram (Vail, 1987).

Objectives

After well logs and seismic sections have been analyzed for sequences, well log and seismic interpretations should be tied together by generating a synthetic seismogram from log information. There are two primary objectives to this step (Vail, 1987):

- To link well log depths to seismic section times.
- To develop an understanding of the causes of constructive and destructive interference patterns of individual wavelets originating from acoustic impedance contrasts.

Using synthetic seismograms

The composite synthetic seismic trace from a synthetic seismogram relates depth information from logs to seismic time. The plots of individual wavelets in a synthetic seismogram show how each impedance interface contributes to the individual reflections. Vail (1987) recommends that seismic sequence analysis and well log sequence analysis be started independently so that boundaries be interpreted as objectively as possible before they are tied together by a synthetic seismogram.

Below is an example of a synthetic seismogram from the Midland basin, Texas.

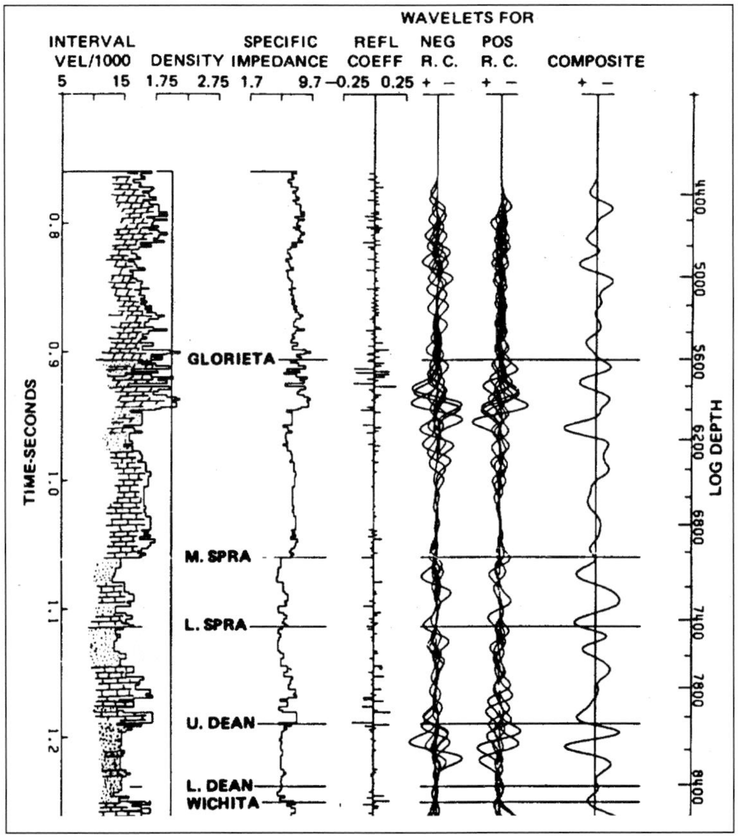

Figure 21–22. After Vail, 1987; courtesy AAPG.

Procedure

Follow this procedure from Vail (1987) to tie well log information to seismic data.

Step	Action
1	Generate a synthetic seismogram from log information (Figure 21–22) using the appropriate software or by asking an expert to create one.
2	Tie well log information to seismic data using the synthetic seismogram.
3	Adjust depositional sequence and systems tract boundaries to the best solution using the ties made in step 2.

Example of integrating synthetics

Synthetic seismograms, or synthetics, can be interactively tied to log, lithologic, and seismic data on geological workstations. The figure below illustrates an example from the Gulf of Suez basin. A wavelet trough forms at a sequence boundary (T55) overlain and sealed by anhydrite and salt. A pronounced wavelet peak forms on an underlying maximum flooding surface. The intervening sequence consists of a lobate deltaic fan formed during a relative highstand. The transgressive systems tract is thin to absent. The geometry of the fan is clear from the well log and seismic integration.

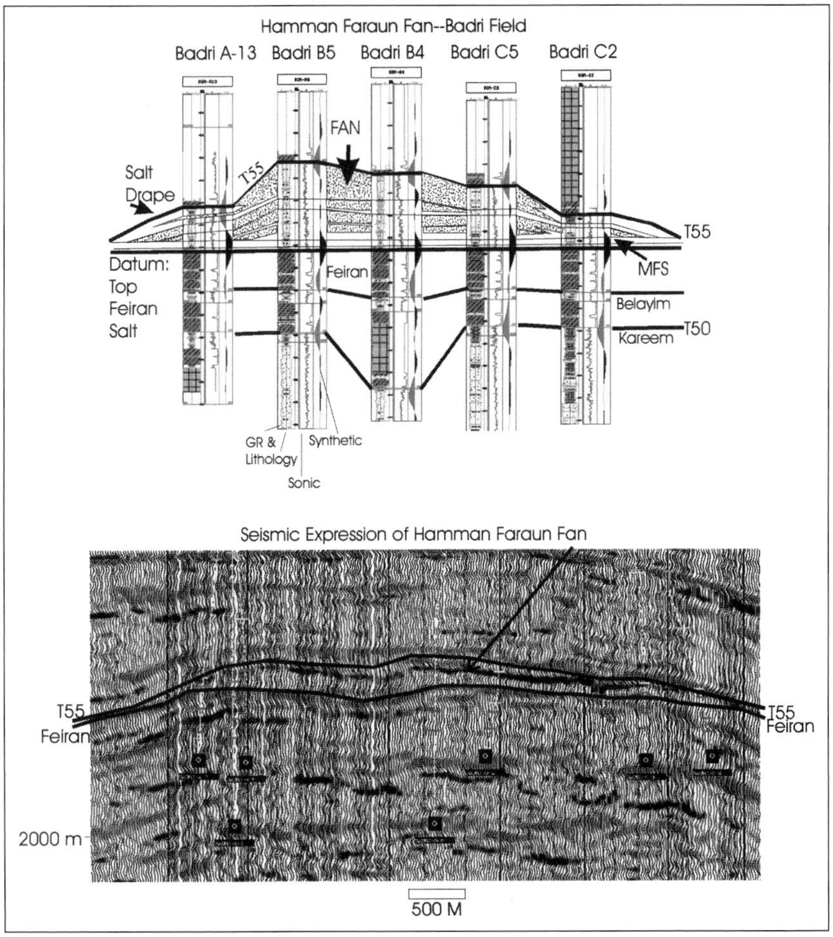

Figure 21–23. From Ramzy et al., 1996; courtesy Egyptian General Petroleum Corp.

Section D

Facies Analysis

Introduction

Seismic facies analysis is the geologic interpretation of seismic parameters as displayed in seismic sequences. Of these parameters, reflection pattern geometries are perhaps the most useful for calibration with lithofacies interpreted from well logs, cores, and cuttings.

In this section

This section contains the following topics.

Basics of Seismic Facies Analysis

Definition and purpose

Seismic facies are mappable, three dimensional seismic units composed of groups of reflections whose parameters differ from those of adjacent facies units" (Mitchum et al., 1977). Seismic facies analysis is the description and interpretation of seismic reflection parameters, such as configuration, continuity, amplitude, and frequency, within the stratigraphic framework of a depositional sequence. Its purpose is to determine all variations of seismic parameters within third-order sequences and their systems tracts in order to determine lateral lithofacies and fluid type changes (Vail, 1987).

Reflection parameters

There are five useful reflection parameters:

- Configuration (reflection geometry)
- Continuity
- Amplitude
- Frequency
- Interval velocity

Depositional environment, sediment source, and lithofacies can be interpreted by grouping these parameters into mappable, three-dimensional seismic facies (Bally, 1987). The table below (after Mitchum et al., 1977) summarizes the information obtained from each parameter.

Reflection Parameter	Geologic Interpretation
Configuration	• Bedding patterns • Depositional properties • Erosion and paleotopography • Fluid contacts
Continuity	• Lateral continuity of strata • Depositional processes
Amplitude	• Velocity–density contrasts of individual interfaces • Bed spacing • Bed thickness
Frequency	• Bed thickness • Fluid content
Interval velocity	• Lithofacies estimations • Porosity estimations • Fluid content

Basics of Seismic Facies Analysis, continued

Seismic facies analysis procedure

The table below outlines a procedure to analyze seismic facies from a grid of sections (vertical) of 2-D or 3-D seismic data (modified from Mitchum and Vail, 1977).

Step	Action
1	Divide each depositional sequence into seismic facies units on all seismic sections.
2	Describe the internal reflection configuration and terminations of each seismic facies unit, i.e., sigmoid, parallel, downlap.
3	Transfer seismic facies descriptions from seismic sections to a shot point map of each sequence.
4	Combine seismic facies distribution and thickness with the map distribution of any other diagnostic parameters, such as interval velocity or localized amplitude anomalies.
5	Integrate well and outcrop data with seismic facies distribution.
6	Interpret the seismic facies maps in terms of depositional settings such as marine or nonmarine, water depth, basin position, energy, transport direction, or any other depositional aspects.
7	Estimate lithology using depositional setting interpretation from step 6 and all available data.

Reflection Configuration Patterns

Groups of configuration patterns

Reflection configuration patterns can be divided into three groups:

- Parallel—including subparallel and divergent
- Discontinuous
- Prograding—caused by lateral accretion of strata

Parallel reflector patterns

Parallel reflections include subparallel, wavy, and divergent. Parallel, subparallel, and wavy reflectors suggest uniform depositional rates on a uniformly subsiding surface, such as a shelf or basin plain. Divergent reflectors suggest lateral variations in depositional rates or progressive tilting of a depositional surface. The figure below shows reflection configurations for this group.

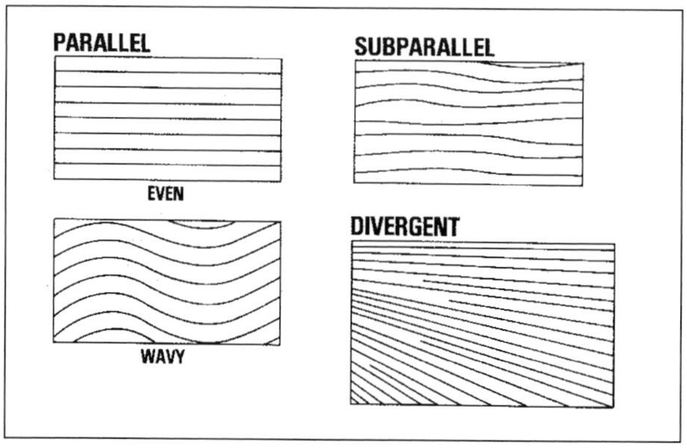

Figure 21–24. From Mitchum et al., 1977; courtesy AAPG.

Discontinuous reflector patterns

Five types of discontinuous reflector patterns that help interdepositional systems are shown in the figure below. Hummocky strata may be discontinuous point bars and crevasse splays. Chaotic reflectors suggest coarse-grained fluvial or turbidite channel fills. Contorted features may be shale-prone debris flows. Precise identification of depositional environments requires integration with other data.

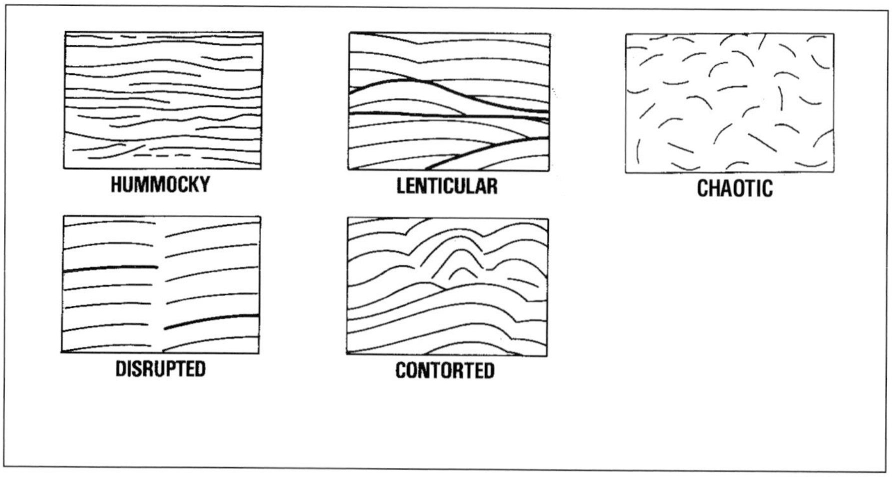

Figure 21–25. After Mitchum et al., 1977; courtesy AAPG.

Reflection Configuration Patterns, continued

Prograding reflector patterns

One of the most common depositional features observed in seismic sections are clinoforms manifested in a configuration pattern called *offlap.* Clinoforms are progradational strata that form through the progressive development of gently sloping surfaces. Paleowater depths can be interpreted from the height of prograding clinoforms. The diagram below shows prograding reflectors and their possible depositional significance.

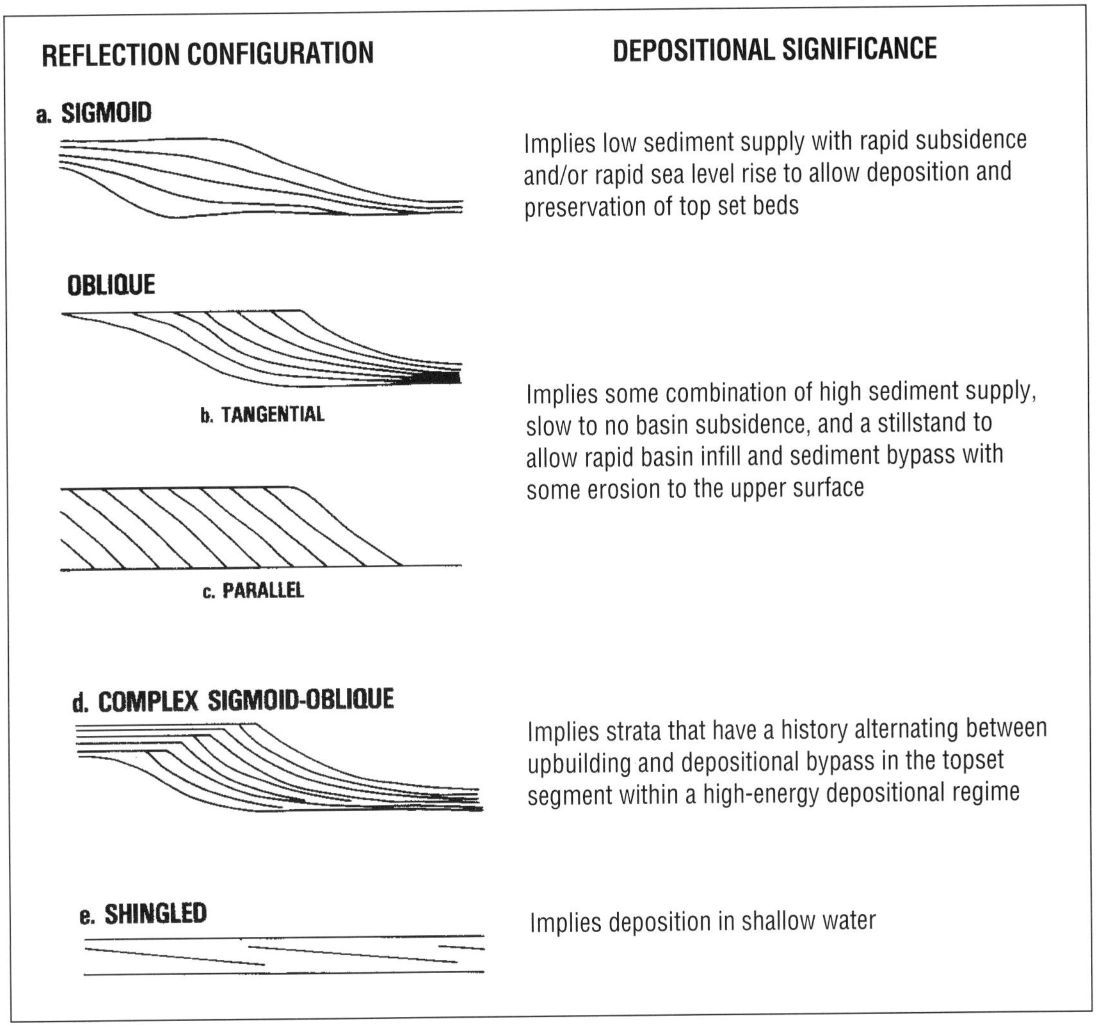
REFLECTION CONFIGURATION
DEPOSITIONAL SIGNIFICANCE
a. SIGMOID
Implies low sediment supply with rapid subsidence and/or rapid sea level rise to allow deposition and preservation of top set beds
OBLIQUE
b. TANGENTIAL
Implies some combination of high sediment supply, slow to no basin subsidence, and a stillstand to allow rapid basin infill and sediment bypass with some erosion to the upper surface
c. PARALLEL
d. COMPLEX SIGMOID-OBLIQUE
Implies strata that have a history alternating between upbuilding and depositional bypass in the topset segment within a high-energy depositional regime
e. SHINGLED
Implies deposition in shallow water

Figure 21–26. After Mitchum et al., 1977; courtesy AAPG.

Reflection Configuration Patterns, continued

Channel fill patterns

Channels are expressed in seismic sections as negative relief features truncating the underlying strata. Fill patterns are shown in the figure below.

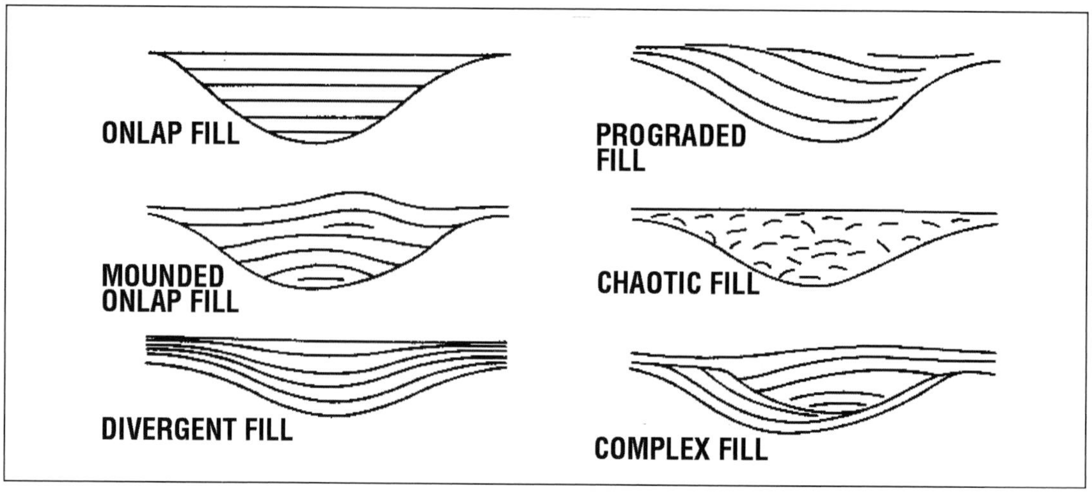

Figure 21–27. From Mitchum et al., 1977; courtesy AAPG.

Seismic Facies Mapping

Introduction

Seismic facies maps show the areal distribution of seismic facies and are useful when making lithofacies interpretations. The most common and useful parameters to be mapped are seismic reflection patterns and isochrons (thickness measured in seconds of two-way time).

Procedure

The table below outlines a suggested procedure for mapping seismic facies.

Step	Action
1	Identify sequences that contain potential traps, seal rocks, reservoir rocks, or source rocks.
2	Make regional seismic reflection pattern maps and isochron maps of those sequences. If possible, make maps of lowstand, transgressive, and highstand systems tracts.

Example

The figure below contains examples of a seismic facies map, an isochron map, and seismic line A–Á (location shown on maps).

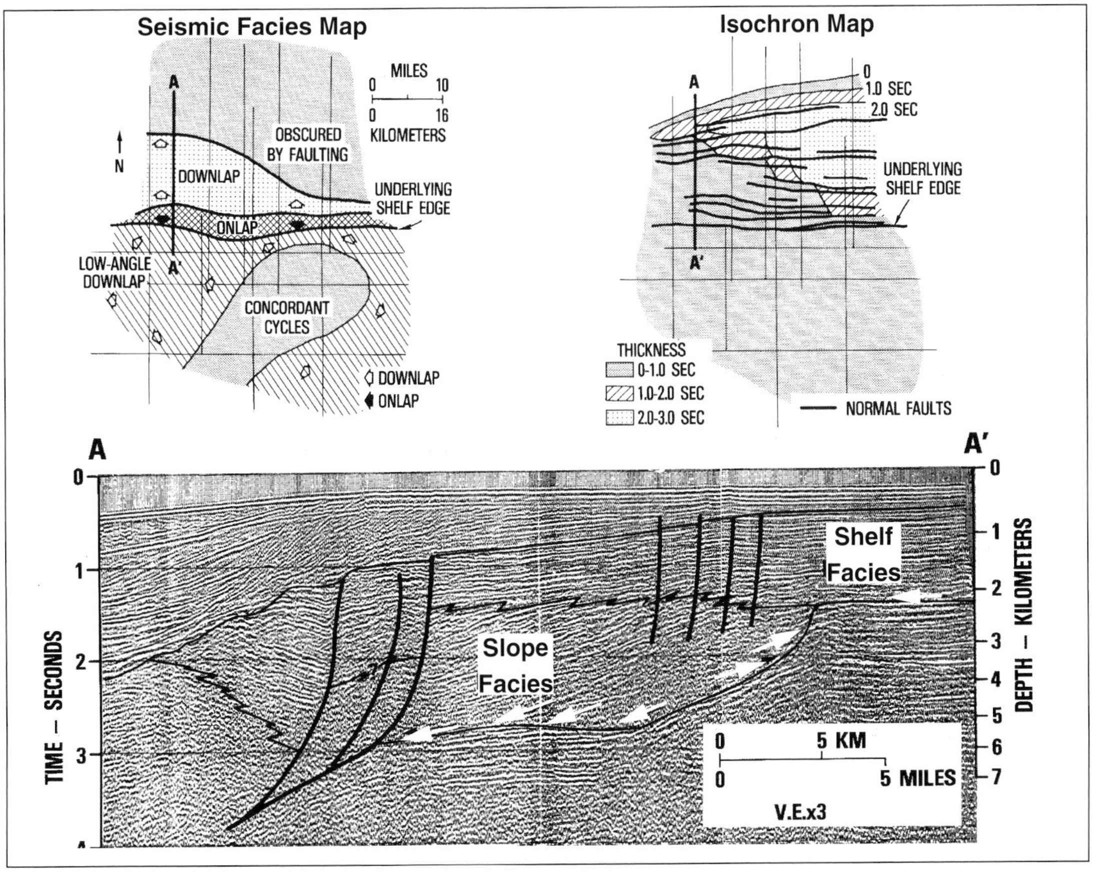

Figure 21–28. Modified from Mitchum and Vail, 1977; courtesy AAPG.

Analyzing Individual Reflectors

Introduction

We can enhance our recognition of stratigraphic features by using seismic data attributes, reflection strength, coherence, and instantaneous phase. These attributes are well suited to stratigraphic interpretation and are an effective interpretive tool when displayed in map view.

Seismic data attributes

Seismic data attributes and their use in seismic facies analysis are listed in the following table.

Attribute	Use
Reflection strength	• Lithologic variation • Facies mapping • Porosity prediction • Thin-bed analysis • Character correlation
Instantaneous phase	• Reflector configuration • Reflector continuity • Reflector terminations
3-D coherence	• Facies mapping • Character correlation • Fault identification • Paleogeomorphology

Reflection strength

Reflection strength is a measure of the total energy of a reflection, manifested in reflection amplitude. It is independent of phase. Reflection strength is also referred to as the instantaneous amplitude, or envelope amplitude. Analysis within specific reflectors can give us clues to changes in lithology or porosity.

Instantaneous phase

Instantaneous phase is an amplitude-independent attribute that highlights reflector continuity. It is useful for enhancing reflector terminations, particularly in areas with weak, low-amplitude events. Reflector terminations appear much clearer, which allows for an easier understanding of the geometry of individual packages of reflectors.

3-D coherence

Three-dimensional coherence is a measure of the similarity of neighboring seismic traces in 3-D data. It is useful for mapping paleogeomorphology and faults (Bahorich et al., 1995).

The map below is a 3-D coherency slice of a Miocene channel complex in the Nile Delta, Egypt.

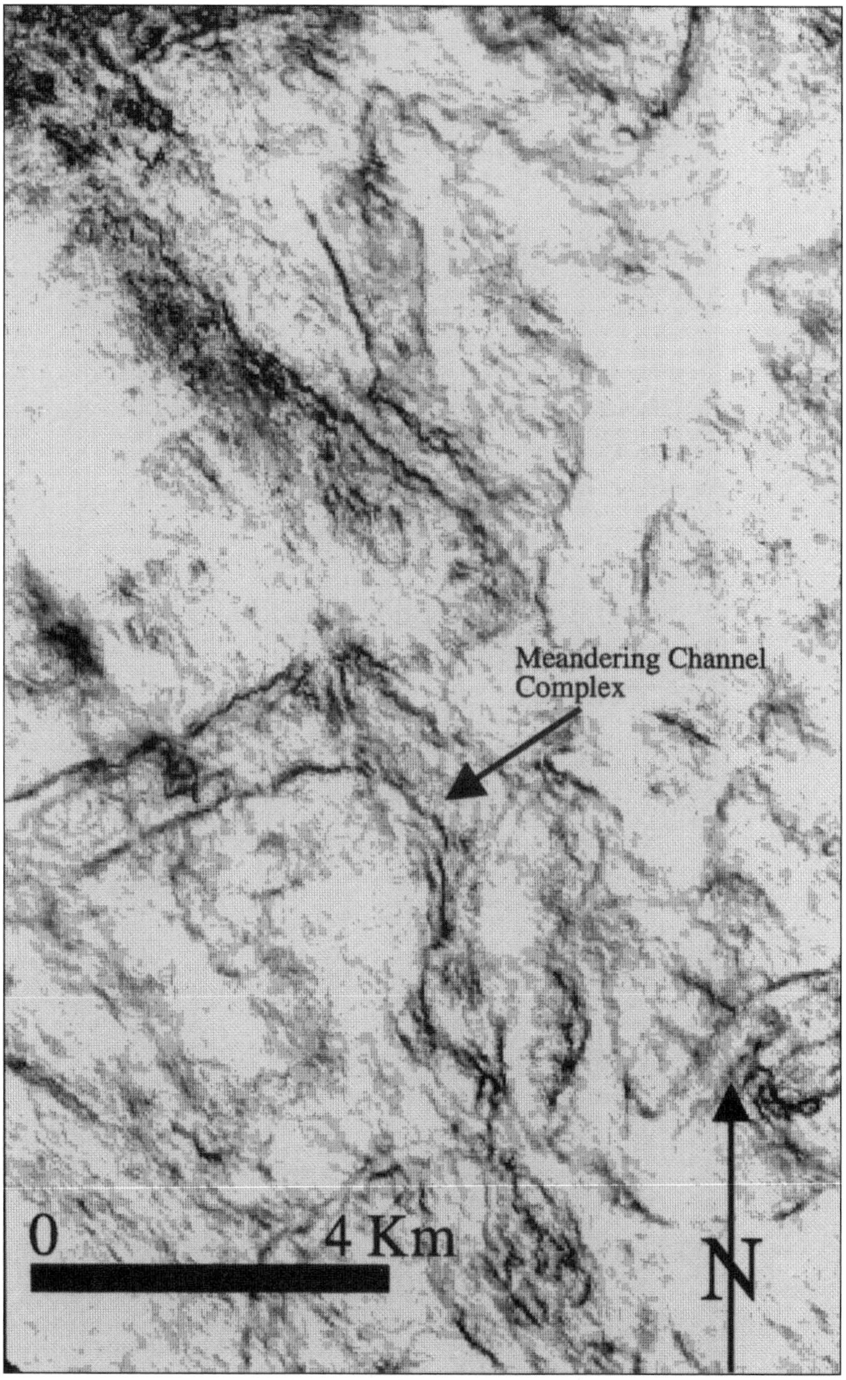

Figure 21–29. From Wescott and Boucher, 1998; courtesy AAPG.

Techniques for Enhancing Seismic Facies Analysis

Introduction

Additional techniques for improving resolution and enhancing interpretations of seismic facies include the following:

- Seismic forward modeling
- Changing display scale for seismic data
- Changing display type for seismic data
- Using 3-D seismic displays

Seismic forward modeling

Forward modeling begins with a model in depth and coverts it to time. Put another way, forward modeling takes a 2-D or 3-D geological model and converts it to a simulated seismic section. The simulated seismic section can be compared to the actual seismic data. The geological model is adjusted until there is a match.

Forward modeling has three purposes (Vail, 1987):

- Interpret stratigraphy and fluid composition at or near the limits of seismic resolution by waveform analysis.
- Simulate a geologic cross section seismically, showing stratal surfaces and impedance contrasts.
- Simulate reflection patterns seen in seismic sections by calculating stratal patterns from rates of subsidence, eustasy, and sediment supply.

Changing display scale

Choice of display scale can be critical in detecting subtle features in seismic data. Minute changes in dip are often difficult to detect on wiggle trace displays plotted at traditional scales. When such displays are horizontally compressed and vertically expanded, stratigraphic changes are magnified accordingly and become more visible. Unfortunately, structural changes are also magnified. This effect can be attenuated by flattening on an interpreted structural horizon.

Changing display type

Choice of display type can also be critical in detecting subtle features in seismic data. Two types that help in seismic facies analysis are horizontally compressed wiggle displays and color amplitude displays. Horizontally compressed wiggle displays also reduce the trace excursion or amplitude of the reflections, making important changes in reflectivity more difficult to discern. Color amplitude displays retain amplitude fidelity regardless of scale and are particularly useful when viewing horizontally compressed, flattened displays. These are often helpful in stratigraphic interpretation of subtle features.

3-D seismic displays

For stratigraphic interpretations, 3-D seismic data has a significant advantage over standard 2-D data because it images the subsurface at a much closer spacing, delineating very subtle changes in reflectors. The ability to map channels, fan lobes, pinch-outs, and other features is greatly enhanced. Amplitude, phase, and frequency can be mapped aerially in considerable detail, resulting in striking visual images of subsurface stratigraphic features. Horizon-based amplitude extractions are one of the most routinely used 3-D seismic display types. Changes in amplitude along a reflector may indicate changes in lithology, porosity, or fluid saturation. For additional details, see Brown (1999).

Example: Compressing vertical scale

Older-vintage 2-D seismic data are often difficult to interpret for subtle stratigraphic changes. The figure below, depicting the northern Powder River basin, Wyoming, shows the impact of compressing seismic sections on a workstation. A 6.4-km, 32-m-deep valley network incised in the Muddy Formation (Lower Cretaceous) is difficult to see on the original data display. However, by compressing the display, the incised valley fill becomes easier to recognize.

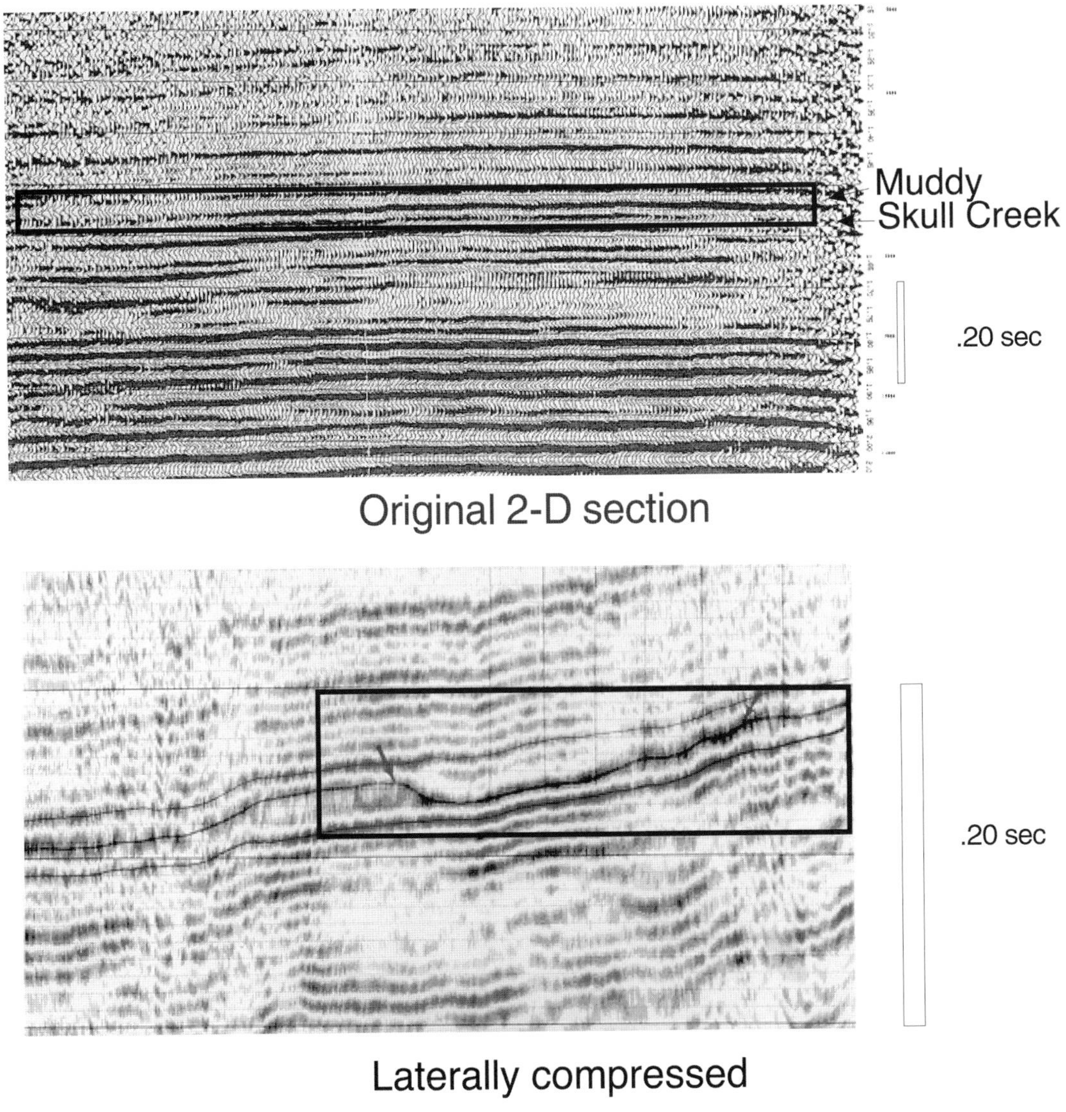

Figure 21–30. Unpublished data courtesy BP-Amoco.

Analyzing Lithofacies

Introduction

Lithofacies are interpreted from well data and seismic facies descriptions. Lithofacies interpretations should be based on all available well and outcrop data and on seismic facies interpretations.

Procedure

Below is a suggested procedure for analyzing lithofacies.

Step	Action
1	Learn as much as possible about the regional geology from well and outcrop control.
2	Describe cores and cuttings from sequences of interest. Besides describing lithology, grain size, and sedimentary structures, also describe pore geometry.
3	Calibrate core and cuttings descriptions to well logs and outcrops. Annotate logs with porosity and permeability data (if available) from potential reservoir and seal intervals.
4	Integrate calibrated well logs into well log cross sections constructed during well log sequence analysis.
5	Interpret depositional environments of lithofacies of depositional sequences using log cross sections and seismic sections with seismic facies analyses.

Petrophysical Analysis of Lithofacies

Introduction

The reservoir or seal quality of a rock is established soon after deposition. It is strongly influenced by its environment of deposition. Diagenesis can alter or completely change the original pore space of a rock, especially for carbonates. However, if the original pore space is not altered too much, then a relationship exists between lithofacies and reservoir- or seal-quality rocks that we can use when prospecting for stratigraphic traps. A petrophysical analysis of the lithofacies of a rock section in a target area can help determine if such a relationship exists.

Procedure

After lithofacies analysis, a careful petrophysical analysis of shows and production should be made and compared to lithofacies distribution. The table below suggests a procedure for petrophysical analysis.

Step	Action
1	Gather all available fluid data regarding production, shows, and pressures from prospective intervals.
2	On structural cross sections, plot intervals that ... • Were perforated • Had DSTs • Had RSTs • Had mud log shows Annotate the intervals with the results.
3	Divide potential reservoir units on the cross sections into intervals of similar petrophysical character (flow units) using log data and, if available, porosity–permeability data. Categorize each flow unit by port type as mega-, macro-, meso-, or microporous.
4	Calculate water saturation (S_w) of intervals that ... • Are productive • Had shows • Are potential reservoirs Annotate the log intervals with S_w values.
5	Estimate the height above free water for zones that appear to have oil or gas.
6	Analyze the fluid data in the context of the petrophysical data. • Do S_w values, shows, and fluid pressures make sense in context with other geological data, including hydrocarbon column height? • Do the shows or S_w values indicate the presence of an updip or downdip trap?
7	Determine whether a relationship exists between the development of reservoir-quality rocks, seal-quality rocks, and lithofacies that can be used to predict location and economic viability of prospective traps.

Example: Calibrating logs to cores and shows

Posting core porosity, permeability, and pore throat radius (r_{35}) data directly on wireline logs next to lithofacies descriptions and show data helps us decide about exploitation for stratigraphic traps. In the figure below, the live oil stain in macroporous strata indicates the direction to move updip. The only macroporous strata present is within an algal mound facies developed in this parasequences at relative highstand. Microporous dolomites comprising the lower portions of the parasequences have poor reservoir characteristics, despite high porosity readings on the logs. Thus, the target of interest is the highstand mound facies.

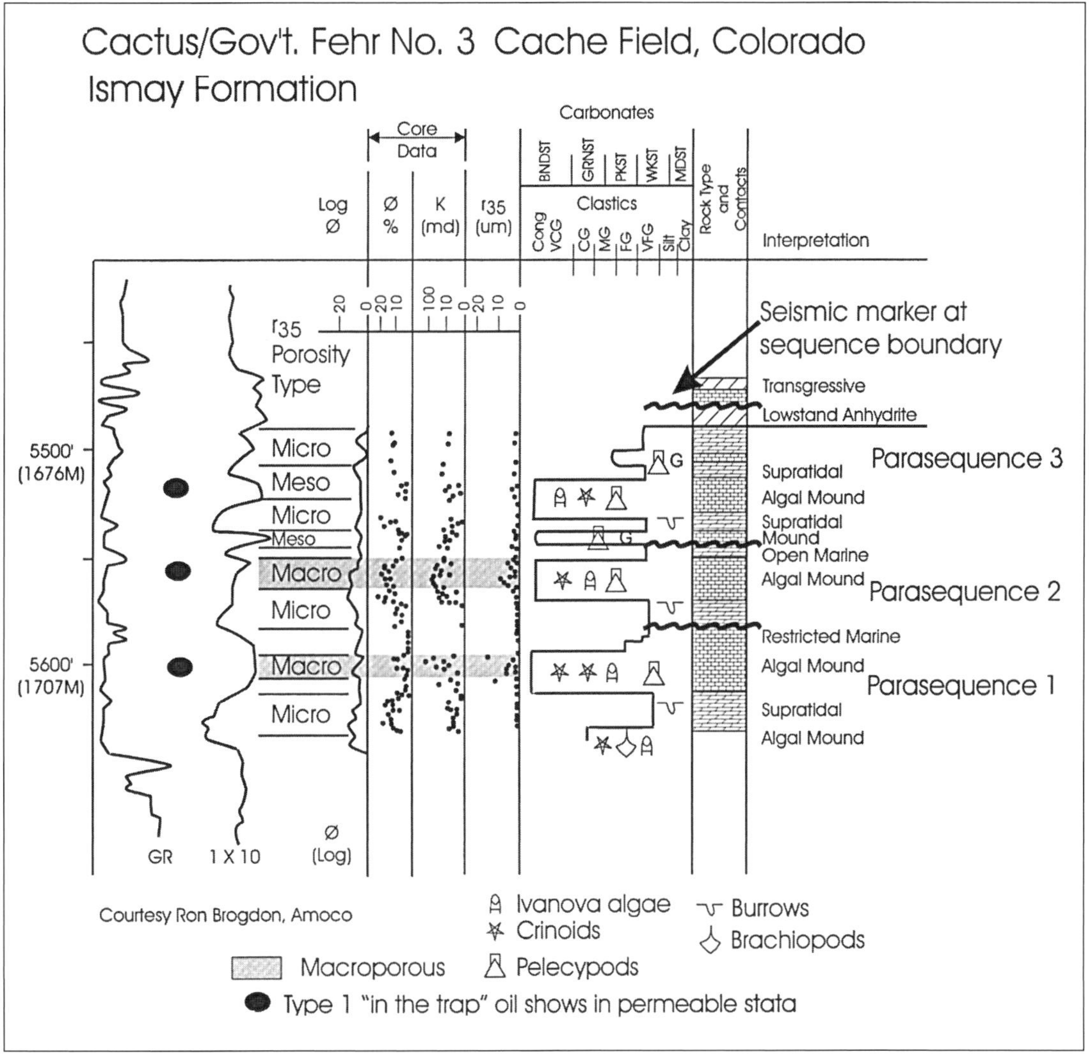

Figure 21–31.

Example: Using pressures

Reservoir scale discontinuities often cannot be detected by primary trapping geometries from sequence stratigraphy alone. Within channel systems of the Lower Cretaceous Mannville Group (Alberta, Canada), fluids distributions may be complex. High-resolution definition of the discrete traps may be possible only by integrating more data.

The figure to the right shows two distinct pressure regimes coinciding with discrete channel systems, delineated with pressure–depth plots. For additional information, refer to Dahlberg (1982).

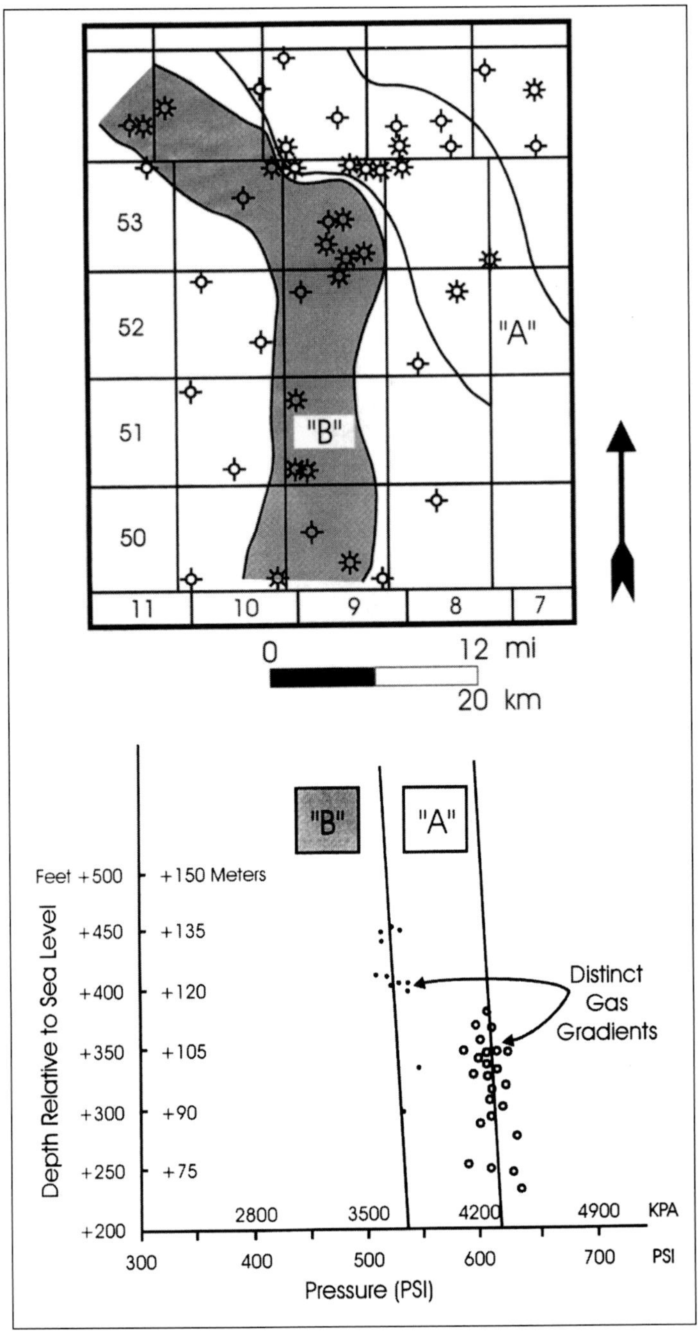

Figure 21–32. From Putnam and Oliver, 1980; courtesy Canadian Society of Petroleum Geologists. Map courtesy Eric Dahlberg.

Section E
Basin-Fill and Trap Analysis

Introduction

A whole basin or part of a basin can be analyzed for stratigraphic trap potential using the sequence stratigraphy approach. Basin-fill analysis is looking for stratigraphic or combination traps by combining paleogeography with the results of the geometric and facies analysis.

In this section

This section contains the following topics.

Procedure for Basin-Fill Analysis

Objective

The objective of basin-fill analysis is to integrate sequence stratigraphy, geometrical analysis, seismic facies analysis, and lithofacies analysis to produce paleogeographic maps of depositional sequences.

Procedure

Below is a suggested procedure for basin-fill analysis.

Step	Action
1	Make a chronostratigraphic chart for the basin.
2	Combine sequence stratigraphic interpretations from seismic sections with sequence stratigraphic interpretations from well log cross sections.
3	Make paleogeographic maps of depositional sequences.
4	Identify the best locations for traps using a combination of paleogeography and sequence stratigraphy.

Chronostratigraphic charts

A chronostratigraphic chart is a correlation chart with geologic time as the Y-axis and distance across the area of interest as the X-axis. A dip-oriented chronostratigraphic chart should be made. But we also should consider making strike-oriented chronostratigraphic charts, depending on the complexity of the stratigraphic section. A chronostratigraphic chart shows the following (Mitchum and Vail, 1977):

- Apparent geologic time of each sequence and time gaps between sequences
- Relationships of sequences to bounding unconformities, highlighting areas of onlap, downlap, toplap, and truncation
- Relationships and correlation of parasequences to a sequence
- Distribution of facies

Chronostratigraphic charts aid in stratigraphic mapping by showing facies relationships across the basin in terms of time so that paleogeographic maps can be made. They are also useful for structural analysis.

Procedure for Basin-Fill Analysis, continued

Chronostratigraphic charts (continued)

Below is an example of a chronostratigraphic chart (A) correlated with a chart showing relative sea level changes (B).

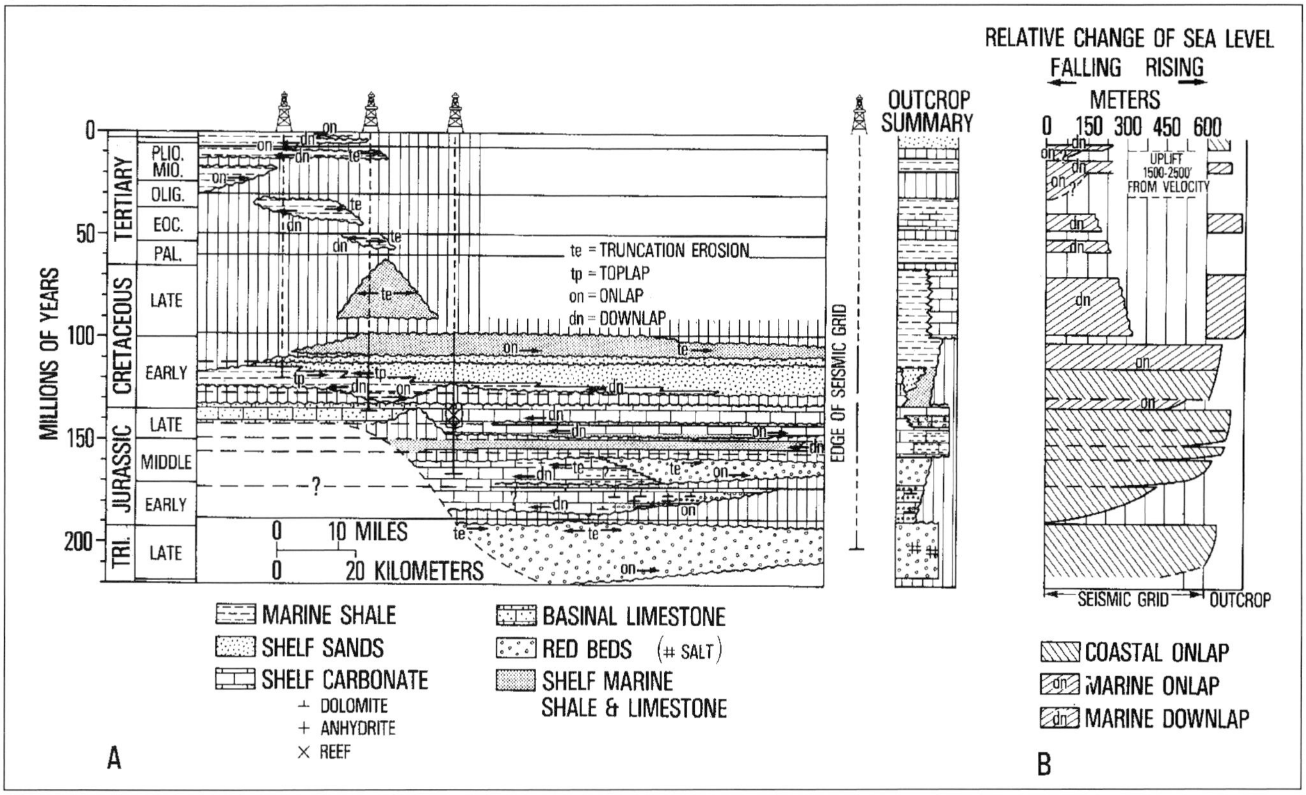

Figure 21–33. From Mitchum and Vail, 1977; courtesy AAPG.

Combining well and seismic data

Combining well and seismic data is simple once the correlation between the two is established. Synthetic seismograms establish these correlations. By combining lithofacies with seismic facies, stronger interpretations of the sedimentary section can be made away from well control. Seismic facies allow accurate correlation of lithofacies between wells. Lithofacies allow more detailed interpretation of seismic parameters, such as reflection patterns.

Mapping Paleogeography

Introduction

Paleogeographic maps are the end product of the sequence stratigraphic analysis. Favorable sites for deposition of reservoir, seal, and source rocks can be ascertained from paleogeographic maps.

Procedure

The table below outlines a procedure for making paleogeographic maps.

Step	Action
1	With objectives in mind, choose intervals to map. Is the target within one depositional sequence? Is the target the entire section?
2	Choose the level of detail. Do you need to map the paleogeography at the level of a depositional sequence or a systems tract?
3	Construct paleogeographic maps using all available information.

Example

Below is a seismic facies map and the corresponding paleogeographic map of the Middle Miocene Taranaki basin, offshore western New Zealand. The paleogeographic map depicts lithofacies and thicknesses in two-way time.

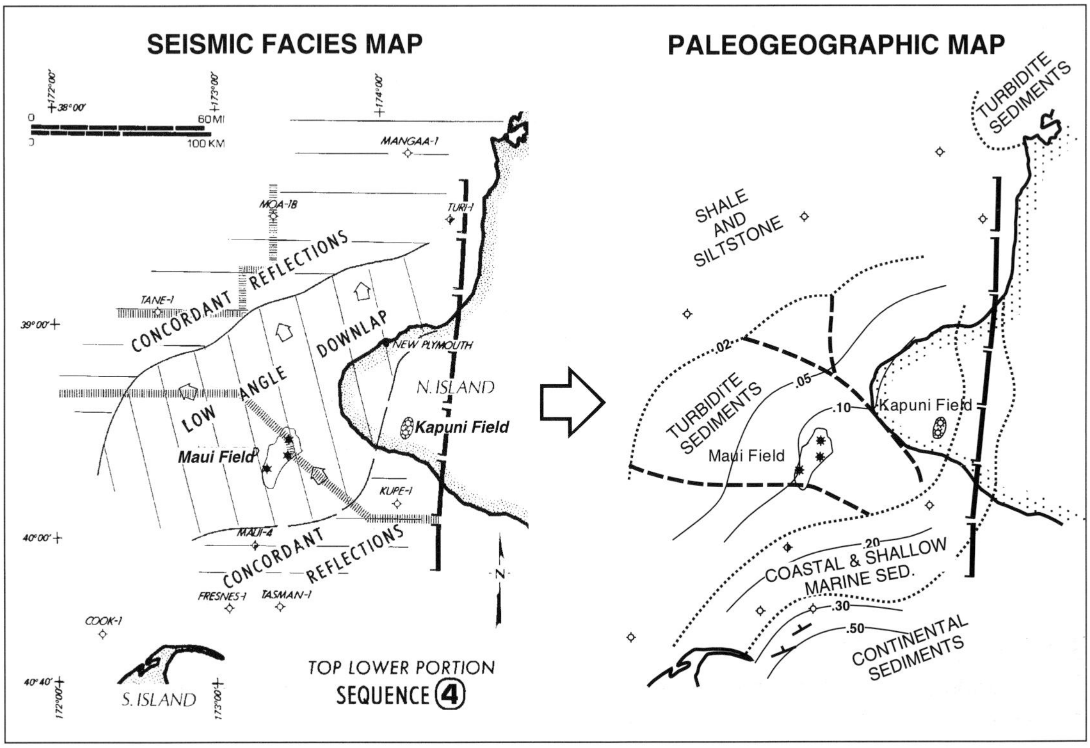

Figure 21–34. From Bally, 1987; courtesy AAPG.

Mapping Unconformities

Introduction

Mapping unconformities (sequence boundaries) is part of an effective exploration effort. Facies, porosity systems, and hydrocarbon shows are evaluated in context with an unconformity surface to predict trap location. Traps can be located above (onlap traps) or below (truncation traps) the unconformity. Seals, reservoir-quality rocks, and shows should be evaluated in terms of their relationship to the unconformity (see Dolson et al., 1994).

Procedure: Mapping unconformities

Follow these suggested steps to map unconformities for prospects.

Step	Action
1	Map subcrop and supercrop lithology and formations.
2	Make an isopach map from the unconformity to a flat datum above or below the unconformity to define paleotopography or paleostructure (see Figure 21–35).
3	Identify the best locations for truncation or onlap traps on the basis of the location seal and reservoir-quality rocks.

Making isopachs

The diagrammatic cross section below shows how to isopach above and below an unconformity. For more explanation, see Busch (1974).

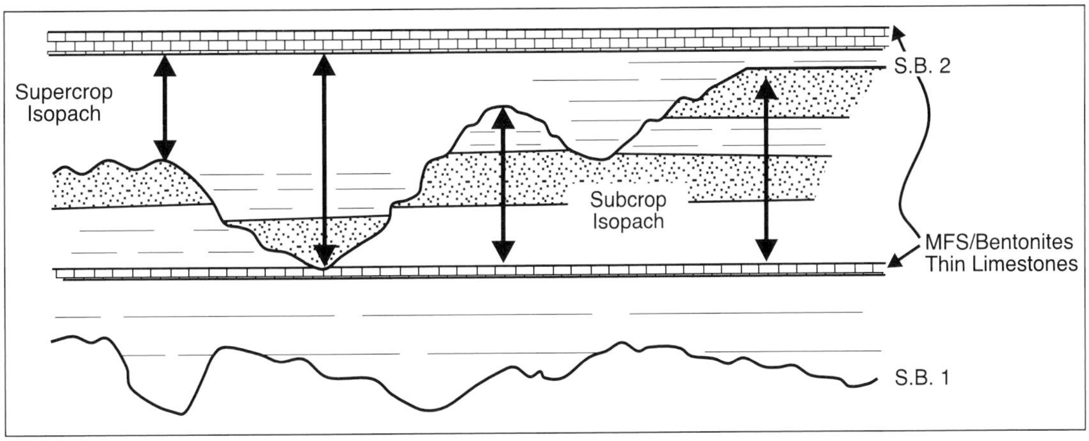

Figure 21–35.

Subcrop and facies mapping example

The Lower Cretaceous Cutbank Sandstone is the largest valley-fill trap in the Rocky Mountains (180 million BOE recoverable) (Dolson et al., 1993). The trap (illustrated below) is a combination valley wall and fossil oil–water contact trap. In this example, a flat datum within the Jurassic Sawtooth Formation was picked as the lowermost datum. Where the Sawtooth Formation is absent by onlap, the erosional top of the Mississippian was used, introducing some error on a local scale. "Thicks" are generally paleohills, and "thins" are incised valleys, although the "thick" to the west of the field is also caused by syndepositional westward thickening of the Jurassic section.

Subcrop and facies mapping example (continued)

Below are subcrop isopach and formation/lithology maps and a cross section whose location is shown on the isopach map. Dashed and hachured areas are shale; stippled areas are sandstone. The arrows on cross section A-A' show the subcrop isopach interval. The north–south trending isopach thin and shaded area on the maps shows the location of the giant Cutbank field.

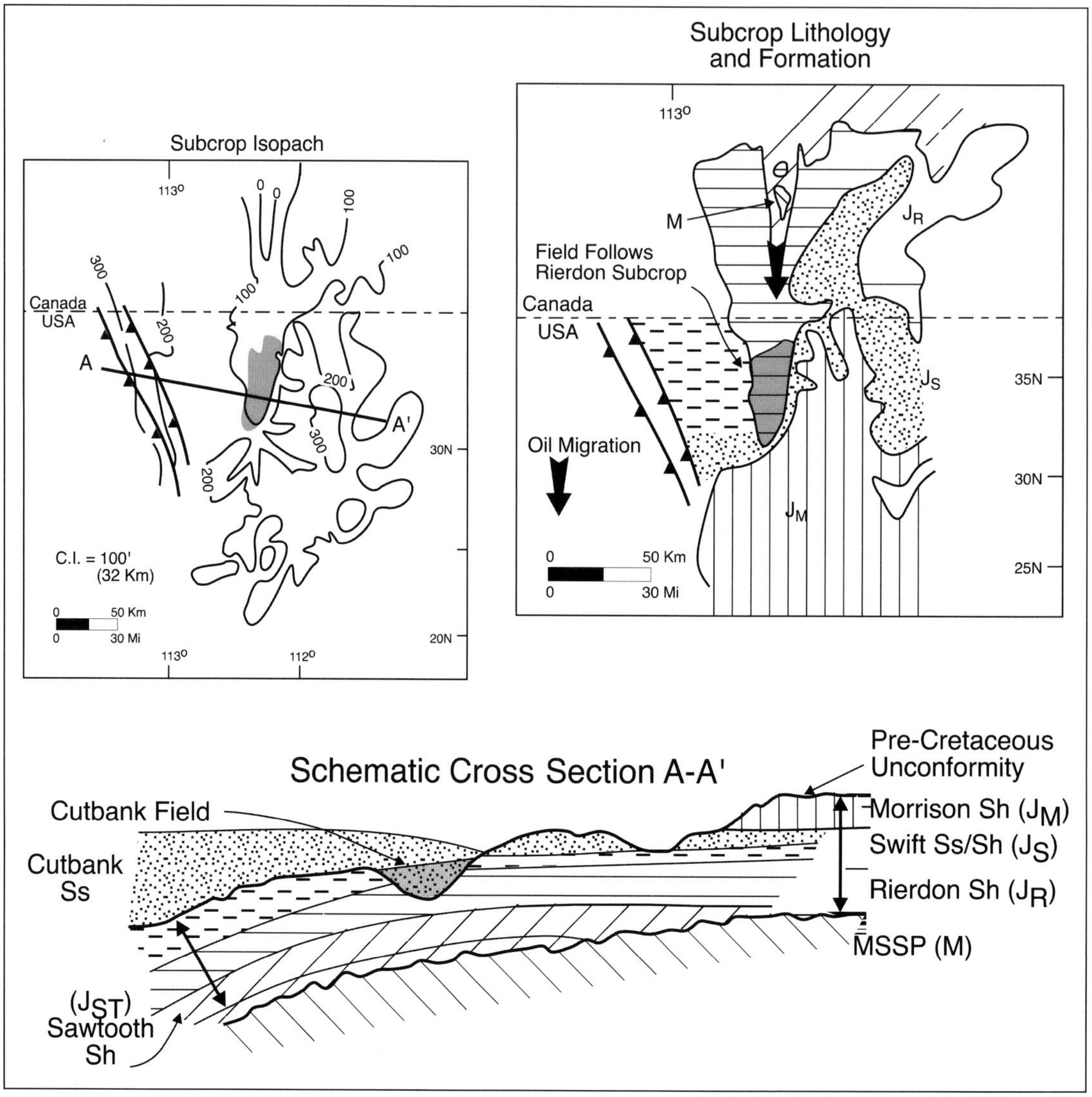

Figure 21–36. Dolson et al., 1993; courtesy Mountain Geologist.

Using subcrop maps to analyze seals

The subcrop lithology and formation map in Figure 21–36 illustrates where regional bottom and lateral seals are located. The trap is found where the porous Cutbank Sandstone abuts impermeable Jurassic shales. Where the Cutbank Sandstone abuts the permeable Swift Sandstone, leakage occurs updip. Oil migrates into the Cutbank where the valley bevels northward into a migration path at the top of the Mississippian strata.

Mapping Unconformities, continued

Using subcrop maps to predict valley fill

Subcrop maps also help us predict lithologic content of the supercropping valley networks. In the example above, fine-grained sandstone and shale entered the Cutbank system from the east and south from eroding hills comprised of fine-grained Morrison and Swift strata. Coarse-grained gravels are confined exclusively to the main alluvial-fan system that eroded Paleozoic strata to the west.

In the Muddy Formation of the Western Interior of the United States, many shale-filled valleys occur where local tributaries have only subcropping Skull Creek Shale for a provenance. These valleys can form seals for subcropping reservoirs (Dolson et al., 1991; Dolson and Muller, 1994). Within deep basins, where the location of coarse gravels may be a primary reason to retain or create porosity, accurate regional reconstructions of erosional networks and their provenance areas are a must (Putnam and Oliver, 1980).

If the sequences are thick enough to image, chaotic seismic signatures within the valley may also suggest reservoir fill; smooth, parallel reflectors suggest shale fill.

Analyzing Depositional Sequences for Traps

Introduction

We can reasonably predict the location of stratigraphic or combination traps using the cross sections, seismic sections, and maps generated during an analysis of the seismic stratigraphy of a basin. This is especially true in basins containing oil or gas traps that can be used as analogs. Sequence stratigraphy, interpreted from seismic, well, and outcrop data, is an effective concept for assessing the quality and location of source, seal, and reservoir rocks. However, most researchers caution against blindly applying published sequence stratigraphic models (Handford and Loucks, 1993; Weimer and Posamentier, 1993). Exxon workers (Van Wagoner, 1990; Sarg, 1988) made assumptions in the models they developed, mainly based on Gulf Coast geology, that might not have universal application. Any model of sequence stratigraphy used for exploration purposes should be based on local geology. Locally based models make more effective exploration tools.

Procedure

Analyzing sequences for stratigraphic or combination traps is simply looking for stratigraphic changes, such as updip pinch-outs of rocks with reservoir potential or mounds of reservoir-quality rocks, in the context of a depositional sequence. Knowing where the target interval and area are within a depositional sequence gives us the ability to predict the presence of certain trap types. Follow the procedure outlined below to predict the location of traps within a sequence.

Step	Action
1	Using seismic lines and/or log cross sections, determine the systems tract type for intervals of interest, i.e., lowstand, transgressive, or highstand.
2	Identify potential seal- and reservoir-quality rocks using seismic facies and lithofacies shown on maps and cross sections.
3	In areas with juxtaposed reservoir- and seal-quality rocks, look for trapping geometries.

Transgressive and highstand systems tracts

Accommodation rates are high during transgressive–early highstand episodes of sea level, forming thick reservoirs of excellent quality. Shales in the upper transgressive systems tract and lower highstand systems tract are generally high-quality seals. Updip and bottom seals can be a problem for stratigraphic traps. Unconformity truncations, onlapping sands, and mounded shoreline sands form stratigraphic traps. Siliciclastics of the late highstand generally are poor reservoirs. Excellent source rocks are associated with the starved portion of the transgressive and early highstand systems tracts. Coals and terrestrial source rocks also are associated with the transgressive and early highstand systems tracts.

Lowstand systems tracts

During lowstands of sea level, sedimentation rates are high. Therefore, organic source potential is generally low. Where depositional sites are euxinic, source potential is higher. Even so, total organic carbon rarely exceeds 1% (Vail, 1987). Reservoir sands can be thick because they tend to aggrade as well as prograde.

Analyzing Depositional Sequences for Traps, continued

Lowstand systems tract traps

The diagrammatic cross section that follows and the corresponding table describe six potential trap types associated with the lowstand systems tract.

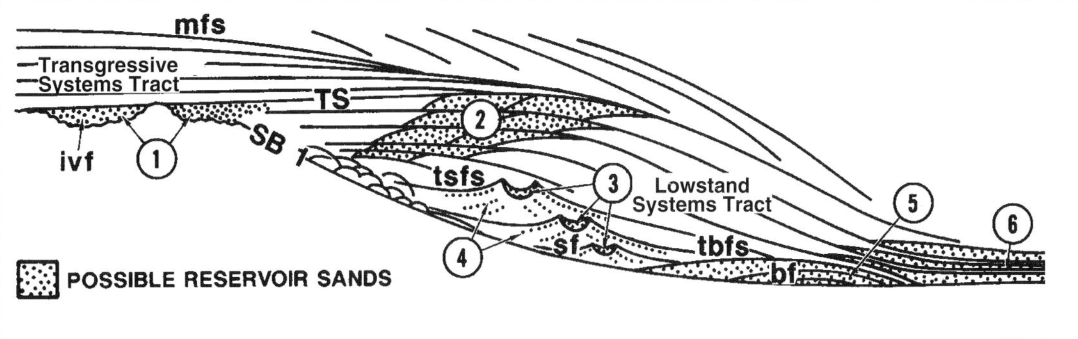

Figure 21–37. From Vail, 1987; courtesy AAPG.

No.	Facies	Trap Description
1	Incised valley sands	Excellent reservoirs. Traps form where valley incises underlying coastal plain shales.
2	Coastal belt sands	Good reservoirs, commonly very thick. Rollover traps common. Strat traps depend on undip seal. If underlying unit is impermeable, they are present where onlapping sands pinch out below preceding shoreline break.
3	Channel/overbank channel sands	Excellent reservoirs. Seal provided by toes of overlying lowstand wedge.
4	Overbank sands	Poor reservoirs. Seal provided by toes of overlying lowstand wedge.
5	Mounded basin floor fan sands	Sands thin or pinchout over contemporaneous highs. Strat traps depend on top and bottom seal. Overlying slope fan not a good seal. Best traps pinch out in a basinward direction.
6	Shingled toe of lowstand prograding wedge sands	Good reservoirs. In sandy systems, basin floor fans are shingled and pinch out between the shale toes of lowstand prograding wedge.

Analyzing Depositional Sequences for Traps, continued

Plays in different margin types

Different margin types in basins have different play types determined by the geometry and history of the margin. The figure below shows play types for shelf-edge and ramp margins.

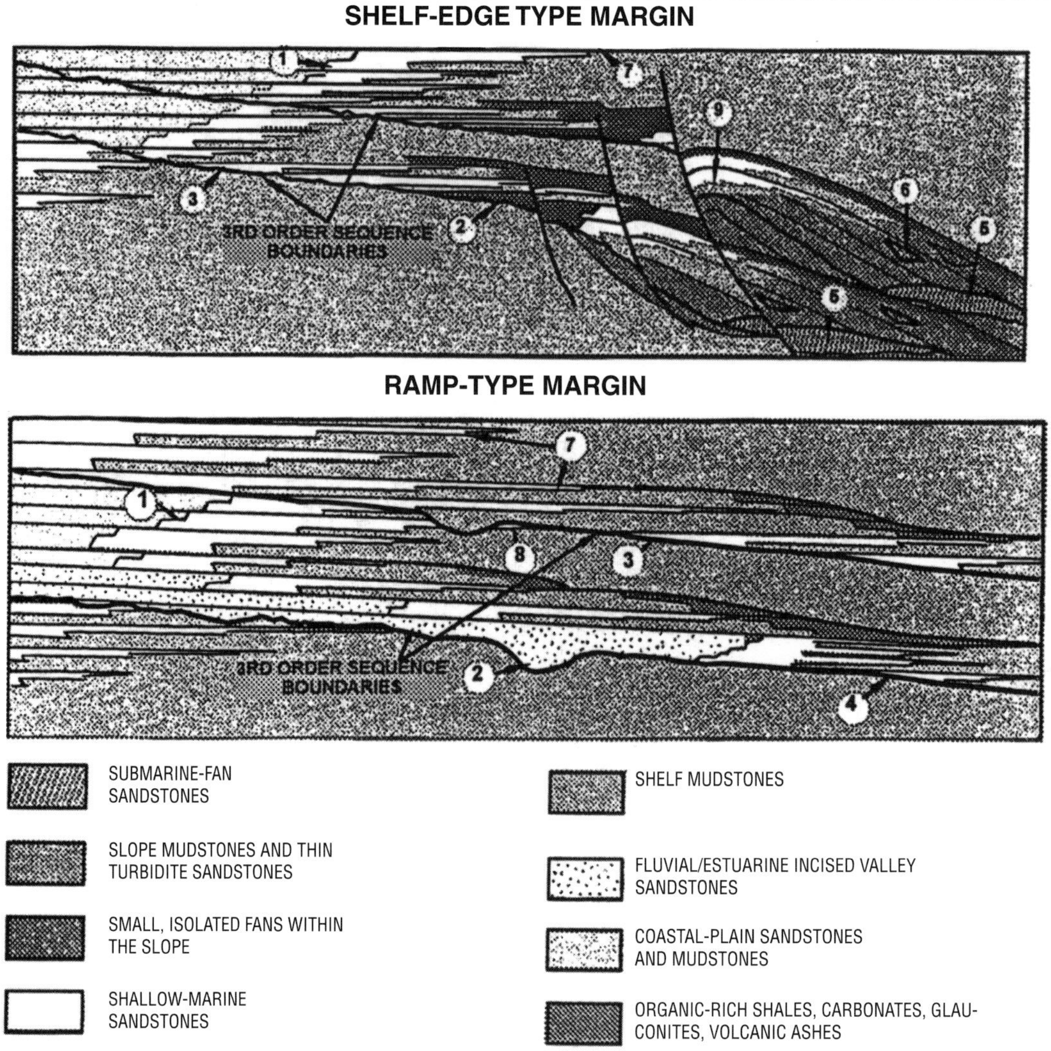

NO.	PLAY TYPE	RESERVOIR
1.	Updip pinchout	Beach or deltaic sandstones
2.	Incised valley	Braided-stream or estuarine sandstones
3.	Shelf onlap	Beach, deltaic, estuarine, or subtidal to tidal-flat sandstones
4.	Basinally restricted onlap	Deltaic sandstones
5.	Submarine fan	Submarine-fan turbidite sandstones
6.	Lowstand wedge	Small, areally restricted fans — composed of thin turbidite sandstones
7.	Downdip pinch-out	Deltaic, beach, or subtidal sandstones (need structural tilt)
8.	Truncation	Beach or deltaic sandstones

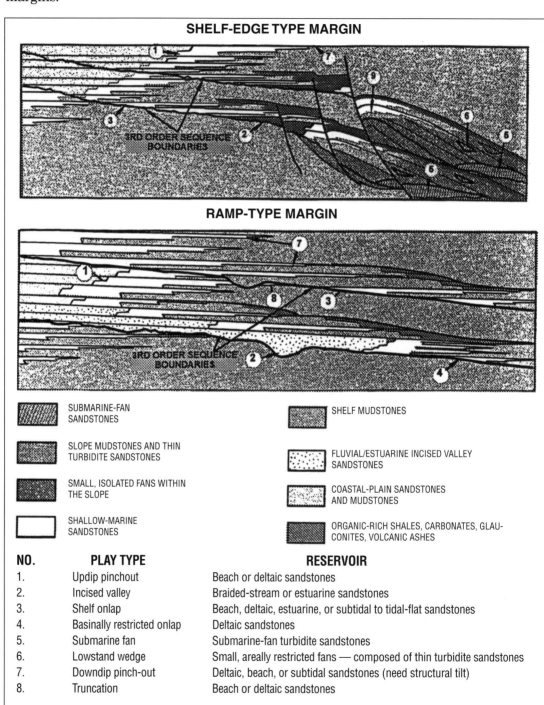

Figure 21–38. From Van Wagoner et al., 1990; courtesy AAPG.

Example: Integrating petrophysics and geology

Unpublished data (courtesy Amoco Production Company) derived from cores and seismic data were used to build an integrated lithofacies map. The figure below is a cross section representing the reservoir properties from representative capillary pressure data. The facies belts shown in the map above the cross section were deposited during maximum highstand of the Ismay (Pennsylvanian) carbonates. The facies are superimposed on an isopach map of the highstand systems tract. Test and show data overlain on the map show that significant reservoirs are restricted generally in the *Ivanovia* algal mound buildups, which flank a highstand basin shown in gray.

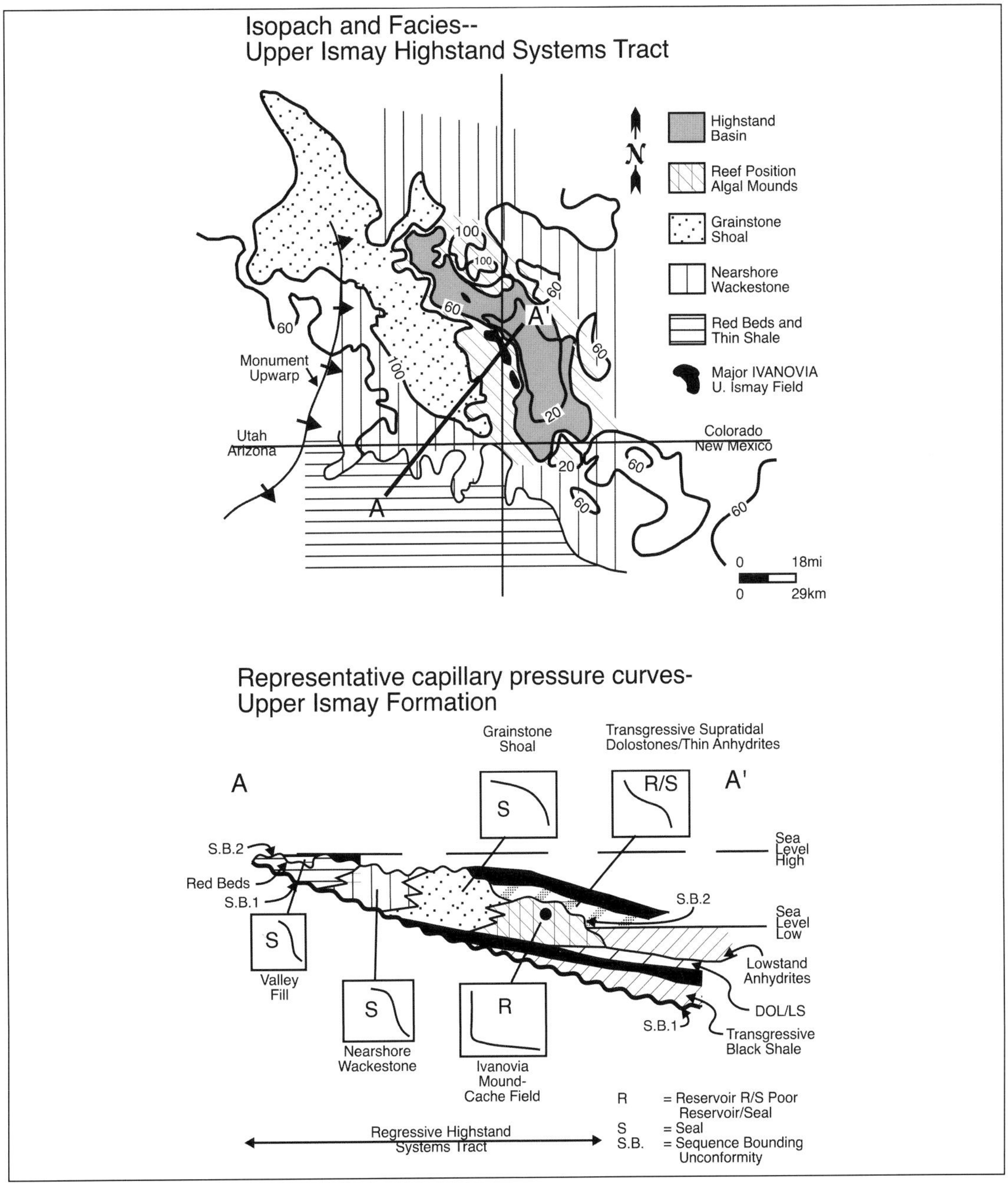

Figure 21–39.

Section F

Diagenetic Modifications of Stratigraphic Traps

Introduction

Diagenetic modifications to primary facies occur in most hydrocarbon accumulations. Understanding diagenetic production controls in existing fields and exploration controls for new fields is an important part of any geologist's role. In mature provinces, these traps form the dominant remaining play type. Although primary facies may exert strong control on diagenetic modifications, diagenetic changes can cross-cut these facies and be very difficult to predict.

In this section

This section contains the following topics.

Types of Diagenetic Traps

Introduction

Diagenetic traps are created by pore throat modifications of primary facies. They can also be created by changes in fluid type within the pore system.

Categories

Diagenetic traps occur in two basic categories: early or near-surface traps and late-burial traps.

Early or near-surface diagenetic traps are created by the following:

- Reservoir destroyed by paleosols, meteoric cementation, karsting, cave development, and/or sediment infill
- Reservoir enhanced by paleo-groundwater movement and/or karsting

Late burial diagenetic traps are created by the following:

- Bottom seal generated below oil–water contacts by late cementation
- Primary porosity preserved due to selective cementation and/or early hydrocarbon emplacement
- Secondary porosity created by cement and/or matrix dissolution

The diagram below shows cross sections of diagenetic trap types.

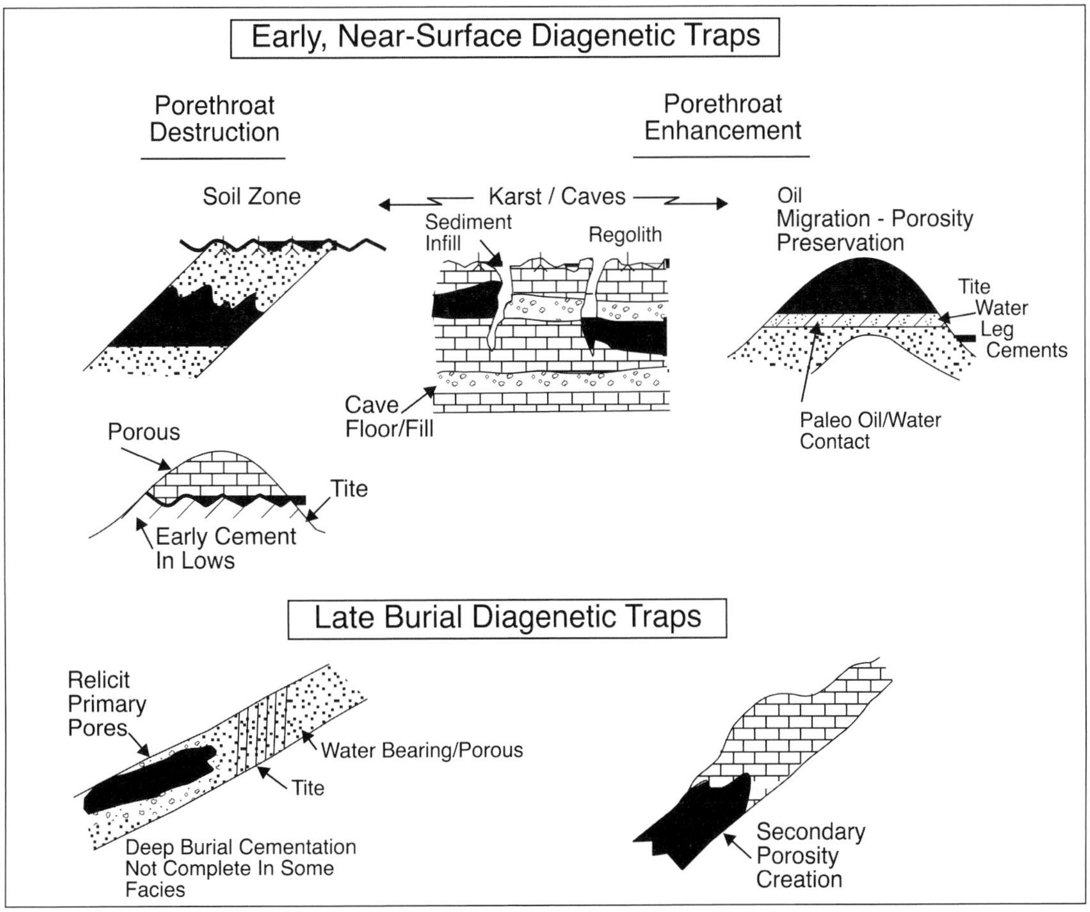

Figure 21–40.

Criteria for Recognizing Diagenetic Traps

Introduction

It is important early on in a play if diagenetic changes play a major role in trap modification. Test, production, geochemical, and show data provide the best criteria to recognize diagenetic modifications.

General geologic indications

Diagenetic traps can exist in the company of the following geologic indicators:

- Geologic setting conducive to development of paleotopographic relief
- Unconformities present
- No relationship between present-day depth and hydrocarbon production for a given zone
- Hydrocarbon accumulations in the absence of structural closure and not following closures created by primary facies changes

Petrographic indicators

Following are petrographic indicators of the potential presence of diagenetic traps:

- Early, pervasive, prehydrocarbon cements present updip from known production within a given facies (updip seal vs. downdip reservoir)
- Late, deep-burial cements or fabrics present, such as saddle or nonplanar dolomite, ferroan poikilotopic calcite, and anhydrite
- Abrupt vertical change in the amount of deep-burial cements present but not coincident with a change in depositional fabric (paleo oil–water contacts)
- Secondary porosity present but not related to subaerial exposure (subsurface deep burial dissolution)
- Zones of secondary porosity interbedded with tight rock in a depositionally homogeneous facies

Production indicators

The following indicate from field production the presence of diagenetic traps.

- Field boundaries within a given formation not coincident with structural closure or facies boundaries
- Tilted oil–water contacts present
- Adjacent structures not in pressure communication
- Pressures in oil-charged reservoirs unusually high
- Most of the wells characterized by high initial potential followed by rapid, sharp decline in flow rates; water cut typically low

Example: Diagenetic trap

Weyburn field, Alberta, is an example of a giant diagenetic trap (1 billion BOE). Primary trap geometries appear to be along the updip termination of the Midale dolomite above the potential bottom seal of the Frobisher anhydrite and beneath the top seal of the Mesozoic section. If only these trapping geometries were used to locate the trap, sequence stratigraphic mapping initially would not have located the trap. However, microporous dolomites are present near the Mesozoic sequence boundary in the updip portion of the Midale dolomite. These Mesoporous dolomites downdip form the reservoir facies.

Example: Diagenetic trap (continued)

The microporous strata form the lateral seal. The sinuous updip edge is a large waste zone that contains live oil shows in microporous strata, indicating the accumulation is downdip.

The figure below contains a cross section, map, and summary of the field.

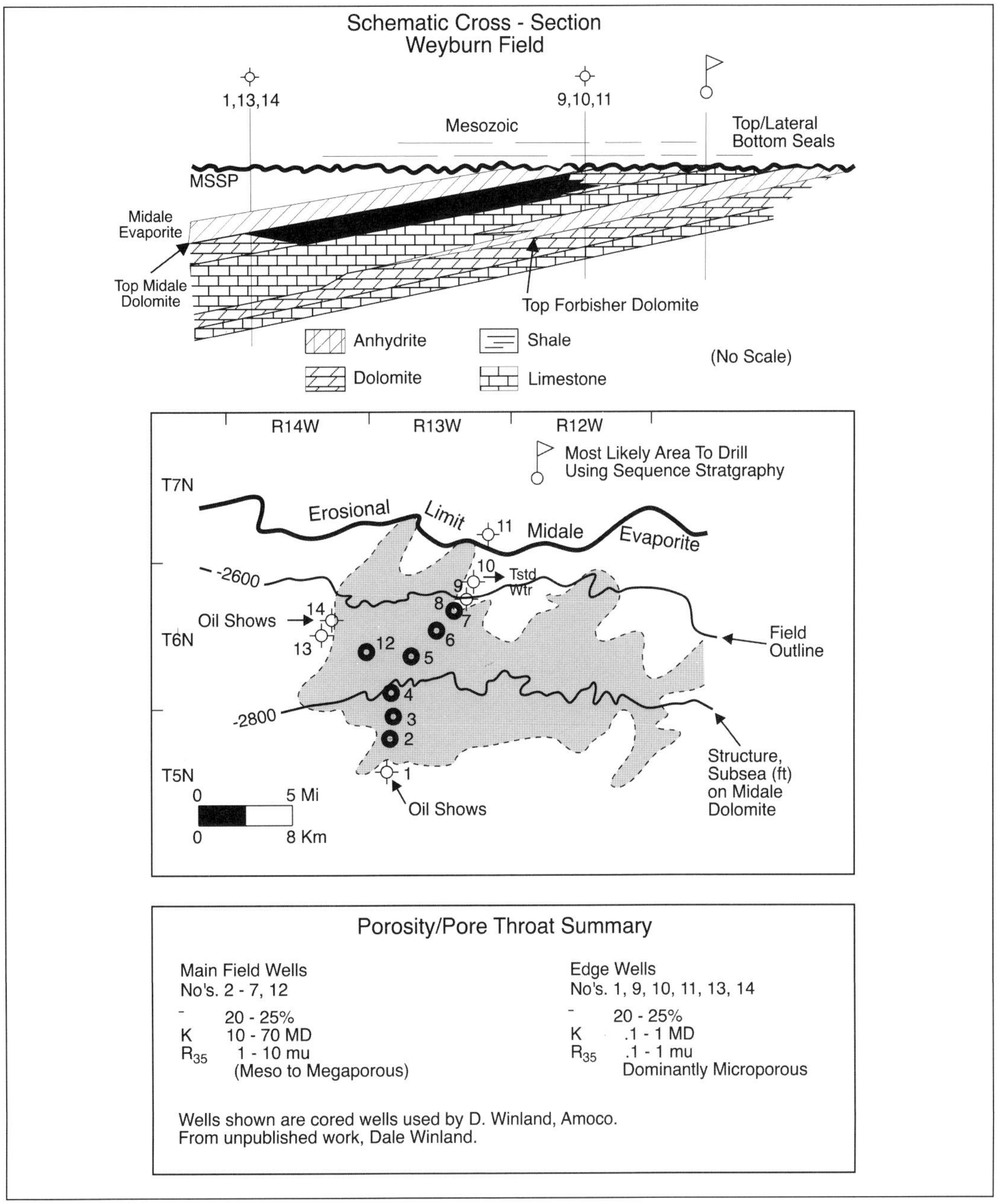

Figure 21–41. From Dale Winland, unpublished data.

Using Petrological Information

Introduction

Petrophysical, petrological, geochemical, production, pressure, and other subsurface data must be used to locate diagenetic traps. Petrological data, in conjunction with subsurface shows, can be a powerful tool in mapping and predicting traps.

Using petrological information

Petrographic data can provide information about migration timing, trap preservation, and facies vs. diagenetic controls on hydrocarbon distribution. The table below lists examples of applying petrological information.

Petrological Information	Exploration Significance	Exploration Application
Oil-filled fluid inclusions in reservoir or carrier beds	Indicates migration pathways and absolute timing of migration	Migration routes that existed during migration
Oil-filled fluid inclusions in seals	Indicates leaky seals and timing of leakage	Column height may be small and/or updip (spilled) accumulations may exist
Primary porosity preservation	Indicates facies patterns may control hydrocarbon distribution	Map depositional facies
Dissolution porosity present	Diagenesis may be critical for trap location; mineralogy and/or facies may control location of dissolution porosity	Use sequence stratigraphy, hydrologic, or thermal maturity models (refer to Tobin, 1991a,b; Read et al., 1995; Wilson, 1994)
Postmigration burial cements present	Indicates potential cementation of water leg	Map diagenetic facies

Example: Using cementation timing

In the example shown in the figure below, Cambrian sandstones in the Lublin basin (Poland) contain fluorescing oil inclusions trapped before the formation of quartz cements, which degraded the reservoir's quality. Oil traps could occur updip if seals were present during the migration event.

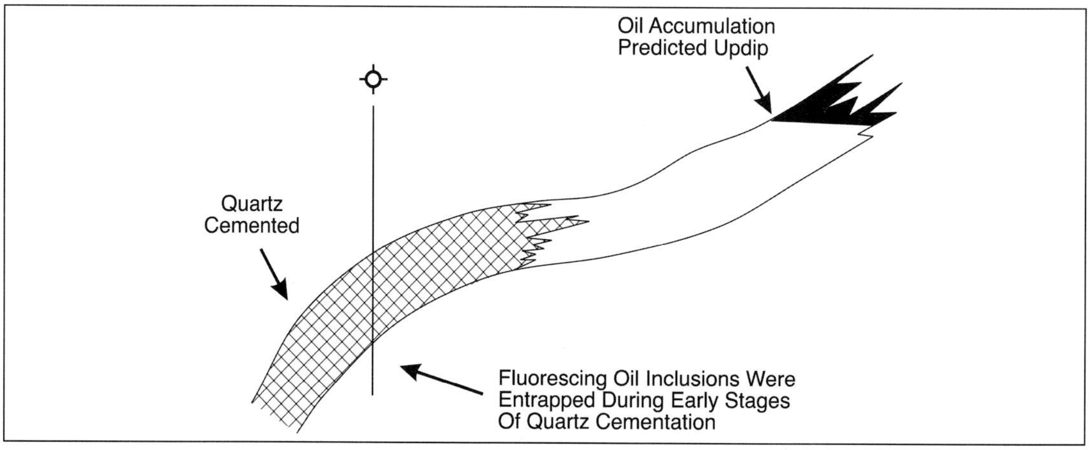

Figure 21–42. From Rick Tobin, unpublished data.

Section G
References

Aitken, J.F., and J.A. Howell, 1996, High-resolution sequence stratigraphy: innovations, applications and future prospects, *in* J.A. Howell and J.F. Aitken, eds., High Resolution Sequence Stratigraphy: Geological Society of London Special Pub. 104, p. 1–9.

Bahorich, M.S., and S.R. Bridges, 1992, The seismic sequence attribute map: Proceedings of the SEG 62nd Annual International Meeting and Exposition, New Orleans, p. 227–230.

_____ and S.L. Farmer, 1994, 3-D seismic discontinuity: the coherence cube for faults and stratigraphic features: U.S. patent 5,563,949; foreign patents pending.

_____ and _____, 1995, 3-D seismic discontinuity for faults and stratigraphic features: the coherence cube: The Leading Edge, vol. 14, no. 10, p. 1053–58.

Bally, A.W., ed., 1987, Atlas of Seismic Stratigraphy: AAPG Studies in Geology 27, vol. 1, 124 p.

Baum, G.R., and P.R. Vail, 1988, Sequence stratigraphic concepts applied to Paleogene outcrops, Gulf and Atlantic basins, *in* C.K. Wilgus, B.S. Hastings, H.M. Posamentier, J. Van Wagoner, C.A. Ross, and G.C.St.C. Kendall, eds., Sea-Level Changes—An Integrated Approach: SEPM Special Publication 42, 407 p.

Brown, A.R., ed., 1999, Interpretation of Three-Dimensional Seismic Data, Fifth Edition, AAPG Memoir 42, 514 p.

Busch, D.A., 1974, Stratigraphic Traps in Sandstone—Exploration Techniques: AAPG Memoir 21, 174 p.

Dahlberg, E.C., 1982, Applied Hydrodynamics in Petroleum Exploration: New York, Springer-Verlag, 161 p.

Dolson, J.C., ed., 1991, Unconformity Related Hydrocarbon Exploitation and Accumulation in Clastic and Carbonate Settings: Rocky Mountain Assoc. of Geologists and Exploration Geoscience Institute (Colorado School of Mines) Core Workshop, Golden, Colorado, 297 p.

_____ and M.H. Franklin, 1991, Sub-Jurassic Sun River (Mississippian) diagenesis, reservoir properties and physical unconformity expression, Sweetgrass Arch, Montana, *in* J.C. Dolson, ed., Unconformity Related Hydrocarbon Exploitation and Accumulation in Clastic and Carbonate Settings: Rocky Mountain Assoc. of Geologists and Exploration Geoscience Institute (Colorado School of Mines) Core Workshop, Golden, Colorado, p. 195–208.

_____ and D.S. Muller, 1994, Stratigraphic evolution of the Lower Cretaceous Dakota Group, Western Interior, U.S.A., *in* M.V. Caputo, J.A. Peterson, and K.J. Franczyk, eds., Mesozoic Systems of the Rocky Mountain Region, U.S.A.: SEPM Rocky Mountain Section, p. 441–456.

_____ and J.T. Piombino, 1994, Giant proximal foreland basin non-marine wedge trap: Lower Cretaceous Cutbank Sandstone, Montana, *in* J.C. Dolson, M.L. Hendricks, and W.A. Wescott, eds., Unconformity-Related Hydrocarbons in Sedimentary Sequences: Rocky Mountain Assoc. of Geologists, p. 135–148.

_____, B. Steer, J. Garing, G. Osborne, A. Gad, and H. Amr, 1997, 3D seismic and workstation technology brings technical revolution to the Gulf of Suez Petroleum Company: The Leading Edge, vol. 16, no. 12, p. 1809–1817.

_____, D.S. Muller, M.J. Evetts, and J.A. Stein, 1991, Paleotopographic trends and production, Muddy Formation (Lower Cretaceous), Central and Northern Rocky Mountains: AAPG Bulletin, vol. 75, p. 405–435.

_____, J.T. Piombino, M.H. Franklin, and R. Harwood, 1993, Devonian oil in Mississippian and Mesozoic reservoirs—unconformity controls on migration and accumulation, Sweetgrass Arch, Montana: The Mountain Geologist, vol. 30, p. 125–146.

Galloway, W.E., 1989, Genetic stratigraphic sequences in basin analysis I: architecture and genesis of flooding-surface bounded depositional units: AAPG Bulletin, vol. 73, p. 125–142.

Gawthorpe, R.L., A.J. Fraser, and E.L. Collier, 1994, Sequence stratigraphy in active extensional basins: implications for the interpretation of ancient basin-fills: Marine and Petroleum Geology, vol. 11, no. 6, p. 642–658.

Gries, R., J.C. Dolson, and R.G.H. Reynolds, 1993, Structural and stratigraphic evolution and hydrocarbon distribution, Rocky Mountain Foreland, *in* R.W. Macqueen and D.A. Leckie, eds., Foreland Basins and Fold Belts: AAPG Memoir 55, p. 395–425.

Halbouty, M.T., ed., 1970, Geology of Giant Petroleum Fields: AAPG Memoir 14, 575 p.

_____, ed., 1980, Giant Oil and Gas Fields of the Decade 1968–1978: AAPG Memoir 30, 596 p.

_____, ed., 1982, The Deliberate Search for the Subtle Trap: AAPG Memoir 32, 351 p.

_____, 1990, Giant Oil and Gas Fields of the Decade 1978–1988: AAPG program abstracts, AAPG Stavanger Conference, Stavanger, Norway.

Handford, C.R., and R.G. Loucks, 1993, Carbonate depositional sequences and systems tracts—responses of carbonate platforms to relative sea-level changes, *in* R.G. Loucks and J.F. Sarg, eds., Carbonate Sequence Stratigraphy: Recent Developments and Applications: AAPG Memoir 57, p. 3–42.

Haq, B.U., J. Hardenbol, and P.R. Vail, 1988, Mesozoic and Cenozoic chronostratigraphy and cycles of sea-level change *in* C.K. Wilgus, B.S. Hastings, H.W. Posamentier, J. Van Wagoner, C.A. Ross, and G.C. St. C. Kendall, eds., Sea-Level Change: An Integrated Approach: Society of Economic Paleontologists and Mineralogists Special Publication 42, p. 71–108.

Howell, J.A., and J.F. Aitken, 1996, eds., High-Resolution Sequence Stratigraphy: Innovations and Applications: Geological Society Publ. 104.

Hunt, D., and M.E. Tucker, 1993, The Mid-Cretaceous Urgonian platform of S.E. France, *in* J.A. Simo, R.W. Scott, and J.P. Masse, eds., Cretaceous Carbonate Platforms: AAPG Memoir 56, p. 409–453.

Hyne, N.J., 1995, Sequence stratigraphy: a new look at old rocks, *in* N.J. Hyne, ed., Sequence Stratigraphy of the Mid Continent: Tulsa Geological Society Special Publication 4, p. 5–20.

Jervey, M.T., 1988, Quantitative geological modeling of siliciclastic rock sequences and their seismic expressions, *in* C.K. Wilgus, B.S. Hastings, H.W. Posamentier, J. Van Wagoner, C.A. Ross, and C.G. St. C. Kendall, eds., Sea Level Changes: An Integrated Approach: Society of Economic Paleontologists and Mineralogists Special Publication 42, p. 47–69.

Loucks, R.G., and J.F. Sarg, eds., 1993, Carbonate Sequence Stratigraphy, Recent Developments and Applications: AAPG Memoir 57, 545 p.

Mitchum, R.M., P.R. Vail, and J.B. Sangree, 1977, Seismic stratigraphy and global changes in sea level, part 6: stratigraphic interpretations of seismic reflection patterns in depositional sequences, *in* C.E. Payton, ed., Seismic Stratigraphy and Applications to Hydrocarbon Exploration: AAPG Memoir 26, p. 117–133.

_____, J.B. Sangree, P.R. Vail, and W.W. Wornardt, 1993, Recognizing sequences and systems tracts from well logs, seismic data, and biostratigraphy: examples from the Late Cenozoic of the Gulf of Mexico, *in* P. Weimer and H.W. Posamentier, eds., Siliciclastic Sequence Stratigraphy, Recent Developments and Applications: AAPG Memoir 58, p. 163–197.

Posamentier, H.W., and P.R. Vail, 1988, Eustatic controls on clastic deposition II—sequence and systems tract models, *in* C.K. Wilgus, B.S. Hastings, H.W. Posamentier, J. Van Wagoner, C.A. Ross, and G.C.St.C. Kendall, eds., Sea-Level Changes—An Integrated Approach: SEPM Special Publication 42, p. 125–154.

Prosser, S., 1993, Rift-related linked depositional systems and their seismic expression, *in* G.D. Williams and A. Dobb, eds., Tectonics and Seismic Sequence Stratigraphy: Geological Society Special Publication 71, p. 35–66.

Putnam, P.E., and T.A. Oliver, 1980, Stratigraphic traps in channel sandstones in the Upper Mannville (Albian) of east-central Alberta: Canadian Society of Petroleum Geologists Bulletin, vol. 28, p. 489–508.

Ramzy, M., B. Steer, F. Abu-Shadi, M. Schlorholtz, J. Mika, J.C. Dolson, and M. Zinger, 1996, Gulf of Suez rift basin sequence models—part B: Miocene sequence stratigraphy and exploration significance in the central and southern Gulf of Suez: Proceedings of the 13th Petroleum Conference, the Egyptian General Petroleum Corp., vol. 2, p. 242–256.

Ravnas, R., and R.J. Steel, 1998, Architecture of marine rift basin succession: AAPG Bulletin, vol. 82, no. 1, p. 110–146.

Read, J.F., C. Kerans, J.F. Sarg, F.M. Wright, 1995, Milankovitch Sea-Level Changes, Cycles, and Reservoirs on Carbonate Platforms in Greenhouse and Ice-House Worlds: SEPM Short Course 35, 79 p.

Sarg, J.F., 1988, Carbonate sequence stratigraphy, *in* C.K. Wilgus et al., eds., Sea-Level Changes—An Integrated Approach: SEPM Special Publication 42, p. 155–181.

References, continued

Tobin, R.C., 1985, Reservoir development in Ellenburger group of West Texas—a diagenetic jambalaya: AAPG Bulletin, vol. 2, p. 312.

_____, 1991a, Diagenesis, thermal maturation and burial history of the Upper Cambrian Bonneterre Dolomite, southeastern Missouri: an interpretation of thermal history from petrographic and fluid inclusion evidence: Organic Geochemistry, vol. 17, no. 2, p 142–152.

_____, 1991b, Pore system evolution vs. paleotemperature in carbonate rocks: a predictable relationship?: Organic Geochemistry, vol. 17, no. 2, p. 271.

Underhill, J.R., and M.A. Partington, 1993, Use of genetic sequence stratigraphy in defining and determining and regional tectonic control on the "Mid-Cimmerian Unconformity"—implications for North Sea basin development and the global sea level chart, *in* P. Weimer and H.W. Posamentier, eds., Siliciclastic Sequence Stratigraphy, Recent Developments and Applications: American Association of Geologists Memoir 58, p. 449–484.

Vail, P.R., 1987, Seismic stratigraphy interpretation procedure, *in* A.W. Bally, ed., Atlas of Seismic Stratigraphy: AAPG Studies in Geology No. 27, p. 2.

Van Wagoner, J.C., 1995, Overview of sequence stratigraphic foreland basin deposits: terminology, summary of papers, and glossary of sequence stratigraphy, *in* J.C. Van Wagoner and G.T. Bertram, eds., Sequence Stratigraphy of Foreland Basin Deposits: Outcrop and Subsurface Examples from the Cretaceous of North America: AAPG Memoir 64, p. ix–xxi.

Van Wagoner, J.C., et al., 1988, An overview of the fundamentals of sequence stratigraphy and key definitions, *in* C.K. Wilgus et al., eds., Sea-Level Changes—An Integrated Approach: SEPM Special Publication 42, p. 39–45.

Van Wagoner, J.C., R.M. Mitchum, K.M. Campion, and V.D. Rahmanian, 1990, Siliciclastic Sequence Stratigraphy in Well Logs, Cores and Outcrops: Concepts for High-Resolution Correlation of Time and Facies: AAPG Methods in Exploration Series No. 7, 55 p.

Weber, L.J., J.F. Sarg, and F.M. Wright, 1995, Sequence stratigraphy and reservoir delineation of the middle Pennsylvanian (Desmoinesian), Paradox basin and Aneth field, southwestern U.S.A., *in* J.F. Read, L.J. Weber, J.F. Sarg, and F.M. Wright, eds., Milankovitch Sea-Level Changes, Cycles, and Reservoirs on Carbonate Platforms in Greenhouse and Ice-House Worlds: SEPM Short Course No. 35, 79 p.

Weimer, P., and H.W. Posamentier, eds., 1993, Siliciclastic Sequence Stratigraphy, Recent Developments and Applications: AAPG Memoir 58, 492 p.

Wescott, W.A., and P.J. Boucher, 1998, Paleohydraulic characteristics of Late Miocene–Early Pliocene submarine channels in the Nile Delta, Egypt: AAPG Bulletin, vol. 82, p. 695.

Wilgus, C.K., B.S. Hastings, et al., eds., Sea-Level Changes—An Integrated Approach: SEPM Special Publication 42, 407 p.

Wilson, M.D., ed., 1994, Reservoir Quality Assessment and Prediction in Clastic Rocks: SEPM (Society of Sedimentary Geology) Short Course 30, 432 p.

Index

Index, continued